PEARSON

Physics

Authors

James E. Ackroyd
Westwind School Division
Cardston, Alberta
formerly *J.T. Foster School*
Livingstone Range School Division
Nanton, Alberta

Mark Anderson
Curriculum Leader
Distributed Learning CBe-learn Online School
Calgary Board of Education
Calgary, Alberta

Carmen Berg
formerly *John G. Diefenbaker High School*
Calgary Board of Education
Calgary, Alberta

Dr. Brian E. Martin
Professor of Physics and Astronomy
The King's University College
University of Alberta
Edmonton, Alberta

Barry L. S. McGuire
formerly *Western Canada High School*
Calgary Board of Education
Calgary, Alberta

Cliff Sosnowski
Department Head of Science
Louis St. Laurent Catholic School
Edmonton Catholic Schools
Edmonton, Alberta

Mike Szojka
St. Francis Xavier High School
Edmonton Catholic Schools
Edmonton, Alberta

Elgin Wolfe
Professor
Department of Curriculum, Teaching
 and Learning
OISE/University of Toronto
Toronto, Ontario

Senior Program Consultant

Lionel Sandner
Saanich School District
Saanichton, British Columbia
formerly *Lead Coordinator,*
Pan Canadian Science Project

Senior Technology Consultant

Josef Martha
Northern Gateway Public Schools
Onoway, Alberta

Program Consultants and Contributors

Igor Nowikow
Markham District High School
York Region District School Board
Markham, Ontario

Paul Williams
Red Deer College
Red Deer, Alberta

PEARSON
Education
Canada

ISBN-13: 978-0-321-30813-9
ISBN-10: 0-321-30813-1

Printed and bound in the United States

3 4 5   QC   11 10 09 08

About the cover photo
Photo permission by Olivier Grunewald/Oxford
Scientific Films/First Light and Courtesy of EISCAT.
The photo shows a radar receptor recording wave
signals of Northern Lights at Research Base
Eiscat, Tromso, Norway. This particular antenna
is a 32-m dish, which is the transmitter part of one
of EISCAT's three big research radars. Two other
antennas similar to this one are in Sweden and Finland.

Managing Editor
Cecilia Chan

Developmental Editors
Nancy Andraos
Lina Mockus
David Peebles
Eileen Pyne-Rudzik, Ph.D.
Yvonne Van Ruskenveld

Coordinating and Production Editors
Anita Reynolds MacArthur
Louise McCauley

Production Editor
Ruth Peckover

Indexer
May Look

Editorial Assistants
Nicole Argyropoulos
Nick Rudzik

Cover and Text Design
ArtPlus Ltd.

Production Coordinators
Suzanne Powell
Sandra Magill

Photo Research
Nancy Belle Cook

Text Composition
ArtPlus Ltd.

Publisher
Reid McAlpine

Product Manager
Patti Henderson

Submission Consultant
Trudy Rising

ACKNOWLEDGEMENTS

The authors and Pearson Education Canada would like to thank
Alberta Education for their guidance in the development of this book.

Advisory Panel

Kevin Engel
St. Joseph High School
Edmonton Catholic Schools

David Paraschuk
Bishop O'Byrne High School
Calgary Catholic School Division

Vladimir Pasek
Archbishop O'Leary High School
Edmonton Catholic Schools

Janet Rhine Herrem
St. Martin de Porres High School
Calgary Catholic School Division

Dean Rootsaert
Archbishop Romero High School
Edmonton Catholic Schools

John Watson
Strathcona High School
Edmonton Public Schools

Paul Williams
Red Deer College

Expert Reviewers

Dr. Jason Carey
Assistant Professor
Mechanical Engineering
University of Alberta

Kerry Kijewski
Mathematics and Physics
SAIT Polytechnic

Hans Laue
Formerly *Department of Physics*
University of Calgary

Muraari Vasudevan
Department of Physics
University of Alberta

Sandra Vidaković
Department of Medical Physics
University of Alberta

Ken Vos
Professor
Department of Physics
University of Lethbridge

Dr. Peter Wright
Professor
Department of Educational Psychology
Faculty of Education
University of Alberta

Tony Yeung
Associate Professor
Chemical and Materials Engineering
University of Alberta

Aboriginal Content Consultants

Steven Daniel
*Coordinator, Mathematics, Science and Secondary
  Education*
Education, Culture and Employment
Government of the Northwest Territories

Karen Decontie
Structural Engineer
Public Works and Government Services, Calgary

Diane Ingraham, Ph. D.
School of Science and Technology
Cape Breton University

Dawn Wiseman
Creative Director
*Mount Pleasant Educational Services Inc., Quebec
  (formerly Native Access to Engineering Program,
  Concordia University)*

Field-test Teachers

Glen Allen
Harry Collinge High School
Grande Yellowhead Regional Division

Ryan Baldry
Raymond High School
Westwind School Division

Timothy Buttler
Parkview Adventist Academy

Bryan Clintberg
Archbishop O'Leary High School
Edmonton Catholic Schools

Susanne Czentye
Bishop Grandin Senior High
Calgary Catholic School Division

Anthony Green
Austin O'Brien Senior High
Edmonton Catholic Schools

Powell Jones
Ross Sheppard Senior High
Edmonton Public Schools

James Kriese
St. Francis Xavier High School
Edmonton Catholic Schools

Cathy MacAdam
Glenmary School
Holy Family Catholic Regional Division

Craig Noad
Magrath Junior/Senior High School
Westwind School Division

Barry Thimer
Sturgeon Composite High School
Sturgeon School Division

The authors and Pearson Education Canada would also like to thank all the
students who participated in the field-test.

Teacher Reviewers

Curtis Blair
St. Albert Catholic High School
Greater St. Albert Catholic Regional Division

Derek Collins
St. Jerome's School
East Central Alberta Catholic Separate Schools

Joan Coy
Peace Academy of Virtual Education
Peace Wapiti School Board

Matt Dyck
J. A. Williams High School
Northern Lights School Division

Don Easton
Formerly *Acadia University*

Michael Enyedy
William E. Hay Composite High School
Clearview School Division

Donald Jamieson
Spruce Grove Composite High School
Parkland School Division

Helen Krol
Edmonton Christian School
Edmonton Public Schools

Wayne Ladner
Chinook Learning Services
Calgary Board of Education

Kari Lagadyn
École Secondaire Ste. Marguerite d'Youville
Greater St. Albert Catholic Regional Division

Karen McMullen
Christ The King School
St. Thomas Aquinas Catholic Schools

Stephen Molesky
École Notre Dame High School
Red Deer Catholic Regional Division

Iain Paton
Didsbury High School
Chinook's Edge School Division

Susan Ruzek
Strathmore High School
Golden Hills School Division

Rachel Sailer
Prairie Christian Academy
Golden Hills School Division

Deana Senn
Grand Centre High School
Northern Lights School Division

Clayton Smiley
E. H. Walter School
Buffalo Trail Public Schools

Duncan Smith
Bishop Grandin High School
Calgary Catholic School Division

Doug Stevens
Foothills Composite High School
Foothills School Division

Robert van Thiel
Father Patrick Mercredi Community High School
Fort McMurray Catholic Board of Education

Natalie Veldhoen
Lord Beaverbrook High School
Calgary Board of Education

Dwayne Wenaas
George McDougall High School
Rocky View School Divisiom

Blaine Woodall
School of Hope
East Central Alberta Catholic Separate Schools

Erin Yeung
formerly *Henry Wise Wood High School*
Calgary Board of Education

UNIT II: DYNAMICS   122

UNIT III: CIRCULAR MOTION, WORK, AND ENERGY   238

UNIT VII: ELECTROMAGNETIC RADIATION   632

UNIT VIII: ATOMIC PHYSICS   750

Pearson Physics provides opportunities for you to explore and understand the natural world and to become aware of the profound influence of physics in your lives. It helps you understand the fundamental concepts that explain many physical phenomena and events. With this book, you will learn physics in relevant contexts and engage in activities that bring physics to life.

The book is organized into eight units, corresponding to the eight units in the Alberta Education Physics 20-30 Program of Studies. The material matches the content required in the Program of Studies. Following is an outline of the organization of the text and features.

UNIT OPENER

The pages that begin a **Unit** show a dramatic photograph that is relevant to the unit content. It provides an excellent opportunity for an introductory discussion about the topic of the unit. Also provided on these pages is the **Unit at a Glance**

✓ a full table of contents of the unit
✓ the general themes of science that are emphasized in the unit
✓ the questions to focus on as you study the unit
✓ a brief link to the project to be completed at the end of the unit
✓ an eWEB link to the *Pearson Physics* website: *www.pearsoned.ca/school/physicssource*

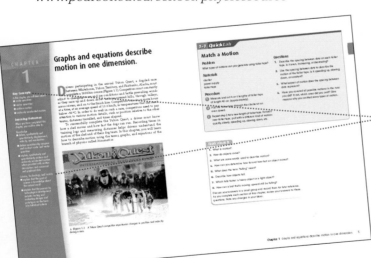

CHAPTER OPENER

Each **chapter** begins with a title in the form of a statement that reflects a General Outcome in the Program of Studies, and an interesting photo relevant to the contents of the chapter.

The **Key Concepts** and **Learning Outcomes** to be addressed in each chapter are listed to provide a clear overview of the material covered in the chapter.

There are always three ways to begin a chapter:

1. The **text narrative** provides the opportunity to develop concept understanding through reading opportunities.

2. **QuickLab** activities provide an opportunity to actively explore initial concepts through short, simple activities.

3. **Think About It** questions provide an opportunity for you to assess what you already know about the chapter's concepts.

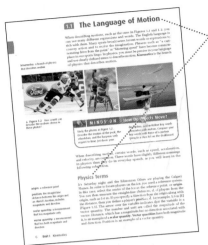

The chapter is further divided into **numbered sections** and **subsections** that organize the contents into appropriate clusters of ideas.

Key terms are shown in bold type in the text. You will also find the definitions of these terms in the margin of the pages. Key equations are highlighted for easy reference.

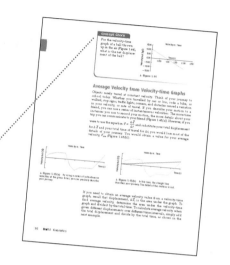

TEXT FEATURES

Within the body of the text, you will find **Concept Checks** that support and build conceptual understanding and promote the development of inquiry and communication skills.

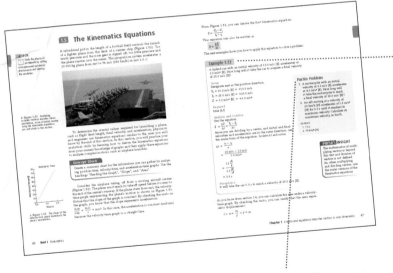

Problem solving is an essential part of learning physics. You will find numerous **Example Problems** that show detailed step-by-step solutions, generally using the GRASP or GRASP V method. This method is explained in detail in the Student References at the end of the book.

Accompanying each Example Problem are **Practice Problems** reflecting the example problem and providing opportunities for further practice. Answers to Practice Problems are provided on the same page in smaller type. Complete solutions for all questions are provided on the teacher's Solutions Manual Disk.

Skills Practice reviews or reinforces skills that are needed to further understand the mathematical treatment of some of the topics.

Minds On activities are designed to stimulate thinking about key aspects of the concept being studied. It is usually suggested that these activities be done in groups.

Then, Now, and Future are active features that illustrate historical items, interesting current events, and possible future innovations. They are designed to help you better establish connections between the content of the book and the broader world of physics.

Features found in the margin include **InfoBits** which offer interesting information relevant to the content of the text.

As well, **Physics Insight** features provide additional support for some of the concepts in the flow of the text. They may also provide alternative problem-solving strategies and different mathematical operations that may be helpful for the Example Problems.

Pearson Physics is fully integrated with a high level of technology support. Icons in the margin indicate possible links on the website *www.pearsoned.ca/school/physicssource*. See page xxiii for details of the technology features.

LAB ACTIVITIES

Lab activities are key to building and consolidating real understanding of physics concepts. *Pearson Physics* offers five kinds of lab activities.

1. **QuickLabs** generally require readily available, simple materials and can be completed in a relatively short time. At the beginning of a chapter, they provide a short, hands-on introduction to key concepts. They may also be included in other appropriate places within the text. In some situations, your teacher may demonstrate the activity.

2. **Inquiry Labs** provide opportunities for you to work in a formal lab setting. You will develop the scientific skills of predicting, observing, measuring, recording, inferring, analyzing and, often, concluding. Inquiry Labs are driven by our curiosity about how things work, i.e., the nature of science. Safety is stressed throughout, and equipment is usually required.

3. **Problem-Solving Labs** provide opportunities for you to solve practical problems that arise from human needs; you may need to build a device or system to solve a problem. The question asked is designed to focus on Science and Technology. You will be asked to identify a problem, make a plan, and construct a solution.

4. **Decision-Making Analysis** activities provide you with activities in which to explore the social, economic, environmental, political, ethical, and moral impacts of a real-world issue related to the unit being studied. You will be asked to work together collecting evidence, and to make a decision based on your research.

5. **Design a Lab** activities can be either scientific inquiry or problem solving in nature. In general, these labs provide minimal direction, asking you to go one step further than either the Inquiry or Problem-Solving Labs by designing the lab yourself.

REVIEW, CONSOLIDATION AND ASSESSMENT

Each numbered section ends in a **Check and Reflect** consisting of numerical
and conceptual problems that allow you to review what you have learned
and to consolidate your understanding.

The **Chapter Summary** at the end of each
chapter lists the key terms and concepts
as well as the key equations pertaining to
the chapter. It also provides a partially-
completed concept map which provides
opportunities for you to demonstrate your
understanding of the relationships among
the concepts presented in the chapter.

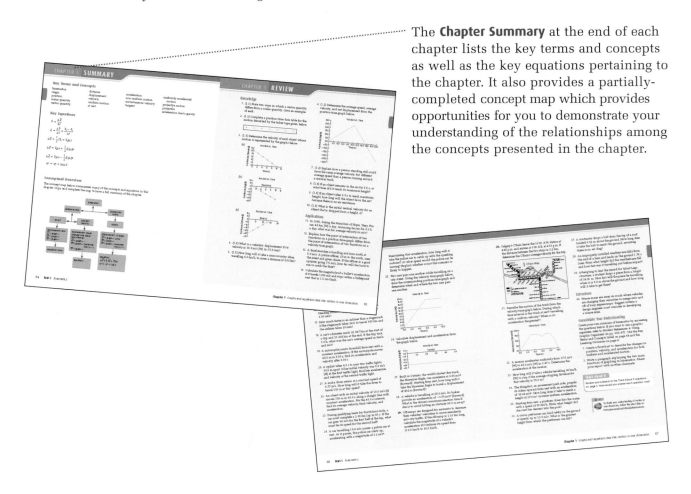

Chapter Review questions at the end of each chapter help you to re-visit
the series of concepts covered in a chapter. Answering these questions
will help you consolidate what you have learned in the various lessons
leading up to this point.

*Note: Due to the fact that Unit V has only one chapter, the Chapter
Summary for Chapter 9 is immediately followed by the end-of-unit-
material described below and a Chapter Review is not included.*

The following features conclude each of the
eight units, and are designed to assist you in
preparing for major assignments.

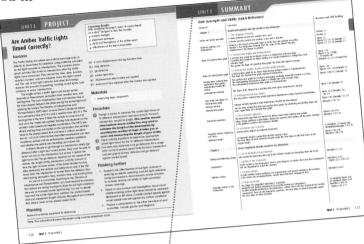

The **Unit Project** provides a hands-on
opportunity for you to demonstrate
what you have learned. The project
requires you to integrate and apply
some of the skills and knowledge that
you have acquired to a new situation.

The **Unit Summary** provides a quick reference
for the entire unit. At a glance, you can find
all the key concepts you have learned within
the unit. This page can help you organize
your notes for studying. You may also use it
as a checklist to track your understanding as
you work through the unit.

The **Unit Review** provides you with
opportunities to:

✓ Review important terms (Vocabulary)
✓ Test your basic understanding of Key Concepts
  and Learning Outcomes (Knowledge)
✓ Test your ability to combine ideas from more than one
  section or chapter to answer questions (Applications)
✓ Test your ability to apply your learning beyond what
  you have studied in the unit. (Extensions)
✓ Test the specific mathematical skills or laboratory skills
  you have learned in the unit (Skills Practice)
✓ Express your thoughts and ideas about the new things
  you have learned (Self-Assessment)

END-OF-BOOK RESOURCES

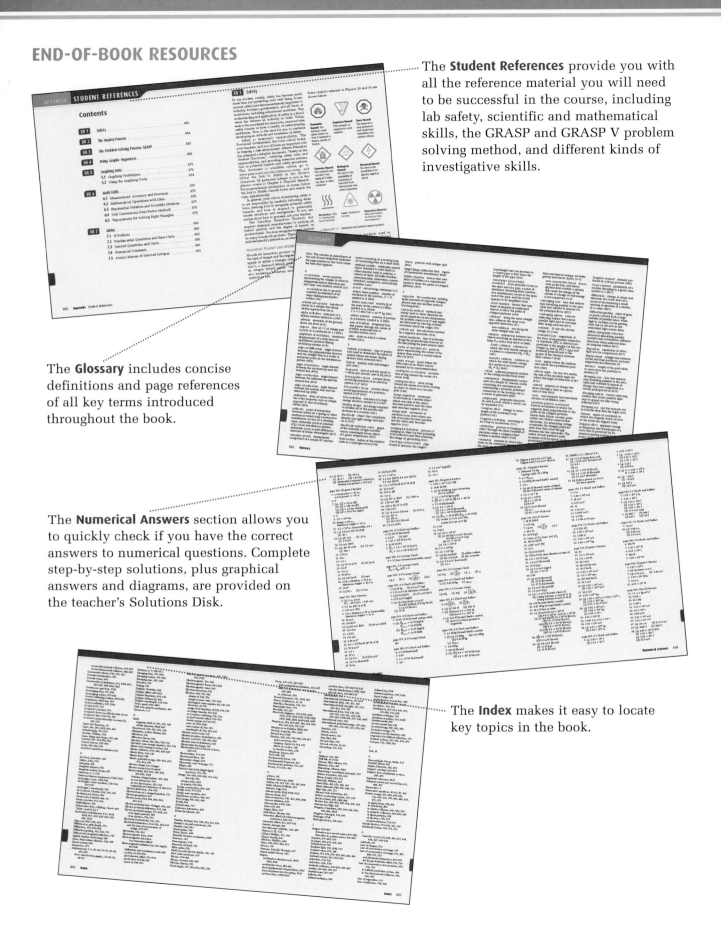

The **Student References** provide you with all the reference material you will need to be successful in the course, including lab safety, scientific and mathematical skills, the GRASP and GRASP V problem solving method, and different kinds of investigative skills.

The **Glossary** includes concise definitions and page references of all key terms introduced throughout the book.

The **Numerical Answers** section allows you to quickly check if you have the correct answers to numerical questions. Complete step-by-step solutions, plus graphical answers and diagrams, are provided on the teacher's Solutions Disk.

The **Index** makes it easy to locate key topics in the book.

TECHNOLOGY INTEGRATION
www.pearsoned.ca/school/physicssource

Pearson Physics is fully integrated with a high level of technology support. Icons throughout the printed Student Edition make references to the website *PhysicsSource* where numerous online resources and support are provided.

While the *Pearson Physics* student book provides complete coverage of the Program of Studies, *PhysicsSource* provides alternative and supplementary treatments of content in a way that may have greater appeal or effectiveness for some students and/or teachers.

Key technology features include:

 eLAB provides Probeware labs that can be done in the place of ones in the text that use conventional equipment. There is also a number of additional eLABs with no direct parallels in the book. These are designed to enhance your depth of understanding

 eMATH provides spreadsheet applications that may enhance your learning of concepts where mathematical approaches may be particularly complex, or a graph might help.

 eSIM provides interactive learning objects. The associated lessons are designed to improve concept understanding and problem solving skills. eSIM objects are a valuable way for you to work independently and to visualize the more complicated concepts in action. They may be used by your teacher for demonstration to the class, for independent student work as part of a lab, or as extensions or remedial work.

 eTECH provides opportunities to use Interactive Physics and VideoPoint activities, to further enhance understanding of some of the key concepts.

 eTESTs are interactive self-tests at the end of every section, chapter, and unit. The eTESTs cover the same content as the Check and Reflect, Chapter Review, and Unit Review features of the textbook with different questions. Feedback on most questions answered is immediate.

 eWEB provides links to potential websites that you can trust as sources of information for further research. Links and topic information are continually updated.

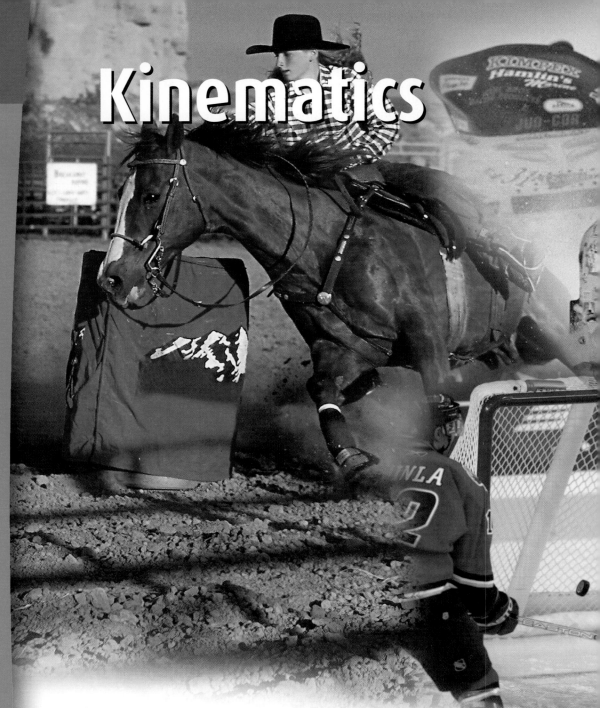

Kinematics

A player on the Calgary Flames hockey team shoots the puck . . .
and scores! A snowmobiler slides around an icy turn on a frozen lake
against a biting cold wind. A rider drives a horse around a barrel at
the Pro Rodeo barrel-racing competition at Writing-on-Stone, Alberta.

Every day, you see and experience motion. In this unit, you will
learn the language of physics that is used to describe motion. You
will then develop a set of equations and graphs that will help you
describe and explain what happens when an object moves.

e WEB

An exciting event at the Calgary Stampede is the fireworks display. To learn more about
the physics of fireworks, follow the links at www.pearsoned.ca/school/physicssource.

Unit at a Glance

Unit Themes and Emphases

- Change and Systems

Focussing Questions

The study of motion requires analyzing and describing how objects move. As you study this unit, consider these questions:

- How do changes in position, velocity, and acceleration allow us to predict the paths of moving objects and systems?
- How do the principles of kinematics influence the development of new mechanical technologies?

Unit Project

Are Amber Traffic Lights Timed Correctly?

- Using the kinematics equations learned in chapter 1, you will determine if the amber traffic lights in your area give drivers enough time to cross an intersection before the lights turn red.

Graphs and equations describe motion in one dimension.

D rivers participating in the annual Yukon Quest, a dogsled race between Whitehorse, Yukon Territory, and Fairbanks, Alaska, must complete a 1600-km course (Figure 1.1). Competitors must constantly adjust to changing snow and ice conditions and battle prevailing winds as they race up and down snow- and ice-covered hills, through valleys, across rivers, and on to the finish line. Competitors run six or more hours at a time, at an average speed of 13.0 km/h, in temperatures that can reach below -50 °C. In order to do well in such a race, competitors need to pay attention to various motion details, such as position relative to the other teams, distances travelled, and times elapsed.

To successfully complete the Yukon Quest, a driver must know how a sled moves and how fast the dogs can run. Recording times in training logs and measuring distances helps drivers understand the motion of the sled and of their dog team. In this chapter, you will learn how to describe motion using the terms, graphs, and equations of the branch of physics called *kinematics*.

▲ **Figure 1.1** A Yukon Quest competitor experiences changes in position and velocity during a race.

Match a Motion

Problem

What types of motions can you generate using ticker tape?

Materials

clacker
power supply
ticker tape

Procedure

1 Measure and cut 4 or 5 lengths of ticker tape of length 40 cm (approximately).

2 Pull the ticker tape through the clacker at an even speed.

3 Repeat step 2 for a new length of ticker tape. For each new ticker tape, pull with a different kind of motion: quickly, slowly, speeding up, slowing down, etc.

Questions

1. Describe the spacing between dots on each ticker tape. Is it even, increasing, or decreasing?

2. Use the spacing between dots to describe the motion of the ticker tape. Is it speeding up, slowing down, or constant?

3. What aspect of motion does the spacing between dots represent?

4. Have you covered all possible motions in the runs you did? If not, which ones did you omit? Give reasons why you omitted some types of motion.

Think About It

1. What is motion?

2. How do objects move?

3. What are some words used to describe motion?

4. How can you determine how far and how fast an object moves?

5. What does the term "falling" mean?

6. Describe how objects fall.

7. Which falls faster: a heavy object or a light object?

8. How can a ball that's moving upward still be falling?

Discuss your answers in a small group and record them for later reference. As you complete each section of this chapter, review your answers to these questions. Note any changes in your ideas.

1.1 The Language of Motion

When describing motions, such as the ones in Figures 1.1 and 1.2, you can use many different expressions and words. The English language is rich with them. Many sports broadcasters invent words or expressions to convey action and to excite the imagination. Phrases such as "a cannonating drive from the point" or "blistering speed" have become commonplace in our sports lingo. In physics, you must be precise in your language and use clearly defined terms to describe motion. **Kinematics** is the branch of physics that describes motion.

kinematics: a branch of physics that describes motion

▲ **Figure 1.2** How would you describe the motions shown in these photos?

> ## MINDS ON   How Do Objects Move?
>
> Study the photos in Figure 1.2. Describe the motion of the puck, the wheelchair, and the harpoon with respect to time. Jot down your descriptions and underline key words associated with motion. Compare your key words with those of a partner. Compile a class list on the chalkboard.

When describing motion, certain words, such as speed, acceleration, and velocity, are common. These words have slightly different meanings in physics than they do in everyday speech, as you will learn in the following subsection.

Physics Terms

origin: a reference point

position: the straight-line distance between the origin and an object's location; includes magnitude and direction

scalar quantity: a measurement that has magnitude only

vector quantity: a measurement that has both magnitude and direction

It's Saturday night and the Edmonton Oilers are playing the Calgary Flames. In order to locate players on the ice, you need a reference system. In this case, select the centre of the ice as the reference point, or **origin**. You can then measure the straight-line *distances*, d, of players from the origin, such as 5.0 m. If you specify a direction from the origin along with the distance, then you define a player's **position**, $\vec{d}$, for example, 5.0 m [E] (Figure 1.3). The arrow over the variable indicates that the variable is a vector quantity. The number and unit are called the *magnitude* of the vector. Distance, which has a magnitude but no direction associated with it, is an example of a **scalar quantity**. **Vector quantities** have both magnitude and direction. Position is an example of a vector quantity.

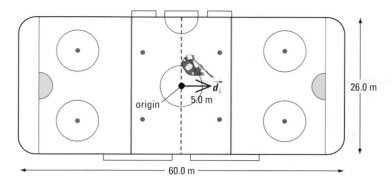

▲ **Figure 1.3** The player's *position* is 5.0 m [east of the origin] or simply 5.0 m [E]. The player is at a *distance* of 5.0 m from the origin.

If the player, initially 5.0 m [east of the origin], skates to the east end of the rink to the goal area, his position changes. It is now 25.0 m [east of the origin] or 25.0 m [E] (Figure 1.4). You can state that he has travelled a straight-line distance of 20.0 m, and has a displacement of 20.0 m [E] relative to his initial position.

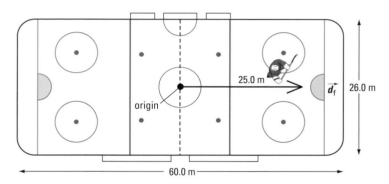

▲ **Figure 1.4** The player's *position* has changed. A change in position is called *displacement*.

Distance travelled is the length of the path taken to move from one position to another, regardless of direction. **Displacement**, $\Delta \vec{d}$, is the change in position. The player's displacement is written as

$$\Delta \vec{d} = 20.0 \text{ m [E]}$$

where Δ is the Greek letter delta that means "change in." Calculate the change in a quantity by subtracting the initial quantity from the final quantity. In algebraic notation, $\Delta R = R_f - R_i$. You can calculate the displacement of the player in the following manner:

$$\Delta \vec{d} = \vec{d}_f - \vec{d}_i$$
$$= 25.0 \text{ m [E]} - 5.0 \text{ [E]}$$
$$= 20.0 \text{ m [E]}$$

PHYSICS INSIGHT

Technically, if you are standing away from the origin, you are displaced a certain distance and in a certain direction. However, the Δ sign is not used with position unless the object you are referring to has moved from the origin to its current position, that is, unless the object has experienced a *change* in position.

distance: the length of the path taken to move from one position to another

displacement: a straight line between initial and final positions; includes magnitude and direction

info **BIT**

Pilots use radar vectors when landing their aircraft. Radar vectors are instructions to fly in a particular direction and usually include altitude and speed restrictions.

Sign Conventions

How would you determine your final distance and displacement if you moved from a position 5.0 m [W] to a position 10.0 m [E] (Figure 1.5)?

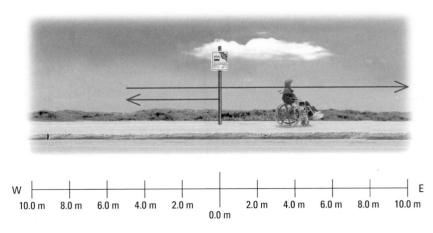

W ├───┼───┼───┼───┼───┼───┼───┼───┼───┤ E
10.0 m 8.0 m 6.0 m 4.0 m 2.0 m   2.0 m 4.0 m 6.0 m 8.0 m 10.0 m
                              0.0 m

▲ **Figure 1.5**   The person travels a distance of 5.0 m + 10.0 m = 15.0 m. What is the person's displacement? What is the person's final position relative to the bus stop?

To calculate the distance travelled, you need only add the magnitudes of the two position vectors.

$$\Delta d = 5.0 \text{ m} + 10.0 \text{ m}$$
$$= 15.0 \text{ m}$$

To find displacement, you need to *subtract* the initial position, $\vec{d}_i$, from the final position, $\vec{d}_f$. Let $\vec{d}_i = 5.0$ m [W] and $\vec{d}_f = 10.0$ m [E].

$$\Delta \vec{d} = \vec{d}_f - \vec{d}_i$$
$$= 10.0 \text{ m [E]} - 5.0 \text{ m [W]}$$

To solve this equation, recall that subtracting a vector is the same as adding its opposite, so the negative west direction is the same as the positive east direction.

$$\Delta \vec{d} = 10.0 \text{ m [E]} - 5.0 \text{ m [W]}$$
$$= 10.0 \text{ m [E]} + 5.0 \text{ m [E]}$$
$$= 15.0 \text{ m [E]}$$

Another way of solving for displacement is to designate the east direction as positive and the west direction as negative (Figure 1.6). The two position vectors become $\vec{d}_i = 5.0$ m [W] $= -5.0$ m and $\vec{d}_f = 10.0$ m [E] $= +10.0$ m. Now calculate displacement:

$$\Delta \vec{d} = \vec{d}_f - \vec{d}_i$$
$$= +10.0 \text{ m} - (-5.0 \text{ m})$$
$$= +15.0 \text{ m}$$

Since east is positive, the positive sign indicates that the person has moved 15.0 m east. Practise finding position and displacement in the next Skills Practice and example.

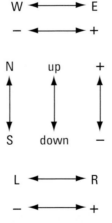

▲ **Figure 1.6**   Let east be positive and west negative. Similarly, north, up, and right are usually designated as positive.

info **BIT**

On April 26, 2004, Stephane Gras of France did 445 chin-ups in one hour. If you consider up as positive, then Gras made 445 positive displacements and 445 negative displacements, meaning that his net displacement was zero!

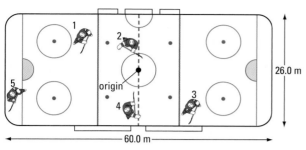

▲ Figure 1.7

1. Create a scale using the dimensions of the hockey rink (Figure 1.7). Measuring from the centre of the player's helmet,
   (a) find each player's position relative to the north and south sides of the rink.
   (b) find each player's position relative to the east and west sides of the rink.
   (c) If the player moves from position 2 to position 4 on the rink, what is his displacement?
   (d) Convert your measurements using your scale.

Example 1.1

Standing 1.5 m to the right of the inukshuk, a traveller moves 3.5 m to the left of the inukshuk (Figure 1.8). Determine the traveller's displacement algebraically
(a) using directions   (b) using plus and minus signs

Given
$\vec{d}_i$ = 1.5 m [right]
$\vec{d}_f$ = 3.5 m [left]

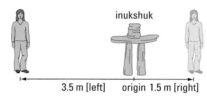

inukshuk

3.5 m [left]   origin 1.5 m [right]

▲ Figure 1.8

Required
displacement ($\Delta\vec{d}$)

Analysis and Solution
To find displacement, use the equation $\Delta\vec{d} = \vec{d}_f - \vec{d}_i$.
(a) $\Delta\vec{d} = \vec{d}_f - \vec{d}_i$

$= 3.5$ m [left] $- 1.5$ m [right]

$= 3.5$ m [left] $- (-1.5$ m [left])

$= 3.5$ m [left] $+ 1.5$ m [left]

$= 5.0$ m [left]

(b) Consider right to be positive.
$\vec{d}_i = 1.5$ m [right] $= +1.5$ m
$\vec{d}_f = 3.5$ m [left] $= -3.5$ m

$\Delta\vec{d} = \vec{d}_f - \vec{d}_i$

$= -3.5$ m $- (+1.5$ m)

$= -3.5$ m $- 1.5$ m

$= -5.0$ m

The answer is negative, so the direction is left.

Paraphrase
The traveller's displacement is 5.0 m [left] of her initial position.

Note that the direction of *displacement* is relative to initial position, whereas the direction of *position* is relative to the designated origin, in this case, the inukshuk.

Practice Problems

1. Sprinting drills include running 40.0 m [N], walking 20.0 m [N], and then sprinting 100.0 m [N]. What is the sprinter's displacement from the initial position?

2. To perform a give and go, a basketball player fakes out the defence by moving 0.750 m [right] and then 3.50 m [left]. What is the player's displacement from the starting position?

3. While building a wall, a bricklayer sweeps the cement back and forth. If she swings her hand back and forth, a distance of 1.70 m, four times, calculate the distance and displacement her hand travels during that time.

Answers
1. 160.0 m [N]
2. 2.75 m [left]
3. 6.80 m, 0 m

Chapter 1 Graphs and equations describe motion in one dimension.   9

For all subsequent problems in this book, you will be using plus and minus signs to indicate direction. This method is more flexible for problem solving and easier to use.

Like distance and displacement, speed and velocity is another scalar-vector pair. *Speed* is the rate at which an object moves. It is a scalar quantity, so it has magnitude only; for example, $v = 50$ km/h (Figure 1.9). *Velocity* is a vector quantity, so it has both magnitude (speed) and direction. If you are travelling south from Fort McMurray to Lethbridge at 50 km/h, your velocity is written as $\vec{v} = 50$ km/h [S]. If you designate south as negative, then $\vec{v} = -50$ km/h. *Acceleration* is a vector quantity that represents the rate of change of velocity. You will study aspects of displacement, velocity, and acceleration, and their interrelationships, in the sections that follow.

▲ **Figure 1.9**   Scalar or vector?

1.1   *Check and Reflect*

Knowledge

1. What two categories of terms describe motion? Give an example of each.

2. Compare and contrast distance and displacement.

3. What is the significance of a reference point?

Applications

4. Draw a seating plan using the statements below.

   (a) Chad is 2.0 m [left] of Dolores.

   (b) Ed is 4.5 m [right] of Chad.

   (c) Greg is 7.5 m [left] of Chad.

   (d) Hannah is 1.0 m [right] of Ed.

   (e) What is the displacement of a teacher who walks from Greg to Hannah?

5. A person's displacement is 50.0 km [W]. What is his final position if he started at 5.0 km [E]?

6. Using an autuk (a type of sealskin racquet), two children play catch. Standing 3.0 m apart, the child on the right tosses the ball to the child on the left, and then moves 5.0 m [right] to catch the ball again. Determine the horizontal distance and displacement the ball travels from its initial position (ignore any vertical motion).

7. Below is a seating plan for the head table at a wedding reception. Relative to the bride, describe the positions of the groom, best man, maid of honour, and flower girl.

e TEST

To check your understanding of scalar and vector quantities, follow the eTest links at www.pearsoned.ca/school/physicssource.

1.2 Position-time Graphs and Uniform Motion

You are competing to win the Masters Golf Tournament. The hole is 5.0 m away (Figure 1.10). You gently hit the ball with your club and hold your breath. Time seems to stop. Then, 5.0 s later, it rolls into the hole. You have won the tournament!

From section 1.1, you know that displacement is the change in an object's position. If you replay the sequence of motions of your winning putt in 1.0-s intervals, you can measure the displacements of the golf ball from you, the putter, to the hole (Figure 1.11).

▲ **Figure 1.10** You can represent motion in sports using vectors and graphs.

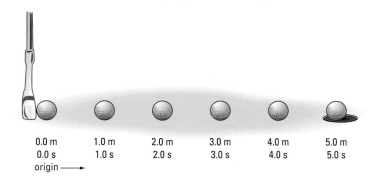

0.0 m	1.0 m	2.0 m	3.0 m	4.0 m	5.0 m
0.0 s	1.0 s	2.0 s	3.0 s	4.0 s	5.0 s
origin ⟶					

▲ **Figure 1.11** What is the golf ball's displacement after each second?

Table 1.1 displays the data from Figure 1.11 for the golf ball's position from you at 1.0-s intervals. By graphing the data, you can visualize the motion of the golf ball more clearly (Figure 1.12).

▼ **Table 1.1** Position-time data

	Time (s)	Position (m [right])
t_0	0.0	0.0
t_1	1.0	1.0
t_2	2.0	2.0
t_3	3.0	3.0
t_4	4.0	4.0
t_5	5.0	5.0

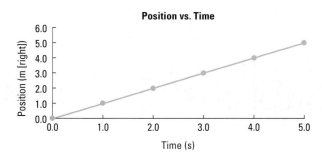

▲ **Figure 1.12** A position-time graph of the golf ball

Velocity

Notice that the graph in Figure 1.12 is a straight line. A straight line has a constant slope. What does constant slope tell you about the ball's motion? To answer this question, calculate the slope and keep track of the units. Designate toward the hole, to the right, as the positive direction.

Recall that slope $= \dfrac{\text{rise}}{\text{run}}$. For position–time graphs, this equation becomes slope $= \dfrac{\text{change in position}}{\text{change in time}}$

A change in position is displacement. So, the equation for slope becomes

$$\text{slope} = \frac{\Delta \vec{d}}{\Delta t}$$

$$= \frac{\vec{d}_f - \vec{d}_i}{t_f - t_i}$$

$$= \frac{+5.0 \text{ m} - 0.0 \text{ m}}{5.0 \text{ s} - 0.0 \text{ s}}$$

$$= +1.0 \text{ m/s}$$

The answer is positive, so the golf ball moves at a rate of 1.0 m/s [right].

Notice that the units are m/s (read metres per second). These units indicate speed or velocity. Since displacement is a vector quantity, the slope of the position-time graph in Figure 1.12 gives you the **velocity**, $\vec{v}$, of the ball: the change in position per unit time. Because you have calculated velocity over a time interval rather than at an instant in time, it is the *average velocity*.

PHYSICS INSIGHT

Speed has magnitude only. Velocity has both magnitude and direction.

velocity: rate of change in position

$$\vec{v} = \frac{\Delta \vec{d}}{\Delta t}$$

Speed and Velocity

Objects travelling at the same speed can have different velocities. For example, a tram carries passengers across a ravine at a constant speed. A passenger going to the observation deck has a velocity of 4 m/s [right] and a passenger leaving the deck has a velocity of 4 m/s [left] (Figure 1.13). Their speeds are the same, but because they are travelling in opposite directions, their velocities are different.

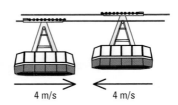

4 m/s   4 m/s

▲ **Figure 1.13** Objects with the same speed can have different velocities.

1-2 *Decision-Making Analysis*

Traffic Safety Is Everyone's Business

The Issue

In an average year in Alberta, traffic accidents claim six times more lives than homicide, eight times more lives than AIDS, and 100 times more lives than meningitis. Collisions represent one of the greatest threats to public safety.

Background Information

In the Canadian 2002 Nerves of Steel: Aggressive Driving Study, speeding was identified as one of two common aggressive behaviours that contribute to a significant percentage of all crashes. The Alberta Motor Association's Alberta Traffic Safety Progress Report has suggested that a province-wide speed management program could significantly improve levels of road safety, decreasing both speed and casualties. One suggested program is the implementation of the vehicle tachograph, a device required in Europe.

Analysis

Your group has been asked to research different traffic safety initiatives. The government will use the results of your research to make the most appropriate decision.

1. Research

   (a) how state- or province-wide speed management programs have influenced driver behaviour

   (b) the societal cost of vehicle crashes

   (c) driver attitudes toward enforcement of and education about traffic safety issues

2. Analyze your research and decide which management program should be used.

3. Once your group has completed a written report recommending a particular program, present the report to the rest of the class, who will act as representatives of the government and the community.

So far, you have learned that the slope of a position-time graph represents a rate of change in position, or velocity. If an object moves at constant velocity (constant magnitude and direction), the object is undergoing **uniform motion**.

A position-time graph for an object **at rest** is a horizontal line (Figure 1.14). An object at rest is still said to be undergoing uniform motion because its change in position remains constant over equal time intervals.

uniform motion: constant velocity (motion or rest)

at rest: not moving; stationary

> ### Concept Check
>
> (a) Describe the position of dots on a ticker tape at rest. Draw the corresponding graph. What is the slope of this graph?
> (b) Describe the shape of a position-time graph for an object travelling at a constant velocity. List three possibilities.

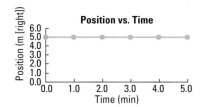

▲ **Figure 1.14** A position-time graph for a stationary object

Frame of Reference

If you were to designate the hole, rather than the putter, as the origin in the golf tournament (Figure 1.15(a)), your data table would start at 5.0 m at time 0.0 s, instead of at 0.0 m and 0.0 s (Table 1.2).

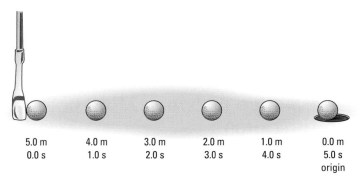

▲ **Figure 1.15(a)** Designating an origin is arbitrary. In this example, the hole is the origin and all positions are measured relative to it.

▼ **Table 1.2** Position-time data

	Time (s)	Position (m [right])
t_0	0.0	5.0
t_1	1.0	4.0
t_2	2.0	3.0
t_3	3.0	2.0
t_4	4.0	1.0
t_5	5.0	0.0

info BIT

On May 31, 2004 in Moscow, Ashrita Furman of the USA walked 1.6 km while continuously hula-hooping in 14 min 25 s. He also holds the world record for the fastest time for pushing an orange with his nose. On August 12, 2004, he pushed an orange 1.6 km in 24 min 36 s. What was his speed, in km/h and m/s, for each case?

The corresponding position-time graph is shown in Figure 1.15(b).

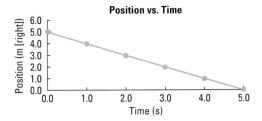

▲ **Figure 1.15(b)**   If you change your reference frame, the position-time graph also changes. Compare this graph with the graph in Figure 1.12.

Consider right (toward the hole) to be positive. From the graph,

$$\text{slope} = \vec{v}$$

$$= \frac{\Delta \vec{d}}{\Delta t}$$

$$= \frac{\vec{d}_f - \vec{d}_i}{t_f - t_i}$$

$$= \frac{0.0 \text{ m} - (+5.0 \text{ m})}{5.0 \text{ s} - 0.0 \text{ s}}$$

$$= -1.0 \text{ m/s}$$

What does the minus sign mean? You still putted in the same direction — toward the hole, to the right! The answer lies in the choice of reference frame. The ball is now moving *toward* the origin as opposed to *away* from it (see Figure 1.11, where the origin was at the putter's position). The sign of the ball's direction is negative because the ball's position from the origin *decreases* each second by 1.0 m, as represented by the downward slope of the graph. The golf ball's velocity is still 1.0 m/s [right] because the ball is moving to the right.

Concept Check

> Determine how the velocity of the golf ball can be positive if the hole is at the origin.

e WEB

In November 2004, at an altitude of 33 000 m, the X-43A recorded a speed of Mach 9. Use the Internet or your local library to research the term "Mach" as used to describe the speed of an object. How did this term originate? What is the difference between Mach and ultrasonic? Write a brief summary of your findings. To learn more about Mach, follow the links at www.pearsoned.ca/school/physicssource.

Below is a summary of what you have learned:
– The slope of a position-time graph represents velocity.
– The velocity is the *average* velocity for the time interval.
– Your choice of reference frame affects the direction (sign) of your answer.

Comparing the Motion of Two or More Objects on a Position-time Graph

You can represent the motions of two objects on one graph, as long as the origin is the same for both objects and they are moving at the same time. You can then use the graph to compare their motions, as in the next example.

Example 1.2

At the end of the school day, student A and student B say goodbye and head in opposite directions. Student B heads north to the bus stop while student A walks south to her house. After 3.0 min, student A is 300 m [S] and student B is 450 m [N] (Figure 1.16).
(a) Graph the position of each student on one graph after 3.0 min.
(b) Determine the velocity of each student algebraically.

Given
Choose north to be positive.
$$\Delta \vec{d}_A = 300 \text{ m [S]} = -300 \text{ m}$$
$$\Delta \vec{d}_B = 450 \text{ m [N]} = +450 \text{ m}$$
$$\Delta t = 3.0 \text{ min}$$

Required
(a) position–time graph
(b) velocity ($\vec{v}_A$ and $\vec{v}_B$)

Analysis and Solution
(a) Since north is the positive direction, plot student B's position (3.0 min, +450 m) above the time axis and student A's position (3.0 min, −300 m) below the time axis (Figure 1.17).

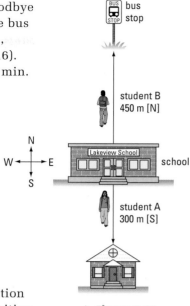
▲ **Figure 1.16**

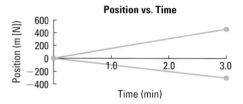

▲ **Figure 1.17**

(b) Convert time in minutes to time in seconds.

Then use the equation $\vec{v} = \dfrac{\Delta \vec{d}}{\Delta t}$ to find the velocity of each student.

$$\Delta t = 3.0 \text{ min} \times \frac{60 \text{ s}}{1 \text{ min}}$$
$$= 180 \text{ s}$$
$$\vec{v}_A = \frac{-300 \text{ m}}{180 \text{ s}}$$
$$= -1.7 \text{ m/s}$$

The sign is negative, so the direction is south.

$$\vec{v}_B = \frac{+450 \text{ m}}{180 \text{ s}}$$
$$= +2.5 \text{ m/s}$$

The sign is positive, so the direction is north.

Paraphrase
(b) Student A's velocity is 1.7 m/s [S] and student B's velocity is 2.5 m/s [N].

Practice Problems

1. A wildlife biologist measures how long it takes four animals to cover a displacement of 200 m [forward].
(a) Graph the data in the table below.
(b) Determine each animal's velocity.

Animal	Time taken (s)
Elk	10.0
Coyote	10.4
Grizzly bear	18.0
Moose	12.9

Answers

1. (a)

Position vs. Time

(b) Elk: 20.0 m/s [forward]
Coyote: 19.2 m/s [forward]
Grizzly bear: 11.1 m/s [forward]
Moose: 15.5 m/s [forward]

So far, you have learned that the slope of a position–time graph represents velocity. By comparing the slopes of two graphs, you can determine which object is moving faster. From the slopes of the graphs in Figure 1.17, which student is moving faster? When you represent the motions of two objects on the same graph, you can also tell whether the objects are approaching or moving apart by checking if the lines are converging or diverging. An important event occurs at the point where the two lines intersect. Both objects have the same position, so the objects meet at this point.

Concept Check

If two objects are approaching each other, how can you represent their motions on a graph?

In the next example, two objects start at different times and have different speeds. You will graphically find their meeting point.

Example 1.3

Two rollerbladers, A and B, are having a race. B gives A a head start of 5.0 s (Figure 1.18). Each rollerblader moves with a constant velocity. Assume that the time taken to reach constant velocity is negligible. If A travels 100.0 m [right] in 20.0 s and B travels 112.5 m [right] in 15.0 s,
(a) graph the motions of both rollerbladers on the same graph.
(b) find the time, position, and displacement at which B catches up with A.

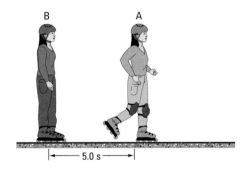

◄ **Figure 1.18**

Practice Problems

1. The two rollerbladers in Example 1.3 are having a race. They start at the same time, but B's initial position is 10.0 m left of A.
   (a) Graph the motions of the rollerbladers.
   (b) Find the time, position, and displacement at which B catches up with A.

Answers

1. (b) t = 4.0 s
   $\vec{d}$ = 20.0 m [right]
   $\Delta \vec{d}$ = 30.0 m [right]

Given
Choose right to be positive.
$\Delta \vec{d}_A = 100.0$ m [right] $= +100.0$ m
$\Delta t_A = 20.0$ s
$\Delta \vec{d}_B = 112.5$ m [right] $= +112.5$ m
$\Delta t_B = 15.0$ s, started 5.0 s later

Required
(a) position-time graph
(b) time (Δt), position ($\vec{d}$), and displacement ($\Delta \vec{d}$) when B catches up with A

Analysis and Solution
(a) Assume that $t = 0.0$ s at the start of A's motion. Thus, the position-time graph of A's motion starts at the origin. A's final position is $+100.0$ m at 20.0 s.

The position-time graph for B's motion starts at 0.0 m and 5.0 s (because B started 5.0 s after A). B starts moving after 5.0 s for 15.0 s. Thus, at 20.0 s (5.0 s + 15.0 s), B's position is $+112.5$ m. Each rollerblader travels with a constant velocity, so the lines connecting their initial and final positions are straight (Figure 1.19(a)).

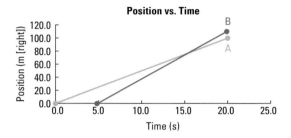

▲ **Figure 1.19(a)**

(b) On the graph in Figure 1.19(a), look for a point of intersection. At this point, both rollerbladers have the same final position. From the graph, you can see that this point occurs at $t = 15.0$ s. The corresponding position is $+75.0$ m (Figure 1.19(b)).

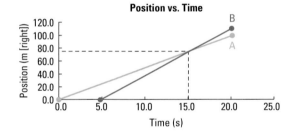

▲ **Figure 1.19(b)**

To find B's displacement, find the change in position: $\Delta \vec{d} = \vec{d}_f - \vec{d}_i$.

Because both A and B started from rest, $\vec{d}_i = 0$. Since they both have the same final position at the point of intersection, $\vec{d}_f = +75.0$ m.

$\Delta \vec{d} = +75.0$ m $- 0.0$ m
$\quad = +75.0$ m

The answer is positive, so the direction is to the right.

Paraphrase
(b) B catches up with A 15.0 s later. B's position and displacement are 75.0 m [right] of the origin.

Example 1.4

From Example 1.3, find the velocities of the two rollerbladers.

Given
Choose right to be positive. At the point of intersection (Figure 1.19(b)),

$$\Delta \vec{d}_A = 75.0 \text{ m [right]} = +75.0 \text{ m}$$
$$\Delta t_A = 15.0 \text{ s}$$
$$\Delta \vec{d}_B = 75.0 \text{ m [right]} = +75.0 \text{ m}$$
$$\Delta t_B = 15.0 \text{ s} - 5.0 \text{ s}$$
$$= 10.0 \text{ s}$$

Required
velocities of A and B ($\vec{v}_A$, $\vec{v}_B$)

Analysis and Solution
To find the velocity of each rollerblader, remember that the slope of a position–time graph is velocity. Because the motions are uniform, the slopes will be constant for each rollerblader.

$$\vec{v} = \frac{\Delta \vec{d}}{\Delta t}$$

$$\vec{v}_A = \frac{+75.0 \text{ m} - 0.0 \text{ m}}{15.0 \text{ s} - 0.0 \text{ s}}$$

$$= +5.0 \text{ m/s}$$

$$\vec{v}_B = \frac{+75.0 \text{ m} - 0.0 \text{ m}}{10.0 \text{ s} - 0.0 \text{ s}}$$

$$= +7.5 \text{ m/s}$$

The answers are both positive, so the direction is to the right. You can see that, in order for B to cover the same distance as A, B must move faster because B started later.

Paraphrase
A's velocity is 5.0 m/s [right] and B's velocity is 7.5 m/s [right].

Practice Problems

1. If rollerblader B's initial position is 10.0 m left of A, find the velocities of the two rollerbladers.

Answers

1. A: 5.0 m/s [right]
   B: 7.5 m/s [right]

Car Activity

Question

What are the speeds of two different toy cars?

If one car is released 3.0 s after the other, where will they meet?

Variables

Identify the manipulated, responding, and controlled variables.

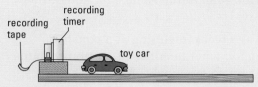

▲ **Figure 1.20**

Materials and Equipment

two battery-operated toy cars

ticker tape	ruler
carbon disk	graph paper
spark timer (60 Hz)	masking tape

Procedure

1 On a flat surface, such as the floor or lab bench, mark the initial starting position of car 1 with masking tape.

2 Using masking tape, attach 1.0 m of ticker tape to the end of car 1.

3 Thread the ticker tape through the spark timer (Figure 1.20).

4 Turn the car on.

5 Turn the spark timer on as you release the car from its initial position.

6 Observe the path of car 1 until the ticker tape is used up. Label the ticker tape "car 1."

7 Repeat steps 2–6 for car 2.

Analysis

1. Draw a line through the first dot on each ticker tape and label it $t = 0$ s.

2. Depending on the calibration of your ticker timer, count from the starting position, and place a mark after a fixed number of dots, e.g., 6, 12, 18, 24, etc. Label each mark t_1, t_2, etc.

3. Measure the distance from $t = 0$ to t_1, $t = 0$ to t_2, $t = 0$ to t_3, etc. Record the data in a position–time table.

4. Using an appropriate scale, graph each set of data for each toy car, separately.

5. Determine the slope of the line of best fit for each graph.

6. What is the speed of each toy car?

7. How do the speeds of car 1 and car 2 compare?

8. Assuming uniform motion, how far would car 1 travel in 15 s?

9. Assuming uniform motion, how long would it take car 2 to travel 30 m?

10. Imagine that you release the faster car 3.0 s after the slower car. Graphically determine the position where the two cars meet. Assume uniform motion.

 e **LAB**

For a probeware activity, go to
www.pearsoned.ca/school/physicssource.

In summary, you can see how a position-time graph helps you visualize the event you are analyzing. Calculating the slope of a position-time graph provides new information about the motion, namely, the object's velocity. In the next sections, you will expand on your graphing knowledge by analyzing motion using a velocity-time graph.

Knowledge

1. For an object at rest, what quantities of motion remain the same over equal time intervals?

2. For an object travelling at a constant velocity, what quantity of motion remains the same over equal time intervals?

3. Match each ticker tape below with the correct position-time graph.

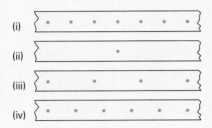

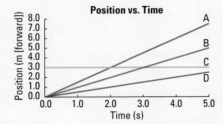

4. Sketch position-time graphs for the ticker tapes given below on one graph.

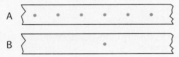

5. A camper kayaks 16 km [E] from a camping site, stops, and then paddles 23 km [W]. What is the camper's final position with respect to the camp site?

6. Sketch a position-time graph for a bear starting 1.2 m from a reference point, walking slowly away at constant velocity for 3.0 s, stopping for 5.0 s, backing up at half the speed for 2.0 s, and finally stopping.

7. Sketch a position-time graph for a student

   (a) walking to school with a constant velocity

   (b) stopping 5 km from the mall

   (c) cycling home with constant velocity

Applications

8. Two children on racing bikes start from the same reference point. Child A travels 5.0 m/s [right] and child B travels 4.5 m/s [right]. How much farther from the point of origin is child A than child B after 5.0 s?

9. Insect A moves 5.0 m/min and insect B moves 9.0 cm/s. Using a position-time graph, determine which insect moves faster.

10. Describe the motion in each lettered stage of the position-time graph below.

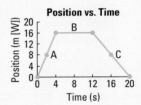

11. A mosquito flies toward you with a velocity of 2.4 km/h [E]. If a distance of 35.0 m separates you and the mosquito, at what point will the mosquito hit your sunglasses if you are travelling toward the mosquito with a speed of 2.0 m/s and the mosquito is travelling in a straight path?

12. Spotting a friend 5.0 m directly in front of you, walking 2.0 m/s [N], you start walking 2.25 m/s [N] to catch up. How long will it take for you to intercept your friend and what will be your displacement?

13. Two vehicles, separated by a distance of 450 m, travel in opposite directions toward a traffic light. When will the vehicles pass one another if vehicle A is travelling 35 km/h and is 300 m [E] of the traffic light while vehicle B is travelling 40 km/h? When will each vehicle pass the traffic light, assuming the light remains green the entire time?

e TEST

To check your understanding of uniform motion, follow the eTest links at www.pearsoned.ca/school/physicssource.

1.3 Velocity-time Graphs: Uniform and Non-uniform Motion

Recently installed video screens in aircraft provide passengers with information about the aircraft's velocity during the flight (Figure 1.21).

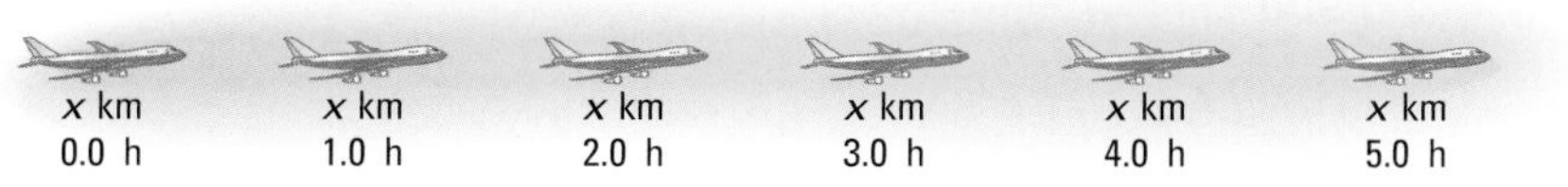

| x km | x km | x km | x km | x km | x km |
| 0.0 h | 1.0 h | 2.0 h | 3.0 h | 4.0 h | 5.0 h |

▲ **Figure 1.22** A plane flies at a constant speed, so the distances within each time interval are equal. Break the plane's motion into a series of snapshots. Record your data in a data table and then graph it.

Figure 1.22 shows the data of the plane's path. Like position-time graphs, velocity-time graphs provide useful information about the motion of an object. The shape of the velocity-time graph reveals whether the object is at rest, moving at constant speed, speeding up, or slowing down. Suppose an airplane has a cruising altitude of 10 600 m and travels at a constant velocity of 900 km/h [E] for 5.0 h. Table 1.3 shows the velocity-time data for the airplane. If you graph the data, you can determine the relationship between the two variables, velocity and time (Figure 1.23).

▲ **Figure 1.21** Video screens are an example of an application of velocity-time graphs.

▼ **Table 1.3**

Time (h)	Velocity (km/h) [E]
0.0	900
1.0	900
2.0	900
3.0	900
4.0	900
5.0	900

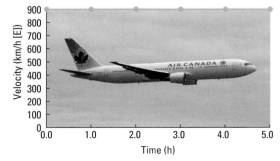

Velocity vs. Time for an Airplane

▲ **Figure 1.23** A velocity-time graph for an airflight

Designating east as the positive direction, the slope of the velocity-time graph is:

$$\text{slope} = \frac{\text{rise}}{\text{run}}$$

$$= \frac{\Delta \vec{v}}{\Delta t}$$

$$= \frac{\vec{v}_f - \vec{v}_i}{t_f - t_i}$$

$$= \frac{+900 \ \dfrac{\text{km}}{\text{h}} - \left(+900 \ \dfrac{\text{km}}{\text{h}}\right)}{5.0 \ \text{h} - 1.0 \ \text{h}}$$

$$= 0 \ \text{km/h}^2$$

From the graph in Figure 1.23, there is no change in the plane's velocity, so the slope of the velocity-time graph is zero.

Notice the units of the slope of the velocity-time graph: km/h^2. These units are units of *acceleration*. Because the plane is moving at a constant velocity, its acceleration is zero.

In general, you can recognize acceleration values by their units, which are always distance divided by time squared. In physics, the standard units for acceleration are metres per second per second, which is generally abbreviated to m/s^2 (read metres per second squared).

e TECH

Determine the velocity of an object based on the shape of its position-time graph. Go to www.pearsoned.ca/school/physicssource.

Concept Check

(a) What does the slope of a position-time graph represent?
(b) What does the slope of a velocity-time graph represent?

Non-uniform Motion

Although objects may experience constant velocity over short time intervals, even a car operating on cruise control has fluctuations in speed or direction (Figure 1.24). How can you describe and illustrate a change of velocity using the concepts of kinematics?

Recall from section 1.2 that an object moving at a constant velocity is undergoing uniform motion. But is uniform motion the only type of motion? Perform the next QuickLab to find out.

◄ **Figure 1.24** Consider the kinds of changes in velocity this car experiences during the trip.

Match a Graph

Problem

What type of motion does each graph describe?

Materials

LM 1-1
ruler
motion sensor
masking tape

Procedure

1. Study the different position-time graphs on LM 1-1. With a partner, decide what type of motion each graph illustrates.

2. Set up the motion sensor to plot position vs. time.

3. Label a starting position with masking tape. Move away from the motion sensor in such a way that the graph of the motion captured approximates the one on the LM.

4. Switch roles with your partner and repeat steps 1–3.

5. Print out the graphs from your experiment. For each graph, construct a table of values for position and time.

Questions

1. Describe the motion of an object that has a horizontal line as its position–time graph.

2. What relationship exists between the type of motion and change in position?

3. Suggest two different ways in which you could classify the motion described by the four graphs.

4. What would the graph look like if you moved away from and then back toward the motion sensor?

5. What happens to the graph when you move away from your initial position and then move back toward and then beyond your initial position?

e LAB

For a probeware activity, go to
www.pearsoned.ca/school/physicssource.

Concept Check

Which ticker tape in Figure 1.25 represents accelerated motion? Explain.

▲ **Figure 1.25**

▲ **Figure 1.26** A drag racer accelerates from rest.

Consider an object, such as a drag racer (Figure 1.26), starting from rest and reaching a constant velocity over a time interval (Figure 1.27). During this time interval, the vehicle has to change its velocity from a value of zero to a final non-zero value. An object whose velocity changes (increases or decreases) over a time interval is undergoing **acceleration**, represented by the variable $\vec{a}$. Acceleration is also called **non-uniform motion** because the object's speed and/or direction are changing.

acceleration: a vector quantity representing the change in velocity (magnitude and/or direction) per unit time

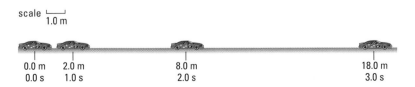

scale ⊢⎯⎯⎯⊣
1.0 m

0.0 m	2.0 m	8.0 m	18.0 m
0.0 s	1.0 s	2.0 s	3.0 s

◀ **Figure 1.27** This sequence illustrates a car undergoing non-uniform motion.

PHYSICS INSIGHT

An object is accelerating if it is speeding up, slowing down, or changing direction.

The following scenario illustrates acceleration.

A drag race is a 402-m (quarter-mile) contest between two vehicles. Starting from rest, the vehicles leave the starting line at the same time, and the first vehicle to cross the finish line is the winner. A fan records the position of her favourite vehicle during the drag race. Her results are recorded in Table 1.4.

The position-time graph for this data is shown in Figure 1.28. From the graph, note that the object is speeding up because the displacement between data points increases for each successive time interval. Which ticker tape in Figure 1.25 matches the graph in Figure 1.28?

▼ **Table 1.4**

Time (s)	Position (m [forward])
0.0	0.0
1.0	2.0
2.0	8.0
3.0	18.0
4.0	32.0
5.0	50.0

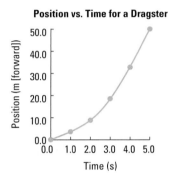

◄ **Figure 1.28**
What does the slope of the graph indicate about the speed of the car?

Instantaneous Velocity

Instantaneous velocity is the moment-to-moment measure of an object's velocity. Imagine recording the speed of your car once every second while driving north. These data comprise a series of instantaneous velocities that describe your trip in detail.

Earlier in this section, you learned that determining the velocity of an object from a position-time graph requires calculating the slope of the position-time graph. But how can you obtain the slope of a curve? Remember that each point on the curve indicates the position of the object (in this case, the dragster) at an instant in time. To determine the velocity of an object at any instant, physicists use tangents. A **tangent** is a straight line that touches a curve at only one point (Figure 1.29(a)). Each tangent on a curve has a unique slope, which represents the velocity at that instant. In order for the object to be at that position, at that time, it must have an *instantaneous velocity* equal to the slope of the tangent at that point. Determining the slopes of the tangents at different points on a position-time curve gives the instantaneous velocities at different times. Consider forward to be the positive direction.

PHYSICS INSIGHT

When you calculate the slope of a line or curve at a single point, you are finding an instantaneous value. When you calculate the slope between two points, you are finding an average value.

tangent: a straight line that touches a curved-line graph at only one point

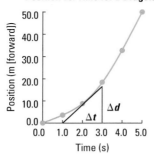

Position vs. Time for a Dragster

▲ **Figure 1.29(a)**

The slope of the tangent at 2.0 s is

$$\text{slope} = \frac{\Delta \vec{d}}{\Delta t}$$

$$= \frac{+14.0 \text{ m} - 0.0 \text{ m}}{3.0 \text{ s} - 1.0 \text{ s}}$$

$$= \frac{+14.0 \text{ m}}{2.0 \text{ s}}$$

$$= +7.0 \text{ m/s}$$

The sign is positive, so at 2.0 s, the velocity of the dragster is 7.0 m/s [forward].

The slope at the point (0.0, 0.0) is a horizontal line, so its value is zero.

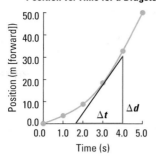

Position vs. Time for a Dragster

▲ **Figure 1.29(b)**

The slope of the tangent at 3.0 s is

$$\text{slope} = \frac{+30.0 \text{ m} - 0.0 \text{ m}}{4.0 \text{ s} - 1.75 \text{ s}}$$

$$= \frac{+30.0 \text{ m}}{2.25 \text{ s}}$$

$$= +13 \text{ m/s}$$

At 3.0 s, the velocity of the dragster is 13 m/s [forward].

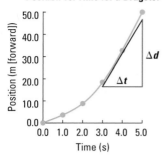

Position vs. Time for a Dragster

▲ **Figure 1.29(c)**

The slope of the tangent at 4.0 s is

$$\text{slope} = \frac{+47.0 \text{ m} - (+15.0 \text{ m})}{5.0 \text{ s} - 3.0 \text{ s}}$$

$$= \frac{+32.0 \text{ m}}{2.0 \text{ s}}$$

$$= +16 \text{ m/s}$$

At 4.0 s, the velocity of the dragster is 16 m/s [forward].

Using Slopes of Position-time Graphs to Draw Velocity-time Graphs

You can now create a new table using the slopes of the position-time graphs in Figures 1.29(a), (b), and (c). See Table 1.5. Remember that the slope of a position-time graph is velocity. These slope values are actually *instantaneous velocities* at the given times. The resulting velocity-time graph is a straight line with a positive slope (Figure 1.30). To find the meaning of slope, check the units of the slope of a velocity-time graph. They are (m/s)/s, which simplify to m/s², which simplify to m/s². These units are the units of acceleration. Since the velocity-time graph in this example is a straight line with non-zero slope, the acceleration of the object is constant, so the object must be undergoing **uniformly accelerated motion.**

uniformly accelerated motion: constant change in velocity per unit time

▼ **Table 1.5**

Time (s)	Velocity (m/s [forward])
0.0	0.0
2.0	7.0
3.0	13
4.0	16

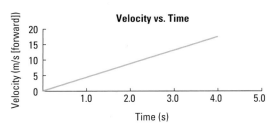

▲ **Figure 1.30** This velocity-time graph represents an object undergoing uniformly accelerated motion.

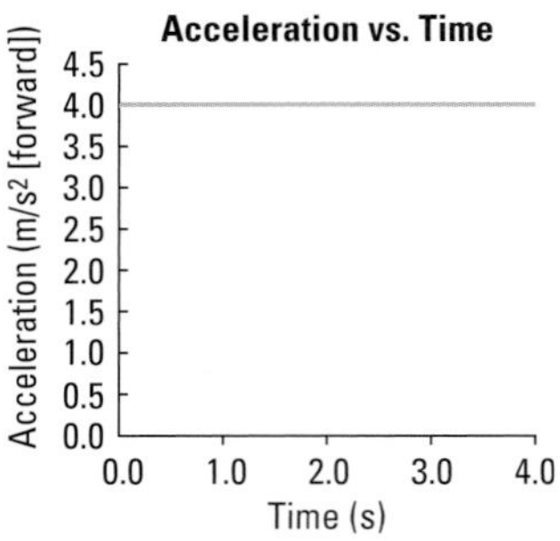

▲ **Figure 1.31** An acceleration-time graph for an object undergoing uniformly accelerated motion is a straight line with zero slope.

Just as the slope of a position-time graph reveals the rate at which position changes (velocity), the slope of a velocity-time graph reveals the rate at which velocity changes (acceleration). Calculate the slope of the line in Figure 1.30 as follows, designating forward as positive:

$$\text{slope} = \frac{\text{rise}}{\text{run}}$$

$$\vec{a} = \frac{\Delta \vec{v}}{\Delta t}$$

$$= \frac{\vec{v}_\text{f} - \vec{v}_\text{i}}{t_\text{f} - t_\text{i}}$$

$$= \frac{+10 \text{ m/s} - (+4 \text{ m/s})}{2.5 \text{ s} - 1.0 \text{ s}}$$

$$= +4 \text{ m/s}^2$$

The answer is positive, so the car is accelerating at 4 m/s² [forward]. The resulting acceleration-time graph is shown in Figure 1.31. You know that the velocity-time graph for an object undergoing uniform motion is a horizontal line (with zero slope, as in Figure 1.23). Similarly, a horizontal line on an acceleration-time graph indicates uniform acceleration.

PHYSICS INSIGHT

If the acceleration-time graph has a non-zero slope, the acceleration is changing (is non-uniform). The slope of an acceleration-time graph is called *jerk*, with units m/s³.

Concept Check

If the position-time graph for an object undergoing positive acceleration is a parabola, such as the one in Figure 1.28, what is the shape of the position-time graph for an object undergoing negative acceleration? What would a ticker tape of the motion of an object that is slowing down look like?

After driving your all-terrain vehicle (ATV, Figure 1.32) through a field, you see a wide river just ahead, so you quickly bring the vehicle to a complete stop. Notice in Figure 1.33 that, as your ATV slows down, the displacement in each time interval decreases.

◀ **Figure 1.32** ATVs can undergo a wide variety of motions.

scale ⊢——⊣ 1.0 m

| 0.0 m | 13.5 m | 24.0 m | 31.5 m | 36.0 m 37.5 m |
| 0.0 s | 1.0 s | 2.0 s | 3.0 s | 4.0 s 5.0 s |

▲ **Figure 1.33** This ATV is undergoing non-uniform motion. It is accelerating, in this case, slowing down.

Example 1.5 shows the calculations and resulting velocity-time graph for an object that is slowing down uniformly.

Example 1.5

The position-time data for an ATV approaching a river are given in Table 1.6. Using these data,
(a) draw a position-time graph
(b) draw a velocity-time graph
(c) calculate acceleration

Analysis and Solution
Designate the forward direction as positive.
(a) For the position-time graph, plot the data in Table 1.6 (Figure 1.34).

▼ **Table 1.6**

Time (s)	Position (m [forward])
0.0	0.0
1.0	13.5
2.0	24.0
3.0	31.5
4.0	36.0
5.0	37.5

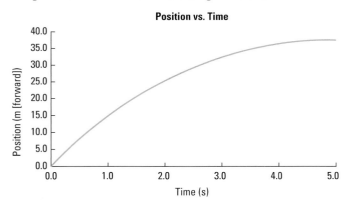

Position vs. Time

▲ **Figure 1.34**

(b) Since the position-time graph is non-linear, find the slope of the tangent at each second (Figures 1.35(a), (b), and (c)).

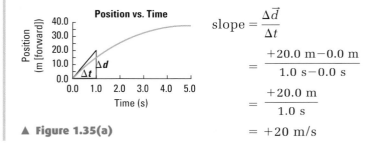

▲ **Figure 1.35(a)**

$$\text{slope} = \frac{\Delta \vec{d}}{\Delta t}$$

$$= \frac{+20.0 \text{ m} - 0.0 \text{ m}}{1.0 \text{ s} - 0.0 \text{ s}}$$

$$= \frac{+20.0 \text{ m}}{1.0 \text{ s}}$$

$$= +20 \text{ m/s}$$

Practice Problems

1. Draw a position-time graph from the velocity-time graph given below.

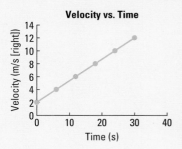

Velocity vs. Time

2. Calculate the acceleration using the graph below.

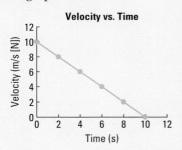

Velocity vs. Time

3. Use the graph below to determine the displacement of the object.

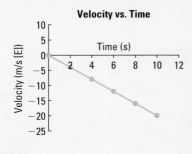

Velocity vs. Time

Answers

2. −1.0 m/s²
3. −100 m [E] or 100 m [W]

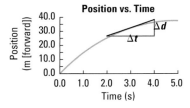

▲ **Figure 1.35(b)**

$$\text{slope} = \frac{\Delta \vec{d}}{\Delta t}$$

$$= \frac{+37.0 \text{ m} - (+26.0 \text{ m})}{4.0 \text{ s} - 2.0 \text{ s}}$$

$$= \frac{+11.0 \text{ m}}{2.0 \text{ s}}$$

$$= +5.5 \text{ m/s}$$

Position vs. Time

▲ **Figure 1.35(c)**

This tangent is a horizontal line, so its slope is zero.

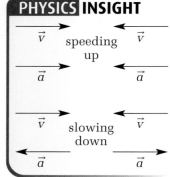

e **MATH**

For an alternative method to create a velocity-time graph from the position-time data points, visit www.pearsoned.ca/school/physicssource.

The slopes of the tangents give the instantaneous velocities (Table 1.7). Positive signs mean that the direction is forward. Plot the data on a velocity-time graph (Figure 1.36).

▼ **Table 1.7**

Time (s)	Velocity (m/s [forward])
0.0	20
3.0	5.5
5.0	0

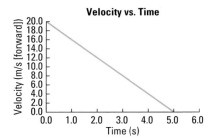

▲ **Figure 1.36**

(c) Find acceleration by calculating the slope of the velocity-time graph.

$$\vec{a} = \frac{\Delta \vec{v}}{\Delta t}$$

$$= \frac{0.0 \, \frac{m}{s} - \left(+20 \, \frac{m}{s} \right)}{5.0 \text{ s} - 0.0 \text{ s}}$$

$$= -4.0 \text{ m/s}^2$$

The acceleration of the ATV is -4.0 m/s^2. Because the forward direction was designated as positive, the negative sign means that the direction of acceleration is backward.

Negative Acceleration Does Not Necessarily Mean Slowing Down

In Example 1.5, the value for acceleration is negative. What is the meaning of negative acceleration? When interpreting the sign of acceleration, you need to compare it to the sign of velocity. For example, for the drag racer that is speeding up, the direction of its velocity is the same as the direction of its acceleration (see the calculation of the slope of the velocity-time graph for Figure 1.30). *When the directions (signs) of velocity and acceleration are the same (positive or negative), the object is speeding up.*

PHYSICS INSIGHT

$\vec{v}$ speeding $\vec{v}$
       up

$\vec{a}$ $\vec{a}$

$\vec{v}$ slowing $\vec{v}$
       down

$\vec{a}$ $\vec{a}$

For the ATV in Example 1.5, the direction of its velocity is opposite to the direction of its acceleration, so it is slowing down. *When velocity and acceleration have opposite directions (signs), the object slows down.*

Concept Check

(a) Think of two more examples of objects not mentioned in this text that are speeding up and slowing down. In each case, indicate the signs or directions of velocity and acceleration.

(b) Under what circumstances can an object have a negative acceleration and be speeding up?

(c) You are given a position-time graph that is a curve. How can you use the slope of the tangent to determine whether the object represented in the graph is speeding up or slowing down? (Hint: How does the slope of the tangent change as you move along the position-time curve?)

THEN, NOW, AND FUTURE   Biomechanics and the Role of the Crash Test Dummy

Understanding how biological systems move is a branch of physics known as biomechanics. For automobile manufacturers, understanding how the human body moves during a car accident is very important. To study, collect, and analyze data on how the human body moves during a vehicular collision requires a test subject.

Human cadavers were the first test subjects used. While live human testing was valuable, it was limited in its scope due to the physical discomfort required and injury potential for some of the tests. Despite the production of reliable applicable data, most automobile manufacturers discontinued live animal testing in 1993 for moral and ethical reasons.

Clearly, a different type of test subject needed to be designed and built. It came in the form of the now recognizable crash test dummy.

Sam W. Alderson created "Sierra Sam" in 1949 to test aircraft ejection seats and pilot restraint harnesses. Then came the VIP-50 series and Sierra Stan in the 1950s. Engineers combined the best features of these different models and debuted Hybrid I in 1971. Hybrid I was known as the "50th percentile male" dummy (meaning approximately 50% of

men are larger and 50% of men are smaller), with a height of 168 cm and a mass of 77 kg. A year later, Hybrid II, with improved shoulder, spine, and knee responses, was produced to test lap and shoulder belts. Still crude, their use was limited, leading to the advent of the Hybrid III family of crash test dummies that include a 50th percentile male, a 50th percentile female, and two child dummies. This family of crash test dummies is designed to measure spine and rib acceleration, and demonstrate neck movement in rear-end collisions.

Equipped with a more human-like spine and pelvis, THOR (Figure 1.37) is the successor of Hybrid III. Its face contains a number of sensors for facial impact analysis. Since front and side air bags have reduced upper body injury, lower extremity injury has become more prevalent. Therefore, THOR is built with an Achilles tendon to better mimic the side-to-side, up-and-down, and rotational movements of the ankle.

Even with sophisticated crash test dummies, plastic and steel can only approximate how the human body will move. The study of soft tissue injury can only be accomplished with real-life subjects. Therefore, the future of crash testing will be in cre-

ating detailed computer models of human systems. Even though it is slow and cumbersome for full body simulations, the computer has the advantage of repeatability and lower cost. The programmer has the ability to control every variable and repeat each and any event.

1. Why are crash test dummies used?

2. What are some of the advantages of THOR over his previous prototypes?

3. Will crash test dummies become obsolete? Explain.

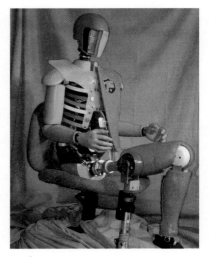

▲ **Figure 1.37**   THOR

Applications

1. A sprinter in a championship race accelerates to his top speed in a short time. The velocity-time data for part of the race are given in the table below. Use the data to find the

   (a) average acceleration from 0.00 s to 0.50 s

   (b) average acceleration from 0.50 s to 3.00 s

   (c) average acceleration from 5.00 s to 6.00 s

   (d) Describe what was happening to the acceleration and velocity over 6.00 s.

Time (s)	Velocity (m/s [forward])
0.00	0.00
0.12	0.00
0.14	0.00
0.50	2.80
1.00	5.00
2.00	8.00
3.00	9.80
4.00	10.80
5.00	11.30
6.00	11.60
7.00	11.70
8.00	11.80
9.00	11.90
9.83	11.95
9.93	11.97

2. Describe the motion of the object as illustrated in the graph below.

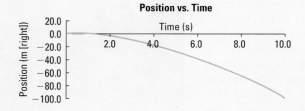

3. Match each velocity-time graph below with the correct statement.

   (i) negative acceleration

   (ii) positive acceleration

   (iii) zero acceleration

   (iv) stationary object

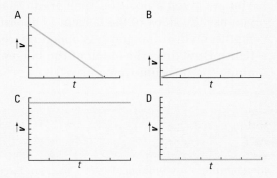

Extensions

4. In your notebook, complete the velocity-time data table for the graph below.

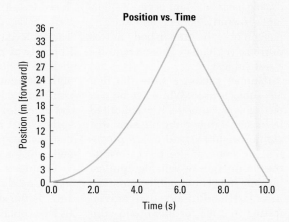

Time (s)	Velocity (m/s [forward])
0.0	
2.0	
4.0	
6.0	
8.0	

e TEST

To check your understanding of uniformly accelerated motion, follow the eTest links at www.pearsoned.ca/school/physicssource.

1.4 Analyzing Velocity-time Graphs

When a plane flies across Alberta with constant speed and direction, it is said to be undergoing *uniform motion* (Figure 1.38(a)). If you were sitting in the plane, you would experience a smooth ride. An all-terrain vehicle (ATV) bouncing and careening along a rough trail is constantly changing speed and direction in order to stay on the road. A ride in the ATV illustrates *non-uniform motion*, or acceleration (Figure 1.39(a)).

You can distinguish between uniform and non-uniform motion by simple observation and gathering data from your observations (see Figures 1.38(b) and 1.39(b)). There are several ways to interpret the data. One way is to analyze graphs by determining their slopes to obtain further information about an object's motion, as you did in section 1.3. In this section, you will develop this method further and learn another method of graphical analysis: how to find the area under a graph. First review the information you can obtain from the slopes of position-time and velocity-time graphs.

▲ **Figure 1.38(a)**   Uniform motion

▲ **Figure 1.39(a)**   Non-uniform motion

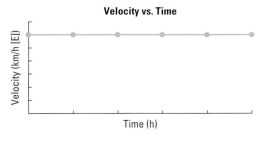

▲ **Figure 1.38(b)**   A graph representing uniform motion

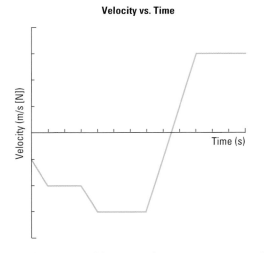

▲ **Figure 1.39(b)**   A graph representing non-uniform motion

Slopes of Graphs Reveal How Objects Move

Consider the three photos and velocity-time graphs in Figure 1.40. You can interpret each graph by reading values from it. To gain new information, you must analyze the graph by calculating its slope. The slope describes the object's motion.

Velocity vs. Time

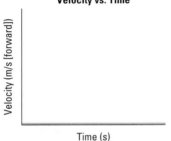

▲ **Figure 1.40(a)** A velocity-time graph for an object at rest

Velocity vs. Time

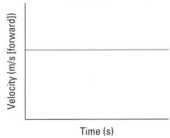

▲ **Figure 1.40(b)** A velocity-time graph for an object undergoing uniform motion

Velocity vs. Time

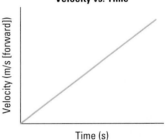

▲ **Figure 1.40(c)** A velocity-time graph for an object undergoing uniformly accelerated motion

Concept Check

1. Sketch all possible position-time graphs for:
   (a) stopped motion
   (b) uniform motion
   (c) uniformly accelerated motion

   Describe each graph in terms of direction of travel and whether the object is speeding up or slowing down.

2. Sketch the corresponding velocity-time graph for each position-time graph in question 1. For each graph, describe how you determined the graph's shape.

By analyzing the units for the slope of a velocity-time graph, m/s², you know from section 1.3 that the slope of a velocity-time graph represents the acceleration of the object.

Concept Check

Sketch all the types of acceleration-time graphs you have encountered thus far. Describe the kind of motion that each graph represents.

Tortoise or Hare?

The Question

In your class, who has the fastest acceleration and the fastest average speed in the 50-m dash?

Design and Conduct Your Investigation

Make a list of variables that you think are likely to influence the acceleration of each participant. For each variable on your list, write a hypothesis that predicts how changes in that variable will affect the participants' acceleration. Write a procedure for an investigation that will test the effect of one of these variables on acceleration. Clearly outline all the steps that you will follow to complete your investigation. Identify the responding and manipulated variables. List all the materials and equipment you will need, as well as all safety precautions. Compare your experimental design and procedure with those of your classmates. Identify any strengths and weaknesses. With your teacher's approval, conduct your investigation. State any problems or questions that you found during your investigation or analysis that would need additional investigation to answer.

The Area Under a Velocity-time Graph Represents Displacement

Occasionally, due to a medical or other emergency, a pilot must turn the aircraft and land at the same or alternate airport. Consider the graph for the uniform motion of a plane travelling east at 300 km/h for 2.0 h only to turn back west for 0.5 h to make an emergency landing (Figure 1.41). What is the plane's displacement for this time interval?

Unit analysis indicates that the area under a velocity-time graph equals displacement. To calculate displacement using a velocity-time graph, look at the units on the axes. To end up with a unit of displacement (km) from the units km/h and h, you need to multiply:

$$\frac{\text{km}}{\cancel{\text{h}}} \times \cancel{\text{h}} = \text{km}$$

The shapes in Figure 1.41 are rectangles, so the area under the velocity-time graph is $l \times w$ (length times width). In this case, find the sum of the areas above and below the time axis. Consider east to be positive. For eastward displacement, the area is *above* the time axis, so it is positive. For westward displacement, the area is *below* the time axis, so it is negative.

For eastward displacement (above the time axis),

$$\text{area} = \Delta \vec{d} = \vec{v}\Delta t$$

$$= \left(+300 \ \frac{\text{km}}{\cancel{\text{h}}} \right)(2.0 \ \cancel{\text{h}})$$

$$= +600 \text{ km}$$

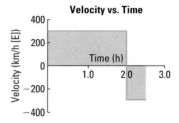

Velocity vs. Time

▲ **Figure 1.41** To calculate net displacement, add the areas above and below the time axis.

For westward displacement (below the time axis),

$$\Delta \vec{d} = \vec{v}\Delta t$$

$$= \left(-300 \ \frac{km}{\cancel{h}}\right)(0.5 \ \cancel{h})$$

$$= -150 \ km$$

To find the plane's net displacement, add the two areas.

area $= \Delta \vec{d} = +600 \ km + (-150 \ km)$

$= +600 \ km - 150 \ km$

$= +450 \ km$

$= 5 \times 10^2 \ km \ [E]$

Because the net area is positive, the plane's displacement is $5 \times 10^2 \ km \ [E]$.

Unlike position-time graphs, where you can only calculate the slope to determine velocity, you can use velocity-time graphs to determine both acceleration and displacement, as in the next example.

Example 1.6

From the graph in Figure 1.42, calculate
(a) displacement
(b) acceleration

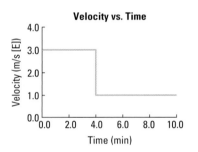

▲ **Figure 1.42**

Analysis and Solution

(a) For displacement, find the sum of the areas under the velocity-time graph (Figure 1.43). Designate east (above the time axis) as the positive direction. Convert minutes to seconds.

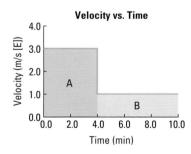

▲ **Figure 1.43**

Practice Problems

1. Calculate the displacement and acceleration for each graph.

(a)

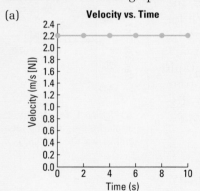

(b)

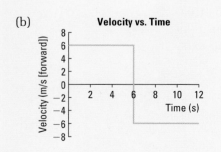

Answers

(a) 22 m [N], 0 m/s² [N]

(b) 0 m, 0 m/s²

Region A:

$$\Delta \vec{d}_A = \vec{v} \Delta t$$

$$= \left(+3.0 \ \frac{m}{s} \right) \left(4.0 \ \text{min} \times \frac{60 \ s}{1 \ \text{min}} \right)$$

$$= \left(+3.0 \ \frac{m}{s} \right) (240 \ s)$$

$$= +720 \ m$$

Region B:

$$\Delta \vec{d}_B = \left(+1.0 \ \frac{m}{s} \right) (10.0 \ \text{min} - 4.0 \ \text{min}) \left(\frac{60 \ s}{1 \ \text{min}} \right)$$

$$= \left(+1.0 \ \frac{m}{s} \right) (6.0 \ \text{min}) \left(\frac{60 \ s}{1 \ \text{min}} \right)$$

$$= +360 \ m$$

$$\Delta \vec{d} = \Delta \vec{d}_A + \Delta \vec{d}_B$$

$$= +720 \ m + 360 \ m$$

$$= +1080 \ m$$

$$= +1.1 \times 10^3 \ m$$

The answer is positive, so the direction is east.

(b) For acceleration, find the slope of each section of the graph. In the first part of the graph,

$$\vec{a} = \frac{\Delta \vec{v}}{\Delta t}$$

$$= \frac{+3.0 \ \dfrac{m}{s} - \left(+3.0 \ \dfrac{m}{s} \right)}{240 \ s}$$

$$= 0.0 \ m/s^2$$

This answer makes sense because the velocity-time graph is a horizontal line. Since the second part of the graph is also a horizontal line, its slope is also zero.

Paraphrase
(a) The displacement is 1.1×10^3 m [E].
(b) The acceleration is zero.

PHYSICS **INSIGHT**

When calculating total displacement from a velocity-time graph, remember to keep track of whether the area is positive or negative.

PHYSICS **INSIGHT**

Check your answer by looking at the units. Do the units reflect the answer that you are asked to find?

For the velocity-time graph of a ball thrown up in the air (Figure 1.44), what is the net displacement of the ball?

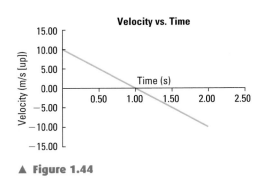

▲ Figure 1.44

Average Velocity from Velocity-time Graphs

Objects rarely travel at constant velocity. Think of your journey to school today. Whether you travelled by car or bus, rode a bike, or walked, stop signs, traffic lights, corners, and obstacles caused a variation in your velocity, or rate of travel. If you describe your motion to a friend, you can use a series of instantaneous velocities. The more time instances you use to record your motion, the more details about your trip you can communicate to your friend (Figure 1.45(a)). However, if you were to use the equation $\vec{v} = \dfrac{\Delta \vec{d}}{\Delta t}$ and substitute your total displacement for $\Delta \vec{d}$ and your total time of travel for Δt, you would lose most of the details of your journey. You would obtain a value for your average velocity, $\vec{v}_{ave}$ (Figure 1.45(b)).

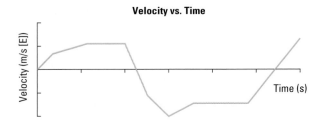

▲ Figure 1.45(a) By using a series of instantaneous velocities at the given times, you can precisely describe your journey.

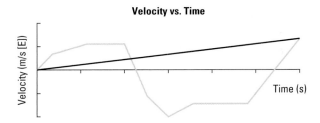

▲ Figure 1.45(b) In this case, the straight line describes your journey. The detail of the motions is lost.

If you need to obtain an average velocity value from a velocity-time graph, recall that displacement, $\Delta \vec{d}$, is the area under the graph. To find average velocity, determine the area under the velocity-time graph and divide it by the total time. To calculate average velocity when given different displacements over different time intervals, simply add the total displacement and divide by the total time, as shown in the next example.

Example 1.7

Find the average velocity of a student who jogs 750 m [E] in 5.0 min, does static stretches for 10.0 min, and then runs another 3.0 km [E] in 30.0 min.

Given

Choose east to be positive. Convert kilometres to metres.

$\Delta \vec{d}_1 = 750$ m [E] = +750 m

$\Delta t_1 = 5.0$ min

$\Delta \vec{d}_2 = 0$ m

$\Delta t_2 = 10.0$ min

$\Delta \vec{d}_3 = 3.0$ km [E]

$$= +3.0 \text{ km} \times \frac{1000 \text{ m}}{1 \text{ km}} = +3000 \text{ m}$$

$\Delta t_3 = 30.0$ min

Required

average velocity ($\vec{v}_{ave}$)

Analysis and Solution

First add the displacement values.

$\Delta \vec{d}_{total} = \Delta \vec{d}_1 + \Delta \vec{d}_2 + \Delta \vec{d}_3$

$\qquad = +750 \text{ m} + 0 \text{ m} + 3000 \text{ m}$

$\qquad = +3750 \text{ m}$

Then add the time intervals and convert to seconds. The total time elapsed is

$\Delta t_{total} = \Delta t_1 + \Delta t_2 + \Delta t_3$

$\qquad = 5.0 \text{ min} + 10.0 \text{ min} + 30.0 \text{ min}$

$\qquad = (45.0 \text{ min}) \left(60 \; \frac{\text{s}}{\text{min}} \right)$

$\qquad = 2700 \text{ s}$

Average velocity equals total displacement divided by total time elapsed:

$\vec{v}_{ave} = \dfrac{\Delta \vec{d}}{\Delta t}$

$\qquad = \dfrac{+3750 \text{ m}}{2700 \text{ s}}$

$\qquad = +1.4 \text{ m/s}$

Since the answer is positive, the direction is east.

Paraphrase

The student's average velocity is, therefore, 1.4 m/s [E].

Practice Problems

1. A person runs 10.0 m [E] in 2.0 s, then 5.0 m [E] in 1.5 s, and finally 30.0 m [W] in 5.0 s. Find the person's average velocity.

2. Donovan Bailey runs the 100-m dash in 9.84 s and then tags Michael Johnson, who runs 200 m in 19.32 s. Johnson then tags an out-of-shape student, who runs 400 m in 1.90 min. Find the average velocity for the trio. Compare it to each individual's average velocity. Assume they are all running in a straight line.

Answers

1. 1.8 m/s [W]

2. 4.89 m/s [forward]

    DB: 10.2 m/s [forward]

    MJ: 10.4 m/s [forward]

    student: 3.51 m/s [forward]

As you have seen, velocity-time graphs are very useful. They provide the following information:

— Reading the velocity-time graph gives you instantaneous velocity values.
— Finding the slope of a velocity-time graph gives you an object's acceleration.
— The area under a velocity-time graph gives you the object's displacement.
— You can also determine the average velocity of an object over a time interval from a velocity-time graph.

The next two examples show you what information you can obtain from velocity-time graphs. Example 1.8 shows you how to obtain information about an object's velocity and acceleration.

Example 1.8

Travelling south, a family sets out for a camping trip. The vehicle's motion is described in the velocity-time graph in Figure 1.46.

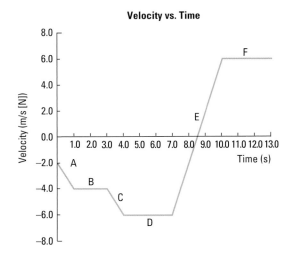

▲ **Figure 1.46**

From the graph, determine
(a) whether acceleration is positive, negative, or zero for each section
(b) the value of the acceleration where it is not zero
(c) when the vehicle changes direction

Analysis and Solution
Consider north to be the positive direction.
(a) Acceleration is the slope of each section of the graph.
   A: Final velocity is less than initial velocity in this section, so the slope of this line is negative. Therefore, the vehicle's acceleration is negative (south).

Practice Problems

1.

(a) Describe the motion of the object from the graph above.
(b) Draw the corresponding velocity-time graph.
(c) Determine the object's displacement.
(d) From your velocity-time graph, find the acceleration in each section.
(e) When is the object stopped?

B: Acceleration is zero because the slope is zero (the graph is a horizontal line).

C: Acceleration is negative because the slope of the line is negative (as in section A).

D: Acceleration is zero because the slope of the line is zero (as in section B).

E: Final velocity is greater than initial velocity, so the slope of this line is positive. Hence, the vehicle's acceleration is positive.

F: Acceleration is zero because the slope of the line is zero.

(b) Acceleration is not zero for sections A, C, and E.

A: $\vec{a} = \dfrac{\vec{v_f} - \vec{v_i}}{t_f - t_i}$

$= \dfrac{-4.0 \dfrac{m}{s} - \left(-2.0 \dfrac{m}{s}\right)}{1.0\ s - 0.0\ s}$

$= -2.0\ m/s^2$

$= 2.0\ m/s^2\ [S]$

C: $\vec{a} = \dfrac{\vec{v_f} - \vec{v_i}}{t_f - t_i}$

$= \dfrac{-6.0 \dfrac{m}{s} - \left(-4.0 \dfrac{m}{s}\right)}{4.0\ s - 3.0\ s}$

$= -2.0\ m/s^2$

$= 2.0\ m/s^2\ [S]$

E: $\vec{a} = \dfrac{\vec{v_f} - \vec{v_i}}{t_f - t_i}$

$= \dfrac{+6.0 \dfrac{m}{s} - \left(-6.0 \dfrac{m}{s}\right)}{10.0\ s - 7.0\ s}$

$= \dfrac{+12.0 \dfrac{m}{s}}{3.0\ s}$

$= +4.0\ m/s^2$

$= 4.0\ m/s^2\ [N]$

(c) The object changes direction at 8.5 s — it crosses the time axis at this instant.

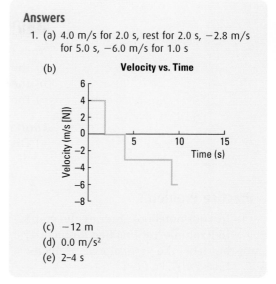

Answers

1. (a) 4.0 m/s for 2.0 s, rest for 2.0 s, −2.8 m/s for 5.0 s, −6.0 m/s for 1.0 s

(b) Velocity vs. Time

(c) −12 m
(d) 0.0 m/s²
(e) 2–4 s

The next example shows you how to use areas to find the displacement of the vehicle and its average velocity from a velocity-time graph.

Example 1.9

From the graph in Figure 1.46, determine
(a) the displacement for each section
(b) the displacement for the entire trip
(c) the average velocity for the trip

Analysis and Solution
(a) Displacement is the area between the graph and the time axis.

$$\text{A:} \quad A = l \times w + \frac{1}{2}bh$$

$$\Delta \vec{d} = (-2.0 \ \frac{m}{s})(1.0 \ s) + \frac{1}{2}(1.0 \ s)(-4.0 \ \frac{m}{s})$$

$$= -4.0 \ m$$

$$\text{B:} \quad A = l \times w$$

$$\Delta \vec{d} = (-4.0 \ \frac{m}{s})(3.0 \ s - 1.0 \ s)$$

$$= -8.0 \ m$$

$$\text{C:} \quad A = l \times w + \frac{1}{2}bh$$

$$\Delta \vec{d} = (-4.0 \ \frac{m}{s})(1.0 \ s) + \frac{1}{2}(1.0 \ s)(-2.0 \ \frac{m}{s})$$

$$= -5.0 \ m$$

$$\text{D:} \quad A = l \times w$$

$$\Delta \vec{d} = (-6.0 \ \frac{m}{s})(7.0 \ s - 4.0 \ s)$$

$$= -18 \ m$$

$$\text{E:} \quad \frac{1}{2}\left(-6.0 \ \frac{m}{s}\right)(1.5 \ s) + \frac{1}{2}\left(+6.0 \ \frac{m}{s}\right)(1.5 \ s) = 0.0 \ m$$

$$\text{F:} \quad A = l \times w$$

$$\Delta \vec{d} = (+6.0 \ \frac{m}{s})(3.0 \ s)$$

$$= +18 \ m$$

(b) Add all the displacements calculated in (a). The displacement over the entire trip is −17 m. Since north is positive, the displacement is 17 m [S].

$$\text{(c)} \quad \vec{v}_{ave} = \frac{\Delta \vec{d}_T}{\Delta t}$$

$$= \frac{-17 \ m}{13.0 \ s}$$

$$= -1.2 \ m/s$$

North is positive, so the average velocity for the trip is 1.2 m/s [S].

Drawing Position-time and Acceleration-time Graphs from Velocity-time Graphs

In this section, you have learned how to use a velocity-time graph to calculate displacement. It is also useful to know how to draw position-time and acceleration-time graphs when given a velocity-time graph.

Consider the following trip. A family travelling from Calgary to go camping in Banff National Park moves at 18.0 m/s [forward] in a camper van. The van accelerates for 4.0 s until it reaches a velocity of 30.0 m/s [forward]. It continues to travel at this velocity for 25.0 s. When approaching a check stop, the driver brakes, bringing the vehicle to a complete stop in 15.0 s. The velocity-time graph for the trip is given in Figure 1.47.

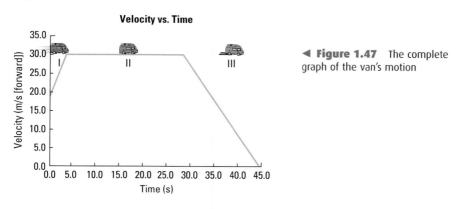

◀ **Figure 1.47** The complete graph of the van's motion

The next example shows you how to create an acceleration-time graph from a velocity-time graph.

Example 1.10

Use the velocity-time graph in Figure 1.47 to draw the corresponding acceleration-time graph.

Analysis and Solution
To find acceleration, calculate the slope for each section of the graph. The velocity-time graph has three distinct sections. The slope in each section is constant. Consider forward to be positive.

Section l
Time: 0.0 s to 4.0 s
t_i = 0.0 s
v_i = +18.0 m/s
t_f = 4.0 s
v_f = +30.0 m/s

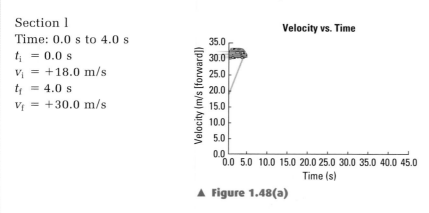

▲ **Figure 1.48(a)**

Practice Problems

1. For each velocity-time graph below, draw the corresponding acceleration-time graph.

(a)

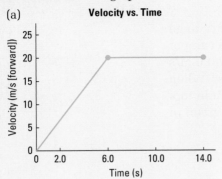

(b)

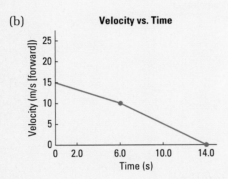

Answers

1. (a)

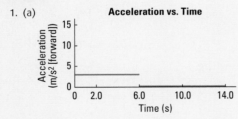

(b)

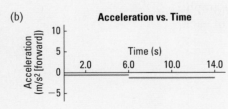

$$\text{slope} = \vec{a} = \frac{\vec{v}_f - \vec{v}_i}{t_f - t_i}$$

$$= \frac{+30.0 \text{ m/s} - (+18.0 \text{ m/s})}{4.0 \text{ s} - 0.0 \text{ s}}$$

$$= +3.0 \text{ m/s}^2$$

Section ll
Time: 4.0 s to 29.0 s
$t_i = 4.0$ s
$v_i = +30.0$ m/s
$t_f = 4.0$ s + 25.0 s
$\quad = 29.0$ s
$v_f = +30.0$ m/s

$$\text{slope} = \vec{a} = \frac{\vec{v}_f - \vec{v}_i}{t_f - t_i}$$

$$= \frac{+30.0 \text{ m/s} - (+30.0 \text{ m/s})}{29.0 \text{ s} - 4.0 \text{ s}}$$

$$= 0.0 \text{ m/s}^2$$

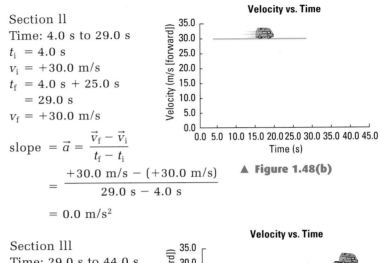

▲ **Figure 1.48(b)**

Section lll
Time: 29.0 s to 44.0 s
$t_i = 29.0$ s
$v_i = +30.0$ m/s
$t_f = 29.0$ s + 15.0 s
$\quad = 44.0$ s
$v_f = 0.0$ m/s

$$\text{slope} = \vec{a} = \frac{\vec{v}_f - \vec{v}_i}{t_f - t_i}$$

$$= \frac{0.0 \text{ m/s} - (+30.0 \text{ m/s})}{44.0 \text{ s} - 29.0 \text{ s}}$$

$$= -2.0 \text{ m/s}^2$$

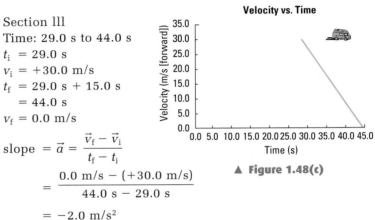

▲ **Figure 1.48(c)**

Now plot the values on the acceleration-time graph (Figure 1.49). Each section of the graph is a horizontal line because acceleration is constant (uniform).

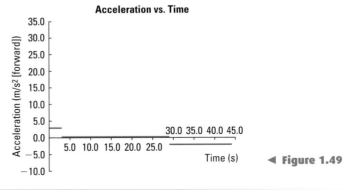

◄ **Figure 1.49**

The next example shows you how to use a velocity-time graph to generate a position-time graph.

Example 1.11

Draw a position-time graph from the velocity-time graph in Figure 1.47.

Analysis and Solution
To draw the position-time graph, find the area under the velocity-time graph. Consider forward to be positive. In the first part of the velocity-time graph (0.0–4.0 s), area (displacement) is a rectangle and a triangle.

$$A = l \times w + \frac{1}{2}bh$$

$$\Delta \vec{d} = \vec{v}_i \Delta t + \frac{1}{2}\Delta t(\vec{v}_f - \vec{v}_i)$$

$$= (+18.0 \text{ m/s})(4.0 \text{ s}) + \frac{1}{2}(4.0 \text{ s})(+30.0 \text{ m/s} - (+18.0 \text{ m/s}))$$

$$= +96 \text{ m}$$

Since the velocity-time graph in this section has a positive slope, the car has positive acceleration, so the corresponding position-time graph is a parabola that curves upward. On the position-time graph, draw a curve from the origin to the point $t = 4.0$ s and $\vec{d} = +96$ m (Figure 1.50(a)).

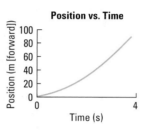

Position vs. Time

▲ **Figure 1.50(a)**

In the second part of the velocity-time graph (4.0–29.0 s), displacement is a rectangle.

$$A = lw$$
$$\Delta \vec{d} = \vec{v}\Delta t$$
$$= (+30.0 \text{ m/s})(29.0 \text{ s} - 4.0 \text{ s})$$
$$= +750 \text{ m}$$

Since the velocity-time graph has zero slope in this section, the car moves with constant velocity and the position-time graph is a straight line with a positive slope that extends from $t = 4.0$ s and $\vec{d} = +96$ m to $t = 29.0$ s and $\vec{d}$
$$= +96 \text{ m} + 750 \text{ m}$$
$$= +846 \text{ m (See Figure 1.50(b).)}$$

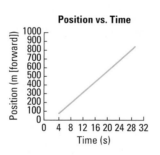

Position vs. Time

▲ **Figure 1.50(b)**

In the third part of the velocity-time graph (29.0–44.0 s), displacement is a triangle.

$$A = \frac{1}{2}bh$$

$$\Delta \vec{d} = \frac{1}{2}\Delta t(\vec{v}_f - \vec{v}_i)$$

$$= \frac{1}{2}(44.0 \text{ s} - 29.0 \text{ s})(0 \text{ m/s} - (+30.0 \text{ m/s}))$$

$$= +225 \text{ m}$$

Practice Problems

1.
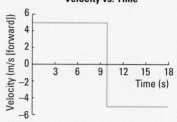
Velocity vs. Time

(a) Describe the motion of the object illustrated above. Calculate its total displacement.
(b) Draw the corresponding position-time graph.

Answers

1. (a) travels with uniform motion, changes direction at 10 s; total displacement: 10 m [forward]

(b)
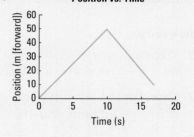
Position vs. Time

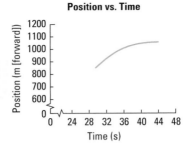

▲ **Figure 1.50(c)**

Since the velocity-time graph has a negative slope, the car undergoes negative acceleration, so the slopes of the tangents of the position-time graph decrease (approach zero). The position-time graph is a parabola that curves down, from $t = 29.0$ s and $\vec{d} = +846$ m to

$t = 44.0$ s and $\vec{d} = +846$ m $+ 225$ m

$\qquad\qquad = +1071$ m (See Figure 1.50(c).)

The resulting position-time graph is shown in Figure 1.51.

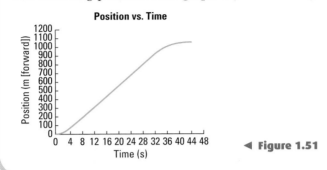

◄ **Figure 1.51**

Concept Check

If north is positive, sketch position-time, velocity-time, and acceleration-time graphs for an object

(a) speeding up and going north

(b) slowing down and going north

(c) speeding up and going south

(d) slowing down and going south

1.4 *Check and Reflect*

Knowledge

1. What quantity of motion can be determined from the area under a velocity-time graph?

2. Describe the velocity-time graph for an object undergoing negative acceleration.

3. If a velocity-time graph is a straight line with a non-zero slope, what kind of motion is the object undergoing?

4. Describe the acceleration-time graph of a car travelling forward and applying its brakes.

5. Use the terms "displacement" and "velocity" to describe how uniformly accelerated motion differs from uniform motion.

6. Compare the shape of a position-time graph for uniform motion with a position-time graph representing uniformly accelerated motion.

7. Determine displacement from the following graph.

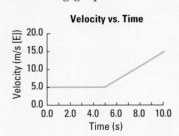

8. Calculate displacement from the velocity-time graph below.

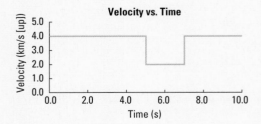

9. Compare and contrast the shape of a velocity-time graph for an object experiencing uniform motion with one experiencing uniformly accelerated motion.

10. On a ticker tape, how can you distinguish between uniform and uniformly accelerated motion?

11. Calculate the acceleration of an object using the velocity-time graph below.

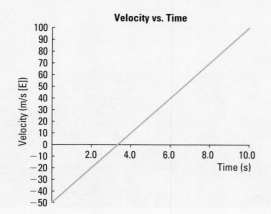

12. Construct an acceleration-time graph using the graph given below.

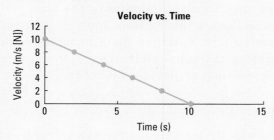

13. What is the relationship between the slope of a position-time graph and velocity?

14. What is the relationship between the slope of a velocity-time graph and acceleration?

Applications

15. A truck travelling forward at 14.0 m/s accelerates at 1.85 m/s² for 6.00 s. It then travels at the new speed for 35.0 s, when a construction zone forces the driver to push on the brakes, providing an acceleration of −2.65 m/s² for 7.0 s. Draw the resulting velocity-time and position-time graphs for this motion.

16. A motorbike increases its velocity from 20.0 m/s [W] to 30.0 m/s [W] over a distance of 200 m. Find the acceleration and the time it takes to travel this distance.

17. (a) While driving north from Lake Louise to Jasper, you travel 75 min at a velocity of 70 km/h [N] and another 96 min at 90 km/h [N]. Calculate your average velocity.

    (b) Create a graph for the question and check your answer using graphing techniques.

18. Determine acceleration from the velocity-time graph given below.

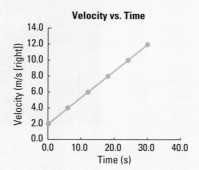

Extension

19. Describe the motion of the object illustrated in the graph below.

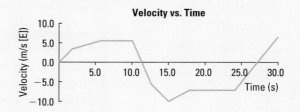

 e **TEST**

To check your understanding of velocity-time graphs follow the eTest links at www.pearsoned.ca/school/physicssource.

1.5 The Kinematics Equations

e TECH

Study the physics of jet takeoffs by visiting www.pearsoned.ca/school/physicssource and viewing the simulation.

A cylindrical piston the length of a football field controls the launch of a fighter plane from the deck of a carrier ship (Figure 1.52). Too much pressure and the nose gear is ripped off; too little pressure and the plane crashes into the ocean. This propulsion system accelerates a 20 000-kg plane from rest to 74 m/s (266 km/h) in just 2.0 s!

▶ **Figure 1.52** Analyzing complex motions requires many calculations, some of which involve using the kinematics equations you will study in this section.

To determine the crucial values required for launching a plane, such as flight deck length, final velocity, and acceleration, physicists and engineers use kinematics equations similar to the ones you will know by the end of this section. In this section, you will practise your analytical skills by learning how to derive the kinematics equations from your current knowledge of graphs and then apply these equations to analyze complex motions such as airplane launches.

Concept Check

Create a summary chart for the information you can gather by analyzing position-time, velocity-time, and acceleration-time graphs. Use the headings "Reading the Graph", "Slope", and "Area".

Consider the airplane taking off from a moving aircraft carrier (Figure 1.52). The plane must reach its takeoff speed before it comes to the end of the carrier's runway. If the plane starts from rest, the velocity-time graph representing the plane's motion is shown in Figure 1.53. Notice that the slope of the graph is constant. By checking the units on the graph, you know that the slope represents acceleration: $\frac{\text{rise}}{\text{run}} = \frac{\text{m/s}}{\text{s}} = \text{m/s}^2$. In this case, the acceleration is constant (uniform) because the velocity-time graph is a straight line.

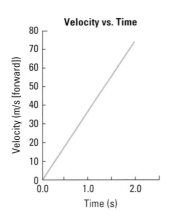

▲ **Figure 1.53** The slope of this velocity-time graph represents the plane's acceleration.

From Figure 1.53, you can derive the first kinematics equation:

$$\vec{a} = \frac{\vec{v}_f - \vec{v}_i}{t_f - t_i}$$

This equation can also be written as

$$\vec{a} = \frac{\Delta \vec{v}}{\Delta t}$$

The next example shows you how to apply this equation to solve a problem.

Example 1.12

A hybrid car with an initial velocity of 10.0 m/s [E] accelerates at 3.0 m/s² [E]. How long will it take the car to acquire a final velocity of 25.0 m/s [E]?

Given
Designate east as the positive direction.

$\vec{v}_i$ = 10.0 m/s [E] = +10.0 m/s

$\vec{v}_f$ = 25.0 m/s [E] = +25.0 m/s

$\vec{a}$ = 3.0 m/s² [E] = +3.0 m/s²

Required
time (Δt)

Analysis and Solution
Use the equation

$$\vec{a} = \frac{\Delta \vec{v}}{\Delta t} = \frac{\vec{v}_f - \vec{v}_i}{\Delta t}$$

Since you are dividing by a vector, and initial and final velocities and acceleration are in the same direction, use the scalar form of the equation. Isolate Δt and solve.

$$\Delta t = \frac{v_f - v_i}{a}$$

$$= \frac{25 \text{ m/s} - 10 \text{ m/s}}{3.0 \text{ m/s}^2}$$

$$= \frac{15 \frac{\text{m}}{\text{s}}}{3.0 \frac{\text{m}}{\text{s}^2}}$$

$$= 5.0 \text{ s}$$

Paraphrase
It will take the car 5.0 s to reach a velocity of 25.0 m/s [E].

Practice Problems

1. A motorcycle with an initial velocity of 6.0 m/s [E] accelerates at 4.0 m/s² [E]. How long will it take the motorcycle to reach a final velocity of 36.0 m/s [E]?

2. An elk moving at a velocity of 20 km/h [N] accelerates at 1.5 m/s² [N] for 9.3 s until it reaches its maximum velocity. Calculate its maximum velocity, in km/h.

Answers

1. 7.5 s
2. 70 km/h [N]

PHYSICS INSIGHT

The mathematics of multiplying vectors is beyond this text and division of vectors is not defined. So, when multiplying and dividing vectors, use the scalar versions of the kinematics equations.

As you know from section 1.4, you can calculate the area under a velocity-time graph. By checking the units, you can verify that the area represents displacement:

$$l \times w = \frac{\text{m}}{\text{s}} \times \text{s} = \text{m}$$

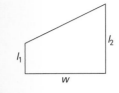
To calculate the displacement (area) from the velocity-time graph in Figure 1.54, you can use the formula for the area of a trapezoid, $A = \frac{1}{2}(l_1 + l_2)w$, which is simply the average of the parallel sides multiplied by the base.

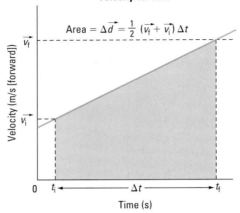

Velocity vs. Time

Area $= \Delta \vec{d} = \frac{1}{2}(\vec{v_f} + \vec{v_i})\,\Delta t$

▲ **Figure 1.54** Use the area under the velocity-time graph to derive the equation $\vec{d} = \vec{v}_{ave}\,\Delta t$.

The second kinematics equation is

$$\Delta \vec{d} = \frac{1}{2}(\vec{v}_i + \vec{v}_f)\Delta t$$

where $l_1 = \vec{v}_i$, $l_2 = \vec{v}_f$, and $w = \Delta t$. The next example shows you how to apply this equation.

Example 1.13

A cattle train travelling west at 16.0 m/s is brought to rest in 8.0 s. Find the displacement of the cattle train while it is coming to a stop. Assume uniform acceleration.

Given
Designate west as the positive direction.

$\vec{v}_i$ = 16.0 m/s [W] = +16.0 m/s

$\vec{v}_f$ = 0 m/s [W] = 0 m/s

Δt = 8.0 s

Required
displacement ($\Delta \vec{d}$)

Analysis and Solution

Use the equation $\Delta \vec{d} = \frac{1}{2}(\vec{v}_i + \vec{v}_f)\Delta t$ and solve for $\Delta \vec{d}$.

$$\Delta \vec{d} = \frac{1}{2}(+16.0 \text{ m/s} + 0 \text{ m/s})(8.0 \text{ s})$$

$$= \left(+8.0 \ \frac{\text{m}}{\text{s}}\right)(8.0 \ \text{s})$$

$$= +64 \text{ m}$$

The sign is positive, so the train's direction is west.

Paraphrase
The cattle train travels 64 m [W] before it stops.

You can also calculate the area under a velocity-time graph by considering that the total area under the graph is made up of a triangle and a rectangle (Figure 1.55).

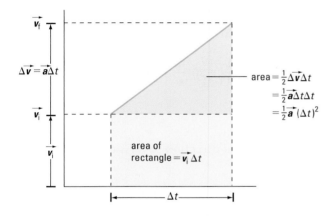

▲ **Figure 1.55** You can divide the area under the velocity-time graph into a triangle and a rectangle.

info **BIT**
The fastest time of covering 1.6 km while flipping tiddly winks — 52 min 10 s — was achieved by E. Wynn and J. Culliongham (UK) on August 31, 2002. Their speed was 1.8 km/h. Using this data and the displacement equation below, verify that they did indeed travel a distance of 1.6 km.

In Figure 1.55, the area of a rectangle represents the displacement of an object travelling with a constant velocity, $\vec{v}_i$. The height of the rectangle is $\vec{v}_i$ and the base is Δt. Therefore, the area of the rectangle is equal to $\vec{v}_i \Delta t$. The area of the triangle represents the additional displacement resulting from the change in velocity. The height of the triangle is $\vec{v}_f - \vec{v}_i = \Delta \vec{v}$ and the base is Δt. The area of the triangle is equal to $\frac{1}{2}(\Delta \vec{v})\Delta t$. But $\Delta \vec{v} = \vec{a}\Delta t$. Therefore, the area of the triangle is equal to $\frac{1}{2}(\vec{a}\Delta t)(\Delta t) = \frac{1}{2}\vec{a}(\Delta t)^2$. Add both displacements to obtain

PHYSICS INSIGHT
$\Delta(t^2) = t_f{}^2 - t_i{}^2$, whereas $(\Delta t)^2 = (t_f - t_i)^2$.

$$\Delta \vec{d} = \vec{v}_i \Delta t + \frac{1}{2}\vec{a}(\Delta t)^2$$

The next example shows you how to apply the third kinematics equation.

Example 1.14

A golf ball that is initially travelling at 25 m/s hits a sand trap and slows down with an acceleration of −20 m/s². Find its displacement after 2.0 s.

Given
Assign a positive direction for forward and a negative direction for backward.

$v_i = +25$ m/s

$\vec{a} = -20$ m/s²

$\Delta t = 2.0$ s

Required
displacement ($\Delta \vec{d}$)

Analysis and Solution
Use the equation $\Delta \vec{d} = \vec{v}_i \Delta t + \frac{1}{2} \vec{a} (\Delta t)^2$ to solve for $\Delta \vec{d}$.

$$\Delta \vec{d} = \left(+25 \ \frac{m}{s} \right)(2.0 \ s) + \frac{1}{2} \left(-20 \ \frac{m}{s^2} \right)(2.0 \ s)^2$$

$$= +50 \ m + (-40 \ m)$$

$$= +10 \ m$$

The sign is positive, so the direction is forward.

Paraphrase
The displacement of the golf ball is 10 m [forward].

Practice Problems

1. A skier is moving down a uniform slope at 3.0 m/s. If the acceleration down the hill is 4.0 m/s², find the skier's displacement after 5.0 s.

2. A motorcycle travelling at 100 km/h on a flat road applies the brakes at 0.80 m/s² for 1.0 min. How far did the motorcycle travel during this time?

Answers

1. 65 m [down]

2. 228 m

To obtain the fourth kinematics equation, derive the value of a required variable in one equation, substitute the derived value into the second equation, and simplify. Start with $\vec{a} = \dfrac{\vec{v}_f - \vec{v}_i}{\Delta t}$ and isolate $\vec{v}_i$.

$$\vec{v}_i = \vec{v}_f - \vec{a} \Delta t$$

Then substitute $\vec{v}_f - \vec{a} \Delta t$ into the equation $\Delta \vec{d} = \frac{1}{2}(\vec{v}_i + \vec{v}_f)\Delta t$. The equation becomes $\Delta \vec{d} = \frac{1}{2}(\vec{v}_f - \vec{a} \Delta t + \vec{v}_f)\Delta t$. This equation simplifies to

$$\Delta \vec{d} = \vec{v}_f \Delta t - \frac{1}{2} \vec{a} (\Delta t)^2$$

Apply this equation in the next example.

info **BIT**

The fastest lava flow ever recorded was 60 km/h in Nyiragongo (Democratic Republic of Congo) on January 10, 1977. At this speed, how far would the lava travel in 2 h 30 min?

Example 1.15

◀ **Figure 1.56**

A speedboat slows to a stop at a rate of 5.0 m/s² (Figure 1.56). If the process took 15 s, find the displacement of the boat.

Given
Let forward be the positive direction.

$\vec{v}_f$ = 0.0 m/s (because the boat comes to rest)

Δt = 15 s

$\vec{a}$ = −5.0 m/s² (Acceleration is negative because the boat is slowing down, so its sign must be opposite to that of velocity (positive).)

Required
displacement $(\Delta \vec{d})$

Analysis and Solution
Use the equation $\Delta \vec{d} = \vec{v}_f \Delta t - \dfrac{1}{2}\vec{a}(\Delta t)^2$ to solve for $\Delta \vec{d}$.

$\Delta \vec{d} = (0.0 \text{ m/s})(15 \text{ s}) - \dfrac{1}{2}(-5.0 \text{ m/s}^2)(15 \text{ s})^2$

$= +562.5 \text{ m}$

$= +560 \text{ m}$

The sign is positive, so the direction of displacement is forward.

Paraphrase
The displacement of the speedboat is 560 m [forward].

Practice Problems

1. If the arresting device on an aircraft carrier stops a plane in 150 m with an acceleration of −15 m/s², find the time the plane takes to stop.

2. The 1968 Corvette took 6.2 s to accelerate to 160 km/h [N]. If it travelled 220 m [N], find its acceleration.

Answers

1. 4.5 s
2. 2.9 m/s² [N]

Deriving the fifth and last kinematics equation involves using the difference of squares, another math technique.

Isolate Δt in the equation $\vec{a} = \dfrac{\vec{v}_f - \vec{v}_i}{\Delta t}$. Remember that, when multiplying or dividing vectors, use the scalar form of the equation:

$\Delta t = \dfrac{v_f - v_i}{a}$

Then substitute the expression for Δt into $\Delta d = \dfrac{1}{2}(v_i + v_f)\Delta t$:

$\Delta d = \dfrac{1}{2}(v_i + v_f)\left(\dfrac{v_f - v_i}{a}\right)$

$\Delta d = \dfrac{1}{2}\left(\dfrac{v_f^2 - v_i^2}{a}\right)$

> **PHYSICS INSIGHT**
>
> Recall that the difference of squares is
> $(a + b)(a - b) = a^2 - b^2$

The more standard form of the fifth kinematics equation is

$$v_f^2 = v_i^2 + 2a\Delta d$$

This equation is applied in the next example.

Example 1.16

A bullet accelerates the length of the barrel of a gun (0.750 m) with a magnitude of 5.35×10^5 m/s². With what speed does the bullet exit the barrel?

Given

$a = 5.35 \times 10^5$ m/s²
$d = 0.750$ m

Required

final speed (v_f)

Analysis and Solution

Use the equation $v_f^2 = v_i^2 + 2a\Delta d$. Since the bullet starts from rest, $v_i = 0$ m/s.

$v_f^2 = 0$ m/s $+ 2(5.35 \times 10^5$ m/s²$)(0.750$ m$)$

$\quad = 802\ 500$ m²/s²

$v_f = 896$ m/s

Paraphrase

The bullet leaves the barrel of the gun with a speed of 896 m/s.

Practice Problems

1. A jetliner lands on a runway at 70 m/s, reverses its engines to provide braking, and comes to a halt 29 s later.
   (a) What is the jet's acceleration?
   (b) What is the minimum length of runway the jet needs to come safely to a complete stop?

2. On-ramps are designed so that motorists can move seamlessly into highway traffic. If a car needs to increase its speed from 50 km/h to 100 km/h and the engine can provide a maximum acceleration of magnitude 3.8 m/s², find the minimum length of the on-ramp.

Answers

1. (a) −2.4 m/s² [forward]
   (b) 1.0 km

2. 76 m

It is important to note that the velocity-time graph used to derive the kinematics equations has a constant slope (see Figure 1.54), so the equations derived from it are for objects undergoing *uniformly accelerated motion* (constant acceleration).

General Method of Solving Kinematics Problems

Now that you know five kinematics equations, how do you know which one to use to solve a problem? To answer this question, notice that each of the five kinematics equations has four variables. Each kinematics problem will provide you with three of these variables, as given values. The fourth variable represents the unknown value. When choosing your equation, make sure that all three known variables and the one unknown variable are represented in the equation (see Table 1.8). You may need to rearrange the equation to solve for the unknown variable.

▼ **Table 1.8** The Variables in the Five Kinematics Equations

Equation	$\Delta \vec{d}$	$\vec{a}$	$\vec{v}_f$	$\vec{v}_i$	Δt
$\vec{a} = \dfrac{\vec{v}_f - \vec{v}_i}{\Delta t}$		X	X	X	X
$\Delta \vec{d} = \dfrac{1}{2}(\vec{v}_i + \vec{v}_f)\Delta t$	X		X	X	X
$\Delta \vec{d} = \vec{v}_i \Delta t + \dfrac{1}{2}\vec{a}(\Delta t)^2$	X	X		X	X
$\Delta \vec{d} = \vec{v}_f \Delta t - \dfrac{1}{2}\vec{a}(\Delta t)^2$	X	X	X		X
$v_f^2 = v_i^2 + 2a\Delta d$	X	X	X	X	

1.5 Check and Reflect

Applications

1. A train's stopping distance, even when full emergency brakes are engaged, is 1.3 km. If the train was travelling at an initial velocity of 90 km/h [forward], determine its acceleration under full emergency braking.

2. Most civilian aircraft are capable of accelerations of magnitude 42.5 m/s². If an aircraft starts from rest, how long will it take the plane to travel down the 2.6-km runway?

3. How far will a humanoid robot travel in 3.0 s, accelerating at 1.0 cm/s² [forward], if its initial velocity is 5.0 cm/s [forward]?

4. Determine a submarine's acceleration if its initial velocity is 9.0 m/s [N] and it travels 1.54 km [N] in 2.0 min.

5. A jet starts from rest and accelerates uniformly for 2.00 s over a displacement of 150 m [W]. Determine the jet's acceleration.

6. If a cyclist travelling at 14.0 m/s skids to a stop in 2.80 s, determine the skidding distance. Assume uniform acceleration.

7. Approaching a flashing pedestrian-activated traffic light, a driver must slow down to a speed of 30 km/h. If the crosswalk is 150 m away and the vehicle's initial speed is 50 km/h, what must be the magnitude of the car's acceleration to reach this speed limit?

8. How far will a car travel if it starts from rest and experiences an acceleration of magnitude 3.75 m/s² for 5.65 s?

9. What is a motorcycle's acceleration if it starts from rest and travels 350.0 m [S] in 14.1 s?

10. Determine the magnitude of a car's acceleration if its stopping distance is 39.0 m for an initial speed of 97.0 km/h.

11. A jet starting from rest reaches a speed of 241 km/h on 96.0 m of runway. Determine the magnitude of the jet's acceleration.

12. What is the displacement of a logging truck accelerating from 10 m/s [right] to 20 m/s [right] in 5.0 s?

13. Determine the acceleration of a bullet starting from rest and leaving the muzzle 2.75×10^{-3} s later with a velocity of 460 m/s [forward].

14. A typical person can handle an acceleration of about -49 m/s² [forward]. If you are in a car travelling at 110 km/h and have a collision with a solid immovable object, over what minimum distance must you stop so as to not exceed this acceleration?

 e TEST

To check your understanding of the kinematics equations, follow the eTest links at www.pearsoned.ca/school/physicssource.

1.6 Acceleration due to Gravity

Many amusement parks and midways showcase a ride based solely on acceleration due to gravity. The ride transports thrill seekers up to a dizzying height, allows them to come to rest, and then, without warning, releases them downward before coming to a controlled stop (Figure 1.57).

In the previous sections, you learned about objects that move in a horizontal plane. Many objects move in a vertical plane. Flipping a coin, punting a football, and a free throw in basketball are all examples of objects experiencing motion in a vertical plane (Figure 1.58). This type of motion is called **projectile motion**. A **projectile** is any object thrown into the air. Projectiles include objects dropped from rest; objects thrown vertically upward, such as a tennis ball for service; and objects moving upward at an angle, such as a punted football. First let's consider projectile motion of an object moving straight up or down. What is the relationship between an object's mass and the speed of its fall? Do the next QuickLab to find out.

▲ **Figure 1.57** Amusement park rides are an application of physics.

projectile motion: motion in a vertical plane

projectile: an object released or thrown into the air

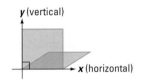

▲ **Figure 1.58**
A plane has two dimensions, *x* and *y*.

1-6 QuickLab

The Bigger They Are . . .

Problem

Does mass affect how quickly an object falls?

Materials

two objects of similar size and shape but different mass, such as a marble and a ball bearing, a die and a sugar cube, a golf ball and a table tennis ball
two pans
chair

Procedure

1. Place a pan on either side of the chair.

2. Standing on the chair, release each pair of objects from the same height at the same time.

3. Listen for the objects hitting the pans.

4. Repeat steps 2 and 3 for other pairs of objects.

5. Repeat steps 2 and 3 from a higher and a lower height.

Questions

1. Did the pair of objects land at the same time?

2. How did a change in height affect how long it took the objects to drop?

3. How did a change in the objects' shape affect how long it took each pair to drop?

---

info **BIT**

In 1971, astronaut David Scott tested Galileo's theory with a feather and a hammer. With no air on the Moon, both objects hit the ground at the same time.

In the 16th century, Galileo conducted experiments that clearly demonstrated that objects falling near Earth's surface have a constant acceleration, called the **acceleration due to gravity**. You can determine the value of the acceleration due to Earth's gravity by performing the following experiment.

Determining the Magnitude of the Acceleration due to Gravity

Question

How can position-time and velocity-time graphs be used to determine the acceleration due to gravity?

Materials and Equipment

60-Hz spark timer	masking tape
ticker tape	C-clamp
carbon disk	retort stand
power supply	graph paper
small mass	cushion
metre-stick or ruler	

Procedure

1 Construct a data table in your notebook for recording time and position.

2 Set up materials as shown in Figure 1.59(a), ensuring that the timer is 1.5 m above the floor.

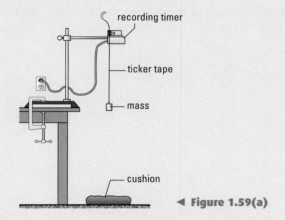

recording timer

ticker tape

mass

cushion

◀ **Figure 1.59(a)**

3 Attach a 1.5-m strip of ticker tape to the mass and thread the ticker tape through the spark timer.

4 Turn on the spark timer just before your partner releases the mass.

5 Repeat steps 3 and 4 for each person in your group.

6 Analyze the ticker tape by drawing a line through the first distinct dot on the tape. Label it "start". (On a 60-Hz timer, every sixth dot represents 0.10 s.) Continue labelling your ticker tape as shown in Figure 1.59(b).

7 Using a ruler, measure the position of the object at each time interval and record it in your data table.

8 Plot your collected data on a position-time graph.

9 With a sweeping motion, practise connecting the dots in a smooth, parabolic curve.

10 Construct a data table in your notebook for recording instantaneous velocity and time.

11 Draw three tangents on the position-time graph.

12 Calculate the instantaneous velocities at these points by determining the slopes of the tangents. Record the data in your table.

13 Plot a velocity-time graph of your collected data.

14 Draw a line of best fit.

15 Calculate the acceleration experienced by the object, in m/s², by finding the slope of the velocity-time graph.

Analysis

1. Determine the experimental value of acceleration by averaging your group's results.

2. Determine the percent error for your experimental value. Assume the magnitude of a is 9.81 m/s².

3. Describe the shape of the position-time graph you drew in step 9.

4. From your graph, describe the relationship between time and displacement for an accelerating object.

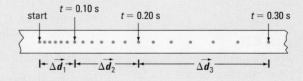

$t = 0.10$ s $t = 0.20$ s $t = 0.30$ s

start

$\Delta \vec{d}_1$ $\Delta \vec{d}_2$ $\Delta \vec{d}_3$

▲ **Figure 1.59(b)**

e **LAB**

For a probeware activity, go to
www.pearsoned.ca/school/physicssource.

Gravity Causes Objects to Accelerate Downward

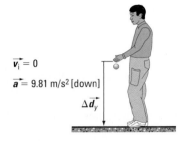

e TECH

Use graphical analysis to determine acceleration due to Earth's gravity. Go to www.pearsoned.ca/school/physicssource.

$\vec{v_i} = 0$

$\vec{a} = 9.81 \text{ m/s}^2 \text{ [down]}$

$\Delta \vec{d_y}$

▲ **Figure 1.60** The time it takes the golf ball to hit the ground depends on the height from which it drops and on the acceleration due to gravity.

PHYSICS INSIGHT

The equations of parabolas are quadratic equations because they include a power of two, for example, $y = x^2$. The equation for the displacement of a vertical projectile is $\Delta \vec{d} = \vec{v_i} \Delta t + \dfrac{1}{2} \vec{a}(\Delta t)^2$.

info BIT

Without a parachute, Vesna Vulovic, a flight attendant, survived a fall of 10 160 m when the DC-9 airplane she was travelling in exploded.

Recall the kinematics equations for accelerated motion from section 1.5:

$$\vec{a} = \frac{\Delta \vec{v}}{\Delta t}$$

$$\Delta \vec{d} = \vec{v_i} \Delta t + \frac{1}{2} \vec{a}(\Delta t)^2$$

$$\Delta \vec{d} = \vec{v_f} \Delta t - \frac{1}{2} \vec{a}(\Delta t)^2$$

$$v_f^2 = v_i^2 + 2a\Delta d$$

You can also apply these equations to motion in a vertical plane. Because vertical acceleration is due to gravity, $\vec{a}$ is the acceleration due to gravity, or 9.81 m/s² [down].

If you drop a golf ball from a height of 1.25 m, how long will it take for the ball to reach the ground (Figure 1.60)?

Because the ball is moving in only one direction, down, choose down to be positive for simplicity. Since the golf ball is accelerating due to gravity starting from rest,

$$\vec{v_i} = 0 \text{ and } \vec{a} = 9.81 \text{ m/s}^2 \text{ [down]} = +9.81 \text{ m/s}^2$$

The ball's displacement can be expressed as 1.25 m [down], or +1.25 m. The equation that includes all the given variables and the unknown variable is $\Delta \vec{d} = \vec{v_i} \Delta t + \dfrac{1}{2} \vec{a}(\Delta t)^2$. The displacement and acceleration vectors are both in the same direction, so use the scalar form of the equation to solve for time. Since $v_i = 0$,

$$\Delta d = \frac{1}{2} a \Delta t^2$$

$$\Delta t = \sqrt{\frac{2\Delta d}{a}}$$

$$= \sqrt{\frac{2(1.25 \text{ m})}{9.81 \dfrac{\text{m}}{\text{s}^2}}}$$

$$= 0.505 \text{ s}$$

The golf ball takes 0.505 s to reach the ground when released from a rest height of 1.25 m.

Note that the height of an object falling due to gravity is directly proportional to the time squared: $\Delta \vec{d} = \dfrac{1}{2} \vec{a} \Delta t^2$. If there is no air resistance, the time it takes for a falling object to reach the ground depends only on the height from which it was dropped. The time does not depend on any other property of the object.

Could You Be a Goalie for the NHL?

Problem
What is your reaction time?

Materials and Equipment
long ruler (30 cm or more)
flat surface

Procedure

1 Rest your arm on a flat surface with your wrist at the edge.

2 Ask your partner to hold the ruler vertically so that the ruler's end is just above your hand.

3 Curl your fingers so that the space between your thumb and index finger is large enough for the ruler to pass through easily.

4 Without watching your partner, ask your partner to let go of the ruler without warning.

5 Try to close your thumb and index finger on the ruler as quickly as possible.

6 Record where your hand is on the ruler.

7 Repeat steps 1–6 several times.

Questions

1. Determine the average distance the ruler falls in each of your trials.

2. Using the average distance, calculate the time.

3. An average NHL goalie has a reaction time of 0.15 s. How do your and your partner's reaction times compare?

4. Certain drugs impair reaction time. What would you expect your results in this lab to be if your reaction time were increased?

Instead of dropping an object such as a golf ball, what if you threw an object down? By throwing an object straight down, you give the object an initial vertical velocity downward. What effect does an initial velocity have on the motion of the object? The next example will show you.

Example 1.17

While cliff diving in Mexico, a diver throws a smooth, round rock straight down with an initial speed of 4.00 m/s. If the rock takes 2.50 s to land in the water, how high is the cliff?

Given
For convenience, choose down to be positive because down is the only direction of the ball's motion.

$\vec{v}_i$ = 4.00 m/s [down] = +4.00 m/s

Δt = 2.50 s

$\vec{a}$ = 9.81 m/s² [down] = +9.81 m/s²

Required
height of cliff (Δd)

Analysis and Solution
The initial velocity and acceleration vectors are both in the same direction, so use the scalar form of the equation $\Delta \vec{d} = \vec{v}_i \Delta t + \dfrac{1}{2} \vec{a}(\Delta t)^2$.

Practice Problems

1. If a rock takes 0.750 s to hit the ground after being thrown down from a height of 4.80 m, determine the rock's initial velocity.

2. Having scored a touchdown, a football player spikes the ball in the end zone. If the ball was thrown down with an initial velocity of 2.0 m/s from a height of 1.75 m, determine how long it is in the air.

3. An elevator moving down at 4.00 m/s accelerates upward at 2.00 m/s² for 1.80 s. What is its velocity at the end of the acceleration and how far has it travelled?

Answers

1. 2.72 m/s [down]
2. 0.43 s
3. 0.400 m/s [down], 3.96 m [down]

$$\Delta d = (4.00 \text{ m/s})(2.50 \text{ s}) + \frac{1}{2}(9.81 \text{ m/s}^2)(2.50 \text{ s})^2$$

$$= 10.0 \text{ m} + 30.6 \text{ m}$$

$$= 40.6 \text{ m}$$

Paraphrase

The cliff is 40.6 m high.

What Goes Up Must Come Down

Circus clowns are often accomplished jugglers (Figure 1.61). If a juggler throws a ball upward, giving it an initial velocity, what happens to the ball (Figure 1.62)?

▲ **Figure 1.61** Juggling is an example of projectile motion.

▲ **Figure 1.62** The ball's motion is called vertical projectile motion.

When you throw an object up, its height (displacement) increases while its velocity decreases. The decrease in velocity occurs because the object experiences acceleration downward due to gravity (Figure 1.63(a)). The ball reaches its maximum height when its vertical velocity equals zero. In other words, it stops for an instant at the top of its path (Figure 1.63(b)). When the object falls back toward the ground, it speeds up because of the acceleration due to gravity (Figure 1.63(c)).

▲ **Figure 1.63(a)**
Stage 1: Velocity and acceleration are in opposite directions, so the ball slows down.

▲ **Figure 1.63(b)**
Stage 2: The ball has momentarily stopped, but its acceleration is still 9.81 m/s² [down], which causes the ball to change direction.

▲ **Figure 1.63(c)**
Stage 3: Velocity and acceleration are in the same direction, so the ball speeds up.

The next two examples analyze different stages of the same object's motion. Example 1.18 analyzes the upward part of the motion of an object thrown upward, whereas Example 1.19 analyzes the same object's downward motion.

Example 1.18

A clown throws a ball upward at 10.00 m/s. Find
(a) the maximum height the ball reaches
(b) the time it takes to do so

Given
Consider up to be positive.

v_i = 10.00 m/s [up] = +10.00 m/s

$\vec{a}$ = 9.81 m/s² [down] = −9.81 m/s²

Required
(a) maximum height (Δd)
(b) time taken to reach maximum height (Δt)

Analysis and Solution
(a) When you throw an object up, as its height increases, its speed *decreases* because the object is accelerating downward due to gravity. The ball, travelling upward away from its initial launch height, reaches its maximum height when its vertical velocity is zero. In other words, the object stops for an instant at the top of its path up, so v_f = 0.00 m/s. To find the object's maximum height, neglecting air friction, use the equation $v_f^2 = v_i^2 + 2a\Delta d$ and substitute scalar quantities.

Practice Problem

1. The Slingshot drops riders 27 m from rest before slowing them down to a stop. How fast are they moving before they start slowing down?

Answer

1. 23 m/s

e **WEB**

Can you shoot an object fast enough so that it does not return to Earth? Research escape velocity. Is it the same regardless of the size of an object? How do you calculate it? Write a brief summary of your findings. To learn more about escape velocity, follow the links at www.pearsoned.ca/school/physicssource.

$$\Delta d = \frac{v_f^2 - v_i^2}{2a}$$

$$= \frac{\left(0.00\ \frac{m}{s}\right)^2 - \left(10.00\ \frac{m}{s}\right)^2}{2\left(-9.81\ \frac{m}{s^2}\right)}$$

$$= 5.10\ \text{m}$$

(b) To find the time taken, use the equation $\vec{a} = \dfrac{\Delta \vec{v}}{\Delta t}$, where $\vec{a}$ is the acceleration due to gravity. Substitute scalar quantities because you are dividing vectors.

$$\Delta t = \frac{v_f - v_i}{a}$$

$$= \frac{0.00\ \frac{m}{s} - \left(10.00\ \frac{m}{s}\right)}{-9.81\ \frac{m}{s^2}}$$

$$= 1.02\ \text{s}$$

Paraphrase
(a) The ball's maximum height is 5.10 m above its launch height.
(b) It takes the ball 1.02 s to reach maximum height.

The next example is a continuation of the previous example: It analyzes the same ball's motion as it falls back down from its maximum height.

Example 1.19

A clown throws a ball upward at 10.00 m/s. Find
(a) the time it takes the ball to return to the clown's hand from maximum height
(b) the ball's final velocity

Given
Consider up to be positive.

$\vec{v}_i = 10.00$ m/s [up] $= +10.00$ m/s
$\vec{a} = 9.81$ m/s² [down] $= -9.81$ m/s²

Required
(a) time taken to land (Δt)
(b) final velocity ($\vec{v}_f$)

Analysis and Solution
(a) For an object starting from rest at maximum height and accelerating downward due to gravity, its motion is described by the equation $\Delta \vec{d} = \vec{v}_i \Delta t + \dfrac{1}{2}\vec{a}(\Delta t)^2$, where $\vec{v}_i = 0$ (at maximum height). For downward motion, the ball's displacement and acceleration are in the same direction, so use the scalar form of the equation. For Δd, substitute 5.10 m (from Example 1.18(a)). Rearrange this equation and substitute the values.

$$\Delta t = \sqrt{\frac{2\Delta d}{a}}$$

$$= \sqrt{\frac{2(5.10\ \cancel{m})}{9.81\ \dfrac{\cancel{m}}{s^2}}}$$

$$= 1.02\ s$$

Compare this time to the time taken to reach maximum height (Example 1.18(b)).

(b) The ball's final velocity (starting from maximum height) when it lands on the ground is

$$\vec{a} = \frac{\vec{v}_f - \vec{v}_i}{\Delta t}$$

$$\vec{v}_f = \vec{v}_i + \vec{a}\Delta t$$

$$= 0.00\ m/s + (-9.81\ m/s^2)(1.02\ s)$$

$$= -10.0\ m/s$$

The negative sign means that the direction is downward.

Paraphrase
(a) It takes the ball 1.02 s to return to the clown's hand.
(b) The final velocity at the height of landing is
10.0 m/s [down].

Concept Check

(a) Why does it make sense that the time taken to travel up to the maximum height is equal to the time to fall back down to the starting height?
(b) What variables determine how long a projectile is in the air? Does the answer surprise you? Why or why not?

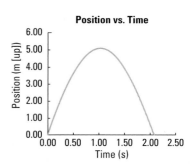

▲ **Figure 1.64** The position-time graph of a ball thrown vertically upward is a parabola.

You can use the data calculated in Examples 1.18 and 1.19 to plot a position-time graph of the ball's motion. Because the ball experiences uniformly accelerated motion, the graph is a *parabola* (Figure 1.64).

A Graphical Representation of a Vertical Projectile

You can now represent the motion of the juggler's ball on a position-time graph. Remember that the ball's motion can be divided into three different stages: Its velocity decreases, becomes zero, and then increases. The graphs that correspond to these three stages of motion are shown in Figure 1.65.

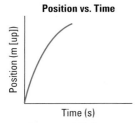

▲ **Figure 1.65(a)** Consider up to be positive. The ball rises until it stops.

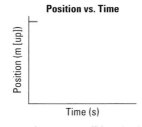

▲ **Figure 1.65(b)** The ball stops momentarily at maximum height.

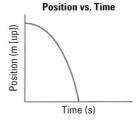

▲ **Figure 1.65(c)** The ball falls back down to its launch height.

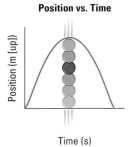

Position vs. Time

▲ **Figure 1.66** A ball thrown straight up in the air illustrates uniformly accelerated motion.

Now put these three graphs together to generate the complete position-time graph of the ball's motion. Remember that the ball is actually moving straight up and down, and not in a parabolic path (Figure 1.66). Why is the graph of its motion a parabola rather than a straight vertical line?

To generate a corresponding velocity-time graph from the position-time graph in Figure 1.66, draw a series of tangents at specific time instances. Choosing strategic points will make your task easier. The best points to choose are those that begin and end a stage of motion because they define that stage (Figure 1.67(a)).

(a)
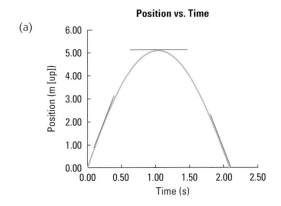

(b)
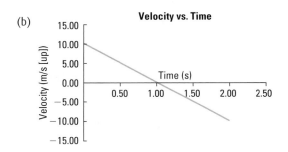

▲ **Figure 1.67** To generate the velocity-time graph in (b) corresponding to the position-time graph in (a), draw tangents at strategic points.

info **BIT**

In 1883, the Krakatoa volcano in Indonesia hurled rocks 55 km into the air. This volcanic eruption was 10 000 times more powerful than the Hiroshima bomb! Can you find the time it took for the rocks to reach maximum height?

In Figure 1.67(a), notice that the initial slope of the tangent on the position-time graph is positive, corresponding to an initial positive (upward) velocity on the velocity-time graph below (Figure 1.67(b)). The last tangent has a negative slope, corresponding to a final negative velocity on the velocity-time graph. The middle tangent is a horizontal line (slope equals zero), which means that the ball stopped momentarily. Remember that the slope of a velocity-time graph represents acceleration.

Concept Check

(a) What is the defining kinematics equation for a ball thrown straight up?
(b) What should be the value of the slope of the velocity-time graph in Figure 1.67(b)?

Knowledge

1. What property of an object determines how long it will take to reach the ground when released with an initial velocity of zero?

2. Define a projectile.

Applications

3. A rock takes 1.575 s to drop 2.00 m down toward the surface of the Moon. Determine the acceleration due to gravity on the Moon.

4. At the beginning of a game, a referee throws a basketball vertically upward with an initial speed of 5.0 m/s. Determine the maximum height above the floor reached by the basketball if it starts from a height of 1.50 m.

5. A student rides West Edmonton Mall's Drop of Doom. If the student falls due to gravity for 2.6 s, what will be his final velocity and how far will he have fallen?

6. If the acceleration due to gravity on Jupiter is 26.2 m/s² [down], determine the time it takes for a tennis ball to fall 1.75 m from rest.

7. During a babysitting assignment, a babysitter is constantly picking up toys dropped from the infant's highchair. If the toys drop from rest and hit the floor 0.56 s later, from what height are they being dropped?

8. If a baseball popped straight up into the air has a hang time (length of time in the air) of 6.25 s, determine its displacement from the ground at its maximum height.

9. A student drops a bran muffin from the roof of the school. From what height is the muffin dropped if it hits the ground 3.838 s later?

10. Jumping straight up, how long will a red kangaroo remain in the air if its maximum height is 3.0 m?

11. The observation deck of the Calgary Tower is 190 m above the street. Determine the time required for a penny to drop from the deck to the street below.

12. A coin tossed straight up into the air takes 2.75 s to go up and down from its initial release point 1.30 m above the ground. What is its maximum height?

13. If a diver starts from rest, determine the amount of time he takes to reach the water's surface from the 10-m platform.

14. A person in an apartment building is 5.0 m above a person walking below. She plans to drop some keys to him. He is currently walking directly toward a point below her at 2.75 m/s. How far away is he if he catches the keys 1.25 m above the ground?

15. What distance does a parachuter have to fall to reach a terminal velocity of 201 km/h, assuming she starts from rest? How long does it take to reach this terminal velocity?

Extensions

16. A ball is fired vertically upward at 5.0 m/s from a cart moving 2.0 m/s [right]. Draw a vector diagram to determine the ball's resultant initial velocity.

17. A rocket launched vertically upward accelerates uniformly for 50 s until it reaches a velocity of 200 m/s [up]. At that instant, its fuel runs out.

    (a) Calculate the rocket's acceleration.

    (b) Calculate the height of the rocket when its fuel runs out.

    (c) Explain why the rocket continues to gain height for 20 s after its fuel runs out.

    (d) Calculate the maximum height of the rocket.

18. A ball is dropped from a height of 60.0 m. A second ball is thrown down 0.850 s later. If both balls reach the ground at the same time, what was the initial velocity of the second ball?

e TEST

To check your understanding of projectiles and acceleration due to gravity, follow the eTest links at **www.pearsoned.ca/school/physicssource**.

Key Terms and Concepts

kinematics	distance	acceleration	uniformly accelerated
origin	displacement	non-uniform motion	motion
position	velocity	instantaneous velocity	projectile motion
scalar quantity	uniform motion	tangent	projectile
vector quantity	at rest		acceleration due to gravity

Key Equations

$$\vec{v} = \frac{\Delta \vec{d}}{\Delta t}$$

$$\vec{a} = \frac{\Delta \vec{v}}{\Delta t} = \frac{\vec{v}_\mathrm{f} - \vec{v}_\mathrm{i}}{\Delta t}$$

$$\Delta \vec{d} = \frac{1}{2}(\vec{v}_\mathrm{f} + \vec{v}_\mathrm{i})\Delta t$$

$$\Delta \vec{d} = \vec{v}_\mathrm{i}\Delta t + \frac{1}{2}\vec{a}(\Delta t)^2$$

$$\Delta \vec{d} = \vec{v}_\mathrm{f}\Delta t - \frac{1}{2}\vec{a}(\Delta t)^2$$

$$v_\mathrm{f}^2 = v_\mathrm{i}^2 + 2a\Delta d$$

Conceptual Overview

The concept map below summarizes many of the concepts and equations in this chapter. Copy and complete the map to have a full summary of the chapter.

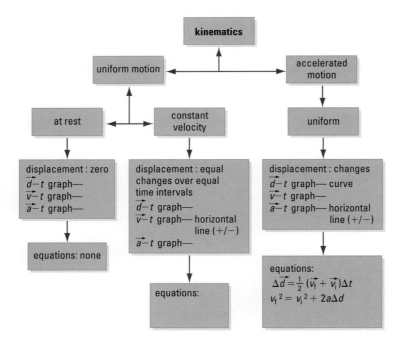

Knowledge

1. (1.1) State two ways in which a vector quantity differs from a scalar quantity. Give an example of each.

2. (1.2) Complete a position-time data table for the motion described by the ticker tape given below.

3. (1.3) Determine the velocity of each object whose motion is represented by the graphs below.

(a)

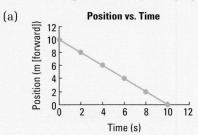

(b)

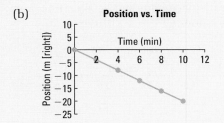

(c)

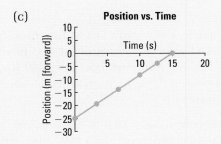

4. (1.5) What is a vehicle's displacement if its velocity is 30.0 m/s [W] in 15.0 min?

5. (1.5) How long will it take a cross-country skier, travelling 5.0 km/h, to cover a distance of 3.50 km?

6. (1.2) Determine the average speed, average velocity, and net displacement from the position-time graph below.

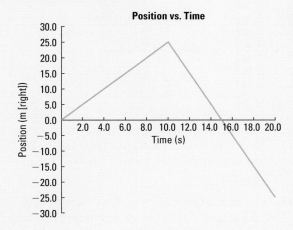

7. (1.2) Explain how a person standing still could have the same average velocity but different average speed than a person running around a circular track.

8. (1.6) If an object remains in the air for 5.6 s, at what time did it reach its maximum height?

9. (1.6) If an object takes 3.5 s to reach maximum height, how long will the object be in the air? Assume there is no air resistance.

10. (1.6) What is the initial vertical velocity for an object that is dropped from a height, h?

Applications

11. In 1980, during the Marathon of Hope, Terry Fox ran 42 km [W] a day. Assuming he ran for 8.0 h a day, what was his average velocity in m/s?

12. Explain how the point of intersection of two functions on a position-time graph differs from the point of intersection of two functions on a velocity-time graph.

13. A thief snatches a handbag and runs north at 5.0 m/s. A police officer, 20 m to the south, sees the event and gives chase. If the officer is a good sprinter, going 7.5 m/s, how far will she have to run to catch the thief?

14. Calculate the magnitude of a bullet's acceleration if it travels 1200 m/s and stops within a bulletproof vest that is 1.0 cm thick.

15. From the velocity-time graph below, determine how far an elk will travel in 30 min.

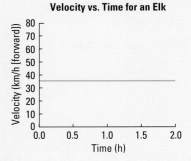

Velocity vs. Time for an Elk

16. The world record for a speedboat is 829 km/h. Heading south, how far will the boat travel in 2.50 min?

17. How much faster is an airliner than a stagecoach if the stagecoach takes 24 h to travel 300 km and the airliner takes 20 min?

18. A car's odometer reads 22 647 km at the start of a trip and 23 209 km at the end. If the trip took 5.0 h, what was the car's average speed in km/h and m/s?

19. A motorcycle coasts downhill from rest with a constant acceleration. If the motorcycle moves 90.0 m in 8.00 s, find its acceleration and velocity after 8.00 s.

20. A cyclist takes 4.0 s to pass two traffic lights, 30.0 m apart. If her initial velocity was 5.0 m/s [N] at the first traffic light, find her acceleration and velocity at the second traffic light.

21. A scuba diver swims at a constant speed of 0.77 m/s. How long will it take the diver to travel 150 m at this speed?

22. An object with an initial velocity of 10.0 m/s [S] moves 720 m in 45.0 s along a straight line with constant acceleration. For the 45.0-s interval, find its average velocity, final velocity, and acceleration.

23. During qualifying heats for the Molson Indy, a car must complete a 2.88-km lap in 65 s. If the car goes 60 m/s for the first half of the lap, what must be its speed for the second half?

24. A car travelling 19.4 m/s passes a police car at rest. As it passes, the police car starts up, accelerating with a magnitude of 3.2 m/s².

Maintaining that acceleration, how long will it take the police car to catch up with the speeding motorist? At what speed would the police car be moving? Explain whether or not this scenario is likely to happen.

25. Two cars pass one another while travelling on a city street. Using the velocity-time graph below, draw the corresponding position-time graph and determine when and where the two cars pass one another.

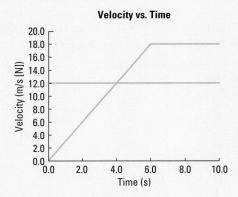

Velocity vs. Time

26. Calculate displacement and acceleration from the graph below.

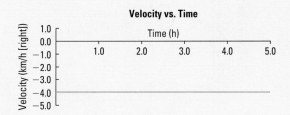

Velocity vs. Time

27. Built in Ontario, the world's fastest fire truck, the Hawaiian Eagle, can accelerate at 9.85 m/s² [forward]. Starting from rest, how long will it take the Hawaiian Eagle to travel a displacement of 402 m [forward]?

28. A vehicle is travelling at 25.0 m/s. Its brakes provide an acceleration of −3.75 m/s² [forward]. What is the driver's maximum reaction time if she is to avoid hitting an obstacle 95.0 m away?

29. Off-ramps are designed for motorists to decrease their vehicles' velocities to move seamlessly into city traffic. If the off-ramp is 1.10 km long, calculate the magnitude of a vehicle's acceleration if it reduces its speed from 110.0 km/h to 60.0 km/h.

30. Calgary's CTrain leaves the 10 St. S.W. station at 4:45 p.m. and arrives at 3 St. S.E. at 4:53 p.m. If the distance between the two stops is 3.2 km, determine the CTrain's average velocity for the trip.

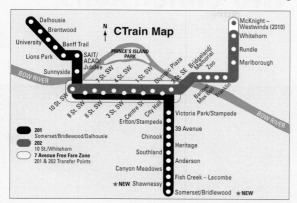

31. Describe the motion of the truck from the velocity-time graph below. During which time interval is the truck at rest? travelling with a uniform velocity? When is its acceleration the greatest?

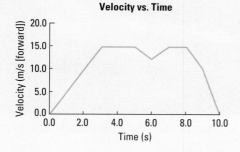

32. A racecar accelerates uniformly from 17.5 m/s [W] to 45.2 m/s [W] in 2.47 s. Determine the acceleration of the racecar.

33. How long will it take a vehicle travelling 80 km/h [W] to stop if the average stopping distance for that velocity is 76.0 m?

34. The Slingshot, an amusement park ride, propels its riders upward from rest with an acceleration of 39.24 m/s^2. How long does it take to reach a height of 27.0 m? Assume uniform acceleration.

35. Starting from rest, a platform diver hits the water with a speed of 55 km/h. From what height did she start her descent into the pool?

36. A circus performer can land safely on the ground at speeds up to 13.5 m/s. What is the greatest height from which the performer can fall?

37. A contractor drops a bolt from the top of a roof located 8.52 m above the ground. How long does it take the bolt to reach the ground, assuming there is no air drag?

38. An improperly installed weathervane falls from the roof of a barn and lands on the ground 1.76 s later. From what height did the weathervane fall and how fast was it travelling just before impact?

39. Attempting to beat the record for tallest Lego structure, a student drops a piece from a height of 24.91 m. How fast will the piece be travelling when it is 5.0 m above the ground and how long will it take to get there?

Extension

40. Weave zones are areas on roads where vehicles are changing their velocities to merge onto and off of busy expressways. Suggest criteria a design engineer must consider in developing a weave zone.

Consolidate Your Understanding

Create your own summary of kinematics by answering the questions below. If you want to use a graphic organizer, refer to Student References 4: Using Graphic Organizers on pp. 869–871. Use the Key Terms and Concepts listed on page 64 and the Learning Outcomes on page 4.

1. Create a flowchart to describe the changes in position, velocity, and acceleration for both uniform and accelerated motion.

2. Write a paragraph explaining the two main functions of graphing in kinematics. Share your report with another classmate.

Think About It

Review your answers to the Think About It questions on page 5. How would you answer each question now?

 e **TEST**

To check your understanding of motion in one dimension, follow the eTest links at www.pearsoned.ca/school/physicssource.

Vector components describe motion in two dimensions.

▲ **Figure 2.1** The motion of Canada's Snowbird precision flight squad can be described using vectors.

Imagine being a pilot for the Canadian Snowbirds (Figure 2.1). This precision flight team, composed of highly trained military personnel, performs at air shows across the country. Unlike the flight crew in the cockpit of a commercial airliner, these pilots execute aerobatic manoeuvres that require motion in both horizontal and vertical directions, while being acutely aware of their positions relative to the ground and to each other.

In this chapter, you will study motion in one and two dimensions by building on the concepts you learned in Chapter 1. You will use vectors to define position, velocity, and acceleration, and their interrelationships. The vector methods you will learn will allow you to study more complex motions.

Taking a One-dimensional Vector Walk

Problem

How can you add vectors to determine displacement?

Materials

30-m tape measure
field marker (tape or flag)

Procedure

1. Starting at the centre of a football field, work out a path sequence using six forward and backward displacements to move from your starting position to the goal line. At least two of your six displacements must be oriented in the direction opposite to the direction of the goal line.

2. On a football or large school field, mark your starting point with a flag or tape. Define direction axes.

3. Ask your partner to walk the displacements of the path sequence chosen in step 1 while holding the end of the measuring tape. Mark your partner's endpoint after each displacement (Figure 2.2).

4. Continue the journey, using the measuring tape, until you have walked all the displacements.

5. Mark the final endpoint.

6. Using the measuring tape, determine the displacement from your starting point.

7. Repeat steps 2–6 using two different sequences of the six displacements you originally chose.

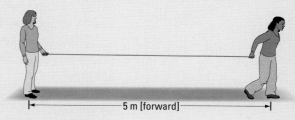

Figure 2.2

Questions

1. What was the total distance you travelled?

2. What was the total displacement?

3. What conclusion can you draw about the order of adding vectors?

Think About It

1. How does the order of a series of displacements affect the final position of an object?

2. Is it better to swim directly across a river or to point yourself directly across the river in order to cross in the shortest time?

3. Why does it take longer to fly across Canada from east to west rather than west to east in the same airplane?

4. How does the angle of a throw affect the time a ball spends in the air?

5. Two objects start from the same height at the same time. One is dropped while the other is given an initial horizontal velocity. Which one hits the ground first?

Discuss your answers in a small group and record them for later reference. As you complete each section of this chapter, review your answers to these questions. Note any changes to your ideas.

2.1 Vector Methods in One Dimension

One of the fastest-growing sports in the world today is snowshoeing (Figure 2.3). The equipment required is minimal and the sport is easy to learn — you need to move forward in a straight line. Despite its simplicity, snowshoeing has great cardiovascular benefits: You can burn up to 1000 calories per hour, which makes it the ultimate cross-training program for athletes. It also allows athletes to explore different terrains and gain a greater appreciation of the outdoors, as well as to test their limits, especially by participating in endurance races!

The motions in a showshoe race can be broken up into one-dimensional vector segments. In this section, you will study motion in one dimension using vectors.

▲ **Figure 2.3** Snowshoeing is a great way of enjoying the great outdoors in winter while improving your health.

Vector Diagrams

In Chapter 1, you used variables and graphs to represent vector quantities. You can also represent vector quantities using vector diagrams. In a diagram, a line segment with an arrowhead represents a vector quantity. Its point of origin is called the *tail*, and its terminal point (arrowhead) is the *tip* (Figure 2.4). If the magnitude of a vector is given, you can draw the vector to scale. The length of the line segment depends on the vector's magnitude. The arrowhead indicates direction. Drawing vector diagrams to represent motion helps you to visualize the motion of an object. Properly drawn, vector diagrams enable you to accurately add vectors and to determine an object's direction.

tail   tip

▲ **Figure 2.4** A vector has a tail and a tip.

Choosing Reference Coordinates

When describing the motion of an object, there are many ways to describe its direction. You could use adjectives such as forward or backward, up or down, into or out of, and left or right. You can also use compass directions, such as north [N], south [S], east [E], and west [W]. When drawing a vector diagram, it is important to choose which directions are positive and to include these directions on every vector diagram. As you learned in section 1.1 (Figure 1.6), in this unit, forward, up, right, north, east, and out of are usually designated as positive, whereas their opposites are usually considered negative. You may choose your own designation of positive and negative when solving problems, but make sure your reference direction is consistent within each problem and clearly communicated at the beginning of your solution.

Practise drawing vectors in the next Skills Practice exercise.

SKILLS PRACTICE   **Representing a Vector**

Using an appropriate scale and direction convention, draw each of the following vectors.

    (a) 5 m [forward]
    (b) 20 m [down]
    (c) 30 km [north]
    (d) 150 km [left]

Adding Vectors in One Dimension

Motion in one dimension involves vectors that are collinear. **Collinear** vectors lie along the same straight line. They may point in the same or in opposite directions (Figure 2.5).

collinear: along the same straight line, either in the same or in opposite directions

▲ **Figure 2.5** (a) Collinear vectors in the same direction (b) Collinear vectors in opposite directions

When more than one vector describes motion, you need to add the vectors. You can add and subtract vectors graphically as well as algebraically, provided they represent the same quantity or measurement. As in mathematics, in which only like terms can be added, you can only add vectors representing the same types of quantities. For example, you can add two or more position vectors, but not a position vector, 5 m [E], to a velocity vector, 5 m/s [E]. In addition, the unit of measurement must be the same. For example, before adding the position vectors 5 m [E] and 10 km [E], you must convert the units of one of the vectors so that both vectors have the same units.

In the next example, determine the sum of all the vector displacements graphically by adding them tip to tail. The sum of a series of vectors is called the **resultant vector**.

resultant vector: a vector drawn from the tail of the first vector to the tip of the last vector

Example 2.1

Contestants in a snowshoe race must move forward 10.0 m, untie a series of knots, move forward 5.0 m, solve a puzzle, and finally move forward 25.0 m to the finish line (Figure 2.6). Determine the resultant vector by adding the vectors graphically.

▲ **Figure 2.6**

Analysis and Solution
1. Choose an appropriate scale and reference direction.
   1.0 cm : 5.0 m, forward is positive.
2. Draw the first vector and label its magnitude and direction (Figure 2.7).

10.0 m [forward]

▲ **Figure 2.7**

3. Place the tail of the second vector at the tip of the first vector. Continue to place all the remaining vectors in order, tip to tail (Figure 2.8).

| 10.0 m | 5.0 m | 25.0 m |
| [forward] | [forward] | [forward] |

▲ **Figure 2.8**

4. Connect the tail of the first vector to the tip of the last vector. This new vector, which points toward the tip of the last vector, is the resultant vector, $\vec{R}$ (the purple arrow in Figure 2.9).

▲ **Figure 2.9**

Find the magnitude of the resultant vector by measuring with a ruler, then convert the measured value using the scale. Remember to include the direction.

$$\Delta \vec{d} = 8.0 \text{ cm [forward]} \times \frac{5.0 \text{ m}}{1.0 \text{ cm}}$$

$$= 40 \text{ m [forward]}$$

Practice Problems

1. The coach of the high-school rugby team made the team members run a series of sprints: 5.0 m [forward], 10 m [backward], 10 m [forward], 10 m [backward], 20 m [forward], 10 m [backward], 40 m [forward], and 10 m [backward]. How far did the players run?
   (a) What is their total distance?
   (b) What is their displacement?

Answers

1. (a) 115 m
   (b) 35 m [forward]

In summary, you can see that adding vectors involves connecting them tip to tail. The plus sign in a vector equation tells you to connect the vectors tip to tail in the vector diagram.

To subtract collinear vectors graphically (Figure 2.10(a)), you may use one of two methods. For the first method, find $\Delta \vec{d}$ using the equation $\Delta \vec{d} = \vec{d}_2 - \vec{d}_1$: Add the negative of $\vec{d}_1$ to $\vec{d}_2$, tip to tail, as you did in Example 2.1. The negative of a vector creates a new vector that points in the opposite direction of the original vector (Figure 2.10(b)). For the second method, connect the vectors tail to tail. This time, $\Delta \vec{d}$ starts at the tip of $\vec{d}_1$ and ends at the tip of $\vec{d}_2$ (Figure 2.10(c)).

(a)

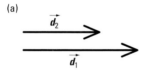

(b)

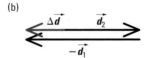

(c)

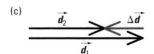

▲ **Figure 2.10**
(a) To subtract two collinear vectors, $\vec{d}_1$ and $\vec{d}_2$, graphically, (b) add the negative of $\vec{d}_1$ to $\vec{d}_2$ or
(c) connect the vectors tail to tail and draw the resultant connecting the tip of $\vec{d}_1$ to the tip of $\vec{d}_2$.

Recall that the definition of displacement is final position minus initial position, or $\Delta\vec{d} = \vec{d}_f - \vec{d}_i$. The next example reviews the algebraic subtraction of vectors, which you learned in Chapter 1, Example 1.1, and also shows you how to subtract vectors graphically.

Example 2.2

A sailboat that is initially 15 m to the right of a buoy sails 35 m to the left of the buoy (Figure 2.11). Determine the sailboat's displacement (a) algebraically and (b) graphically.

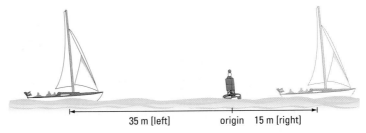

35 m [left]　　origin　15 m [right]

▲ **Figure 2.11**

Practice Problems

1. Sprinting drills include running 40.0 m [N], walking 20.0 m [N], and then sprinting 100.0 m [N]. Using vector diagrams, determine the sprinter's displacement from his initial position.

2. To perform a give and go, a basketball player fakes out the defence by moving 0.750 m [right] and then 3.50 m [left]. Using vector diagrams, determine the player's displacement from the starting position.

3. While building a wall, a bricklayer sweeps the cement back and forth. If she swings her hand back and forth, a distance of 1.70 m, four times, use vector diagrams to calculate the distance and displacement her hand travels during that time.

Check your answers against those in Example 1.1 Practice Problem 1.

Answers

1. 160.0 m [N]
2. 2.75 m [left]
3. 6.80 m, 0 m

Given
Consider left to be positive.
$\vec{d}_i = 15$ m [right] $= -15$ m
$\vec{d}_f = 35$ m [left] $= +35$ m

Required
displacement ($\Delta\vec{d}$)

Analysis and Solution
(a) To find displacement algebraically, use the equation
$$\Delta\vec{d} = \vec{d}_f - \vec{d}_i$$
$$= +35 \text{ m} - (-15 \text{ m})$$
$$= +35 \text{ m} + 15 \text{ m}$$
$$= +50 \text{ m}$$

The sign is positive, so the direction is to the left.

(b) To find displacement graphically, subtract the two position vectors. Draw the vectors tail to tail and draw the resultant from the tip of the initial position vector to the tip of the final position vector (Figure 2.12).

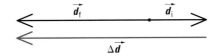

$\vec{d}_f$　　　　$\vec{d}_i$

$\Delta\vec{d}$

▲ **Figure 2.12**

Paraphrase
The sailboat's displacement is 50 m [left].

For collinear vectors, find displacement by subtracting initial position from final position. Subtract vectors graphically by connecting them tail to tail or by reversing the direction of the initial position vector. Recall from Chapter 1 that direction for displacement is given with respect to initial position.

2.1 Check and Reflect

Knowledge

1. Describe the similarities and differences between the two vectors drawn below.

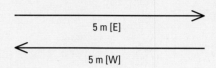

2. Using the same scale and reference coordinates, compare the vectors 5 m [N] and 10 m [S].

3. If the scale vector diagram of 5.0 m [S] is 6.0 cm long, what is the length of the scale vector diagram of 20 m [S]?

4. What scale is being used if 5.0 cm represents 100 km?

Applications

5. The scale on a *National Geographic* world map is 1.0 cm : 520 km. On the map, 4.0 cm separates Alberta's north and south provincial boundaries. What is the separation in kilometres?

6. During a tough drill on a field of length 100 yards, players run to each 10-yard line and back to the starting position until they reach the other end of the field.

   (a) Write a vector equation that includes all the legs of the run.

   (b) What is the players' final displacement?

   (c) How far did they run?

7. A car drives north 500 km. It then drives three sequential displacements south, each of which is 50 km longer than the previous displacement. If the final position of the car is 50 km [N], find the three displacements.

8. Are vectors A and B equal? Why or why not?

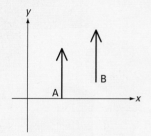

9. A bouncy ball dropped from a height of 10.0 m bounces back 8.0 m, then drops and rebounds 4.0 m and finally 2.0 m. Find the distance the ball travels and its displacement from the drop point.

 e TEST

To check your understanding of vectors in one dimension, follow the eTest links at www.pearsoned.ca/school/physicssource.

Motion in Two Dimensions

From the boot, the ball flies across the grass into the net and the crowd roars. The enormously successful FIFA Under-19 Women's World Championship, held in 2002, raised the profile of women's soccer in Canada and drew crowds totalling almost 200 000 to venues in Edmonton, Vancouver, and Victoria (Figure 2.13). Stars like Charmaine Hooper, Brittany Timko, and Christine Sinclair continue to amaze. From World Championship team members to the Under-6s on the local soccer pitch, performance depends on understanding and coordinating the movement of players and ball across the surface of the field.

▲ **Figure 2.13**   Motion in sports such as soccer can be described by vectors in two dimensions.

Playbooks are available for fast-paced games such as hockey and soccer to allow coaches and players to plan the strategies that they hope will lead to success. Sometimes a team can charge straight up the rink or field, but, more often, a series of angled movements is needed to advance the puck or ball (Figure 2.14). For everyone to understand the play, a system is needed to understand motion in two dimensions.

Components of Vectors

Imagine that you are at one corner of a soccer field and you have to get to the far opposite corner. The shortest path from one corner to the other is a straight diagonal line. Figure 2.15 shows this path to be 150 m.

Another way to describe this motion is to imagine an x-axis and a y-axis placed onto the soccer field, with you standing at the point (0, 0). You could move along the length of the field 120 m and then across the field 90 m and end up at the same spot (Figure 2.15).

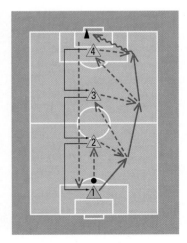

▲ **Figure 2.14**   This page is taken from a soccer playbook. How many players are involved in this wall pass-in-succession manoeuvre?

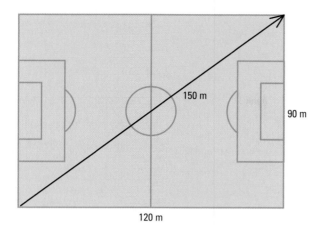

◀ **Figure 2.15**
The diagonal distance
from one corner to the
opposite corner of a
soccer field is 150 m.

150 m

90 m

120 m

In this example, the sideline of the soccer field could be considered the *x*-axis, and the goal line could be the *y*-axis. The diagonal motion vector can then be separated, or resolved, into two perpendicular parts, or **components**: the *x* component and the *y* component. The diagonal vector is the resultant vector.

components: perpendicular parts into which a vector can be separated

If you walked along the sideline or *x*-axis, you would move through a distance of 120 m. This distance is the *x* component of the diagonal vector. The second part of the walk along the goal line, parallel to the *y*-axis, is the *y* component of the diagonal vector. This motion has a distance of 90 m. Figure 2.16 shows the *x* and *y* components of the diagonal motion across the soccer field.

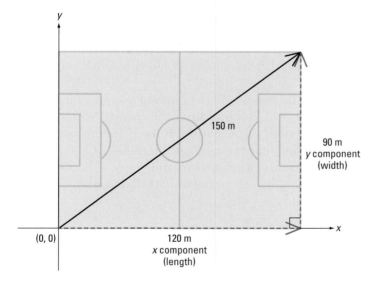

150 m

90 m
y component
(width)

(0, 0)

120 m
x component
(length)

◀ **Figure 2.16**   The resultant vector representing the diagonal walk across the soccer field can be resolved into *x* and *y* components.

Vector Directions

Recall that a vector must have a magnitude and a direction. You have just studied how to resolve a vector into its components. Before going further, you need to know how to indicate the direction of vectors in two dimensions. There are two methods commonly used to show direction for vector quantities in two dimensions: the **Cartesian method** and the **navigator method**. Both methods are considered valid ways to describe the direction of a vector.

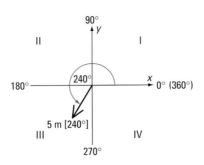

▲ **Figure 2.17** The Cartesian method for stating vector direction

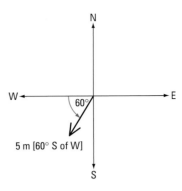

▲ **Figure 2.18** The navigator method for stating vector direction

Cartesian Method

With the Cartesian method, the positive x-axis is at 0° and angles are measured by moving counterclockwise about the origin. One complete rotation is 360° — a complete circle. In Figure 2.17, the displacement vector, 5 m [240°], is located in the third quadrant. This vector is rotated 240° counterclockwise starting from the positive x-axis.

Navigator Method

Another method for indicating vector direction is the navigator method. This method uses the compass bearings north [N], south [S], east [E], and west [W] to identify vector directions. In Figure 2.18, the displacement vector 5 m [60° S of W] is between the west and south compass bearings. To draw this vector, start with the second compass bearing you are given in square brackets, west, then move 60° in the direction of the first compass bearing you are given, south.

The type of problem will determine the method you use for stating vector directions. Often, it will be clear from the context of the problem which method is preferred. For example, if the question is about a boat sailing [30° N of W], then use the navigator method. If a plane has a heading of 135°, then use the Cartesian method.

In the problems below, you can practise identifying and drawing vectors using the two methods.

SKILLS PRACTICE Directions

1. For each of the following vectors, identify the method used for indicating direction. Then draw each vector in your notebook, using an appropriate scale and reference coordinates.
   (a) 3 m [0°]
   (b) 17 m/s [245°]
   (c) 7 m [65°]
   (d) 8 m/s [35° W of N]
   (e) 2 m [98°]
   (f) 12 m/s [30° S of E]

2. For each vector in question 1, state the direction using the alternative method. Then draw each vector using an appropriate scale and reference coordinates.

Concept Check

Write the direction [60° S of W] another way using a different start-ing axis but keeping the angle less than 90°.

2-2 *QuickLab*

Vector Walk

Problem

How can you add vectors to determine displacement?

Materials

30-m measuring tape
large chalkboard protractor
field marker (tape or flag)

Procedure

1 Using a tree diagram, determine the number of pathways you could take to walk the series of displacement vectors below. Assume that you will start on the centre line of a football field and mark it 0°.

  (a) 5 m [0°]

  (b) 12 m [270°]

  (c) 15 m [90°]

  (d) 3 m [180°]

2 On a football or large school field, mark your starting point with a flag or tape. Define direction axes.

3 Ask your partner to walk the displacement given in (a) while you hold the end of the measuring tape. Mark your partner's endpoint (Figure 2.19).

4 Continue the journey, using the protractor and measuring tape, until you have walked all the vectors.

5 Mark the final endpoint.

6 Using the measuring tape, determine the displacement from your starting point.

7 Use the protractor to estimate the angle of displacement.

8 Repeat steps 3–7 for all the pathways you determined in step 1.

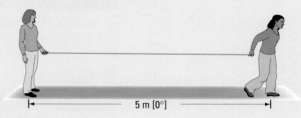

5 m [0°]

▲ **Figure 2.19**

 NOTE: Use the same method for determining direction throughout the lab.

Questions

1. What was the total distance you travelled?

2. What was the total displacement?

3. What conclusion can you draw about the order of adding vectors?

Adding Two-dimensional Vectors Graphically

To sink the eight ball in the front side pocket of a billiard table, you must cause the ball to travel down and across the table (Figure 2.20). The ball's motion occurs in a plane, or two dimensions, even though its path is linear (Figure 2.21).

▲ **Figure 2.20** Playing billiards involves two-dimensional motion.

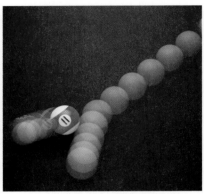

▲ **Figure 2.21** The path of the billiard ball is linear, but it occurs in two dimensions.

Recall from section 2.1 that the plus sign (+) in a vector equation indicates that you need to connect the vectors tip to tail. Up to this point, you have added collinear vectors only. In this section, you will learn how to add non-collinear vectors. The plus sign still indicates you need to connect the vectors tip to tail while keeping track of their directions.

Adding Non-collinear Vectors

non-collinear: not along a straight line

In section 2.1, you learned that vectors that lie along the same straight line are collinear. Vectors that are *not* along the same straight line are **non-collinear** (Figure 2.22). To determine the magnitude and direction of the sum of two or more non-collinear vectors *graphically*, use an accurately drawn scale vector diagram. To add two non-collinear vectors *algebraically*, use trigonometry. When the vectors are perpendicular, you can add them using the Pythagorean theorem. If the vectors to be added are not perpendicular, first resolve them into their x and y components.

▲ **Figure 2.22** Non-collinear vectors lie along different lines.

Imagine you are walking north a distance of 40 m. Your initial position from your starting point is $\vec{d}_1$. You stop, head west a distance of 30 m, and stop again. Your final position is $\vec{d}_2$. To find your displacement, you cannot simply subtract your initial position from your final position because the vectors are not collinear. To find your displacement in two dimensions, you need to *add* the two position vectors: $\Delta\vec{d} = \vec{d}_1 + \vec{d}_2$.

From Figure 2.23, you can see that the answer is *not* 70 m. You would obtain the answer 70 m if you walked in the same direction for both parts of your walk. Because you did not, you cannot directly substitute values into the displacement equation $\Delta\vec{d} = \vec{d}_1 + \vec{d}_2$. Instead, you must draw the vectors to scale, connect them tip to tail (because of the plus sign), and measure the magnitude of the resultant. Since $\Delta\vec{d}$ is a vector quantity, you must also indicate its direction. You can find the direction of the resultant using a protractor (Figure 2.24).

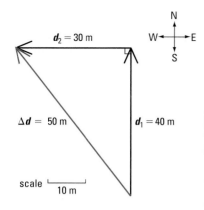

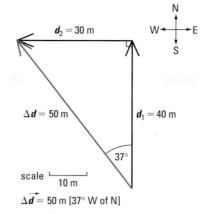

$\Delta \vec{d} = 50$ m [37° W of N]

▲ **Figure 2.23** What is the sum of $\vec{d}_1$ and $\vec{d}_2$?

▲ **Figure 2.24** When adding non-collinear vectors graphically, use a protractor to find the direction of the resultant.

Eight Steps for Adding Non-collinear Vectors Graphically

To find the resultant vector in a non-collinear vector addition statement using the graphical method, follow these eight steps (see Figure 2.25):

1. Create an appropriate scale.
2. Choose a set of reference coordinates.
3. Draw vector 1 to scale. Measure its direction from the tail.
4. Draw vector 2 to scale. Draw its tail at the tip (arrowhead) of vector 1.
5. Draw the resultant vector by connecting the tail of vector 1 to the tip of vector 2.
6. Measure the magnitude (length) of the resultant. Measure the angle of the resultant from its tail.
7. Use your scale to convert the magnitude of the resultant to its original units.
8. State the resultant vector. Remember to include both magnitude and direction.

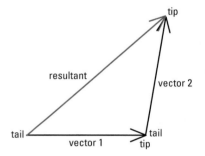

▲ **Figure 2.25** Adding vectors

This method also works for more than two vectors. You can add the vectors in any order. The next example shows you how to add more than two non-collinear vectors graphically.

Example 2.3

A camper left her tent to go to the lake. She walked 0.80 km [S], then 1.20 km [E] and 0.30 km [N]. Find her resultant displacement.

Given
$\Delta \vec{d}_1 = 0.80$ km [S]
$\Delta \vec{d}_2 = 1.20$ km [E]
$\Delta \vec{d}_3 = 0.30$ km [N]

Required
resultant displacement ($\Delta \vec{d}_R$)

Practice Problems

1. For Example 2.3, add the vectors in two different orders and obtain the resultant for each case.

2. A student runs through a field 100 m [E], then 200 m [S], and finally 50 m [45° S of E]. Find her final position relative to her starting point.

Answers

1. 1.30 km [67° E of S]
2. 272 m [60° S of E]

Analysis and Solution

The three vectors are non-collinear, so add them tip to tail to find the resultant (Figure 2.26).

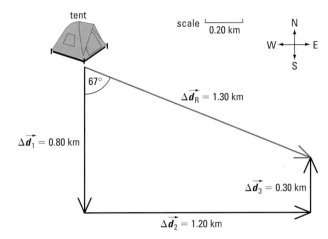

$$\Delta \vec{d}_R = \Delta \vec{d}_1 + \Delta \vec{d}_2 + \Delta \vec{d}_3$$

▲ **Figure 2.26**

Paraphrase

The camper's resultant displacement is 1.30 km [67° E of S].

SKILLS PRACTICE   Distance, Displacement, and Position

Figure 2.27 shows the distances a bicycle courier travelled in going along the path from A to D, passing through B and C on the way. Use the information in the diagram, a ruler calibrated in mm, and a protractor to complete the distance, displacement, and position information required in Table 2.1. Assume the bicycle courier's reference point is A. Complete Table 2.1, then draw and label the displacement vectors AB, BC, and CD, and the position vectors AB, AC, and AD.

▼ **Table 2.1**   Distance, Displacement, and Position

	Distance Δd (m)	Final position $\vec{d}$ (m) [direction] reference point	Displacement $\Delta \vec{d}$ (m) [direction]
AB			
BC			
CD			
AC			
AD			

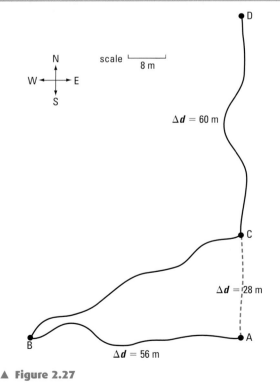

▲ **Figure 2.27**

Determining Components

You may have noticed the symbol θ used with angles in illustrations such as Figure 2.28. This symbol is the Greek letter theta, and it represents the angle between the x-axis and the vector $\vec{R}$. In Figure 2.28, θ is 37°. You can also see in Figure 2.28 that the components R_x and R_y form a right triangle with the vector $\vec{R}$.

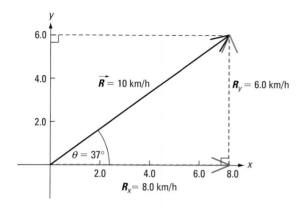

◀ **Figure 2.28**
Drawing components

Because the triangle is a right triangle, you can determine components algebraically by using the trigonometric functions sine, cosine, and tangent. You can define each of the trigonometric functions in terms of the sides of a right triangle, like the one in Figure 2.29. Knowing these definitions, you can use the trigonometric functions to help you solve for the components of a vector.

To calculate R_x, use the cosine function:

$$\cos \theta = \frac{\text{adjacent}}{\text{hypotenuse}} = \frac{R_x}{R} \text{ or } R_x = R \cos \theta$$

In Figure 2.28, the x component is:

$R_x = (10 \text{ km/h})(\cos 37°)$
$\quad = 8.0 \text{ km/h}$

To calculate R_y, use the sine function:

$$\sin \theta = \frac{\text{opposite}}{\text{hypotenuse}} = \frac{R_y}{R} \text{ or } R_y = R \sin \theta$$

In Figure 2.28, the y component is:

$R_y = (10 \text{ km/h})(\sin 37°)$
$\quad = 6.0 \text{ km/h}$

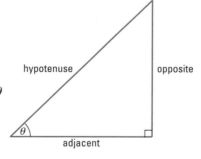

▲ **Figure 2.29** Labelled sides of a right triangle

Example 2.4 shows the steps for finding the velocity components of a car travelling in a northeasterly direction using trigonometry. This example uses the navigator method to indicate the direction of the velocity vector. Note that the east direction [E] is the same as the positive x direction in the Cartesian method, and north [N] is the same as the positive y direction. So, for any vector $\vec{R}$, the x component is the same as the east component, and the y component is the same as the north component.

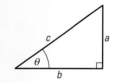

Example 2.4

Determine the north and east velocity components of a car travelling at 100 km/h [25° N of E].

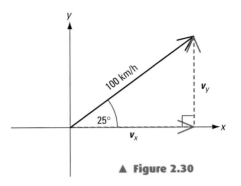

▲ **Figure 2.30**

Given
$\vec{v} = 100$ km/h [25° N of E]

Required
velocity component north (y component, v_y)
velocity component east (x component, v_x)

Analysis and Solution
The vector lies between the north and east directions, so the x and y components are both positive. Since the north direction is parallel to the y-axis, use the sine function, $R_y = R \sin \theta$, to find the north component. Since the east direction lies along the x-axis, use the cosine function, $R_x = R \cos \theta$, to find the east component.

$R_y = R \sin \theta$
$v_y = (100$ km/h$)(\sin 25°)$
$\quad = 42$ km/h

$R_x = R \cos \theta$
$v_x = (100$ km/h$)(\cos 25°)$
$\quad = 91$ km/h

Paraphrase
The north component of the car's velocity is 42 km/h and the east component is 91 km/h.

Practice Problems

1. A hiker's displacement is 15 km [40° E of N]. What is the north component of his displacement?

2. A cyclist's velocity is 10 m/s [245°]. Determine the x and y components of her velocity.

3. A snowmobile travels 65 km [37° E of S]. How far east does it travel?

Answers

1. 11 km [N]
2. $v_x = -4.2$ m/s, $v_y = -9.1$ m/s
3. 39 km [E]

Concept Check

For a vector $\vec{R}$ in the first quadrant, are R_x and R_y always positive? Determine whether R_x and R_y are positive or negative for vectors in the second, third, and fourth quadrants.

Adding Vectors Using Components

You can write the magnitude of any two-dimensional vector as the sum of its x and y components. Note that x and y components are perpendicular. Because motion along the x direction is perpendicular to motion along the y direction, a change in one component does not affect the other component. Whether it is movement across a soccer field or any other type of two-dimensional motion, you can describe the motion in terms of x and y components.

In Example 2.4, you learned how to determine the x and y components, R_x and R_y, for a general vector $\vec{R}$. In some situations, you already know R_x and R_y, and you must find the magnitude and direction of the resultant vector $\vec{R}$. For example, a toy moves 9.0 m right and then 12.0 m across a classroom floor (Figure 2.31). What is the toy's displacement? Solving this problem algebraically requires two steps:

Step 1: Find the magnitude of $\vec{R}$.

To find the magnitude of the resultant vector, use the Pythagorean theorem. You can use this theorem because the two components, R_x and R_y, form a right triangle with the resultant vector. You are given that R_x = 9.0 m and R_y = 12.0 m.

$$R^2 = R_x{}^2 + R_y{}^2$$

$$R = \sqrt{(9.0 \text{ m})^2 + (12.0 \text{ m})^2}$$

$$= 15 \text{ m}$$

Step 2: Find the angle of $\vec{R}$.

To find the angle of $\vec{R}$, use the tangent function:

$$\tan \theta = \frac{\text{opposite}}{\text{adjacent}}$$

$$= \frac{12.0 \text{ m}}{9.0 \text{ m}}$$

$$= 1.33$$

$$\theta = \tan^{-1}(1.33)$$

$$= 53.1°$$

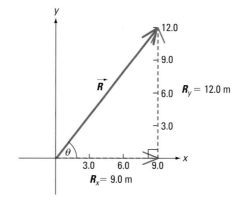

▲ **Figure 2.31**   Vector components of the movement of a toy across a classroom floor

Using the Cartesian method, the resultant vector direction is [53.1°].
Using the navigator method, the direction is [53.1° N of E].

SKILLS PRACTICE   Using Components

1. Find R_x and R_y for the following vectors:
   (a) A boat travelling at 15 km/h [45° N of W]
   (b) A plane flying at 200 km/h [25° E of S]
   (c) A mountain bike travelling at 10 km/h [N]

2. Find $\vec{R}$ and θ for the following R_x and R_y values:
   (a) R_x = 12 m, R_y = 7 m
   (b) R_x = 40 km/h, R_y = 55 km/h
   (c) R_x = 30 cm, R_y = 10 cm

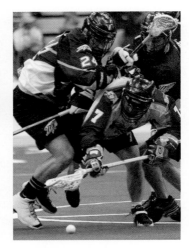

▲ Figure 2.32 The movement of the players and the ball in a lacrosse game could be tracked using vectors.

In general, most vector motion involves adding non-collinear vectors. Consider the following scenario. During a lacrosse game, players pass the ball from one person to another (Figure 2.32). The ball can then be redirected for a shot on goal. Each of the displacements could involve different angles. In order to find the net displacement, you would use the following sequence of calculations.

Four Steps for Adding Non-collinear Vectors Algebraically

1. Determine the x and y components of each vector.

2. Add all components in the x direction. Add all components in the y direction. The sums of the x and y components are the two (perpendicular) components of the resultant vector.

3. To find the magnitude of the resultant vector, use the Pythagorean theorem.

4. To find the angle of the resultant vector, use $\theta = \tan^{-1}\left(\dfrac{\text{opposite}}{\text{adjacent}}\right)$.

The following example illustrates how to apply these steps.

In a lacrosse game (Figure 2.33(a)), player A passes the ball 12.0 m to player B at an angle of 30°. Player B relays the ball to player C, 9.0 m away, at an angle of 155°. Find the ball's resultant displacement.

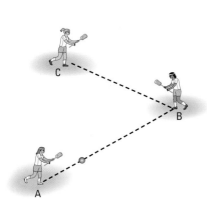

▲ Figure 2.33(a) The path of the ball on the lacrosse field

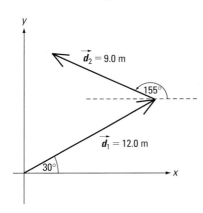

▲ Figure 2.33(b) The path of the ball as vectors

Figure 2.33(b) shows the path of the lacrosse ball as vectors. This problem is different from previous examples because the two vectors are not at right angles to each other. Even with this difference, you can follow the same general steps to solve the problem.

Step 1: Determine the x and y components of each vector.
Since you are solving for displacement, resolve each displacement vector into its components (Figure 2.34). Table 2.2 shows how to calculate the x and y components. In this case, designate up and right as positive directions.

x direction	y direction
$d_{1_x} = (12.0 \text{ m})(\cos 30°)$ $= 10.4 \text{ m}$	$d_{1_y} = (12.0 \text{ m})(\sin 30°)$ $= 6.0 \text{ m}$
$d_{2_x} = -(9.0 \text{ m})(\cos 25°)$ $= -8.16 \text{ m}$	$d_{2_y} = (9.0 \text{ m})(\sin 25°)$ $= 3.8 \text{ m}$

(Note that d_{2_x} is negative because it points to the left, and up and right were designated as positive.)

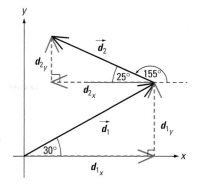

▲ **Figure 2.34**   The path of the lacrosse ball

Step 2: Add the x components and the y components separately.

Add all the x components together, then add all the y components (see Table 2.3 and Figure 2.35).

▼ **Table 2.3**   Adding x and y Components in Figure 2.35

x direction	y direction
$d_x = d_{1_x} + d_{2_x}$ $= 10.4 \text{ m} + (-8.16 \text{ m})$ $= 10.4 \text{ m} - 8.16 \text{ m}$ $= 2.2 \text{ m}$	$d_y = d_{1_y} + d_{2_y}$ $= 6.0 \text{ m} + 3.8 \text{ m}$ $= 9.8 \text{ m}$

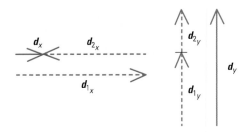

▲ **Figure 2.35**   Add the x and y components separately first to obtain two perpendicular vectors.

Step 3: Find the magnitude of the resultant, $\vec{d}$.

To find the magnitude of the resultant, use the Pythagorean theorem (Figure 2.36).

$$d = \sqrt{(d_x)^2 + (d_y)^2}$$
$$= \sqrt{(2.2 \text{ m})^2 + (9.8 \text{ m})^2}$$
$$= 10 \text{ m}$$

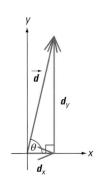

▲ **Figure 2.36**   The component method allows you to convert non-perpendicular vectors into perpendicular vectors that you can then combine using the Pythagorean theorem.

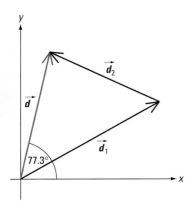

y

$\vec{d}_2$

$\vec{d}$

$\vec{d}_1$

77.3°

x

▲ **Figure 2.37** Determine the angle by looking at the position of the resultant.

Step 4: Find the angle of $\vec{d}$.
Use the tangent function to find the angle (Figure 2.37).

$$\tan \theta = \frac{\text{opposite}}{\text{adjacent}}$$

$$= \frac{9.8 \text{ m}}{2.2 \text{ m}}$$

$$= 4.45$$

$$\theta = \tan^{-1}(4.45)$$

$$= 77.3°$$

From Figure 2.37, the ball's displacement is, therefore, 10 m [77.3°].

The following example illustrates another situation where the displacement vectors are not at right angles.

Example 2.5

Practice Problems

1. Find the displacement of a farmer who walked 80.0 m [0°] and then 60.0 m [335°].

2. Find the displacement of a soccer player who runs 15 m [15° N of E] and then 13 m [5° W of N].

3. While tracking a polar bear, a wildlife biologist travels 300 m [S] and then 550 m [75° N of E]. What is her displacement?

Answers

1. 137 m [349°]
2. 21 m [52° N of E]
3. 2.7×10^2 m [58° N of E]

Use components to determine the displacement of a cross-country skier who travelled 15.0 m [220°] and then 25.0 m [335°] (Figure 2.38).

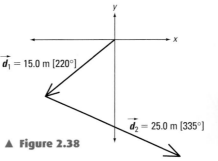

$\vec{d}_1 = 15.0$ m [220°]

$\vec{d}_2 = 25.0$ m [335°]

▲ **Figure 2.38**

Given
$\vec{d}_1 = 15.0$ m [220°]
$\vec{d}_2 = 25.0$ m [335°]

Required
displacement $(\vec{d})$

Analysis and Solution
Step 1: Use $R_x = R \cos \theta$ and $R_y = R \sin \theta$ to resolve each vector into its x and y components. Designate up and to the right as positive. Work with acute angles (Figure 2.39).

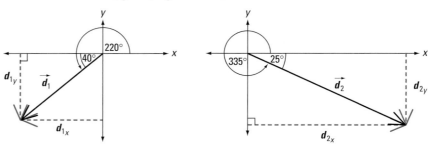

▲ **Figure 2.39**

x direction:
$$d_{1_x} = -(15.0 \text{ m})(\cos 40°)$$
$$= -11.49 \text{ m}$$

y direction:
$$d_{1_y} = -(15.0 \text{ m})(\sin 40°)$$
$$= -9.642 \text{ m}$$

$$d_{2_x} = (25.0 \text{ m})(\cos 25°)$$
$$= 22.66 \text{ m}$$

$$d_{2_y} = -(25.0 \text{ m})(\sin 25°)$$
$$= -10.57 \text{ m}$$

Step 2: Add the x and y components.

$$d_x = d_{1_x} + d_{2_x}$$
$$= -11.49 \text{ m} + 22.66 \text{ m}$$
$$= 11.17 \text{ m}$$

$$d_y = d_{1_y} + d_{2_y}$$
$$= -9.642 \text{ m} + (-10.57 \text{ m})$$
$$= -20.21 \text{ m}$$

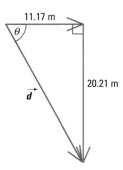

▲ **Figure 2.40**

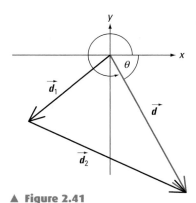

▲ **Figure 2.41**

Step 3: To find the magnitude of the resultant, calculate d using the Pythagorean theorem (Figure 2.40).

$$d = \sqrt{(11.17 \text{ m})^2 + (20.21 \text{ m})^2}$$
$$= 23.09 \text{ m}$$

Figure 2.41 shows that the resultant lies in the fourth quadrant.

Step 4: To find the angle, use the tangent function (see Figure 2.40).

$$\tan \theta = \frac{\text{opposite}}{\text{adjacent}}$$
$$= \frac{20.21 \text{ m}}{11.17 \text{ m}}$$
$$= 1.810$$
$$\theta = \tan^{-1}(1.810)$$
$$= 61.1°$$

From Figure 2.41, note that the angle, θ, lies below the positive x-axis. Using the Cartesian system, the angle is 299°.

Paraphrase
The cross-country skier's displacement is 23.1 m [299°].

e **SIM**

Practise the numerical addition of two or more vectors. Follow the eSim links at www.pearsoned.ca/school/ physicssource.

In summary, in order to solve a two-dimensional motion problem, you need to split the motion into two one-dimensional problems by using the vectors' x and y components. Then add the x and y components separately. To find the magnitude of the resultant, use the Pythagorean theorem. To find the angle of the resultant, use the tangent function.

Knowledge

1. What trigonometric function is used to determine the *x* or horizontal component of a vector?

2. True or false? Explain.

   (a) The order in which vectors are added is important.

   (b) Displacement and distance are always equal.

3. Describe when you would use the navigator method to indicate the direction of a vector.

Applications

4. A student has created a short computer program that calculates components of vectors drawn with a computer mouse. To demonstrate his program, he drags the mouse to create a vector at 55 cm [30° W of S]. What are the components of the vector?

5. Determine the distance travelled and the displacement for each of the following.

   (a) After leaving her cabin, a camper snowshoes 750 m [90°] and then 2.20 km [270°].

   (b) Blading through Fish Creek Park in Calgary takes you 5.0 km [W], 3.0 km [N], 2.0 km [E], and 1.5 km [S].

   (c) A swimmer travels in a northerly direction across a 500-m-wide lake. Once across, the swimmer notices that she is 150 m east of her original starting position.

6. A boat sails 5.0 km [45° W of N]. It then changes direction and sails 7.0 km [45° S of E]. Where does the boat end up with reference to its starting point?

7. A pellet gun fires a pellet with a velocity of 355 m/s [30°]. What is the magnitude of the vertical component of the velocity at the moment the pellet is fired?

8. Tourists on a jet ski move 1.20 km [55° N of E] and then 3.15 km [70° S of E]. Determine the jet ski's displacement.

9. A jogger runs with a velocity of 6.0 km/h [25° N of W] for 35 min and then changes direction, jogging for 20 min at 4.5 km/h [65° E of N]. Using a vector diagram, determine the jogger's total displacement and his average velocity for the workout.

10. On second base, a baseball player's displacement from home plate is 38 m [90°]. Given that a baseball diamond is a square, assume that the first-base line is the horizontal axis to solve the following.

    (a) What are the components of the player's displacement from home plate?

    (b) Has the runner standing on second base travelled a distance of 38 m? Why or why not?

11. Determine the resultant displacement of a skateboarder who rolls 45.0 m [310°] and 35.0 m [135°].

 e **TEST**

To check your understanding of two-dimensional motion, follow the eTest links at www.pearsoned.ca/school/physicssource.

2.3 Relative Motion

Conveyor belts in the oil sands mines of Northern Alberta are 50 km long (Figure 2.42). Every hour, they move 25 200 t of oil sand from the mine to the extraction plant. What is the speed of the oil with respect to the conveyor belt? How fast is the oil sand moving with respect to the ground? How fast is it moving relative to a 21 240-t mechanical drive truck going in the opposite direction?

▲ **Figure 2.42**   A conveyor belt represents an example of uniform and relative motion.

Sometimes objects move within a medium that is itself moving. Wind (moving air) affects the motion of objects such as kites, sailboats, and airplanes. Current (moving water) affects the motion of watercraft, wildlife, and swimmers. An Olympic kayak competitor who can paddle with a speed of 5.0 m/s in still water may appear to be going faster to an observer on shore if she is paddling in the same direction as the current. In this case, the velocity of the moving object depends on the location of the observer: whether the observer is on the moving object or observing the moving object from a stationary position. **Relative motion** is motion measured with respect to an observer.

relative motion: motion measured with respect to an observer

Concept Check

An observer is on a train moving at a velocity of 25 m/s [forward]. A ball moves at 25 m/s [forward] on the moving train. What is the velocity of the ball relative to the observer on the train? What is the velocity of the ball relative to an observer standing on the ground? What happens if the ball moves 25 m/s [backward]?

How does a moving medium affect the motion of a table tennis ball?

Table Tennis in the Wind

Problem

How does air movement affect the motion of a table tennis ball?

Materials

large upright fan
table tennis table
paddles
table tennis ball

Procedure

1 With a partner, practise hitting the table tennis ball to each other (Figure 2.43).

2 Set up the fan on one side of the table tennis table.

3 Hit the table tennis ball straight across the length of the table

   (a) against the wind

   (b) with the wind

   (c) perpendicular to the wind's direction

4 Record how the moving air influences the motion of the ball in each case.

▲ **Figure 2.43**

Questions

1. When did the ball move the fastest? the slowest?

2. When the air movement was perpendicular to the ball's path, did it change the ball's speed? Did it change the ball's velocity? Explain.

3. Given your results, speculate as to why golfers release a tuft of grass before teeing off.

4. Describe how wind direction might influence a beach volleyball player's serve.

e LAB

For a probeware activity, go to
www.pearsoned.ca/school/physicssource.

Relative Motion in the Air

ground velocity: velocity relative to an observer on the ground

air velocity: an object's velocity relative to still air

wind velocity: velocity of the wind relative to the ground

A flight from Edmonton to Toronto takes about 3.5 h. The return flight on the same aircraft takes 4.0 h. If the plane's air speed is the same in both directions, why does the trip east take less time? The reason is that, when travelling eastward from Edmonton, a tailwind (a wind that blows from the rear of the plane, in the same direction as the plane's motion) increases the airplane's **ground velocity** (velocity relative to an observer on the ground), hence reducing the time of travel and, therefore, fuel consumption and cost.

A Canadian regional jet travels with an **air velocity** (the plane's velocity in still air) of 789 km/h [E]. The jet encounters a **wind velocity** (the wind's velocity with respect to the ground) of 56.3 km/h [E] (Figure 2.44). (This wind is a west wind, blowing eastward from the west.) What is the velocity of the airplane relative to an observer on the ground? The resultant velocity of the airplane, or ground velocity, is the vector sum of the plane's air velocity and the wind velocity (Figure 2.45). Let the positive direction be east.

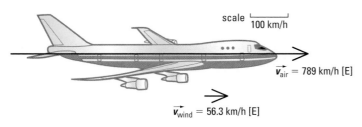

scale $\overline{\text{100 km/h}}$

$\vec{v}_{air}$ = 789 km/h [E]

$\vec{v}_{wind}$ = 56.3 km/h [E]

▲ **Figure 2.44** The air velocity and wind velocity are in the same direction.

$$\vec{v}_{\text{ground}} = \vec{v}_{\text{air}} + \vec{v}_{\text{wind}}$$
$$= +789 \text{ km/h} + 56.3 \text{ km/h}$$
$$= +845 \text{ km/h}$$

The sign is positive, so the ground velocity is 845 km/h [E].

▲ **Figure 2.45**

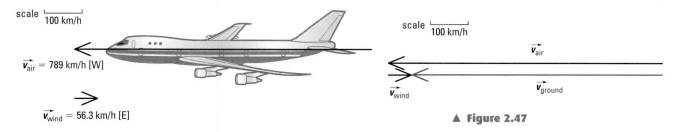

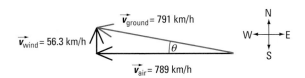

▲ **Figure 2.47**

▲ **Figure 2.46** The air velocity and wind velocity are in opposite directions.

If the jet heads west, from Toronto to Edmonton (Figure 2.46), its resultant velocity becomes
$$\vec{v}_{\text{ground}} = \vec{v}_{\text{air}} + \vec{v}_{\text{wind}}$$
$$= -789 \text{ km/h} + 56.3 \text{ km/h}$$
$$= -733 \text{ km/h}$$

(See Figure 2.47.) The sign is negative, so the ground velocity is 733 km/h [W]. The plane's speed decreases due to the headwind (wind that approaches from the front).

Non-collinear Relative Motion

Suppose the jet travelling west from Toronto encounters a crosswind of 56.3 km [N] (Figure 2.48).

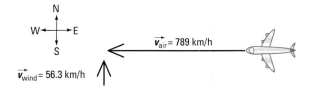

▲ **Figure 2.48** A plane flies in a crosswind.

▲ **Figure 2.49** A plane that flies in a crosswind needs to adjust its direction of motion.

In this case, the velocity of the plane is not aligned with the wind's velocity. The defining equation for this case is still the same as for the collinear case: $\vec{v}_{\text{ground}} = \vec{v}_{\text{air}} + \vec{v}_{\text{wind}}$. From section 2.2, recall that the plus sign in a two-dimensional vector equation tells you to connect the vectors tip to tail. The resultant vector is the ground velocity, $\vec{v}_{\text{ground}}$. The ground velocity indicates the actual path of the plane (Figure 2.49).

To solve for the ground velocity, notice that the triangle formed is a right triangle, meaning that you can use the Pythagorean theorem to solve for the magnitude of the ground velocity.

$$(v_{ground})^2 = (v_{air})^2 + (v_{wind})^2$$

$$
\begin{aligned}
v_{ground} &= \sqrt{(v_{air})^2 + (v_{wind})^2} \\
&= \sqrt{(789 \text{ km/h})^2 + (56.3 \text{ km/h})^2} \\
&= 791 \text{ km/h}
\end{aligned}
$$

PHYSICS INSIGHT

To determine the angle, substitute the magnitudes of the relative velocities into the tangent function. To determine the direction, refer to the vector diagram for the problem.

Using the tangent function, the direction of the ground velocity is

$$
\begin{aligned}
\tan \theta &= \frac{\text{opposite}}{\text{adjacent}} \\
&= \frac{56.3 \text{ km/h}}{789 \text{ km/h}} \\
&= 0.07136 \\
\theta &= \tan^{-1}(0.07136) \\
&= 4.1°
\end{aligned}
$$

From Figure 2.49, the wind blows the airplane off its westerly course in the northerly direction. Hence, the airplane's ground velocity is 791 km/h [4.1° N of W]. The pilot must take into consideration the effect of the wind blowing the airplane off course to ensure that the plane reaches its destination.

What path would the pilot have to take to arrive at a point due west of the point of departure? Remember that, if the vectors are not perpendicular, resolve them into components first before adding them algebraically.

Example 2.6

A plane flies west from Toronto to Edmonton with an air speed of 789 km/h.
(a) Find the direction the plane should have to compensate for a wind velocity of 56.3 km/h [N].
(b) Find the plane's speed relative to the ground.

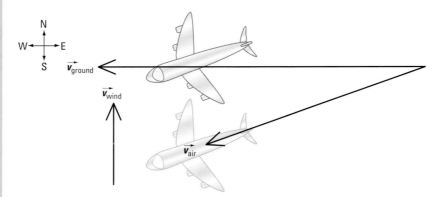

▲ **Figure 2.50**

Given

$\vec{v}_{wind} = 56.3$ km/h [N]

$\vec{v}_{air} = 789$ km/h

direction of ground velocity is west

Required

(a) the plane's direction
(direction of air velocity)
(b) ground speed (v_{ground})

Analysis and Solution

(a) First construct a diagram
based on the defining
equation,

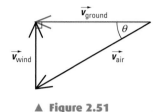

▲ **Figure 2.51**

$$\vec{v}_{ground} = \vec{v}_{air} + \vec{v}_{wind}$$

The rules of vector addition tell you to connect
the vectors $\vec{v}_{air}$ and $\vec{v}_{wind}$ tip to tail.

To find the direction required in order to compensate
for the wind velocity, find the angle, θ. Because the
connection of the vectors forms a right triangle, and
you know the magnitude of the opposite side ($\vec{v}_{wind}$)
and the hypotenuse ($\vec{v}_{air}$), you can use the sine
function to find the angle (Figure 2.51).

$$\sin \theta = \frac{\text{opposite}}{\text{hypotenuse}}$$

$$\theta = \sin^{-1}\left(\frac{\text{opposite}}{\text{hypotenuse}}\right)$$

$$= \sin^{-1}\left(\frac{56.3 \text{ km/h}}{789 \text{ km/h}}\right)$$

$$= 4.1°$$

From Figure 2.51, the angle is [4.1° S of W].

(b) To find the magnitude of the ground velocity, use the Pythagorean
theorem. From Figure 2.51, note that the hypotenuse in this case
is the air velocity, $\vec{v}_{air}$.

$$(v_{air})^2 = (v_{wind})^2 + (v_{ground})^2$$
$$(v_{ground})^2 = (v_{air})^2 - (v_{wind})^2$$
$$= (789 \text{ km/h})^2 - (56.3 \text{ km/h})^2$$
$$= 6.1935 \times 10^5 \text{ (km/h)}^2$$
$$v_{ground} = 787 \text{ km/h}$$

Notice that there is a small change in the magnitude of the ground
velocity from the previous example of the plane heading west. As
the magnitude of the wind velocity increases, the magnitude of the
ground velocity and the compensating angle will significantly change.

Paraphrase

(a) The plane's heading must be [4.1° S of W].
(b) The plane's ground speed is 787 km/h.

Practice Problems

1. A swimmer can swim at a speed
   of 1.8 m/s. The river is 200 m wide
   and has a current of 1.2 m/s [W]. If
   the swimmer points herself north,
   directly across the river, find
   (a) her velocity relative to
      the ground.
   (b) the time it takes her to cross.

2. For a river flowing west with a
   current of 1.2 m/s, a swimmer
   decides she wants to swim directly
   across. If she can swim with a
   speed of 1.8 m/s, find
   (a) the angle at which she must
      direct herself.
   (b) the time it takes her to cross
      if the river is 200 m wide.

Answers

1. (a) 2.2 m/s [34° W of N]
   (b) 111 s

2. (a) [42° E of N]
   (b) 149 s

To calculate the time it takes to fly from Toronto to Edmonton, use the equation $\vec{v} = \dfrac{\Delta \vec{d}}{\Delta t}$. The distance between Edmonton and Toronto is about 2335 km, but you must decide which value for velocity to use: air velocity or ground velocity. To answer this question, rearrange the equation and solve for time: $\Delta t = \dfrac{\Delta \vec{d}}{\vec{v}}$.

Both displacement and velocity are vectors. To substitute values into this equation, both vectors must be collinear. Since you are assuming that displacement is in the west direction, the appropriate velocity to use is the one that is in the westerly direction. In this example, it is the ground velocity, $\vec{v}_{ground}$ (Figure 2.52).

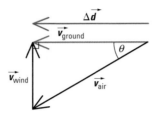

◄ **Figure 2.52**   For calculating time, choose the velocity vector that matches the direction of the displacement vector.

Consider west to be positive. Since both vectors are in the same direction (west), use the scalar form of the equation to solve for time.

$$\Delta t = \frac{\Delta d}{v}$$
$$= \frac{2335 \text{ km}}{787 \dfrac{\text{km}}{\text{h}}}$$
$$= 2.97 \text{ h}$$

It takes 2.97 h to fly from Toronto to Edmonton.

In the following example, the three velocity vectors do not form a right triangle. In order to solve the problem, you will need to use components.

Example 2.7

As a pilot of a small plane, you need to transport three people to an airstrip 350.0 km due west in 2.25 h. If the wind is blowing at 40.0 km/h [65° N of W], what should be the plane's air velocity in order to reach the airstrip on time?

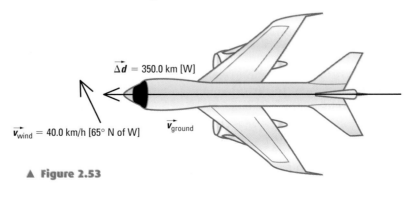

$\vec{\Delta d} = 350.0$ km [W]

$\vec{v}_{wind} = 40.0$ km/h [65° N of W] $\vec{v}_{ground}$

▲ **Figure 2.53**

Given
$\vec{v}_{wind}$ = 40.0 km/h [65° N of W]
$\Delta \vec{d}$ = 350.0 km [W]
Δt = 2.25 h

Required
plane's air velocity ($\vec{v}_{air}$)

Analysis and Solution
First draw a vector diagram of the problem (Figure 2.54).

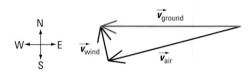

▲ **Figure 2.54**

Designate north and west as the positive directions.
Then calculate the ground velocity from the given
displacement and time.
If the plane must fly 350.0 km [W] in 2.25 h, its ground
velocity is

$$\vec{v}_{ground} = \frac{\Delta \vec{d}}{\Delta t}$$

$$= \frac{350.0 \text{ km [W]}}{2.25 \text{ h}}$$

$$= 155.6 \text{ km/h [W]}$$

Now find the components of the wind velocity (Figure 2.55).

x direction: *y* direction:
v_{wind_x} = (40.0 km/h)(cos 65°) v_{wind_y} = (40.0 km/h)(sin 65°)
  = 16.9 km/h   = 36.25 km/h

The ground velocity is directed west, so its *x* component is 155.6 km/h
and its *y* component is zero.
Since $\vec{v}_{ground} = \vec{v}_{air} + \vec{v}_{wind}$, rearrange this equation to solve for $\vec{v}_{air}$.

$$\vec{v}_{air} = \vec{v}_{ground} - \vec{v}_{wind}$$

Use this form of the equation to solve for the components of the air velocity.

Add the *x* (west) components: Add the *y* (north) components:
v_{air_x} = v_{ground_x} − v_{wind_x} v_{air_y} = v_{ground_y} − v_{wind_y}
  = 155.6 km/h − 16.9 km/h   = 0 − 36.25 km/h
  = 138.7 km/h   = −36.25 km/h

Use the Pythagorean theorem to find the magnitude of the air velocity.

$$v_{air} = \sqrt{\left(v_{air_x}\right)^2 + \left(v_{air_y}\right)^2}$$

$$= \sqrt{(138.7 \text{ km/h})^2 + (36.25 \text{ km/h})^2}$$

$$= 143 \text{ km/h}$$

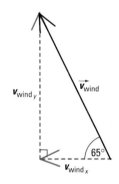

▲ **Figure 2.55**

Practice Problems

1. An airplane can fly with a maximum
   air velocity of 750 km/h [N]. If the
   wind velocity is 60 km/h [15° E
   of N], what must be the plane's
   ground velocity if it is to remain
   on a course going straight north?

2. What is the air velocity of a jetliner
   if its ground velocity is 856 km/h
   [25.0° W of S] and the wind
   velocity is 65.0 km/h [S]?

3. How long will it take a plane to
   travel 100 km [N] if its ground
   velocity is 795 km/h [25° W of N]?

Answers
1. 8.1 × 10² km/h [1.1° W of N]
2. 798 km/h [27.0° W of S]
3. 0.139 h

To find the direction of air velocity, use the tangent function (Figure 2.56).

$$\tan \theta = \frac{\text{opposite}}{\text{adjacent}}$$

$$= \frac{36.25 \ \cancel{\text{km/h}}}{138.7 \ \cancel{\text{km/h}}}$$

$$= 0.261$$

$$\theta = \tan^{-1}(0.261)$$

$$= 14.6°$$

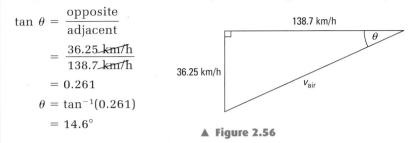

▲ **Figure 2.56**

The x component is positive, so its direction is west. Since the y component is negative, its direction is to the south. Thus, the direction of the air velocity is [14.6° S of W].

Paraphrase
The airplane's air velocity is 143 km/h [14.6° S of W].

Relative Motion in the Water

Whereas wind velocity affects the speed and direction of flying objects, watercraft and swimmers experience currents. As with flying objects, an object in the water can move with the current (ground velocity increases), against the current (ground velocity decreases), or at an angle (ground velocity increases or decreases). When the object moves at an angle to the current that is not 90°, both the object's speed and direction change. The following example illustrates how to use components to find velocity.

Example 2.8

The *Edmonton Queen* paddleboat travels north on the Saskatchewan River at a speed of 5.00 knots or 9.26 km/h. If the *Queen*'s ground velocity is 10.1 km/h [23° E of N], what is the velocity of the Saskatchewan River?

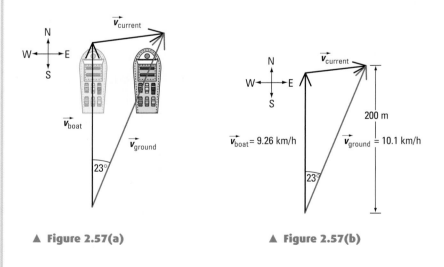

▲ **Figure 2.57(a)**   ▲ **Figure 2.57(b)**

Given

$\vec{v}_{boat}$ = 9.26 km/h [N]

$\vec{v}_{ground}$ = 10.1 km/h [23° E of N]
(Note that the angle is given with respect to the vertical (y) axis (Figure 2.57(a).)

Required

velocity of current ($\vec{v}_{current}$)

Analysis and Solution

Let north and east be positive.
Calculate the current's velocity using components. First find the components of the ground velocity (Figure 2.58).

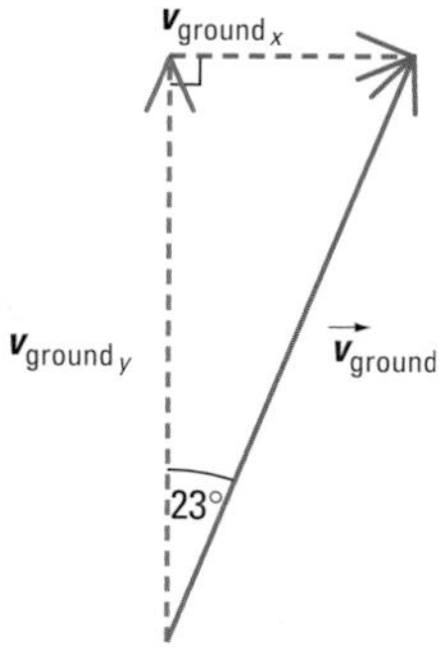

▲ **Figure 2.58**

x direction:

$v_{ground_x} = v_{ground}\sin\theta$
$\quad = (10.1 \text{ km/h})(\sin 23°)$
$\quad = 3.946 \text{ km/h}$

y direction:

$v_{ground_y} = v_{ground}\cos\theta$
$\quad = (10.1 \text{ km/h})(\cos 23°)$
$\quad = 9.297 \text{ km/h}$

Since the boat's velocity is directed north, its y component is 9.26 km/h and its x component is zero.

$\vec{v}_{ground} = \vec{v}_{boat} + \vec{v}_{current}$

You are asked to find $\vec{v}_{current}$, so rearrange the vector equation accordingly:

$\vec{v}_{current} = \vec{v}_{ground} - \vec{v}_{boat}$

Use this form of the equation to solve for the components of the current's velocity.

$v_{current_x} = v_{ground_x} - v_{boat_x}$
$\quad = 3.946 \text{ km/h} - 0$
$\quad = 3.946 \text{ km/h}$

$v_{current_y} = v_{ground_y} - v_{boat_y}$
$\quad = 9.297 \text{ km/h} - 9.26 \text{ km/h}$
$\quad = 0.03700 \text{ km/h}$

To the find the magnitude of the current's velocity, use the Pythagorean theorem.

$v_{current} = \sqrt{(v_{current_x})^2 + (v_{current_y})^2}$

$\quad = \sqrt{(3.946 \text{ km/h})^2 + (0.03700 \text{ km/h})^2}$

$\quad = 3.946 \text{ km/h}$

To find the direction of the current's velocity, use the tangent function (Figure 2.59).

$\tan\theta = \dfrac{\text{opposite}}{\text{adjacent}}$

$\theta = \tan^{-1}\left(\dfrac{0.03700 \text{ km/h}}{3.946 \text{ km/h}}\right)$

$\quad = 0.5°$

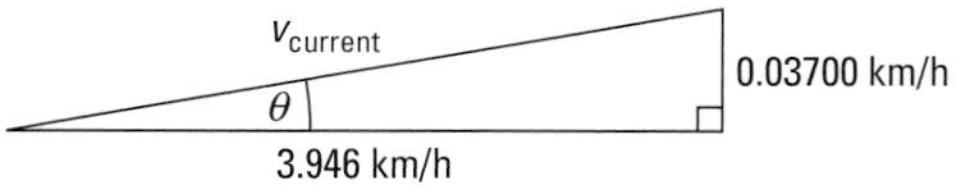

$v_{current}$

θ

3.946 km/h

0.03700 km/h

▲ **Figure 2.59**

Since both the x and y components are positive, the directions are east and north, respectively. Therefore, the current's direction is [0.5° N of E].

Paraphrase

The current's velocity is 3.95 km/h [0.5° N of E].

Practice Problems

1. Determine a Sea Doo's ground velocity if it travels with a constant velocity of 4.50 m/s [W] and encounters a current of 2.0 m/s [20° W of N].

2. A jogger runs with a velocity of 3.75 m/s [20° N of E] on an Alaskan cruise ship heading north at 13 m/s. What is the jogger's ground velocity?

3. A ship travelling 55° [W of N] is 65.0 km farther north after 3.0 h. What is the ship's velocity?

Answers

1. 5.5 m/s [20° N of W]

2. 15 m/s [76° N of E]

3. 38 km/h [55° W of N]

In order to find the time required to cross the river, you need to use the velocity value that corresponds to the direction of the object's displacement, as you will see in the next example.

Example 2.9

From Example 2.8, if the river is 200 m wide, how much time, in seconds, does it take for the *Edmonton Queen* to travel from shore to shore?

Given

$\vec{v}_{boat} = 9.26$ km/h [N]

$\Delta d = 200$ m

Required
time of travel (Δt)

Analysis and Solution
Let north and east be positive.

Use the equation $\vec{v} = \dfrac{\Delta \vec{d}}{\Delta t}$ and the boat's velocity to find the time, because the boat's velocity is in the same direction as the given displacement — north (see Figure 2.57). From $\vec{v} = \dfrac{\Delta \vec{d}}{\Delta t}$, isolate Δt and solve. Both vectors are in the same direction, so use the scalar form of the equation.

$$\Delta t = \frac{\Delta d}{v_{boat}}$$

$$= \frac{0.200 \text{ km}}{9.26 \dfrac{\text{km}}{\text{h}}}$$

$$= 0.0216 \text{ h} \times \frac{60 \text{ min}}{1 \text{ h}} \times \frac{60 \text{ s}}{1 \text{ min}}$$

$$= 77.8 \text{ s}$$

Paraphrase
It takes the *Edmonton Queen* 77.8 s to cross the river.

Relative motion problems describe the motion of an object travelling in a medium that is also moving. Both wind and current can affect the magnitude and direction of velocity. To solve relative motion problems in two dimensions, resolve the vectors into components and then add them using trigonometry.

Knowledge

1. Describe a situation where a wind or current will increase an object's speed.

2. Describe a situation where a wind or current will change an object's direction but not its speed in a moving medium.

3. Describe a situation when a wind or current will cause zero displacement.

4. Provide an example other than in the text that illustrates that perpendicular components of motion are independent of one another.

Applications

5. A swimmer needs to cross a river as quickly as possible. The swimmer's speed in still water is 1.35 m/s.

   (a) If the river's current speed is 0.60 m/s and the river is 106.68 m wide, how long will it take the swimmer to cross the river if he swims so that his body remains in the same lateral position in the river while crossing, and he ends up on the far bank directly across from where he started?

   (b) If he lets himself be carried downstream by the current, how long will it take to get across the river and how far downstream from his starting point will he end up?

6. A small plane can travel with a speed of 265 km/h with respect to the air. If the plane heads north, determine its resultant velocity if it encounters

   (a) a 32.0-km/h headwind

   (b) a 32.0-km/h tailwind

   (c) a 32.0-km/h [W] crosswind

7. The current in a river has a speed of 1.0 m/s. A woman swims 300 m downstream and then back to her starting point without stopping. If she can swim 2.0 m/s in still water, find the time of her round trip.

8. What is the ground velocity of an airplane if its air velocity is 800 km/h [E] and the wind velocity is 60 km/h [42° E of N]?

9. A person can swim 3.0 m/s in still water. If a swimmer heads east across a 3.20-km-wide river, what is the swimmer's velocity with respect to an observer on shore if the current has a velocity of 1.75 m/s [25° W of S]? How long will it take the swimmer to reach the opposite shore?

10. An airplane is observed to be flying at a speed of 600 km/h. The plane's nose points west. The wind's velocity is 100 km/h [45° W of S]. Find the plane's velocity relative to the ground.

11. A canoe can move at a speed of 4.0 m/s [N]. If the velocity of the current is 2.5 m/s [W] and the river is 0.80 km wide, find

   (a) the velocity of the canoe relative to the ground

   (b) the time it takes to cross the river

 e **TEST**

To check your understanding of relative motion, follow the eTest links at www.pearsoned.ca/school/physicssource.

2.4 Projectile Motion

Sports are really science experiments in action. Consider golf balls, footballs, and tennis balls. All of these objects are projectiles (Figure 2.60). You know from personal experience that there is a relationship between the distance you can throw a ball and the angle of loft. In this section, you will learn the theory behind projectile motion and how to calculate the values you need to throw the fastball or hit the target dead on.

Try the next QuickLab and discover what factors affect the trajectory of a projectile.

Figure 2.60 Sports is projectile motion in action.

Projectiles

Problem

What factors affect the trajectory of a marble?

Materials

wooden board (1 m × 1 m)	two nails
hammer	elastic band
paint	spoon
marble	brick
newspaper	masking tape
white paper to cover the board	gloves

Procedure

1 Spread enough newspaper on the floor so that it covers a larger workspace than the wooden board.

2 Hammer two nails, 7.0 cm apart, at the bottom left corner of the board. Stretch the elastic between them.

3 Cover the board with white paper and affix the paper to the board using masking tape.

4 Prop the board up on the brick (Figure 2.61).

5 Wearing gloves, roll the marble in a spoonful of paint.

6 Pull the elastic band back at an angle and rest the marble in it.

7 Release the elastic band and marble. Label the marble's trajectory on the paper track 1.

8 Repeat steps 5–7 for different launch angles and extensions of the elastic band.

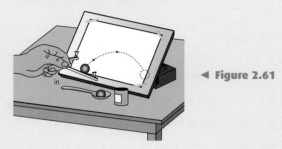

◀ **Figure 2.61**

Questions

1. What is the shape of the marble's trajectory, regardless of speed and angle?

2. How did a change in the elastic band's extension affect the marble's path?

3. How did a change in launch angle affect the marble's path?

LAB

For a probeware activity, go to www.pearsoned.ca/school/physicssource.

Galileo studied projectiles and found that they moved in two directions at the same time. He determined that the motion of a projectile follows the curved path of a parabola. The parabolic path of a projectile is called its **trajectory** (Figure 2.62). The shape of a projectile's trajectory depends on its initial velocity — both its initial speed and direction — and on the acceleration due to gravity. To understand and analyze projectile motion, you need to consider the horizontal (*x* direction) and vertical (*y* direction) components of the object's motion separately.

trajectory: the parabolic motion of a projectile

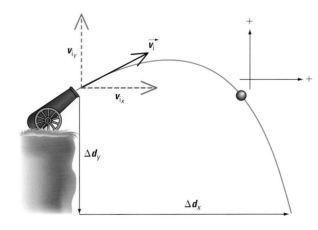

▶ **Figure 2.62** A projectile has a parabolic trajectory.

Which Lands First?

Problem

What is the relationship between horizontal and vertical motion of objects on a ramp?

Materials

Galileo apparatus (Figure 2.63)
steel balls

Procedure

1 Set up the Galileo apparatus at the edge of a lab bench.

2 Place a steel ball at the top of each ramp.

3 Release the balls at the same time.

4 Listen for when each ball hits the ground.

5 Using a different ramp, repeat steps 1–4.

Questions

1. Which ball landed first?

2. Did the balls' initial velocity affect the result? If so, how?

3. What inference can you make about the relationship between horizontal and vertical motion?

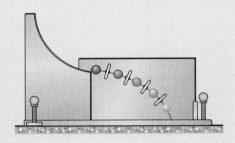

▲ **Figure 2.63**

From section 1.6, you know that gravity influences the vertical motion of a projectile by accelerating it downward. From Figure 2.64, note that gravity has no effect on an object's horizontal motion. So, the two components of a projectile's motion can be considered independently. As a result, a projectile experiences both uniform motion and uniformly accelerated motion at the same time! The *horizontal motion* of a projectile is an example of uniform motion; the projectile's horizontal velocity component is constant. The *vertical motion* of a projectile is an example of uniformly accelerated motion. The object's acceleration is the constant acceleration due to gravity or 9.81 m/s² [down] (neglecting friction).

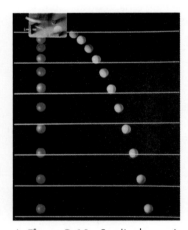

▲ **Figure 2.64** Gravity does not affect the horizontal motion of a projectile because perpendicular components of motion are independent.

Concept Check

In a table, classify the horizontal and vertical components of position, velocity, and acceleration of a horizontally launched projectile as uniform or non-uniform motion.

PHYSICS INSIGHT

When a projectile is launched, for a fraction of a second, it accelerates from rest to a velocity that has *x* and *y* components.

Objects Launched Horizontally

Suppose you made a new game based on a combination of shuffleboard and darts. The goal is to flick a penny off a flat, horizontal surface, such as a tabletop, and make it land on a target similar to a dartboard beyond the table. The closer your penny lands to the bull's eye, the more points you score (Figure 2.65).

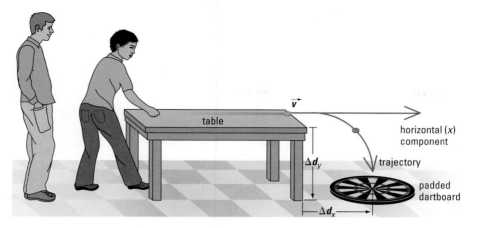

▲ **Figure 2.65** An object launched horizontally experiences uniform horizontal motion and uniformly accelerated vertical motion.

In the game, once the penny leaves the tabletop, it becomes a projectile and travels in a parabolic path toward the ground. In section 1.6, you studied motion that was caused by acceleration due to gravity. The velocity of an object falling straight down has no horizontal velocity component. In this game, the penny moves both horizontally and vertically, like the ball on the right in Figure 2.64. In this type of projectile motion, the object's initial vertical velocity is zero.

Because the projectile has a horizontal velocity component, it travels a horizontal distance along the ground from its initial launch point. This distance is called the projectile's **range** (Figure 2.66). The velocity component in the y direction increases because of the acceleration due to gravity while the x component remains the same. The combined horizontal and vertical motions produce the parabolic path of the projectile.

range: the distance a projectile travels horizontally over level ground

Concept Check

(a) What factors affecting projectile motion in the horizontal direction are being neglected?

(b) What causes the projectile to finally stop?

(c) If the projectile's initial velocity had a vertical component, would the projectile's path still be parabolic? Give reasons for your answer.

Solving Projectile Motion Problems

In this chapter, you have been working with components, so you know how to solve motion problems by breaking the motion down into its horizontal (x) and vertical (y) components.

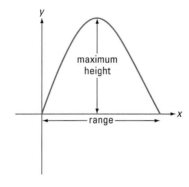

▲ **Figure 2.66** The range of a projectile is its horizontal distance travelled.

Before you solve a projectile motion problem, review what you already know (Figure 2.67).

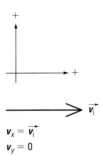

$v_x = \vec{v_i}$
$v_y = 0$

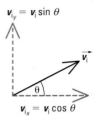

$v_{i_y} = v_i \sin \theta$
$v_{i_x} = v_i \cos \theta$

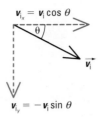

$v_{i_x} = v_i \cos \theta$
$v_{i_y} = -v_i \sin \theta$

▲ **Figure 2.67(a)**
The projectile is given an initial horizontal velocity.

▲ **Figure 2.67(b)**
The projectile is given an initial horizontal velocity and an upward vertical velocity.

▲ **Figure 2.67(c)**
The projectile is given an initial horizontal velocity and a downward vertical velocity.

e MATH

To explore and graph the relationship between the velocity and position of an object thrown vertically into the air, visit www.pearsoned.ca/school/physicssource.

x direction
– There is no acceleration in this direction, so $a_x = 0$. In this text, a_x will always be zero.
– The general equation for the initial x component of the velocity can be written as $v_{i_x} = v_i \cos \theta$.
– The range is Δd_x.
– Because the projectile is moving in both the horizontal and vertical directions at the same time, Δt is a common variable.

y direction
– If up is positive, the acceleration due to gravity is down or negative, so $a_y = -9.81$ m/s².
– The y component of the initial velocity can be written as $v_{i_y} = v_i \sin \theta$.
– The displacement in the y direction is Δd_y.
– Time (Δt) is the same in both the x and y directions.

▼ **Table 2.4** Projectile Problem Setup

x direction	y direction
$a_x = 0$	$a_y = -9.81$ m/s²
$v_{i_x} = v_i \cos \theta$	$v_{i_y} = v_i \sin \theta$
	v_{i_y} can be positive or negative depending on the direction of $\vec{v_i}$.
$\Delta d_x = v_x \Delta t$	$\Delta d_y = v_{i_y} \Delta t + \frac{1}{2} a_y (\Delta t)^2$

If you check the variables, you can see that they are v_i, Δt, Δd, and a, all of which are present in the equation $\Delta \vec{d} = \vec{v_i} \Delta t + \frac{1}{2} \vec{a} (\Delta t)^2$. In the horizontal direction, the acceleration is zero, so this equation simplifies to $\Delta \vec{d} = \vec{v_i} \Delta t$. The next example shows you how to apply these equations.

Example 2.10

Head-Smashed-In Buffalo Jump, near Fort Macleod, Alberta, is a UNESCO heritage site (Figure 2.68). Over 6000 years ago, the Blackfoot people of the Plains hunted the North American bison by gathering herds and directing them over cliffs 20.0 m tall. Assuming the plain was flat and the bison were moving at their maximum speed of 18.0 m/s at the time of the fall, determine how far from the base of the cliff the bison landed.

▲ **Figure 2.68**

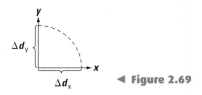

◄ **Figure 2.69**

Given

For convenience, choose forward and down to be positive because the motion is forward and down (Figure 2.69).

x direction	y direction
$v_{i_x} = 18.0$ m/s	$a_y = 9.81$ m/s² [down] = +9.81 m/s²
	$\Delta d_y = 20.0$ m

Required

distance from the base of the cliff (Δd_x)

Analysis and Solution

Since there is no vertical component to the initial velocity of the bison, $v_{i_y} = 0$ m/s. Therefore, the bison experience uniformly accelerated motion due to gravity in the vertical direction but uniform motion in the horizontal direction resulting from the run.

From the given values, note that, in the y direction, you have all the variables except for time. So, you can solve for time in the y direction, which is the time taken to fall.

y direction:

$$\Delta d_y = v_{i_y}\Delta t + \frac{1}{2}a_y(\Delta t)^2$$

$$= 0 + \frac{1}{2}a_y\Delta t^2$$

PHYSICS INSIGHT

For projectile motion in two dimensions, the time taken to travel horizontally equals the time taken to travel vertically.

e **SIM**

Analyze balls undergoing projectile motion. Follow the eSim links at www.pearsoned.ca/school/physicssource.

$$\Delta t = \sqrt{\frac{2\Delta d_y}{a_y}}$$

$$= \sqrt{\frac{2(20.0 \text{ m})}{9.81 \text{ m/s}^2}}$$

$$= 2.02 \text{ s}$$

x direction:
The time taken for the bison to fall vertically equals the time they travel horizontally. Substitute the value for time you found in the *y* direction to find the range. Since the bison had an initial horizontal speed of 18.0 m/s, use the equation $\Delta d_x = v_{i_x}\Delta t$.

$$\Delta d_x = (18.0 \text{ m/s})(2.02 \text{ s})$$

$$= 36.0 \text{ m}$$

Paraphrase
The bison would land 36.0 m from the base of the cliff.

▼ **Figure 2.70** Baseball is all about projectile motion.

Objects Launched at an Angle

Baseball is a projectile game (Figure 2.70). The pitcher throws a ball at the batter, who hits it to an open area in the field. The outfielder catches the ball and throws it to second base. The runner is out. All aspects of this sequence involve projectile motion. Each sequence requires a different angle on the throw and a different speed. If the player miscalculates one of these variables, the action fails: Pitchers throw wild pitches, batters strike out, and outfielders overthrow the bases. Winning the game depends on accurately predicting the components of the initial velocity!

For objects launched at an angle, such as a baseball, the velocity of the object has both a horizontal and a vertical component. Any vector quantity can be resolved into *x* and *y* components using the trigonometric ratios $R_x = R \cos \theta$ and $R_y = R \sin \theta$, when θ is measured relative to the *x*-axis. To determine the horizontal and vertical components of velocity, this relationship becomes $v_x = v \cos \theta$ and $v_y = v \sin \theta$, as shown in Figure 2.71.

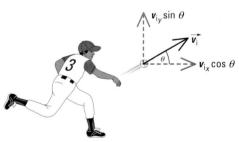

▲ **Figure 2.71** The horizontal and vertical components of velocity

Solving problems involving objects launched at an angle is similar to solving problems involving objects launched horizontally. The object experiences uniform motion in the horizontal direction, so use the equation $\Delta d_x = v_{i_x}\Delta t$. In the vertical direction, the object experiences uniformly accelerated motion. The general equation $\Delta d_y = v_{i_y}\Delta t + \frac{1}{2}a_y(\Delta t)^2$ still applies, but in this case, v_{i_y} is not zero. The next example shows you how to apply these equations to objects launched at an angle.

Example 2.11

Baseball players often practise their swing in a batting cage, in which a pitching machine delivers the ball (Figure 2.72). If the baseball is launched with an initial velocity of 22.0 m/s [30.0°] and the player hits it at the same height from which it was launched, for how long is the baseball in the air?

▲ **Figure 2.72**

Given

$\vec{v}_i = 22.0$ m/s [30.0°]

Required

time (Δt)

Analysis and Solution

Choose forward and up to be positive (Figure 2.73). First find the components of the baseball's initial velocity.

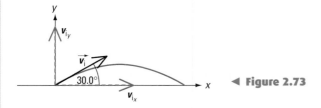

◄ **Figure 2.73**

x direction	y direction
$v_{i_x} = v_i \cos \theta$	$v_{i_y} = v_i \sin \theta$
$\quad = (22.0 \text{ m/s})(\cos 30.0°)$	$\quad = (22.0 \text{ m/s})(\sin 30.0°)$
$\quad = 19.05$ m/s	$\quad = 11.00$ m/s

Since the ball returns to the same height from which it was launched, $\Delta d_y = 0$. With this extra known quantity, you now have enough information in the y direction to find the time the ball spent in the air.

PHYSICS INSIGHT

Be careful to follow the sign convention you chose. If you chose up as positive, a_y becomes -9.81 m/s².

info **BIT**

The world's fastest bird is the peregrine falcon, with a top vertical speed of 321 km/h and a top horizontal speed of 96 km/h.

e **WEB**

The fastest speed for a projectile in any ball game is approximately 302 km/h in jai-alai. To learn more about jai-alai, follow the links at www.pearsoned.ca/school/physicssource.

$$\Delta d_y = v_{i_y}\Delta t + \frac{1}{2}a_y(\Delta t)^2$$

$$0 = (11.00 \text{ m/s})\Delta t + \frac{1}{2}(-9.81 \text{ m/s}^2)(\Delta t)^2$$

Isolate Δt and solve.

$$(4.905 \text{ m/s}^2)(\Delta t)^2 = (11.00 \text{ m/s})(\cancel{\Delta t})$$

$$\Delta t = \frac{11.00 \frac{\cancel{m}}{\cancel{s}}}{4.905 \frac{\cancel{m}}{s^{\cancel{2}}}}$$

$$= 2.24 \text{ s}$$

Paraphrase

The baseball is in the air for 2.24 s.

How far will the baseball in Example 2.11 travel horizontally if it lands at the same height from which it was launched? Since horizontal velocity is constant,

$$\Delta d_x = v_{i_x}\Delta t$$

$$= (19.05 \text{ m/s})(2.24 \text{ s})$$

$$= 42.7 \text{ m}$$

The baseball travels a horizontal distance of 42.7 m.

In the next example, you are given the time and are asked to solve for one of the other variables. However, the style of solving the problem remains the same. In any problem that you will be asked to solve in this course, you will always be able to solve for one quantity in either the x or y direction, and then you can substitute your answer to solve for the remaining variable(s).

Example 2.12

A ball of paint directed at a target is shot with an angle of 25.0°. If paint splats on its intended target at the same height from which it was launched, 3.00 s later, find the distance from the shooter to the target.

Given

Choose down and right to be positive.

$$\vec{a} = a_y = 9.81 \text{ m/s}^2 \text{ [down]} = +9.81 \text{ m/s}^2$$

$$\theta = 25.0°$$

$$\Delta t = 3.00 \text{ s}$$

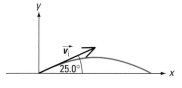

▲ **Figure 2.74**

Required

range (Δd_x)

Analysis and Solution

Use the equation $\Delta d_y = v_{i_y}\Delta t + \frac{1}{2}a_y(\Delta t)^2$. Since the height of landing is the same as the launch height, $\Delta d_y = 0$.

y direction:

$$\begin{aligned}\Delta d_y &= v_{i_y}\Delta t + \frac{1}{2}a_y(\Delta t)^2 \\ 0 &= v_{i_y}\Delta t + \frac{1}{2}a_y(\Delta t)^2 \\ v_{i_y}\Delta t &= -\frac{1}{2}a_y(\Delta t)^2 \\ v_{i_y} &= -\frac{1}{2}a_y\Delta t \\ &= -\frac{1}{2}\left(9.81\ \frac{\text{m}}{\text{s}^2}\right)(3.00\ \cancel{\text{s}}) \\ &= -14.7\ \text{m/s}\end{aligned}$$

Since down is positive, the negative sign means that the direction of the vertical component of initial velocity is up.

x direction:

Find the initial horizontal speed using the tangent function. Because there is no acceleration in the x direction, the ball's horizontal speed remains the same during its flight: $a_x = 0$.

$$\begin{aligned}\tan\theta &= \frac{\text{opposite}}{\text{adjacent}} \\ \text{adjacent} &= \frac{\text{opposite}}{\tan\theta} \\ &= \frac{14.7\ \text{m/s}}{\tan 25.0°} \\ &= 31.56\ \text{m/s}\end{aligned}$$

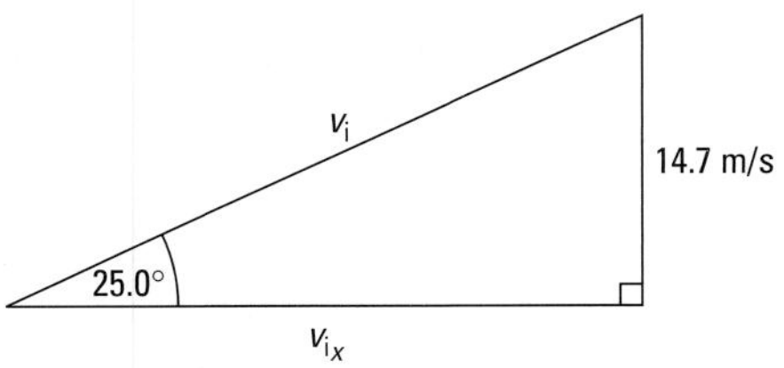

▲ **Figure 2.75**

From Figure 2.75, the adjacent side is v_{i_x} and it points to the right, so $v_{i_x} = 31.56$ m/s.

Now find the horizontal distance travelled.

$$\begin{aligned}\Delta d_x &= v_{i_x}\Delta t \\ &= (31.56\ \text{m/s})(3.00\ \text{s}) \\ &= 94.7\ \text{m}\end{aligned}$$

Paraphrase

The distance that separates the target from the shooter is 94.7 m.

PHYSICS INSIGHT

Alternatively, the time taken to reach maximum height is the same time taken to fall back down to the same height. So, the paintball is at its maximum height at 1.50 s. The speed at maximum height is zero. If up is positive,

$$\begin{aligned}\vec{a} &= \frac{\Delta\vec{v}}{\Delta t} \\ &= \frac{\vec{v}_f - \vec{v}_i}{\Delta t} \\ \vec{v}_i &= \vec{v}_f - \vec{a}\Delta t \\ &= 0\ \text{m/s} - \vec{a}\Delta t \\ &= -(-9.81\ \text{m/s}^2)(\Delta t) \\ &= +(9.81\ \text{m/s}^2)(1.50\ \text{s}) \\ &= +14.7\ \text{m/s}\end{aligned}$$

The sign is positive, so the direction is up.

Practice Problems

1. Determine the height reached by a baseball if it is released with a velocity of 17.0 m/s [20°].
2. Flying fish can launch themselves into the air with speeds of 56.0 km/h and remain airborne for 30.0 s. If a fish travels 198 m horizontally during that time, determine the angle at which it left the water.
3. A German U2 rocket from the Second World War had a range of 300 km, reaching a maximum height of 100 km. Determine the rocket's maximum initial velocity.

Answers

1. 1.72 m
2. 64.9°
3. 1.75×10^3 m/s [53.1°]

The points below summarize what you have learned in this section.

- To solve problems involving projectiles, first resolve the motion into its components using the trigonometric functions, then apply the kinematics equations.
- Perpendicular components of motion are independent of one another.
- Horizontal motion is considered uniform and is described by the equation $\Delta \vec{d} = \vec{v}\Delta t$, whereas vertical motion is a special case of uniformly accelerated motion, where the acceleration is the acceleration due to gravity or 9.81 m/s² [down].
- A projectile's path is a parabola.
- In the vertical direction, a projectile's velocity is greatest at the instant of launch and just before impact, whereas at maximum height, vertical velocity is zero.

2.4 Check and Reflect

Knowledge

1. Platform divers receive lower marks if they enter the water a distance away from the platform, whereas speed swimmers dive as far out into the pool as they can. Compare and contrast the horizontal and vertical components of each type of athlete's motion.

2. For a fixed speed, how does the range depend on the angle, θ?

3. (a) How does the amount of time the projectile remains in the air vary with the range?
   (b) Does the maximum time correspond to the maximum range? Explain.

4. Water safety instructors tell novice swimmers to put their toes over the edge and jump out into the pool. Explain why, using concepts from kinematics and projectile motion.

Applications

5. Participants in a road race take water from a refreshment station and throw their empty cups away farther down the course. If a runner has a forward speed of 6.20 m/s, how far in advance of a garbage pail should he release his water cup if the horizontal distance between the lid of the garbage can and the runner's point of release is 0.50 m?

6. A baseball is thrown with a velocity of 27.0 m/s [35°]. What are the components of the ball's initial velocity? How high and how far will it travel?

7. A football is thrown to a moving receiver. The football leaves the quarterback's hands 1.75 m above the ground with a velocity of 17.0 m/s [25°]. If the receiver starts 12.0 m away from the quarterback along the line of flight of the ball when it is thrown, what constant velocity must she have to get to the ball at the instant it is 1.75 m above the ground?

8. At the 2004 Olympic Games in Athens, Dwight Phillips won the gold medal in men's long jump with a jump of 8.59 m. If the angle of his jump was 23°, what was his takeoff speed?

9. A projectile is fired with an initial speed of 120 m/s at an angle of 55.0° above the horizontal from the top of a cliff 50.0 m high. Find
   (a) the time taken to reach maximum height
   (b) the maximum height
   (c) the total time in the air
   (d) the range
   (e) the components of the final velocity just before the projectile hits the ground

Extension

10. Design a spreadsheet to determine the maximum height and range of a projectile with a launch angle that increases from 0° to 90° and whose initial speed is 20.0 m/s.

 e TEST

To check your understanding of projectile motion, follow the eTest links at www.pearsoned.ca/school/physicssource.

Key Terms and Concepts

collinear	Cartesian method	relative motion	wind velocity
resultant vector	navigator method	ground velocity	trajectory
components	non-collinear	air velocity	range

Key Equations

$$\vec{a} = \frac{\Delta \vec{v}}{\Delta t} \qquad \Delta \vec{d} = \vec{v}_i \Delta t + \frac{1}{2}\vec{a}(\Delta t)^2 \qquad \Delta \vec{d} = \vec{v}\Delta t$$

Conceptual Overview

The concept map below summarizes many of the concepts and equations in this chapter. Copy and complete the map to have a full summary of the chapter.

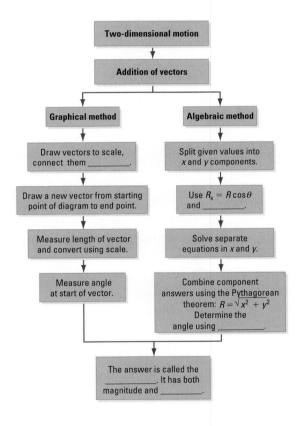

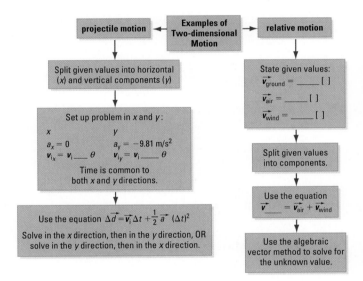

Knowledge

1. (2.2) During the Terry Fox Run, a participant travelled A to D, passing through B and C on the way. Copy and complete the table using the information in the diagram, a ruler calibrated in millimetres, and a protractor. In your notebook, draw and label the displacement vectors AB, BC, and CD and the position vectors AB, AC, and AD.

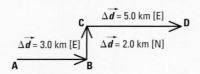

	Distance	Final position	Displacement
AB			
BC			
CD			
AC			
AD			

2. (2.2) Determine the x and y components of the displacement vector 55 m [222°].

3. (2.4) What is the vertical component for velocity at the maximum height of a projectile's trajectory?

4. (2.4) During a field goal kick, as the football rises, what is the effect on the vertical component of its velocity?

5. (2.1) Fort McMurray is approximately 500 km [N] of Edmonton. Using a scale of 1.0 cm : 50.0 km, draw a displacement vector representing this distance.

6. (2.1) Give one reason why vector diagrams must be drawn to scale.

7. (2.2) Using an appropriate scale and reference coordinates, graphically solve each of the following:
   (a) 5.0 m [S] and 10.0 m [N]
   (b) 65.0 cm [E] and 75.0 cm [E]
   (c) 1.0 km [forward] and 3.5 km [backward]
   (d) 35.0 km [right] −45.0 km [left]

8. (2.4) For an object thrown vertically upward, what is the object's initial horizontal velocity?

Applications

9. The air medivac, King Air 200, flying at 250 knots (1 knot = 1.853 km/h), makes the trip between Edmonton and Grande Prairie in 50 min. What distance does the plane travel during this time?

10. A golf ball is hit with an initial velocity of 30.0 m/s [55°]. What are the ball's range and maximum height?

11. Off the tee box, a professional golfer can drive a ball with a velocity of 80.0 m/s [10°]. How far will the ball travel horizontally and for how long is the ball airborne?

12. A canoeist capable of paddling at a speed of 4.0 m/s wishes to cross a river 120 m wide. The river is flowing at 5.0 m/s [E]. Find
   (a) her velocity relative to the ground
   (b) the time it takes her to cross

13. An object is thrown horizontally off a cliff with an initial speed of 7.50 m/s. The object strikes the ground 3.0 s later. Find
   (a) the object's vertical velocity component when it reaches the ground
   (b) the distance between the base of the cliff and the object when it strikes the ground
   (c) the horizontal velocity of the object 1.50 s after its release

14. If a high jumper reaches her maximum height as she travels across the bar, determine the initial velocity she must have to clear a bar set at 2.0 m if her range during the jump is 5.0 m.

15. An alligator wishes to swim directly across a channel 500 m wide. There is a current of 2.0 m/s flowing east. The alligator is capable of swimming at 4.0 m/s. Find
   (a) the angle at which the alligator must point its body in order to swim directly across
   (b) its velocity relative to the ground
   (c) the time it takes to cross

16. A baseball player throws a ball horizontally at 45.0 m/s. How far will the ball drop before reaching first base 27.4 m away?

17. How much time can you save travelling diagonally instead of walking 750 m [N] and then 350 m [E] if your walking speed is 7.0 m/s?

18. How long will an arrow be in flight if it is shot at an angle of 25° and hits a target 50.0 m away, at the same elevation?

19. A pilot of a small plane wishes to fly west. The plane has an airspeed of 100 km/h. If there is a 30-km/h wind blowing north, find
    (a) the plane's heading
    (b) the plane's ground speed

20. At what angle was an object thrown if its initial launch speed is 15.7 m/s, it remains airborne for 2.15 s, and travels 25.0 m horizontally?

21. A coin rolls off a 25.0° incline on top of a 2.5-m bookcase with a speed of 30 m/s. How far from the base of the bookcase will the coin land?

22. Starting from the left end of the hockey rink, the goal line is 3.96 m to the right of the boards, the blue line is 18.29 m to the right of the goal line, the next blue line is 16.46 m to the right of the first blue line, the goal line is 18.29 m right, and the right board is 3.96 m right of the goal line. How long is a standard NHL hockey rink?

23. A plane with a ground speed of 151 km/h is moving 11° south of east. There is a wind blowing at 40 km/h, 45° south of east. Find
    (a) the plane's airspeed
    (b) the plane's heading, to the nearest degree

24. How long will a soccer ball remain in flight if it is kicked with an initial velocity of 25.0 m/s [35.0°]? How far down the field will the ball travel and what will be its maximum height?

25. At what angle is an object launched if its initial vertical speed is 3.75 m/s and its initial horizontal speed is 4.50 m/s?

Extensions

26. During the Apollo 14 mission, Alan Shepard was the first person to hit a golf ball on the Moon. If a golf ball was launched from the Moon's surface with a velocity of 50 m/s [35°] and the acceleration due to gravity on the Moon is −1.61 m/s²,
    (a) how long was the golf ball in the air?
    (b) what was the golf ball's range?

27. An airplane is approaching a runway for landing. The plane's air velocity is 645 km/h [forward], moving through a headwind of 32.2 km/h. The altimeter indicates that the plane is dropping at a velocity of 3.0 m/s [down]. If the plane is at a height of 914.4 m and the range from the plane to the start of the runway is 45.0 km, does the pilot need to make any adjustments to her descent in order to land the plane at the start of the runway?

Consolidate Your Understanding

Create your own summary of kinematics by answering the questions below. If you want to use a graphic organizer, refer to Student References 4: Using Graphic Organizers on pp. 869–871. Use the Key Terms and Concepts listed on page 113 and the Learning Outcomes on page 68.

1. Create a flowchart to describe the different components required to analyze motion in a horizontal plane and in a vertical plane.

2. Write a paragraph describing the similarities and differences between motion in a horizontal plane and motion in a vertical plane. Share your thoughts with another classmate.

Think About It

Review your answers to the Think About It questions on page 69. How would you answer each question now?

e TEST

To check your understanding of two-dimensional motion, follow the eTest links at www.pearsoned.ca/school/physicssource.

Are Amber Traffic Lights Timed Correctly?

Scenario

The Traffic Safety Act allows law enforcement agencies in Alberta to issue fines for violations using evidence provided by red light cameras at intersections. The cameras photograph vehicles that enter an intersection *after* the traffic lights have turned red. They record the time, date, location, violation number, and time elapsed since the light turned red. The use of red light cameras and other technology reduces the amount of speeding, running of red lights, and collisions at some intersections.

The length of time a traffic light must remain amber depends on three factors: perception time, reaction time, and braking time. The sum of perception time and reaction time is the time elapsed between the driver seeing the amber light and applying the brakes. The Ministry of Infrastructure and Transportation's (MIT) *Basic Licence Driver's Handbook* allows for a perception time of 0.75 s and a reaction time of 0.75 s. The braking time is the time it takes the vehicle to come to a full stop once the brakes are applied. Braking time depends on the vehicle's initial speed and negative acceleration. The MIT's predicted braking times are based on the assumption that vehicles travel at the posted speed limit and have a uniform acceleration of -3.0 m/s^2. Other factors that affect acceleration are road conditions, vehicle and tire performance, weather conditions, and whether the vehicle was travelling up or down hill.

If drivers decide to go through an intersection safely (go distance) after a light has turned amber, they must be able to travel not only to the intersection but across it before the light turns red. The go distance depends on the speed of the vehicle, the length of the intersection, and the amount of time the light remains amber. If the driver decides to stop (stop distance), the vehicle can safely do so only if the distance from the intersection is farther than the distance travelled during perception time, reaction time, and braking time.

As part of a committee reporting to the Ministry of Infrastructure and Transportation, you must respond to concerns that drivers are being improperly fined for red light violations because of improper amber light timing. You are to decide how well the amber light time matches the posted speed limit and intersection length. Assume throughout your analysis that drivers travel at the posted speed limits.

Planning

Research or derive equations to determine

(a) a car's displacement during reaction time

(b) stop distance

(c) go distance

(d) amber light time

(e) displacement after brakes are applied

(f) amount of time elapsed after the brakes are applied

Materials

• measuring tape, stopwatch

Procedure

1 Design a survey to measure the amber light times at 10 different intersections near your school. For each intersection, record its length. ***Use caution around intersections due to traffic! You may wish to estimate the length of the intersection by counting the number of steps it takes you to cross and measuring the length of your stride.***

2 Apply suitable equations to determine appropriate amber light times for the 10 different intersections.

3 Calculate stop distances and go distances for a range (± 10 km/h) of posted speed limits for each intersection and plot graphs of stop distance and go distance against posted speed.

Thinking Further

1. Research the effectiveness of red light cameras in reducing accidents, speeding, and red light violations. Using your research, recommend a course of action to increase vehicle-rail safety at light-controlled railway crossings.

2. Based on your surveys and investigation, recommend whether existing amber light times should be increased, decreased, or left alone. Consider posted speeds against actual speeds and wet against dry surface conditions.

3. Prepare a presentation to the other members of your committee. Include graphs and diagrams.

*Note: Your instructor will assess the project using a similar assessment rubric.

Unit Concepts and Skills: Quick Reference

Concepts	Summary	Resources and Skill Building
Chapter 1	**Graphs and equations describe motion in one dimension.**	
	1.1 The Language of Motion	
Scalar and vector quantities	A scalar quantity consists of a number and a unit.	Section 1.1
	A vector quantity consists of a number, a unit, and a direction.	Section 1.1
Distance, position, and displacement	Distance is the length of the path taken to travel from one position to another.	Figure 1.5
	Position is the straight-line distance from the origin to the object's location.	Figures 1.3, 1.4, 1.5, Example 1.1
	Displacement is the change in position.	Figures 1.3, 1.4, 1.5, Example 1.1
	1.2 Position-time Graphs and Uniform Motion	
Slope of a position-time graph	A position-time graph for an object at rest is a straight line with zero slope.	Figure 1.14
	A position-time graph for an object moving at a constant velocity is a straight line with non-zero slope.	Figures 1.12, 1.15(b), 1-3 Inquiry Lab
	The greater the slope of a position-time graph, the faster the object is moving.	Examples 1.2, 1.3, 1-3 Inquiry Lab
	1.3 Velocity-time Graphs: Uniform and Non-uniform Motion	
Slope of a velocity-time graph	A velocity-time graph for an object experiencing uniform motion is a horizontal line.	Figure 1.24
	The slope of a velocity-time graph represents acceleration.	Figures 1.24, 1.30, Example 1.5
Position-time, velocity-time, acceleration-time graphs representing accelerated motion	The position-time graph for an object undergoing uniformly accelerated motion is a curve.	Figures 1.28–1.31, Example 1.5
	The corresponding velocity-time graph is a straight line with non-zero slope.	
	The corresponding acceleration-time graph is a horizontal line.	
Instantaneous velocity	The slope of the tangent on a position-time curve gives instantaneous velocity.	Figure 1.29, Example 1.5
	1.4 Analyzing Velocity-time Graphs	
Area under and slope of a velocity-time graph	The area under a velocity-time graph represents displacement; slope represents acceleration.	Figure 1.41, Examples 1.6, 1.8, 1.9
Average velocity	Average velocity represents total displacement divided by time elapsed.	Figure 1.45, Examples 1.7, 1.9
Velocity-time graphs	You can draw acceleration-time and position-time graphs by calculating and plotting slope and area, respectively, of a velocity-time graph.	Examples 1.10, 1.11
	1.5 The Kinematics Equations	
Kinematics equations	The kinematics equations are derived by finding areas under velocity-time graphs.	Figures 1.53–1.55
	When solving problems in kinematics, choose the equation that contains all the given variables in the problem as well as the unknown variable.	Examples 1.12–1.16
	1.6 Acceleration Due to Gravity	
Projectile motion straight up and down	Gravity causes objects to accelerate downward.	1-6 QuickLab, 1-7 Inquiry Lab, 1-8 QuickLab, Examples 1.17–1.19
Maximum height	At maximum height, a projectile's vertical velocity is zero.	Figures 1.63–1.65
	The time taken to reach maximum height equals the time taken to fall back down to the original height.	Examples 1.18, 1.19
Chapter 2	**Vector components describe motion in two dimensions.**	
	2.1 Vector Methods in One Dimension	
Adding and subtracting vectors	Add vectors by connecting them tip to tail. Subtract vectors by connecting them tail to tail.	Examples 2.1, 2.2
	2.2 Motion in Two Dimensions	
Components	To add vectors in two dimensions, draw a scale diagram, or resolve them into their components and use trigonometry to find the resultant.	Examples 2.3–2.5, Figures 2.31, 2.33–2.37
	2.3 Relative Motion	
Relative motion	To solve relative motion problems, use trigonometry, with ground velocity as the resultant.	Examples 2.6–2.9
	If the vectors are not perpendicular, resolve them into their components first.	
	2.4 Projectile Motion	
Projectile motion in two dimensions	The shape of a projectile's trajectory is a parabola.	2-4 QuickLab, Figure 2.62
	Horizontal and vertical components of projectile motion are independent.	2-5 QuickLab, Figure 2.64
	To solve projectile problems in two dimensions, resolve them into their horizontal and vertical components. Then use the kinematics equations. The time taken to travel horizontally equals the time taken to travel vertically.	Examples 2.10–2.12, Figures 2.67, 2.71

Vocabulary

1. Using your own words, define these terms:
   acceleration
   acceleration due to gravity
   air velocity
   at rest
   Cartesian method
   collinear
   components
   displacement
   distance
   ground velocity
   instantaneous velocity
   kinematics
   navigator method
   non-collinear
   non-uniform motion
   origin
   position
   projectile
   projectile motion
   range
   relative motion
   resultant vector
   scalar quantity
   tangent
   trajectory
   uniform motion
   uniformly accelerated motion
   vector quantity
   velocity
   wind velocity

Knowledge

CHAPTER 1

2. Describe how scalar quantities differ from vector quantities.

CHAPTER 2

3. Resolve the following vectors into their components:
   (a) 5.0 m [90°]
   (b) 16.0 m/s [20° S of W]

4. Using an appropriate scale and reference coordinates, draw the following vectors:
   (a) 5.0 m/s [0°]
   (b) 25.0 m/s² [60° N of E]
   (c) 1.50 km [120°]

5. Using a scale of 1.0 cm : 3.5 km, determine the magnitude and direction of the vector below.

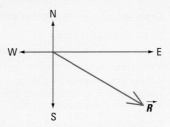

Applications

6. A wildlife biologist records a moose's position as it swims away from her. Using the graph below, determine the moose's velocity.

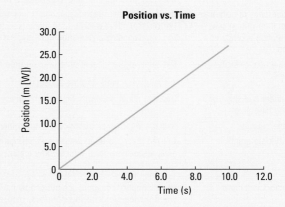

Position vs. Time

7. Sketch a position-time graph for each statement below. Assume that right is positive.
   (a) object accelerating to the right
   (b) object accelerating to the left
   (c) object travelling at a constant velocity left
   (d) object at rest
   (e) object travelling with constant velocity right

8. Hockey pucks can be shot at speeds of 107 km/h. If a puck is shot at an angle of 30°, determine how long the puck is in the air, how far it will travel, and how high it will be at the peak of its trajectory.

9. Sketch two different position-time graphs for objects with a negative velocity.

10. Sketch two different velocity-time graphs for objects with a negative acceleration.

11. From the position-time graph below, determine which object has the greatest velocity.

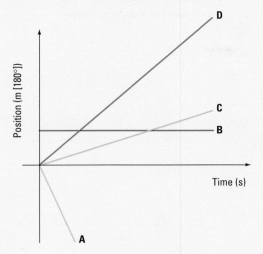

12. Solve each of the following equations for initial velocity, $\vec{v}_i$, algebraically.

(a) $\vec{a} = \dfrac{\vec{v}_f - \vec{v}_i}{\Delta t}$

(b) $\Delta \vec{d} = \vec{v}_i \Delta t + \dfrac{1}{2}\vec{a}\Delta t^2$

(c) $\Delta \vec{d} = \dfrac{1}{2}(\vec{v}_i + \vec{v}_f)\Delta t$

13. The longest kickoff in CFL history is 83.2 m. If the ball remains in the air for 5.0 s, determine its initial speed.

14. Determine the speed of a raven that travels 48 km in 90 min.

15. Describe the motion of the object illustrated in the graph below.

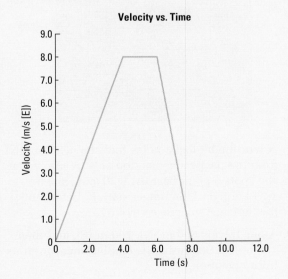

16. (a) What is the change in velocity in 10.0 s, as illustrated in the acceleration-time graph below?

(b) If the object had an initial velocity of 10 m/s [90°], what is its final velocity after 10.0 s?

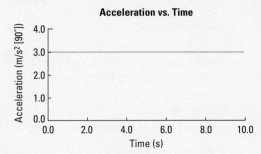

17. How far will a crow fly at 13.4 m/s for 15.0 min?

18. How long will it take a car to travel from Valleyview to Grande Prairie if its speed is 100 km/h? The map's scale is 1 cm : 118 km.

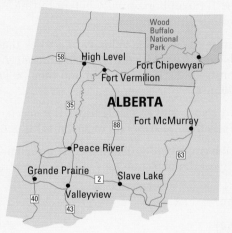

19. A baseball player hits a baseball with a velocity of 30 m/s [25°]. If an outfielder is 85.0 m from the ball when it is hit, how fast will she have to run to catch the ball before it hits the ground?

20. Determine the magnitude of the acceleration of a Jeep Grand Cherokee if its stopping distance is 51.51 m when travelling at 113 km/h.

21. What is the velocity of an aircraft with respect to the ground if its air velocity is 785 km/h [S] and the wind is blowing 55 km/h [22° S of W]?

22. An object with an initial speed of 11.0 m/s travels 350 m in 3.00 s. Determine the magnitude of its acceleration.

23. Improperly installed air conditioners can occasionally fall from apartment windows down onto the road below. How long does a pedestrian have to get out of the way of an air conditioner falling eight stories (24 m)?

24. An object is launched from the top of a building with an initial velocity of 15 m/s [32°]. If the building is 65.0 m high, how far from the base of the building will the object land?

25. Two friends walk at the same speed of 4.0 km/h. One friend steps onto a travelator moving at 3.0 km/h. If he maintains the same initial walking speed,

    (a) how long will it take him to reach the end of the 100-m-long travelator?

    (b) what must be the magnitude of the acceleration of the other friend to arrive at the end of the travelator at the same time?

26. How far will a vehicle travel if it accelerates uniformly at 2.00 m/s² [forward] from 2.50 m/s to 7.75 m/s?

27. An object is thrown into the air with a speed of 25.0 m/s at an angle of 42°. Determine how far it will travel horizontally before hitting the ground.

28. Determine the average velocity of a truck that travels west from Lloydminster to Edmonton at 110 km/h for 1.0 h and 20 min and then 90 km/h for 100 min.

29. What distance will a vehicle travel if it accelerates uniformly from 15.0 m/s [S] to 35.0 m/s [S] in 6.0 s?

30. From the graph below, determine the instantaneous velocity of the object at 5.0 s, 10.0 s, and 15.0 s.

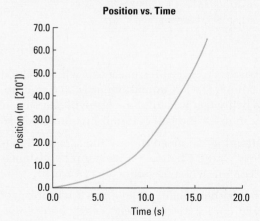

Position vs. Time

31. A speedboat's engine can move the boat at a velocity of 215 km/h [N]. What is the velocity of the current if the boat's displacement is 877 km [30° E of N] 3.5 h later?

32. An object starts from rest and travels 50.0 m along a frictionless, level surface in 2.75 s. What is the magnitude of its acceleration?

33. Determine the displacement of the blue jay from the velocity-time graph below.

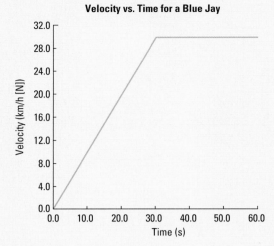

Velocity vs. Time for a Blue Jay

34. Sketch a position-time graph for an object that travels at a constant velocity of 5.0 m/s for 10 s, stops for 10 s, then travels with a velocity of −2.0 m/s for 20 s.

35. Determine the height reached by a projectile if it is released with a velocity of 18.0 m/s [20°].

36. (a) From the map below, determine Becky's house position with respect to the school.

    (b) Determine how far Becky would have to travel from her house to get to school if she must stay on the roads (no shortcuts).

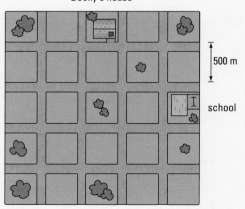

37. A wildlife biologist notes that she is 350 m [N] from the park ranger station at 8:15 a.m. when she spots a polar bear. At 8:30 a.m., she is 1.75 km [N] of the ranger station. Determine the biologist's average velocity.

38. A bus travels 500 m [N], 200 m [E], and then 750 m [S]. Determine its displacement from its initial position.

39. Match the motion with the correct position-time graph given below. Identify the motion as at rest, uniform motion, or uniformly accelerated motion.

(a) an airplane taking off

(b) an airplane landing

(c) passing a car on the highway

(d) waiting at the red line at Canada Customs

(e) standing watching a parade

(f) travelling along the highway on cruise control

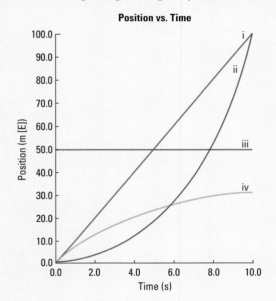

Position vs. Time

40. Determine the magnitude of the acceleration of a Jeep Grand Cherokee that can reach 26.9 m/s from rest in 4.50 s.

Extensions

41. A penny is released from the top of a wishing well and hits the water's surface 1.47 s later. Calculate

(a) the velocity of the penny just before it hits the water's surface

(b) the distance from the top of the well to the water's surface

42. A balloonist drops a sandbag from a balloon that is rising at a constant velocity of 3.25 m/s [up]. It takes 8.75 s for the sandbag to reach the ground. Determine

(a) the height of the balloon when the sandbag is dropped

(b) the height of the balloon when the sandbag reaches the ground

(c) the velocity with which the sandbag hits the ground

43. A motorcycle stunt rider wants to jump a 20.0-m-wide row of cars. The launch ramp is angled at 30° and is 9.0 m high. The landing ramp is also angled at 30° and is 6.0 m high. Find the minimum launch velocity required for the stunt rider to reach the landing ramp.

Skills Practice

44. Draw a Venn diagram to compare and contrast vector and scalar quantities.

45. Draw a Venn diagram to illustrate the concepts of graphical analysis.

46. A swimmer wants to cross the Athabasca River in Fort McMurray. The swimmer's speed in still water is 3.0 m/s, the current's velocity is 4.05 m/s [N], and the river is 550 m wide. Draw a vector diagram for this problem.

47. For an experiment to measure the velocity of an object, you have a radar gun, probeware, and motion sensors. Explain to a classmate how you would decide which instrument to use.

48. Design an experiment to determine the acceleration of an object rolling down an inclined plane.

49. Construct a concept map for solving a two-dimensional motion problem involving a projectile thrown at an angle.

50. Explain how you can use velocity-time graphs to describe the motion of an object.

Self-assessment

51. Describe to a classmate which kinematics concepts and laws you found most interesting when studying this unit. Give reasons for your choices.

52. Identify one issue pertaining to motion studied in this unit that you would like to investigate in greater detail.

53. What concept in this unit did you find most difficult? What steps could you take to improve your understanding?

54. As a future voter, what legislation would you support to improve vehicular and road safety?

55. Assess how well you are able to graph the motion of an object. Explain how you determine a reference point.

e TEST

To check your understanding of kinematics, follow the eTest links at
www.pearsoned.ca/school/physicssource.

Dynamics

The design of equipment used in many activities, such as ice climbing, involves understanding the cause of motion. How does gravity affect the climber and the icy cliff? How can understanding the cause of motion help you predict motion?

e WEB

Explore the physics principles that apply to ice and mountain climbing. Write a summary of your findings. Begin your search at www.pearsoned.ca/school/physicssource.

Unit at a Glance

Unit Themes and Emphases

- Change and Systems
- Social and Environmental Contexts
- Problem-Solving Skills

Focussing Questions

In this study of dynamics and gravitation, you will investigate different types of forces and how they change the motion of objects and affect the design of various technological systems. As you study this unit, consider these questions:

- How does an understanding of forces help humans interact with their environment?
- How do the principles of dynamics affect mechanical and other systems?
- What role does gravity play in the universe?

Unit Project

Tire Design, Stopping Distance, and Vehicle Mass

- By the time you complete this unit, you will have the skills to evaluate how tire treads, road surfaces, and vehicle mass affect stopping distances. You will need to consider human reaction times and the amount of moisture on road surfaces to investigate this problem.

Forces can change velocity.

Screeching tires on the road and the sound of metal and fibreglass being crushed are familiar sounds of a vehicle collision. Depending on the presence of airbags and the correct use of seat belts and headrests, a motorist may suffer serious injury. In order to design these safety devices, engineers must understand what forces are and how forces affect the motion of an object.

When a driver suddenly applies the brakes, the seat belts of all occupants lock. If the vehicle collides head-on with another vehicle, airbags may become deployed. Both seat belts and airbags are designed to stop the forward motion of motorists during a head-on collision (Figure 3.1).

Motorists in a vehicle that is rear-ended also experience forces. The car seats move forward quickly, taking the lower part of each person's body with it. But each person's head stays in the same place until yanked forward by the neck. It is this sudden yank that causes whiplash. Adjustable headrests are designed to prevent whiplash by supporting the head of each motorist.

In this chapter, you will investigate how forces affect motion and how to explain and predict the motion of an object using Newton's three laws.

▲ **Figure 3.1** To design cars with better safety features, accident researchers use dummies to investigate the results of high-speed collisions.

Accelerating a Cart

Problem

If you pull an object with a force, how do force and mass affect the acceleration of the object?

Materials

dynamics cart with hook
two 200-g standard masses
one 1-kg standard mass
spring scale (0–5 N)
smooth, flat surface (about 1.5 m long)

Procedure

1 Place the 200-g standard masses on the cart and attach the spring scale to the hook on the cart.

2 Pull the spring scale so that the cart starts to accelerate forward (Figure 3.2). Make sure that the force reading on the spring scale is 2 N and that the force remains as constant as possible while pulling the cart. Observe the acceleration of the cart.

3 Replace the 200-g masses on the cart with the 1-kg standard mass. Then pull the cart, applying the same force you used in step 2. Observe the acceleration of the cart.

4 Remove all the objects from the cart. Then pull the cart, applying the same force you used in step 2. Observe the acceleration of the cart.

5 Repeat step 4 but this time pull with a force of 1 N.

6 Repeat step 4 but this time pull with a force of 3 N.

7 Repeat step 4 but now only pull with just enough force to start the cart moving. Measure the force reading on the spring scale.

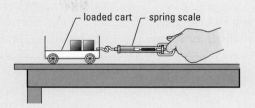
loaded cart — spring scale

▲ **Figure 3.2**

Questions

1. Why do you think it was difficult to apply a constant force when pulling the cart each time?

2. Describe how the acceleration of the cart changed from what it was in step 2 when

(a) you used the 1-kg standard mass instead of the 200-g masses,

(b) you removed all the objects from the cart,

(c) you decreased the pulling force to 1 N, and

(d) you increased the pulling force to 3 N.

3. What force was required to start the cart moving in step 7?

4. Suppose, instead of hooking a spring scale to the cart in steps 2 to 4, you gave the cart a push of the same magnitude each time.

(a) Which cart would you expect to travel the farthest distance?

(b) Which cart would you expect to slow down sooner?

(c) What force do you think makes the cart eventually come to a stop?

Think About It

1. Describe the motion of a large rocket during liftoff using the concept of force. Include diagrams in your explanation.

2. Is a plane during takeoff accelerating or moving with constant velocity? Explain in words and with diagrams.

Discuss your answers in a small group and record them for later reference. As you complete each section of this chapter, review your answers to these questions. Note any changes to your ideas.

3.1 The Nature of Force

dynamics: branch of mechanics dealing with the cause of motion

The Petronas Twin Towers in Kuala Lumpur, Malaysia, are currently the world's tallest twin towers. Including the spire on top, each tower measures 452 m above street level. To allow for easier movement of people within the building, architects designed a bridge to link each tower at the 41st floor. What is interesting is that this bridge is *not* stationary. In order for the bridge to not collapse, it must move with the towers as they sway in the wind (Figure 3.3).

In Unit I, you learned that kinematics describes the motion of an object without considering the cause. When designing a structure, the kinematics quantities that an architect considers are displacement, velocity, and acceleration. But to predict how and explain why a structure moves, an architect must understand **dynamics**. Dynamics deals with the effects of forces on objects.

Structures such as bridges and buildings are required to either remain stationary or move in appropriate ways, depending on the design, so that they are safe to use. Architects must determine all the forces that act at critical points of the structure. If the forces along a particular direction do not balance, acceleration will occur.

Before you can predict or explain the motion of an object, it is important to first understand what a force is and how to measure and calculate the sum of all forces acting on an object.

▶ **Figure 3.3** The design of tall buildings involves understanding forces. Towering buildings are susceptible to movement from the wind.

Force Is a Vector Quantity

You experience a **force** when you push or pull an object. A push or a pull can have different magnitudes and can be in different directions. For this reason, force is a vector quantity. In general, any force acting on an object can change the shape and/or velocity of the object (Figure 3.4). If you want to deform an object yet keep it stationary, at least two forces must be present.

force: a quantity measuring a push or a pull on an object

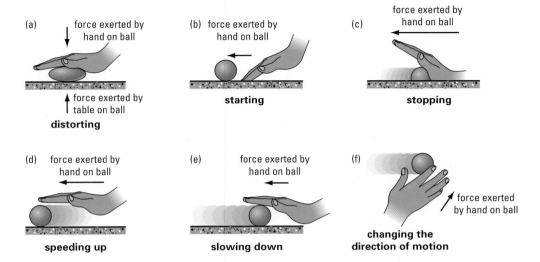

▲ **Figure 3.4** Different forces acting on a ball change either the shape or the motion of the ball. (a) The deformation of the ball is caused by both the hand and the table applying opposing forces on the ball. (b)–(f) The motion of the ball is changed, depending on the magnitude and the direction of the force applied by the hand.

The symbol of force is $\vec{F}$ and the SI unit for force is the newton (N), named in honour of physicist Isaac Newton (1642–1727). One newton is equal to one kilogram-metre per second squared (1 kg·m/s²), which is the force required to move a 1-kg object with an acceleration of 1 m/s².

The direction of a force is described using reference coordinates that you choose for a particular situation. You may use [forward] or [backward], compass directions, or Cartesian x and y axes. When stating directions using Cartesian axes, measure angles counterclockwise from the positive x-axis (Figure 3.5).

info **BIT**
One newton is roughly equal to the magnitude of the weight of a medium-sized apple or two golf balls.

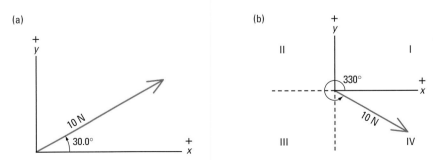

▲ **Figure 3.5** Two vectors of the same magnitude but with different directions in the Cartesian plane. (a) 10 N [30°] (b) 10 N [330°]

Measuring Force

One way you could measure forces involves using a calibrated spring scale. To measure the force of gravity acting on an object, attach the object to the end of a vertical spring and observe the stretch of the spring. The **weight** of an object is the force of gravity acting on the object. The symbol of weight is $\vec{F}_g$.

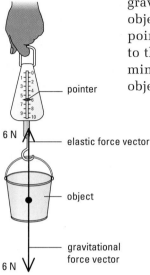

pointer

6 N — elastic force vector

object

gravitational force vector

6 N

When the spring stops stretching, the gravitational and elastic forces acting on the object balance each other (Figure 3.6). At this point, the elastic force is equal in magnitude to the weight of the object. So you can determine the magnitude of the weight of an object by reading the pointer position on a calibrated spring scale once the spring stops stretching.

Find out the relationship between the stretch of a spring and the weight of an object by doing 3-2 QuickLab.

◄ **Figure 3.6** A spring scale is one type of instrument that can be used to measure forces.

3-2 QuickLab

Measuring Force Using a Spring Scale

Problem

How is the amount of stretch of a calibrated spring related to the magnitude of the force acting on an object?

Materials

set of standard masses with hooks
spring scale (0–10 N)

Procedure

1 Hold the spring scale vertically and make sure the pointer reads zero when nothing is attached.

2 Gently suspend a 100-g standard mass from the spring. Use a table to record the mass and the magnitudes of the gravitational and elastic forces acting on the object.

3 Hang additional objects from the spring, up to a total mass of 1000 g. Each time, record the mass and the magnitudes of the corresponding gravitational and elastic forces.

Questions

1. What was the reading on the spring scale when the 100-g mass was attached?

2. What happened to the stretch of the spring when the mass of the object attached to the spring scale
   (a) doubled?
   (b) tripled?
   (c) changed by a factor of 10?

3. Why is a spring scale ideal for measuring force?

Representing Forces Using Free-Body Diagrams

A **free-body diagram** is a powerful tool that can be used to analyze situations involving forces. This diagram is a sketch that shows the object by itself, isolated from all others with which it may be interacting. Only the force vectors exerted *on* the object are included and, in this physics course, the vectors are drawn with their tails meeting at the centre of the object (Figure 3.7). However, it does not necessarily mean that the centre of the object is *where* the forces act.

When drawing a free-body diagram, it is important to show the reference coordinates that apply to the situation in a given problem. Remember to always include which directions you will choose as positive. Figure 3.8 shows the steps for drawing free-body diagrams.

free-body diagram: vector diagram of an object in isolation showing all the forces acting *on* it

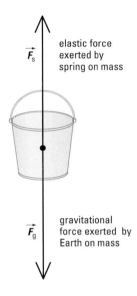

elastic force exerted by spring on mass

$\vec{F}_s$

gravitational force exerted by Earth on mass

$\vec{F}_g$

▲ **Figure 3.7** The free-body diagram for the object in Figure 3.6 that is suspended from the spring scale. The spring scale is not included here because it is not the object being studied.

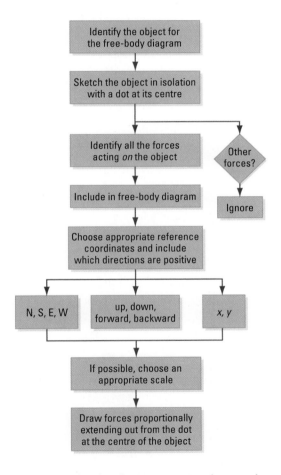

▲ **Figure 3.8** Flowchart summarizing the steps for drawing a free-body diagram

Some Types of Forces

There are different types of forces and scientists distinguish among them by giving these forces special names. When an object is in contact with another, the objects will have a common surface of contact, and the two objects will exert a normal force on each other. The **normal force**, $\vec{F}_N$, is a force that is perpendicular to this common surface. Depending on the situation, another force called **friction**, $\vec{F}_f$, may be present, and this force acts parallel to the common surface.

The adjective "normal" simply means perpendicular. Figure 3.9 (a) shows a book at rest on a level table. The normal force exerted by the table on the book is represented by the vector directed upward. If the table top were slanted and smooth as in Figure 3.9 (b), the normal force acting on the book would not be directed vertically upward. Instead, it would be slanted, but always perpendicular to the contact surface.

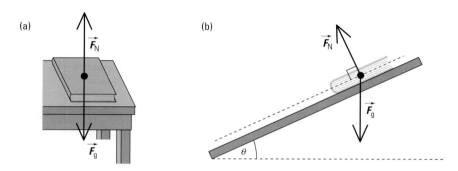

▲ **Figure 3.9** Forces acting on (a) a stationary book on a level table and on (b) a book accelerating down a smooth, slanted table.

A stationary object may experience an **applied force**, $\vec{F}_{app}$, if, say, a person pushes against the object (Figure 3.10). In this case, the force of friction acting on the object will oppose the direction of impending motion.

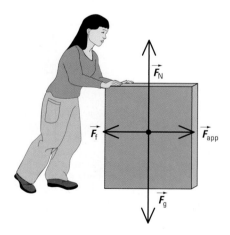

▲ **Figure 3.10** The forces acting on a stationary box

Example 3.1 demonstrates how to draw a free-body diagram for a car experiencing different types of forces. In this situation, the normal force acting on the car is equal in magnitude to the weight of the car.

Example 3.1

A car with a weight, $\vec{F}_g$, of 10 000 N [down] is coasting on a level road. The car experiences a normal force, $\vec{F}_N$, of 10 000 N [up], a force of air resistance, $\vec{F}_{air}$, of 2500 N [backward], and a force of friction, $\vec{F}_f$, exerted by the road on the tires of 500 N [backward]. Draw a free-body diagram for this situation.

Analysis and Solution

While the car is coasting, there is no forward force acting on the car.
The free-body diagram shows four forces (Figure 3.11).

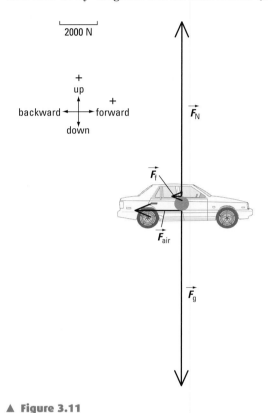

▲ **Figure 3.11**

Practice Problems

1. The driver in Example 3.1 sees a pedestrian and steps on the brakes. The force of air resistance is 2500 N [backward]. With the brakes engaged, the force of friction exerted on the car is 5000 N [backward]. Draw a free-body diagram for this situation.

2. A car moving at constant velocity speeds up. The weight of the car is 12 000 N [down]. The force of air resistance is 3600 N [backward]. With the engine engaged, the force of friction exerted by the road on the tires is 7200 N [forward]. Draw a free-body diagram for this situation.

Answers

1. and 2. See page 898.

Using Free-Body Diagrams to Find Net Force

Free-body diagrams are very useful when you need to calculate the **net force**, $\vec{F}_{net}$, on an object. The net force is a *vector sum* of all the forces acting simultaneously on an object. The force vectors can be added using either a scale vector diagram or using components.

net force: vector sum of two or more forces acting simultaneously on an object

Concept Check

Can the net force on an object ever equal zero? Explain using an example and a free-body diagram.

Adding Collinear Forces

e SIM

Learn how to use free-body diagrams to find the net force on an object. Follow the eSim links at www.pearsoned.ca/school/physicssource.

Vectors that are parallel are collinear, even if they have opposite directions. Example 3.2 demonstrates how to find the net force on an object given two collinear forces. In this example, a canoe is dragged using two ropes. The magnitude of the force $\vec{F}_T$ exerted by a rope on an object at the point where the rope is attached to the object is called the **tension** in the rope.

In this physics course, there are a few assumptions that you need to make about ropes or cables to simplify calculations. These assumptions and the corresponding inferences are listed in Table 3.1. Note that a "light" object means that it has negligible mass.

▼ **Table 3.1** Assumptions about Ropes or Cables

Assumption	Inference
The mass of the rope is negligible.	The tension is uniform throughout the length of the rope.
The rope has a negligible thickness.	$\vec{F}_T$ acts parallel to the rope and is directed away from the object to which the rope is attached.
The rope is taut and does not stretch.	Any objects attached to the rope will have the same magnitude of acceleration as the rope.

Example 3.2

Two people, A and B, are dragging a canoe out of a lake onto a beach using light ropes (Figure 3.12). Each person applies a force of 60.0 N [forward] on the rope. The force of friction exerted by the beach on the canoe is 85.0 N [backward]. Starting with a free-body diagram, calculate the net force on the canoe.

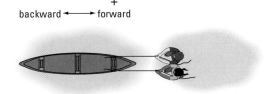

backward ← → forward

Given

$\vec{F}_{T_1}$ = 60.0 N [forward]

$\vec{F}_{T_2}$ = 60.0 N [forward]

$\vec{F}_f$ = 85.0 N [backward]

▲ **Figure 3.12**

Required

net force on canoe ($\vec{F}_{net}$)

Analysis and Solution

Draw a free-body diagram for the canoe (Figure 3.13).

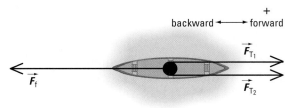

backward ← → forward

▲ **Figure 3.13**

Practice Problems

1. Two dogs, A and B, are pulling a sled across a horizontal, snowy surface. Dog A exerts a force of 200 N [forward] and dog B a force of 150 N [forward]. The force of friction exerted by the snow on the sled is 60 N [backward]. The driver attempts to slow down the sled by pulling on it with a force of 100 N [backward]. Starting with a free-body diagram, calculate the net force on the sled.

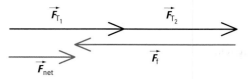

backward ← + → forward

▲ **Figure 3.14**

Add the force vectors shown in the vector addition diagram (Figure 3.14).

$$\vec{F}_{net} = \vec{F}_{T_1} + \vec{F}_{T_2} + \vec{F}_f$$
$$F_{net} = F_{T_1} + F_{T_2} + F_f$$
$$= 60.0 \text{ N} + 60.0 \text{ N} + (-85.0 \text{ N})$$
$$= 60.0 \text{ N} + 60.0 \text{ N} - 85.0 \text{ N}$$
$$= 35.0 \text{ N}$$
$$\vec{F}_{net} = 35.0 \text{ N [forward]}$$

Paraphrase
The net force on the canoe is 35.0 N [forward].

Adding Non-Collinear Forces

Example 3.3 demonstrates how to find the net force on an object if the forces acting on it are neither parallel nor perpendicular. By observing the relationship between the components of the force vectors, you can greatly simplify the calculations.

Example 3.3

Refer to Example 3.2 on page 132. Person A thinks that if A and B each pull a rope forming an angle of 20.0° with the bow, the net force on the canoe will be greater than in Example 3.2 (Figure 3.15). The canoe is being dragged along the beach using ropes that are parallel to the surface of the beach. Starting with a free-body diagram, calculate the net force on the canoe. Is person A's thinking correct?

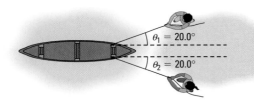

▲ **Figure 3.15**

Given

$\vec{F}_{T_1} = 60.0 \text{ N [along rope]}$ $\vec{F}_{T_2} = 60.0 \text{ N [along rope]}$

$\vec{F}_f = 85.0 \text{ N [backward]}$ $\theta_1 = \theta_2 = 20.0°$

Required
net force on canoe ($\vec{F}_{net}$)

Analysis and Solution
Draw a free-body diagram for the canoe (Figure 3.16).

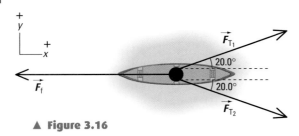

▲ **Figure 3.16**

Practice Problems

1. Refer to Example 3.3. Suppose person A pulls a rope forming an angle of 40.0° with the bow and person B pulls a rope forming an angle of 20.0° with the bow. The canoe and ropes are parallel to the surface of the beach. If the canoe is being dragged across a horizontal, frictionless surface, calculate the net force on the canoe.

2. Two people, A and B, are dragging a sled on a horizontal, icy surface with two light ropes. Person A applies a force of 65.0 N [30.0°] on one rope. Person B applies a force of 70.0 N [300°] on the other rope. The force of friction on the sled is negligible and the ropes are parallel to the icy surface. Calculate the net force on the sled.

Answers

1. 1.04×10^2 N [10.0°]
2. 95.5 N [343°]

Resolve all forces into x and y components.

Vector	x component	y component
$\vec{F}_{T_1}$	(60.0 N)(cos 20.0°)	(60.0 N)(sin 20.0°)
$\vec{F}_{T_2}$	(60.0 N)(cos 20.0°)	−(60.0 N)(sin 20.0°)
$\vec{F}_f$	−85.0 N	0

From the chart, $F_{T_{1y}} = -F_{T_{2y}}$.

So $\quad \vec{F}_{net_y} = \vec{F}_{T_{1y}} + \vec{F}_{T_{2y}}$
$\qquad F_{net_y} = F_{T_{1y}} + F_{T_{2y}} = 0$ N

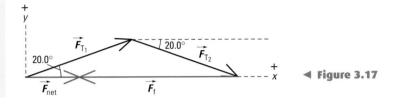

◄ **Figure 3.17**

Add the x components of all force vectors in the vector addition diagram (Figure 3.17).

x direction

$\vec{F}_{net_x} = \vec{F}_{T_{1x}} + \vec{F}_{T_{2x}} + \vec{F}_f$

$F_{net_x} = F_{T_{1x}} + F_{T_{2x}} + F_f$

$\qquad = (60.0\ N)(\cos 20.0°) + (60.0\ N)(\cos 20.0°) + (-85.0\ N)$

$\qquad = (60.0\ N)(\cos 20.0°) + (60.0\ N)(\cos 20.0°) - 85.0\ N$

$\qquad = 27.8\ N$

$\vec{F}_{net} = 27.8\ N\ [0°]$

Paraphrase

The net force is 27.8 N [0°]. Since the net force in Example 3.3 is less than that in Example 3.2, person A's thinking is incorrect.

Applying Free-Body Diagrams to Objects in Equilibrium

At the beginning of this section, you learned that architects consider the net force acting at critical points of a building or bridge in order to prevent structure failure. Example 3.4 demonstrates how free-body diagrams and the concept of net force apply to a stationary object.

Example 3.4

A 25-kg store sign is suspended as shown in Figure 3.18. Calculate the forces $\vec{F}_{T_1}$ and $\vec{F}_{T_2}$ exerted at the point at which the sign is suspended.

▶ **Figure 3.18**

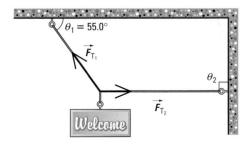

Given

$m = 25$ kg $\qquad \theta_1 = 55.0°$ $\qquad \theta_2 = 90.0°$ $\qquad \vec{g} = 9.81$ m/s^2 [down]

Required

forces ($\vec{F}_{T_1}$ and $\vec{F}_{T_2}$)

Analysis and Solution

Draw a free-body diagram for the sign (Figure 3.19).
Resolve all forces into x and y components.

Vector	x component	y component
$\vec{F}_{T_1}$	$-F_{T_1}\cos 55.0°$	$F_{T_1}\sin 55.0°$
$\vec{F}_{T_2}$	F_{T_2}	0
$\vec{F}_g$	0	$-mg$

Since the sign is not accelerating, the net force in both the x and y directions is zero.

$$F_{\text{net}_x} = F_{\text{net}_y} = 0 \text{ N}$$

Add the x and y components of all force vectors separately.

x direction

$$\vec{F}_{\text{net}_x} = \vec{F}_{T_{1x}} + \vec{F}_{T_{2x}}$$
$$F_{\text{net}_x} = F_{T_{1x}} + F_{T_{2x}}$$
$$0 = -F_{T_1}\cos 55.0° + F_{T_2}$$

$$F_{T_2} = F_{T_1}\cos 55.0°$$

y direction

$$\vec{F}_{\text{net}_y} = \vec{F}_{T_{1y}} + \vec{F}_g$$
$$F_{\text{net}_y} = F_{T_{1y}} + F_g$$
$$0 = F_{T_1}\sin 55.0° + (-mg)$$
$$0 = F_{T_1} - \frac{mg}{\sin 55.0°}$$

$$F_{T_1} = \frac{mg}{\sin 55.0°}$$
$$= \frac{(25\text{kg})\left(9.81\dfrac{\text{m}}{\text{s}^2}\right)}{\sin 55.0°}$$
$$= 299\ \frac{\text{kg} \cdot \text{m}}{\text{s}^2}$$
$$= 3.0 \times 10^2 \text{ N}$$

Substitute F_{T_1} into the equation for F_{T_2}.

$$F_{T_2} = F_{T_1}\cos 55.0°$$
$$= (299 \text{ N})(\cos 55.0°)$$
$$= 1.7 \times 10^2 \text{ N}$$
$$\vec{F}_{T_2} = 1.7 \times 10^2 \text{ N } [0°]$$

From Figure 3.19, the direction of $\vec{F}_{T_1}$ measured counterclockwise from the positive x-axis is $180° - 55.0° = 125°$.

$$\vec{F}_{T_1} = 3.0 \times 10^2 \text{ N } [125°]$$

Paraphrase

$\vec{F}_{T_1}$ is 3.0×10^2 N [125°] and $\vec{F}_{T_2}$ is 1.7×10^2 N [0°].

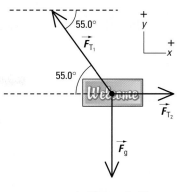

▲ **Figure 3.19**

Practice Problems

1. If the sign in Example 3.4 had half the mass, how would the forces $\vec{F}_{T_1}$ and $\vec{F}_{T_2}$ compare?

2. Suppose the sign in Example 3.4 is suspended as shown in Figure 3.20. Calculate the forces $\vec{F}_{T_1}$ and $\vec{F}_{T_2}$.

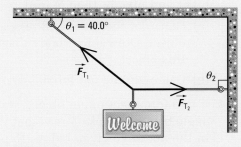

▲ **Figure 3.20**

3. Refer to the solutions to Example 3.4 and Practice Problem 2 above.
   (a) As θ_1 decreases, what happens to $\vec{F}_{T_1}$ and $\vec{F}_{T_2}$?
   (b) Explain why θ_1 can never equal zero.

Answers

1. directions of $\vec{F}_{T_1}$ and $\vec{F}_{T_2}$ would remain the same as before, but the respective magnitudes would be half

2. $\vec{F}_{T_1} = 3.8 \times 10^2$ N [140°]
   $\vec{F}_{T_2} = 2.9 \times 10^2$ N [0°]

3. (a) $\vec{F}_{T_1}$ and $\vec{F}_{T_2}$ increase in value
   (b) magnitude of $\vec{F}_{T_{1y}}$ must always equal mg

Knowledge

1. (a) Explain what a force is, and state the SI unit of force.

   (b) Why is force a dynamics quantity and not a kinematics quantity?

Applications

2. Sketch a free-body diagram for

   (a) a bicycle moving west on a level road with decreasing speed

   (b) a ball experiencing forces of 45 N [12.0°], 60 N [100°], and 80 N [280°] simultaneously

3. The total weight of a biker and her motorbike is 1800 N [down]. With the engine engaged, the force of friction exerted by the road on the tires is 500 N [forward]. The air resistance acting on the biker and bike is 200 N [backward]. The normal force exerted by the road on the biker and bike is 1800 N [up].

   (a) Consider the biker and bike as a single object. Draw a free-body diagram for this object.

   (b) Calculate the net force.

4. If two forces act on an object, state the angle between these forces that will result in the net force given below. Explain using sketches.

   (a) maximum net force

   (b) minimum net force

5. Two people, A and B, are pulling on a tree with ropes while person C is cutting the tree down. Person A applies a force of 80.0 N [45.0°] on one rope. Person B applies a force of 90.0 N [345°] on the other rope. Calculate the net force on the tree.

6. Three forces act simultaneously on an object: $\vec{F}_1$ is 65 N [30.0°], $\vec{F}_2$ is 80 N [115°], and $\vec{F}_3$ is 105 N [235°]. Calculate the net force acting on the object.

Extensions

7. Suppose the sign in Example 3.4 on page 134 is suspended as shown below. Calculate the forces $\vec{F}_{T_1}$ and $\vec{F}_{T_2}$.

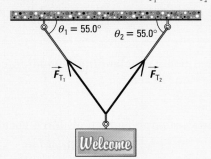

8. The blanket toss is a centuries-old hunting technique that the Inuit used to find herds of caribou. During the toss, several people would hold a hide taut while the hunter would jump up and down, much like on a trampoline, increasing the jump height each time. At the top of the jump, the hunter would rotate 360° looking for the herd. Draw a free-body diagram for a hunter of weight 700 N [down] while

   (a) standing at rest on the taut hide just before a jump

   (b) at the maximum jump height

9. Construct a flowchart to summarize how to add two or more non-collinear forces using components. Refer to Figure 3.8 on page 129 or Student References 4: Using Graphic Organizers on page 869.

_e_ TEST

To check your understanding of forces, follow the eTest links at www.pearsoned.ca/school/physicssource.

3.2 Newton's First Law

At the 2006 Winter Olympics in Turin, Italy, Duff Gibson charged head-first down a 1.4-km icy track with 19 challenging curves. He reached speeds well over 125 km/h and ended up clinching the gold medal in the men's skeleton event (Figure 3.21). Gibson's success had a lot to do with understanding the physics of motion.

Imagine an ideal situation in which no friction acts on the sled and no air resistance acts on the athlete. Scientist Galileo Galilei (1564–1642) thought that an object moving on a level surface would continue moving forever at constant speed and in the same direction if no external force acts on the object. If the object is initially stationary, then it will remain stationary, provided no external force acts on the object.

In the real world, friction and air resistance are external forces that act on all moving objects. So an object that is in motion will eventually slow down to a stop, unless another force acts to compensate for both friction and air resistance. Galileo recognized the existence of friction, so he used thought experiments, as well as experiments with controlled variables, to understand motion. Thought experiments are theoretical, idealized situations that can be imagined but cannot be created in the real world.

info **BIT**

The skeleton is an Olympic sledding sport believed to have originated in St. Moritz, Switzerland.

◄ **Figure 3.21**   In the 2006 Winter Olympics, Calgary residents Duff Gibson (shown in photo) and Jeff Pain competed in the men's skeleton. Gibson edged Pain by 0.26 s to win the gold medal. Pain won the silver medal.

The Concept of Inertia

Since ancient times, many thinkers attempted to understand how and why objects moved. But it took thousands of years before satisfactory explanations were developed that accounted for actual observations. A major stumbling block was not identifying friction as a force that exists in the real world.

In his study of motion, Galileo realized that every object has **inertia**, a property that resists acceleration. A stationary curling stone on ice requires a force to start the stone moving. Once it is moving, the curling stone requires a force to stop it.

To better understand the concept of inertia, try the challenges in 3-3 QuickLab.

inertia: property of an object that resists acceleration

Concept Check

Compare the inertia of an astronaut on Earth's surface, in orbit around Earth, and in outer space. Can an object ever have an inertia of zero? Explain.

3-3 QuickLab

Challenges with Inertia

Problem

What role does inertia play in each of these challenges?

Materials

glass tumbler
small, stiff piece of cardboard
several loonies
empty soft-drink bottle
plastic hoop (about 2 cm wide, cut from a large plastic bottle)
small crayon with flat ends
ruler (thinner than thickness of one loonie)

Procedure

➊ Set up the tumbler, piece of cardboard, and loonie as shown in Figure 3.22 (a). Remove the cardboard so the loonie falls into the tumbler.

➋ Set up the soft-drink bottle, plastic hoop, and a crayon as shown in Figure 3.22 (b). Remove the hoop so the crayon falls into the bottle.

➌ Set up a stack of loonies and the ruler as shown in Figure 3.22 (c). Use the ruler to remove the loonie at the very bottom without toppling the stack.

> ⚠ **Caution: Keep your eyes well above the coin stack.**

Questions

1. (a) What method did you use to successfully perform each step in the procedure?

   (b) Apply the concept of inertia to explain why each of your procedures was effective.

(a)   (b)   (c)

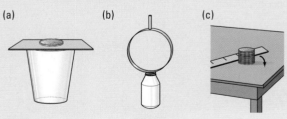

▲ **Figure 3.22**

Newton's First Law and Its Applications

Newton modified and extended Galileo's ideas about inertia in a law, called Newton's first law of motion (Figure 3.23).

An object will continue either being at rest or moving at constant velocity unless acted upon by an external non-zero net force.

If $\vec{F}_{net} = 0$, then $\Delta \vec{v} = 0$.

So if you want to change the motion of an object, a non-zero net force must act on the object.

Concept Check

The Voyager 1 and 2 space probes are approaching interstellar space. If the speed of Voyager 1 is 17 km/s and no external force acts on the probe, describe the motion of the probe (Figure 3.24).

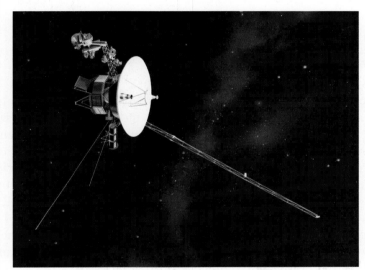

▲ **Figure 3.24** The Voyager planetary mission is NASA's most successful in terms of the number of scientific discoveries.

Newton's First Law and Sliding on Ice

Many winter sports involve a person sliding on ice. In the case of the skeleton event in the Winter Olympics, an athlete uses a sled to slide along a bobsled track. In hockey, a player uses skates to glide across the icy surface of a rink.

Suppose a person on a sled is sliding along a horizontal, icy surface. If no external force acts on the person-sled system, then according to Newton's first law, the person would maintain the same speed. In fact, the person would not stop at all (Figure 3.25).

In real life, the external forces of friction and air resistance act on all moving objects. So the system would eventually come to a stop.

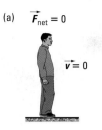

(a) $\vec{F}_{net} = 0$

$\vec{v} = 0$

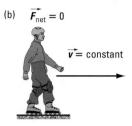

(b) $\vec{F}_{net} = 0$

$\vec{v} = $ constant

▲ **Figure 3.23** If the net force on an object is zero, (a) a stationary object will remain at rest, and (b) an object in motion will continue moving at constant speed in the same direction.

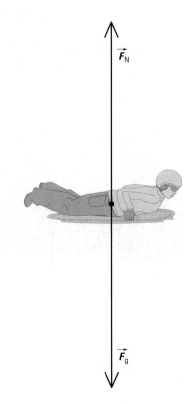

$\vec{F}_N$

$\vec{F}_g$

▲ **Figure 3.25** Free-body diagram of a person-sled system sliding on a horizontal, frictionless surface

Newton's First Law and Vehicle Safety Devices

When you are in a moving car, you can feel the effects of your own inertia. If the car accelerates forward, you feel as if your body is being pushed back against the seat, because your body resists the increase in speed. If the car turns a corner, you feel as if your body is being pushed against the door, because your body resists the change in the direction of motion. If the car stops suddenly, you feel as if your body is being pushed forward, because your body resists the decrease in speed (Figure 3.26).

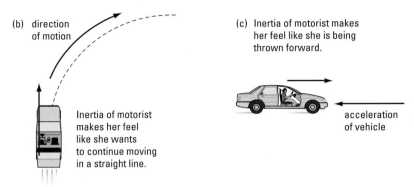

(a) Inertia of motorist makes her feel like she is being pushed backward.

acceleration of vehicle

(b) direction of motion

Inertia of motorist makes her feel like she wants to continue moving in a straight line.

(c) Inertia of motorist makes her feel like she is being thrown forward.

acceleration of vehicle

▲ **Figure 3.26** The inertia of a motorist resists changes in the motion of a vehicle. (a) The vehicle is accelerating, (b) the vehicle is changing direction, and (c) the vehicle is stopping suddenly.

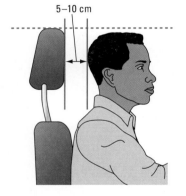

5–10 cm

▲ **Figure 3.27** The ideal position for a headrest

When a car is rear-ended, a motorist's body moves forward suddenly as the car seat moves forward. However, the motorist's head resists moving forward. A properly adjusted headrest can minimize or prevent whiplash, an injury resulting from the rapid forward accelerations in a rear-end collision (Figure 3.27). Research shows that properly adjusted headrests can reduce the risk of whiplash-related injuries by as much as 40%. A poorly adjusted headrest, however, can actually worsen the effects of a rear-end collision on the neck and spine.

When a car is involved in a head-on collision, the motorist continues to move forward. When a seat belt is worn properly, the forward motion of a motorist is safely restricted.

If a head-on collision is violent enough, sodium azide, a deadly poison, undergoes a rapid chemical reaction to produce non-toxic nitrogen gas, which inflates an airbag. The inflated airbag provides a protective cushion to slow down the head and body of a motorist (Figure 3.28).

 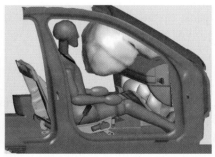 

▲ **Figure 3.28** Airbag systems in vehicles are designed to deploy during vehicle collisions.

The Airbag Debate

The Issue

Front airbags were introduced in the 1990s to help prevent injury to motorists, especially during head-on collisions. Side airbags can also help. Yet front airbags have also been the cause of serious injury, even death. Furthermore, some airbags, such as side airbags, add to the cost of a vehicle. Airbag advocates want both front and side airbags installed, better airbags, and greater control over their operation. Opponents want airbags removed from cars altogether.

Background Information

Airbags are connected to sensors that detect sudden changes in acceleration. The process of triggering and inflating an airbag occurs in about 40 ms. It is in that instant that arms and legs have been broken and children have been killed by the impact of a rapidly inflating airbag. Tragically, some of these deaths occurred during minor car accidents.

Manufacturers have placed on/off switches for airbags on some vehicles, and some engineers are now developing "smart" airbags, which can detect the size of a motorist and the distance that person is sitting from an airbag. This information can then be used to adjust the speed at which the airbag inflates.

Analysis

1. Identify the different stakeholders involved in the airbag controversy.

2. Research the development and safety history of airbags in cars. Research both front and side airbags. Consider head, torso, and knee airbags. Analyze your results, and identify any trends in your data.

3. Propose a solution to this issue, based on the trends you identified.

4. Propose possible changes to current airbag design that could address the issues of safety and cost.

5. Plan a class debate to argue the pros and cons of airbag use. Identify five stakeholders to represent each side in the debate. Support your position with research. Participants will be assessed on their research, organizational skills, debating skills, and attitudes toward learning.

Concept Check

Use Newton's first law to explain why
(a) steel barriers usually separate the cab of a truck from the load (Figure 3.29),
(b) trucks carrying tall loads navigate corners slowly, and
(c) customers who order take-out drinks are provided with lids.

*e***TECH**

Explore the motion of an object that experiences a net force of zero. Follow the *e*TECH links at www.pearsoned.ca/school/physicssource.

◀ **Figure 3.29**

Knowledge

1. In your own words, state Newton's first law.

2. Give two examples, other than those in the text, that illustrate the property of inertia for both a stationary and a moving object.

3. Use Newton's first law to describe the motion of

   (a) a car that attempts to go around an icy curve too quickly, and

   (b) a lacrosse ball after leaving the lacrosse stick.

4. Apply Newton's first law and the concept of inertia to each of these situations.

   (a) How could you remove the newspaper without toppling the plastic beaker?

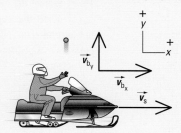

   (b) While moving at constant speed on a level, snowy surface, a snowmobiler throws a ball vertically upward. If the snowmobile continues moving at constant velocity, the ball returns to the driver. Why does the ball land ahead of the driver if the snowmobile stops? Assume that the air resistance acting on the ball is negligible.

Applications

5. Design an experiment using an air puck on an air table or spark air table to verify Newton's first law. Report your findings.

> ⚠ **Caution: A shock from a spark air table can be dangerous.**

6. Imagine you are the hockey coach for a team of 10-year-olds. At a hockey practice, you ask the players to skate across the ice along the blue line (the line closest to the net), and shoot the puck into the empty net. Most of the shots miss the net. The faster the children skate, the more they miss. Newton's first law would help the players understand the problem, but a technical explanation might confuse them.

   (a) Create an explanation that would make sense to the 10-year-olds.

   (b) With the aid of a diagram, design a drill for the team that would help the players score in this type of situation.

Extensions

7. Research why parents use booster seats for young children using information from Safe Kids Canada. Summarize the "seat belt test" that determines whether a child is big enough to wear a seat belt without a booster seat. Begin your search at www.pearsoned.ca/school/physicssource.

8. During a sudden stop or if a motorist tries to adjust a seat belt suddenly, the seat belt locks into position. Research why seat belts lock. Write a brief report, including a diagram, of your findings. Begin your search at www.pearsoned.ca/school/physicssource.

9. Make a web diagram to summarize concepts and ideas associated with Newton's first law. Label the oval in the middle as "Newton's first law." Cluster your words or ideas in other ovals around it. Connect these ovals to the central one and one another, where appropriate, with lines. See Student References 4: Using Graphic Organizers on page 869 for an example.

 e TEST

To check your understanding of inertia and Newton's first law, follow the eTest links at www.pearsoned.ca/school/physicssource.

3.3 Newton's Second Law

If a speed skater wants to win a championship race, the cardiovascular system and leg muscles of the athlete must be in peak condition. The athlete must also know how to effectively apply forces to propel the body forward. World-class speed skaters such as Cindy Klassen know that maximizing the forward acceleration requires understanding the relationship among force, acceleration, and mass (Figure 3.30).

Newton spent many years of his life trying to understand the motion of objects. After many experiments and carefully analyzing the ideas of Galileo and others, Newton eventually found a simple mathematical relationship that models the motion of an object.

This relationship, known as Newton's second law, relates the net force acting on an object, the acceleration of the object, and its mass. Begin by doing 3-5 Inquiry Lab to find the relationship between the acceleration of an object and the net force acting on it.

info **BIT**

Cindy Klassen won a total of five medals during the 2006 Winter Olympics, a Canadian record, and is currently Canada's most decorated Olympian with six medals.

▲ **Figure 3.30** Cindy Klassen, originally from Winnipeg but now a Calgary resident, won the gold medal in the 1500-m speed skating event in the 2006 Winter Olympics in Turin, Italy.

Relating Acceleration and Net Force

The kinematics equation $\vec{d} = \vec{v}_i \Delta t + \dfrac{1}{2}\vec{a}(\Delta t)^2$ relates displacement $\vec{d}$, initial velocity $\vec{v}_i$, time interval Δt, and acceleration $\vec{a}$. If $\vec{v}_i = 0$, the equation simplifies to $\vec{d} = \dfrac{1}{2}\vec{a}(\Delta t)^2$. If you solve for acceleration, you get $\vec{a} = \dfrac{2\vec{d}}{(\Delta t)^2}$. Remember to use the scalar form of this equation when solving for acceleration.

Question

How is the acceleration of an object related to the net force acting on the object?

Hypothesis

State a hypothesis relating acceleration and net force. Remember to write an "if/then" statement.

Variables

The variables involved in this lab are the mass of the system, the applied force acting on the system, friction acting on the system, time interval, the distance the system travels, and the acceleration of the system. Read the procedure and identify the controlled, manipulated, and responding variable(s).

Materials and Equipment

C-clamp
dynamics cart
three 100-g standard masses
pulley
smooth, flat surface (about 1.5 m)
string (about 2 m)
recording tape
recording timer with power supply
metre-stick
masking tape
graph paper

e LAB

For a probeware activity, go to
www.pearsoned.ca/school/physicssource.

Procedure

1. Copy Tables 3.2 and 3.3 on page 145 into your notebook.

2. Measure the mass of the cart. Record the value in Table 3.2.

3. Set up the recording timer, pulley, and cart loaded with three 100-g standard masses on a lab bench (Figure 3.31). Make a loop at each end of the string. Hook one loop to the end of the cart and let the other loop hang down over the pulley.

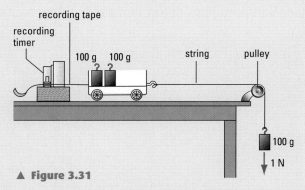

▲ **Figure 3.31**

> ⚠ **Caution: Position a catcher person near the edge of the lab bench. Do not let the cart or hanging objects fall to the ground.**

4. Attach a length of recording tape to the cart and thread it through the timer.

5. While holding the cart still, transfer one 100-g mass from the cart to the loop of string over the pulley and start the timer. When you release the cart, the hanging 100-g mass will exert a force of about 1 N on the system. Release the cart but stop it before it hits the pulley. Label the tape "trial 1; magnitude of $\vec{F}_{app} = 1$ N."

6. Repeat steps 4 and 5 using the same cart but this time transfer another 100-g mass from the cart to the first hanging object. Label the tape "trial 2; magnitude of $\vec{F}_{app} = 2$ N." By transferring objects from the cart to the end of the string hanging over the pulley, the mass of the system remains constant but the net force acting on the system varies.

7. Repeat steps 4 and 5 using the same cart but this time transfer another 100-g mass from the cart to the two hanging masses. Label the tape "trial 3; magnitude of $\vec{F}_{app} = 3$ N."

Analysis

1. Calculate the mass of the system, m_T. Record the value in Table 3.2.

2. Using the tape labelled "trial 3," label the dot at the start $t = 0$ and mark off a convenient time interval. If the period of the timer is $\frac{1}{60}$ s, a time interval of 30 dot spaces represents 0.5 s ($30 \times \frac{1}{60}$ s = 0.5 s). Record the time interval in Table 3.2.

3. Measure the distance the system travelled during this time interval. Record this value in Table 3.2.

4. Use the equation $a = \frac{2d}{(\Delta t)^2}$ to calculate the magnitude of the acceleration of the system. Record the value in Tables 3.2 and 3.3.

5. Using the same time interval, repeat questions 3 and 4 for the tapes labelled "trial 1" and "trial 2."

6. Why is it a good idea to choose the time interval using the tape labelled "trial 3"?

7. Plot a graph of the magnitude of the acceleration vs. the magnitude of the applied force (Table 3.3).

8. (a) Describe the graph you drew in question 7.

   (b) Where does the graph intersect the x-axis? Why? What conditions would have to be present for it to pass through the origin?

   (c) For each trial, subtract the x-intercept from the applied force to find the net force. Record the values in Table 3.3. Then plot a graph of the magnitude of the acceleration vs. the magnitude of the net force.

9. When the magnitude of the net force acting on the system is doubled, what happens to the magnitude of the acceleration of the system?

10. What is the relationship between the magnitude of the acceleration and the magnitude of the net force? Write this relationship as a proportionality statement. Does this relationship agree with your hypothesis?

▼ **Table 3.2** Mass, Time, Distance, and Acceleration

Trial	Mass of Cart m_c (kg)	Mass of Load on Cart m_l (kg)	Mass of Load Hanging over Pulley m_h (kg)	Total Mass $m_T = m_c + m_l + m_h$ (kg)	Time Interval Δt (s)	Distance d (m)	Magnitude of $\vec{a}$ (m/s²)
1		0.200	0.100				
2		0.100	0.200				
3		0	0.300				

▼ **Table 3.3** Force and Acceleration

Trial	Magnitude of $\vec{F}_{app}$ Acting on System (N)	Magnitude of $\vec{F}_{net}$ Acting on System (N)	Magnitude of $\vec{a}$ of System (m/s²)
1	1		
2	2		
3	3		

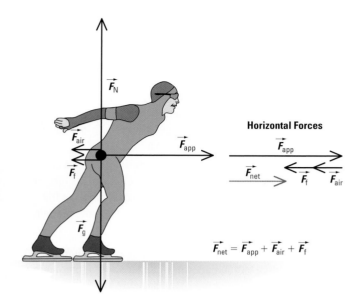

Relating Acceleration and Net Force

For the system in 3-5 Inquiry Lab, you discovered that there is a linear relationship between acceleration and net force. This relationship can be written as a proportionality statement:

$$a \propto F_{net}$$

This relationship applies to speed skating. In the short track relay event, a speed skater pushes the next teammate forward onto the track when it is the teammate's turn to start skating.

While the teammate is being pushed, the horizontal forces acting on the skater are the push force, friction, and air resistance (Figure 3.32). As long as the push force is greater in magnitude than the sum of the force of friction acting on the skates and the air resistance acting on the skater's body, the net force on the teammate acts forward.

The harder the forward push, the greater will be the forward net force on the teammate (Figure 3.33). So the acceleration of the teammate will be greater. Note that the acceleration is in the same direction as the net force.

Find out the relationship between the acceleration of an object and its mass by doing 3-6 Design a Lab.

▲ **Figure 3.32** (left) Free-body diagram showing the forces acting on a speed skater being pushed by a teammate in the short track relay event; (right) vector addition diagram for the horizontal forces.

▶ **Figure 3.33**
For the same mass, a greater net force results in a greater acceleration.

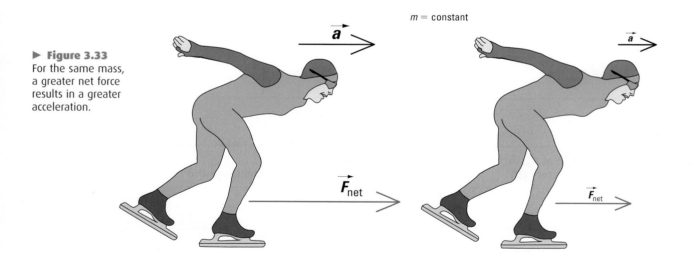

Concept Check

What is the difference between a net force and an applied force? Can a net force ever equal an applied force? Explain using an example and a free-body diagram.

Relating Acceleration and Mass

In this lab, you will investigate the relationship between acceleration and mass when the net force acting on the system is constant.

The Question

How is the acceleration of an object related to the mass of the object?

e LAB

For a probeware activity, go to www.pearsoned.ca/school/physicssource.

Design and Conduct Your Investigation

- State a hypothesis relating acceleration and mass.
- Then use the set-up in Figure 3.31 on page 144 to design an experiment. List the materials you will use as well as a detailed procedure. Use the procedure and questions in 3-5 Inquiry Lab to help you.
- Plot a graph of the magnitude of the acceleration vs. the mass of the system. Then plot a graph of the magnitude of the acceleration vs. the reciprocal of the mass of the system.
- Analyze your data and form conclusions. How well did your results agree with your hypothesis?

Relating Acceleration and Mass

In 3-6 Design a Lab, you discovered that the relationship between acceleration and mass is non-linear. But if you plot acceleration as a function of the reciprocal of mass, you get a straight line. This shows that there is a linear relationship between acceleration and the reciprocal of mass. This relationship can be written as a proportionality statement:

$$a \propto \frac{1}{m}$$

In speed skating, evidence of this relationship is the different accelerations that two athletes of different mass have. Suppose athlete A has a mass of 60 kg and athlete B a mass of 90 kg. If the net force acting on A and B is the same, you would expect A to have a greater acceleration than B (Figure 3.34).

This observation makes sense in terms of inertia, because the inertia of B resists the change in motion more so than the inertia of A does. In fact, you observed this relationship in 3-1 QuickLab when you compared the acceleration of an empty cart and a cart loaded with a 1-kg standard mass.

e TECH

Explore how the net force on an object and its mass affect its acceleration. Follow the eTech links at www.pearsoned.ca/school/physicssource.

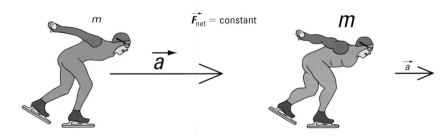

▲ **Figure 3.34** For the same net force, a more massive person has a smaller acceleration than a less massive one does.

Newton's Second Law and Inertial Mass

e MATH

Use technology to explore the relationship among F_{net}, m, and a in Newton's second law. Follow the eMath links at www.pearsoned.ca/school/physicssource to download sample data.

The proportionality statements $a \propto F_{net}$ and $a \propto \dfrac{1}{m}$ can be combined into one statement, $a \propto \dfrac{F_{net}}{m}$ or $a = k\dfrac{F_{net}}{m}$ where k is the proportionality constant. Since 1 N is defined as the net force required to accelerate a 1-kg object at 1 m/s², k is equal to 1. So the equation can be written as $a = \dfrac{F_{net}}{m}$.

This mathematical relationship is Newton's second law.

> When an external non-zero net force acts on an object, the object accelerates in the direction of the net force. The magnitude of the acceleration is directly proportional to the magnitude of the net force and inversely proportional to the mass of the object.

The equation for Newton's second law is usually written with $\vec{F}_{net}$ on the left side:

$$\vec{F}_{net} = m\vec{a}$$

The Concept of Inertial Mass

All objects have mass, so all objects have inertia. From experience, it is more difficult to accelerate a curling stone than to accelerate a hockey puck (Figure 3.35). This means that the inertia of an object is related to its mass. The greater the mass of the object, the greater its inertia.

The mass of an object in Newton's second law is determined by finding the ratio of a known net force acting on an object to the acceleration of the object. In other words, the mass is a measure of the inertia of an object. Because of this relationship, the mass in Newton's second law is called **inertial mass**, which indicates *how* the mass is measured.

inertial mass: mass measurement based on the ratio of a known net force on an object to the acceleration of the object

$$m = \dfrac{F_{net}}{a}$$

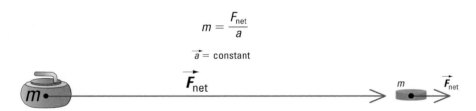

$\vec{a} = $ constant

▲ **Figure 3.35** If the acceleration of the curling stone and the hockey puck is the same, $\vec{F}_{net}$ on the curling stone would be 95 times greater than $\vec{F}_{net}$ on the hockey puck because the inertial mass of the curling stone is that much greater than the hockey puck.

Concept Check

What happens to the acceleration of an object if
(a) the mass and net force both decrease by a factor of 4?
(b) the mass and net force both increase by a factor of 4?
(c) the mass increases by a factor of 4, but the net force decreases by the same factor?
(d) the mass decreases by a factor of 4, and the net force is zero?

Applying Newton's Second Law to Horizontal Motion

Example 3.5 demonstrates how to use Newton's second law to predict the average acceleration of a lacrosse ball. In this situation, air resistance is assumed to be negligible to simplify the problem.

Example 3.5

A lacrosse player exerts an average net horizontal force of 2.8 N [forward] on a 0.14-kg lacrosse ball while running with it in the net of his stick (Figure 3.36). Calculate the average horizontal acceleration of the ball while in contact with the lacrosse net.

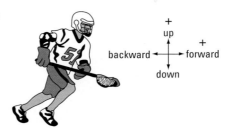

▲ **Figure 3.36**

Given

$\vec{F}_{net} = 2.8$ N [forward]

$m = 0.14$ kg

Required

average horizontal acceleration of ball ($\vec{a}$)

Analysis and Solution

The ball is not accelerating up or down.
So in the vertical direction, $\vec{F}_{net} = 0$ N.
In the horizontal direction, the acceleration of the ball is in the direction of the net force. So use the scalar form of Newton's second law.

$$F_{net} = ma$$
$$a = \frac{F_{net}}{m}$$
$$= \frac{2.8 \text{ N}}{0.14 \text{ kg}}$$
$$= \frac{2.8 \text{ kg} \cdot \frac{m}{s^2}}{0.14 \text{ kg}}$$
$$= 20 \text{ m/s}^2$$
$$\vec{a} = 20 \text{ m/s}^2 \text{ [forward]}$$

Paraphrase

The average acceleration of the lacrosse ball is 20 m/s² [forward].

Practice Problems

1. The net force acting on a 6.0-kg grocery cart is 12 N [left]. Calculate the acceleration of the cart.

2. A net force of 34 N [forward] acts on a curling stone causing it to accelerate at 1.8 m/s² [forward] on a frictionless icy surface. Calculate the mass of the curling stone.

Answers

1. 2.0 m/s² [left]

2. 19 kg

In Example 3.6, a free-body diagram is used to first help determine the net force acting on a canoe. Then Newton's second law is applied to predict the average acceleration of the canoe.

Example 3.6

Two athletes on a team, A and B, are practising to compete in a canoe race (Figure 3.37). Athlete A has a mass of 70 kg, B a mass of 75 kg, and the canoe a mass of 20 kg. Athlete A can exert an average force of 400 N [forward] and B an average force of 420 N [forward] on the canoe using the paddles. During paddling, the magnitude of the water resistance on the canoe is 380 N. Calculate the average acceleration of the canoe from the starting point.

◀ **Figure 3.37**

Practice Problem

1. In the men's four-man bobsled event in the Winter Olympics, the maximum mass of a bobsled with two riders, a pilot, and a brakeman is 630 kg (Figure 3.39).

▲ **Figure 3.39**

During a practice run, riders A and B accelerate a bobsled of mass 255 kg, a pilot of mass 98 kg, and a brakeman of mass 97 kg, then jump in for the challenging ride down a 1300-m course. Riders A and B exert average forces of magnitudes 1220 N and 1200 N respectively on the bobsled. During the pushing, the magnitude of the force of friction acting on the bobsled is 430 N. Calculate the average acceleration of the bobsled, pilot, and brakeman.

Answer

1. 4.4 m/s² [forward]

Given

$m_A = 70$ kg $\qquad m_B = 75$ kg $\qquad m_c = 20$ kg

$\vec{F}_A = 400$ N [forward] $\qquad \vec{F}_B = 420$ N [forward]

$\vec{F}_f = 380$ N [backward]

Required

average acceleration of canoe ($\vec{a}$)

Analysis and Solution

The canoe and athletes are a system because they move together as a unit. Find the total mass of the system.

$$m_T = m_A + m_B + m_c$$

$$= 70 \text{ kg} + 75 \text{ kg} + 20 \text{ kg}$$

$$= 165 \text{ kg}$$

Draw a free-body diagram for the system (Figure 3.38).

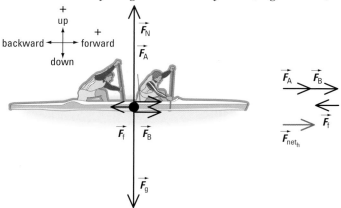

▲ **Figure 3.38**

The system is not accelerating up or down.
So in the vertical direction, $F_{net_v} = 0$ N.
Write equations to find the net force on the system in both the horizontal and vertical directions.

horizontal direction

$$\vec{F}_{net_h} = \vec{F}_A + \vec{F}_B + \vec{F}_f$$

$$F_{net_h} = F_A + F_B + F_f$$

$$= 400 \text{ N} + 420 \text{ N} + (-380 \text{ N})$$

$$= 400 \text{ N} + 420 \text{ N} - 380 \text{ N}$$

$$= 440 \text{ N}$$

vertical direction

$$\vec{F}_{net_v} = \vec{F}_N + \vec{F}_g$$

$$F_{net_v} = 0$$

Calculations in the vertical direction are not required in this problem.

Apply Newton's second law to the horizontal direction.

$$F_{net_h} = m_T a$$

$$a = \frac{F_{net_h}}{m_T}$$

$$= \frac{440 \text{ N}}{165 \text{ kg}}$$

$$= \frac{440 \frac{\text{kg} \cdot \text{m}}{\text{s}^2}}{165 \text{ kg}}$$

$$= 2.7 \text{ m/s}^2$$

$$\vec{a} = 2.7 \text{ m/s}^2 \text{ [forward]}$$

Paraphrase
The canoe will have an average acceleration of 2.7 m/s² [forward].

Applying Newton's Second Law to Vertical Motion

Example 3.7 demonstrates how to apply Newton's second law to determine the vertical acceleration of a person riding an elevator. To determine the net force on the elevator, use a free-body diagram.

Example 3.7

A person and an elevator have a combined mass of 6.00×10^2 kg (Figure 3.40). The elevator cable exerts a force of 6.50×10^3 N [up] on the elevator. Find the acceleration of the person.

Given

$$m_T = 6.00 \times 10^2 \text{ kg}$$

$$\vec{F}_T = 6.50 \times 10^3 \text{ N [up]}$$

$$\vec{g} = 9.81 \text{ m/s}^2 \text{ [down]}$$

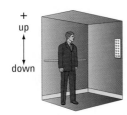

Required
acceleration of person ($\vec{a}$)

▲ **Figure 3.40**

Analysis and Solution
Draw a free-body diagram for the person-elevator system [Figure 3.41 (a)].

The system is not accelerating left or right.

So in the horizontal direction, $\vec{F}_{net} = 0$ N.

Since the person is standing on the elevator floor, both the person and the elevator will have the same vertical acceleration.

▲ **Figure 3.41 (a)**

For the vertical direction, write an equation to find the net force on the system [Figure 3.41 (b)].

$$\vec{F}_{net} = \vec{F}_T + \vec{F}_g$$

Apply Newton's second law.

$$m\vec{a} = \vec{F}_T + \vec{F}_g$$

$$ma = F_T + F_g$$

$$ma = F_T + mg$$

$$a = \frac{F_T}{m} + g$$

$$= \frac{6.50 \times 10^3 \text{ N}}{6.00 \times 10^2 \text{ kg}} + (-9.81 \text{ m/s}^2)$$

$$= \frac{6.50 \times 10^3 \ \frac{\text{kg}\cdot\text{m}}{\text{s}^2}}{6.00 \times 10^2 \ \text{kg}} - 9.81 \text{ m/s}^2$$

$$= 1.02 \text{ m/s}^2$$

$$\vec{a} = 1.02 \text{ m/s}^2 \text{ [up]}$$

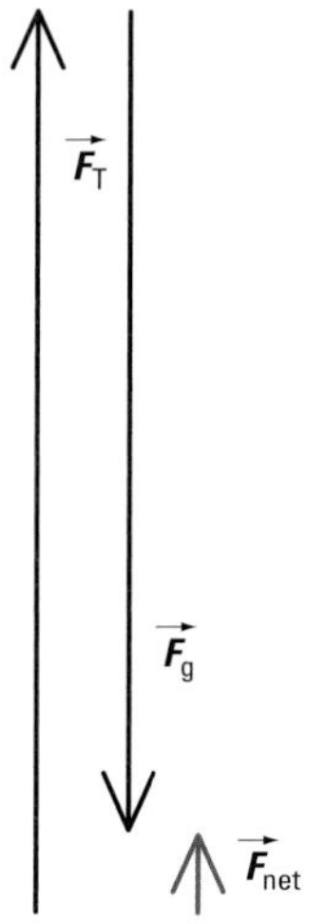

Paraphrase

The acceleration of the person is 1.02 m/s² [up].

▲ **Figure 3.41 (b)**

Practice Problems

1. The person in Example 3.7 rides the same elevator when the elevator cable exerts a force of 5.20×10^3 N [up] on the elevator. Find the acceleration of the person.

2. An electric chain hoist in a garage exerts a force of 2.85×10^3 N [up] on an engine to remove it from a car. The acceleration of the engine is 1.50 m/s² [up]. What is the mass of the engine?

Answers

1. 1.14 m/s² [down]
2. 252 kg

e WEB

Air resistance is the frictional force that acts on all objects falling under the influence of gravity. Research how this force affects the maximum speed that an object reaches during its fall. Write a brief summary of your findings. Begin your search at www.pearsoned.ca/school/physicssource.

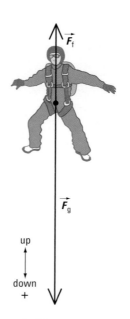

▲ **Figure 3.42**

In Example 3.8, the force of gravity causes a skydiver to accelerate downward. Since the only motion under consideration is that of the skydiver and the direction of motion is down, it is convenient to choose *down* to be positive.

Example 3.8

A skydiver is practising jumping out of an airplane. During the first few seconds of one jump, the parachute is unopened, and the magnitude of the air resistance acting on the skydiver is 250 N. The acceleration of the skydiver during this time is 5.96 m/s² [down]. Calculate the mass of the skydiver.

Given

$\vec{F}_f = 250$ N [up] $\vec{a} = 5.96$ m/s² [down]

$\vec{g} = 9.81$ m/s² [down]

Required

mass of skydiver (m)

Analysis and Solution

Draw a free-body diagram for the skydiver (Figure 3.42).
The skydiver is not accelerating left or right. So in the horizontal direction, $\vec{F}_{net} = 0$ N.
For the vertical direction, write an equation to find the net force on the skydiver (Figure 3.43).

$$\vec{F}_{net} = \vec{F}_g + \vec{F}_f$$

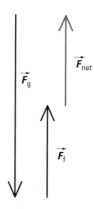

▲ **Figure 3.43**

Apply Newton's second law.

$$m\vec{a} = \vec{F}_g + \vec{F}_f$$

$$ma = F_g + F_f$$

$$m(5.96 \text{ m/s}^2) = mg + (-250 \text{ N})$$

$$= m(9.81 \text{ m/s}^2) - 250 \text{ N}$$

$$250 \text{ N} = m(9.81 \text{ m/s}^2) - m(5.96 \text{ m/s}^2)$$

$$= m(9.81 \text{ m/s}^2 - 5.96 \text{ m/s}^2)$$

$$= m(3.85 \text{ m/s}^2)$$

$$m = \frac{250 \text{ N}}{3.85 \text{ m/s}^2}$$

$$= \frac{250 \text{ kg} \cdot \frac{\not{m}}{\not{s}^2}}{3.85 \frac{\not{m}}{\not{s}^2}}$$

$$= 64.9 \text{ kg}$$

Paraphrase
The mass of the skydiver is 64.9 kg.

Applying Newton's Second Law to Two-Body Systems

When two objects are connected by a light rope as in Example 3.9, applying a force on one of the objects will cause both objects to accelerate at the same rate and in the same direction. In other words, the applied force can be thought to act on a single object whose mass is equivalent to the total mass.

Example 3.9

Two blocks of identical material are connected by a light rope on a level surface (Figure 3.44). An applied force of 55 N [right] causes the blocks to accelerate. While in motion, the magnitude of the force of friction on the blocks is 44.1 N. Calculate the acceleration of the blocks.

Given
$m_A = 20$ kg
$m_B = 10$ kg
$\vec{F}_{app} = 55$ N [right]
$\vec{F}_f = 44.1$ N [left]

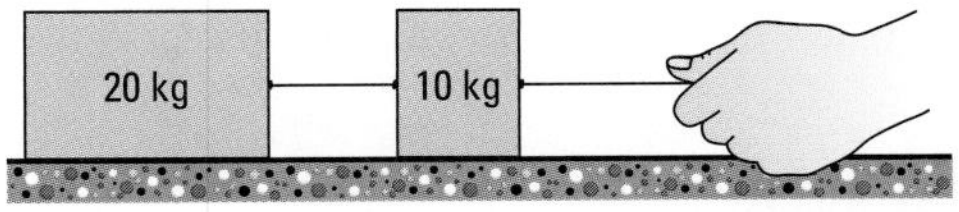

▲ **Figure 3.44**

Required
acceleration ($\vec{a}$)

Analysis and Solution
The two blocks move together as a unit with the same acceleration. So consider the blocks to be a single object. Find the total mass of both blocks.

$$m_T = m_A + m_B$$

$$= 20 \text{ kg} + 10 \text{ kg}$$

$$= 30 \text{ kg}$$

Practice Problems

1. A 55-kg female bungee jumper fastens one end of the cord (made of elastic material) to her ankle and the other end to a bridge. Then she jumps off the bridge. As the cord is stretching, it exerts an elastic force directed up on her. Calculate her acceleration at the instant the cord exerts an elastic force of 825 N [up] on her.

2. During a bungee jump, the velocity of the 55-kg woman at the lowest point is zero and the cord stretches to its maximum.
   (a) Compare the direction of her acceleration at this point to the part of the jump where she is accelerating due to gravity.
   (b) At this point, what is the direction of her acceleration?

Answers
1. 5.2 m/s² [up]
2. (b) up

Practice Problems

1. Two buckets of nails are hung one above the other and are pulled up to a roof by a rope. Each bucket has a mass of 5.0 kg. The tension in the rope connecting the buckets is 60 N. Calculate the acceleration of the buckets.

2. Refer to Example 3.9. The force of friction on the 10-kg block has a magnitude of 14.7 N.
   (a) Calculate the tension in the rope connecting the two blocks.
   (b) Calculate the tension in the rope between the hand and the 10-kg block.

Answers
1. 2.2 m/s² [up]
2. (a) 37 N
   (b) 55 N

Draw a free-body diagram for this single object (Figure 3.45). The single object is not accelerating up or down.
So in the vertical direction, $\vec{F}_{net} = 0$ N.
Write equations to find the net force on the single object in both the horizontal and vertical directions.

horizontal direction

$$\vec{F}_{net_h} = \vec{F}_{app} + \vec{F}_f$$

Apply Newton's second law.

$$m_T \vec{a} = \vec{F}_{app} + \vec{F}_f$$

$$m_T a = F_{app} + F_f$$

$$a = \frac{F_{app} + F_f}{m_T}$$

$$= \frac{55 \text{ N} + (-44.1 \text{ N})}{30 \text{ kg}}$$

$$= 0.36 \text{ m/s}^2$$

$$\vec{a} = 0.36 \text{ m/s}^2 \text{ [right]}$$

vertical direction

$$\vec{F}_{net_v} = \vec{F}_N + \vec{F}_g$$

$$F_{net_v} = 0$$

Calculations in the vertical direction are not required in this problem.

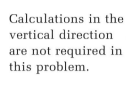
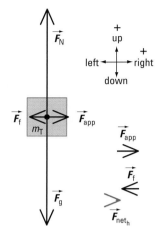

▲ Figure 3.45

Paraphrase
The acceleration of the blocks is 0.36 m/s² [right].

Applying Newton's Second Law to a Single Pulley System

e SIM

Apply Newton's second law to determine the motion of two blocks connected by a string over a pulley. Follow the eSim links at www.pearsoned.ca/school/physicssource.

In Example 3.10, two objects are attached by a rope over a pulley. The objects, the rope, and the pulley form a system. You can assume that the rope has a negligible mass and thickness, and the rope does not stretch or break.

To simplify calculations in this physics course, you need to also assume that a pulley has negligible mass and has no frictional forces acting on its axle(s).

In Example 3.10, the external forces on the system are the gravitational forces acting on the hanging objects. The internal forces on the system are the forces along the string that pull on each object. The magnitude of both the internal and external forces acting on the system are not affected by the pulley. The pulley simply redirects the forces along the string that pulls on each object.

Example 3.10

Two objects, A and B, are connected by a light rope over a light, frictionless pulley (Figure 3.46). A has a mass of 25 kg and B a mass of 35 kg. Determine the motion of each object once the objects are released.

Given

$$m_A = 25 \text{ kg} \qquad m_B = 35 \text{ kg}$$

$$\vec{g} = 9.81 \text{ m/s}^2 \text{ [down]}$$

Required
acceleration of each object ($\vec{a}_A$ and $\vec{a}_B$)

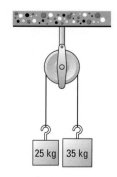

▲ Figure 3.46

Analysis and Solution

The difference in mass between objects A and B will provide the net force that will accelerate both objects. Since $m_B > m_A$, you would expect m_B to accelerate down while m_A accelerates up.
The rope has a negligible mass.
So the tension in the rope is the same on both sides of the pulley.
The rope does not stretch.
So the magnitude of $\vec{a}_A$ is equal to the magnitude of $\vec{a}_B$.
Find the total mass of both objects.

$$m_T = m_A + m_B$$
$$= 25 \text{ kg} + 35 \text{ kg}$$
$$= 60 \text{ kg}$$

Choose an equivalent system in terms of m_T to analyze the motion [Figure 3.47 (a)].

left ←———→ right $\vec{F}_A$ m_T $\vec{F}_B$

▲ **Figure 3.47 (a)**

$\vec{F}_A$ is equal to the gravitational force acting on m_A, and $\vec{F}_B$ is equal to the gravitational force acting on m_B.
Apply Newton's second law to find the net force acting on m_T [Figure 3.47 (b)].

$$\vec{F}_{net} = \vec{F}_A + \vec{F}_B$$
$$F_{net} = F_A + F_B$$
$$= -m_A g + m_B g$$
$$= (m_B - m_A)g$$
$$= (35 \text{ kg} - 25 \text{ kg})(9.81 \text{ m/s}^2)$$
$$= 98.1 \, \frac{\text{kg} \cdot \text{m}}{\text{s}^2}$$
$$= 98.1 \text{ N}$$

$\vec{F}_A$
$\vec{F}_B$
$\vec{F}_{net}$

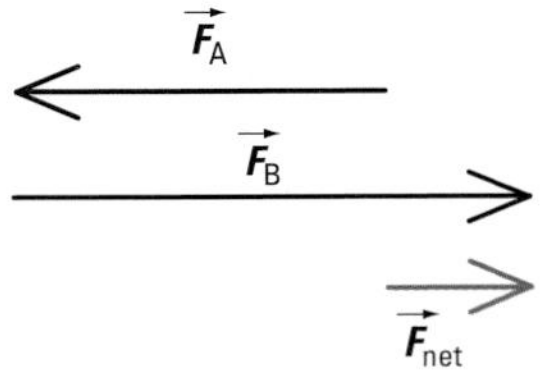

▲ **Figure 3.47 (b)**

Use the scalar form of Newton's second law to calculate the magnitude of the acceleration.

$$F_{net} = m_T a$$
$$a = \frac{F_{net}}{m_T}$$
$$= \frac{98.1 \text{ N}}{60 \text{ kg}}$$
$$= \frac{98.1 \, \frac{\text{kg} \cdot \text{m}}{\text{s}^2}}{60 \text{ kg}}$$
$$= 1.6 \text{ m/s}^2$$

$\vec{a}_A = 1.6 \text{ m/s}^2$ [up] and $\vec{a}_B = 1.6 \text{ m/s}^2$ [down]

Paraphrase
Object A will have an acceleration of 1.6 m/s² [up] and object B will have an acceleration of 1.6 m/s² [down].

Practice Problems

1. Determine the acceleration of the system shown in Example 3.10 for each situation below. State the direction of motion for each object. Express your answer in terms of g.

   (a) $m_A = \left(\frac{1}{3}\right)m_B$

   (b) $m_A = 2m_B$

   (c) $m_A = m_B$

2. Use the result of Example 3.10 and a free-body diagram to calculate the tension in the rope.

3. Draw a free-body diagram for each object in Example 3.10.

Answers

1. (a) $a = \frac{1}{2}g$, m_A moves up, m_B moves down

   (b) $a = \frac{1}{3}g$, m_A moves down, m_B moves up

   (c) $a = 0$, neither mass moves

2. 2.9×10^2 N

3.

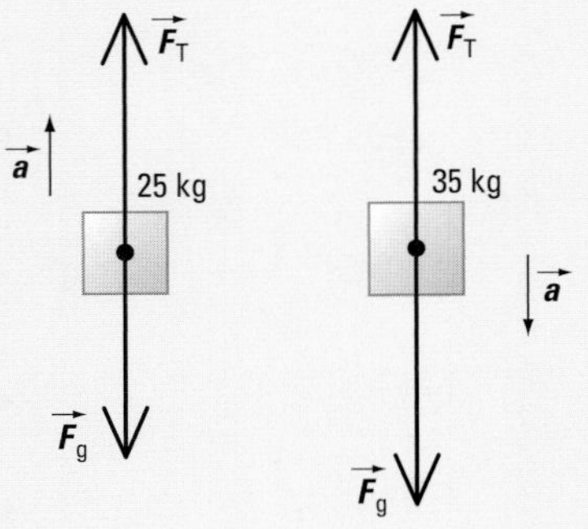

$\vec{F}_T$ $\vec{F}_T$
$\vec{a}$ 25 kg   35 kg $\vec{a}$
$\vec{F}_g$ $\vec{F}_g$

Applying Newton's Second Law to a Two-Pulley System

In Example 3.11, the system is made up of three objects (A, B, and C). As in Example 3.10, the difference in weight between objects B and C will provide the net force that will accelerate the system.

Example 3.11

A 20-kg truck tire (object A) is lying on a horizontal, frictionless surface. The tire is attached to two light ropes that pass over light, frictionless pulleys to hanging pails B and C (Figure 3.48). Pail B has a mass of 8.0 kg and C a mass of 6.0 kg. Calculate the magnitude of the acceleration of the system.

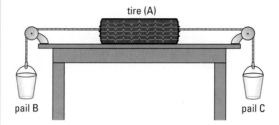

tire (A)

pail B   pail C

▲ **Figure 3.48**

Given

$m_A = 20$ kg $m_B = 8.0$ kg $m_C = 6.0$ kg

$\vec{g} = 9.81$ m/s² [down]

Required

magnitude of the acceleration of the system (a)

Analysis and Solution

Since $m_B > m_C$, you would expect m_B to accelerate down while m_C accelerates up. Since object A will accelerate left, choose left to be positive.

The rope has a negligible mass and the rope does not stretch.

So the magnitude of $\vec{a}_A$ is equal to the magnitude of $\vec{a}_B$, which is also equal to $\vec{a}_C$.

Find the total mass of the system.

$m_T = m_A + m_B + m_C$

$\quad = 20$ kg $+ 8.0$ kg $+ 6.0$ kg

$\quad = 34.0$ kg

Choose an equivalent system in terms of m_T to analyze the motion (Figure 3.49).

+
left ←——→ right

$\vec{F}_B$ m_T $\vec{F}_C$

▲ **Figure 3.49**

$\vec{F}_B$ is equal to the gravitational force acting on m_B, and $\vec{F}_C$ is equal to the gravitational force acting on m_C.

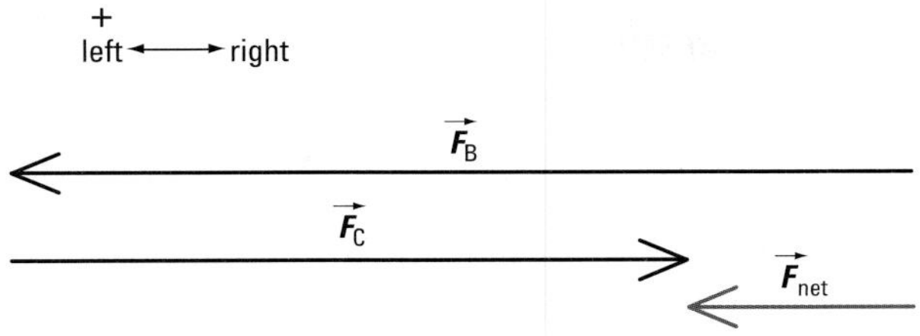

▲ **Figure 3.50**

Apply Newton's second law to find the net force acting on m_T (Figure 3.50).

$$\vec{F}_{net} = \vec{F}_B + \vec{F}_C$$

$$\begin{aligned} F_{net} &= F_B + F_C \\ &= m_B g - m_C g \\ &= (m_B - m_C)g \\ &= (8.0 \text{ kg} - 6.0 \text{ kg})(9.81 \text{ m/s}^2) \\ &= 19.6 \frac{\text{kg}\cdot\text{m}}{\text{s}^2} \\ &= 19.6 \text{ N} \end{aligned}$$

Use the scalar form of Newton's second law to calculate the magnitude of the acceleration.

$$\begin{aligned} F_{net} &= m_T a \\ a &= \frac{F_{net}}{m_T} \\ &= \frac{19.6 \text{ N}}{34.0 \text{ kg}} \\ &= \frac{19.6 \frac{\cancel{\text{kg}}\cdot\text{m}}{\text{s}^2}}{34.0 \cancel{\text{kg}}} \\ &= 0.58 \text{ m/s}^2 \end{aligned}$$

Paraphrase

The system will have an acceleration of magnitude 0.58 m/s^2.

Practice Problems

1. Calculate the acceleration of the tire in Example 3.11 if the mass of pail B is increased to 12 kg, without changing the mass of pail C.
2. If the tire in Example 3.11 is replaced by a car tire of mass 15 kg, calculate the acceleration of each object.

Answers

1. 1.5 m/s^2 [left]
2. (A) 0.68 m/s^2 [left], (B) 0.68 m/s^2 [down], (C) 0.68 m/s^2 [up]

Knowledge

1. In your own words, state Newton's second law.

2. An applied force $\vec{F}_{app}$ acting on an object of constant mass causes the object to accelerate. Sketch graphs to show the relationship between a and F_{app} when friction is

   (a) present, and

   (b) absent.

   Refer to Student References 5.1: Graphing Techniques on pp. 872–873.

3. Sketch a graph to show the relationship between the magnitude of acceleration and mass for constant net force.

4. Explain why vehicles with more powerful engines are able to accelerate faster.

Applications

5. While in the water, a force of 320 N [up] exerted by the water on a dolphin causes the dolphin to jump up. The acceleration of the dolphin is 2.6 m/s² [up].

   (a) Calculate the mass of the dolphin.

   (b) What would be the acceleration of the dolphin if it had the same strength but half the mass?

6. An ice hut used for winter fishing is resting on a level patch of snow. The combined mass of the hut and angler inside is 80 kg. A wind exerts a horizontal force of 205 N on the hut, and causes it to accelerate. While in motion, the magnitude of the force of friction acting on the hut is 196 N. What is the acceleration of the hut?

7. Suppose the only horizontal forces acting on a 20-N object are 36 N [45°] and 60 N [125°].

   (a) What is the net force acting on the object?

   (b) Calculate the acceleration of the object.

8. Two boxes, A and B, are touching each other and are at rest on a horizontal, frictionless surface. Box A has a mass of 25 kg and box B a mass of 15 kg. A person applies a force of 30 N [right] on box A which, in turn, pushes on box B. Calculate the acceleration of the boxes.

9. A 4.0-kg oak block on a horizontal, rough oak surface is attached by a light string that passes over a light, frictionless pulley to a hanging 2.0-kg object. The magnitude of the force of friction on the 4.0-kg block is 11.8 N.

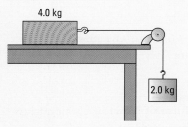

4.0 kg

2.0 kg

   (a) Calculate the acceleration of the system.

   (b) Calculate the tension in the string.

Extension

10. Summarize concepts and ideas associated with Newton's second law using a graphic organizer of your choice. See Student References 4: Using Graphic Organizers on pp. 869–871 for examples of different graphic organizers. Make sure that the concepts and ideas are clearly presented and are linked appropriately.

e TEST

To check your understanding of Newton's second law, follow the eTest links at www.pearsoned.ca/school/physicssource.

3.4 Newton's Third Law

Volleyball is a sport that involves teamwork and players knowing how to apply forces to the ball to redirect it. When the acceleration of the ball is large, a player will usually bump the ball to slow it down so that another player can redirect it over the net (Figure 3.51).

At the instant the player bumps the ball, the ball exerts a large force on the player's arms, often causing sore arms. Immediately after the interaction, the ball bounces upward. To explain the motion of each object during and after this interaction requires understanding Newton's third law.

Newton's first two laws describe the motion of an object or a system of objects *in isolation*. But to describe the motion of objects that are interacting, it is important to examine how the force exerted by one object on another results in a change of motion for both objects. Find out what happens when two initially stationary carts interact by doing 3-7 QuickLab.

info **BIT**

In order to walk, you must apply a force backward on the ground with one foot. The ground then pushes forward on that foot.

▲ **Figure 3.51** Conrad Leinemann of Kelowna, British Columbia, bumps the ball while teammate Jody Holden of Shelburne, Nova Scotia, watches during the beach volleyball competition at the 1999 Pan Am Games in Winnipeg, Manitoba.

Exploding Carts

Problem

If a stationary cart exerts a net force on another identical cart, what will be the motion of both carts after the interaction?

Materials

dynamics cart with spring
dynamics cart without spring
500-g standard mass

Procedure

1 Note the position of the spring on the one cart, and how to cock and release the spring.

2 Cock the spring and place the cart on the table. Release the spring.

> ⚠ **CAUTION: Do not cock the spring unless it is safely attached to the cart. Do not point the spring at anyone when releasing it.**

3 Repeat step 2, this time making the cart with the spring touch the second cart (Figure 3.52). Release the spring.

4 Repeat step 3 but add a 500-g standard mass to one of the carts before releasing the spring.

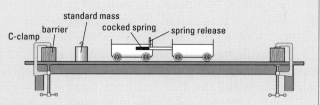

▲ **Figure 3.52**

Questions

1. What did you observe when you released the spring when the cart was initially at rest and not touching the other cart?

2. (a) What did you observe when you released the spring when one cart was touching the other cart?

(b) What evidence do you have that two forces were present?

(c) What evidence do you have that a force was exerted on each cart?

(d) How do the magnitudes and directions of the two forces compare?

3. Compare and contrast the results from steps 3 and 4.

Forces Always Exist in Pairs

action force: force initiated by object A on object B

reaction force: force exerted by object B on object A

When two objects interact, two forces will always be involved. One force is the **action force** and the other is the **reaction force**. The important points to remember are that the reaction force *always* acts on a different object than the action force, and that the reaction force acts in the opposite direction.

> ### Concept Check
>
> Is it possible to have an action force without a reaction force?

Newton's Third Law and Its Applications

Newton found that the reaction force is equal in magnitude to the action force, but opposite in direction. This relationship is called Newton's third law of motion.

> If object A exerts a force on object B, then B exerts a force on A that is equal in magnitude and opposite in direction.

$$\vec{F}_{\text{A on B}} = -\vec{F}_{\text{B on A}}$$

Some people state Newton's third law as "for every action force, there is an equal and opposite reaction force." However, remembering Newton's third law this way does not emphasize that the action and reaction forces are acting on *different* objects (Figure 3.53).

PHYSICS INSIGHT

In order to show action-reaction forces, you must draw *two* free-body diagrams, one for each object.

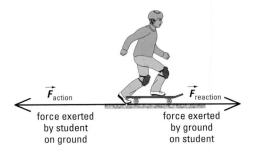

◀ **Figure 3.53** The action force is the backward force that the student exerts on the ground. The reaction force is the forward force that the ground exerts on the student.

Concept Check

If the action force is equal in magnitude to the reaction force, how can there ever be an acceleration? Explain using an example and free-body diagrams.

Action-Reaction Forces Acting on Objects in Contact

Let's revisit the scenario of the volleyball player bumping the ball. At the instant that both the ball and the player's arms are in contact, the action force is the upward force that the player exerts on the ball. The reaction force is the downward force that the ball exerts on the player's arms. During the collision, the ball accelerates upward and the player's arms accelerate downward (Figure 3.54).

TECH

Explore how a stranded astronaut can return to a spacecraft by throwing away tools. Follow the eTech links at www.pearsoned.ca/school/ physicssource.

◀ **Figure 3.54** The action-reaction forces at collision time when a volleyball player bumps the ball

A similar reasoning applies when a baseball bat strikes a baseball. The action force is the forward force that the bat exerts on the ball. The reaction force is the backward force that the ball exerts on the bat. During the collision, the ball accelerates forward and the bat slows down as it accelerates backward (Figure 3.55).

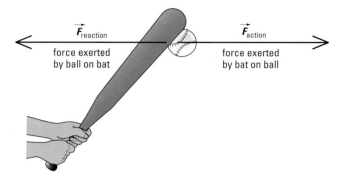

$\vec{F}_{reaction}$ $\vec{F}_{action}$

force exerted by ball on bat   force exerted by bat on ball

▲ **Figure 3.55** The action-reaction forces at collision time when a baseball bat strikes a baseball

Action-Reaction Forces Acting on Objects Not in Contact

Sometimes an object can exert a force on another without actually touching the other object. This situation occurs when an object falls toward Earth's surface, or when a magnet is brought close to an iron nail. Action-reaction forces still exist in these interactions.

When an apple falls toward the ground, the action force is the force of gravity that Earth exerts on the apple. The falling apple, in turn, exerts a reaction force upward on Earth. So while the apple is accelerating down, Earth is accelerating up (Figure 3.56).

You see the acceleration of the apple but not of Earth because the inertial mass of the apple is far less than that of Earth. In fact, Earth does accelerate but at a negligible rate because the magnitude of the acceleration is inversely proportional to mass.

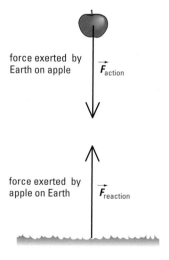

force exerted by Earth on apple $\vec{F}_{action}$

force exerted by apple on Earth $\vec{F}_{reaction}$

▲ **Figure 3.56** The action-reaction forces when an apple falls toward Earth's surface

When a magnet is brought close to an iron nail, the action force is the magnetic force that the magnet exerts on the nail. The reaction force is the force that the nail exerts on the magnet. So the nail accelerates toward the magnet, and at the same time the magnet is accelerating toward the nail (Figure 3.57).

Investigate the validity of Newton's third law by doing 3-8 QuickLab.

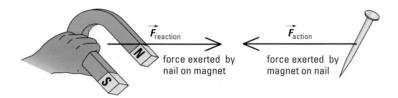

▲ **Figure 3.57** The action-reaction forces when a magnet is brought close to an iron nail

3-8 *QuickLab*

Skateboard Interactions

Problem

How does Newton's third law apply to interactions involving skateboards?

Materials

two skateboards

 CAUTION: Wear a helmet and knee pads when doing this activity.

Procedure

1 Choose a partner with a mass about the same as yours.

2 Sit on skateboards on a hard, level surface with your feet toward one another and touching (Figure 3.58).

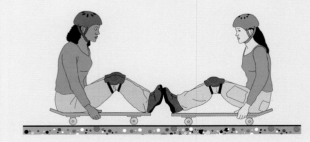

▲ **Figure 3.58**

3 Give your partner a gentle push with your feet. Observe what happens to both skateboards.

4 Repeat steps 2 and 3 but this time, give your partner a harder push. Observe what happens to both skateboards.

5 Repeat steps 2 and 3 but this time, have you and your partner push simultaneously. Observe what happens to both skateboards.

6 Choose a partner with a significantly different mass than yours.

7 Repeat steps 2 to 5 with your new partner.

8 Sit on a skateboard near a wall. Then push against the wall. Observe the motion of your skateboard.

Questions

1. Describe the motion of each skateboard when
   (a) you pushed a partner of equal mass, and
   (b) you pushed a partner of significantly different mass.

2. Compare and contrast the results from steps 4 and 5.

3. What happened to your skateboard when you pushed against the wall?

4. Explain each interaction in this activity using Newton's laws. Draw a sketch showing the action-reaction forces in each situation.

Applying Newton's Third Law to Situations Involving Frictionless Surfaces

In Example 3.12, an applied force acts on box A, causing all three boxes to accelerate. Newton's third law is used to calculate the force that box C exerts on box B.

Example 3.12

Three boxes, A, B, and C, are positioned next to each other on a horizontal, frictionless surface (Figure 3.59). An applied force acting on box A causes all the boxes to accelerate at 1.5 m/s² [right]. Calculate the force exerted by box C on box B.

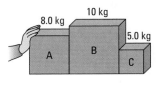

▲ **Figure 3.59**

Practice Problems

1. For the situation in Example 3.12, calculate the force that box B exerts on box A.

2. For the situation in Example 3.9 Practice Problem 1 on page 153, calculate the applied force needed to lift both buckets up.

Answers

1. 23 N [left]
2. 1.2×10^2 N [up]

Given

$m_A = 8.0$ kg $m_B = 10$ kg $m_C = 5.0$ kg

$\vec{a} = 1.5$ m/s² [right]

Required

force exerted by box C on box B ($\vec{F}_{\text{C on B}}$)

Analysis and Solution

Draw a free-body diagram for box C (Figure 3.60).

Box C is not accelerating up or down. So in the vertical direction, $\vec{F}_{\text{net}} = 0$ N. Write equations to find the net force on box C in both the horizontal and vertical directions.

horizontal direction	vertical direction
$\vec{F}_{\text{net}_h} = \vec{F}_{\text{B on C}}$	$\vec{F}_{\text{net}_v} = \vec{F}_N + \vec{F}_g$
$F_{\text{net}_h} = F_{\text{B on C}}$	$F_{\text{net}_v} = 0$

Calculations in the vertical direction are not required in this problem.

Apply Newton's second law.

$F_{\text{B on C}} = m_C a$

$\qquad = (5.0 \text{ kg})\left(1.5 \dfrac{\text{m}}{\text{s}^2}\right)$

$\qquad = 7.5 \dfrac{\text{kg} \cdot \text{m}}{\text{s}^2}$

$\qquad = 7.5$ N

$\vec{F}_{\text{B on C}} = 7.5$ N [right]

Apply Newton's third law.

$\vec{F}_{\text{C on B}} = -\vec{F}_{\text{B on C}}$

$\qquad = 7.5$ N [left]

Paraphrase

The force exerted by box C on box B is 7.5 N [left].

▲ **Figure 3.60**

Applying Newton's Third Law to Situations Involving Friction

In Example 3.13, a rough surface exerts a force of friction on two boxes. Newton's third law is used to calculate the force exerted by box B on box A in this situation.

Example 3.13

Two boxes, A and B, of identical material but different mass are placed next to each other on a horizontal, rough surface (Figure 3.61). An applied force acting on box A causes both boxes to accelerate at 2.6 m/s² [right]. If the magnitude of the force of friction on box B is 28.3 N, calculate the force exerted by box B on box A.

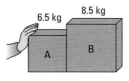

▲ **Figure 3.61**

Given

$m_A = 6.5$ kg $\qquad m_B = 8.5$ kg

$\vec{F}_{f \text{ on } B} = 28.3$ N [left] $\qquad \vec{a} = 2.6$ m/s² [right]

Required

force exerted by box B on box A ($\vec{F}_{B \text{ on } A}$)

Analysis and Solution

Draw a free-body diagram for box B (Figure 3.62). Box B is not accelerating up or down. So in the vertical direction, $\vec{F}_{net} = 0$ N. Write equations to find the net force on box B in both the horizontal and vertical directions.

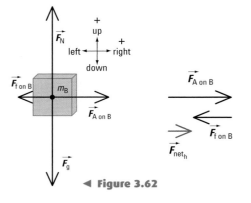

◀ **Figure 3.62**

horizontal direction

$\vec{F}_{net_h} = \vec{F}_{A \text{ on } B} + \vec{F}_{f \text{ on } B}$

$F_{net_h} = F_{A \text{ on } B} + F_{f \text{ on } B}$

vertical direction

$\vec{F}_{net_v} = \vec{F}_N + \vec{F}_g$

$F_{net_v} = 0$

Calculations in the vertical direction are not required in this problem.

Apply Newton's second law.

$m_B a = F_{A \text{ on } B} + F_{f \text{ on } B}$

$F_{A \text{ on } B} = m_B a - F_{f \text{ on } B}$

$\qquad = (8.5 \text{ kg})(2.6 \text{ m/s}^2) - (-28.3 \text{ N})$

$\qquad = (8.5 \text{ kg})(2.6 \text{ m/s}^2) + 28.3 \text{ N}$

$\qquad = 50 \text{ N}$

$\vec{F}_{A \text{ on } B} = 50 \text{ N [right]}$

Apply Newton's third law.

$\vec{F}_{B \text{ on } A} = -\vec{F}_{A \text{ on } B}$

$\qquad = 50 \text{ N [left]}$

Paraphrase

The force exerted by box B on box A is 50 N [left].

Practice Problem

1. To minimize the environmental impact of building a road through a forest, a logger uses a team of horses to drag two logs, A and B, from the cutting location to a nearby road. A light chain connects log A with a mass of 150 kg to the horses' harness. Log B with a mass of 250 kg is connected to log A by another light chain.
   (a) The horses can pull with a combined force of 2600 N. The ground exerts a force of friction of magnitude 2400 N on the logs. Calculate the acceleration of the logs.
   (b) If the force of friction on log A is 900 N, calculate the force exerted by log B on log A.

Answer

1. (a) 0.500 m/s² [forward]
   (b) 1.63 × 10³ N [backward]

Applying Newton's Second and Third Laws to Propeller Aircraft

The acceleration of many devices such as propeller aircraft can be controlled in midair. To explain how these machines accelerate involves applying Newton's second and third laws.

A propeller airplane can move through air because as the propeller rotates, it exerts an action force on the air, pushing the air backward. According to Newton's third law, the air, in turn, exerts a reaction force on the propeller, pushing the airplane forward (Figure 3.63).

Propeller blades are slanted so that they scoop new air molecules during each revolution. The faster a propeller turns, the greater is the mass of air accelerated backward and, by Newton's second law, the force exerted by the air on the propeller increases.

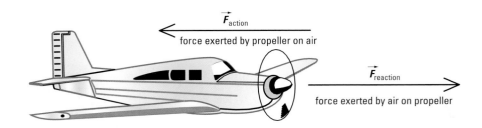

$\vec{F}_{action}$
force exerted by propeller on air

$\vec{F}_{reaction}$
force exerted by air on propeller

▲ **Figure 3.63**   The action-reaction forces when a propeller airplane is in flight

---

 THEN, NOW, AND FUTURE   **Wallace Rupert Turnbull (1870–1954)**

Wallace Rupert Turnbull was an aeronautical engineer interested in finding ways to make aircraft wings stable (Figure 3.64). In 1902, he built the first wind tunnel in Canada at Rothesay, New Brunswick, for his experiments on propeller design.

In 1909, Turnbull was awarded a bronze medal from the Royal Aeronautical Society for his research on efficient propeller design. One of his major inventions was the variable-pitch propeller, which is still used on aircraft today.

During takeoff, the angle of the blades is adjusted to scoop more air. Air moving at a high speed backward gives a plane thrust, which causes the plane to accelerate forward. Once a plane maintains a constant altitude, the blade angle, or pitch, is decreased, reducing fuel consumption. This allows greater payloads to be carried efficiently and safely through the sky.

By 1925, Turnbull had perfected a propeller that used an electric motor to change its pitch. In 1927, the Canadian Air Force successfully tested the propeller at Borden, Ontario. Turnbull was later inducted into the Canadian Aviation Hall of Fame in 1977.

Questions

1. Research the forces that act on airplanes in flight. Define these forces and compare them to forces already discussed in this chapter.

2. Explain how and where the forces on an airplane act to cause changes in its horizontal motion. Use Newton's laws and diagrams to support your explanations.

▶ **Figure 3.64**   Canadian inventor Wallace Rupert Turnbull

Applying Newton's Third Law to Rockets

The motion of rockets is a little different from that of propeller airplanes because a rocket does not have propellers that scoop air molecules. In fact, a rocket can accelerate in outer space where there is a vacuum.

When a rocket engine is engaged, the highly combustible fuel burns at a tremendous rate. The action force of the exhaust gas leaving the rocket, according to Newton's third law, causes a reaction force that pushes against the rocket. It is the action force of the exhaust gas being directed backward that accelerates the rocket forward (Figure 3.65). That is why a rocket can accelerate in outer space.

Test out Newton's third law with a toy rocket by doing 3-9 Design a Lab.

force exerted by rocket on exhaust gas

force exerted by exhaust gas on rocket

▲ **Figure 3.65**   The action-reaction forces when a rocket is in flight

3-9 *Design a Lab*

Motion of a Toy Rocket

Figure 3.66 shows a toy rocket partially filled with water about to be released from an air pump. The pump is used to add pressurized air into the rocket.

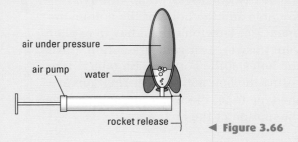

air under pressure

air pump   water

rocket release

◀ **Figure 3.66**

The Question
What effect does increasing each of these quantities have on the motion of the rocket?
• the amount of water inside the rocket
• the air pressure inside the rocket

Design and Conduct Your Investigation
• State a hypothesis. Then design and conduct an experiment to test your hypothesis. Be sure to identify all variables and to control the appropriate ones.

 Caution: Never point the rocket at anyone. Perform this activity outside.

• Compare the direction of motion of the water and the rocket when the rocket is released.
• Explain the motion of the rocket, water, and air in terms of Newton's third law. Include sketches showing at least three action-reaction pairs of forces.
• How well did your results agree with your hypothesis?

Knowledge

1. In your own words, state Newton's third law.

2. Explain why

   (a) a swimmer at the edge of a pool pushes backward on the wall in order to move forward, and

   (b) when a person in a canoe throws a package onto the shore, the canoe moves away from shore.

3. No matter how powerful a car engine is, a car cannot accelerate on an icy surface. Use Newton's third law and Figure 3.53 on page 161 to explain why.

4. State and sketch the action-reaction forces in each situation.

   (a) Water pushes sideways with a force of 600 N on the centreboard of a sailboat.

   (b) An object hanging at the end of a spring exerts a force of 30 N [down] on the spring.

Applications

5. An object is resting on a level table. Are the normal force and the gravitational force acting on the object action-reaction forces? Explain your reasoning.

6. A vehicle pushes a car of lesser mass from rest, causing the car to accelerate on a rough dirt road. Sketch all the action-reaction forces in this situation.

7. Suppose you apply a force of 10 N to one spring scale. What is the reading on the other spring scale? What is the force exerted by the anchored spring scale on the wall?

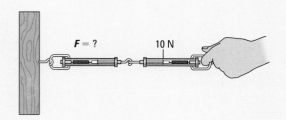

8. Blocks X and Y are attached to each other by a light rope and can slide along a horizontal, frictionless surface. Block X has a mass of 10 kg and block Y a mass of 5.0 kg. An applied force of 36 N [right] acts on block X.

   (a) Calculate the action-reaction forces the blocks exert on each other.

   (b) Suppose the magnitudes of the force of friction on blocks X and Y are 8.0 N and 4.0 N respectively. Calculate the action-reaction forces the blocks exert on each other.

9. A rectangular juice box has two holes punched near the bottom corners on opposite sides, and another hole at the top. The box is hung from a rigid support with a string. Predict what will happen if the box is filled with water through the top hole and the holes at the bottom are open. Use Newton's third law to explain your answer. Test your prediction. Cover the holes at the bottom with tape before filling the box with water. Then remove the tape to let the water out and observe the motion of the box.

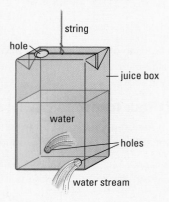

 TEST

To check your understanding of Newton's third law, follow the eTest links at www.pearsoned.ca/school/physicssource.

3.5 Friction Affects Motion

Throughout this chapter, you encountered friction in all the lab activities and when solving several problems. Friction is a force that is present in almost all real-life situations. In some cases, friction is desirable while in other cases, friction reduces the effectiveness of mechanical systems.

Without friction, you would not be able to walk. The wheels on a vehicle would have no traction on a road surface and the vehicle would not be able to move forward or backward. Parachutists would not be able to land safely (Figure 3.67).

On the other hand, friction causes mechanical parts to seize and wear out, and mechanical energy to be converted to heat. For example, snowmobiles cannot move for long distances over bare ice. Instead, snowmobilers must detour periodically through snow to cool the moving parts not in contact with the ice.

To determine the direction of the force of friction acting on an object, you need to first imagine the direction in which the object would move if there were no friction. The force of friction, then, opposes motion in that direction.

info **BIT**

Olympic cyclists now wear slipperier-than-skin suits with seams sown out of the airflow to reduce friction and improve race times by as much as 3 s.

friction: force that opposes either the motion of an object or the direction the object would be moving in if there were no friction

◄ **Figure 3.67** When a person falls in midair, the air resistance that acts on a parachute slows the fall. In this case, friction allows a parachutist to land without injury.

In a sport such as curling, friction affects how far the stone will travel along the ice. Sweeping the ice in front of a moving stone reduces the force of friction acting on the stone (Figure 3.68). The result is that the stone slides farther.

To better understand how the nature of a contact surface affects the force of friction acting on an object, do 3-10 QuickLab.

◄ **Figure 3.68** Brad Gushue, from St. John's, Newfoundland, and his team won the gold medal in men's curling at the 2006 Winter Olympics in Turin, Italy.

3-10 QuickLab

Friction Acting on a Loonie

Problem

What factors affect the ability of a loonie to start sliding?

Materials

textbook   two loonies
protractor   tape
coarse, medium, and fine sandpaper: a 10 cm × 25 cm piece of each

Procedure

1 Read the procedure and design a chart to record your results.

2 Place your textbook flat on a lab bench and place a loonie at one end of the book.

3 Slowly raise this end of the textbook until the loonie starts to slide down the incline (Figure 3.69).

Use the protractor to measure the angle the textbook makes with the lab bench when the loonie first starts to slide. Repeat this step several times, and find the average of the angles.

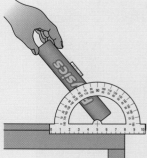

◄ **Figure 3.69**

4 Use a piece of tape to fasten the fine sandpaper on the textbook, sandy-side facing up. Repeat step 3.

5 Repeat step 4 for the medium sandpaper and then for the coarse sandpaper. Carefully remove and save the sandpaper.

6 Repeat steps 2 and 3 but this time increase the mass (not the surface area) by stacking one loonie on top of the other. Use a piece of tape between the two loonies to fasten them together.

Questions

1. How consistent were your results for each trial?

2. Explain how the angle needed to start the loonie sliding down the incline was affected by
   • the roughness of the contact surface
   • the mass of the coins (number of stacked coins) in contact with the contact surface

3. Identify the controlled, manipulated, and responding variables in this activity.

Static Friction

In 3-10 QuickLab, you discovered that the force of friction depends on the nature of the two surfaces in contact. If you drag an object on a smooth surface, the force of friction acting on the object is less than if you drag it on a rough or bumpy surface. If you drag a smooth block and a rough block on the same surface, the force of friction acting on each block will be different. Although there are different types of friction, the force of friction that acts on objects sliding across another surface is the main focus in this section.

Suppose an object A (the desk) is in contact with another object B (the floor) as in Figure 3.70. The contact surface would be the horizontal surface at the bottom of each leg of the desk.

Now suppose that a force acts on the desk, say $\vec{F}_{app}$, such that $\vec{F}_{app}$ has a vertical component as well as a horizontal component. If the desk remains at rest, even though $\vec{F}_{app}$ acts on it, then the net force on the desk is zero, $\vec{F}_{net} = 0$ N.

e SIM

Learn how friction is created and how it affects the net force on an object. Follow the eSim links at www.pearsoned.ca/school/physicssource.

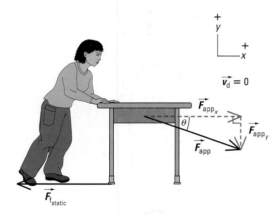

▲ **Figure 3.70** An applied force $\vec{F}_{app}$ is acting on the desk at a downward angle θ. The floor exerts a force of static friction on the bottom of each leg of the desk.

In the x direction, $F_{net_x} = 0$ N, which means that $\vec{F}_{app_x}$ must be balanced by another force. This balancing force is the **force of static friction**, $\vec{F}_{f_{static}}$. The equation for the net force acting on the desk in the x direction would then be

$$\vec{F}_{net_x} = \vec{F}_{app_x} + \vec{F}_{f_{static}}$$

$$F_{net_x} = F_{app_x} + F_{f_{static}}$$

$$0 = F_{app}\cos\theta + F_{f_{static}}$$

$$F_{f_{static}} = -F_{app}\cos\theta$$

So the direction of $\vec{F}_{f_{static}}$ opposes the x component of the applied force acting on the desk.

static friction: force exerted on an object at rest that prevents the object from sliding on another object

The Magnitude of Static Friction

An important point about static friction is that its magnitude does not have a fixed value. Instead, it varies from zero to some maximum value. This maximum value is reached at the instant the object starts to move.

If you push on a table with a force of ever-increasing magnitude, you will notice that the table remains at rest until you exceed a critical value. Because of Newton's second law, the magnitude of the force of static friction must increase as the applied force on the table increases, if the forces are to remain balanced.

Static Friction on a Horizontal Surface

Suppose the applied force acting on the desk in Figure 3.70 on page 171 is given. Example 3.14 demonstrates how to calculate the force of static friction by using a free-body diagram to help write the equation for the net force on the desk. Since $\vec{F}_{app}$ acts at an angle to the surface of the desk, it is convenient to use Cartesian axes to solve this problem.

Example 3.14

The magnitude of the applied force in Figure 3.71 is 165 N and $\theta = 30.0°$. If the desk remains stationary, calculate the force of static friction acting on the desk.

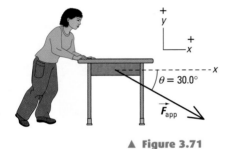

Given
magnitude of $\vec{F}_{app}$ = 165 N

$\theta = 30.0°$

▲ **Figure 3.71**

Required
force of static friction ($\vec{F}_{f_{static}}$)

Analysis and Solution
Draw a free-body diagram for the desk (Figure 3.72).

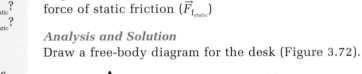

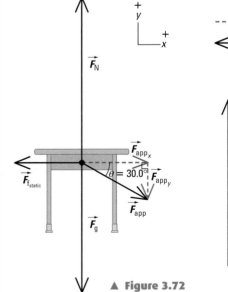

▲ **Figure 3.72**

Practice Problems

1. Refer to Example 3.14. What value of θ would
   (a) maximize the magnitude of $\vec{F}_{f_{static}}$?
   (b) minimize the magnitude of $\vec{F}_{f_{static}}$?

2. A mountain climber stops during the ascent of a mountain (Figure 3.73). Sketch all the forces acting on the climber, and *where* those forces are acting.

▲ **Figure 3.73**

Since the desk is not accelerating, $\vec{F}_{\text{net}} = 0$ N in both the x and y directions.

Write equations to find the net force on the desk in both directions.

x direction	y direction
$\vec{F}_{\text{net}_x} = \vec{F}_{\text{app}_x} + \vec{F}_{\text{f}_{\text{static}}}$	$\vec{F}_{\text{net}_y} = \vec{F}_{\text{N}} + \vec{F}_{\text{app}_y} + \vec{F}_{\text{g}}$
$F_{\text{net}_x} = F_{\text{app}_x} + F_{\text{f}_{\text{static}}}$	$F_{\text{net}_y} = 0$
$0 = F_{\text{app}_x} + F_{\text{f}_{\text{static}}}$	Calculations in the y direction are not required in this problem.

$$F_{\text{f}_{\text{static}}} = -F_{\text{app}_x}$$
$$= -(165 \text{ N})(\cos \theta)$$
$$= -(165 \text{ N})(\cos 30.0°)$$
$$= -143 \text{ N}$$

$\vec{F}_{\text{f}_{\text{static}}}$ prevents the desk from sliding in the x direction. The negative value for $F_{\text{f}_{\text{static}}}$ indicates that the direction of $\vec{F}_{\text{f}_{\text{static}}}$ is along the negative x-axis or [180°].

$$\vec{F}_{\text{f}_{\text{static}}} = 143 \text{ N } [180°]$$

Paraphrase

The force of static friction acting on the desk is 143 N [180°].

Answers

1. (a) 0°
   (b) 90.0°

2.

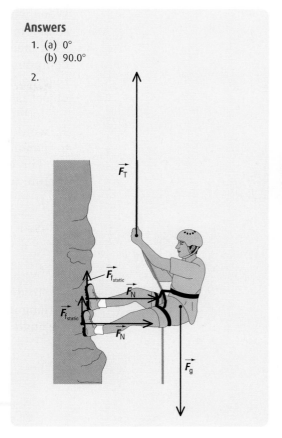

Static Friction on an Incline

If an object is at rest on an incline, the net force acting on the object is zero, $\vec{F}_{\text{net}} = 0$ N. Let's first examine the forces acting on the object (Figure 3.74).

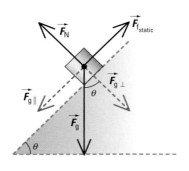

◀ **Figure 3.74** (left) Free-body diagram for an object at rest on an incline; (below) vector addition diagrams for the ∥ and ⊥ forces

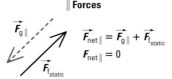

∥ **Forces**

$$\vec{F}_{\text{net} \parallel} = \vec{F}_{\text{g} \parallel} + \vec{F}_{\text{f}_{\text{static}}}$$
$$F_{\text{net} \parallel} = 0$$

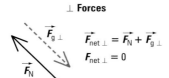

⊥ **Forces**

$$\vec{F}_{\text{net} \perp} = \vec{F}_{\text{N}} + \vec{F}_{\text{g} \perp}$$
$$F_{\text{net} \perp} = 0$$

When working with inclines, it is easier to rotate the reference coordinates so that motion along the incline is described as either uphill or downhill. This means that only the gravitational force needs to be resolved into components, one parallel to the incline $\vec{F}_{g\parallel}$ and one perpendicular to the incline $\vec{F}_{g\perp}$. Usually, uphill is chosen to be positive unless the object is accelerating downhill.

In Figure 3.74 on page 173, if there were no friction, the component $\vec{F}_{g\parallel}$ would cause the object to accelerate down the incline. So for the object to remain at rest, a balancing force $(\vec{F}_{f_{static}})$ must be acting *up* the incline.

The equation for the net force acting on the object parallel to the incline would then be

$$\vec{F}_{net\parallel} = \vec{F}_{g\parallel} + \vec{F}_{f_{static}}$$
$$F_{net\parallel} = F_{g\parallel} + F_{f_{static}}$$
$$0 = F_{g\parallel} + F_{f_{static}}$$
$$F_{f_{static}} = -F_{g\parallel}$$

To determine the expression for $\vec{F}_{g\parallel}$ requires using the geometry of a triangle. In Figure 3.75, the angle between $\vec{F}_{g\parallel}$ and $\vec{F}_g$ is $90.0° - \theta$. Since the angle between $\vec{F}_{g\parallel}$ and $\vec{F}_{g\perp}$ is $90.0°$, the angle between $\vec{F}_g$ and $\vec{F}_{g\perp}$ is θ.

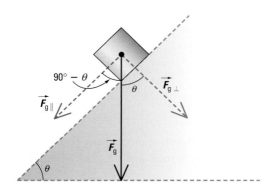

◀ **Figure 3.75** Diagram for an object at rest on an incline showing only the force of gravity vector resolved into components

Since the object is not accelerating perpendicular to the incline, the equation for the net force acting on the object in this direction is

$$\vec{F}_{net\perp} = \vec{F}_N + \vec{F}_{g\perp}$$
$$F_{net\perp} = F_N + F_{g\perp}$$
$$0 = F_N + F_{g\perp}$$
$$F_N = -F_{g\perp}$$

In 3-10 QuickLab, the sandpaper exerted a force of static friction on the loonie, preventing the coin from sliding down the incline. Example 3.15 demonstrates how to calculate the force of static friction acting on a loonie at rest on an incline of $25.0°$.

Example 3.15

A loonie with a mass of 7.0 g is at rest on an incline of 25.0° (Figure 3.76). Calculate the force of static friction acting on the loonie.

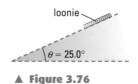

▲ **Figure 3.76**

Given
$m = 7.0$ g or 7.0×10^{-3} kg $\theta = 25.0°$
$g = 9.81$ m/s^2

Required
force of static friction ($\vec{F}_{f_{static}}$)

Analysis and Solution
Draw a free-body diagram for the loonie (Figure 3.77).

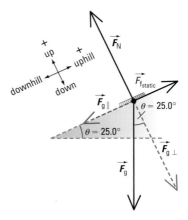

▲ **Figure 3.77**

Since the loonie is not accelerating, $\vec{F}_{net} = 0$ N both parallel and perpendicular to the incline.
Write equations to find the net force on the loonie in both directions.

⊥ direction

$\vec{F}_{net\perp} = \vec{F}_N + \vec{F}_{g\perp}$

$F_{net\perp} = 0$

Calculations in the ⊥ direction are not required in this problem.

‖ direction

$\vec{F}_{net\|} = \vec{F}_{g\|} + \vec{F}_{f_{static}}$

$F_{net\|} = F_{g\|} + F_{f_{static}}$

$F_{f_{static}} = F_{net\|} - F_{g\|}$

Now, $F_{g\|} = -mg \sin \theta$

So, $F_{f_{static}} = 0 - (-mg \sin \theta)$

$\qquad = mg \sin \theta$

$\qquad = (7.0 \times 10^{-3} \text{ kg})(9.81 \text{ m/s}^2)(\sin 25.0°)$

$\qquad = 2.9 \times 10^{-2}$ N

$\vec{F}_{f_{static}}$ prevents the loonie from sliding downhill. The positive value for $F_{f_{static}}$ indicates that the direction of $\vec{F}_{f_{static}}$ is uphill.

$\qquad \vec{F}_{f_{static}} = 2.9 \times 10^{-2}$ N [uphill]

Paraphrase

The force of static friction acting on the loonie is 2.9×10^{-2} N [uphill].

Practice Problems

1. A loonie of mass 7.0 g is taped on top of a toonie of mass 7.3 g and the combination stays at rest on an incline of 30.0°. Calculate the force of static friction acting on the face of the toonie in contact with the incline.

2. A loonie of mass 7.00 g is placed on the surface of a rough book. A force of static friction of magnitude 4.40×10^{-2} N acts on the coin. Calculate the maximum angle at which the book can be inclined before the loonie begins to slide.

Answers
1. 7.0×10^{-2} N [uphill]
2. $39.8°$

Kinetic Friction

Suppose you apply a force to the desk in Figure 3.78 and the desk starts to slide across the floor at constant velocity. In this situation, the force of static friction is not able to balance the applied force, so motion occurs. Now the floor will exert a force of friction on the desk that opposes the direction of motion of the desk. This force is the **force of kinetic friction**, $\vec{F}_{f_{kinetic}}$

Kinetic friction is present any time an object is sliding on another, whether or not another force acts on the sliding object. If you stop pushing the desk once it is in motion, the desk will coast and eventually stop. While the desk is sliding, the floor exerts a force of kinetic friction on the desk. This frictional force is directed backward, and causes the desk to eventually come to a stop.

kinetic friction: force exerted on an object in motion that opposes the motion of the object as it slides on another object

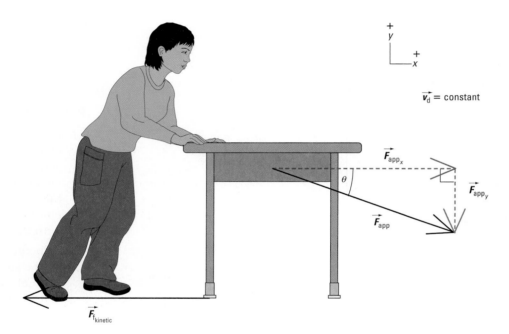

▲ **Figure 3.78** The applied force $\vec{F}_{app}$ overcomes the force of static friction acting on the desk, causing the desk to slide. While the desk is in motion, the floor exerts a force of kinetic friction that opposes the motion of the desk.

The Direction of Kinetic Friction on an Incline

If an object is on an incline and the object begins to slide, the surface of the incline exerts a force of kinetic friction on the object that opposes its motion. Whether the object is accelerating uphill or downhill, $\vec{F}_{net} \neq 0$ N parallel to the incline.

Accelerating Down an Incline

Let's first consider the case where an object accelerates downhill (Figure 3.79). In this situation, $\vec{F}_{g\parallel}$ causes the object to accelerate downhill. The force of kinetic friction acts to oppose the motion of the object. So $\vec{F}_{f_{kinetic}}$ is uphill as shown below.

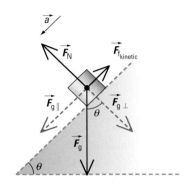

◀ **Figure 3.79** (left) Free-body diagram for an object accelerating downhill; (below) vector addition diagrams for the ∥ and ⊥ forces

∥ Forces

$$\vec{F}_{net\parallel} = \vec{F}_{g\parallel} + \vec{F}_{f_{kinetic}}$$
$$F_{net\parallel} \neq 0$$

⊥ Forces

$$\vec{F}_{net\perp} = \vec{F}_{N} + \vec{F}_{g\perp}$$
$$F_{net\perp} = 0$$

The equation for the net force acting on the object parallel to the incline is

$$\vec{F}_{net\parallel} = \vec{F}_{g\parallel} + \vec{F}_{f_{kinetic}}$$

If you apply Newton's second law, the equation for $\vec{F}_{net\parallel}$ becomes

$$m\vec{a} = \vec{F}_{g\parallel} + \vec{F}_{f_{kinetic}}$$
$$ma = F_{g\parallel} + F_{f_{kinetic}}$$

In Figure 3.79, $\vec{F}_{g\parallel}$ acts downhill and $\vec{F}_{f_{kinetic}}$ acts uphill. For the object to accelerate downhill, the net force on the object, $\vec{F}_{net\parallel}$, is directed downhill. So the magnitude of $\vec{F}_{g\parallel}$ must be greater than the magnitude of $\vec{F}_{f_{kinetic}}$.

Since the object is not accelerating perpendicular to the incline, the net force acting on the object in this direction is zero. The equation for the net force on the object in the perpendicular direction is

$$\vec{F}_{net\perp} = \vec{F}_{N} + \vec{F}_{g\perp}$$
$$F_{net\perp} = F_{N} + F_{g\perp}$$
$$0 = F_{N} + F_{g\perp}$$
$$F_{N} = -F_{g\perp}$$

Accelerating Up an Incline

If an object is accelerating uphill, the force of kinetic friction acts downhill to oppose the motion. $\vec{F}_{g\parallel}$ also acts downhill. A force, $\vec{F}_{app}$, must act uphill on the object that is great enough to overcome both $\vec{F}_{f_{kinetic}}$ and $\vec{F}_{g\parallel}$ (Figure 3.80).

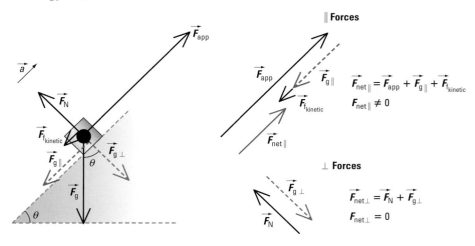

▲ **Figure 3.80**　(left) Free-body diagram for an object accelerating uphill; (right) vector addition diagrams for the ∥ and ⊥ forces

The equation for the net force acting on the object parallel to the incline is

$$\vec{F}_{net\parallel} = \vec{F}_{app} + \vec{F}_{g\parallel} + \vec{F}_{f_{kinetic}}$$

If you apply Newton's second law, the equation for $\vec{F}_{net\parallel}$ becomes

$$m\vec{a} = \vec{F}_{app} + \vec{F}_{g\parallel} + \vec{F}_{f_{kinetic}}$$

$$ma = F_{app} + F_{g\parallel} + F_{f_{kinetic}}$$

In Figure 3.80, both $\vec{F}_{g\parallel}$ and $\vec{F}_{f_{kinetic}}$ act downhill and $\vec{F}_{app}$ acts uphill. For the object to accelerate uphill, $\vec{F}_{net\parallel}$ is directed uphill. So the magnitude of $\vec{F}_{app}$ must be greater than the sum of the magnitudes of $\vec{F}_{g\parallel}$ and $\vec{F}_{f_{kinetic}}$.

Since the object is not accelerating perpendicular to the incline, the net force acting on the object in this direction is zero. The equation for the net force on the object in the perpendicular direction is

$$\vec{F}_{net\perp} = \vec{F}_{N} + \vec{F}_{g\perp}$$

$$F_{net\perp} = F_{N} + F_{g\perp}$$

$$0 = F_{N} + F_{g\perp}$$

$$F_{N} = -F_{g\perp}$$

Concept Check

What is the angle between the normal force and the force of friction? Is this angle always the same size? Explain your reasoning.

Example 3.16 demonstrates how to calculate the acceleration of a block sliding down an incline. Since the direction of motion of the block is downhill, it is convenient to choose *downhill* to be positive.

Example 3.16

A 3.5-kg block is sliding down an incline of 15.0° (Figure 3.81). The surface of the incline exerts a force of kinetic friction of magnitude 3.9 N on the block. Calculate the acceleration of the block.

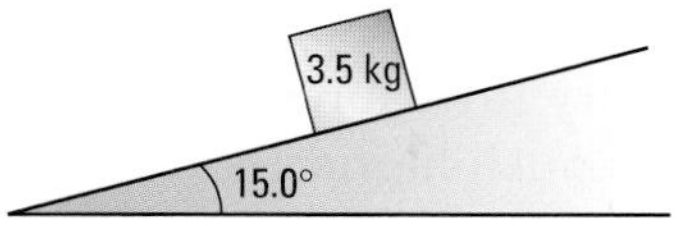

▲ **Figure 3.81**

Given

$m = 3.5$ kg $\qquad\qquad \theta = 15.0°$

magnitude of $\vec{F}_{f_{kinetic}} = 3.9$ N $\qquad g = 9.81$ m/s^2

Required
acceleration of block $(\vec{a})$

Analysis and Solution
Draw a free-body diagram for the block (Figure 3.82).

Since the block is accelerating downhill, $\vec{F}_{net} \neq 0$ N parallel to the incline, but $\vec{F}_{net} = 0$ N perpendicular to the incline.

Write equations to find the net force on the block in both directions.

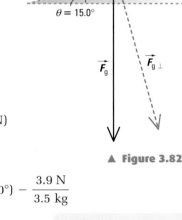

$\perp$ direction	$\parallel$ direction
$\vec{F}_{net\perp} = \vec{F}_N + \vec{F}_{g\perp}$	$\vec{F}_{net\parallel} = \vec{F}_{g\parallel} + \vec{F}_{f_{kinetic}}$
$F_{net\perp} = 0$	$F_{net\parallel} = F_{g\parallel} + F_{f_{kinetic}}$

Calculations in the $\perp$ direction are not required in this problem.

$ma = F_{g\parallel} + F_{f_{kinetic}}$

Now, $F_{g\parallel} = mg \sin\theta$

So, $ma = mg \sin\theta + (-3.9$ N$)$

$= mg \sin\theta - 3.9$ N

$a = g \sin\theta - \dfrac{3.9 \text{ N}}{m}$

$= (9.81 \text{ m/s}^2)(\sin 15.0°) - \dfrac{3.9 \text{ N}}{3.5 \text{ kg}}$

$= 1.4$ m/s^2

▲ **Figure 3.82**

The positive value for a indicates that the direction of $\vec{a}$ is downhill.

$\vec{a} = 1.4$ m/s^2 [downhill]

Paraphrase
The acceleration of the block is 1.4 m/s^2 [downhill].

Practice Problems

1. Determine the acceleration of the block in Example 3.16 if friction is not present.

2. A 55.0-kg skier is accelerating down a 35.0° slope. The magnitude of the skier's acceleration is 4.41 m/s^2. Calculate the force of kinetic friction that the snowy surface exerts on the skis.

Answers

1. 2.5 m/s^2 [downhill]
2. 66.9 N [uphill]

Comparing the Magnitudes of Static and Kinetic Friction

The magnitude of the force of kinetic friction is *never* greater than the maximum magnitude of the force of static friction. Often, the magnitude of $\vec{F}_{f_{kinetic}}$ is *less* than the magnitude of $\vec{F}_{f_{static}}$.

Figure 3.83 shows a graph of a situation where a person is applying very little force to an object during the first 2 s. Then the person begins to push harder, and at $t = 4$ s, the object starts to move. The graph does not provide any information about the applied force after 4 s.

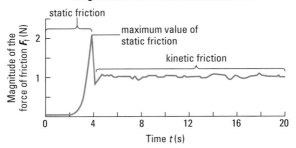

Magnitude of the Force of Friction vs. Time

◀ **Figure 3.83** The force of static friction increases up to a maximum value.

> ### Concept Check
>
> Explain why it makes sense that the magnitude of the force of kinetic friction does not exceed the maximum magnitude of the force of static friction.

Determining the Magnitude of Frictional Forces

e WEB

Leonardo da Vinci was as creative in science as he was in art. Research some of da Vinci's scientific ideas. Write a brief report of your findings, including diagrams where appropriate. Begin your search at www.pearsoned.ca/school/physicssource.

Leonardo da Vinci (1452–1519) was one of the first people to experimentally determine two important relationships about friction. He discovered that for hard contact surfaces, the force of friction does *not* depend on the contact surface area. If you push a heavy box across the floor, the force of friction acting on the box is the same whether you push it on its bottom or on its side [Figure 3.84 (a) and (b)].

Da Vinci also discovered that the force of friction acting on an object depends on the normal force acting on that object. Find out what this relationship is by doing 3-11 Inquiry Lab.

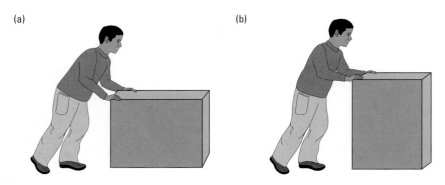

(a)   (b)

▲ **Figure 3.84** The force of friction acting on the box in each of these pictures is the same. For hard contact surfaces, the force of friction does not depend on contact surface area.

Relating Static Friction and the Normal Force

Question

What is the relationship between the maximum magnitude of the force of static friction and the magnitude of the normal force acting on an object?

Hypothesis

State a hypothesis relating the magnitude of $\vec{F}_{f_{static}}$ and the magnitude of $\vec{F}_N$. Write an "if/then" statement.

Variables

Read the procedure and identify the controlled, manipulated, and responding variable(s).

Materials and Equipment

balance
wooden block with different face areas and a hook
horizontal board
spring scale, calibrated in newtons
set of standard masses

Procedure

1. Read the steps of the procedure and design a chart to record your results.

2. Measure the mass of the block using the balance.

3. Place the largest face of the block on the horizontal board. Attach the spring scale to the block. Pull with an ever-increasing horizontal force until the block just starts to move. Record this force, which is the maximum magnitude of the force of static friction.

4. Increase the mass of the block system by placing a standard mass on the upper surface. Record the total mass of the block with the standard mass. Use the spring scale to determine the maximum magnitude of the force of static friction for this system (Figure 3.85).

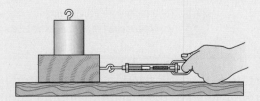

▲ **Figure 3.85**

5. Repeat step 4 three more times, increasing the added mass each time until you have five different masses and five corresponding maximum magnitudes of static friction.

6. Calculate the magnitude of the weight corresponding to each mass system. Record the magnitude of the normal force.

7. (a) Graph the maximum magnitude of the force of static friction as a function of the magnitude of the normal force.

   (b) Draw the line of best fit and calculate the slope of the graph.

Analysis

1. Describe the graph you drew in step 7.

2. As the magnitude of the normal force acting on the mass system increased, what happened to the maximum magnitude of the force of static friction?

3. What is the relationship between the maximum magnitude of the force of static friction and the magnitude of the normal force? Write this as a proportionality statement. Does this relationship agree with your hypothesis?

4. On a level surface, how does the magnitude of the weight of an object affect the magnitude of the normal force and the maximum magnitude of the force of static friction?

5. Explain why adding a bag of sand to the trunk of a rear-wheel-drive car increases its traction.

6. Design and conduct an experiment to verify that contact surface area does not affect the maximum magnitude of the force of static friction for a sliding object. Identify the controlled, manipulated, and responding variables. Analyze your data and form conclusions.

e **LAB**

For a probeware activity, go to
www.pearsoned.ca/school/physicssource.

How will the force of static friction acting on each vehicle in the Unit II Project on page 232 affect the stopping distance?

How will the types of treads of the tires affect the force of static friction?

coefficient of static friction: proportionality constant relating $(F_{f_{static}})_{max}$ and F_N

Coefficient of Static Friction

In 3-11 Inquiry Lab, you found that the maximum magnitude of the force of static friction is directly proportional to the magnitude of the normal force. This proportionality can be written mathematically:

$$(F_{f_{static}})_{max} \propto F_N$$

As an equation, the relationship is

$$(F_{f_{static}})_{max} = \mu_s F_N$$

where μ_s is a proportionality constant called the **coefficient of static friction**. Since the magnitude of the force of static friction can be anywhere from zero to some maximum value just before motion occurs, the general equation for the magnitude of the force of static friction must have an inequality sign.

$$F_{f_{static}} \leq \mu_s F_N \text{ for static friction}$$

Coefficient of Kinetic Friction

Find out how the force of kinetic friction acting on an object is related to the normal force on that object by doing 3-12 Design a Lab.

3-12 *Design a Lab*

Relating Kinetic Friction and the Normal Force

In this lab, you will investigate the relationship between the force of kinetic friction acting on an object and the normal force acting on that object.

The Question

What is the relationship between the magnitude of the force of kinetic friction and the magnitude of the normal force acting on an object?

Design and Conduct Your Investigation

- State a hypothesis relating the magnitudes of $\vec{F}_{f_{kinetic}}$ and $\vec{F}_N$.
- Then use the set-up in Figure 3.85 on page 181 to design an experiment. List the materials you will use as well as a detailed procedure. You will need to place objects of different mass on the block for each trial.
- For each trial, measure the force that must be applied to keep the block system moving at constant velocity. Then calculate the magnitude of the normal force.
- Plot a graph of $F_{f_{kinetic}}$ as a function of F_N.
- Analyze your data and form conclusions. How well did your results agree with your hypothesis?

  e **LAB**

For a probeware activity, go to www.pearsoned.ca/school/physicssource.

From 3-12 Design a Lab, just as with static friction, the magnitude of kinetic friction is directly proportional to the magnitude of the normal force. This proportionality can be written mathematically:

$$F_{f_{kinetic}} \propto F_N$$

As an equation, the relationship is

$$F_{f_{kinetic}} = \mu_k F_N \text{ for kinetic friction}$$

where μ_k is a proportionality constant called the **coefficient of kinetic friction**. The force of kinetic friction has only one value, unlike the force of static friction which varies from zero to some maximum value. So the equation for the force of kinetic friction has an equal sign, not an inequality as does the equation for the force of static friction.

coefficient of kinetic friction: proportionality constant relating $F_{f_{kinetic}}$ and F_N

Characteristics of Frictional Forces and Coefficients of Friction

There are a few important points to keep in mind about the force of friction and the variables that affect its magnitude:

- The equations for static friction and kinetic friction are not fundamental laws. Instead, they are approximations of experimental results.
- The equations $(F_{f_{static}})_{max} = \mu_s F_N$ and $F_{f_{kinetic}} = \mu_k F_N$ cannot be written as vector equations because the vectors $\vec{F}_f$ and $\vec{F}_N$ are perpendicular to each other.
- Both μ_s and μ_k are proportionality constants that have no units.
- For a given pair of surfaces, the coefficient of static friction is usually *greater* than the coefficient of kinetic friction.
- The coefficients of friction depend on the materials forming the contact surface, how smooth or rough a surface is, whether the surface is wet or dry, the temperature of the two contact surfaces, and other factors.
  Table 3.4 lists coefficients of friction between pairs of materials.

▼ **Table 3.4** Approximate Coefficients of Friction for Some Materials

Material	Coefficient of Static Friction μ_s	Coefficient of Kinetic Friction μ_k
Copper on copper	1.6	1.0
Steel on dry steel	0.41	0.38
Steel on greased steel	0.15	0.09
Dry oak on dry oak	0.5	0.3
Rubber tire on dry asphalt	1.2	0.8
Rubber tire on wet asphalt	0.6	0.5
Rubber tire on dry concrete	1.0	0.7
Rubber tire on wet concrete	0.7	0.5
Rubber tire on ice	0.006	0.005
Curling stone on ice	0.003	0.002
Teflon™ on Teflon™	0.04	0.04
Waxed hickory skis on dry snow	0.06	0.04
Waxed hickory skis on wet snow	0.20	0.14
Synovial fluid	0.01	0.01

▲ **Figure 3.86** The amount of synovial fluid present depends on the need for a joint to move in a particular direction.

How Friction Affects Motion

Movable joints in the human body, such as elbows, knees, and hips, have membranes that produce a lubricating fluid called synovial fluid. Among other factors, the amount of synovial fluid and the smoothness of adjacent bone surfaces affect the coefficients of friction in synovial joints (Figure 3.86).

The movement of synovial joints is very complicated because various biological processes are involved. In diseases such as arthritis, physical changes in joints and/or the presence of too much or too little synovial fluid affect the coefficients of friction. This, in turn, results in limited and painful movement.

The effect of temperature on the coefficients of friction plays a role in drag racing. Drag racers often warm the tires on their cars by driving for a while. Tires that are warm stick to a racing track better than cooler tires. This increased coefficient of static friction increases traction and improves the acceleration of the car.

The amount of moisture on a road surface, the temperature of the road surface and tires, and the type of tire treads are some factors that determine if a vehicle will skid. For a given tire, the coefficients of static and kinetic friction are greater on a dry road than if the same road is wet. The result is that vehicles are less likely to skid on a dry road than on a wet road.

Tire treads and road surfaces also affect the force of friction acting on a vehicle (Figure 3.87). A ribbed tire increases friction acting sideways which helps a driver steer better. A lug tread provides more traction than a ribbed tire. Slicks, the tires on drag racing cars, have no treads at all to increase the surface area of the tire in contact with the racing track to better dissipate heat.

(a)

(b)

(c)

▲ **Figure 3.87** Different types of tires: (a) a ribbed tire with chains on it for better traction on snowy and icy surfaces, (b) a lug tread, and (c) slicks on a racing car

Example 3.17 demonstrates how to use the coefficients of friction in Table 3.4 on page 183 to calculate the mass of a sled. Since the sled is at rest, the snowy surface exerts a force of static friction on the sled.

Example 3.17

A sled with waxed hickory runners rests on a horizontal, dry snowy surface (Figure 3.88). Calculate the mass of the sled if an applied force of 46 N [forward] causes the sled to start moving. Refer to Table 3.4 on page 183.

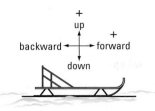

▲ **Figure 3.88**

Given

$\vec{F}_{app}$ = 46 N [forward] $\vec{g}$ = 9.81 m/s² [down]

μ_s = 0.06 from Table 3.4
(waxed hickory skis on dry snow)

Required

mass of sled (*m*)

Analysis and Solution

Draw a free-body diagram for the sled (Figure 3.89).
Since the sled is not accelerating, $\vec{F}_{net}$ = 0 N in both the horizontal and vertical directions. Write equations to find the net force on the sled in both directions.

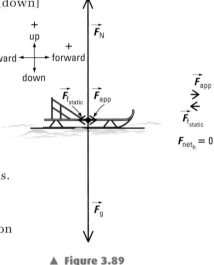

▲ **Figure 3.89**

horizontal direction	vertical direction
$\vec{F}_{net_h} = \vec{F}_{app} + \vec{F}_{f_{static}}$	$\vec{F}_{net_v} = \vec{F}_N + \vec{F}_g$
$F_{net_h} = F_{app} + F_{f_{static}}$	$F_{net_v} = F_N + F_g$
$0 = F_{app} + F_{f_{static}}$	$0 = F_N + (-mg)$
$\quad = F_{app} + (-\mu_s F_N)$	$\quad = F_N - mg$
$\quad = F_{app} - \mu_s F_N$	$F_N = mg$

$F_{app} = \mu_s F_N$

Substitute $F_N = mg$ into the equation for F_{app}.

$F_{app} = \mu_s mg$

$m = \dfrac{F_{app}}{\mu_s g}$

$\quad = \dfrac{46 \text{ N}}{(0.06)\left(9.81\dfrac{\text{m}}{\text{s}^2}\right)}$

$\quad = \dfrac{46 \text{ kg}\cdot\dfrac{\cancel{m}}{\cancel{s}^2}}{(0.06)\left(9.81\dfrac{\cancel{m}}{\cancel{s}^2}\right)}$

$\quad = 8 \times 10^2 \text{ kg}$

Paraphrase

The mass of the sled is 8×10^2 kg.

Practice Problems

1. An applied force of 24 N [forward] causes a steel block to start moving across a horizontal, greased steel surface. Calculate the mass of the block. Refer to Table 3.4 on page 183.

2. Suppose the sled in Example 3.17 is resting on a horizontal, wet snowy surface. Would the sled move if the applied force is 125 N? Explain. Refer to Table 3.4 on page 183.

Answers

1. 16 kg

2. no

In Example 3.18, a toboggan is initially at rest on a snowy hill. By knowing only the angle of the incline, it is possible to determine the coefficient of static friction for the toboggan on the hill.

Example 3.18

A 50-kg toboggan is on a snowy hill. If the hill forms an angle of at least 20.0° with the horizontal, the toboggan just begins to slide downhill (Figure 3.90). Calculate the coefficient of static friction for the toboggan on the snow.

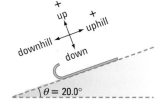

▲ **Figure 3.90**

Given

$m = 50$ kg $\qquad \theta = 20.0°$ $\qquad g = 9.81$ m/s^2

Required

coefficient of static friction (μ_s)

Analysis and Solution

Draw a free-body diagram for the toboggan [Figure 3.91 (a)]. When the angle of the incline is just enough for the toboggan to start moving, the surface of the incline is exerting the maximum magnitude of the force of static friction on the toboggan.

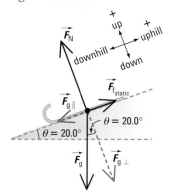

▲ **Figure 3.91 (a)**

Just before the toboggan begins to slide, $\vec{F}_{net} = 0$ N in both the parallel and perpendicular directions to the incline.

Write equations to find the net force on the toboggan in both directions [Figure 3.91 (b)].

⊥ direction	∥ direction
$\vec{F}_{net\perp} = \vec{F}_N + \vec{F}_{g\perp}$	$\vec{F}_{net\parallel} = \vec{F}_{g\parallel} + \vec{F}_{f_{static}}$
$F_{net\perp} = F_N + F_{g\perp}$	$F_{net\parallel} = F_{g\parallel} + F_{f_{static}}$
$0 = F_N + F_{g\perp}$	$0 = F_{g\parallel} + F_{f_{static}}$
$F_N = -F_{g\perp}$	$F_{f_{static}} = -F_{g\parallel}$

Now, $F_{g\perp} = -mg \cos\theta$ $\qquad F_{g\parallel} = -mg \sin\theta$

So, $F_N = -(-mg \cos\theta)$ $\qquad F_{f_{static}} = -(-mg \sin\theta)$

$ = mg \cos\theta$ $\qquad\qquad = mg \sin\theta$

$\qquad\qquad\qquad\qquad \mu_s F_N = mg \sin\theta$

$\vec{F}_{g\parallel}$

$\vec{F}_{f_{static}}$

$\vec{F}_{net\parallel} = 0$

▲ **Figure 3.91 (b)**

Substitute $F_N = mg \cos\theta$ into the last equation for the ∥ direction.

$$\mu_s(mg \cos\theta) = mg \sin\theta$$
$$\mu_s \cos\theta = \sin\theta$$
$$\mu_s = \frac{\sin\theta}{\cos\theta}$$
$$= \tan\theta$$
$$= \tan 20.0°$$
$$= 0.36$$

Paraphrase

The coefficient of static friction for the toboggan on the snow is 0.36. Note that μ_s does *not* depend on the mass of the toboggan, only on the angle of the hill.

Practice Problems

1. Calculate the coefficient of static friction if the toboggan in Example 3.18 is 20 kg and the hill forms an angle of 30.0° with the horizontal.

2. An 80-kg skier uses waxed hickory skis on wet snow. The skier starts moving down a hill forming an angle of at least 25.0° with the horizontal.
   (a) Determine the coefficient of static friction.
   (b) Calculate the maximum force of static friction on the skier.

Answers

1. 0.58
2. (a) 0.47
   (b) 3.3 × 10^2 N [uphill]

---

info **BIT**

The trigonometric function tan θ can be expressed in terms of sin θ and cos θ.

$$\tan\theta = \frac{\sin\theta}{\cos\theta}$$

Kinetic Friction Applies to Skidding Tires

When the tires of a vehicle lock or if the tires skid on a road surface, the tires no longer rotate. Instead, the tires slide along the road surface. At the area where the tire and the road are in contact, the road surface exerts a force of kinetic friction directed backward on the tire (Figure 3.92).

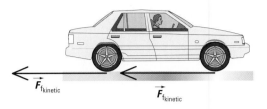

▲ **Figure 3.92** Diagram showing the force of kinetic friction acting on the tires of a skidding car

Safety features on vehicles such as anti-lock braking systems are designed to prevent the wheels of a vehicle from locking when a driver steps on the brakes. If the wheels lock, the tires no longer rotate on the road surface and the vehicle ends up skidding. As long as the wheels continue to turn, the road surface exerts a force of static friction on the tires. Anti-lock braking systems maximize the force of static friction acting on the tires, allowing the driver of a vehicle to come to a more controlled stop.

In Example 3.19, a lift truck is skidding on a concrete surface. Since the wheels are not rotating, the concrete surface is exerting a force of kinetic friction on the tires.

e TECH

Explore how the initial velocity of a skidding car and its mass affect the braking distance. Follow the eTech links at www.pearsoned.ca/school/physicssource.

e WEB

Research how anti-lock braking systems work, and identify the strengths and weaknesses. Interview a car salesperson and/or an owner. Write a brief report of your findings, including diagrams where appropriate. Begin your search at www.pearsoned.ca/school/physicssource.

Example 3.19

A 1640-kg lift truck with rubber tires is skidding on wet concrete with all four wheels locked (Figure 3.93). Calculate the acceleration of the truck. Refer to Table 3.4 on page 183.

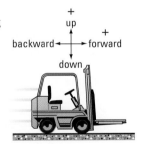

▲ **Figure 3.93**

Given

$m = 1640$ kg $\vec{g} = 9.81$ m/s^2 [down]

$\mu_k = 0.5$ from Table 3.4 (rubber on wet concrete)

Required

acceleration of lift truck ($\vec{a}$)

Analysis and Solution

Draw a free-body diagram for the lift truck (Figure 3.94).

Since the lift truck is accelerating forward, $\vec{F}_{net} \neq 0$ N in the horizontal direction, but $\vec{F}_{net} = 0$ N in the vertical direction.

Write equations to find the net force on the lift truck in both directions.

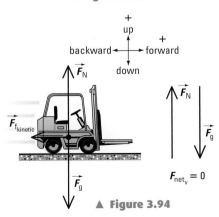

▲ **Figure 3.94**

Practice Problems

1. An applied force of 450 N [forward] is needed to drag a 1000-kg crate at constant speed across a horizontal, rough floor. Calculate the coefficient of kinetic friction for the crate on the floor.

2. Calculate the force of kinetic friction if the truck in Example 3.19 is skidding downhill at constant speed on a hill forming an angle of 15.0° with the horizontal.

Answers

1. 4.59×10^{-2}
2. 4.16×10^3 N [uphill]

horizontal direction

$$\vec{F}_{\text{net}_h} = \vec{F}_{\text{f}_{\text{kinetic}}}$$

$$F_{\text{net}_h} = F_{\text{f}_{\text{kinetic}}}$$

$$ma = F_{\text{f}_{\text{kinetic}}}$$

$$= -\mu_k F_N$$

vertical direction

$$\vec{F}_{\text{net}_v} = \vec{F}_N + \vec{F}_g$$

$$F_{\text{net}_v} = F_N + F_g$$

$$0 = F_N + (-mg)$$

$$= F_N - mg$$

$$F_N = mg$$

Substitute $F_N = mg$ into the equation for $F_{\text{f}_{\text{kinetic}}}$.

$$\cancel{m}a = -\mu_k \cancel{m}g$$

$$a = -\mu_k g$$

$$= -(0.5)\left(9.81 \frac{\text{m}}{\text{s}^2}\right)$$

$$= -5 \text{ m/s}^2$$

The negative value for a indicates that the direction of $\vec{a}$ is backward.

$$\vec{a} = 5 \text{ m/s}^2 \text{ [backward]}$$

Paraphrase

The acceleration of the truck is 5 m/s² [backward].

Example 3.20 involves a snowmobile accelerating uphill while towing a sled. Since the motion of the sled is uphill, it is convenient to choose uphill to be positive.

Example 3.20

A person wants to drag a 40-kg sled with a snowmobile up a snowy hill forming an angle of 25.0° (Figure 3.95). The coefficient of kinetic friction for the sled on the snow is 0.04. Calculate the force the snowmobile must exert to accelerate the sled at 2.5 m/s² [uphill].

▼ **Figure 3.95**

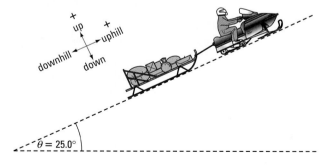

Given

$m = 40$ kg

$\theta = 25.0°$

$\mu_k = 0.04$

$g = 9.81$ m/s²

$\vec{a} = 2.5$ m/s² [uphill]

Required

applied force on sled ($\vec{F}_{\text{app}}$)

Analysis and Solution

Draw a free-body diagram for the sled (Figure 3.96).

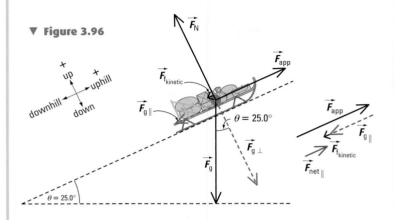

▼ Figure 3.96

Since the sled is accelerating uphill, $\vec{F}_{net} \neq 0$ N parallel to the incline, but $\vec{F}_{net} = 0$ N perpendicular to the incline.

Write equations to find the net force on the sled in both directions.

⊥ direction	∥ direction
$\vec{F}_{net\perp} = \vec{F}_N + \vec{F}_{g\perp}$	$\vec{F}_{net\parallel} = \vec{F}_{app} + \vec{F}_{g\parallel} + \vec{F}_{f_{kinetic}}$
$F_{net\perp} = F_N + F_{g\perp}$	$F_{net\parallel} = F_{app} + F_{g\parallel} + F_{f_{kinetic}}$
$0 = F_N + F_{g\perp}$	$ma = F_{app} + F_{g\parallel} + F_{f_{kinetic}}$
$F_N = -F_{g\perp}$	$F_{app} = ma - F_{g\parallel} - F_{f_{kinetic}}$

Now, $F_{g\perp} = -mg \cos \theta$
So, $F_N = -(-mg \cos \theta)$
$ = mg \cos \theta$

Also, $F_{g\parallel} = -mg \sin \theta$ and
$ F_{f_{kinetic}} = -\mu_k F_N$
$F_{app} = ma - (-mg \sin \theta)$
$\phantom{F_{app} =} - (-\mu_k F_N)$
$\phantom{F_{app}} = ma + mg \sin \theta$
$\phantom{F_{app} = ma} + \mu_k F_N$

Substitute $F_N = mg \cos \theta$ into the equation for F_{app}.

$F_{app} = ma + mg \sin \theta + \mu_k mg \cos \theta$

$\phantom{F_{app}} = ma + mg(\sin \theta + \mu_k \cos \theta)$

$\phantom{F_{app}} = (40 \text{ kg})(2.5 \text{ m/s}^2) + (40 \text{ kg})(9.81 \text{ m/s}^2) [(\sin 25.0°) + (0.04)(\cos 25.0°)]$

$\phantom{F_{app}} = 3 \times 10^2 \text{ N}$

The positive value for F_{app} indicates that the direction of $\vec{F}_{app}$ is uphill.

$\vec{F}_{app} = 3 \times 10^2 \text{ N [uphill]}$

Paraphrase

The snowmobile must apply a force of 3×10^2 N [uphill].

Practice Problems

1. A roofer is shingling a roof that rises 1.0 m vertically for every 2.0 m horizontally. The roofer is pulling one bundle of shingles (A) with a rope up the roof. Another rope connects bundle A to bundle B farther down the roof (Figure 3.97).

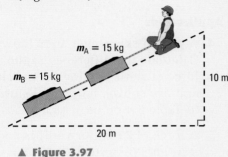

▲ Figure 3.97

Each of the two bundles of shingles has a mass of 15 kg. The coefficient of kinetic friction for the bundles on plywood sheeting is 0.50.
   (a) What force must the roofer exert up the roof to drag the bundles at constant speed?
   (b) Calculate the force exerted by bundle A on bundle B.
   (c) What total force would the roofer have to exert to accelerate both bundles at 2.0 m/s² [up roof]?

Answers
1. (a) 2.6×10^2 N [up roof]
   (b) 1.3×10^2 N [up roof]
   (c) 3.2×10^2 N [up roof]

Knowledge

1. In your own words, define friction.

2. What are some situations where friction is so small that it could be neglected?

3. Distinguish between static friction and kinetic friction.

Applications

4. A pair of skis weigh 15 N [down]. Calculate the difference in the maximum force of static friction for the skis on a wet and dry snowy, horizontal surface. Refer to Table 3.4 on page 183.

5. A force of 31 N [forward] is needed to start an 8.0-kg steel slider moving along a horizontal steel rail. What is the coefficient of static friction?

6. A biker and his motorcycle have a weight of 2350 N [down]. Calculate the force of kinetic friction for the rubber tires and dry concrete if the motorcycle skids. Refer to Table 3.4 on page 183.

7. A 15-kg box is resting on a hill forming an angle with the horizontal. The coefficient of static friction for the box on the surface is 0.45. Calculate the maximum angle of the incline just before the box starts to move.

8. The coefficient of static friction for a wheelchair with its brakes engaged on a conveyor-type ramp is 0.10. The average mass of a person including the wheelchair is 85 kg. Determine if a ramp of 8.0° with the horizontal will prevent motion.

9. A truck loaded with a crate of mass m is at rest on an incline forming an angle of 10.0° with the horizontal. The coefficient of static friction for the crate on the truck bed is 0.30. Find the maximum possible acceleration uphill for the truck before the crate begins to slip backward.

10. A loaded dogsled has a mass of 400 kg and is being pulled across a horizontal, packed snow surface at a velocity of 4.0 m/s [N]. Suddenly, the harness separates from the sled. If the coefficient of kinetic friction for the sled on the snow is 0.0500, how far will the sled coast before stopping?

Extensions

11. A warehouse employee applies a force of 120 N [12.0°] to accelerate a 35-kg wooden crate from rest across a wooden floor. The coefficient of kinetic friction for the crate on the floor is 0.30. How much time elapses from the time the employee starts to move the crate until it is moving at 1.2 m/s [0°]?

12. Make a Venn diagram to summarize the similarities and differences between static and kinetic friction. See Student References 4: Using Graphic Organizers on page 869 for an example.

13. Research how the type of tread on a tire affects the coefficients of static friction and kinetic friction given the same road surface. Find out what hydroplaning is and how tires are designed to minimize this problem. Write a brief report of your findings, including diagrams where appropriate. Begin your search at www.pearsoned.ca/school/physicssource.

14. Design an experiment to determine the coefficients of static and kinetic friction for a curling stone on an icy surface. Perform the experiment at a local arena or club. Ask the icemaker to change the temperature of the ice, and repeat the experiment to determine if there is a difference in your values. Write a brief report of your findings.

eTEST

To check your understanding of friction and inclines, follow the eTest links at www.pearsoned.ca/school/physicssource.

Key Terms and Concepts

dynamics	net force	reaction force	coefficient of
force	inertia	friction	static friction
free-body diagram	inertial mass	static friction	coefficient of
normal force	action force	kinetic friction	kinetic friction

Key Equations

Newton's first law: $\vec{F}_{net} = 0$ when $\Delta\vec{v} = 0$ Static friction: $F_{f_{static}} \leq \mu_s F_N$

Newton's second law: $\vec{F}_{net} = m\vec{a}$ Kinetic friction: $F_{f_{kinetic}} = \mu_k F_N$

Newton's third law: $\vec{F}_{A\ on\ B} = -\vec{F}_{B\ on\ A}$

Conceptual Overview

The concept map below summarizes many of the concepts and equations in this chapter. Copy and complete the map to have a full summary of the chapter.

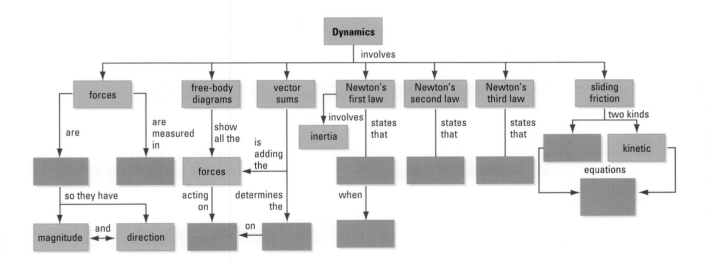

▲ **Figure 3.98**

Knowledge

1. (3.1, 3.3) Two people, A and B, are pushing a stalled 2000-kg truck along a level road. Person A exerts a force of 300 N [E]. Person B exerts a force of 350 N [E]. The magnitude of the force of friction on the truck is 550 N. Calculate the acceleration of the truck.

2. (3.2) Use a free-body diagram and Newton's first law to explain the motion of
   (a) a figure skater during a glide, and
   (b) a hockey puck during a cross-ice pass.

3. (3.4) A transport truck pulls a trailer with a force of 1850 N [E]. What force does the trailer exert on the transport truck?

4. (3.5) An inexperienced driver, stuck in snow, tends to spin the car tires to increase the force of friction exerted by the snow on the tires. What advice would you give to the driver? Why?

Applications

5. A device used to treat a foot injury is shown below. The pulley is attached to the foot, and the weight of the 3.0-kg object provides a tension force to each side of the pulley. The pulley is at rest because the foot applies a force $\vec{F}$ to the pulley, which is balanced by the forces $\vec{F}_{T_1}$ and $\vec{F}_{T_2}$ in the rope. The weight of the leg and foot is supported by the pillow.
   (a) Using a free-body diagram for the pulley, determine the force $\vec{F}$.
   (b) What will happen to the magnitude of $\vec{F}$ if the angle between $\vec{F}_{T_1}$ and $\vec{F}_{T_2}$ decreases? Why?

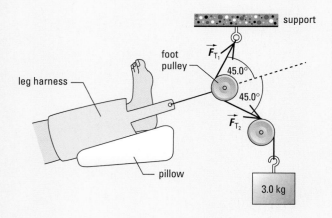

6. Refer to Example 3.6 Practice Problem 1 on page 150. In a second practice run, the initial acceleration of the bobsled, pilot, and brakeman is 4.4 m/s² [forward]. Rider A exerts an average force of magnitude 1200 N on the bobsled, and the force of friction decreases to 400 N. What average force does rider B exert?

7. During its ascent, a loaded jet of mass 4.0×10^5 kg is flying at constant velocity 20.0° above the horizontal. The engines of the plane provide a thrust $\vec{T}$ of 4.60×10^6 N [forward] to provide the lift force $\vec{L}$ [perpendicular to wings]. The air resistance $\vec{R}$ opposes the motion of the jet. Determine the magnitudes of $\vec{L}$ and $\vec{R}$.

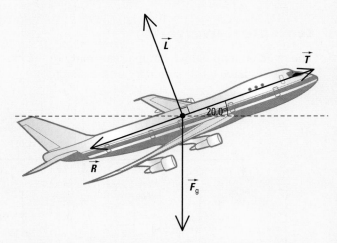

8. Suppose the force of kinetic friction on a sliding block of mass m is 2.5 N [backward]. What is the force of kinetic friction on the block if another block of mass $2m$ is placed on its upper surface?

9. A 1385-kg pickup truck hitched to a 453-kg trailer accelerates along a level road from a stoplight at 0.75 m/s² [forward]. Ignore friction and air resistance. Calculate
   (a) the tension in the hitch,
   (b) the force of friction exerted by the road on the pickup truck to propel it forward, and
   (c) the force the trailer exerts on the pickup truck.

10. Two curlers, A and B, have masses of 50 kg and 80 kg respectively. Both players are standing on a carpet with shoes having Teflon™ sliders. The carpet exerts a force of friction of 24.5 N [E] on player A and a force of friction of 39.2 N [W] on player B. Player A pushes player B with a force of 60 N [E].
    (a) Calculate the net force acting on each player.
    (b) Calculate the acceleration of each player.

11. A force of 15 N [S] moves a case of soft drinks weighing 40 N [down] across a level counter at constant velocity. Calculate the coefficient of kinetic friction for the case on the counter.

12. A 1450-kg car is towing a trailer of mass 454 kg. The force of air resistance on both vehicles is 7471 N [backward]. If the acceleration of both vehicles is 0.225 m/s², what is the coefficient of static friction for the wheels on the ground?

13. Two bags of potatoes, $m_1 = 60$ kg and $m_2 = 40$ kg, are connected by a light rope that passes over a light, frictionless pulley. The pulley is suspended from the ceiling using a light spring scale.

    (a) What is the reading on the scale if the pulley is prevented from turning?

    (b) Draw a free-body diagram for each bag when the pulley is released.

        (i) Calculate the acceleration of the system.

        (ii) Calculate the tension in the rope.

    (c) What is the reading on the scale when the bags are accelerating?

    (d) Explain the difference between your answers in parts (a) and (c).

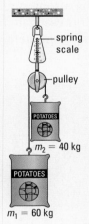

14. A drag racing car initially at rest can reach a speed of 320 km/h in 6.50 s. The wheels of the car can exert an average horizontal force of 1.52×10^4 N [backward] on the pavement. If the force of air resistance on the car is 5.2×10^3 N [backward], what is the mass of the car?

15. A tractor and tow truck have rubber tires on wet concrete. The tow truck drags the tractor at constant velocity while its brakes are locked. If the tow truck exerts a horizontal force of 1.0×10^4 N on the tractor, determine the mass of the tractor. Refer to Table 3.4 on page 183.

16. Create a problem involving an object of mass m on an incline of angle θ. Write a complete solution, including an explanation of how to resolve the gravitational force vector into components.

17. The table below shows some coefficients of static and kinetic friction (μ_s and μ_k) for rubber tires in contact with various road surfaces.

Coeffi-cient	Dry Concrete	Wet Concrete	Dry Asphalt	Wet Asphalt
μ_s	1.0	0.7	1.2	0.6
μ_k	0.7	0.5	0.6	0.5

    (a) Which road surface exerts more static friction on a rubber tire, dry concrete or dry asphalt? Explain.

    (b) On which surface does a car slide more easily, on wet concrete or on wet asphalt? Why?

    (c) On which surface will a moving car begin to slide more easily, on dry concrete or on dry asphalt? Why?

    (d) On which surface will a car with locked brakes slide a shorter distance, on dry concrete or on dry asphalt? Explain.

Extensions

18. An 80-kg baseball player slides onto third base. The coefficient of kinetic friction for the player on the ground is 0.70. His speed at the start of the slide is 8.23 m/s.

    (a) Calculate his acceleration during the slide.

    (b) For how long does he slide until he stops?

    (c) Show that the time it takes the player to come to a stop is given by the equation $\Delta t = \dfrac{v_i}{\mu_k g}$.

Consolidate Your Understanding

19. Write a paragraph explaining the similarities and differences among Newton's three laws. Include an example that involves all three laws and explain how each law applies. Use the example to teach the laws to a student who has not studied dynamics.

20. Write a paragraph describing the differences between static and kinetic friction, and between the coefficients of static and kinetic friction. Include an example with a free-body diagram for each type of friction.

Think About It

Review your answers to the Think About It questions on page 125. How would you answer each question now?

 e TEST

To check your understanding of forces and Newton's laws of motion, follow the eTest links at www.pearsoned.ca/school/physicssource.

Gravity extends throughout the universe.

Skydiving, hang-gliding, bungee jumping, and hot-air ballooning are just a few activities that involve accelerating under the influence of gravity for a thrill (Figure 4.1). Gravitational force attracts all objects in the universe. It holds you to Earth, and Earth in its orbit around the Sun.

In 1665, Isaac Newton began his study of gravity when he attempted to understand why the Moon orbits Earth. His theories led him to an understanding of the motion of planets and their moons in the solar system. Several centuries later, these theories led to the launch of satellites and the success of various space missions such as Mariner and Voyager.

Gravity is one of the four basic forces of nature, called **fundamental forces**, that physicists think underlie all interactions in the universe. These forces are the gravitational force, the electromagnetic force, the weak nuclear force, and the strong nuclear force.

In this chapter, you will investigate how gravity affects the motion of objects on Earth and on other planets, and how it affects the motion of satellites orbiting Earth.

▲ **Figure 4.1** Understanding how forces and gravity affect motion determines how successful the design of a hot-air balloon will be and the best way to navigate it.

Falling Coins

Problem

Suppose you drop two coins of different shapes and sizes from the same height. How do the rates of both coins falling compare?

Materials

variety of coins (penny, nickel, dime, quarter, loonie, and toonie)
ruler
Styrofoam™ disk (size of a loonie)

Procedure

1. Choose any two different coins and place them at the edge of a table above an uncarpeted floor.

2. Using a ruler, push the coins off the table so they leave at the same time (Figure 4.2).

3. Listen carefully for the sounds of the coins as they hit the floor.

4. Repeat this activity with different combinations of two coins, including the loonie with the Styrofoam™ disk. Record your observations.

▲ **Figure 4.2**

Questions

1. When the coins landed, how many sounds did you hear? Did all combinations of two coins give the same result? Explain.

2. If all the coins fall at the same rate, how many sounds would you expect to hear when they land?

3. How would the results compare if two coins were released at the same time from a greater height, such as 10 m?

4. How did the average acceleration of the loonie differ from that of the Styrofoam™ disk? Explain why.

Think About It

1. (a) What factors affect the weight of an astronaut during a rocket flight?

   (b) How does the astronaut's weight change?

2. What would be the motion of Earth if the Sun's gravity were zero? Assume that no other celestial bodies affect Earth.

Discuss your answers in a small group and record them for later reference. As you complete each section of this chapter, review your answers to these questions. Note any changes to your ideas.

4.1 Gravitational Forces due to Earth

info **BIT**

Gravitational force is an attraction force only. There is no such thing as a repulsive gravitational force.

gravitational force: attractive force between any two objects due to their masses

One of Newton's great achievements was to identify the force that causes objects to fall near Earth's surface as the same force that causes the Moon to orbit Earth. He called this force "gravity," and he reasoned that this force is present throughout the universe.

Gravitational force, $\vec{F}_g$, is the force that attracts any two objects together. Although this force is the weakest fundamental force, you can feel its effect when you interact with an object of very large mass such as Earth.

When you slide down a waterslide, you can feel the gravitational force exerted by Earth pulling you downward toward the bottom of the slide (Figure 4.3). But if you want to feel the gravitational force exerted by the person sitting next to you, you will not be able to sense anything because the magnitude of the force is so small.

▶ **Figure 4.3** The attractive force between Earth and you is far greater than that between you and another person coming down a waterslide.

Gravitational force is a force that always exists in pairs. This is another example of Newton's third law. If Earth exerts a gravitational force of magnitude 700 N on you, then you exert a gravitational force of magnitude 700 N on Earth. Earth attracts you and you attract Earth.

The force you exert on Earth has a negligible effect because Earth's mass is huge in comparison to yours (5.97×10^{24} kg). However, the gravitational force that Earth exerts on you causes a noticeable acceleration because of your relatively small mass.

Concept Check

Which diagram best represents the gravitational force acting on you and on Earth (Figure 4.4)? Explain your reasoning.

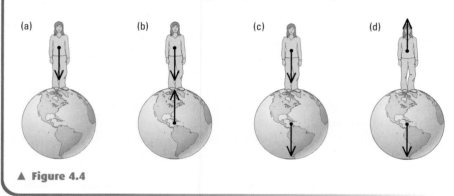

(a)   (b)   (c)   (d)

▲ **Figure 4.4**

The Concept of Weight

In a vacuum, all objects near Earth's surface will fall with the same acceleration, no matter what the objects consist of or what their masses are. The only force acting on a falling object in a vacuum is the gravitational force exerted by Earth on the object (Figure 4.5). Suppose you analyze this situation using a free-body diagram and Newton's second law.

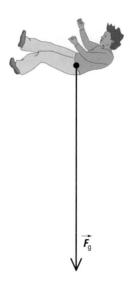

$\vec{F}_g$

▲ **Figure 4.5**   Free-body diagram for a falling object in a vacuum

▲ **Figure 4.6** Diagram showing the forces acting on an object that is suspended from a spring scale

weight: gravitational force exerted on an object by a celestial body

The equation for the net force acting on the falling object is

$$\vec{F}_{net} = \vec{F}_g$$

$$m\vec{a} = \vec{F}_g$$

Since the object is accelerating due to gravity, $\vec{a} = \vec{g}$. So the equation for the net force becomes

$$m\vec{g} = \vec{F}_g$$

or

$$\vec{F}_g = m\vec{g}$$

The equation $\vec{F}_g = m\vec{g}$ is valid in general, because the gravitational force acting on an object is the same, whether or not the object is at rest or is moving. This equation relates the gravitational force acting on an object, the so-called **weight** of the object, to its mass.

One way to measure the magnitude of the weight of an object directly involves using a spring scale (Figure 4.6). When the object stops moving at the end of the spring, Earth exerts a downward gravitational force on the object while the spring exerts an upward elastic force of equal magnitude on the object.

Find out what the relationship is between mass and gravitational force in the vicinity of your school by doing 4-2 QuickLab.

4-2 *QuickLab*

Relating Mass and Weight

Problem

What is the relationship between the mass of an object and the local value of the gravitational force exerted on that object?

Materials

set of standard masses with hooks
spring scale (0−10 N)
graph paper

Procedure

① Design a procedure to determine the gravitational force acting on a set of standard masses (Figure 4.7).

② Use a table to record the magnitude of the gravitational force and mass. Add another column in the table for the ratio of F_g to m.

③ Calculate the ratio of F_g to m for each standard mass. Calculate the average ratio for all masses. Include units.

▲ **Figure 4.7**

④ Plot a graph of F_g vs. m. Draw a line of best fit through the data points. Calculate the slope of the graph.

Questions

1. What does the ratio of F_g to m represent? How constant is this value?

2. Describe the graph of F_g vs. m. How does the slope compare to the average ratio calculated in step 3?

3. Write an equation relating F_g and m. Use the symbol g for the proportionality constant.

4. (a) The Moon exerts a gravitational force that is about $\frac{1}{6}$ that exerted by Earth. If you did this activity on the Moon using an appropriate spring scale and the same standard masses, would
   • the graph be a straight line?
   • the slope be the same as before?
   • the line go through the origin?
   • the proportionality constant g be the same as before?

   (b) Why would a 0−5 N spring scale be more ideal to use on the Moon, rather than a 0−10 N spring scale?

Gravitational Mass

The mass in the equation $\vec{F}_g = m\vec{g}$ is determined by finding the ratio of the gravitational force acting on an object to the acceleration due to gravity. Since $\vec{F}_g$ and $\vec{g}$ are in the same direction, the scalar form of the equation may be used:

$$F_g = mg$$

$$m = \frac{F_g}{g}$$

A practical way to measure this mass involves using a balance. In Figure 4.8, an object of unknown mass (A) is placed on one pan and standard masses (B) are added to the other pan until both pans balance. This method involves comparing the weights of two objects: one unknown and the other known. Mass measured using the concept of weight is called **gravitational mass**.

gravitational mass: mass measurement based on comparing the known weight of one object to the unknown weight of another object

gravitational force exerted on standard masses gravitational force exerted on an unknown mass

◄ **Figure 4.8** When both pans are balanced, the gravitational force acting on the unknown mass is equal to the gravitational force acting on the standard masses.

If the balance in Figure 4.8 were moved to the Moon, the process of determining the gravitational mass of object A would be the same. However, the weight of A and B would be different from that at Earth's surface because the acceleration due to gravity at the Moon's surface, g_{Moon}, is 1.62 m/s² compared to 9.81 m/s² at Earth's surface.

$$F_{g_A} = F_{g_B}$$

$$m_A g_{Moon} = m_B g_{Moon}$$

$$m_A = m_B$$

But since both objects A and B experience the same value of g_{Moon}, $m_A = m_B$. So the gravitational mass of an object is the same whether the object is on Earth, the Moon, or anywhere else in the universe. Both gravitational mass and inertial mass are properties of an object that do not depend on the location of the object.

e **SIM**

Explore how mass and weight are measured. Follow the eSim links at www.pearsoned.ca/school/physicssource.

Is Inertial Mass the Same as Gravitational Mass?

You can determine the mass of an object by using either the concept of inertia or weight. Experiments since Newton's day have shown that for any object, the numerical value of its inertial mass is equal to its gravitational mass. Later, Albert Einstein (1879–1955) showed that inertial mass is actually equivalent to gravitational mass. So it does not matter whether you determine the mass of an object using inertia or weight, because the numerical value of the mass is the same.

Describing Gravitational Force as a Field

Gravitational force is an example of a force that acts on objects whether or not they actually touch each other, even if the objects are in a vacuum. These forces are referred to as **action-at-a-distance forces**.

Since Newton's time, physicists have introduced the concept of a field to explain action-at-a-distance forces. You encountered some fields in previous science courses when you worked with magnets.

Imagine you are moving the north pole of a magnet close to the north pole of a fixed magnet. As you move the magnet closer to the fixed magnet, you can feel an increasing resistance. Somehow, the fixed magnet has created a region of influence in the space surrounding it. Physicists refer to a three-dimensional region where there is some type of an influence, whether it is an attraction or a repulsion, on a suitable object as a **field**.

Since every object exerts a gravitational force in three dimensions, it influences the space around it (Figure 4.9). This region of influence is a **gravitational field**, and it is through this region that two objects interact.

info **BIT**

Physicists are attempting to find a way to view all fundamental forces as different aspects of a single concept. So far, physicists have successfully unified the electromagnetic and the weak nuclear forces into the electroweak interaction.

action-at-a-distance force: force that acts even if the objects involved are not touching

field: three-dimensional region of influence

gravitational field: region of influence surrounding any object that has mass

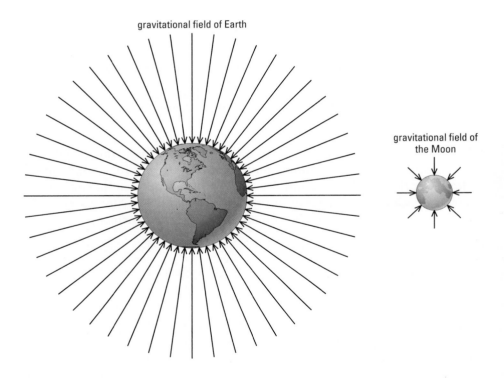

gravitational field of Earth

gravitational field of the Moon

▲ **Figure 4.9** This figure shows a two-dimensional representation of Earth's and the Moon's gravitational field. A gravitational field is three-dimensional and is directed toward the centre of the object.

To determine the magnitude and direction of a gravitational field created by an object, you could use a test mass m_{test}. At different locations around the object, this test mass will experience a gravitational force that has a certain magnitude and direction. The direction of the gravitational force will be directed toward the centre of the object.

Gravitational field strength is defined as the gravitational force per unit mass, $\vec{g} = \dfrac{\vec{F}_g}{m_{test}}$. If you release the test mass, it will accelerate toward the object with an acceleration equal to g.

Figure 4.10 shows how the magnitude of Earth's gravitational field strength changes as a test mass is moved farther away from Earth's centre. The farther the test mass is moved, the more significant is the decrease in g. In fact, the graph in Figure 4.10 shows an inverse square relationship:

$$g \propto \frac{1}{r^2}$$

gravitational field strength:
gravitational force per unit mass at a specific location

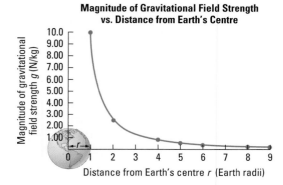

▲ **Figure 4.10**   The magnitude of the gravitational field strength as a function of distance from Earth's centre

Since force is measured in newtons and mass in kilograms, the units of gravitational field strength are newtons per kilogram, or N/kg. The ratio you determined in 4-2 QuickLab was the gravitational field strength at the vicinity of your school.

Concept Check

What happens to the magnitude of the gravitational field strength if
(a) r decreases by a factor of four?
(b) r increases by a factor of two?
(c) m_{test} doubles?
(d) m_{test} is halved?

Knowledge

1. Distinguish between mass and weight. Explain using an example and a diagram.

2. Distinguish between inertial mass and gravitational mass.

3. In your own words, define gravitational acceleration and gravitational field strength. State the units and symbol for each quantity.

4. In your own words, explain the concept of a gravitational field. Include an example of how a gravitational field affects another object.

5. Why do physicists use the concept of a field to describe gravity?

6. In a vacuum, a feather and a bowling ball are released from rest at the same time from the same height. Compare the time it takes for each object to fall. Explain your answer.

Applications

7. The Moon exerts a gravitational force that is about $\frac{1}{6}$ that exerted by Earth. Explain why the mass of an object measured on the Moon using a balance is the same as if the object were on Earth's surface.

8. Describe a situation where measuring the inertial mass of an object is easier than measuring its gravitational mass.

9. The table below shows the magnitude of the gravitational force on objects of different mass in Banff, Alberta.

Mass (kg)	0	1.50	3.00	4.50	6.00	7.50	10.0
Magnitude of Gravitational Force (N)	0	14.7	29.4	44.1	58.9	73.6	98.1

(a) Graph the data.

(b) Calculate the slope of the line.

(c) What does the slope represent?

10. How could you distinguish between a 5.0-kg medicine ball and a basketball in outer space without looking at both objects?

Extensions

11. Visit a local fitness gymnasium. Find out how athletes use gravitational and elastic forces to improve their fitness. Is friction a help or a hindrance? Write a brief report of your findings.

12. List some occupations that might require a knowledge of gravitational field strength. Briefly explain how gravitational field strength applies to these occupations.

13. Complete the gathering grid below to summarize the similarities and differences among gravitational mass, inertial mass, and gravitational force.

	Gravitational Mass	Inertial Mass	Gravitational Force
Definition			
SI unit			
Measuring Instrument(s)			
How the Quantity Is Measured			
Factors It Depends On			
Variability with Location			

 e **TEST**

To check your understanding of gravitational force, weight, mass, and gravitational field strength, follow the eTest links at www.pearsoned.ca/school/physicssource.

4.2 Newton's Law of Universal Gravitation

Gravity affects all masses in the universe. No matter where you are on Earth or in outer space, you exert a gravitational force on an object and an object exerts a gravitational force, of equal magnitude but opposite direction, on you. Because gravitational force acts over any distance, the range of its effect is infinite.

Near Earth's surface, the magnitude of the gravitational force exerted by Earth (object A) on object B is given by the equation $F_{\text{A on B}} = m_{\text{B}}g$. But object B also exerts a gravitational force of equal magnitude on Earth, $F_{\text{B on A}} = m_{\text{A}}g$. Newton hypothesized that, given two objects A and B, the magnitude of the gravitational force exerted by one object on the other is directly proportional to the product of both masses:

$$F_{\text{g}} \propto m_{\text{A}}m_{\text{B}}$$

Figure 4.11 shows the magnitude of the gravitational force acting on an object at Earth's surface (r_{Earth}), one Earth radius above Earth ($2r_{\text{Earth}}$), and two Earth radii above Earth ($3r_{\text{Earth}}$). If the separation distance from Earth's centre to the centre of the object doubles, F_{g} decreases to $\frac{1}{4}$ of its original value. If the separation distance from Earth's centre to the centre of the object triples, F_{g} decreases to $\frac{1}{9}$ of its original value. So, just as $g \propto \frac{1}{r^2}$, F_{g} is inversely proportional to the square of the separation distance (Figure 4.12):

$$F_{\text{g}} \propto \frac{1}{r^2}$$

***info* BIT**
Gravity is the dominant force throughout the universe. This force is attractive and has an infinite range.

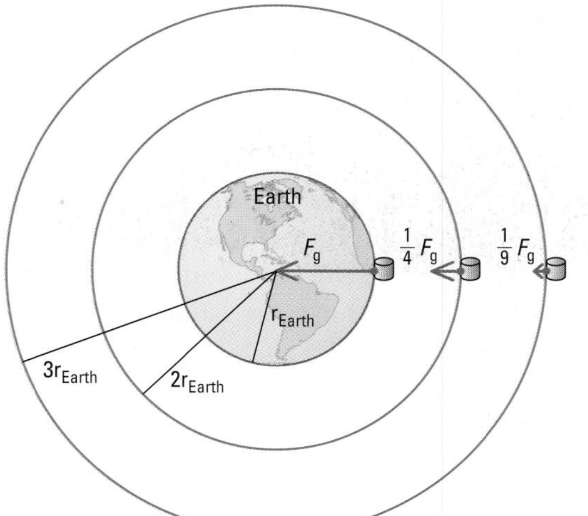

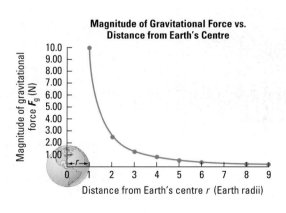

▲ **Figure 4.11** The magnitude of the gravitational force acting on an object some distance from Earth varies inversely with the square of the separation distance.

▲ **Figure 4.12** The magnitude of the gravitational force acting on a 1.00-kg object as a function of distance from Earth's centre

eSIM

Explore the relationship among m_A, m_B, r, and F_g in Newton's law of gravitation. Follow the eSim links at www.pearsoned.ca/school/physicssource.

If you combine both proportionalities into one statement, you get $F_g \propto \dfrac{m_A m_B}{r^2}$ or $F_g = \dfrac{G m_A m_B}{r^2}$ (Figure 4.13). This mathematical relationship is Newton's law of universal gravitation.

Any two objects, A and B, in the universe exert gravitational forces of equal magnitude but opposite direction on each other. The forces are directed along the line joining the centres of both objects. The magnitude of the gravitational force is given by $F_g = \dfrac{G m_A m_B}{r^2}$,

where m_A and m_B are the masses of the two objects, r is the separation distance between the centres of both objects, and G is a constant called the **universal gravitational constant**.

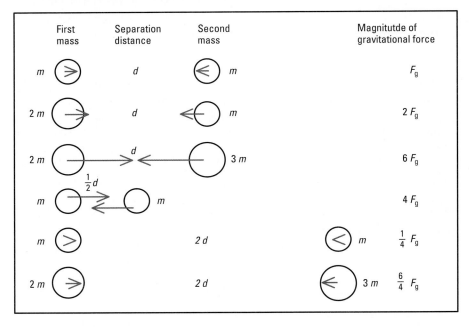

▲ **Figure 4.13** The magnitude of the gravitational force is directly proportional to the product of the two masses, and inversely proportional to the square of the separation distance.

Experiments have shown that the magnitude of the gravitational force acting on any pair of objects does not depend on the medium in which the objects are located (Figure 4.14). In other words, given two fish, the gravitational force acting on either fish will have the same magnitude if both fish are underwater or in midair.

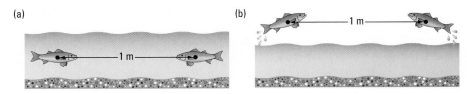

▲ **Figure 4.14** The magnitude of the gravitational force acting on either fish is the same whether both fish are (a) underwater or (b) above water.

e WEB

Edmund Halley, an associate of Newton, paid for the publication of some of Newton's famous work. Find out about Edmund Halley and his contributions to Newton's work. Begin your search at www.pearsoned.ca/school/physicssource.

Determining the Value of the Universal Gravitational Constant

Although Newton found a mathematical relationship for gravitational force, he was unable to determine the value of G. In 1798, scientist Henry Cavendish (1731–1810) confirmed experimentally that Newton's law of gravitation is valid, and determined the density of Earth. Cavendish's experimental set-up was later used to determine the value of G.

The magnitude of the gravitational force acting on most pairs of objects is very weak and the magnitude decreases significantly as the separation distance between the objects increases. However, if you use two light spheres (each of mass m) and two heavy spheres (each of mass M) that are very close to each other, it is possible to determine the magnitude of the gravitational force exerted by M on m.

The trick is to use a device that can accurately measure the very small gravitational force. A modern **torsion balance** is a device that uses a sensitive fibre and a beam of light to measure very minute forces due to gravity, magnetic fields, or electric charges. Cavendish used a modified torsion balance invented by John Michell (1724–1793) to verify Newton's law of gravitation.

A modern torsion balance consists of a small, light, rigid rod with two identical, light, spheres (m) attached to each end (Figure 4.15). The rod is suspended horizontally by a thin fibre connected to the centre of the rod. A mirror is also attached to the fibre and rod so that when the rod turns, the mirror also turns by the same amount. The entire assembly is supported in an airtight chamber. The torsion balance initially experiences no net force and the spheres m are stationary.

torsion balance: device used to measure very small forces

info BIT

Charles de Coulomb invented the torsion balance in 1777 to measure small magnetic forces and forces in fluids. However, John Michell independently invented the same type of device in 1784.

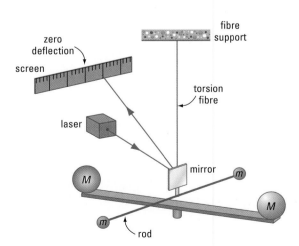

◀ **Figure 4.15** A modern torsion balance uses a laser beam to measure the amount of twist in the fibre. The most accurate value of G has been determined using such a device.

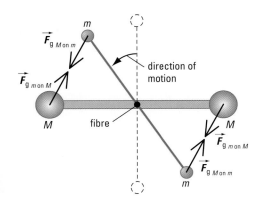

▲ **Figure 4.16** This figure shows the top view of spheres *m* and *M* from Figure 4.15. The original position of spheres *m* is shown with dashed lines. The gravitational force exerted by *M* on *m* causes *m* to rotate toward *M*. The greater the magnitude of the gravitational force, the greater the angle of rotation.

When two identical, heavy, spheres (*M*) are moved close to spheres *m*, the gravitational force exerted by *M* on *m* causes *m* to rotate horizontally toward *M*. This rotation causes the fibre to twist slightly (Figure 4.16). As the fibre twists, the mirror attached to both the fibre and the rod turns through an angle in the horizontal plane. A beam of light reflected from the mirror becomes deflected as spheres *m* rotate. The amount of deflection is an indication of how much the spheres rotate. The greater the magnitude of the gravitational force, the more the fibre twists, and the greater the angle of rotation.

By measuring the amount of deflection, the gravitational force exerted by *M* on *m* can be determined. Spheres *M* are then moved to a symmetrical position on the opposite side of *m*, and the procedure is repeated.

Since the separation distance between *m* and *M*, the values of *m* and *M*, and the gravitational force can all be measured, it is possible to calculate *G* using Newton's law of gravitation.

$$F_{\mathrm{g}} = \frac{GmM}{r^2}$$

$$\frac{F_{\mathrm{g}}r^2}{mM} = G$$

$$G = \frac{F_{\mathrm{g}}r^2}{mM}$$

The current accepted value of *G* to three significant digits is 6.67×10^{-11} N·m²/kg².

In Example 4.1, Newton's law of gravitation is used to show that a person weighs slightly less at the top of the mountain than at its base.

Example 4.1

Mount Logan in the Yukon is 5959 m above sea level, and is the highest peak in Canada. Earth's mass is 5.97×10^{24} kg and Earth's equatorial radius is 6.38×10^6 m. What would be the difference in the magnitude of the weight of a 55.0-kg person at the top of the mountain as compared to at its base (Figure 4.17)? Assume that Earth's equatorial radius is equal to the distance from Earth's centre to sea level.

Given

$$m_{\mathrm{p}} = 55.0 \text{ kg}$$
$$h = 5959 \text{ m}$$
$$m_{\mathrm{Earth}} = 5.97 \times 10^{24} \text{ kg}$$
$$r_{\mathrm{Earth}} = 6.38 \times 10^6 \text{ m}$$

Required
difference in magnitude of weight (ΔF_{g})

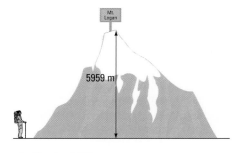

▲ **Figure 4.17**

Analysis and Solution

Assume that the separation distance between the person at the base of the mountain and Earth is equal to Earth's equatorial radius.

Base of mountain: $r_B = r_{Earth} = 6.38 \times 10^6$ m

Top of mountain: $r_T = 6.38 \times 10^6$ m + 5959 m

The person's weight is equal to the gravitational force exerted by Earth on the person, and is directed toward Earth's centre both at the base and at the top of the mountain.

Calculate F_g at the base of the mountain using Newton's law of gravitation.

$$(F_g)_B = \frac{Gm_p m_{Earth}}{(r_B)^2}$$

$$= \frac{\left(6.67 \times 10^{-11}\ \dfrac{N \cdot m^2}{kg^2}\right)(55.0\ kg)(5.97 \times 10^{24}\ kg)}{(6.38 \times 10^6\ m)^2}$$

$$= 538.049\ N$$

Calculate F_g at the top of the mountain using Newton's law of gravitation.

$$(F_g)_T = \frac{Gm_p m_{Earth}}{(r_T)^2}$$

$$= \frac{\left(6.67 \times 10^{-11}\ \dfrac{N \cdot m^2}{kg^2}\right)(55.0\ kg)(5.97 \times 10^{24}\ kg)}{(6.38 \times 10^6\ m + 5959\ m)^2}$$

$$= 537.045\ N$$

The difference in the magnitude of the weight is equal to the difference in magnitude of both gravitational forces.

$$\Delta F_g = (F_g)_B - (F_g)_T$$

$$= 538.049\ N - 537.045\ N$$

$$= 1.00\ N$$

Paraphrase

The difference in the magnitude of the person's weight is 1.00 N.

Using Proportionalities to Solve Gravitation Problems

Example 4.2 demonstrates how to solve gravitation problems using proportionalities. This technique is useful if you are given how the separation distance and masses change from one situation to another.

Practice Problems

1. Two people, A and B, are sitting on a bench 0.60 m apart. Person A has a mass of 55 kg and person B a mass of 80 kg. Calculate the magnitude of the gravitational force exerted by B on A.

2. The mass of the *Titanic* was 4.6×10^7 kg. Suppose the magnitude of the gravitational force exerted by the *Titanic* on the fatal iceberg was 61 N when the separation distance was 100 m. What was the mass of the iceberg?

Answers

1. 8.2×10^{-7} N
2. 2.0×10^8 kg

Example 4.2

Object A exerts a gravitational force of magnitude 1.3×10^{-10} N on object B. Determine the magnitude of the gravitational force if the separation distance is doubled, m_A increases by 6 times, and m_B is halved. Explain your reasoning.

Analysis and Solution

From Newton's law of gravitation, $F_g \propto m_A m_B$ and $F_g \propto \dfrac{1}{r^2}$. Figure 4.18 represents the situation of the problem.

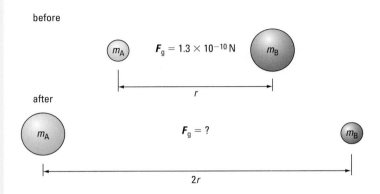

▲ **Figure 4.18**

$$F_g \propto (6m_A)\left(\frac{1}{2}m_B\right) \qquad \text{and} \qquad F_g \propto \frac{1}{(2r)^2}$$

$$\propto (6)\left(\frac{1}{2}\right)m_A m_B \qquad\qquad\qquad \propto \left(\frac{1}{2^2}\right)\left(\frac{1}{r^2}\right)$$

$$\propto 3m_A m_B \qquad\qquad\qquad\qquad \propto \left(\frac{1}{4}\right)\left(\frac{1}{r^2}\right)$$

Calculate the factor change of F_g.

$$3 \times \frac{1}{4} = \frac{3}{4}$$

Calculate F_g.

$$\frac{3}{4}F_g = \frac{3}{4} \times (1.3 \times 10^{-10} \text{ N})$$

$$= 1 \times 10^{-10} \text{ N}$$

The new magnitude of the gravitational force will be 1×10^{-10} N.

Practice Problem

1. Object A exerts a gravitational force of magnitude 5.9×10^{-11} N on object B. For each situation, determine the magnitude of the gravitational force. Explain your reasoning.
   (a) the separation distance increases to $\dfrac{4}{3}$ of its original value, m_A increases to $\dfrac{3}{2}$ of its original value, and m_B is halved
   (b) the separation distance decreases to $\dfrac{1}{6}$ of its original value, m_A is halved, and m_B increases to $\dfrac{5}{4}$ of its original value

Answer

1. (a) 2.5×10^{-11} N
   (b) 1.3×10^{-9} N

Using Superposition to Find the Net Gravitational Force on an Object

Example 4.3 demonstrates how to calculate the gravitational force exerted by both the Moon and the Sun on Earth. A free-body diagram is used to determine the gravitational forces acting on Earth. The technique of adding the gravitational force due to each pair of objects (Earth and the Moon, and Earth and the Sun) to find the net gravitational force is called superposition.

Example 4.3

During a lunar eclipse, Earth, the Moon, and the Sun are aligned on the same plane as shown in Figure 4.19. Using the data in the chart below, calculate the net gravitational force exerted by both the Moon and the Sun on Earth.

Celestial Body	Mass* (kg)	Mean Separation Distance from Earth* (m)
Earth	5.97×10^{24}	—
Earth's Moon	7.35×10^{22}	3.84×10^{8}
Sun	1.99×10^{30}	1.50×10^{11}

*Source: Jet Propulsion Laboratory, California Institute of Technology
(See JPL link at www.pearsoned.ca/school/physicssource.)

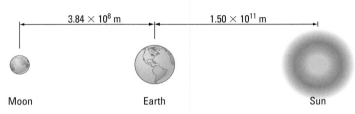

▲ **Figure 4.19**

Given

$m_{\text{Earth}} = 5.97 \times 10^{24}$ kg

$m_{\text{Moon}} = 7.35 \times 10^{22}$ kg $\qquad r_{\text{E to M}} = 3.84 \times 10^{8}$ m

$m_{\text{Sun}} = 1.99 \times 10^{30}$ kg $\qquad r_{\text{E to S}} = 1.50 \times 10^{11}$ m

Required

net gravitational force on Earth ($\vec{F}_{\text{g}}$)

Analysis and Solution

Draw a free-body diagram for Earth (Figure 4.20).

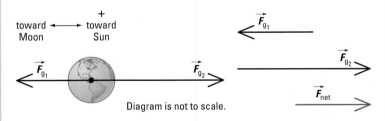

Diagram is not to scale.

▲ **Figure 4.20**

Calculate F_{g} exerted by the Moon on Earth using Newton's law of gravitation.

$$(F_{\text{g}})_1 = \frac{Gm_{\text{Earth}}m_{\text{Moon}}}{(r_{\text{E to M}})^2}$$

$$= \frac{\left(6.67 \times 10^{-11} \dfrac{\text{N·m}^2}{\text{kg}^2}\right)(5.97 \times 10^{24} \text{ kg})(7.35 \times 10^{22} \text{ kg})}{(3.84 \times 10^{8} \text{ m})^2}$$

$$= 1.985 \times 10^{20} \text{ N}$$

$\vec{F}_{\text{g}_1} = 1.985 \times 10^{20}$ N [toward Moon's centre]

Practice Problems

1. During a solar eclipse, Earth, the Moon, and the Sun are aligned on the same plane as shown in Figure 4.21. Calculate the net gravitational force exerted by both the Moon and the Sun on Earth.

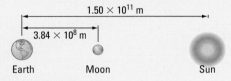

▲ **Figure 4.21**

2. During the third quarter phase of the Moon, Earth, the Moon, and the Sun are positioned as shown in Figure 4.22. Calculate the net gravitational force exerted by both the Moon and the Sun on Earth.

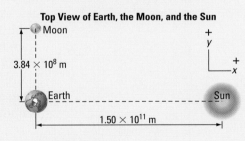

▲ **Figure 4.22**

Answers

1. 3.54×10^{22} N [toward Sun's centre]
2. 3.52×10^{22} N [0.3°]

Calculate F_g exerted by the Sun on Earth using Newton's law of gravitation.

$$(F_g)_2 = \frac{Gm_{Earth}m_{Sun}}{(r_{E\ to\ S})^2}$$

$$= \frac{\left(6.67 \times 10^{-11}\ \frac{N\cdot m^2}{kg^2}\right)(5.97 \times 10^{24}\ kg)(1.99 \times 10^{30}\ kg)}{(1.50 \times 10^{11}\ m)^2}$$

$$= 3.522 \times 10^{22}\ N$$

$$\vec{F}_{g_2} = 3.522 \times 10^{22}\ N\ \text{[toward Sun's centre]}$$

Find the net gravitational force on Earth.

$$\vec{F}_{g_{net}} = \vec{F}_{g_1} + \vec{F}_{g_2}$$

$$F_{g_{net}} = F_{g_1} + F_{g_2}$$

$$= -1.985 \times 10^{20}\ N + 3.522 \times 10^{22}\ N$$

$$= 3.50 \times 10^{22}\ N$$

$$\vec{F}_{g_{net}} = 3.50 \times 10^{22}\ N\ \text{[toward Sun's centre]}$$

Paraphrase

The net gravitational force on Earth due to the Sun and Moon during a lunar eclipse is 3.50×10^{22} N [toward Sun's centre].

The Role of Gravitational Force on Earth's Tides

Newton used the concept of gravitational force to account for Earth's tides. Although he correctly identified the gravitational force exerted by the Moon and the Sun on Earth as the major cause, a complete understanding of tides must take into account other factors as well.

The height of the tides varies depending on the location on Earth (Figure 4.23). In the middle of the Pacific Ocean, the difference between high and low tides is about 0.5 m. But along the coastline of the continents, the difference may be considerably greater.

▲ **Figure 4.23** The tides in the Bay of Fundy are the highest in the world. In some locations, the water level rises up to 18 m between low and high tides.

Some factors that affect tides are
- the shape of the coastline
- the topography of the ocean floor near the coastline
- friction between Earth and the ocean water
- Earth's position in its orbit around the Sun
- Earth's rotation about its axis
- the tilt of Earth's axis
- the alignment of Earth, the Moon, and the Sun

First consider only the Moon's influence on Earth. Since the Moon exerts a gravitational force on Earth, the Moon is in a sense pulling Earth closer to it. So the land mass and ocean water on Earth are all "falling" toward the Moon. In Figure 4.24, this gravitational force is greatest at side A, then decreases at the midpoints of A and B, and is least at side B, because the magnitude of the gravitational force varies inversely with the square of the separation distance.

e **WEB**

Newspapers in cities near an ocean, such as Halifax, often publish tidal charts listing the times of local high and low tides. Find an example of a tidal chart and suggest how different people would find this information useful. Begin your search at www.pearsoned.ca/school/physicssource.

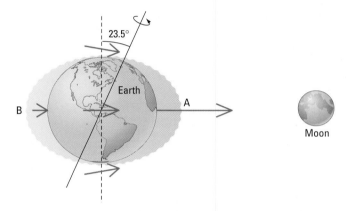

▲ **Figure 4.24** Earth experiences high tides on sides A and B at the same time. The vectors show the relative gravitational force exerted by the Moon on a test mass at various locations near Earth's surface.

The bulges at A and B are the **high tides**. The **low tides** occur at the midpoints of A and B. The bulge at B occurs because the land mass of Earth at B is pulled toward the Moon, leaving the ocean water behind.

Next consider the fact that Earth rotates on its axis once every 24 h. As the bulges remain fixed relative to the Moon, Earth rotates underneath those bulges. So at a given location on Earth's surface, a high tide is replaced by a low tide about 6 h later, followed again by a high tide about 6 h later, and so on. These time intervals are actually a bit longer than 6 h because the Moon is orbiting Earth every $27\frac{1}{3}$ days with respect to distant stars, and the Moon is taking the bulges along with it.

Now consider that Earth is tilted on its axis. When the northern hemisphere is under the bulge at A, the southern hemisphere is under the bulge at B. So the high tides that are 12 h apart are not equally high, and low tides that are 12 h apart are not equally low.

Example 4.4 demonstrates how to calculate the gravitational force exerted by the Moon on 1.0000 kg of water at A.

info **BIT**

Io, one of Jupiter's moons, has tidal bulges of up to 100 m compared to typical tidal bulges of 1 m on Earth.

Example 4.4

Calculate the gravitational force exerted by the Moon on 1.0000 kg of water at A (Figure 4.25). Use $G = 6.672\ 59 \times 10^{-11}$ N·m²/kg².

Celestial Body	Mass* (kg)	Equatorial Radius* (m)	Mean Separation Distance from Earth* (m)
Earth	5.9742×10^{24}	6.3781×10^6	—
Earth's Moon	7.3483×10^{22}	1.7374×10^6	3.8440×10^8

*Source: Jet Propulsion Laboratory, California Institute of Technology (See JPL link at www.pearsoned.ca/school/physicssource.)

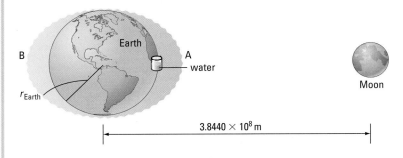

▲ **Figure 4.25**

Given

$$m_w = 1.0000 \text{ kg}$$

$$m_{Earth} = 5.9742 \times 10^{24} \text{ kg} \qquad r_{Earth} = 6.3781 \times 10^6 \text{ m}$$

$$m_{Moon} = 7.3483 \times 10^{22} \text{ kg} \qquad r_{Moon} = 1.7374 \times 10^6 \text{ m}$$

$$r_{E \text{ to } M} = 3.8440 \times 10^8 \text{ m}$$

Required

gravitational force exerted by Moon on water ($\vec{F}_g$)

Analysis and Solution

Draw a free-body diagram for the water showing only $\vec{F}_g$ due to the Moon (Figure 4.26).

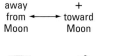

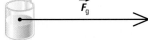

▲ **Figure 4.26**

Find the separation distance between the water and the Moon.

$$r = r_{\text{E to M}} - r_{\text{Earth}}$$

$$= 3.8440 \times 10^8 \text{ m} - 6.3781 \times 10^6 \text{ m}$$

$$= 3.780\ 22 \times 10^8 \text{ m}$$

Calculate F_g exerted by the Moon on the water using Newton's law of gravitation.

$$F_\text{g} = \frac{Gm_\text{w}m_\text{Moon}}{r^2}$$

$$= \frac{\left(6.672\ 59 \times 10^{-11}\ \dfrac{\text{N}\cdot\text{m}^2}{\text{kg}^2}\right)(1.0000\ \cancel{\text{kg}})(7.3483 \times 10^{22}\ \cancel{\text{kg}})}{(3.780\ 22 \times 10^8\ \text{m})^2}$$

$$= 3.4312 \times 10^{-5}\text{ N}$$

$$\vec{F}_\text{g} = 3.4312 \times 10^{-5}\text{ N [toward Moon's centre]}$$

Paraphrase
The gravitational force exerted by the Moon on the water at A is 3.4312×10^{-5} N [toward Moon's centre].

The Role of Gravitational Force on Interplanetary Travel

Scientists who plan space missions take advantage of the gravitational force exerted by planets and other celestial bodies to change the speed and direction of spacecraft. Distances between celestial bodies are huge compared to distances on Earth. So a space probe leaving Earth to study Jupiter and Saturn and their moons would take many years to arrive there.

Scientists have to calculate the position and velocity of all the celestial bodies that will affect the motion of the probe many years in advance. If several planets are moving in the same direction and their positions are aligned, a space probe launched from Earth can arrive at its destination many years sooner, provided the probe moves near as many of those planets as possible (Figure 4.27).

info **BIT**

The Voyager mission was intended to take advantage of a geometric alignment of Jupiter, Saturn, Uranus, and Neptune. This arrangement occurs approximately every 175 years. By using the concept of gravity assist, the flight time to Neptune was reduced from 30 to 12 years, and a minimum of onboard propellant on the spacecraft was required.

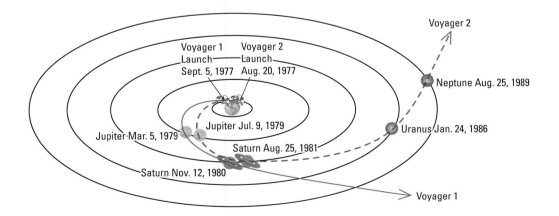

▲ **Figure 4.27** Both Voyager spacecraft were launched from Cape Canaveral, Florida, in 1977. Voyager 1 had close encounters with Jupiter and Saturn, while Voyager 2 flew by all four of the gaseous planets in the solar system.

Each time the probe gets near enough to one of these planets, the gravitational field of the planet causes the path of the probe to curve (Figure 4.28). The planet deflects the space probe and, if the planet is moving in the same direction as the probe, the speed of the probe after its planetary encounter will increase. The use of the gravitational force exerted by celestial bodies to reduce interplanetary travel times is called **gravity assist**.

▼ **Figure 4.28** Voyager 1 passed close to Io, Ganymede, and Callisto, three of Jupiter's moons. Jupiter has a total of 62 moons.

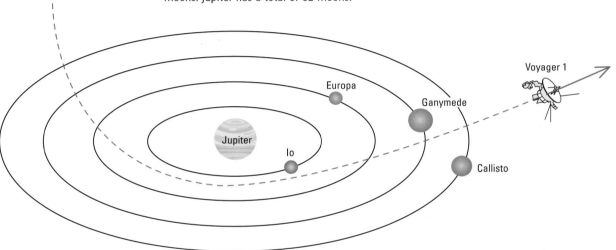

THEN, NOW, AND FUTURE   Small Steps Lead to New Models

When Newton began his study of gravity in 1665, he was not the first person to tackle the challenge of explaining planetary motion.

Ancient Greek astronomer Ptolemy (Claudius Ptolemaeus, 2nd century A.D.) and eventually Nicolaus Copernicus (1473–1543) proposed two different models of the solar system: one Earth-centred and the other Sun-centred. Later Johannes Kepler (1571–1630) developed three empirical laws describing planetary motion using astronomical data compiled by astronomer Tycho Brahe (1546–1601).

Kepler's laws confirmed that a Sun-centred system is the correct model, because it was possible to predict the correct position of plan-

ets. However, Kepler was unable to explain *why* planets move.

Newton was the first scientist to explain the motion of planets in terms of forces. By using his three laws of motion and his law of gravitation, Newton derived Kepler's laws, providing further evidence of the validity of his force laws and of the model of a Sun-centred solar system.

Newton was able to develop his law of gravitation because many scientists before him developed theories and made observations about planetary motion. Newton's laws and the concept of gravity could describe the motion of objects on Earth and throughout the universe.

This was a tremendous breakthrough because up until that time,

scientists were unable to predict or explain motion. While Newton's model can still be used today for most everyday situations, scientists have further modified it. The process of developing new models and theories has helped scientists tackle questions about the universe in ways Newton could never have imagined.

Questions

1. Research the scientific developments that led to Newton's law of gravitation.

2. What are some benefits of developing new scientific models and theories?

Knowledge

1. Why is G called a "universal" constant?

2. Describe how a torsion balance can be used to measure the constant G.

3. Suppose F_g is the magnitude of the gravitational force between two people with a separation distance of 1.0 m. How would F_g change if

   (a) the separation distance became 2.0 m?

   (b) one person was joined by an equally massive friend while at this 2.0-m separation distance?

Applications

4. The Moon has a mass of 7.35×10^{22} kg and its equatorial radius is 1.74×10^6 m. Earth's mass is 5.97×10^{24} kg and its equatorial radius is 6.38×10^6 m.

   (a) Calculate the magnitude of the gravitational force exerted by

      (i) the Moon on a 100-kg astronaut standing on the Moon's surface, and

      (ii) Earth on a 100-kg astronaut standing on Earth's surface.

   (b) Explain why the values of F_g in part (a) are different.

5. Mars has two moons, Deimos and Phobos, each named after an attendant of the Roman war god Mars. Deimos has a mass of 1.8×10^{15} kg and its mean distance from Mars is 2.3×10^7 m. Phobos has a mass of 1.1×10^{16} kg and its mean distance from Mars is 9.4×10^6 m.

   (a) Without doing any calculations, predict which moon will exert a greater gravitational force on Mars. Explain your reasoning.

   (b) Check your prediction in part (a) by calculating the magnitude of the gravitational force exerted by each moon on Mars. Mars' mass is 6.42×10^{23} kg. Show complete solutions.

6. Suppose the equatorial radius of Earth was the same as the Moon, but Earth's mass remained the same. The Moon has an equatorial radius of 1.74×10^6 m. Earth's mass is 5.97×10^{24} kg and its equatorial radius is 6.38×10^6 m.

   (a) Calculate the gravitational force that this hypothetical Earth would exert on a 1.00-kg object at its surface.

   (b) How does the answer in part (a) compare to the actual gravitational force exerted by Earth on this object?

Extensions

7. Prepare a problem involving Newton's law of gravitation for each situation. Work with a partner to solve each problem, and discuss the steps you use.

   (a) Choose the values of the two masses and the separation distance.

   (b) Use values of m_A, m_B, and r that are multiples of those in part (a). Use proportionalities to solve the problem.

8. During Newton's time, scientists often

   • worked alone and contact with other scientists working on similar problems was difficult.

   • had very strong religious beliefs and some scientists, such as Kepler, were members of the clergy.

   • were knowledgeable in many different fields. Newton, for example, spent many years doing chemistry.

   (a) In paragraph form, assess the impacts that these factors might have had on science in Newton's day.

   (b) In a paragraph, describe the effects these factors might have on scientists today.

e TEST

To check your understanding of Newton's law of gravitation, follow the eTest links at www.pearsoned.ca/school/physicssource.

4.3 Relating Gravitational Field Strength to Gravitational Force

info **BIT**

A *g* force is a force that causes an acceleration with a magnitude of some multiple of *g*. A force of 2*g* means the magnitude of the acceleration is 2 × 9.81 m/s² = 19.6 m/s².

The acceleration due to gravity $\vec{g}$ near or on Earth's surface is about 9.81 m/s² [down]. But where does the value of 9.81 m/s² come from?

Consider the forces acting on a test mass m_{test} some distance above Earth's surface, where Earth has a mass of M_{source}. The only force acting on m_{test} is the gravitational force exerted by Earth on the test mass (Figure 4.29).

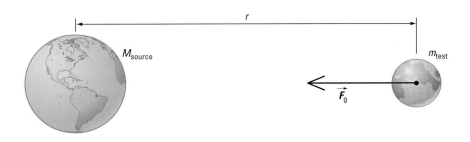

▲ **Figure 4.29**   The gravitational force exerted by Earth on test mass m_{test}

info **BIT**

During a roller coaster ride, riders may experience a 4*g* change in acceleration between the top and bottom of a loop. This dramatic change in acceleration causes the thrill and occasional dizziness experienced by riders.

The magnitude of $\vec{F}_{\text{g}}$ can be evaluated two ways: using the concept of weight or using Newton's law of gravitation.

Weight	Newton's law of gravitation
$F_{\text{g}} = m_{\text{test}}g$	$F_{\text{g}} = \dfrac{Gm_{\text{test}}M_{\text{source}}}{r^2}$

Since the value of F_{g} is the same no matter which equation you use, set both equations equal to each other.

$$m_{\cancel{\text{test}}}\, g = \frac{Gm_{\cancel{\text{test}}}\, M_{\text{source}}}{r^2}$$

$$g = \frac{GM_{\text{source}}}{r^2}$$

So no matter where the test mass is located in the universe, you can calculate the magnitude of the gravitational field strength (or gravitational acceleration) at any distance from a celestial body if you know the mass of the celestial body M_{source} and the separation distance between the centre of the test mass and the celestial body r.

Find out the relationship between gravitational field strength and the acceleration due to gravity by doing 4-3 Design a Lab.

Comparing Gravitational Field Strength to Gravitational Acceleration

The Question

What is the relationship between gravitational field strength and the local value of the gravitational acceleration?

Design and Conduct Your Investigation

State a hypothesis. Then design an experiment. Identify the controlled, manipulated, and responding variables. Review the procedure in 4-2 QuickLab on page 198. List the materials you will use, as well as a detailed procedure. Check the procedure with your teacher and then do the investigation. Analyze your data and form a conclusion. How well did your results agree with your hypothesis?

How Is Gravitational Field Strength Related to Gravitational Acceleration?

To determine how gravitational field strength is related to gravitational acceleration, use the definition of a newton, $1 \text{ N} = 1 \text{ kg·m/s}^2$. Then substitute kilogram-metres per second squared for newtons in the equation for gravitational field strength:

$$1 \, \frac{\text{N}}{\text{kg}} = 1 \, \frac{\cancel{\text{kg}} \cdot \frac{\text{m}}{\text{s}^2}}{\cancel{\text{kg}}}$$

$$= 1 \, \frac{\text{m}}{\text{s}^2}$$

Metres per second squared are the units of acceleration. So in terms of units, gravitational field strength and gravitational acceleration are equivalent (Figure 4.30).

◀ **Figure 4.30** Jennifer Heil of Spruce Grove, Alberta, won the gold medal in the women's freestyle skiing moguls in the 2006 Winter Olympics in Turin, Italy. The gravitational field strength at the surface of the Moon is about $\frac{1}{6}$ that at Earth's surface. How would Jennifer's jump on Earth compare with one on the Moon?

Calculating the Gravitational Acceleration of an Object on Two Celestial Bodies

e WEB

Globular clusters are groups of about 1 000 000 stars that are bound together by gravity. Find out who discovered the first cluster and how many have been identified so far. Research the approximate size and shape of a globular cluster and the forces involved in its formation. Summarize your findings. Begin your search at www.pearsoned.ca/school/physicssource.

Example 4.5 demonstrates how to calculate the gravitational acceleration at the equator on Earth's surface and that on the surface of the Moon. These two values are then compared to find the ratio of g_{Earth} to g_{Moon}.

To solve the problem requires using data in Table 4.1, which shows the mass and equatorial radius of the Sun, the Moon, and each planet in the solar system.

▼ **Table 4.1** Masses and Radii for Celestial Bodies in the Solar System*

Celestial Body	Mass (kg)	Equatorial Radius (m)
Sun	1.99×10^{30}	6.96×10^{8}
Mercury	3.30×10^{23}	2.44×10^{6}
Venus	4.87×10^{24}	6.05×10^{6}
Earth	5.97×10^{24}	6.38×10^{6}
Earth's Moon	7.35×10^{22}	1.74×10^{6}
Mars	6.42×10^{23}	3.40×10^{6}
Jupiter	1.90×10^{27}	7.15×10^{7}
Saturn	5.68×10^{26}	6.03×10^{7}
Uranus	8.68×10^{25}	2.56×10^{7}
Neptune	1.02×10^{26}	2.48×10^{7}

*Source: Jet Propulsion Laboratory, California Institute of Technology (See JPL link at www.pearsoned.ca/school/physicssource.)

Example 4.5

(a) Calculate the magnitude of the gravitational acceleration of an object at the equator on the surface of Earth and the Moon (Figure 4.31). Refer to Table 4.1 above.
(b) Determine the ratio of g_{Earth} to g_{Moon}. How different would your weight be on the Moon?

$g_{Earth} = ?$ $g_{Moon} = ?$

Earth   Moon

▲ **Figure 4.31**

Given

$m_{Earth} = 5.97 \times 10^{24}$ kg $r_{Earth} = 6.38 \times 10^{6}$ m

$m_{Moon} = 7.35 \times 10^{22}$ kg $r_{Moon} = 1.74 \times 10^{6}$ m

Required

(a) magnitude of gravitational acceleration at equator on Earth and the Moon (g_{Earth} and g_{Moon})
(b) ratio of g_{Earth} to g_{Moon}

Analysis and Solution

(a) Use the equation $g = \dfrac{GM_{source}}{r^2}$ to calculate the magnitude of the gravitational field strength on each celestial body. The magnitude of the gravitational acceleration is numerically equal to the magnitude of the gravitational field strength.

Earth

$$
\begin{aligned}
g_{Earth} &= \frac{Gm_{Earth}}{(r_{Earth})^2} \\[2mm]
&= \frac{\left(6.67 \times 10^{-11} \dfrac{N \cdot m^2}{kg^2}\right)(5.97 \times 10^{24} \, kg)}{(6.38 \times 10^6 \, m)^2} \\[2mm]
&= 9.783 \text{ N/kg} \\
&= 9.783 \text{ m/s}^2
\end{aligned}
$$

The Moon

$$
\begin{aligned}
g_{Moon} &= \frac{Gm_{Moon}}{(r_{Moon})^2} \\[2mm]
&= \frac{\left(6.67 \times 10^{-11} \dfrac{N \cdot m^2}{kg^2}\right)(7.35 \times 10^{22} \, kg)}{(1.74 \times 10^6 \, m)^2} \\[2mm]
&= 1.619 \text{ N/kg} \\
&= 1.619 \text{ m/s}^2
\end{aligned}
$$

(b) Calculate the ratio of g_{Earth} to g_{Moon}.

$$
\begin{aligned}
\frac{g_{Earth}}{g_{Moon}} &= \frac{9.783 \, \dfrac{m}{s^2}}{1.619 \, \dfrac{m}{s^2}} \\[2mm]
&= 6.04
\end{aligned}
$$

Paraphrase

(a) The magnitude of the gravitational acceleration at the equator on the surface of Earth is 9.78 m/s² and of the Moon is 1.62 m/s².

(b) The ratio of g_{Earth} to g_{Moon} is 6.04. So your weight would be about 6 times less on the surface of the Moon than on Earth.

Practice Problems

1. A satellite orbits Earth at a distance of $3r_{Earth}$ above Earth's surface. Refer to Table 4.1 on page 218.
   (a) How many Earth radii is the satellite from Earth's centre?
   (b) What is the magnitude of the gravitational acceleration of the satellite?

2. An 80.0-kg astronaut is in orbit 3.20×10^4 km from Earth's centre. Refer to Table 4.1 on page 218.
   (a) Calculate the magnitude of the gravitational field strength at the location of the astronaut.
   (b) What would be the magnitude of the gravitational field strength if the astronaut is orbiting the Moon with the same separation distance?

3. The highest satellites orbit Earth at a distance of about $6.6r_{Earth}$ from Earth's centre. What would be the gravitational force on a 70-kg astronaut at this location?

Answers

1. (a) $4r_{Earth}$
   (b) 6.11×10^{-1} m/s²

2. (a) 3.89×10^{-1} N/kg
   (b) 4.79×10^{-3} N/kg

3. 16 N [toward Earth's centre]

Calculating the Weight of an Object on Mars

The equation $g = \dfrac{GM_{source}}{r^2}$ can be used to calculate the weight of an object on any celestial body. In Example 4.6, the weight of a student on Mars is calculated. This quantity is then compared with the student's weight on Earth's surface.

An interesting application of the variation in the weight of an object involves the Mars rover (Figure 4.32). The rover had a mass of about 175 kg, but on the surface of Mars, the rover weighed about 2.5 times less than on Earth's surface. The rover was designed to avoid inclines greater than 30° but because $g_{Mars} < g_{Earth}$, the rover could travel farther up an incline on Mars than on Earth using the same battery charge.

▲ **Figure 4.32** In full sunlight, a 140-W battery enabled the Mars rover to travel about 100 m per day on level ground with an average speed of 1.0 cm/s between charges.

Example 4.6

(a) What is the mass of a 60.0-kg student on Mars and on Earth?

(b) What is the student's weight at the equator on the surface of Mars and of Earth (Figure 4.33). Refer to Table 4.1 on page 218.

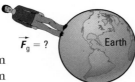

Given

(a) $m_s = 60.0$ kg

(b) $m_{Mars} = 6.42 \times 10^{23}$ kg $r_{Mars} = 3.40 \times 10^6$ m
    $m_{Earth} = 5.97 \times 10^{24}$ kg $r_{Earth} = 6.38 \times 10^6$ m

Required

(a) mass on Mars and on Earth (m)

(b) weight on Mars and on Earth ($\vec{F}_{g_{Mars}}$ and $\vec{F}_{g_{Earth}}$)

▲ **Figure 4.33**

Analysis and Solution

(a) Mass is a scalar quantity and does not depend on location. So the student's mass will be the same on Mars as on Earth.

(b) Use the equation $g = \dfrac{GM_{source}}{r^2}$ to calculate the magnitude of the gravitational field strength on Mars and on Earth.

Mars

$$g_{Mars} = \frac{Gm_{Mars}}{(r_{Mars})^2}$$

$$= \frac{\left(6.67 \times 10^{-11} \dfrac{\text{N}\cdot\text{m}^2}{\text{kg}^2}\right)(6.42 \times 10^{23} \text{ kg})}{(3.40 \times 10^6 \text{ m})^2}$$

$$= 3.704 \text{ N/kg}$$

Earth

$$g_{Earth} = \frac{Gm_{Earth}}{(r_{Earth})^2}$$

$$= \frac{\left(6.67 \times 10^{-11} \dfrac{\text{N}\cdot\text{m}^2}{\text{kg}^2}\right)(5.97 \times 10^{24} \text{ kg})}{(6.38 \times 10^6 \text{ m})^2}$$

$$= 9.783 \text{ N/kg}$$

Since the direction of $\vec{F}_g$ will be toward the centre of each celestial body, use the scalar equation $F_g = mg$ to find the magnitude of the weight.

Mars

$$F_{g_{Mars}} = m_s g_{Mars}$$

$$= (60.0 \text{ kg})\left(3.704 \frac{\text{N}}{\text{kg}}\right)$$

$$= 222 \text{ N}$$

Earth

$$F_{g_{Earth}} = m_s g_{Earth}$$

$$= (60.0 \text{ kg})\left(9.783 \frac{\text{N}}{\text{kg}}\right)$$

$$= 587 \text{ N}$$

Practice Problems

1. What would be the weight of a 22.0-kg dog at the equator on Saturn's surface? Refer to Table 4.1 on page 218.

2. (a) Do you think your skeleton could support your weight on Jupiter?
   (b) Compared to Earth, how much stronger would your bones need to be?

3. (a) What is the magnitude of the gravitational field strength at the equator on Uranus' surface?
   (b) Compared to Earth, how would your weight change on Uranus?

Answers

1. 229 N [toward Saturn's centre]

2. (a) no
   (b) 2.53 times

3. (a) 8.83 N/kg, (b) 0.903 $F_{g_{Earth}}$

Different Values of Gravitational Field Strength on Earth

For a long time, people thought that the magnitude of the gravitational field strength was constant at any location on Earth's surface. However, scientists discovered that the value of g depends on both latitude and altitude. **Latitude** is the angular distance north or south of the equator. **Altitude** is the elevation of the ground above sea level. Figure 4.34 shows how the magnitude of the gravitational field strength at sea level varies with latitude.

info **BIT**

The value 9.81 N/kg is an average of the magnitude of the gravitational field strength at different locations on Earth's surface.

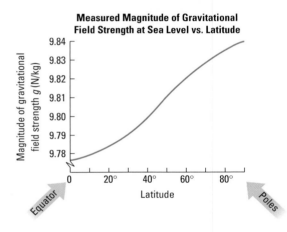

◀ **Figure 4.34** Gravitational field strength at sea level as a function of latitude. At what location on Earth's surface would you weigh the least? The most?

The value of g increases as you move toward either the North or South Pole, because Earth is not a perfect sphere. It is flatter at the poles and it bulges out slightly at the equator. In fact, Earth's radius is 21 km greater at the equator than at the poles. So an object at the equator is farther away from Earth's centre than if the object were at the North Pole. Since $g \propto \dfrac{1}{r^2}$, the farther an object is from Earth's centre, the smaller the value of g will be.

Other factors affect the value of g at Earth's surface. The materials that make up Earth's crust are not uniformly distributed. Some materials, such as gold, are more dense than materials such as zinc. Earth's rotation about its axis also reduces the measured value of g, but the closer an object is to the North or South Pole, the less effect Earth's rotation has on g.

Concept Check

Leo weighs 638 N [down] in Calgary, Alberta. What are some problems with Leo saying he weighs 638 N [down] anywhere on Earth? What property of matter would he be more accurate to state?

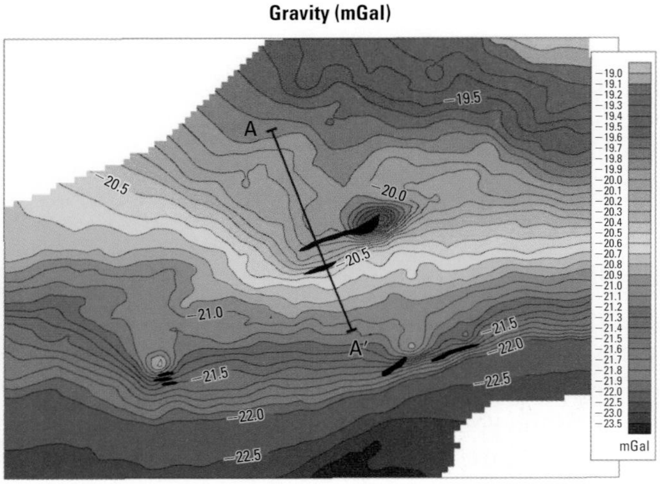

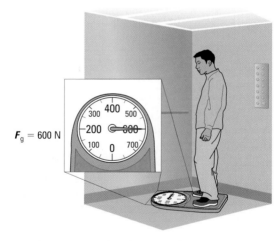

Gravity (mGal)
A
A′
−19.5
−20.5
−20.0
−20.5
−21.0
−21.5
−22.0
−22.5
−21.5
−22.0
−22.5
−19.0 −19.1 −19.2 −19.3 −19.4 −19.5 −19.6 −19.7 −19.8 −19.9 −20.0 −20.1 −20.2 −20.3 −20.4 −20.5 −20.6 −20.7 −20.8 −20.9 −21.0 −21.1 −21.2 −21.3 −21.4 −21.5 −21.6 −21.7 −21.8 −21.9 −22.0 −22.5 −23.0 −23.5
mGal

▲ **Figure 4.35** A map showing the location of sulphide deposits in northern New Brunswick (shown in black)

Applications of the Variation in *g* in Geology

The variation in the value of g on Earth is used to detect the presence of minerals and oil. Geophysicists and geologists use sensitive instruments, called **gravimeters**, to detect small variations in g when they search for new deposits of ore or oil. Gold and silver deposits increase the value of g, while deposits of oil and natural gas decrease g. Figure 4.35 is an example of a map that shows different measured values of g as lines, where each line represents a specific value of g.

True Weight vs. Apparent Weight

true weight: gravitational force acting on an object that has mass

So far, you used the equation $\vec{F}_g = m\vec{g}$ to calculate the weight of an object at any location in the universe. The gravitational force that you calculate with this equation is really called the **true weight**, $\vec{F}_g$, of an object.

Suppose a student is standing on a scale calibrated in newtons in an elevator (Figure 4.36). If the elevator is at rest or is moving at constant velocity, the scale reads 600 N.

F_g = 600 N
300
400
500
200
600
100
0
700

▲ **Figure 4.36** The elevator and student are either at rest or moving at constant velocity.

$\vec{a} = 0$
$\vec{v}$ = constant
$\vec{F}_N$
$\vec{F}_g$

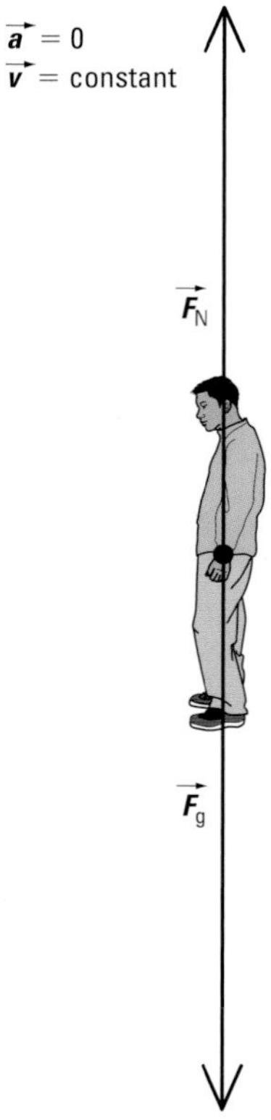

▲ **Figure 4.37** The free-body diagram for the student in Figure 4.36

Using the free-body diagram for the student (Figure 4.37), the equation for the net force on the student is

$$\vec{F}_{net} = \vec{F}_g + \vec{F}_N$$
$$0 = \vec{F}_g + \vec{F}_N$$
$$0 = F_g + F_N$$
$$0 = -mg + F_N$$
$$F_N = mg$$

So when $\vec{F}_{net} = 0$ N on the student, the magnitude of the normal force is equal to the magnitude of the student's weight.

Now suppose the elevator is accelerating up uniformly (Figure 4.38). In this situation, the scale reads 750 N.

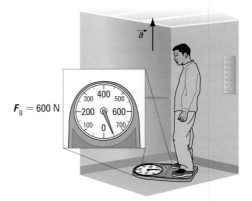

$F_g = 600$ N

▲ **Figure 4.38** The elevator and student are accelerating up uniformly.

To understand why the reading on the scale is different, draw the free-body diagram for the student (Figure 4.39) and write the equation for the net force:

$$\vec{F}_{net} = \vec{F}_g + \vec{F}_N$$
$$m\vec{a} = \vec{F}_g + \vec{F}_N$$
$$\vec{F}_N = m\vec{a} - \vec{F}_g$$
$$= m\vec{a} - m\vec{g}$$
$$= m(\vec{a} - \vec{g})$$

The equation for $\vec{F}_N$ is valid whether the student is accelerating up or down. In Figure 4.38, the student feels heavier than usual because the scale is pushing up on him with a force greater than mg.

If the elevator is accelerating down uniformly, the scale reads 525 N (Figure 4.40). As before, $\vec{F}_N = m(\vec{a} - \vec{g})$ but this time $\vec{a}$ and $\vec{g}$ are in the same direction. So F_N is less than mg, and the student feels lighter than usual.

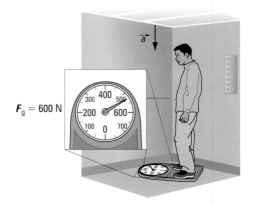

$F_g = 600$ N

▲ **Figure 4.40** The elevator and student are accelerating down uniformly.

▲ **Figure 4.39** The free-body diagram for the student in Figure 4.38

e **SIM**

Calculate the true weight, normal force, and apparent weight of a person during an elevator ride. Follow the eSim links at www.pearsoned.ca/school/physicssource.

The quantity $-\vec{F}_N$ is called the **apparent weight**, $\vec{w}$, of an object. For the situations shown in Figures 4.38 and 4.40 on page 223, the equation for the apparent weight of the student is

$$\boxed{\vec{w} = -\vec{F}_N}$$
$$= -m(\vec{a} - \vec{g})$$
$$= m(\vec{g} - \vec{a})$$

Example 4.7 demonstrates how to calculate the true weight and apparent weight of an astronaut in a rocket during liftoff on Earth's surface.

Example 4.7

A 100.0-kg astronaut in a spacesuit is standing on a scale in a rocket (Figure 4.41). The acceleration of the rocket is 19.6 m/s² [up]. Calculate her true weight and apparent weight during liftoff on Earth. The acceleration due to gravity on Earth's surface is 9.81 m/s² [down].

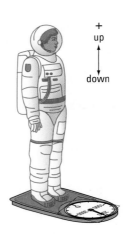

Given
$m = 100.0$ kg
$\vec{a} = 19.6$ m/s² [up] $\vec{g} = 9.81$ m/s² [down]

Required
true weight and apparent weight during liftoff
($\vec{F}_g$ and $\vec{w}$)

▲ **Figure 4.41**

Analysis and Solution
Draw a free-body diagram and a vector addition diagram for the astronaut (Figure 4.42).

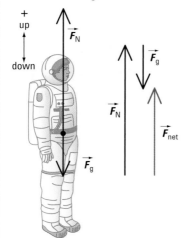

◀ **Figure 4.42**

Use the equation $\vec{F}_g = m\vec{g}$ to find the astronaut's true weight.

$$\vec{F}_g = m\vec{g}$$
$$= (100.0 \text{ kg})\left(-9.81\,\frac{\text{m}}{\text{s}^2}\right)$$
$$= -9.81 \times 10^2 \text{ N}$$

The astronaut is not accelerating left or right. So in the horizontal direction, $\vec{F}_{net} = 0$ N.

For the vertical direction, write an equation to find the net force on the astronaut.

$$\vec{F}_{net} = \vec{F}_N + \vec{F}_g$$

Apply Newton's second law.

$$m\vec{a} = \vec{F}_N + \vec{F}_g$$

$$\vec{F}_N = m\vec{a} - \vec{F}_g$$

$$\begin{aligned} F_N &= ma - F_g \\ &= (100.0 \text{ kg})\left(19.6 \, \frac{\text{m}}{\text{s}^2}\right) - (-9.81 \times 10^2 \text{ N}) \\ &= (100.0 \text{ kg})\left(19.6 \, \frac{\text{m}}{\text{s}^2}\right) + 9.81 \times 10^2 \text{ N} \\ &= 2.94 \times 10^3 \text{ N} \end{aligned}$$

$$\vec{F}_N = 2.94 \times 10^3 \text{ N [up]}$$

Use the equation $\vec{w} = -\vec{F}_N$ to find the astronaut's apparent weight.

$$\begin{aligned} \vec{w} &= -\vec{F}_N \\ &= -(2.94 \times 10^3 \text{ N}) \\ &= -2.94 \times 10^3 \text{ N} \end{aligned}$$

Paraphrase
During liftoff, the astronaut's true weight is 9.81×10^2 N [down] and her apparent weight is 2.94×10^3 N [down].

In Example 4.8, an astronaut is accelerating in deep space, a location in which the gravitational force acting on an object is not measurable. So in deep space, $\vec{F}_g = 0$.

Example 4.8

Refer to Example 4.7 on pages 224 and 225. What is the magnitude of the astronaut's true weight and apparent weight if the rocket is in deep space? The magnitude of the acceleration of the rocket is 19.6 m/s².

Given
$m = 100.0$ kg

magnitude of $\vec{a} = 19.6$ m/s² $\vec{g} = 0$ m/s²

Required
magnitude of true weight and apparent weight in deep space ($\vec{F}_g$ and $\vec{w}$)

Analysis and Solution
In deep space, the mass of the astronaut is still 100.0 kg, but $\vec{g} = 0$ m/s².

So $\vec{F}_g = m\vec{g}$
              $= 0$ N

The astronaut is not accelerating left or right.
So in the horizontal direction, $\vec{F}_{net} = 0$ N.

Practice Problems

1. In Example 4.7, draw the free-body diagram for the scale during liftoff.

2. Suppose the rocket in Example 4.7 has an acceleration of 19.6 m/s² [down] while it is near Earth's surface. What will be the astronaut's apparent weight and true weight?

Answers

1. See page 898.
2. 9.79×10^2 N [down], 9.81×10^2 N [down]

Practice Problems

1. An 80.0-kg astronaut is standing on a scale in a rocket leaving the surface of the Moon. The acceleration of the rocket is 12.8 m/s² [up]. On the Moon, $\vec{g} = 1.62$ N/kg [down]. Calculate the magnitude of the true weight and apparent weight of the astronaut
   (a) during liftoff, and
   (b) if the rocket has the same acceleration in deep space.

2. A 60.0-kg astronaut is standing on a scale in a rocket about to land on the surface of Mars. The acceleration of the rocket is −11.1 m/s² [down]. Refer to Table 4.1 on page 218. Calculate the true weight and apparent weight of the astronaut
   (a) as the rocket lands, and
   (b) if the rocket is accelerating at 7.38 m/s² [up] when leaving Mars.

For the vertical direction, write an equation to find the net force on the astronaut. Refer to the free-body diagram in Figure 4.42 on page 224.

$$\vec{F}_{net} = \vec{F}_g + \vec{F}_N$$
$$= 0 + \vec{F}_N$$
$$= \vec{F}_N$$

Apply Newton's second law.

$$\vec{F}_N = m\vec{a}$$

$$F_N = ma$$
$$= (100.0 \text{ kg})\left(19.6 \ \frac{\text{m}}{\text{s}^2}\right)$$
$$= 1.96 \times 10^3 \text{ N}$$

Use the equation $\vec{w} = -\vec{F}_N$ to find the astronaut's apparent weight.

$$\vec{w} = -\vec{F}_N$$
$$= -(1.96 \times 10^3 \text{ N})$$
$$= -1.96 \times 10^3 \text{ N}$$

Paraphrase
In deep space, the astronaut's true weight is zero and the magnitude of her apparent weight is 1.96×10^3 N.

Free Fall

Let's revisit the elevator scenario on pages 222 and 223. Suppose the elevator cable breaks (Figure 4.43). Assuming that frictional forces are negligible, the elevator, student, and scale all fall toward Earth with an acceleration of g. The student is now in **free fall**, the condition in which the only force acting on an object is $\vec{F}_g$.

free fall: situation in which the only force acting on an object that has mass is the gravitational force

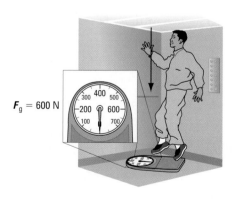

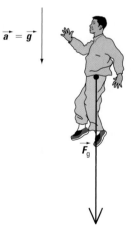

▲ **Figure 4.43** The elevator, student, and scale are in free fall.

▲ **Figure 4.44** The free-body diagram for the student in Figure 4.43

To understand free fall, draw the free-body diagram for the student (Figure 4.44) and write the equation for the net force:

$$\vec{F}_{net} = \vec{F}_g$$

$$m\vec{a} = \vec{F}_g$$

$$\cancel{m}\vec{a} = \cancel{m}\vec{g}$$

$$\vec{a} = \vec{g}$$

So in free fall, $\vec{a} = \vec{g}$ and both the student and the scale are accelerating at g downward. In Figure 4.43 on page 226, the scale reads zero because it no longer exerts a normal force on the student, so $\vec{F}_N = 0$. Since $\vec{F}_N = 0$, the student's apparent weight is also zero. Sometimes an object in free fall is described as being "weightless." However, this description is incorrect. In free fall, $\vec{F}_N = \vec{w} = 0$ but $\vec{F}_g \neq 0$.

Observe the motion of water in a cup while in free fall by doing 4-4 QuickLab.

4-4 QuickLab

Water in Free Fall

Problem

What is the motion of water in a cup when the cup is dropped from several metres above Earth's surface?

> ⚠ **CAUTION: Do this activity outside. Have someone steady the ladder and be careful when climbing it.**

Materials

paper cup
pointed pen or pencil
water
dishpan
stepladder

Procedure

1. Make two holes on opposite sides of the cup near the bottom using the pen or pencil. Cover the holes with your thumb and forefinger. Then fill the cup with water.

e LAB

For a probeware activity, go to www.pearsoned.ca/school/physicssource.

2. Hold the cup at shoulder height above a dishpan, and uncover the holes. Observe what happens to the water (Figure 4.45). Have a partner sketch the path the water takes.

3. Repeat step 1 but climb the ladder and drop the cup toward the dishpan from a height of several metres. Observe the motion of the water during the fall.

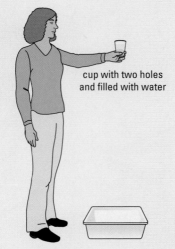

cup with two holes and filled with water

Questions

1. Describe the path and motion of the water
   (a) when the cup was held stationary, and

▲ **Figure 4.45**

   (b) when the cup was dropped from the ladder. Give a reason for your observations.

Weightlessness

Videos transmitted from a space shuttle or the space station often show astronauts floating in their cabin (Figure 4.46). Are the astronauts weightless in space? The answer is no. Then why do they appear to be weightless?

Since the shuttle is some distance above Earth, g is less than its value at Earth's surface, because $g \propto \dfrac{1}{r^2}$. While the shuttle orbits Earth at high speed in an almost circular path, Earth exerts a gravitational force on the shuttle and everything in it. So the shuttle is able to remain in orbit.

If an astronaut were standing on a scale in the shuttle, the scale would read zero, because the shuttle and everything in it are in free fall. The astronaut would feel "weightless" because the gravitational force exerted by Earth pulls the shuttle and the astronaut toward Earth.

Suppose an astronaut is in a rocket in deep space and the acceleration of the rocket is zero. The astronaut would experience no measurable gravitational forces from any celestial bodies, and the astronaut's acceleration would be zero. In this situation, the astronaut would have a true weight of zero and an apparent weight of zero, a condition called **true weightlessness**.

true weightlessness: situation in which $\vec{w} = 0$ for an object and $\vec{F}_g = 0$ on the object

▲ **Figure 4.46** At the altitude of the shuttle, the value of g is about 90% of its value at Earth's surface.

Knowledge

1. (a) What is the difference between true weight and apparent weight?

   (b) Describe a situation in which the true weight of an object is zero but its apparent weight is not zero.

2. A person orbiting Earth in a spacecraft has an apparent weight of zero. Explain if the person still experiences a gravitational force.

3. List two factors that affect the magnitude of the gravitational field strength at Earth's surface.

Applications

4. Is there a place in the universe where true weightlessness actually exists? Where or why not?

5. Calculate the gravitational field strength at the location of a 70-kg astronaut $2.0r_{Earth}$ from Earth's centre. Refer to Table 4.1 on page 218.

6. Graph the equation $g = \dfrac{Gm_{Moon}}{r^2}$ using technology. Refer to Student References 5: Graphing Data on pp. 872–874. Plot g on the y-axis (range of $0-2.0$ N/kg) and r on the x-axis (range of $1-5r_{Moon}$). Toggle through to read values of g corresponding to specific values of r_{Moon} to answer these questions:

   (a) Describe the graph of g vs. r_{Moon}. How is it similar to Figure 4.10 on page 201?

   (b) What is the value of g

   (i) on the surface?

   (ii) at $\dfrac{1}{2} r_{Moon}$ above the surface?

   (iii) at r_{Moon} above the surface?

   (c) At what distance from the Moon's surface is g negligible?

7. At the top of Mount Robson in British Columbia, a 7.5-kg turkey weighs 73.6 N [down]. Calculate the magnitude of the gravitational field strength at this location.

8. An astronaut in a rocket has an apparent weight of 1.35×10^3 N [down]. If the acceleration of the rocket is 14.7 m/s² [up] near Earth's surface, what is the astronaut's true weight? The acceleration due to gravity on Earth's surface is about 9.81 m/s² [down].

9. A 50-kg astronaut experiences an acceleration of $5.0g$ [up] during liftoff.

   (a) Draw a free-body diagram for the astronaut during liftoff.

   (b) What is the astronaut's true weight and apparent weight?

10. Calculate the acceleration of the elevator in Figures 4.38 and 4.40 on page 223.

Extensions

11. Draw a flowchart to summarize the steps needed to find the apparent weight of an object. Refer to Student References 4: Using Graphic Organizers on page 869.

12. Research how geophysicists and geologists use gravitational field strength to locate minerals, oil, and natural gas in Canada. Prepare a half-page report on your findings. Begin your search at www.pearsoned.ca/school/physicssource.

13. Suppose you are wearing a spacesuit. Where could you walk faster, on Earth or on the Moon? Explain your answer.

14. Draw a concept map to identify and link the concepts needed to understand gravitational acceleration and gravitational field strength near a celestial body other than Earth. Refer to Student References 4: Using Graphic Organizers on page 869. Create and solve a problem to demonstrate your understanding of these concepts.

e **TEST**

To check your understanding of gravitational field strength, true weight, apparent weight, and free fall, follow the eTest links at www.pearsoned.ca/school/physicssource.

Key Terms and Concepts

gravitational force
weight
gravitational mass
action-at-a-distance force

field
gravitational field
gravitational field
   strength

torsion balance
true weight
apparent weight

free fall
true weightlessness

Key Equations

True weight: $\vec{F}_g = m\vec{g}$

Newton's law of gravitation: $F_g = \dfrac{Gm_A m_B}{r^2}$

Gravitational field strength (or gravitational acceleration): $g = \dfrac{GM_{source}}{r^2}$

Apparent weight: $\vec{w} = -\vec{F}_N$

Conceptual Overview

The concept map below summarizes many of the concepts and equations in this chapter. Copy and complete the map to have a full summary of the chapter.

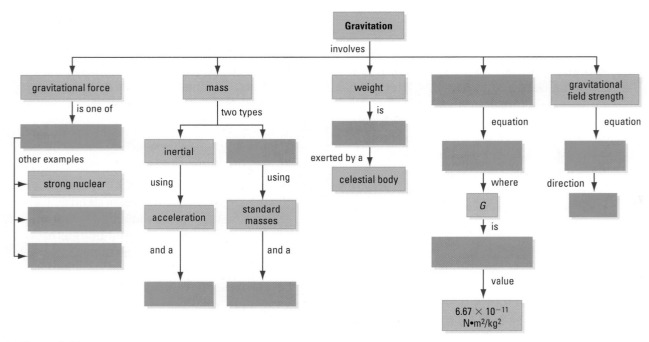

▲ **Figure 4.47**

Knowledge

1. (4.2) What is the significance of the term "universal" in Newton's law of universal gravitation?

2. (4.1, 4.3) A brick placed on an equal arm balance requires 5.0 kg to just balance it. When the brick is hung from a spring scale, the scale reads 48 N. The balance, standard masses, spring scale, and brick are moved to a planet where the gravitational field strength is 2.0 times that on Earth. What will be the reading on the balance and on the spring scale in this new location?

3. (4.1, 4.3) How does gravitational field strength vary with the mass of a celestial body? Assume that the radius is constant.

4. (4.3) The gravitational field strength at Earth's surface is about 9.81 N/kg [down]. What is the gravitational field strength $1.6r_{Earth}$ from Earth's centre?

Applications

5. A 1.0-kg object, initially at rest, is dropped toward Earth's surface. It takes 2.26 s for the object to fall 25 m. Determine how long it takes a 2.0-kg object to fall this distance from rest on Jupiter. Refer to Table 4.1 on page 218.

6. Describe the steps you would use to determine the distance from Earth's centre where the gravitational force exerted by Earth on a spacecraft is balanced by the gravitational force exerted by the Moon. Assume that you know the distance from Earth's centre to the centre of the Moon. Do not do the calculations.

7. Refer to Table 4.1 on page 218. Calculate the true weight of a 60.0-kg astronaut on
   (a) the surface of Mars, and
   (b) the surface of Saturn.

8. Objects A and B experience a gravitational force of magnitude 2.5×10^{-8} N. Determine the magnitude of the gravitational force if the separation distance is halved, m_A increases by 8 times, and m_B is reduced to $\frac{1}{4}$ of its original value.

9. Suppose a 65-kg astronaut on Mars is standing on a scale calibrated in newtons in an elevator. What will be the reading on the scale when the acceleration of the elevator is
   (a) zero?
   (b) 7.2 m/s² [up]?
   (c) 3.6 m/s² [down]?

10. A 50-kg rock in a Nahanni River canyon breaks loose from the edge of a cliff and falls 500 m into the water below. The average air resistance is 125 N.
    (a) What is the average acceleration of the rock?
    (b) How long does the rock take to reach the water?
    (c) What is the true weight of the rock?
    (d) Does the rock have an apparent weight? Explain.

Extensions

11. Research why astronauts do exercises in space and why they have difficulty walking when they return to Earth. Write a short paragraph of your findings. Begin your search at www.pearsoned.ca/school/physicssource.

12. Pilots in high-speed planes are subject to *g* forces. Healthy people can withstand up to 3–4 *g*s. Beyond that limit, the blood will pool in the lower half of the body and not reach the brain, causing the pilot to lose consciousness. Research how Dr. Wilbur Franks from Toronto found a solution to this problem. What connection does this problem have to human survival during a space flight? Begin your search at www.pearsoned.ca/school/physicssource.

Consolidate Your Understanding

13. Write a paragraph summarizing Newton's law of gravitation. Include a numerical example that illustrates the law. Show a detailed solution.

Think About It

Review your answers to the Think About It questions on page 195. How would you answer each question now?

 e **TEST**

To check your understanding of gravitation concepts, follow the eTest links at www.pearsoned.ca/school/physicssource.

Tire Design, Stopping Distance, and Vehicle Mass

Scenario

Imagine that you work for Alberta Infrastructure and Transportation. A level section of highway in the mountains has an abnormally large number of accidents. The surface of one lane of the highway is concrete and the other is asphalt. You are a member of a research team formed to determine the stopping distances in the summer for both wet and dry days for different types of tires and for different masses of vehicles. Your team is to prepare a written report on your findings for the Traffic Branch of the Ministry. Assume that the vehicles are travelling at the posted speed limit of 90 km/h when the brakes are applied and that the vehicles are not equipped with anti-lock braking systems (ABS). Assume that the reaction time of drivers before they apply the brakes is 1.8 s.

Planning

Form a team of three to five members. Summarize the question your group is researching. Make hypotheses about how tire tread, surface condition, and vehicle mass might affect stopping distance. Assign roles to different team members. Some examples are team leader, materials manager, liaison officer, record keeper, and safety officer. Brainstorm strategies for researching and reporting on the question and create a timeline. Research tire designs that are designed to work well on both wet and dry road surfaces. Use the Internet and consult local tire suppliers.

Materials

- a digital camera and a computer
- force-measuring equipment
- mass-measuring equipment
- new and used tires having different treads and designs
- vehicle brochures

Procedure

1. Research the Internet and interview different tire suppliers to identify tires designed to work well at above-freezing temperatures on both wet and dry pavement.

Assessing Results

After completing the project, assess its success based on a rubric designed in class* that considers

- research strategies
- experiment techniques
- clarity and thoroughness of the written report
- effectiveness of the team's presentation
- quality and fairness of the teamwork

2. Visit a local tire supplier and borrow new and used tires of different designs. Photograph the tires to record the tread designs.

3. Design and conduct an experiment to determine the coefficients of static and kinetic friction for the tires on wet and dry asphalt, and wet and dry concrete. Recall that you will need the mass of the tires and the local value of gravitational field strength.

⚠ **CAUTION: Take all your measurements on parking lots or sidewalks, and beware of traffic. Consult the local police department and ask for supervision while doing your experiments.**

4. Research the masses of at least four small, medium, and large vehicles travelling highways that would use these tires. Determine the average mass of each class of vehicle. Sales brochures from vehicle dealers have mass information.

5. Determine the average deceleration on both wet and dry roadways for the vehicles of different mass equipped with these tires. Remember that some drivers may lock their brakes while braking.

6. Determine the stopping distance for the different vehicles under different conditions. Remember to consider driver reaction time.

7. Write a report of your findings. Use graphs and tables where appropriate. Prepare the report in a format suitable for publishing in a school magazine or local newspaper.

Thinking Further

Write a three-paragraph addition to your team's report hypothesizing how driver education, changing the posted speed limit, and requiring that vehicles be equipped with ABS brakes might affect the results.

*Note: Your instructor will assess the project using a similar assessment rubric.

Unit Concepts and Skills: Quick Reference

Concepts	Summary	Resources and Skill Building
CHAPTER 3	**Forces can change velocity.**	
	3.1 The Nature of Force	
Force	Force is a push or a pull on an object. Force is a vector quantity measured in newtons ($1\ N = 1\ kg \cdot m/s^2$).	3-1 QuickLab 3-2 QuickLab Examples 3.1–3.4
Net force	Net force is the vector sum of two or more forces acting simultaneously on an object. A free-body diagram helps you write the net force acting on an object.	Examples 3.2–3.4
	3.2 Newton's First Law of Motion	
Newton's first law	Newton's first law states that an object will continue being at rest or moving at constant speed in a straight line unless acted upon by a non-zero net force.	3-3 QuickLab
	3.3 Newton's Second Law of Motion	
Newton's second law	Newton's second law states that when a non-zero net force acts on an object, the object accelerates in the direction of the net force. The magnitude of the acceleration is directly proportional to the magnitude of the net force and inversely proportional to the mass of the object.	3-5 Inquiry Lab Figures 3.33–3.35 3-6 Design a Lab Examples 3.5–3.11
	3.4 Newton's Third Law of Motion	
Newton's third law	Newton's third law states that if object A exerts a force on object B, then B exerts a force on A that is equal in magnitude and opposite in direction.	3-7 QuickLab Figures 3.53–3.57, 3.63, 3.65 3-8 QuickLab Examples 3.12, 3.13 3-9 Design a Lab
	3.5 Friction Affects Motion	
Types of friction	Friction is a force that opposes either the motion of an object or the direction the object would be moving in if there were no friction. Static friction is present when an object is stationary but experiences an applied force. Kinetic friction is present when an object is moving.	3-10 QuickLab Figures 3.70, 3.74, 3.78–3.80 Examples 3.14–3.16
Factors affecting friction	The magnitude of the force of friction acting on an object is directly proportional to the normal force on the object.	3-11 Inquiry Lab
Coefficients of static and kinetic friction	The coefficients of friction are proportionality constants that relate the magnitude of the force of friction to the magnitude of the normal force. Temperature, moisture, and the smoothness or roughness of the contact surfaces, and the materials forming the contact surface are some factors that affect the value of the coefficients of friction.	Table 3.4 Examples 3.17–3.20
CHAPTER 4	**Gravity extends throughout the universe.**	
	4.1 Gravitational Forces due to Earth	
Gravitational force	Gravitational force is a fundamental force, and can be described as an action-at-a-distance force or as a field.	4-1 QuickLab
Gravitational field strength	Gravitational field strength is the ratio of gravitational force to mass at a specific location. The units of gravitational field strength are N/kg.	4-2 QuickLab Figure 4.10
	4.2 Newton's Law of Universal Gravitation	
Newton's law of universal gravitation	Newton's law of universal gravitation states that the gravitational force of attraction between any two masses is directly proportional to the product of the masses and inversely proportional to the square of the separation distance between the centres of both masses.	Figures 4.11–4.13, 4.16, 4.24 Examples 4.1–4.4
	4.3 Relating Gravitational Field Strength to Gravitational Force	
Calculating g anywhere in the universe	Newton's law of gravitation can be used to determine the magnitude of gravitational field strength anywhere in the universe. The magnitude of gravitational field strength at a location is numerically equal to the magnitude of gravitational acceleration.	4-3 Design a Lab Examples 4.5–4.6
Variations of g	The value of g at Earth's surface depends on latitude, altitude, the composition of Earth's crust, and Earth's rotation about its axis.	Figures 4.34, 4.35
True weight, apparent weight, free fall, and weightlessness	The true weight of an object is equal to the gravitational force acting on the mass, and depends on location. Apparent weight is the negative of the normal force acting on an object. Free fall is the condition where the only force acting on an object is the gravitational force. True weightlessness is the condition in which $\vec{w} = 0$ for an object and $\vec{F}_g = 0$ on the object.	Figures 4.36–4.40, 4.43, 4.44, 4.46 4-4 QuickLab Examples 4.7, 4.8

Vocabulary

1. Using your own words, define these terms, concepts, principles, or laws.

   action-at-a-distance force
   action force
   apparent weight
   coefficient of friction
   field
   free-body diagram
   free fall
   gravitational field strength
   gravitational force
   gravitational mass
   inertia
   inertial mass
   kinetic friction
   net force
   Newton's first law
   Newton's law of gravitation
   Newton's second law
   Newton's third law
   normal force
   reaction force
   static friction
   tension
   true weight

Knowledge

CHAPTER 3

2. An object experiences three forces: $\vec{F}_1$ is 60 N [22.0°], $\vec{F}_2$ is 36 N [110°], and $\vec{F}_3$ is 83 N [300°]. Explain, using words and diagrams, how to calculate the net force on the object. What is the net force?

3. An object experiences zero net force. Work with a partner to describe the possibilities for its motion.

4. A person with a plaster cast on an arm or leg experiences extra fatigue. Use Newton's laws to explain to a classmate the reason for this fatigue.

5. Use inertia and Newton's first law to explain how the spin cycle in a washing machine removes water from wet clothes.

6. A load is placed on a 1.5-kg cart. A force of 6.0 N [left] causes the cart and its load to have an acceleration of 3.0 m/s² [left]. What is the inertial mass of the load?

7. What happens to the acceleration of an object if the mass is constant and the net force

   (a) quadruples?

   (b) is divided by 4?

   (c) becomes zero?

8. Two people, A and B, are pulling a wagon on a horizontal, frictionless surface with two ropes. Person A applies a force [50°] on one rope. Person B applies a force of 25.0 N [345°] on the other rope. If the net force on the wagon is 55.4 N [26°], calculate the magnitude of person A's applied force.

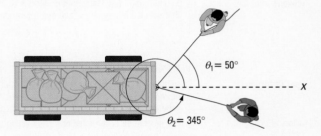

9. A book is at rest on a table. The table is exerting an upward force on the book that is equal in magnitude to the downward force exerted by the book on the table. What law does this example illustrate?

10. A pencil exerts a force of 15 N [down] on a notebook. What is the reaction force? What object is exerting the reaction force?

11. Explain why the coefficients of static and kinetic friction are numerals without units.

12. Draw a free-body diagram for a stationary 5.0-kg block resting on a rough incline forming an angle of 30.0° with the horizontal.

    (a) Explain why the block is stationary.

    (b) Explain why a free-body diagram is helpful to describe the situation.

13. How does the ability of a car slowing down on wet asphalt compare to it slowing down on wet concrete? Refer to Table 3.4 on page 183.

14. Compare the acceleration due to gravity and the gravitational field strength at the top of a tall skyscraper on Earth.

15. Consider the quantities gravitational force, mass, and gravitational field strength. Which of these quantities affects the inertia of an object?

16. Suppose an athlete were competing in the 2010 Winter Olympics in Vancouver and Whistler, British Columbia. Whistler has an elevation of 2182 m at the top and 652 m at the base. If the ski jumping and bobsled events are held near the top of the mountain rather than at the base, how might the results of these events be affected?

17. Two bags, each containing 10 oranges of equal mass, are hung 4 m apart. In a small group, describe two situations, one involving mass and the other involving separation distance, that would double the gravitational force exerted by one bag on the other. Explain your answer.

18. A student working on a satellite problem got an answer of 57.3 $\dfrac{\text{N} \cdot \text{s}^2}{\text{m}}$. What physical quantity was the student solving for?

19. Use an example to explain the meaning of the statement: "The gravitational force exerted by Mars on a space probe varies inversely as the square of the separation distance between the centre of Mars and the centre of the probe."

20. Is an object in free fall weightless? Explain your reasoning.

21. Compare the gravitational force exerted by Earth (mass M) on two satellites (masses m and $2m$) in orbit the same distance from Earth.

22. Compare the magnitude of Earth's gravitational field strength at the equator and at the North Pole. Explain your answer to a classmate.

23. On Earth, how does the mass of an object affect the values of the quantities below? Explain your answers.
    (a) acceleration due to gravity
    (b) gravitational field strength

Applications

24. Two horizontal forces act on a soccer player: 150 N [40.0°] and 220 N [330°]. Calculate the net force on the player.

25. Calculate the acceleration of a 1478-kg car if it experiences a net force of 3100 N [W].

26. A car is stopped at a stoplight facing due east. When the light turns green, the car gradually speeds up from rest to the city speed limit, and cruises at the speed limit for a while. It then enters a highway on-ramp and gradually speeds up to the highway speed limit all the while heading due east. Sketch a free-body diagram for the car during each stage of its motion (five diagrams in total).

27. A net force of magnitude 8.0 N acts on a 4.0-kg object, causing the velocity of the object to change from 10 m/s [right] to 18 m/s [right]. For how long was the force applied?

28. Two people, on opposite banks, are towing a boat down a narrow river. Each person exerts a force of 65.0 N at an angle of 30.0° to the bank. A force of friction of magnitude 104 N acts on the boat.
    (a) Draw a free-body diagram showing the horizontal forces acting on the boat.
    (b) Calculate the net force on the boat.

29. A force acting on train A causes it to have an acceleration of magnitude 0.40 m/s². Train A has six cars with a total mass of 3.0×10^5 kg, and a locomotive of mass 5.0×10^4 kg. Train B has a locomotive of the same mass as train A, and four cars with a total mass of 2.0×10^5 kg. If the same force acts on train B, what will be its acceleration? Ignore friction.

30. A submarine rescue chamber has a mass of 8.2 t and safely descends at a constant velocity of 10 cm/s [down]. If $g = 9.81$ m/s², what is the upward force exerted by the cable and water on the chamber?

31. A 240-kg motorcycle and 70-kg rider are travelling on a horizontal road. The air resistance acting on the rider-bike system is 1280 N [backward]. The road exerts a force of static friction on the bike of 1950 N [forward]. What is the acceleration of the system?

32. The velocity of a 0.25-kg model rocket changes from 15 m/s [up] to 40 m/s [up] in 0.60 s. Calculate the force that the escaping gas exerts on the rocket.

33. Two boxes, A and B, are in contact and initially stationary on a horizontal, frictionless surface. Box A has a mass of 60 kg and box B a mass of 90 kg. A force of 800 N [right] acts on box A causing it to push on box B.
    (a) What is the acceleration of both boxes?
    (b) What is the magnitude of the action-reaction forces between the boxes?

34. A person exerts a force of 1.5 N [right] to pull a 2.0-kg block of glass at constant velocity along a horizontal surface on the Moon ($g_{Moon} = 1.62$ m/s²). What is the coefficient of kinetic friction for the glass on the surface?

35. Three oak blocks, $m_A = 4.0$ kg, $m_B = 6.0$ kg, and $m_C = 3.0$ kg, are positioned next to each other on a dry, horizontal oak surface. Refer to Table 3.4 on page 183.

(a) What horizontal force must be applied to accelerate the blocks at 1.4 m/s² [forward]?

(b) Calculate the force exerted by m_B on m_C.

(c) Calculate the force exerted by m_B on m_A.

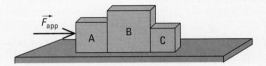

36. A 10.0-kg block is placed on an incline forming an angle of 30.0° with the horizontal. Calculate the acceleration of the block if the coefficient of kinetic friction for the block on the incline is 0.20.

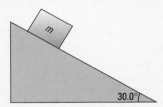

37. A rehabilitation clinic has a device consisting of a light, frictionless pulley attached to a wall support. A patient pulls with a force of magnitude 416 N. The rope exerts a force of friction of magnitude 20 N on the pulley. Calculate the acceleration of m_A and m_B.

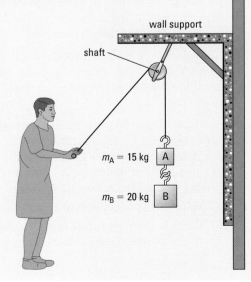

38. Three objects, A, B, and C, are connected together by light strings that pass over light, frictionless pulleys. The coefficient of kinetic friction for object B on the surface is 0.200.

(a) What is the acceleration of object B?

(b) What is the tension in each string? Explain why the tensions are different.

(c) Draw a free-body diagram for object B.

(d) Identify four action-reaction pairs associated with object B.

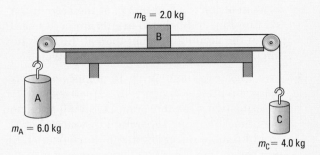

39. The gravitational force on an object located $2r_{Earth}$ from Earth's centre is 200 N [toward Earth's centre]. What is the gravitational force if the object is $10r_{Earth}$ from Earth's centre?

40. A 50-kg diver steps off a 9.0-m diving tower at the same time as a 100-kg diver. Work with a partner to compare the times taken for the two divers to reach the water. Ignore air resistance.

41. Skylab 1, the first American space station, had a mass of about 68 t. It was launched into orbit 435 km above Earth's surface. Calculate the gravitational field strength at the location of Skylab 1 at this altitude. Refer to Table 4.1 on page 218.

42. A spring scale is used to measure the gravitational force acting on a 4.00-kg silver block on Earth's surface. If the block and spring scale are taken to the surface of Mars, by how much does the reading on the spring scale change? Refer to Table 4.1 on page 218.

43. A 60-kg student is standing on a scale in an elevator on Earth. What will be the reading on the scale when the elevator is

(a) (i) moving down at constant speed?

(ii) at rest at a floor?

(iii) accelerating at 4.9 m/s² [up]?

(iv) accelerating at 3.3 m/s² [down]?

(b) What is the student's apparent weight and true weight in all the situations in part (a)?

44. A 60-kg skydiver falls toward Earth with an unopened parachute. The air resistance acting on the skydiver is 200 N [up]. What is the true weight and acceleration of the skydiver?

45. A group of tourists on a ledge overlooking Pulpit Rock, Northwest Territories, dislodge a 25-kg boulder. The rock takes 8.0 s to fall 300 m into the water below. At this location, the gravitational field strength is 9.81 N/kg [down].

(a) Calculate the acceleration of the boulder.

(b) Calculate the air resistance acting on the boulder.

(c) What was the apparent weight of the boulder during its fall?

Extensions

46. The value of g on the Moon is less than that on Earth. So a pendulum on the Moon swings slower than it would on Earth. Suppose a pendulum is 36 cm long. Use the equation

$$T = 2\pi \frac{\sqrt{l}}{\sqrt{g}}$$ to calculate the period, T, at the

equator on Earth and on the Moon. Refer to Table 4.1 on page 218.

47. During the last seconds of a hockey game, the losing team replaces their goalie with a good shooter. The other team shoots the 150-g puck with an initial speed of 7.0 m/s directly toward the unguarded net from a distance of 32 m. The coefficient of kinetic friction for the puck on the ice is 0.08.

(a) What is the force of kinetic friction acting on the puck?

(b) What is the acceleration of the puck?

(c) How long does it take the puck to stop?

(d) Will the puck reach the net if no other player touches it?

48. Construct a gathering grid to distinguish among Newton's three laws. In the left column, identify the criteria you will use to compare and contrast the laws. Add three additional columns, one for each law. Then place checkmarks in the appropriate columns to compare the laws.

49. During the 2000 Sydney Olympics, some swimmers wore special swimsuits designed to reduce water resistance. Compare the arguments that people might make to defend or oppose the standardization of athletic equipment in the interests of fair play.

50. List two different stakeholders in the airbag debate and describe how their positions on the issue compare.

51. The G rocket of the former Soviet Union has a mass of about 3.8×10^6 kg and its first-stage engines exert a thrust of about 5.0×10^7 N [forward].

(a) What is the true weight of the rocket on Earth's surface?

(b) Calculate the net force acting on the rocket at liftoff.

(c) Calculate the initial acceleration of the rocket.

(d) What should happen to the acceleration if the force exerted by the engines remains constant as the fuel burns?

(e) Why is the first stage jettisoned after the fuel is consumed?

52. People who believe in astrology claim that distant planets affect the forces acting on people on Earth. In a small group, answer the questions below.

(a) Suppose the mass of the person sitting next to you is 70 kg and the separation distance between you and that person is 1.0 m. The mass of Mars is 6.42×10^{23} kg and the separation distance between Mars and Earth is 2.3×10^{11} m. Compare the gravitational force exerted by Mars on you and the gravitational force exerted by the person sitting next to you on you.

(b) Comment on the claim made by astrologers based on your answer to part (a).

53. In a small group, research the materials being used to make artificial joints such as hips and knees. Find out how they are designed to provide enough friction for stability but not so much friction that the joints cannot move. Begin your search at www.pearsoned.ca/school/physicssource.

54. Manufacturers of skis recommend different waxes for different snow temperatures. Design and carry out an experiment to test the recommendations for three different waxes.

55. Research gait analysis, the study of how humans walk and run. This topic is central to physiotherapy, orthopedics, the design of artificial joints and sports footwear, and the manufacture of orthotics. How do Newton's three laws apply to gait analysis? Interview people associated with rehabilitation and sports. Write a brief summary of your findings. Begin your search at www.pearsoned.ca/school/physicssource.

 e TEST

To check your understanding of dynamics, follow the eTest links at www.pearsoned.ca/school/physicssource.

Circular Motion, Work, and Energy

The International Space Station is a silent companion to Earth, placed into an orbit that is a precise balance of kinetic and gravitational potential energies. The International Space Station stays in orbit because physicists and engineers applied the laws of physics for circular motion and conservation of energy to determine the satellite's speed and height above Earth.

e WEB

To learn more about the types of satellites placed in orbit, and the paths that they take, follow the links at www.pearsoned.ca/school/physicssource.

Unit at a Glance

Unit Themes and Emphases

- Energy, Equilibrium, and Systems
- Nature of Science
- Scientific Inquiry

Focussing Questions

This unit focusses on circular motion, work, and energy. You will investigate the conditions necessary to produce circular motion and examine some natural and human examples. You will consider energy, its transfer, and how it interacts with objects. As you study this unit, consider these questions:

- What is necessary to maintain circular motion?
- How does an understanding of conservation laws contribute to an understanding of the Universe?
- How can mechanical energy be transferred and transformed?

Unit Project

Building a Persuader Apparatus

- When you have finished this unit, you will understand how energy is transferred when objects interact. You will be able to use this understanding in the design and construction of a persuader apparatus that is able to protect its passenger from injury in different types of collisions.

Newton's laws can explain circular motion.

If humans hadn't invented the wheel — the first circular motion machine — it's hard to imagine what life would be like. The number of devices that make use of the properties of circular motion is almost too large to count. Bicycles, gears, drills, transmissions, clutches, cranes, watches, and electric motors are just a few examples.

The wheel and the many technologies derived from it are a uniquely human creation (Figure 5.1). But the principles of circular motion have always existed in nature. In fact, as you read this, you are spinning around in a large circle as Earth rotates on its axis. In Alberta, your speed is approximately 1000 km/h because of this rotation. At the same time, you are flying through space at an amazing speed of approximately 107 000 km/h as Earth revolves around the Sun. And you thought your car was fast!

How is circular motion unique? What are the properties of objects moving with circular motion? In this chapter, you will explore the physics of circular motion that define and control these many technologies, as well as the motion of the planets in the solar system.

▲ **Figure 5.1**

Characteristics of Circular Motion

Problem

In what direction will an object moving in a circular path go when released?

Materials

a marble
a circular barrier (e.g., rubber tubing, embroidery hoop)

▲ Figure 5.2

Procedure

1. Place the circular barrier on an unobstructed section of a table or the floor, then place the marble against the inside rim of the barrier (Figure 5.2).

2. You will be rolling a marble around inside the barrier. Before you do, predict where you think the marble will go when you remove the barrier. Now roll the marble around the inside rim of the barrier.

3. As the marble is rolling around the rim, lift the barrier and make a note of the direction the marble rolls. Also pay attention to the position of the marble when you lift the barrier.

4. Sketch the circular path that the marble took inside the barrier, the position of the marble when you lifted the barrier, and the path that it rolled after the barrier was lifted.

5. Repeat steps 3 and 4 several times. Each time release the marble when it is in a different position.

Questions

1. Was your prediction correct? Why or why not?

2. What similarities, if any, exist between your sketches?

3. What conclusions can you draw about the motion of the marble when it was released?

4. In each sketch that you made, draw a line from the centre of the circular motion to the position of the marble when it was released. What is the angle between this line and the path of the marble when it was released?

Think About It

1. Can you predict the position the marble would have to be in for it to move away from your body when it was released?

2. What can you say about the direction of the velocity of the marble at any moment in its circular path?

Discuss your answers in a small group and record them for later reference. As you complete each section of this chapter, review your answers to these questions. Note any changes to your ideas.

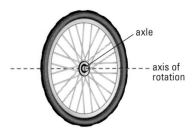

▲ **Figure 5.3** The axle of a wheel is part of the axis of rotation.

axle: shaft on which a wheel rotates

axis of rotation: imaginary line that passes through the centre of rotation perpendicular to the circular motion

uniform circular motion: motion in a circular path at a constant speed

5.1 Defining Circular Motion

The bicycle is not the most sophisticated machine ever created, but it does have a lot going for it. It is easy to maintain; it does not require any fuel; it is a very efficient form of transportation; and it is full of parts moving in circular motion. Perhaps most importantly for this lesson, it is easy for us to examine.

When you pedal a bike, the force is transferred through the chain to the **axle** where it turns the wheel (Figure 5.3). The wheel transmits the force to the road, which, according to Newton's third law, pushes back, and the bicycle moves forward. The wheel's axle is referred to as the **axis of rotation** because the entire wheel rotates around this shaft. If the wheels of the bike are moving at a constant speed, they are moving with **uniform circular motion**. That means their rotational speed is uniform. Because the wheel is circular, it can also provide a constant and uniform force to the road. This is important if you want the bike to move forward at a uniform speed.

In the sections that follow, we will restrict our study of circular motion to two dimensions. In other words, the circular motion described in this chapter has only one axis of rotation and the motion is in a plane.

Speed and Velocity in Circular Motion

If you ride through puddles after a rainfall, you'll come home with muddy water splashed on your back. Why is this? It has to do with the properties of an object moving in circular motion. As the wheel passes through the puddle, some of the water adheres to it.

As the wheel rotates upward out of the puddle, excess water flies off. When it flies off, it moves along a path that is tangential to the wheel. Recall from Unit I that a tangent is a line that touches the circle at only one point and is perpendicular to the radius of the circle. In the case of the bicycle, that is the point where the water drops break free of the wheel. Unless the splashguard is big enough, it will not protect you from all the water that is flying off the wheel (Figure 5.4).

▲ **Figure 5.4** Water that flies off the wheel at point A hits the rider in the back. The direction that the water drops fly is determined by the place where they leave the wheel.

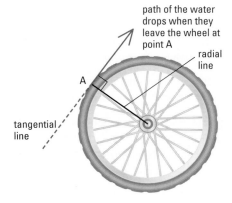

▲ **Figure 5.5** Water leaves the wheel at point A and flies off at a tangent.

A line drawn from point A in Figure 5.5 to the centre of the circle is called a radial line. The radial line and the tangential line are perpendicular to each other when they intersect at the same point on the circle. The tangential line represents the direction that the water drops are moving at any instant. The speed of the water drops is determined by their speed at the wheel.

It is worth taking some time to review the difference between speed and velocity. Speed is a magnitude only (a scalar quantity) that does not have a direction. If a wheel is rotating with uniform circular motion, then the speed is constant, even though the wheel is continually turning and the water on the wheel is continually changing direction. Velocity, on the other hand, has a magnitude and a direction: it is a vector quantity. Because of this, even though the wheel is spinning at constant speed, the velocity of the water on the wheel is continually changing as the wheel's direction of motion changes.

It is correct to say that the speed of the water drops on the wheel represents the magnitude of the velocity. Knowing that the object moves in a circular path is often sufficient. However, we must specify the object's velocity if we need to know its speed and direction at any instant in its circular path.

Since we can assume the speed and direction of the water drop are known at any instant, we know its velocity. A velocity vector can be drawn at position A, and the drawing can be simplified as shown in Figure 5.6.

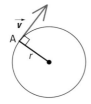

▲ **Figure 5.6** The velocity vector $\vec{v}$ shows the velocity of a particle at any instant as it moves on a circular path.

Concept Check

1. Imagine a Frisbee in level flight. Where is its axis of rotation, and what is its orientation?
2. Identify all the axes of rotation in a typical bicycle.

▲ **Figure 5.7** A mountain bike has many axes of rotation.

Centripetal Acceleration and Force

Now imagine that you drive over a small pebble that gets lodged in the treads of your bicycle wheel. As you ride, the pebble circles around with the wheel, as shown in Figure 5.8. At one moment it is in position A, and a fraction of a second later, it is in position B. A short time has passed as the pebble moved from point A to point B. This small change in time is written as Δt.

The pebble has experienced a very small displacement from point A to point B, which is written as $\Delta\vec{d}$. The velocities of the pebble at point A and point B are $\vec{v}_A$ and $\vec{v}_B$, respectively (Figure 5.9). C represents the centre of the circle (the axis of rotation).

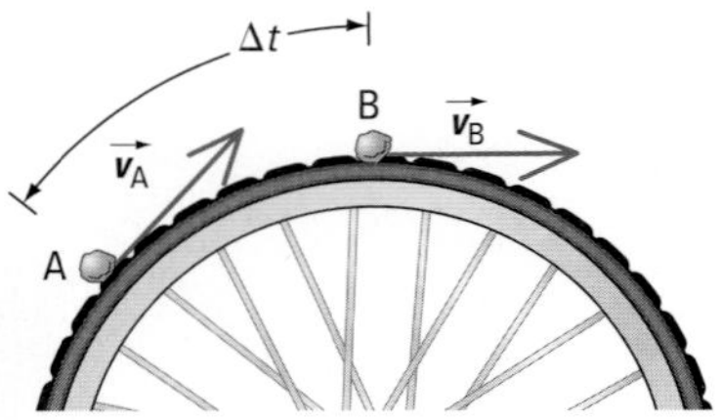

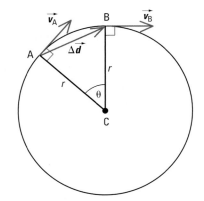

▲ **Figure 5.9** As the pebble moves from point A to point B, it moves through angle θ and experiences a change in velocity.

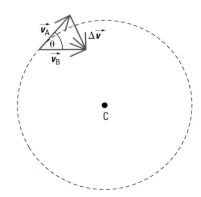

▲ **Figure 5.10** The change in velocity $\vec{v}$ is toward the centre of the circle.

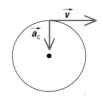

▲ **Figure 5.8** A pebble caught in the wheel of a bike moves from position A to B in a small time Δt, and experiences a change in velocity.

The speed of the pebble does not change, but its direction does. Therefore, its velocity also changes. The change in velocity ($\Delta\vec{v}$) can best be shown by subtracting the velocity at B from the velocity at A (using the rules of graphical vector addition) as shown in Figure 5.10. Angle θ is the same in both Figures 5.9 and 5.10, and the two triangles are similar. Something subtle but significant happens when we subtract the two velocity vectors. The difference between them is designated as $\Delta\vec{v}$, and it is pointing in toward the centre of the circle!

Velocity and Acceleration Toward the Centre

The changing velocity ($\Delta\vec{v}$) represents the change in direction of the object, not its speed. If an object has a changing velocity, then it must be accelerating. Since the changing velocity is pointing inward toward the centre of the circle, the acceleration must also be in that direction (Figure 5.11). It is called **centripetal acceleration** ($\vec{a}_c$). For an object to move with circular motion, it must experience centripetal acceleration. If the circular motion is uniform, then so is the centripetal acceleration.

According to Newton's second law, if a mass is accelerating, it must also experience a non-zero net force. This non-zero net force is called the **centripetal force** ($\vec{F}_c$). In our example, the pebble stuck in the wheel is experiencing a force that attempts to pull it toward the centre of the circle. This is the centripetal force.

Why doesn't the pebble actually move toward the centre of the wheel? It does, in a way. Remember: if the pebble were to break free of the tire's grip, it would fly off at a tangent to its circular motion. While it remains stuck in the tire, it is forced to follow the circular path because the centripetal force attempts to pull it toward the centre. In other words, centripetal force is pulling the pebble toward the centre of the circle while at the same time, the pebble is moving off in a direction at a tangent to the circle. The result is the circular path in which it actually moves.

▲ **Figure 5.11** Although the velocity of an object moving with uniform circular motion is tangential, the centripetal acceleration (and centripetal force) is acting toward the centre of the circle.

centripetal acceleration: acceleration acting toward the centre of a circle

centripetal force: force acting toward the centre of a circle causing an object to move in a circular path

Speed and Radius

Question

For an object moving with uniform circular motion, what relationship exists between the radius of its path and its speed? (Assume the object is experiencing a constant centripetal force.)

Hypothesis

State a hypothesis relating the radius and speed. Remember to use an "if/then" statement.

Variables

The variables in this lab are the radius of the circular path, mass of the rubber stopper, mass of the hanging weight, number of revolutions, elapsed time, period, and speed. Read the procedure and identify the controlled, manipulated, and responding variables.

Materials and Equipment

1-hole rubber stopper (mass $\leq$ 25 g)
1.5 m of string or fishing line
small-diameter plastic tube
100-g mass
metre-stick
felt marker
safety goggles
stopwatch

⚠️ **CAUTION: Remember to swing the rubber stopper over your head and in a place clear of obstructions.**

Procedure

1. Copy Table 5.1, shown at the bottom of this page, into your notebook.

2. Secure the rubber stopper to one end of the string.

3. Run the other end of the string through the plastic tube and attach the 100-g mass to it.

4. Hold the end of the string attached to the stopper at the zero mark of a metre-stick laid on a table. The zero mark of the ruler should line up with the centre of the stopper. While holding the stopper in position, pull the string taut along the ruler.

5. With the felt marker, mark the string at 20, 30, 40, 50, and 60 cm.

6. Adjust the string's position so that the 20-cm mark is positioned on the lip of the plastic tube. Record 20 cm in the "Radius" column of the table.

7. Grasp the plastic tube in one hand and pinch the string to the lip of the tube using your thumb or forefinger.

8. Put on your safety goggles. Begin spinning the rubber stopper in a horizontal circle above your head as you release the string. Make sure the 100-g mass is hanging freely (Figure 5.12). At first, you may have to pull the string up or down using your other hand to position the mark as the stopper is spinning.

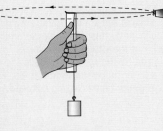

▲ **Figure 5.12**

▼ **Table 5.1** Data for 5-2 Inquiry Lab

Radius (m)	Time for 20 Revolutions (s)		Average Time (s)	Period (s)	Speed (m/s)
	Time 1	Time 2			

9 Adjust the rate at which you spin the rubber stopper so that the string does not slip up or down and the mark stays in position at the lip of the tube. Once you have reached a steady rate, your partner can begin timing. Do not pull the string up or down with the other hand.

10 Your partner should time 20 complete revolutions of the rubber stopper using a stopwatch. While your partner does this, be sure to monitor the speed of the stopper so that the mark does not move off the lip. Record the time in the "Time 1" column of the table.

11 Repeat step 10 and record the time in the "Time 2" column of the table.

12 Increase the radius by 10 cm, and record this radius in the "Radius" column of the table. Repeat steps 7 to 12 until all radii are used.

Analysis

1. For each trial, average the two times and place the result in the "Average Time" column.

2. For each trial, divide the average time by the number of revolutions the stopper made. Record the values in the "Period" column.

3. For each trial, determine the speed of the stopper using the equation $v = \dfrac{2\pi r}{T}$, and record the value in the "Speed" column.

4. Identify the controlled, responding, and manipulated variables.

5. Identify the force that acted as the centripetal force, and determine its value.

6. Plot a graph of velocity versus radius. Remember to plot the manipulated variable on the horizontal axis and the responding variable on the vertical axis.

7. Complete the statement, "The speed varies with …"

8. Was your hypothesis accurate? If not, how can you modify it to reflect your observations from this lab?

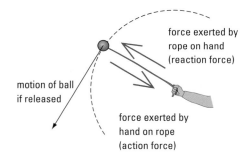

force exerted by rope on hand (reaction force)

motion of ball if released

force exerted by hand on rope (action force)

▲ **Figure 5.13** The hand exerts a centripetal force on the rope and ball, but feels the reaction force exerted by the rope. This leads to a false impression that the centripetal force is acting outward.

Misconceptions About Centripetal Force

A common misconception is that centripetal force acts radially outward from the centre of a circle. This is not what happens. The change in the velocity of the object is *inward*, and therefore, so is the centripetal acceleration and force. What causes confusion is that when you spin an object in a circle at the end of a rope, you feel the force pulling outward on your hand (Figure 5.13). This outward pull is mistakenly thought to be the centripetal force.

Newton's third law states that for every action there is an equal and opposite reaction. If we apply this law to our example, then the action force is the hand pulling on the rope to make the object move in a circle. This is the centripetal force. The reaction force is the force the rope exerts on your hand. It is outward. This is the force that people often believe is the centripetal force. The rope would not exert a force on your hand unless your hand exerted a force on the rope first.

Another misconception is that centripetal force is a unique and separate force responsible for circular motion. This is not true. It is best to think of centripetal force as a generic term given to any force that acts toward the centre of the circular path. In fact, the translation from Latin of the word centripetal is "centre seeking."

Many different forces could actually be the centripetal force. For example, when a car turns a corner, the frictional force of the tires on the road acts as the centripetal force. If you spin an object around in a horizontal circle on a rope, the tension of the rope is the centripetal force. The force of gravity the Sun exerts on the planets is another example of a centripetal force. Sometimes several forces working together act as a centripetal force. For an object spinning in a vertical circle on a rope, two forces, gravity and tension, work together to act as the centripetal force at the top of the circle. This is because the centripetal force is a net force. It is often convenient to use it in place of the actual force or forces acting toward the centre. Table 5.2 summarizes circular motion quantities and their directions.

PHYSICS INSIGHT

Some texts refer to centrifugal force. This refers to the reaction force that exists as a result of centripetal force. If the centripetal force is removed, there is no centrifugal force.

Concept Check

A pebble caught in the tread of a tire experiences a centripetal force as the tire turns. What force is responsible for it?

e **SIM**

For an interactive demonstration that explores the relationship among centripetal acceleration, force, and velocity, visit www.pearsoned.ca/school/physicssource.

▼ **Table 5.2** Circular Motion Quantities and Their Direction

Quantity	Direction
Velocity ($\vec{v}$)	tangential to the circle
Centripetal acceleration ($\vec{a}$)	toward the centre
Centripetal force ($\vec{F}_c$ or $\vec{F}_{net}$)	toward the centre
Change in velocity ($\Delta\vec{v}$)	toward the centre

5.1 Check and Reflect

Knowledge

1. Give an example of an object that moves with uniform circular motion and one that moves with non-uniform circular motion.

2. Identify the force acting as the centripetal force in each of the following situations:

   (a) A car makes a turn without skidding.

   (b) A ball is tied to the end of a rope and spun in a horizontal circle.

   (c) The Moon moves in a circular orbit around Earth.

Applications

3. What is the relationship between the speed and radius of an object moving with uniform circular motion if the centripetal force is constant?

4. What is the relationship between the speed and velocity of an object moving with uniform circular motion?

Extensions

5. Imagine pedalling a bike at a constant rate. Describe the motion of the bicycle if the wheels were not circular but oval.

6. Consider the relative speed between a pebble stuck in the tread of a bicycle tire and the ground. Explain why the pebble is not dislodged when it comes in contact with the ground. Suggest a method to dislodge the pebble while still riding the bike.

e **TEST**

To check your understanding of the definition of circular motion, follow the eTest links at www.pearsoned.ca/school/physicssource.

5.2 Circular Motion and Newton's Laws

Soccer players put a spin on the ball when they kick it that makes it curve around opposing players. Professional golfers routinely strike the golf ball so that it has a spin that curves it into the wind or prevents it from rolling when it hits the ground. A baseball pitcher can throw a curving fastball at 144 km/h, making the batter's job of hitting the ball much more difficult (Figure 5.14).

▲ **Figure 5.14** Pitchers can put a spin on a ball that causes it to curve. This curve is predictable.

In these sports and many others, putting a spin on the ball is an essential skill. Even though the pitch from a pitcher may be extremely difficult to predict, the behaviour of the ball isn't. If players perform the same motion reliably when they kick, throw, or hit the ball, it will always behave the same way. That is why good players, when faced with the curving soccer ball or fastball, can anticipate where the ball will be and adjust their positions.

It is accurate to say that the physical properties of a spinning ball or anything moving with circular motion can be predicted. In fact, the rotational velocity, frequency, centripetal force, and radius of a spinning object can be related mathematically.

MINDS ON | **Spinning Objects in Sports**

In groups of two or three, think of as many sports as you can that involve a spinning motion. It may be the player or an object that has the spin.

Indicate what advantages the spinning motion has for the player and what type of motion is used to cause the spin. Discuss your answers with the class.

Period and Frequency of Circular Motion

A baseball pitcher can throw a baseball at speeds of about 145 km/h. By flicking his wrist, he can give the ball a spin so that, in effect, it has two velocities: a velocity as it approaches the batter, and a rotational velocity because of its spin (Figure 5.15). The rotational velocity can be measured indirectly by measuring the time it takes for one complete rotation. One complete rotation is called a **cycle** or **revolution**, and the time for one cycle is the **period** (T), measured in s/cycle.

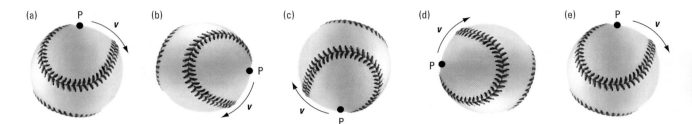

▲ **Figure 5.15** Point P on the spinning baseball makes one complete rotation from (a) to (e). The time for this is called the period and is measured in s/cycle. This is frequently abbreviated to s for convenience.

If an object is spinning quickly, the period may be a fraction of a second. For example, a hard drive in a computer makes one complete revolution in about 0.00833 s. This value is hard to grasp and is inconvenient to use. It is often easier to measure the number of rotations in a certain amount of time instead of the period.

Frequency (f) is a measurement that indicates the number of cycles an object makes in a certain amount of time, usually one second. The SI units for frequency are cycles/s or hertz (Hz). You might have noticed that the units for frequency are cycles/s while the units for period are s/cycle. Each is the inverse of the other, so the relationship can be expressed mathematically as:

$$T = \frac{1}{f} \text{ or } f = \frac{1}{T}$$

You may also have seen rotational frequency expressed in **rpm**. Even though this unit for measuring frequency is not an SI unit, it is commonly used commercially in products such as power tools. An rpm is a revolution per minute and is different from a hertz. It represents the number of revolutions in one minute instead of one second, so it is always 60 times bigger than the value in Hz. A simple method can be used to convert Hz to rpm and vice versa:

$$\text{Hz} \xrightarrow[\div\ 60\ \text{s/min}]{\times\ 60\ \text{s/min}} \text{rpm}$$

Example 5.1

The hard drive in Figure 5.16 stores data on a thin magnetic platter that spins at high speed. The platter makes one complete revolution in 0.00833 s. Determine its frequency in Hz and rpm.

Given
$T = 0.00833$ s

Required
frequency in Hz and rpm

Analysis and Solution
The frequency is the inverse of the period. Solve the frequency of the hard drive in the SI unit for frequency (Hz) and then convert the Hz to rpm.

$$T = \frac{1}{f}$$

$$f = \frac{1}{0.00833 \text{ s}}$$

$$= 120 \text{ Hz}$$

direction of rotation

hard drive case

read/write head

▲ **Figure 5.16**

Now convert the SI units of frequency to rpm:

$$\text{Hz} \xrightarrow[\div \, 60 \text{ s/min}]{\times \, 60 \text{ s/min}} \text{rpm}$$

$$120 \text{ Hz} \times 60 \, \frac{\text{s}}{\text{min}} = 7.20 \times 10^3 \text{ rpm}$$

Paraphrase
The frequency of the hard drive is 120 Hz or 7.20×10^3 rpm.

Practice Problems

1. The propeller of a toy airplane rotates at 300 rpm. What is its frequency?

2. An electric motor rotates at a frequency of 40 Hz. What is its rotational frequency in rpm?

3. A medical centrifuge is a device that separates blood into its parts. The centrifuge can spin at up to 6.0×10^4 rpm. What is its frequency in hertz and what is its period?

Answers

1. 5.00 Hz
2. 2.4×10^3 rpm
3. 1.0×10^3 Hz; 1.0×10^{-3} s

Speed and Circular Motion

At the beginning of this chapter you learned that, at this moment, you are moving at approximately 107 000 km/h as Earth moves in its orbit around the Sun. It's hard to imagine that Earth is moving that fast through our solar system. How was the speed determined?

The answer is the simple application of an equation you learned in section 1.2 of chapter 1:

$$v = \frac{\Delta d}{\Delta t}$$

where Δd is the distance travelled and Δt is the time that it takes the object to travel that distance.

In the case of circular motion, the distance around a circle is the circumference (C), given by $C = 2\pi r$. The time it takes for one revolution is the period (T). Therefore, the speed of anything moving with uniform circular motion can be described by the equation:

$$v = \frac{2\pi r}{T}$$ (1)

PHYSICS INSIGHT

Remember: The SI units for distance and time are metres and seconds, respectively.

where r is the radius in metres, T is the period in seconds, and v is the speed in metres per second.

Let's look at Earth as it follows a circular orbit around the Sun. Earth has an orbital radius of approximately 1.49×10^8 km, and makes one complete revolution in 365.25 days. By substituting these values into the equation for speed, we can do the following calculation:

$$v = \frac{2\pi r}{T}$$

$$= \frac{2\pi(1.49 \times 10^{11}\ \text{m})}{3.16 \times 10^7\ \text{s}}$$

$$= 2.97 \times 10^4\ \text{m/s}$$

Then convert this to kilometres per hour:

$$2.97 \times 10^4\ \frac{\text{m}}{\text{s}} \times \frac{1\ \text{km}}{1000\ \text{m}} \times \frac{3600\ \text{s}}{1\ \text{h}} = 1.07 \times 10^5\ \text{km/h}$$

Earth's speed as it orbits the Sun is approximately 107 000 km/h.

The speed of a planet as it rotates on its axis can be determined in the same way but varies depending on the latitude. We will explore the reasons for this later in "Centripetal Force, Acceleration, and Frequency" in section 5.2.

Example 5.2

A pebble is stuck in the treads of a tire at a distance of 55.0 cm from the axle (Figure 5.17). It takes just 0.40 s for the wheel to make one revolution. What is the speed of the pebble at any instant?

Given
$r = 0.550$ m
$T = 0.40$ s

Required
speed (v) of the pebble

Analysis and Solution
Determine the speed by using equation 1:

$$v = \frac{2\pi r}{T}$$

$$= \frac{2\pi(0.550\ \text{m})}{0.40\ \text{s}}$$

$$= 8.6\ \text{m/s}$$

Paraphrase
The speed of the pebble caught in the tire tread is 8.6 m/s.

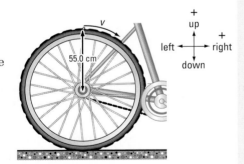

▲ **Figure 5.17** The speed of the pebble is determined by its distance from the axis of rotation, and the wheel's period (T).

Practice Problems

1. How much time does it take for the tires of a racecar to make one revolution if the car is travelling at 261.0 km/h and the wheels have a radius of 0.350 m?

2. In 2006, an Alberta astronomer discovered the fastest spinning collapsed star (called a pulsar) ever found. It has a radius of only 16.1 km and is spinning at a rate of 716 Hz (faster than a kitchen blender). What is its speed at its equator?

Answers
1. 0.0303 s
2. 7.24×10^7 m/s

A Closer Look at Centripetal Acceleration and Force

In Unit II, you learned that, just before a race, dragster drivers spin their tires to make them hot and sticky so that the coefficient of friction increases between the tire and the road. When the race starts, the tires will have a better grip and the dragster will be able to accelerate at a greater rate. While the dragster performs the tire-spin, the tires change shape (Figure 5.18). The rear tires start off being fat and thick. During the spin they become thin and their diameter increases. Clearly, this must have something to do with the spinning motion of the wheel, and therefore centripetal force, but what?

▲ **Figure 5.18** (a) At first, the dragster's wheels have a low rotational speed and don't stretch noticeably. The centripetal acceleration and force are small. (b) The dragster's wheels are spinning very fast and stretch away from the rim. The centripetal acceleration and force are large.

Before the tires start spinning, they are in their natural shape. When they are spinning, they experience a strong centripetal acceleration and force. Both act toward the centre of the wheel. Each tire is fastened to a rim, so the rim is pulling the tire inward. However, the tire moves the way Newton's first law predicts it will — it attempts to keep moving in a straight line in the direction of the velocity. Thus the tire, being made of rubber, stretches. Dragster tires and the tires of trucks and passenger cars are designed to endure high speeds without being torn apart. The faster a wheel spins, the greater the centripetal acceleration and force.

Car tires are thoroughly tested to ensure they can handle a centripetal force much greater than the centripetal force at the speed that you would normally drive in the city or on the highway. However, if you drove at a speed that exceeded the tires' capabilities, the tires could be torn apart.

Is speed the only factor that affects centripetal acceleration and force, or are there other factors? Are the factors that affect centripetal acceleration the same as those that affect the centripetal force? To answer these questions, let's start by taking a closer look at centripetal acceleration.

Factors Affecting the Magnitude of Centripetal Acceleration

The rotational speed is one factor that determines the magnitude of the centripetal acceleration, but what other factors play a role? To answer this question, look at Figure 5.19. It shows the two diagrams you saw earlier as Figures 5.9 and 5.10 in section 5.1. Using these figures, we can derive an equation for centripetal acceleration.

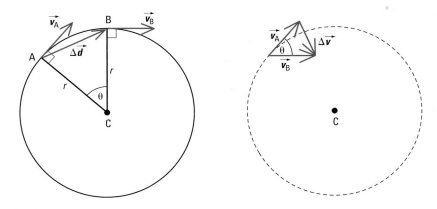

▲ **Figure 5.19** An object following in a circular path moves through a displacement $\Delta \vec{d}$ as there is a change in velocity $\Delta \vec{v}$. The triangles formed by these two vectors will help us solve for centripetal acceleration.

As already stated, the two triangles are similar. Therefore, we can compare them. For convenience, the triangles have been redrawn below without the circles (Figure 5.20). Since v_A and v_B have the same value, we have dropped the designations A and B in Figure 5.20. We have omitted the vector arrows because we are solving only for the magnitude of the centripetal acceleration.

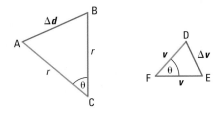

▲ **Figure 5.20** Triangles ABC and DEF are similar, so we can use a ratio of similar sides.

Triangle ABC is similar to triangle DEF in Figure 5.20. Therefore, a ratio of similar sides can be created:

$$\frac{\Delta v}{v} = \frac{\Delta d}{r}$$

or

$$\Delta v = \frac{v \Delta d}{r} \tag{2}$$

Remember, Δv is directed toward the centre of the circle. The time it took for the velocity vectors to move the small distance Δd can be designated Δt. In this time, the Δv vector was created.

Since $v = \dfrac{\Delta d}{\Delta t}$, we can manipulate the equation so that:

$$\Delta t = \frac{\Delta d}{v} \qquad (3)$$

To find acceleration toward the centre of the circle (centripetal acceleration), divide the Δv by Δt.

$$a_c = \frac{\Delta v}{\Delta t} \qquad (4)$$

Now we can substitute equations 2 and 3 into equation 4:

$$a_c = \frac{\dfrac{v\Delta d}{r}}{\dfrac{\Delta d}{v}}$$

By taking the reciprocal of the denominator and multiplying the two fractions, we have:

$$a_c = \frac{v\cancel{\Delta d}}{r} \times \frac{v}{\cancel{\Delta d}}$$

Simplified, this becomes:

$$a_c = \frac{v^2}{r} \qquad (5)$$

where a_c is the centripetal acceleration in metres per second squared toward the centre of the circle, v is the rotational speed of the object moving with uniform circular motion in metres per second, and r is the radius of the circular motion in metres.

The centripetal acceleration depends only on the speed and radius of the circular motion. Mass does not affect it, just as the mass of a falling object does not affect the acceleration of gravity caused by Earth. A truck or a marble will both experience a gravitational acceleration of 9.81 m/s² [down]. Two objects of different masses moving in a circular path will experience the same centripetal acceleration if they have the same radius and speed.

Mass does not affect centripetal acceleration, but companies that manufacture racing tires, jet engines, and other equipment know they cannot ignore it. In fact, the mass of a tire or fan blade is important to them. These companies are continually looking for ways to reduce mass without decreasing the strength of their products. Why? The answer has to do with the centripetal force that these devices experience.

If a fan blade or tire has a large mass, it will experience a large centripetal force and might break apart at high speeds. Reducing the mass decreases the centripetal force these parts experience, but often with a trade-off in strength. Next, we will examine the factors that influence centripetal force.

Example 5.3

A DVD disc has a diameter of 12.0 cm and a rotational period of 0.100 s (Figure 5.21). Determine the centripetal acceleration at the outer edge of the disc.

Given
$D = 0.120$ m
$T = 0.100$ s

Required
centripetal acceleration (a_c)

Analysis and Solution
The magnitude of the centripetal acceleration depends on speed and radius. Convert the diameter to a radius by dividing it by 2.

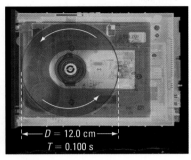

$\leftarrow D = 12.0$ cm $\rightarrow$
$T = 0.100$ s

▲ **Figure 5.21**

$$r = \frac{D}{2}$$

$$= \frac{0.120 \text{ m}}{2}$$

$$= 0.600 \text{ m}$$

Determine the speed of the outer edge of the disc:

$$v = \frac{2\pi r}{T}$$

$$= \frac{2\pi (0.600 \text{ m})}{0.100 \text{ s}}$$

$$= 3.77 \text{ m/s}$$

Now use equation 5 to determine the centripetal acceleration:

$$a_c = \frac{v^2}{r}$$

$$= \frac{\left(3.77 \dfrac{\text{m}}{\text{s}}\right)^2}{0.0600 \text{ m}}$$

$$= 2.37 \times 10^2 \text{ m/s}^2$$

Note that no vector arrows appear on a_c or v because we are solving for their magnitude only.

Paraphrase
The centripetal acceleration at the edge of the DVD disc is 2.37×10^2 m/s^2.

Practice Problems

1. You throw a Frisbee to your friend. The Frisbee has a diameter of 28.0 cm and makes one turn in 0.110 s. What is the centripetal acceleration at its outer edge?

2. A child playing with a top spins it so that it has a centripetal acceleration of 125.0 m/s^2 at the edge, a distance of 3.00 cm from the axis of rotation. What is the speed at the edge of the top?

3. A helicopter blade has a diameter of 14.0 m and a centripetal acceleration at the tip of 2527.0 m/s^2. What is the period of the helicopter blade?

Answers

1. 4.57×10^2 m/s^2
2. 1.94 m/s
3. 0.331 s

Factors Affecting the Magnitude of Centripetal Force

Mass does not affect centripetal acceleration, but it does influence the force needed to move an object in a circular path. From Newton's second law, we know that the net force is the product of mass and the net acceleration. Therefore, centripetal force must simply be the product of the mass and centripetal acceleration:

$$F_{net} = ma$$

$$F_c = ma_c$$

or

$$F_c = \frac{mv^2}{r} \tag{6}$$

where m is the mass in kilograms, v is the rotational speed in metres per second of the object moving with uniform circular motion, and r is the radius of the circular motion in metres. Notice that v and r are the same as in equation 5. Therefore, all the factors that affect centripetal acceleration also affect the centripetal force; namely, speed and the radius of rotation. However, the mass affects only the centripetal force.

Example 5.4

Determine the magnitude of the centripetal force exerted by the rim of a dragster's wheel on a 45.0-kg tire. The tire has a 0.480-m radius and is rotating at a speed of 30.0 m/s (Figure 5.22).

Given
$m = 45.0$ kg
$r = 0.480$ m
$v = 30.0$ m/s

Required
centripetal force exerted on the tire by the rim (F_c)

Analysis and Solution
Use equation 6 to solve for the centripetal force.

$$F_c = \frac{mv^2}{r}$$

$$= \frac{(45.0\ \text{kg})\left(30.0\ \dfrac{\text{m}}{\text{s}}\right)^2}{0.480\ \text{m}}$$

$$= 8.44 \times 10^4\ \text{N}$$

Paraphrase
The magnitude of the centripetal force exerted on the tire by the rim is 8.44×10^4 N.

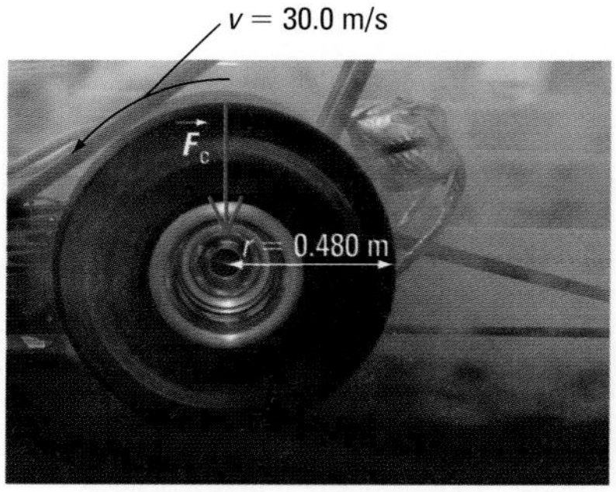

▲ **Figure 5.22** The dragster wheel experiences a centripetal force pulling it inward.

v = 30.0 m/s

r = 0.480 m

Practice Problems

1. An intake fan blade on a jet engine has a mass of 7.50 kg. As it spins, the middle of the blade has a speed of 365.9 m/s and is a distance of 73.7 cm from the axis of rotation. What is the centripetal force on the blade?

2. A 0.0021-kg pebble is stuck in the treads of a dirt bike's wheel. The radius of the wheel is 23.0 cm and the pebble experiences a centripetal force with a magnitude of 0.660 N. What is the speed of the wheel?

Answers

1. 1.36×10^6 N
2. 8.50 m/s

Speed and Centripetal Force

Question

What is the relationship between centripetal force and the speed of a mass moving in a horizontal circle?

Hypothesis

State a hypothesis relating centripetal force and speed. Remember to use an "if/then" statement.

Variables

The variables in this lab are the radius of the circular path, mass of the rubber stopper, mass of the hanging mass, number of revolutions, elapsed time, period, and speed. Read the procedure and identify the controlled, manipulated, and responding variables.

Materials and Equipment

1-hole rubber stopper (mass $\leqq$ 25 g)
1.5 m of string or fishing line
0.5-cm-diameter plastic tube
5 masses: 50 g, 100 g, 150 g, 200 g, 250 g
metre-stick
felt marker
safety goggles
stopwatch

⚠ **CAUTION: Remember to swing the rubber stopper over your head and in a place clear of obstructions.**

Procedure

1. Copy Table 5.3, at the bottom of this page, into your notebook.

2. Secure the rubber stopper to one end of the string.

3. Run the other end of the string through the plastic tube and attach the 50-g mass to it. Record this mass in the "Mass" column of the table. The force of gravity exerted on this mass is the centripetal force.

4. Hold the end of the string attached to the stopper at the zero mark of a metre-stick laid on a table. The zero mark of the ruler should line up with the centre of the stopper. While holding the stopper in position, pull the string taut along the ruler.

5. With the felt marker, mark the string at 40 cm.

6. Hold the rubber stopper in one hand and the plastic tube in the other. Adjust the string's position so that the 40-cm mark is positioned on the lip of the plastic tube. With the hand holding the plastic tube, pinch the string to the lip of the tube using your thumb or forefinger.

7. Put on your safety goggles. Begin spinning the rubber stopper in a horizontal circle above your head as you release the string (Figure 5.23). Make sure the mass is hanging freely. At first, you may have to pull the string up or down using your other hand to position the mark as the stopper is spinning.

8. Adjust the rate at which you spin the rubber stopper so that the string does not slip up or down and the mark stays in position at the lip at the top of the tube. Once you have reached a steady rate, your partner can begin timing. Do not pull the string up or down with the other hand.

▼ **Table 5.3** Data for 5-3 Inquiry Lab

Mass (k)	Time for 20 Revolutions (s)		Average Time (s)	Period (s)	Speed (m/s)	Centripetal Force ($\times 10^{-1}$ N)
	Time 1	Time 2				

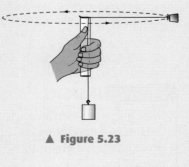

▲ **Figure 5.23**

9. Your partner should time 20 complete revolutions of the rubber stopper using a stopwatch. While your partner does this, be sure to monitor the speed of the stopper so that the mark does not move off the lip. Record the time in the "Time 1" column of Table 5.3.

10. Repeat step 9 and record the time in the "Time 2" column of Table 5.3.

11. Increase the hanging mass by 50 g, and record this mass in the "Mass" column of the table. Repeat steps 6 to 10 until all the masses are used.

Analysis

1. For each trial, average the two times, and place the result in the "Average Time" column of the table.

2. For each trial, divide the average time by the number of revolutions the stopper made. Record the value in the "Period" column of the table.

3. For each trial, determine the speed of the stopper using the equation $v = \dfrac{2\pi r}{T}$. Record the value in the "Speed" column of the table.

4. For each trial determine the force of gravity acting on the mass hanging from the string using the equation $F_g = mg$. Record these values in the "Centripetal Force" column of the table.

5. Identify the controlled, responding, and manipulated variables.

6. Plot a graph of speed versus centripetal force. Remember to plot the manipulated variable on the horizontal axis and the responding variable on the vertical axis.

7. Complete the statement, "The speed varies with …."

8. Was your hypothesis accurate? If not, how can it be modified to reflect your observations in this lab?

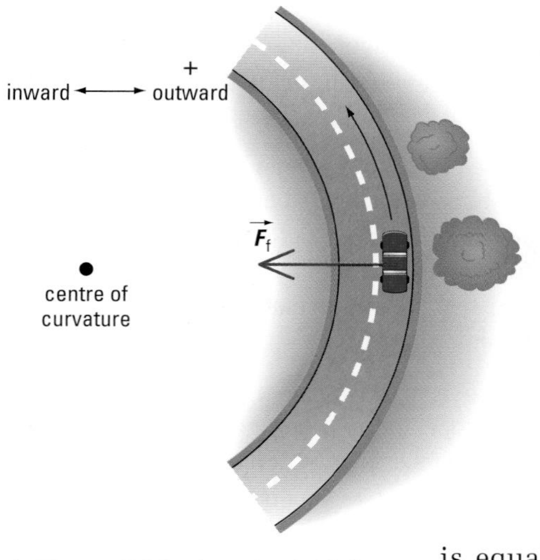

▲ **Figure 5.24** A car turning left. The force of friction of the tires on the road is the centripetal force.

PHYSICS INSIGHT

On a horizontal surface the force of gravity (F_g) is equal and opposite to the normal force (F_N).

A Horizontal System in Circular Motion

Imagine that a car is following a curve to the left on a flat road (Figure 5.24). As the car makes the turn its speed remains constant, and it experiences a centripetal force. The centripetal force is caused by the wheels turning to the left, continually changing the direction of the car. If it weren't for the frictional force between the tire and the road, you would not be able to make a turn. Hence, the frictional force between the tires and the road is the centripetal force. For simplicity, this is written as:

$$F_c = F_f$$

Recall that the magnitude of the force of friction is represented by the equation $F_f = \mu F_N$, where F_N is the normal force, or perpendicular force exerted by the surface on the object. It is equal and opposite to the force of gravity on a horizontal surface. Recall from Unit II that the coefficient of friction, μ, is the magnitude of the force of friction divided by the magnitude of the normal force. Think of it as a measure of how well two surfaces slide over each other. The lower the value, the easier the surfaces move over one another.

Assume that the driver increases the speed as the car turns the corner. As a result, the centripetal force also increases (Figure 5.25). Suppose the force of friction cannot hold the tires to the road. In other words, the force of friction cannot exert the needed centripetal force because of the increase in speed. In that case, the car skids off the road tangentially. Recall that kinetic friction is present when a car slides with its wheels locked. If a car turns a corner without skidding, static friction is present.

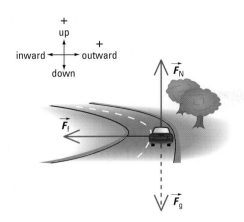

◀ **Figure 5.25** $\vec{F}_c = \vec{F}_f$ The maximum frictional force that can be exerted between the road and the tires determines the maximum speed the car can go around the turn without skidding. For horizontal surfaces, the normal force is equal and opposite to the force of gravity ($\vec{F}_N = -\vec{F}_g$).

Example 5.5

Determine the maximum speed at which a 1500.0-kg car can round a curve that has the radius of 40.0 m, if the coefficient of friction between the tires and the road is 0.60.

Given

$m = 1500.0$ kg

$\mu_s = 0.60$

$r = 40.0$ m

$g = 9.81$ m/s^2

Required
maximum speed (v)

Analysis and Solution
First draw a free-body diagram to show the direction of the forces (Figure 5.26). The normal force is equal to the force of gravity on a horizontal surface.

$$F_c = F_f$$

$$\frac{mv^2}{r} = \mu F_N$$

$$F_N = mg$$

$$\frac{\cancel{m}v^2}{r} = \mu(\cancel{m}g)$$

$$v^2 = \mu gr$$

$$v = \sqrt{\mu gr}$$

$$= \sqrt{(0.60)\left(9.81\ \frac{m}{s^2}\right)(40.0\ m)}$$

$$= 15.3\ \text{m/s}$$

Paraphrase
The fastest that the car can round the curve is 15.3 m/s or 55.2 km/h. If it attempts to go faster, the force of static friction will be insufficient to prevent skidding.

Figure 5.26

$m = 1500.0$ kg

Practice Problems

1. An Edmonton Oiler ($m = 100$ kg) carves a turn with a radius of 7.17 m while skating and feels his skates begin to slip on the ice. What is his speed if the coefficient of static friction between the skates and the ice is 0.80?

2. Automotive manufacturers test the handling ability of a new car design by driving a prototype on a test track in a large circle ($r = 100$ m) at ever-increasing speeds until the car begins to skid. A prototype car ($m = 1200$ kg) is tested and found to skid at a speed of 95.0 km/h. What is the coefficient of static friction between the car tires and the track?

3. A 600.0-g toy radio-controlled car can make a turn at a speed of 3.0 m/s on the kitchen floor where the coefficient of static friction is 0.90. What is the radius of its turn?

Answers

1. 7.5 m/s

2. 0.710

3. 1.0 m

Centripetal Force and Gravity

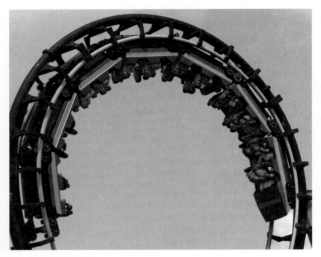

▲ **Figure 5.27** Why doesn't this car fall off the track at the top of the loop?

The designers of amusement park rides know their physics. Rides will toss you around, but leave you unharmed. Many of these rides spin you in circles — the Ferris wheel and the roller coaster, for example. The roller coaster often has a vertical loop somewhere along its track (Figure 5.27). Why is it that when you reach the top of the loop, where the car is inverted, you don't fall out? It isn't because of the harness that they put over you before you start the ride. That just keeps you strapped into the car so you don't do something silly like stand up while the roller coaster is moving. No, the answer lies in the physics of the roller coaster's design.

A Vertical System in Circular Motion

All roller coasters, regardless of their appearance, are designed so that each car has sufficient velocity to remain in contact with the track at the top of the loop. At the top, the centripetal force is exerted by two forces working in the same direction: the track on the car, which is the normal force ($\vec{F}_N$) and the force of gravity ($\vec{F}_g$). Both forces push the car toward the centre of the loop.

The speed of the car determines the amount of centripetal force needed to maintain a certain radius. As you saw from equation 6, the centripetal force is directly related to the square of the speed. Here is equation 6 again:

$$F_c = \frac{mv^2}{r} \tag{6}$$

But the force of gravity is independent of speed, and will always pull the car downward with the same force. To demonstrate the role that gravity plays as a portion of the centripetal force, we can look at a hypothetical situation of a roller coaster going around a loop as shown in Figures 5.28(a), (b), and (c).

Assume a roller coaster car like the one in Figure 5.28 on the opposite page experiences a force of gravity that is 1000 N. This value won't change regardless of the car's position on the track or its speed. Remember, the centripetal force is the net force. In this case, it is equal to the sum of the gravitational force ($\vec{F}_g$) and the track's force ($\vec{F}_N$) on the car.

Figure 5.28 illustrates how speed affects the roller coaster car's motion when it is sent through the loop three times. Each time, it is sent with less speed.

► **Figure 5.28(a)**   The first time through the loop, the speed is such that the roller coaster requires a centripetal force of 1500 N to keep it moving in a circular path. At the top of the loop, the roller coaster car will experience a centripetal force that is the sum of the force of gravity and the force exerted by the track, pushing the car inward to the centre of the circle. The centripetal force acts down, so it is −1500 N. The force of gravity is constant at 1000 N so the track pushes inward with 500 N to produce the required centripetal force. The car goes around the loop with no problem.

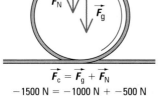

$$\vec{F}_c = \vec{F}_g + \vec{F}_N$$
−1500 N = −1000 N + −500 N

► **Figure 5.28(b)**   Suppose the next time the car goes around the track, it is moving more slowly, so that the centripetal force required is only 1000 N. In this case, the force of gravity alone can provide the required centripetal force. Therefore, the track does not need to exert any force on the car to keep it moving on the track. There is no normal force, so the force of gravity alone is the centripetal force. The car goes around the loop again with no problem.

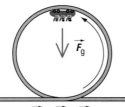

$$\vec{F}_c = \vec{F}_g + \vec{F}_N$$
−1000 N = −1000 N + 0 N

► **Figure 5.28(c)**   Now suppose the last time the car goes around the track, it is moving very slowly. The required centripetal force is just 800 N, but the force of gravity is constant, so it is still 1000 N; that is, 200 N more than the centripetal force required to keep the car moving in a circular path with this radius. If the track could somehow pull upward by 200 N to balance the force of gravity, the car would stay on the track. This is something it can't do in our hypothetical case. Since the gravitational force cannot be balanced by the track's force, it pulls the car downward off the track.

$$\vec{F}_c = \vec{F}_g + \vec{F}_N$$
−800 N = −1000 N + 200 N

Since the normal force cannot pull upward, it cannot generate +200 N. 200 N more is needed to keep the car on a track of this radius, so the car falls off.

The slowest that any car can go around the track would be at a speed that requires a centripetal force that has a magnitude equal to gravity. Gravity would make up all of the centripetal force. This can be expressed as:

$$F_c = F_g$$

Remember that this equality doesn't mean that the centripetal force is a different force than the force of gravity. It means that it *is* the force of gravity.

All roller coasters are designed so that the cars' speed is enough to create a centripetal force greater than the force of gravity to minimize the chance of the car leaving the track. The wheels of roller coaster cars also wrap around both sides of the track so the track can indeed pull upwards.

Concept Check

The centripetal force exerted on the Moon as it orbits Earth is caused by Earth's gravity. What would happen to the Moon's orbit if the Moon's velocity increased or slowed down?

Example 5.6

A 700.0-kg roller coaster car full of people goes around a vertical loop that has a diameter of 50.0 m (Figure 5.29). What minimum speed must the roller coaster car have at the top of the vertical loop to stay on the track?

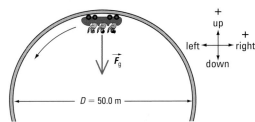

▲ **Figure 5.29**   When the roller coaster is moving with the minimum speed to maintain its circular path, the force of gravity alone is the centripetal force. The track exerts no force on the car.

Analysis and Solution

For the roller coaster to stay on the track at the top of the loop with the minimum speed, the centripetal force is the force of gravity.

To determine the radius of the loop, divide the diameter by 2.

$$r = \frac{50.0 \text{ m}}{2}$$
$$= 25.0 \text{ m}$$

Use the equality of the centripetal force and gravity to solve for the speed:

$$F_{\text{net}} = F_g$$
$$F_c = F_g$$
$$\frac{\not{m}v^2}{r} = \not{m}g$$
$$\frac{v^2}{r} = g$$
$$v = \sqrt{rg}$$
$$= \sqrt{25.0 \text{ m}\left(9.81 \, \frac{\text{m}}{\text{s}^2}\right)}$$
$$= 15.7 \text{ m/s}$$

The roller coaster car must have a minimum speed of 15.7 m/s to stay on the track.

Practice Problems

1. Neglecting friction, what is the minimum speed a toy car must have to go around a vertical loop of diameter 15.0 cm without falling off?

2. What is the maximum radius a roller coaster loop can be if a car with a speed of 20.0 m/s is to go around safely?

Answers

1. 1.21 m/s
2. 40.8 m

e LAB

For a probeware activity that investigates circular motion in a vertical plane, follow the links at www.pearsoned.ca/physicssource.

PHYSICS INSIGHT

All objects fall at a rate of 9.81 m/s² regardless of their mass.

You can swing a full pail of water around in a circle over your head without getting wet for the same reason that a roller coaster can go around a loop without falling off the track. Let's examine the case of a mass on the end of a rope, moving in a vertical circle, and see how it compares to the roller coaster.

A bucket of water is tied to the end of a rope and spun in a vertical circle. It has sufficient velocity to keep it moving in a circular path. Figures 5.30(a), (b), and (c) show the bucket in three different positions as it moves around in a vertical circle.

▶ **Figure 5.30(a)** The bucket is at the top of the circle. In this position, two forces are acting on the bucket: the force of gravity and the tension of the rope. Both are producing the centripetal force and are acting downward. The equation to represent this situation is:
$$\vec{F}_c = \vec{F}_g + \vec{F}_T$$

(a)

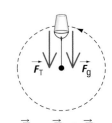

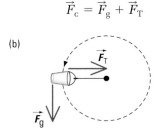

$$\vec{F}_c = \vec{F}_g + \vec{F}_T$$

▶ **Figure 5.30(b)** When the bucket has moved to the position where the rope is parallel to the ground, the force of gravity is perpendicular to the tension. It does not contribute to the centripetal force. The tension alone is the centripetal force. We can write this mathematically as:
$$\vec{F}_c = \vec{F}_T$$

(b)

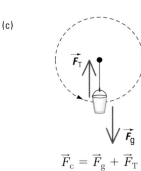

$$\vec{F}_c = \vec{F}_T$$

▶ **Figure 5.30(c)** As the bucket moves through the bottom of the circle, it must have a centripetal force that overcomes gravity. The tension is the greatest here because gravity is acting opposite to the centripetal force. The equation is the same as in (a) above, but tension is acting upward, so when the values are placed into the equation this time, $\vec{F}_T$ is positive and $\vec{F}_g$ is negative. The effect is demonstrated in Example 5.7.

(c)

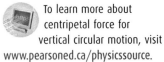

$$\vec{F}_c = \vec{F}_g + \vec{F}_T$$

Concept Check

1. A bucket filled with sand swings in a vertical circle at the end of a rope with increasing speed. At some moment, the tension on the rope will exceed the rope's strength, and the rope will break. In what position in the bucket's circular path is this most likely to happen? Explain.
2. Is it necessary to know the position of an object moving in a vertical circle with uniform speed if you are determining centripetal force? Explain.

e **SIM**

To learn more about centripetal force for vertical circular motion, visit www.pearsoned.ca/physicssource.

Forces Affecting an Object Moving in a Vertical Circle

In summary, an object moving in a vertical circle is affected by the following forces:

- The centripetal force is the net force on the object in any position.
- The centripetal force is determined by the object's mass, speed, and radius. In the case of the roller coaster and bucket of water, their mass and radius of curvature are constant so only their speed affects the centripetal force.
- The force of gravity is one of the forces that contributes to the centripetal force.
- The force of gravity remains constant regardless of the position of the object.

Example 5.7

A bucket of water with a mass of 1.5 kg is spun in a vertical circle on a rope. The radius of the circle is 0.75 m and the speed of the bucket is 3.00 m/s. What is the tension on the rope in position C, as shown in Figure 5.31?

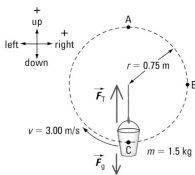

Given

$r = 0.75$ m
$m = 1.5$ kg
$v = 3.00$ m/s
$g = 9.81$ m/s²

Required

tension ($\vec{F}_T$)

▲ **Figure 5.31**

Practice Problems

1. Using the information in Example 5.7, determine the tension in the rope at position A in Figure 5.31.

2. Using the information in Example 5.7, determine the tension in the rope in position B in Figure 5.31.

3. A 0.98-kg rock is attached to a 0.40-m rope and spun in a vertical circle. The tension on the rope when the rock is at the top of the swing is 79.0 N [down]. What is the speed of the rock?

Answers

1. 3.3 N [down]
2. 18 N [left]
3. 6.0 m/s

Analysis and Solution

The centripetal force acting on the bucket will not change as the bucket moves in a vertical circle. The tension will change as the bucket moves in its circular path because gravity will work with it at the top and against it at the bottom.

In position C, the force of gravity works downward (negative), but the centripetal force and tension act upward (positive). Tension must overcome gravity to provide the centripetal force (Figure 5.32).

Remember that the centripetal force is the net force and is the vector sum of all the forces acting on the bucket. Therefore, the equation is:

$$\vec{F}_{net} = \vec{F}_g + \vec{F}_T$$

$$\vec{F}_c = \vec{F}_g + \vec{F}_T$$

$$F_c = F_g + F_T$$

$$F_T = F_c - F_g$$

▲ **Figure 5.32**

$$= \frac{mv^2}{r} - (-mg)$$

$$= \frac{(1.5 \text{ kg})\left(3.0 \frac{\text{m}}{\text{s}}\right)^2}{0.75 \text{ m}} - \left[-(1.5 \text{ kg})\left(9.81 \frac{\text{m}}{\text{s}^2}\right)\right]$$

$$= 18\text{N} - [-14.715 \text{ N}]$$

$$= 33 \text{ N}$$

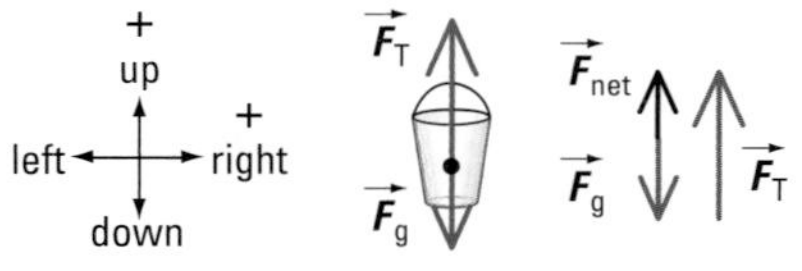

Paraphrase

The tension on the rope at position C is 33 N [up]. This is the maximum tension the system will experience because gravity acts in the opposite direction of the centripetal force.

Centripetal Force, Acceleration, and Frequency

At your local hardware store, you will find a variety of rotary power tools that operate by circular motion. The table saw, circular saw, impact wrench, reciprocating saw, and rotary hammer are a few (Figure 5.33). One of the selling features listed on the box of most of these tools is the rotational frequency (in rpm). At the beginning of this chapter, you learned that rpm refers to the frequency of rotation measured in revolutions per minute. This is an Imperial measurement that has been around for hundreds of years. It has probably persisted because people have a "feel" for what it means.

Even though revolutions per minute (rpm) is not, strictly speaking, the correct way to represent the frequency of rotation, it is a very useful measurement nevertheless. Why is the frequency of rotation often a more useful measure than the speed? The answer has to do with the nature of a rotating object.

▲ **Figure 5.33** Most tools, motors, and devices that rotate with high speed report the frequency of rotation using rpm instead of the speed.

The Effect of Radius on Speed, Period, and Frequency

Imagine a disc spinning about its axis with uniform circular motion (Figure 5.34). Positions A, B, and C are at different radii from the axis of rotation, but all the positions make one complete revolution in exactly the same time, so they have the same period. Of course, if the periods for points A, B, and C are the same, so are their frequencies, and we can make the following generalization: For any solid rotating object, regardless of its shape, the frequency of rotation for all points on the object will be the same.

Compare the speeds of points A, B, and C. Point A is the closest to the axis of rotation and has the smallest radius, followed by B, and then C with the largest radius. As already discussed, all three points make one complete revolution in the same amount of time, so point C, which has the farthest distance to cover, moves the fastest. Point B moves more slowly than C because it has less distance to travel. Point A has the slowest speed because it has the least distance to cover in the same amount of time. In essence, the speed of the spinning disc changes depending on which point you are referring to. In other words, the speed of a point on a disc changes with respect to its radius.

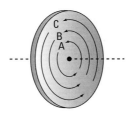

▲ **Figure 5.34** The velocities at A, B, and C are all different, whereas the rotational frequency of this disc is the same at any point.

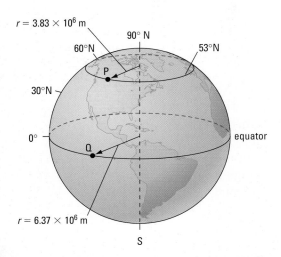

$r = 3.83 \times 10^6$ m

90° N

60°N   53°N

P

30°N

0°   equator

Q

$r = 6.37 \times 10^6$ m

S

▲ **Figure 5.35** The speed of any point on Earth depends on its latitude (which determines its rotational radius). Point P moves more slowly than point Q, but they both have the same period and frequency.

At the beginning of this chapter, you learned that the speed of an Albertan is roughly 1000 km/h as Earth rotates on its axis. However, not every point on Earth's surface moves with the same speed. Remember: Speed changes with radius, and on Earth, the distance from the axis of rotation changes with latitude (Figure 5.35). The fastest motion is at the equator and the slowest is at the poles, but every point on Earth has the same *period* of rotation — one day.

Determining Centripetal Force Using Period and Frequency

In earlier example problems, such as Example 5.3, a given rotational frequency or period had to be converted to speed before the centripetal acceleration or force could be determined. It would be simpler to derive the equations for centripetal acceleration and force using rotational frequency or period to save a step in our calculations. The equations for centripetal acceleration and force are:

$$a_c = \frac{v^2}{r} \text{ and } F_c = \frac{mv^2}{r}$$

Recall that:

$$v = \frac{2\pi r}{T}$$

By substituting the velocity equation into the centripetal acceleration equation, the result is:

$$a_c = \frac{(2\pi r)^2}{rT^2}$$

$$= \frac{4\pi^2 r^2}{rT^2}$$

$$a_c = \frac{4\pi^2 r}{T^2} \tag{7}$$

The centripetal force is $F_c = ma$, so the centripetal acceleration is:

$$F_c = \frac{4\pi^2 mr}{T^2} \tag{8}$$

Period is just the inverse of frequency, so it is relatively simple to express equations 7 and 8 in terms of frequency:

$$a_c = 4\pi^2 r f^2 \tag{9}$$

and

$$F_c = 4\pi^2 mr f^2 \tag{10}$$

To convert rpm to hertz, simply divide by 60.

Example 5.8

The compressor blades in a jet engine have a diameter of 42.0 cm and turn at 15 960 rpm (Figure 5.36). Determine the magnitude of the centripetal acceleration at the tip of each compressor blade.

▲ **Figure 5.36** The centripetal acceleration at the tip of a blade can be determined from the frequency of the blade's rotation.

Analysis and Solution

First convert the frequency to SI units (Hz) and determine the radius. Then use equation 9.

$$f = \frac{15\ 960\ \text{rev}}{1\ \text{min}} \times \frac{1\ \text{min}}{60\ \text{s}}$$

$$= 266.00\ \text{Hz}$$

$$r = \frac{D}{2}$$

$$= \frac{0.420\ \text{m}}{2}$$

$$= 0.210\ \text{m}$$

$$a_c = 4\pi^2 r f^2$$

$$= 4\pi^2 (0.210\ \text{m})(266.00\ \text{Hz})^2$$

$$= 5.87 \times 10^5\ \text{m/s}^2$$

The magnitude of the centripetal acceleration at the tip of each compressor blade is $5.87 \times 10^5\ \text{m/s}^2$.

Practice Problems

1. A space station shaped like a wheel could be used to create artificial gravity for astronauts living in space. The astronauts would work on the rim of the station as it spins. If the radius of the space station is 30.0 m, what would its frequency have to be to simulate the gravity of Earth ($g = 9.81\ \text{m/s}^2$)?

2. A 454.0-g mass, attached to the end of a 1.50-m rope, is swung in a horizontal circle with a frequency of 150.0 rpm. Determine the centripetal force acting on the mass.

Answers

1. 9.10×10^{-2} Hz
2. 1.68×10^2 N

Knowledge

1. A car heading north begins to make a right turn. One-quarter of a whole turn later, in what direction is the centripetal force acting?

2. Does the Moon experience centripetal acceleration? Why?

3. What two things could you do to increase the centripetal force acting on an object moving in a horizontal circle?

4. An object moves in a vertical circle at the end of a rope. As the object moves, explain what happens to:

   (a) the force of gravity, and

   (b) the tension.

5. What force acts as the centripetal force for a plane that is making a horizontal turn?

Applications

6. A car's wheels have a radius of 0.5 m. If the car travels at a speed of 15.0 m/s, what is the period of rotation of the wheels?

7. A propeller blade has a period of rotation of 0.0400 s. What is the velocity of the outer tip of the propeller blade if the tip is 1.20 m from the hub?

8. A 1500-kg car is making a turn with a 100.0-m radius on a road where the coefficient of static friction is 0.70. What is the maximum speed the car can go without skidding?

9. A car rounds a curve of radius 90.0 m at a speed of 100.0 km/h. Determine the centripetal acceleration of the car.

10. NASA uses a centrifuge that spins astronauts around in a capsule at the end of an 8.9-m metallic arm. The centrifuge spins at 35 rpm. Determine the centripetal acceleration that the astronauts feel. How many times greater is this acceleration than the acceleration of gravity?

11. What minimum speed must a toy racecar have to move successfully through a vertical loop that has a diameter of 30.0 cm?

12. Determine the centripetal acceleration acting on a person standing at the equator ($r_{Earth} = 6.37 \times 10^6$ m).

13. An ant climbs onto the side of a bicycle tire a distance of 0.40 m from the hub. If the 0.010-g ant can hold onto the tire with the force of 4.34×10^{-4} N, at what frequency would the tire fling the ant off?

Extensions

14. Two pulleys are connected together by a belt as shown in the diagram below. If the pulley connected to the motor spins at 200.0 rpm, what is the frequency of the larger pulley? (Hint: Both pulleys have the same velocity at their outer edge.)

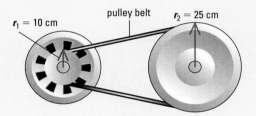

$r_1 = 10$ cm   pulley belt $r_2 = 25$ cm

15. Two NASCAR racecars go into a turn beside each other. If they remain side by side in the turn, which car has the advantage coming out of the turn?

e TEST

To check your understanding of circular motion and Newton's laws, follow the eTest links at www.pearsoned.ca/school/physicssource.

5.3 Satellites and Celestial Bodies in Circular Motion

Johannes Kepler (1571–1630) was a German mathematician with a strong interest in astronomy. When he started working for renowned Danish astronomer Tycho Brahe (1546–1601) in 1600, he was given the problem of determining why the orbit of Mars didn't completely agree with mathematical predictions. Brahe probably gave Kepler this job to keep him busy since he didn't share Kepler's ideas that the planets revolved around the Sun. At this time, most people, including scientists, believed that the planets and the Sun revolved around Earth.

info **BIT**

Comets are objects in space that have very elliptical orbits. They are often difficult to detect because they are relatively small and their orbits take them a great distance from the Sun. It is likely there are many comets orbiting the Sun that we have yet to discover.

Kepler's Laws

Brahe had made very meticulous observations of the orbital position of Mars. Kepler used this data to determine that the planet must revolve around the Sun. Kepler also hypothesized that Mars had an elliptical orbit, not a circular one. Until this time, all mathematical predictions of a planet's position in space were based on the assumption that it moved in a circular orbit. That is why Brahe's observations disagreed with mathematical predictions at the time. By recognizing that planets move in elliptical orbits, Kepler could account for the discrepancy.

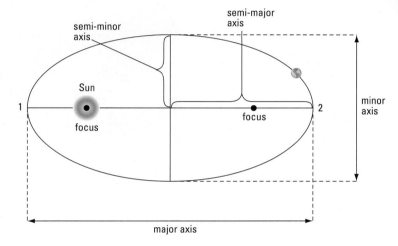

▲ **Figure 5.37** Kepler described the motion of planets as an ellipse with a semi-major axis and a semi-minor axis. The average orbital radius is the semi-major axis.

Kepler's First Law

An ellipse is an elongated circle. Figure 5.37 is an example of an ellipse. There are two foci, as well as major and minor axes. In Kepler's model, the Sun is at one focus and the planet's orbit is the path described by the shape of the ellipse. It is clear from Figure 5.37 that the planet will be closer to the Sun in position 1 than in position 2. This means that the planet's orbital radius must be changing as time goes by.

Why then is a planet's orbital radius often written as a fixed number? There are two reasons:

- The radius used is an average value. Mathematically, this average radius can be shown to be the same length as the semi-major axis.
- The orbit of the planet, although an ellipse, is very close to being a circle, so the orbital radius really doesn't change much from position 1 to position 2.

Figure 5.37 is an exaggeration of a planet's orbit for the purposes of clarity.

The degree to which an ellipse is elongated is called the eccentricity. It is a number between 0 and 1, with 0 being a perfect circle and 1 being a parabola. Table 5.4 shows the eccentricities of the orbits of the planets and other celestial bodies in our solar system.

▼ Table 5.4 Eccentricities of
Orbits of Celestial Bodies

Celestial Body	Eccentricity
Mercury	0.205
Venus	0.007
Earth	0.017
Mars	0.093
Ceres	0.080
Jupiter	0.048
Saturn	0.054
Uranus	0.047
Neptune	0.009
Pluto	0.249
Eris	0.437
Sedna	0.857

Kepler's Second Law

When Kepler stated his theory, the time was right and the scientific climate was such that it wasn't rejected. He went on to state two more revolutionary ideas relating to the orbits of planets in the solar system. His second law stated that planets move through their elliptical orbit in such a manner as to sweep out equal areas in equal times. Imagine a line that extends from the Sun to the planet. As the planet moves in its orbit, the line moves with it and sweeps out an area. In the same amount of time, at any other position in the planet's orbit, the planet will again sweep out the same area (Figure 5.38).

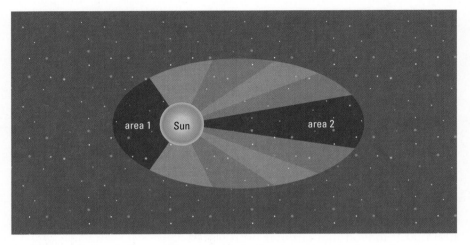

▲ Figure 5.38 Kepler's second law states that a line drawn from the Sun to the planet sweeps out equal areas in equal times.

e **WEB**

Sedna was discovered in 2004 and is the largest object yet found in a region of space known as the Oort cloud. On July 29, 2005, an object now named Eris was confirmed. It is larger than Pluto but also in the Kuiper belt. To learn more about these celestial bodies, the Kuiper belt, and the Oort cloud, follow the links at:www.pearsoned.ca/school/physicssource.

One consequence of this rule is that a planet's speed must change throughout its orbit. Consider Figure 5.39 where area 1 is equal to area 2. As the planet approaches the Sun, the orbital radius decreases. If it is to sweep out an area equal to area 2, the planet must speed up and cover a larger distance to compensate for the smaller radius. As the planet gets farther from the Sun, the orbital radius gets larger. The planet slows down and sweeps out the same area again in the same amount of time (Figure 5.39).

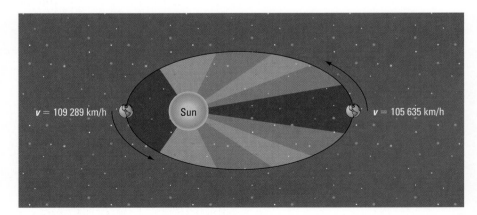

▲ Figure 5.39 Earth's speed varies from 105 635 km/h at its farthest distance from the Sun to 109 289 km/h when it is closest. Its speed changes to compensate for the change in its orbital radius.

Kepler's Third Law

Kepler's third law states that the ratio of a planet's orbital period squared divided by its orbital radius cubed is a constant that is the same for all the planets orbiting the Sun. Written mathematically, it is:

$$\frac{T_a^2}{r_a^3} = K \qquad (11)$$

where T_a is the orbital period of planet A, r_a is the orbital radius of planet A, and K is Kepler's constant.

Since the constant K applies to all planets orbiting the Sun, we can equate the ratio T^2/r^3 between any two planets and write the equation:

$$\frac{T_a^2}{r_a^3} = \frac{T_b^2}{r_b^3} \qquad (12)$$

Until Kepler noticed this relationship between the planets, there was really no indication that the third law would be true. If it hadn't been for Tycho Brahe's accurate measurements of the planets' orbital positions throughout their year, it is unlikely that Kepler would have made this discovery. Once the relationship was known, it was easy to verify, and it further bolstered the credibility of the heliocentric (Sun-centred) model of the solar system. It is important to note that when Kepler derived his third law, he applied it only to planets orbiting the Sun. However, this law can be extended to moons that orbit a planet. In fact, in the most general sense, Kepler's third law is applicable to all celestial bodies that orbit the same focus. For bodies orbiting a different focus, *Kepler's constant will be different*.

Kepler's three laws can be summarized this way:

1. All planets in the solar system have elliptical orbits with the Sun at one focus.

2. A line drawn from the Sun to a planet sweeps out equal areas in equal times.

3. The ratio of a planet's orbital period squared to its orbital radius cubed is a constant. All objects orbiting the same focus (e.g., planets, the Sun) have the same constant. $\dfrac{T_a^2}{r_a^3} = \dfrac{T_b^2}{r_b^3}$

Determining Kepler's Constant

Kepler's third law states that the constant K is the same for all planets in a solar system. The period and orbital radius of Earth are well known, so they are used to compute the constant. The mean (average) orbital distance for Earth from the Sun is 1.49×10^{11} m, and Earth's orbital period is 31 557 600 s. Kepler's constant can be calculated as shown below:

$$K = \frac{T_E^2}{r_E^3}$$

$$= \frac{(3.15576 \times 10^7 \text{ s})^2}{(1.49 \times 10^{11} \text{ m})^3}$$

$$= 3.01 \times 10^{-19} \text{ s}^2/\text{m}^3$$

e **SIM**

To learn more about Kepler's second law regarding eccentricity, orbital period, and speed of a planet, visit www.pearsoned.ca/school/physicssource.

e **WEB**

The Titius-Bode law is another mathematical description that predicts the orbital radius of the planets. To learn more about the Titius-Bode law, follow the links at www.pearsoned.ca/school/physicssource.

PHYSICS INSIGHT

The orbital radius is always measured from the centre of the orbiting body to the centre of the body being orbited.

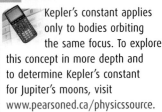
However, you will not often find Kepler's constant written with this value. The reason is twofold. If different units for distance and time are used (something other than metres and seconds), then the constant can be made to equal 1. This has obvious mathematical benefits. The other reason is that using metres and seconds as the units of measurement is impractical when dealing with the scale of our solar system. To represent astronomical distances, it becomes necessary to use units bigger than a metre or even a kilometre. For example, measuring the distance from Earth to the Sun in kilometres (149 000 000 km) is roughly like measuring the distance from Edmonton to Red Deer in millimetres.

Astronomical Units

A more suitable measurement for astronomical distances has been adopted. It is called the astronomical unit (AU). One astronomical unit is the mean orbital distance from Earth to the Sun (the length of the semi-major axis of Earth's orbit). This is a more manageable unit to use. For example, Neptune is only 30.1 AU away from the Sun on average.

Kepler's constant, using units of years and AU, can be determined as follows:

$$K = \frac{T_E^2}{r_E^3}$$

$$= \frac{(1\ y)^2}{(1\ AU)^3}$$

$$= 1\ y^2/AU^3$$

The advantage of using the units of an Earth year and astronomical units becomes clear as Kepler's constant works out to 1. Any other planet in our solar system must also have the same constant because it orbits the same focus (the Sun). Be careful not to use this value of Kepler's constant for all systems. For example, if Kepler's third law is used for moons orbiting a planet, or planets orbiting a different sun, the constant will be different.

Example 5.9

Mars has an orbital radius of 1.52 AU (Figure 5.40). What is its orbital period?

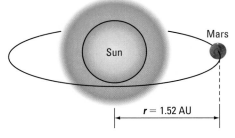

▲ **Figure 5.40** Mars has a mean orbital radius of 1.52 AU (not drawn to scale). Kepler's third law can be used to determine its period.

Practice Problems

1. Use Kepler's third law to determine the orbital period of Jupiter. Its orbital radius is 5.203 AU.

2. Pluto takes 90 553 Earth days to orbit the Sun. Use this value to determine its mean orbital radius.

3. A piece of rocky debris in space has a mean orbital distance of 45.0 AU. What is its orbital period?

Analysis and Solution

Start with the equation for determining Kepler's constant:

$$K = \frac{T^2_{\text{Mars}}}{r^3_{\text{Mars}}}$$

where T_{Mars} is the the orbital period of Mars, and r_{Mars} is the mean orbital radius of Mars.

$$T^2_{\text{Mars}} = Kr^3_{\text{Mars}}$$

$$T_{\text{Mars}} = \sqrt{\left(1\ \frac{y^2}{\text{AU}^3}\right)(1.52\ \text{AU})^3}$$

$$= 1.87\ y$$

The orbital period of Mars is 1.87 Earth years. In other words, it takes 1.87 Earth years for Mars to go around the Sun once.

A close examination of Table 5.5 shows that as the orbital radius of a planet increases, so does its orbital period. Planets nearest the Sun orbit fastest; that is, they have the shortest years. Planets farthest from the Sun have the longest years.

Kepler's laws don't apply just to planets orbiting the Sun. They apply to all bodies that orbit the same focus in an ellipse. This means that moons orbiting a planet are also subject to Kepler's laws and have their own Kepler's constant. Earth has only one Moon (natural satellite) but Jupiter and Saturn have many, and more are being found all the time. Table 5.6 shows the planets and some of their known moons.

PHYSICS INSIGHT

Kepler's third law can only be applied to bodies orbiting the same object.

▼ **Table 5.5**   Solar Celestial Bodies

Celestial Body	Mass (kg)	Equatorial Radius (m)	Orbital Period (days)	Mean Orbital Radius (m)	Distance (AU)
Sun	1.99×10^{30}	6.96×10^8	—	—	—
Mercury	3.34×10^{23}	2.44×10^6	87.97	5.79×10^{10}	0.387
Venus	4.87×10^{24}	6.05×10^6	224.7	1.08×10^{11}	0.723
Earth	5.98×10^{24}	6.37×10^6	365.24	1.49×10^{11}	1
Mars	6.40×10^{23}	3.40×10^6	686.93	2.28×10^{11}	1.524
Ceres	9.5×10^{20}	4.88×10^5	1679.8	4.14×10^{11}	2.778
Jupiter	1.90×10^{27}	7.15×10^7	4330.6	7.78×10^{11}	5.203
Saturn	5.69×10^{26}	6.00×10^7	10 755.7	1.43×10^{12}	9.537
Uranus	8.68×10^{25}	2.59×10^7	30 687.2	2.87×10^{12}	19.191
Neptune	1.03×10^{26}	2.48×10^7	60 190	4.50×10^{12}	30.069
Pluto	1.20×10^{22}	1.70×10^6	90 553	5.91×10^{12}	39.482
Eris	?	~1.43×10^6	204 540	~1.01×10^{13}	67.940
Sedna	4.21×10^{21}	8.5×10^5	3 835 020	7.14×10^{13}	479.5

info **BIT**

As of August 2006, the International Astronomical Union (IAU) finally developed a definition of a planet. To be a planet, a celestial body must orbit a star, be large enough that its own gravity forms it into a spherical shape, and have cleared the neighbourhood around its orbit. Pluto fails to satisfy the last criterion as its orbit is near many other Kuiper belt objects. There are now officially only eight planets in our solar system.

1. What type of orbit would a planet have if the semi-minor axis of its orbit equalled the semi-major axis?
2. Why can't Kepler's third law be applied to Earth's Moon and Jupiter's moon Callisto using the same value for Kepler's constant?
3. Assume astronomers discover a planetary system in a nearby galaxy that has 15 planets orbiting a single star. One of the planets has twice the mass, but the same orbital period and radius as Earth. Could Kepler's constant for our solar system be used in the newly discovered planetary system? Explain.
4. Assume astronomers discover yet another planetary system in a nearby galaxy that has six planets orbiting a single star, but all of the planets' orbits are different from Earth's. Explain how Kepler's third law could apply to this planetary system.
5. Compare planets orbiting a star with points on a rotating solid disc (Figure 5.34).

▼ **Table 5.6**   The Planets and Their Large Moons

Planet	Moons	Mass (kg)	Equatorial Radius (m)	Orbital Period (Earth days)	Mean Orbital Radius (m)	Eccentricity	Discovered (Year)
Earth	Moon	7.36×10^{22}	1.737×10^6	27.322	3.844×10^8	0.0549	—
Mars	Phobos	1.063×10^{16}	1.340×10^4	0.3189	9.378×10^6	0.015	1877
	Deimos	2.38×10^{15}	7.500×10^3	1.262	2.346×10^7	0.0005	1877
Jupiter (4 most massive)	Io	8.9316×10^{22}	1.830×10^6	1.769	4.220×10^8	0.004	1610
	Europa	4.79982×10^{22}	1.565×10^6	3.551	6.710×10^8	0.009	1610
	Ganymede	1.48186×10^{23}	2.634×10^6	7.154	1.070×10^9	0.002	1610
	Callisto	1.07593×10^{23}	2.403×10^6	16.689	1.883×10^9	0.007	1610
Saturn (7 most massive)	Mimas	3.75×10^{19}	2.090×10^5	0.942	1.855×10^8	0.0202	1789
	Enceladus	7×10^{19}	2.560×10^5	1.37	2.380×10^8	0.00452	1789
	Tethys	6.27×10^{20}	5.356×10^5	1.887	2.947×10^8	0.00	1684
	Dione	1.10×10^{21}	5.600×10^5	2.74	3.774×10^8	0.002	1684
	Rhea	2.31×10^{21}	7.640×10^5	4.52	5.270×10^8	0.001	1672
	Titan	1.3455×10^{23}	2.575×10^6	15.945	1.222×10^9	0.0292	1655
	Iapetus	1.6×10^{21}	7.180×10^5	79.33	3.561×10^9	0.0283	1671
Uranus (5 most massive)	Miranda	6.6×10^{19}	2.400×10^5	1.41	1.299×10^8	0.0027	1948
	Ariel	1.35×10^{21}	5.811×10^5	2.52	1.909×10^8	0.0034	1851
	Umbriel	1.17×10^{21}	5.847×10^5	4.14	2.660×10^8	0.005	1851
	Titania	3.53×10^{21}	7.889×10^5	8.71	4.363×10^8	0.0022	1787
	Oberon	3.01×10^{21}	7.614×10^5	13.46	5.835×10^8	0.0008	1787
Neptune (3 most massive)	Proteus	5.00×10^{19}	2.080×10^5	1.12	1.176×10^8	0.0004	1989
	Triton	2.14×10^{22}	1.352×10^6	5.8766	3.548×10^8	0.000016	1846
	Nereid	2.00×10^{19}	1.700×10^5	360.14	5.513×10^9	0.7512	1949

Example 5.10

Mars has two moons, Deimos and Phobos (Figure 5.41). Phobos has an orbital radius of 9378 km and an orbital period of 0.3189 Earth days. Deimos has an orbital period of 1.262 Earth days. What is the orbital radius of Deimos?

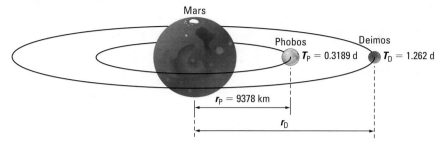

▲ **Figure 5.41** The orbital period and radius of Phobos can be used with the orbital period of Deimos to determine its orbital radius (not drawn to scale).

Given

$T_P = 0.3189$ d

$r_P = 9378$ km

$T_D = 1.262$ d

Required
orbital radius of Deimos (r_D)

Analysis and Solution
Both Phobos and Deimos orbit the same object, Mars, so Kepler's third law can be used to solve for the orbital radius of Deimos. The units of days and kilometres do not need to be changed to years and astronomical units because Kepler's third law is simply a ratio. It is important to be consistent with the units. If we use the units of kilometres for the measure of orbital radius, then the answer will be in kilometres as well.

$$\frac{T_D{}^2}{r_D{}^3} = \frac{T_P{}^2}{r_P{}^3}$$

$$r_D{}^3 = \frac{T_D{}^2 r_P{}^3}{T_P{}^2}$$

$$= \frac{(1.262 \text{ d})^2 (9378 \text{ km})^3}{(0.3189 \text{ d})^2}$$

$$= 1.2916 \times 10^{13} \text{ km}^3$$

$$r_D = \sqrt[3]{1.2916 \times 10^{13} \text{ km}^3}$$

$$= 2.346 \times 10^4 \text{ km}$$

Paraphrase
The orbital radius of Deimos is 2.346×10^4 km. This answer is reasonable since a planet with a larger orbital radius than Deimos will also have a larger period.

Practice Problems

1. Titan is one of the largest moons in our solar system, orbiting Saturn at an average distance of 1.22×10^9 m. Using the data for Dione, another moon of Saturn, determine Titan's orbital period.

2. The Cassini-Huygens probe began orbiting Saturn in December 2004. It takes 147 days for the probe to orbit Saturn. Use Tethys, one of Saturn's moons, to determine the average orbital radius of the probe.

3. Astronomers are continually finding new moons in our solar system. Suppose a new moon X is discovered orbiting Jupiter at an orbital distance of 9.38×10^9 m. Use the nearest moon to determine its orbital period.

Answers

1. 15.9 d

2. 5.38×10^6 km

3. 186 d

Orbital Period and Radius

Kepler determined that planets have slightly elliptical orbits. He also determined empirically that the period and radius of the planet's orbit were related. The purpose of this lab is to examine the relationship between the period and radius of planets' orbits around the Sun.

The Question

What relationship exists between the orbital period and orbital radius of planets orbiting the Sun?

Design and Conduct Your Investigation

This lab should be designed to investigate the relationship between period and radius. State a hypothesis relating the orbital period to the radius for planets orbiting the Sun. Remember to use an "if/then" statement. The lab should show how a planet's orbital radius affects its orbital period. To do this, use Table 5.5 to select data for at least five planets' periods and orbital radii.

Organize the relevant data from Table 5.5 into a chart in a suitable order that can be used to plot a graph using a graphing calculator or other acceptable means. Choose appropriate units for the manipulated and responding variables.

Look at the type of graph that results to draw a conclusion relating period and radius. Test the relationship you discovered from this lab with the relationship that exists between the orbital radius and period of a planet's moons. Do this by picking a planet from Table 5.6 that has several moons and perform the same procedure and analysis. Compare the relationships of orbital radius and period of the planets with that of the moons. Comment on any similarities or differences.

e **WEB**

In August 2006, the IAU decided to create three classifications of solar system objects: planets, dwarf planets, and small solar system objects. Pluto is now classified as a dwarf planet, along with Eris and Ceres (formerly an asteroid). To be a dwarf planet, the celestial body must orbit the Sun and be large enough that its own gravity forms it into a spherical shape, but not large enough that it has cleared the neighbourhood around its orbit. To learn about dwarf planets, follow the links at: www.pearsoned.ca/school/physicssource.

Newton's Version of Kepler's Third Law

Some stories suggest that Newton was sitting under a tree when an apple fell to the ground and inspired him to discover gravity. This is definitely not what happened, as gravity was already known to exist. But the falling apple did lead him to wonder if the force of gravity that caused the apple to fall could also be acting on the Moon pulling it toward Earth. This revelation might seem obvious but that's only because we have been taught that it's true. In his day, Kepler theorized that magnetism made the Moon orbit Earth, and planets orbit the Sun!

For most of the 1600s, scientists had been trying to predict where planets would be in their orbit at specific times. They failed to grasp the underlying mechanism responsible for the elliptical orbits that Kepler had shown to exist. In 1665, Newton finally recognized what no one else did: the centripetal force acting on the Moon was the force of gravity (Figure 5.42). The Moon was being pulled toward Earth like a falling apple. But the Moon was also moving off tangentially so that the rate at which it was falling matched the rate at which Earth curved away from it. In fact, the same mechanism was responsible for the planets orbiting the Sun.

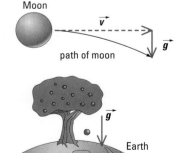

▲ **Figure 5.42** The Moon is falling to Earth with the acceleration of gravity just like the apple does. But the Moon also has a tangential velocity ($\vec{v}$) keeping it at the same distance from Earth at all times.

By recognizing that the centripetal force and force of gravity were the same, Newton solved the mystery of planetary motion. His derivations mathematically proved Kepler's third law. The implications of Newton's work were huge because scientists now had the mathematical tools necessary to explore the solar system in more depth.

Determining the Speed of a Satellite

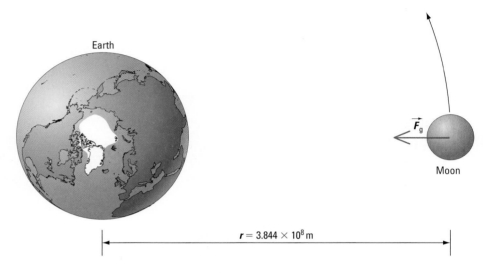

Earth

$\vec{F_g}$

Moon

$r = 3.844 \times 10^8 \, \text{m}$

▲ **Figure 5.43** The Moon experiences a centripetal force that is the force of gravity of Earth on the Moon.

Two of Newton's derivations deserve close examination. The first derivation uses the orbital radius of a body orbiting a planet or the Sun to determine the body's velocity.

Recall from Chapter 4 that Newton had determined the equation for the force of gravity that one object exerts on another:

$$F_g = \frac{Gm_1m_2}{r^2}$$

He correctly reasoned that the gravitational force exerted by the Moon and Earth must be the centripetal force acting on the Moon (Figure 5.43). So:

$$F_c = F_g$$

If we substitute the equations for centripetal force and gravity into this equation, we obtain:

$$\frac{m_{\text{Moon}}v^2}{r} = \frac{Gm_{\text{Moon}}m_{\text{Earth}}}{r^2}$$

where G is the universal gravitational constant, m_{Moon} is the mass of the Moon in kilograms, m_{Earth} is the mass of Earth in kilograms, v is the speed of the Moon in metres per second, and r is the orbital radius of the Moon in metres.

info **BIT**
Pluto and its moon Charon are close enough in mass that they have a common centre of gravity between them in space (see Extrasolar Planets on page 283). Charon does not orbit Pluto — both bodies orbit their common centre of gravity. Since their centre of gravity is in space and not below the surface of Pluto, they form a binary system. Astronomers have been aware of binary stars in our universe for many years (i.e., two stars that have a common centre of gravity in space around which they revolve). Pluto and Charon are unique because they are the only planet-moon system like this in our solar system.

PHYSICS INSIGHT

Equation 13 uses the mass of Earth, but is not restricted to it. In a more general sense, the mass refers to the object being orbited.

The mass of the Moon cancels, leaving:

$$\frac{v^2}{r} = \frac{Gm_{\text{Earth}}}{r^2}$$

Solving for v gives:

$$v = \sqrt{\frac{Gm_{\text{Earth}}}{r}} \qquad (13)$$

In its current form, this equation determines the speed of any object orbiting Earth. The speed of an object orbiting any planet, the Sun, or another star for that matter, can be determined by using the mass of the object being orbited in place of the mass of Earth.

Example 5.11

Earth's Moon is 3.844×10^5 km from Earth (Figure 5.44). Determine the orbital speed of the Moon.

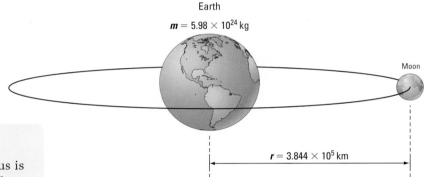

▲ Figure 5.44 The orbital speed of the Moon can be determined from its orbital radius and the mass of Earth.

Analysis and Solution
Convert the radius of the Moon's orbit to SI units. Then use the mass of Earth in equation 13.

$$r = (3.844 \times 10^5 \text{ km}) \times \frac{1000 \text{ m}}{\text{km}}$$

$$= 3.844 \times 10^8 \text{ m}$$

$$v = \sqrt{\frac{Gm_{\text{Earth}}}{r}}$$

$$= \sqrt{\frac{\left(6.67 \times 10^{-11} \frac{\text{N·m}^2}{\text{kg}^2}\right)(5.98 \times 10^{24} \text{ kg})}{3.844 \times 10^8 \text{ m}}}$$

$$= 1.02 \times 10^3 \text{ m/s}$$

The orbital speed of the Moon is 1.02×10^3 m/s or 3.67×10^3 km/h.

Practice Problems

1. Neptune's average orbital radius is 4.50×10^{12} m from the Sun. The mass of the Sun is 1.99×10^{30} kg. What is Neptune's orbital speed?

2. The moon Miranda orbits Uranus at a speed of 6.68×10^3 m/s. Use this speed and the mass of Uranus to determine the radius of Miranda's orbit. The mass of Uranus is 8.68×10^{25} kg.

Answers

1. 5.43×10^3 m/s
2. 1.30×10^8 m

Measuring the Orbital Height of a Satellite

Recall from Chapter 4 that the radius is always measured from the centre of one object to the centre of the other. This means that the orbital radius refers to the distance from centre to centre when measuring the distance from Earth to the Moon or from the Sun to the planets. Figure 5.45 shows the Earth-Moon system drawn to scale.

For an artificial (human-made) satellite, the height of its orbit is usually measured from Earth's surface. To determine the velocity of an artificial satellite, you must first find its proper orbital height (from the centre of Earth). This is done by adding Earth's radius to the height of the satellite above Earth's surface.

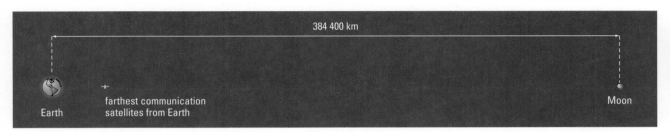

384 400 km

Earth   farthest communication   Moon
         satellites from Earth

▲ **Figure 5.45**   The Earth-Moon system drawn to scale. The radius of Earth doesn't need to be considered when comparing the distance between Earth and the Moon because it is insignificant compared to the great distance separating the two bodies. The distance between Earth and a communication satellite (35 880 km away) is small, so Earth's radius must be included in calculations involving orbital radius and period.

Example 5.12

LandSat is an Earth-imaging satellite that takes pictures of Earth's ozone layer and geological features. It orbits Earth at the height of 912 km (Figure 5.46). What are its orbital speed and its period?

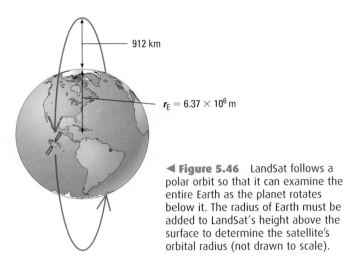

912 km

$r_E = 6.37 \times 10^6$ m

◀ **Figure 5.46**   LandSat follows a polar orbit so that it can examine the entire Earth as the planet rotates below it. The radius of Earth must be added to LandSat's height above the surface to determine the satellite's orbital radius (not drawn to scale).

Practice Problems

1. The International Space Station orbits Earth at a height of 359.2 km. What is its orbital speed?

2. The Chandra X-ray satellite takes X-ray pictures of high-energy objects in the universe. It is orbiting Earth at an altitude of 114 593 km. What is its orbital period?

Answers

1. 7.70×10^3 m/s
2. 4.19×10^5 s

Given
height of the satellite above Earth's surface = 912 km

Required
LandSat's orbital speed (v) and period (T)

Analysis and Solution

The radius of LandSat's orbit must be measured from the centre of Earth. To do this, add Earth's radius to the satellite's height above the planet's surface. Then determine the speed and period of the satellite.

$$r = r_{Earth} + 912\,000 \text{ m}$$

$$= (6.37 \times 10^6 \text{ m}) + (9.12 \times 10^5 \text{ m})$$

$$= 7.28 \times 10^6 \text{ m}$$

$$F_c = F_g$$

$$\frac{m_{Moon}v^2}{r} = \frac{Gm_{Moon}m_{Earth}}{r^2}$$

$$v = \sqrt{\frac{Gm_{Earth}}{r}}$$

$$= \sqrt{\frac{\left(6.67 \times 10^{-11} \, \frac{\text{N}\cdot\text{m}^2}{\text{kg}^2}\right)(5.98 \times 10^{24} \text{ kg})}{7.28 \times 10^6 \text{ m}}}$$

$$= 7.40 \times 10^3 \text{ m/s}$$

$$T = \frac{2\pi r}{v}$$

$$= \frac{2\pi(7.28 \times 10^6 \text{ m})}{7.40 \times 10^3 \, \frac{\text{m}}{\text{s}}}$$

$$= 6.18 \times 10^3 \text{ s}$$

Paraphrase

The speed of the satellite is 7.40×10^3 m/s (26 640 km/h). It orbits Earth once every 6.18×10^3 s (103 minutes).

Determining the Mass of a Celestial Body

A second derivation from Newton's version of Kepler's third law has to do with determining the mass of a planet or the Sun from the period and radius of a satellite orbiting it.

For any satellite in orbit around a planet, you can determine its speed if you know the mass of the planet. But just how do you determine the mass of the planet? For example, how can you "weigh" Earth? Newton realized that this was possible. Let's look at the equality $F_c = F_g$ again, but this time we will use equation 8 for centripetal force. Recall that:

$$F_c = \frac{4\pi^2 m_{Moon}r}{T^2_{Moon}}$$

where m_{Moon} is the mass of the Moon in kilograms, and T_{Moon} is the orbital period of the Moon in seconds.

e TECH

For an interactive simulation of the effect of a star's mass on the planets orbiting it, follow the links at www.pearsoned.ca/physicssource.

Since $F_c = F_g$, then

$$\frac{4\pi^2 m_{\text{Moon}} r}{T^2_{\text{Moon}}} = \frac{Gm_{\text{Moon}} m_{\text{Earth}}}{r^2}$$

Solve for m_{Earth}:

$$m_{\text{Earth}} = \frac{4\pi^2 r^3}{T^2_{\text{Moon}} G} \qquad (14)$$

You can determine Earth's mass by using the orbital radius and period of its satellite, the Moon. From Table 5.6 on page 274, the Moon's period and radius are:

- period of the Moon (T_{Moon}) = 27.3 days or 2.36×10^6 s
- radius of the Moon's orbit (r_{Moon}) = 384 400 km or 3.844×10^8 m

$$m_{\text{Earth}} = \frac{4\pi^2 (3.844 \times 10^8 \text{ m})^3}{(2.36 \times 10^6 \text{ s})^2 \left(6.67 \times 10^{-11} \dfrac{\text{N} \cdot \text{m}^2}{\text{kg}^2}\right)}$$

$$= 6.04 \times 10^{24} \text{ kg}$$

The mass of Earth is 6.04×10^{24} kg, which is close to the accepted value of 5.98×10^{24} kg.

Of course, this equation is not restricted to the Earth-Moon system. It applies to any celestial body that has satellites. For example, the Sun has eight planets that are natural satellites. Any one of them can be used to determine the mass of the Sun.

PHYSICS INSIGHT

Equation 14 uses the mass of Earth and the period of its Moon. This equation can be used for any celestial body with a satellite orbiting it. In a more general sense, the mass refers to the object being orbited, and the period is the period of the orbiting object.

Concept Check

1. What insight did Newton have that helped him explain the motion of the planets?
2. If Newton were told that our solar system is orbiting the centre of our galaxy, how would he explain this?
3. What previously immeasurable quantity was Newton able to determine once he developed his version of Kepler's third law?

Orbital Perturbations

At about the same time as Kepler was figuring out the mechanism of the solar system, Galileo Galilei (1564–1642) pointed a relatively new invention at the sky. He began using a telescope to closely examine Jupiter. Only a few planets are visible to the naked eye: Mercury, Venus, Mars, Saturn, and Jupiter. Until the early 1600s, any observations of these planets were done without the aid of a telescope. Within a few months of using only an 8-power telescope, Galileo had discovered four moons of Jupiter. It quickly became apparent how useful a telescope would be in the field of astronomy.

e WEB

To learn more about Galileo's discoveries with the telescope in 1609 and 1610, follow the links at www.pearsoned.ca/school/physicssource.

Within the space of 100 years, telescope technology improved dramatically, and the field of astronomy began its golden age. Astronomers plotted the positions of the planets more accurately than ever before and could peer deeper into the solar system. William Herschel (1738–1822) discovered the new planet Uranus in 1781, which created enormous interest. However, it wasn't long before astronomers noticed something strange about the orbit of Uranus. The orbital path of Uranus deviated from its predicted path slightly, just enough to draw attention. Astronomers called this deviation, or disturbance, an **orbital perturbation**.

The Discovery of Neptune

It had been over 120 years since Kepler and Newton had developed the mathematical tools necessary to understand and predict the position of the planets and their moons. Confident in the reliability of these laws, astronomers looked for a reason for the perturbation in the orbit of Uranus. According to mathematical predictions, Uranus should have been farther along in its orbit and closer to the Sun than it actually was. Somehow its progress was being slowed, and it was being pulled away from the Sun.

Recall that anything with mass creates a gravitational field. The strength of this field depends on the mass of the object and the separation distance from it. The orbit of Uranus was minutely perturbed. Could another as-yet-undiscovered planet be exerting a gravitational pull or tug on Uranus whenever the orbital path took these two planets close together? If there was a planet X farther out and behind Uranus, it would exert a gravitational pull that would slow Uranus down and pull its orbit outward (Figure 5.47). This could explain the perturbation in the orbit of Uranus and was precisely the assumption that two astronomers, Urbain Le Verrier (1811–1877) of France and John Adams (1819–1892) of Britain, made in 1845.

By examining exactly how much Uranus was pulled from its predicted position, Le Verrier and Adams could use Newton's law of gravitation to mathematically predict the size and position of this mysterious planet — if it existed. Working independently, both scientists gave very similar predictions of where to look for the planet. In September 1846, at the request of Le Verrier, German astronomer Johann Gottfried Galle (1812–1910) looked for the planet where Le Verrier predicted it would be and he found it! Le Verrier called the planet Neptune. It remained the solar system's outermost planet for the next 84 years until astronomers discovered Pluto in 1930 by analyzing the orbital perturbations of Neptune. (In 2006, Pluto was reclassified as a dwarf planet.)

The Search for Other Planets

The search for more planets in our solar system continues. A large band of rocky debris called the Kuiper belt lies 30 to 50 AU from the Sun. Pluto is a resident in this belt. Many scientists believed that Pluto was unlikely to be the only large resident of the belt and that the belt very likely contained more planet-sized objects.

orbital perturbation: irregularity or disturbance in the predicted orbit of a planet

e **WEB**

Telescopes and space technologies are continually improving, and new planetary objects are being found all the time. For the most up-to-date list of planets and celestial bodies in our solar system, follow the links at www.pearsoned.ca/school/physicssource.

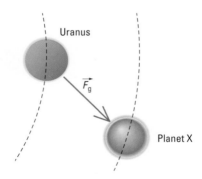

▲ **Figure 5.47** If a planet X existed and was behind Uranus in its orbit, it would pull Uranus back and outward.

In July 2005, a Kuiper belt object about 1.5 times bigger than Pluto was found. The scientific community has now given it the status of a dwarf planet, but at the time of publication of this book, it did not yet have an official name. Do other larger-than-Pluto bodies exist in the Kuiper belt? Probably, but their low reflectivity and extreme distance make them difficult to detect.

THEN, NOW, AND FUTURE   Extrasolar Planets

For many centuries, humans have wondered if they were the only intelligent life in the universe. It seems unlikely, given the multitude of stars in our galaxy alone. However, for any life to exist, it's pretty safe to assume that it must have a planet to inhabit. Until 1995, there was no conclusive proof that any other star besides our Sun had planets.

In October 1995, the first extrasolar planet was found orbiting a star similar in size to our Sun. It is called "extrasolar" because it is outside ("extra") our solar system. This planet was named 51 Pegasi b after the star around which it revolves (Figure 5.48).

It is huge but its orbital radius is extremely small. It is unlikely to support life as its gravitational field strength and temperature are extreme. Yet the discovery was a milestone since finding a planet orbiting a bright star 48 light years away is a very difficult task. A planet doesn't produce any light of its own, and it would be relatively dark compared to the very bright star beside it.

The light coming from a star is so bright it makes direct observation of a nearby planet difficult. Imagine staring into a car's headlight on a dark night and trying to see an ant crawling on the bumper. Now imagine the car is 23 000 km away, and you get an idea of the magnitude of the problem. However, the increasing power of telescopes and innovative detection techniques are yielding new planet findings all the time.

How is this accomplished? There are several different ways, but the most common and productive way is not to look for the planet directly but to look at the star that it is orbiting and watch for perturbations (also called wobble) in the star's movement.

That's right, stars move. If they don't have a planet or planets orbiting them, then they simply move in a linear fashion through space. If they have a planet or planets in orbit around them, not only do they move linearly, but they also wobble in a circular path. This is because a planet exerts a gravitational pull on its star just as the star exerts the same pull on the planet.

They both revolve around each other, just like you and a very heavy object would if you spun the object around in a circle at the end of a rope. Since the star is much more massive than the planet, its orbital radius is very small. This perturbation of the star is detectable and is indirect evidence that a planet must be orbiting it.

As you can imagine, for a star to have a noticeable wobble, the planet that orbits it must be relatively large and fairly close to the star. This would make conditions on the planet inhospitable for life as we know it. But the search goes on and as our technology improves, who knows what we may find?

Questions

1. Why is it so hard to detect an extrasolar planet?

2. What new technologies and techniques are making it possible to detect extrasolar planets?

3. Why is it unlikely that any life exists on the extrasolar planets discovered so far?

▲ **Figure 5.48** An artist's conception of 51 Pegasi b — the first extrasolar planet found orbiting a star similar to our own.

Artificial Satellites

▲ **Figure 5.49** A satellite in low Earth orbit

At present, there are well over 600 working artificial satellites orbiting Earth. About half of them are in a low or medium Earth orbit, ranging from 100 to 20 000 km above Earth's surface (Figure 5.49). The other half are geostationary satellites that orbit Earth at a distance of precisely 35 880 km from Earth's surface, directly above the equator. Depending on their design and orbit, satellites perform a variety of tasks. Weather, communication, observation, science, broadcast, navigation, and military satellites orbit Earth at this moment. These include a ring of GPS (global positioning system) satellites that are used to triangulate the position of a receiver wherever it may be. With the help of a GPS receiver, you could find your position on the planet to within a few metres.

All satellites are designed to receive information from and transmit information to Earth. Each satellite has an antenna that is used to receive radio signals from satellite stations on the ground. At the same time, satellites send information back down to Earth for people to use.

5-5 *Decision-Making Analysis*

Required Skills
- Initiating and Planning
- Performing and Recording
- Analyzing and Interpreting
- Communication and Teamwork

The Costs and Benefits of Putting a Satellite into Orbit

The Issue

Satellites perform a variety of tasks that make them almost indispensable. They map Earth, find geological formations and minerals, help us communicate over great distances and in remote areas, and help predict the movement of weather systems such as hurricanes. Opponents of the continued unregulated use of satellites argue that the cost of deploying satellites is enormous; they don't have a long lifespan; and their failure rate is high. Furthermore, once a satellite is in a medium or geostationary orbit, it will stay there even after it becomes inoperative. It turns into nothing more than very expensive and dangerous space junk.

Background Information

The first satellite in orbit was Sputnik in 1957. Since that time there have been over 4000 launches, and space has become progressively more crowded. The best estimates suggest that there are about 600 active satellites in orbit, and about 6000 pieces of space debris that are being tracked. The space debris can be very hazardous for missions carrying astronauts to low Earth orbit. If hit by even a small piece of orbiting debris, a spacecraft could be destroyed.

To limit the overcrowding of space, satellite manufacturers are designing more sophisticated satellites that can handle a higher flow of information so that fewer satellites have to be deployed. This drives up the cost of manufacturing satellites because they are more technologically advanced than their predecessors. Unfortunately, as well as being more sophisticated, they are more prone to failure.

Analyze and Evaluate

1. Identify two different types of satellites based on the type of job they perform.

2. For each type of satellite from question 1:
   (a) Identify the type of orbit that it occupies and explain the job that it performs.
   (b) Determine the approximate cost of deployment (getting it into space).
   (c) Determine its expected lifespan.

3. Suggest an alternative technology that could be used in place of each of these satellites. Analyze the effectiveness and cost of this technology compared with the satellite.

4. Propose possible changes that could be made to the way satellites are built and deployed that could lessen the overcrowding of space.

Geostationary Satellites

Geostationary satellites may be the most interesting of all satellites because they appear to be stationary to an observer on Earth's surface, even though they travel around Earth at high velocity. They are placed at a specific altitude so that they make one complete orbit in exactly 24 h, which is the same as Earth's rotational period (Figure 5.50). These satellites are placed in the plane of the equator, so they will have exactly the same axis of rotation as Earth, and will stay fixed over the same spot on the planet (Figure 5.51). To an observer on the ground, geostationary satellites appear motionless.

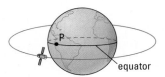

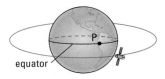

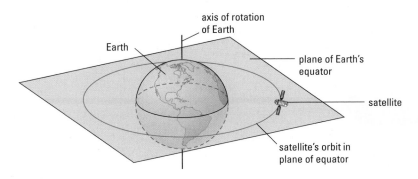

▲ **Figure 5.50** Geostationary satellites orbit in the plane of the equator with the same axis of rotation as Earth.

▲ **Figure 5.51** A geostationary satellite moves with a fixed point (P) on the Earth since both revolve around the same axis with the same period. To an observer on the ground, the satellite does not appear to be moving.

Communication satellites are geostationary. A communication signal, such as a telephone or TV signal, can be sent from the ground at any time of the day to the nearest geostationary satellite located over the equator. That satellite can then relay the signal to other geostationary satellites located over different spots on Earth, where the signal is then transmitted back down to the nearest receiving station.

Weather satellites also make use of this orbit. They may be "parked" near a landmass such as North America, using cameras to map the weather. Weather forecasters receive a continuous stream of information from the satellites that allows them to predict the weather in their area.

This type of orbit is in high demand and is filled with satellites from many different countries. Unfortunately, the orbit must be fixed at 35 880 km from Earth's surface and be directly over the equator. This orbit risks being overcrowded. If satellites are placed too close together, their signals can interfere with each other. Satellites also tend to drift slightly in their orbit and therefore cannot be placed close to each other. Many derelict satellites that were placed in geostationary orbits are still there taking up room, since they continue to orbit even after they no longer function. The limited room available is filling up fast. At present, about half (at least 300) of the active satellites in orbit are geostationary.

An artificial satellite obeys the same laws of physics as a natural satellite does. The orbital radius determines its orbital period and speed, and it is governed by the same laws that describe the motion of moons around a planet or planets around the Sun. That means low Earth orbit satellites make one complete orbit in about 90 min, while geostationary satellites take exactly one day.

info **BIT**

Geostationary satellites are also referred to as geosynchronous satellites.

e **WEB**

To learn more about real-time tracking of satellites in orbit around Earth, follow the links at www.pearsoned.ca/school/physicssource.

In the short space of time since the first satellite, Sputnik, was launched in October 1957, satellites have become indispensable (Figure 5.52). They have enabled us to see areas of our planet and atmosphere never seen before. They have enabled us to know our location anywhere on Earth within a few metres, and have allowed us to communicate with the remotest places on Earth. The future of satellites seems assured.

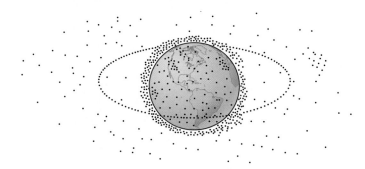

▶ **Figure 5.52** Around Earth, space is crowded with the multitude of satellites currently in orbit. The large ring farthest from Earth is made up of geostationary satellites.

5.3 Check and Reflect

Knowledge

1. What is an astronomical unit?

2. Why is the orbital radius of a planet not constant?

3. An eccentricity of 0.9 indicates what kind of shape?

4. Where in a planet's orbit is its velocity the greatest? The smallest? Why?

5. State the condition necessary for Kepler's third law to be valid.

6. Is Kepler's constant the same for moons orbiting a planet as it is for planets orbiting the Sun? Why?

7. Does our Sun experience orbital perturbation? Explain.

Applications

8. Sketch a graph that shows the trend between the planets' orbital radius and their period.

9. Venus has an average orbital period of 0.615 years. What is its orbital radius?

10. Another possible planet has been discovered, called Sedna. It has an average orbital radius of 479.5 AU. What is its average orbital velocity?

11. Jupiter's moon Io has an orbital period of 1.769 d and an average orbital radius of 422 000 km. Another moon of Jupiter, Europa, has an average orbital radius of 671 000 km. What is Europa's orbital period?

12. Determine the average orbital speed of Mimas using orbital data from Table 5.6 on page 274.

13. Using the orbital period and radius of Venus from Table 5.5 on page 273, determine the mass of the Sun.

Extensions

14. As more satellites are put into space, the amount of orbital debris increases. What solutions can you suggest to decrease the amount of space junk?

15. Using a graphing calculator or other suitable software, plot a graph of velocity versus radius for an artificial satellite orbiting Earth.

e TEST

To check your understanding of satellites and celestial bodies in circular motion, follow the eTest links at www.pearsoned.ca/school/physicssource.

Key Terms and Concepts

axle	cycle	Kepler's laws	satellite
axis of rotation	revolution	ellipse	artificial satellite
uniform circular motion	period	eccentricity	orbital perturbation
centripetal acceleration	frequency	orbital period	extrasolar planet
centripetal force	rpm	orbital radius	

Key Equations

$$v = \frac{2\pi r}{T}$$

$$a_c = \frac{4\pi^2 r}{T^2}$$

$$\frac{T_a^2}{r_a^3} = \frac{T_b^2}{r_b^3}$$

$$a_c = \frac{v^2}{r}$$

$$F_c = \frac{4\pi^2 mr}{T^2}$$

$$F_c = \frac{mv^2}{r}$$

$$\frac{T_a^2}{r_a^3} = K$$

Conceptual Overview

The concept map below summarizes many of the concepts and equations in this chapter.
Copy and complete the map to have a full summary of the chapter.

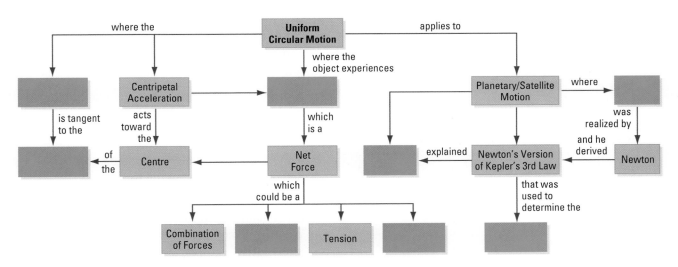

▲ **Figure 5.53**

Knowledge

1. (5.1) What is the direction of centripetal acceleration?

2. (5.1) Describe what produces the centripetal force in the following cases:

(a) A boat makes a turn.

(b) A plane makes a horizontal turn.

(c) A satellite orbits Earth.

3. (5.1) What force is responsible for the tug your hand feels as you spin an object around at the end of a rope?

4. (5.1) Sketch a diagram of a mass moving in a vertical circle. Draw the velocity, centripetal acceleration, and centripetal force vectors at a point on the circle's circumference.

5. (5.2) Why do spinning tires tend to stretch?

6. (5.2) A heavy mass attached to the end of a cable is spinning in a vertical circle. In what position is the cable likely to break?

7. (5.2) What force acts as the centripetal force for a motorcycle making a turn?

8. (5.2) Explain why a truck needs a larger turning radius than a car when they move at the same speed.

9. (5.3) In what position of its orbit does a planet move the fastest?

10. (5.3) In the orbit of a planet, what does the semi-major axis of an ellipse represent?

11. (5.3) Equation 14 can be confusing because it uses the mass of one object and the period of another.

(a) Explain what m_{Earth} and T_{Moon} represent.

(b) Explain how equation 14 is used in the most general case.

12. (5.3) Use Kepler's second law to explain why planets move more quickly when they are nearer to the Sun than when they are farther away in their orbital path.

13. (5.3) Why can't Kepler's constant of 1 y^2/AU^3 be used for moons orbiting planets or planets in other solar systems?

Applications

14. If the frequency of a spinning object is doubled, what effect does this have on the centripetal acceleration?

15. A slingshot containing rocks is spun in a vertical circle. In what position must it be released so that the rocks fly vertically upward?

16. People of different masses are able to ride a roller coaster and go through a vertical loop without falling out. Show the mathematical proof of this.

17. An eagle circles above the ground looking for prey. If it makes one complete circle with the radius of 25.0 m in 8.0 s, what is its speed?

18. A ride at the fair spins passengers around in a horizontal circle inside a cage at the end of a 5.0-m arm. If the cage and passengers have a speed of 7.0 m/s, what is the centripetal force the cage exerts on an 80.0-kg passenger?

19. What is the minimum speed that a glider must fly to make a perfect vertical circle in the air if the circle has a radius of 200.0 m?

20. A child spins an 800.0-g pail of water in a vertical circle at the end of a 60.0-cm rope. What is the tension of the rope at the top of the swing if it is spinning with the frequency of 2.0 Hz?

21. A driver is negotiating a turn on a mountain road that has a radius of 40.0 m when the 1600.0-kg car hits a patch of ice. The coefficient of friction between the ice and the wheels is 0.500. If the car is moving at 30.0 km/h, determine if it skids off the road.

22. The blade of a table saw has a diameter of 25.4 cm and rotates with a frequency of 750 rpm. What is the centripetal acceleration at the edge of the blade?

23. The tip of a propeller on an airplane has a radius of 0.90 m and experiences a centripetal acceleration of 8.88×10^4 m/s². What is the frequency of rotation of the propeller in rpm?

24. Using information and equations from this chapter, verify that the speed of Earth in orbit around the Sun is approximately 107 000 km/h.

25. A car rounds a corner of radius 25.0 m with the centripetal acceleration of 6.87 m/s² and a hubcap flies off. What is the speed of the hubcap?

26. An electron ($m = 9.11 \times 10^{-31}$ kg) caught in a magnetic field travels in a circular path of radius 30.0 cm with a period of 3.14×10^{-8} s.

    (a) What is the electron's speed?

    (b) What is the electron's centripetal acceleration?

27. Halley's comet has an orbital period of 76.5 y. What is its mean orbital radius?

28. An extrasolar planet is found orbiting a star in the Orion nebula. Determine the mass of the star if the planet has an orbital period of 400.0 Earth days and an orbital radius of 1.30×10^{11} m.

29. The Milky Way is a spiral galaxy with all the stars revolving around the centre where there is believed to be a super-massive black hole. The black hole is 2.27×10^{20} m from our Sun, which revolves around it at a speed of 1234 m/s.

    (a) What is the period of our solar system's orbit around the black hole?

    (b) How massive is the black hole?

    (c) What centripetal acceleration does our solar system experience as a result of the black hole's gravity?

30. Newton hypothesized that a cannonball fired parallel to the ground from a cannon on the surface of Earth would orbit Earth if it had sufficient speed and if air friction were ignored.

    (a) What speed would the cannonball have to have to do this?

    (b) From the speed determined in part (a), determine the mass of Earth.

    (c) If the mass of the cannonball were doubled, what time would it take to orbit Earth once?

31. Use the Moon's period (27.3 d), its mass, and its distance from Earth to determine its centripetal acceleration and force.

32. Neptune has a moon Galatea that orbits at an orbital radius of 6.20×10^7 m. Use data from Table 5.6 on page 274 to determine Galatea's orbital period.

33. Determine the orbital speed of Ariel, a moon of Uranus, using Table 5.5 (page 273) and Table 5.6 (page 274).

34. A star in the Andromeda galaxy is found to have a planet orbiting it at an average radius of 2.38×10^{10} m and an orbital period of 4.46×10^4 s.

    (a) What is the star's mass?

    (b) A second planet is found orbiting the same star with an orbital period of 6.19×10^6 s. What is its orbital radius?

Extensions

35. Paraphrase two misconceptions about centripetal force mentioned in this book. How do these misconceptions compare with your preconceptions of centripetal force?

36. Explain why a person standing at the equator weighs less than the same person standing at the North or South Pole.

Consolidate Your Understanding

Create your own summary of uniform circular motion, Kepler's laws, and planetary and satellite motion by answering the questions below. If you want to use a graphic organizer, refer to Student References 4: Using Graphic Organizers pp. 869–871. Use the Key Terms and Concepts listed above and the Learning Outcomes on page 240.

1. In a few sentences, summarize how frequency, period, and velocity affect centripetal acceleration.

2. Explain to a classmate in writing why the velocity at different radii on a spinning disc will vary while the rotational frequency remains constant.

Think About It

Review your answers to the Think About It questions on page 241. How would you answer each question now?

e TEST

To check your understanding of circular motion, follow the eTest links at www.pearsoned.ca/school/physicssource.

In an isolated system, energy is transferred from one object to another whenever work is done.

▲ **Figure 6.1**

Tension mounts as the motor pulls you slowly to the top of the first hill. Slowly you glide over the top, then suddenly, you are plunging down the hill at breathtaking speed. Upon reaching the bottom of the hill, you glide to the top of the next hill and the excitement begins all over again. As you race around the roller coaster track, each hill gets a bit lower until, at last, you coast to a gentle stop back at the beginning. You probably realize that because of friction the trolley can never regain the height of the previous hill, unless it is given a boost. It seems obvious to us that as objects move, kinetic energy is always lost.

Energy is the most fundamental concept in physics. Everything that occurs in nature can be traced back to energy. The complicating factor is that there are so many forms of energy it is often very difficult to keep track of what happens to the energy when it is transferred. This chapter concentrates on gravitational potential energy, kinetic energy, and elastic potential energy.

In this chapter you will take the first steps to understanding the role of energy in nature. Specifically, you will learn how energy is given to and taken from objects when they interact with each other.

Energy Changes of a Roller Coaster

e WEB

This activity uses the roller coaster simulation found at www.pearsoned.ca/school/physicssource.

Problem

How does the energy of a roller coaster vary as it travels on its track?

Materials

computer connected to the Internet
clear plastic ruler

Procedure

1. Click on the start button for the simulation.

2. Observe the motion of the cart.

3. Click on "continue" and note what happens to the motion of the trolley as it moves along the track.

4. Repeat step 3 until the simulation is complete.

5. Reset the simulation.

6. Use a see-through plastic ruler to measure the lengths of the potential energy bar (blue) and the kinetic energy bar (green) before you start the simulation. Record your measurements.

7. Start the simulation.

8. Each time the trolley pauses, measure the length of the potential energy and the kinetic energy bars and record the results in a table similar to Table 6.1.

Questions

1. What assumptions are you making when you measure the lengths of the energy bars?

2. What is the effect on the potential energy of the trolley as it moves upward and downward?

3. What is the effect on the kinetic energy of the trolley as it moves upward and downward? Is this true as the trolley moves upward to the top of the first hill? Explain.

4. From the table, what happens to the energy of the trolley as it moves from the start to position "a"?

5. For each of the positions at which the trolley pauses, how does the sum of lengths of the bars change? What does the sum of these lengths represent?

6. Is there an energy pattern as the trolley moves along the track? Describe the pattern.

7. Do you think that this pattern is representative of nature? Explain.

▼ **Table 6.1**

Position	Length of Potential Energy Bar (mm)	Length of Kinetic Energy Bar (mm)	Sum of Lengths (mm)
start			
a			
b			

Think About It

1. If two cars are identical except for the size of their engines, how will that affect their performance on the highway?

2. What is the "law of conservation of energy"? When does this law apply?

3. When work is done on an object, where does the energy used to do the work go?

Discuss your answers in a small group and record them for later reference. As you complete each section of this chapter, review your answers to these questions. Note any changes in your ideas.

e LAB

 For a probeware activity, go to www.pearsoned.ca/school/physicssource.

info BIT

Inuit hunters devised unusual ways of storing potential energy in a bow. One way they accomplished this was to tie cords of sinew along the back of the bow (Figure 6.3). The sinew was more heavily braided where strength was needed and less heavily braided where flexibility was important. When the bow was bent, the cords would stretch like a spring to store energy. In the absence of a wood source, bows were often made of antler or bone segments.

e WEB

To see photographs and to learn more about the technology of Inuit bows, follow the links at www.pearsoned.ca/school/physicssource.

6.1 Work and Energy

▲ **Figure 6.2**   When the string on a bow is pulled back, elastic potential energy is stored in the bow.

energy: the ability to do work

▲ **Figure 6.3**   Sinew-backed bow of the Inuit Copper people of the Central Arctic.

Maximum gravitational potential energy is stored in the skier at the top of the run.

Gravitational potential energy changes to kinetic energy and heat during the run.

▲ **Figure 6.4**   During the downhill run, the skier's gravitational potential energy is continually converted into kinetic energy and heat.

An archer is pulling back her bowstring (Figure 6.2). She does work on the bow transforming chemical energy in her muscles into elastic potential energy in the bow. When she releases the string, the bow does work on the arrow transforming its elastic potential energy into the energy of motion of the arrow, called kinetic energy.

As skiers ride up a lift, the lift's motor is transforming chemical energy of the fuel into gravitational potential energy of the individuals. As they go downhill, gravity does work on the skiers transforming their gravitational potential energy into kinetic energy and heat.

In both these examples, work transfers **energy**. In the case of the archer, energy is transformed from chemical energy into elastic potential energy and then into kinetic energy (from the archer to the bow to the arrow). In the case of the skier, energy is transformed from the chemical energy of the motor's fuel into the gravitational potential energy of the skier at the top of the run and then into a combination of changing kinetic energy, gravitational potential energy, and heat of the skier as she speeds downhill. All these processes involve work.

Work Is Done When Force Acts Over a Displacement

When a force ($\vec{F}$) acts on an object resulting in a displacement ($\Delta\vec{d}$), a transfer of energy occurs. This energy transfer is defined as the **work** done by the force. In introductory courses the quantity of work is usually defined by the equation $W = F\Delta d$.

Work is a scalar quantity. However, the relative directions of the vectors $\vec{F}$ and $\Delta\vec{d}$ are important. If the applied force ($\vec{F}$) does not act parallel to the displacement (Figure 6.5), you must resolve the force into components that are parallel ($F_\parallel$) and perpendicular ($F_\perp$) to the displacement. Only the component of the force parallel to the displacement actually does work. The component of the force acting perpendicular to the displacement does no work.

work: a measure of the amount of energy transferred when a force acts over a given displacement. It is calculated as the product of the magnitude of applied force and the displacement of the object in the direction of that force.

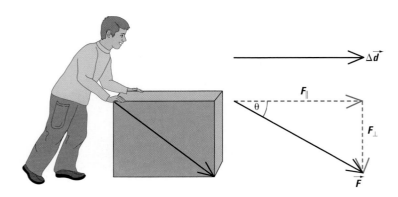

▲ **Figure 6.5** When a force acts on an object, resulting in a displacement, only the component of the force that acts parallel to the displacement does work. If the box moves horizontally, only the horizontal component, $\vec{F}_\parallel$, does work.

Thus, the equation for work is often written as

$$W = F_\parallel \Delta d$$

where $F_\parallel$ is the magnitude of the component of the force that acts parallel to the displacement. In Figure 6.5, where the angle between the direction of the force and the direction of the displacement is θ, the component of the force parallel to the displacement is given by

$$F_\parallel = F\cos\theta$$

If you replace $F_\parallel$ by $F\cos\theta$, the calculation for work becomes

$$W = (F\cos\theta)\Delta d$$

Let's look at two special cases. First, when the force acts parallel to the displacement, the angle $\theta = 0°$ so that $\cos\theta = 1$, making $F_\parallel = F$. This results in the maximum value for the work that the force could do over that displacement (Figure 6.6). Second, if the force acts perpendicular to the displacement, there is no parallel component. Mathematically, since $\theta = 90°$ then $\cos\theta = 0$ making $F_\parallel = 0$. In this case, the applied force does no work on the object (Figure 6.7).

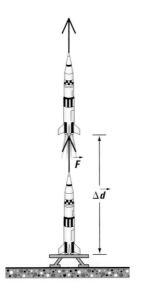

▲ **Figure 6.6**

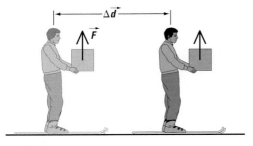

▲ **Figure 6.7**

When a centripetal force acts on an object, the object shows no increase in kinetic energy. In terms of the work done by the centripetal force, explain why this is true.

Example 6.1

Figure 6.8 shows a force of 150 N [0°] acting on an object that moves over a displacement of 25.0 m [25.0°] while the force acts. What is the work done by this force?

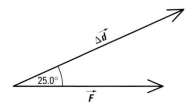

▲ **Figure 6.8**

Practice Problems

1. You pull a sled along a horizontal surface by applying a force of 620 N at an angle of 42.0° above the horizontal. How much work is done to pull the sled 160 m?

2. A force acts at an angle of 30.0° relative to the direction of the displacement. What force is required to do 9600 J of work over a displacement of 25.0 m?

3. A force of 640 N does 12 500 J of work over a displacement of 24.0 m. What is the angle between the force and the displacement?

4. A bungee jumper with a mass of 60.0 kg leaps off a bridge. He is in free fall for a distance of 20.0 m before the cord begins to stretch. How much work does the force of gravity do on the jumper before the cord begins to stretch?

Answers

1. 7.37×10^4 J
2. 443 N
3. 35.5°
4. 1.18×10^4 J

Given
$\vec{F} = 1.50 \times 10^2$ N [0°]
$\Delta \vec{d} = 25.0$ m [25.0°]

Required
work done by the force (W)

Analysis and Solution
From Figure 6.8, the angle between the force and the displacement is 25.0°. Draw a component diagram (Figure 6.9). The component that does work is F (cos 25.0°). Solve using the equation for work.

$$W = (F\cos \theta)\Delta d$$
$$= (1.50 \times 10^2 \text{ N})(\cos 25.0°)(25.0 \text{ m})$$
$$= 3.399 \times 10^3 \text{ N·m}$$
$$= 3.40 \times 10^3 \text{ J}$$

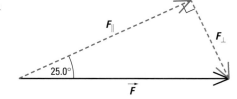

▲ **Figure 6.9**   Component diagram

Paraphrase and Verify
The work done by the force is 3.40×10^3 J. If the force had acted parallel to the displacement, the maximum amount of work done would have been 3.75×10^3 J. Since cos 25.0° is about 0.91, the answer of 3.40×10^3 J, or 0.91 times the maximum value for W, is reasonable.

Gravitational Potential Energy

Imagine a ride at the fair where the passengers are lifted vertically before being allowed to drop in free fall, as in Figure 6.10. Ignoring friction, the work done by the machinery to lift the passengers and car to a height, h, is equal to the change in **gravitational potential energy, ΔE_P**. To lift the object straight up at a constant speed, the force applied must be equal but opposite to the force of gravity on the object. The equation for calculating work can be used to develop the equation for change in gravitational potential energy.

$$\Delta E_P = W$$
$$= F\Delta d$$

where F is the magnitude of the force acting *parallel* to the displacement, and Δd is the magnitude of the displacement.

To lift an object of mass m upward at a constant speed, the force is equal in magnitude and parallel, but opposite in direction, to the gravitational force, $\vec{F}_g$. Recall from Unit II that $F_g = mg$ where g is the magnitude of the acceleration due to gravity, which has a constant value of 9.81 m/s^2 near Earth's surface. It follows that

$$F = mg$$

If the object is moved through a change in height Δh, so that $\Delta d = \Delta h$, the change in potential energy equation becomes

$$\Delta E_P = mg\Delta h$$

So, when an object is moved upward, h increases and Δh is positive, and the potential energy increases (positive change). When an object is moved downward, h decreases and Δh is negative, and the potential energy decreases (negative change).

▲ **Figure 6.10** A motor works transferring energy to the ride car. The gravitational potential energy gained produces the exciting free fall.

gravitational potential energy: the energy of an object due to its position above the surface of Earth

Concept Check

Does the above equation for change in gravitational potential energy apply to objects that move over very large changes in height? Explain.

Example 6.2

If the car and its passengers in Figure 6.10 have a mass of 500 kg, what is their change in potential energy when they are lifted through a height of 48.0 m?

Practice Problems

1. An elevator car has a mass of 750 kg. Three passengers of masses 65.0 kg, 30.0 kg, and 48.0 kg, ride from the 8th floor to the ground floor, 21.0 m below. Find the change in gravitational potential energy of the car and its passengers.

2. A book with a mass of 1.45 kg gains 25.0 J of potential energy when it is lifted from the floor to a shelf. How high is the shelf above the floor?

3. The Mars rover lifts a bucket of dirt from the surface of Mars into a compartment on the rover. The mass of the dirt is 0.148 kg and the compartment is 0.750 m above the surface of Mars. If this action requires 0.400 J of energy, what is the gravitational acceleration on Mars?

Answers

1. -1.84×10^5 J
2. 1.76 m
3. 3.60 m/s^2

Given

$m = 500$ kg

$g = 9.81$ m/s^2

$\Delta h = +48.0$ m

Required

change in gravitational potential energy (ΔE_p)

Analysis and Solution

Sketch the movement of the car as in Figure 6.11 and solve for ΔE_p.

$\Delta E_p = mg\Delta h$

$= (5.00 \times 10^2 \text{ kg})\left(9.81\frac{\text{m}}{\text{s}^2}\right)(+48.0 \text{ m})$

$= +2.35 \times 10^5 \left(\left(\text{kg} \cdot \frac{\text{m}}{\text{s}^2}\right) \cdot \text{m}\right)$

$= +2.35 \times 10^5$ (N·m)

$= +2.35 \times 10^5$ J

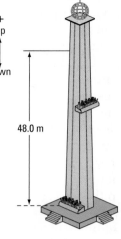

▲ **Figure 6.11**

Paraphrase

The change in potential energy of the car and its passengers is a gain of 2.3×10^5 J. The object moved upward, gaining gravitational potential energy.

If E_{p_1} represents the potential energy of an object at height h_1 and E_{p_2} its potential energy when it is lifted to a height h_2, then the change in potential energy is, by definition,

$$\Delta E_p = E_{p_2} - E_{p_1}$$

Since $\Delta E_p = mg\Delta h$

$$E_{p_2} - E_{p_1} = mg(h_2 - h_1)$$

Consider an object at ground level as having zero potential energy. If the object is raised from the ground level, $h_1 = 0$. It follows that

$$E_{p_2} - 0 = mg(h_2 - 0)$$

$$E_{p_2} = mgh_2$$

In general, the potential energy of an object at height h, measured from the ground, is

$$E_p = mgh$$

Choosing a Reference Point

You see from the equation for the change in potential energy on page 295 that ΔE depends only on the change in height, Δh. The values of h may be measured from any convenient **reference point**, as long as the reference point is kept the same for all the measurements when solving a problem. The change in height, and therefore the change in gravitational potential energy, is the same regardless of your frame of reference.

Look at the book resting on the shelf in Figure 6.12. The value of h for the shelf can be defined relative to the floor (h_f), relative to the table (h_t), or even relative to the ceiling above the shelf (h_c), in which case h_c will have a negative value. Usually, you choose the frame of reference that most simplifies your measurements and calculations for Δh. For example, if you were trying to determine how much gravitational potential energy the book would lose as it fell from the shelf to the tabletop, then it would be logical to use the tabletop as your reference point. If you used another position as a reference point, your calculations might be slightly more complex, but the final answer for the amount of gravitational potential energy the book loses would be the same.

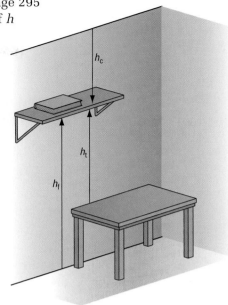

▲ **Figure 6.12** The book has gravitational potential energy due to its position on the shelf.

reference point: an arbitrarily chosen point from which distances are measured

Change in gravitational potential energy depends only on change in vertical height.

The change in gravitational potential energy of an object depends only on the change in height. For example, the change in gravitational potential energy of a cart rolling down a frictionless ramp as in Figure 6.13 depends only on the vertical measurement, h. The actual distance an object travels, while it moves through a given change in height, does not affect its change in gravitational potential energy.

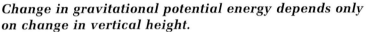

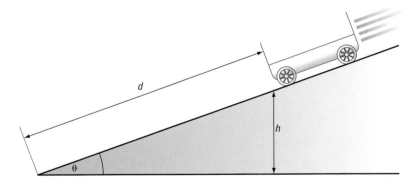

▲ **Figure 6.13** As the cart rolls down the ramp, only the change in height h affects its change in gravitational potential energy.

PHYSICS INSIGHT

The calculation of h from Figure 6.13 involves the use of the trigonometric ratio $\sin \theta = \dfrac{h}{d}$.

Example 6.3

Figure 6.14 shows a toy car track set up on a tabletop.
(a) What is the gravitational potential energy of the car, which has a mass of 0.0250 kg, relative to the floor?
(b) Calculate the change in gravitational potential energy of the car when it arrives at the bottom of the hill.

Given
$m = 0.0250$ kg
$g = 9.81$ m/s^2
$h_1 = 2.15$ m
$h_2 = 0.950$ m

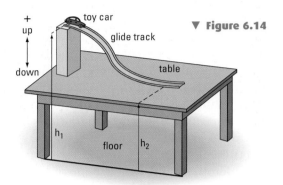

▼ **Figure 6.14**

Required
(a) gravitational potential energy at the top of the hill relative to the floor (E_{p_1})
(b) change in the gravitational potential energy as the car moves from the top to the bottom of the hill (ΔE_p)

Analysis and Solution
(a) To find gravitational potential energy relative to the floor, use that surface to define $h = 0$ and make all height measurements from there.

$$E_{p_1} = mgh_1$$
$$= (0.0250 \text{ kg})\left(9.81 \frac{\text{m}}{\text{s}^2}\right)(2.15 \text{ m})$$
$$= +0.527 \frac{\text{kg·m}^2}{\text{s}^2}$$
$$= 0.527 \text{ J}$$

(b) To find the change in gravitational potential energy, use the data and Figure 6.14 to calculate the change in height $(\Delta h = h_2 - h_1)$.

$$\Delta h = h_2 - h_1$$
$$= 0.950 \text{ m} - 2.15 \text{ m}$$
$$= -1.20 \text{ m}$$

$$\Delta E_p = mg(\Delta h)$$
$$= (0.0250 \text{ kg})\left(9.81 \frac{\text{m}}{\text{s}^2}\right)(-1.20 \text{ m})$$
$$= -0.294 \text{ J}$$

Paraphrase and Verify
(a) The gravitational potential energy relative to the floor is 0.527 J.
(b) The change in gravitational potential energy is -0.294 J. As the car rolls down the hill it loses 0.294 J of gravitational potential energy.

Note: You could calculate E_{p_2} first and then use $\Delta E_p = E_{p_2} - E_{p_1}$

Practice Problems

1. A pile driver drops a mass of 550 kg from a height of 12.5 m above the ground onto the top of a pile that is 2.30 m above the ground. Relative to ground level, what is the gravitational potential energy of the mass
   (a) at its highest point?
   (b) at its lowest point?
   (c) What is the change in the gravitational potential energy of the mass as it is lifted from the top of the pile to its highest point?

2. A roller coaster trolley begins its journey 5.25 m above the ground. As the motor tows it to the top of the first hill, it gains 4.20×10^5 J of gravitational potential energy. If the mass of the trolley and its passengers is 875 kg, how far is the top of the hill above the ground?

3. A winch pulls a 250-kg block up a 20.0-m-long inclined plane that is tilted at an angle of 35.0° to the horizontal. What change in gravitational potential energy does the block undergo?

Answers

1. (a) 6.74×10^4 J
   (b) 1.24×10^4 J
   (c) 5.50×10^4 J

2. 54.2 m

3. 2.81×10^4 J

Hooke's Law

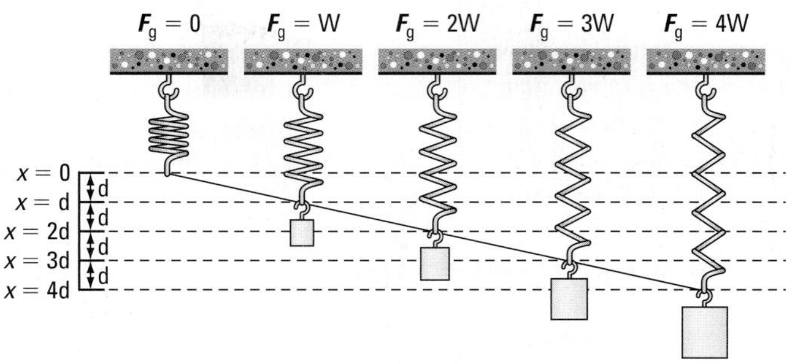

In 1676, Robert Hooke, an English physicist, showed that the stretch produced by a force applied to a spring was proportional to the magnitude of the force. This relationship is known as Hooke's Law and applies to any elastic substance when a force is exerted upon it. Thus, if a mass is suspended from a spring (Figure 6.15) the position (x) of the mass changes in proportion to the force (the weight (F_g) of the mass) exerted on the spring.

In an experiment to test this prediction, students suspended a series of masses from a spring and measured the position for each mass. Their data are shown in Table 6.2.

Stretch Produced by a Force Applied to a Spring

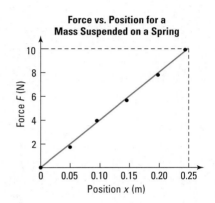

▲ **Figure 6.15** The stretch produced by a force applied on a spring is proportional to the magnitude of the force.

▼ **Table 6.2** Students' experimental data

Mass m (g)	Weight F_g (N)	Position x (m)
0	0	0
200	1.96	0.050
400	3.92	0.099
600	5.87	0.146
800	7.85	0.197
1000	9.81	0.245

◀ **Figure 6.16** Graph of data from Table 6.2

The students then plotted a graph of the magnitude of the applied force (F_g) as a function of the position (x) of the spring. The resulting line is a straight line with a constant slope (Figure 6.16). The equation of this line is $F = kx$ where k is the slope of the line. The slope of the line is determined by the properties of the spring and is defined as the **elastic** or **spring constant** (k).

For the graph in Figure 6.16, the slope is found as shown below:

$$k = \frac{\Delta F}{\Delta x}$$

$$= \frac{F_f - F_i}{x_f - x_i}$$

$$= \frac{10.0 \text{ N} - 3.0 \text{ N}}{0.250 \text{ m} - 0.075 \text{ m}}$$

$$= 40.0 \frac{\text{N}}{\text{m}}$$

This force-position graph is characteristic for all springs whether the force stretches or compresses the spring. When a heavier or lighter spring is used, the slope of the line changes but the line is still straight.

You will deal with Hooke's Law in greater depth when you study simple harmonic motion in Chapter 7.

Elastic Potential Energy

elastic potential energy: the energy resulting from an object being altered from its standard shape, without permanent deformation

When the archer in Figure 6.2 draws her bow she stores another form of potential energy, **elastic potential energy**, in the bow. Both gravitational potential energy and elastic potential energy form part of mechanical energy. The study of elastic potential energy requires the use of Hooke's law.

The amount of energy stored in the spring is equal to the work done to stretch (or compress) the spring, without causing any permanent deformation. The force is not constant, so the equation for work used earlier, ($W = F\Delta d$) does not apply, because that equation requires a constant force acting over the displacement. However, when force-position graphs are used, work is equivalent to the area under the curve. The units for this area are N·m, equivalent to joules, the unit for work. You can therefore determine the amount of work done to stretch the spring from its equilibrium position to the position x by calculating the area of the shaded portion of Figure 6.17.

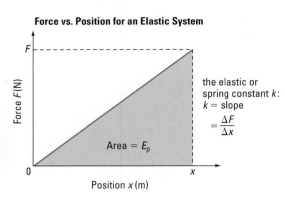

Force vs. Position for an Elastic System

the elastic or spring constant k:
k = slope
$= \dfrac{\Delta F}{\Delta x}$

Area = E_p

▲ **Figure 6.17** The area under the force-position curve is equal to the work done by the force to stretch the spring to that position.

Calculation of Elastic Potential Energy

The area under the curve in Figure 6.17 is the shaded triangle whose area is calculated by $A = \dfrac{1}{2}hb$. The base (b) is equal to the magnitude of the position (x), and the height (h) is equal to the magnitude of the force (F) at that position. Thus, in terms of force and position, the equation for the area under the curve is

$$W = \frac{1}{2}Fx$$

From Hooke's law, the magnitude of the force (F) is equal to $F = kx$, so the work done to stretch the spring can be written as:

$$W = \frac{1}{2}(kx)(x)$$

$$= \frac{1}{2}kx^2$$

The work done to stretch (or compress) a spring from its equilibrium position to any position (x) results in storing elastic potential energy (E_p) in the spring. Therefore, the equation for the elastic potential energy stored in the spring is given by

$$E_p = \frac{1}{2}kx^2$$

Concept Check

Explain why it is incorrect to try to find the change in elastic potential energy of a stretched spring from the measurement of the change in the stretch.

Example 6.4

A spring is stretched to a position 35.0 cm from its equilibrium position. At that point the force exerted on the spring is 10.5 N.
(a) What is the elastic potential energy stored in the spring?
(b) If the stretch in the spring is allowed to reduce to 20.0 cm, what is the change in the elastic potential energy?

Given
$x_1 = 0.350$ m
$F_1 = 10.5$ N
$x_2 = 0.200$ m

Required
(a) elastic potential energy in the spring stretched to 0.350 m (E_{p_1})
(b) change in potential energy when the stretch is reduced from 0.350 m to 0.200 m (ΔE_p)

Analysis and Solution
(a) Calculate the value for k, the elastic constant for the spring, using Hooke's law.

$$F_1 = kx_1$$

$$k = \frac{F_1}{x_1}$$

$$= \frac{10.5 \text{ N}}{0.350 \text{ m}}$$

$$= 30.0 \ \frac{\text{N}}{\text{m}}$$

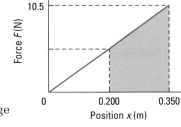

Graph Showing Change in Elastic Potential Energy

From the data given, plot the graph of change in elastic potential energy, Figure 6.18. Next, use $E_p = \frac{1}{2}kx^2$, to find the elastic potential energy for a stretch of 0.350 m. This is equivalent to finding the area of the large triangle in Figure 6.18.

▲ **Figure 6.18**

$$E_{p_1} = \frac{1}{2}kx_1^2$$

$$= \frac{1}{2}\left(30.0 \ \frac{\text{N}}{\text{m}}\right)(0.350 \text{ m})^2$$

$$= 1.8375 \left(\frac{\text{N}}{\text{m}} \cdot \text{m}^2\right)$$

$$= 1.84 \text{ N} \cdot \text{m}$$

$$= 1.84 \text{ J}$$

(b) To find the change in the elastic potential energy, first find the elastic potential energy at a stretch of 0.200 m and then subtract from that value the answer to part (a). This is equivalent to finding the shaded area of the graph in Figure 6.18.

Practice Problems

1. A force of 125 N causes a spring to stretch to a length of 0.250 m beyond its equilibrium position.
   (a) What is the elastic potential energy stored in the spring?
   (b) If the spring contracts to a stretch of 0.150 m, what is the change in elastic potential energy?

2. An engineer is designing the suspension system for a car. He decides that the coil spring used in this car should compress 4.00 cm when a force of 1000 N is applied to it.
   (a) What is the spring constant of the spring?
   (b) If the spring is compressed a distance of 14.0 cm, what force must have been exerted on it?

3. The elastic constant for a spring is 750 N/m.
   (a) How far must you stretch a spring from its equilibrium position in order to store 45.0 J of elastic potential energy in it?
   (b) If you wanted to double the elastic potential energy stored in the spring, how much farther would you need to stretch it?

4. A spring has an elastic constant of 4.40×10^4 N/m. What is the change in elastic potential energy stored in the spring when its stretch is increased from 12.5 cm to 15.0 cm?

5. When a spring is stretched by 0.400 m from its equilibrium position, its elastic potential energy is 5.00×10^2 J.
   (a) What is the magnitude of the force required to produce this amount of stretch?
   (b) If the force causing the stretch is changed to 1000 N, how much change in elastic potential energy results?

The elastic potential energy for a stretch of 0.200 m is:

$$E_{P_2} = \frac{1}{2}kx_2{}^2$$

$$= \frac{1}{2}\left(30.0\ \frac{N}{m}\right)(0.200\ m)^2$$

$$= 0.600\ N \cdot m$$

$$= 0.600\ J$$

The change in the elastic potential energy is:

$$\Delta E_P = E_{P_2} - E_{P_1}$$

$$= 0.600\ J - 1.84\ J$$

$$= -1.24\ J$$

Paraphrase

(a) The energy stored in the spring at the initial stretch is 1.84 J.

(b) When the stretch is reduced from 0.350 m to 0.200 m, the elastic potential energy stored in the spring reduced by 1.24 J to 0.600 J.

Kinetic Energy

Examine Figure 6.19. When the archer releases the arrow, the bowstring exerts a non-zero force on the arrow, which accelerates the arrow toward its target. As the arrow gains speed, it gains **kinetic energy (E_k)**.

kinetic energy: the energy due to the motion of an object

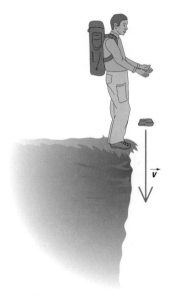

▲ **Figure 6.19**

▲ **Figure 6.20** When an object is in free fall, gravity is working to increase its kinetic energy.

When the hiker in Figure 6.20 drops the rock off the cliff, the force of gravity accelerates the rock downward increasing its speed and thus its kinetic energy. Kinetic energy is a scalar quantity. The kinetic energy of an object is calculated using the equation

$$E_k = \frac{1}{2}mv^2$$

Concept Check

If the kinetic energy of an object doubles, by what factor does its speed increase?

Example 6.5

On a highway, a car of mass 1.2×10^3 kg, travelling at 20 m/s, has kinetic energy equal to a loaded van of mass 4.8×10^3 kg. What is the speed of the van?

Given
$$m_1 = 1.2 \times 10^3 \text{ kg}; \quad m_2 = 4.8 \times 10^3 \text{ kg};$$
$$v_1 = 20 \text{ m/s}$$
$$E_{k_{car}} = E_{k_{van}}$$

Required
the speed of the van (v_2)

Analysis and Solution
The two vehicles have equal kinetic energy $\left(\dfrac{1}{2} mv^2\right)$.

Find the kinetic energy of the car and then use that value to solve for the speed of the van.

$$E_{k_{car}} = \frac{1}{2} mv_{car}^2 \qquad\qquad E_{k_{van}} = 2.4 \times 10^5 \text{ J}$$

$$= \frac{1}{2}(1.2 \times 10^3 \text{ kg})\left(20\frac{\text{m}}{\text{s}}\right)^2 \qquad = \frac{1}{2} mv_{van}^2$$

$$= 2.4 \times 10^5 \frac{\text{kg} \cdot \text{m}^2}{\text{s}^2} \qquad v_{van} = \sqrt{\frac{(2.4 \times 10^5 \text{ J})(2)}{4.8 \times 10^3 \text{ kg}}}$$

$$= 2.4 \times 10^5 \text{ J} \qquad\qquad = 10 \text{ m/s}$$

Paraphrase
The van is travelling at 10 m/s.

Practice Problems

1. A 45.0-kg girl pedals a 16.0-kg bicycle at a speed of 2.50 m/s. What is the kinetic energy of the system?

2. A car travelling at 80.0 km/h on a highway has kinetic energy of 4.2×10^5 J. What is the mass of the car?

3. A skateboarder with a mass of 65.0 kg increases his speed from 1.75 m/s to 4.20 m/s as he rolls down a ramp. What is the increase in his kinetic energy?

Answers

1. 1.91×10^2 J
2. 1.7×10^3 kg
3. 474 J

Project **LINK**

How will the concept of the kinetic energy of a moving vehicle relate to the design of your persuader apparatus?

MINDS ON **Energy of Impact**

There is evidence that many meteors have hit Earth's surface. The vast quantity of kinetic energy that these meteors have at the time of impact is revealed by the size of the craters that they create (Figure 6.21).

1. What types of measurements would scientists need to make in order to estimate the kinetic energy of the meteor at the instant of impact?

2. What types of experiments could be done to verify the scientists' assumptions?

3. Investigate the incidence of meteor collisions in Canada. Where is the meteor impact crater that is closest to where you live? Approximately how many meteors have landed in Alberta? What was the greatest kinetic energy for a meteor that landed (a) in Alberta (b) in Canada?

▶ **Figure 6.21** Meteor impact craters are found in all regions of Earth. This one, called the Barringer crater, is in Arizona.

Example 6.6

A man on a trampoline has a mass of 75.0 kg. At the instant he first touches the surface of the trampoline (at its rest position) he is descending with a speed of 8.00 m/s. At his lowest point, the man is 0.650 m below the trampoline's rest position. (a) What is the kinetic energy of the man when he first contacts the trampoline? (b) If you assume that, at his lowest point, all of the man's kinetic energy is transformed into elastic potential energy, what is the elastic constant for the trampoline?

Given

m = 75.0 kg

v = 8.00 m/s

x = 0.650 m

▲ **Figure 6.22**

Required

(a) kinetic energy of the man (E_k)

(b) the spring constant of the trampoline (k)

Analysis and Solution

(a) Find the initial kinetic energy, by using $E_k = \dfrac{1}{2}mv^2$

$$E_k = \frac{1}{2}mv^2$$

$$= \frac{1}{2}(75.0 \text{ kg})\left(800 \ \frac{\text{m}}{\text{s}}\right)^2$$

$$= 2.40 \times 10^3 \text{ kg} \cdot \frac{\text{m}^2}{\text{s}^2}$$

$$= 2.40 \times 10^3 \text{ J}$$

(b) Assume that the elastic potential energy at 0.650 m is 2.40×10^3 J and solve for the spring constant.

$$E_p = \frac{1}{2}kx^2$$

Solve for k.

$$k = \frac{2E_p}{x^2}$$

$$= \frac{2(2.40 \times 10^3 \text{ J})}{(0.650 \text{ m})^2}$$

$$= 1.136 \times 10^4 \ \frac{\text{N}}{\text{m}}$$

$$= 1.14 \times 10^4 \ \frac{\text{N}}{\text{m}}$$

Paraphrase

(a) The kinetic energy of the man is 2.40×10^3 J.

(b) The elastic constant of a spring that stores 2.40×10^3 J of elastic potential energy when it is stretched 0.650 m is 1.14×10^4 N/m.

Practice Problems

1. A bow that has an elastic constant of 2500 N/m is stretched to a position of 0.540 m from its rest position.
   (a) What is the elastic potential energy stored in the bow?
   (b) If all of the elastic potential energy of the bow were to be transformed into kinetic energy of a 95.0-g arrow, what would be the speed of the arrow?

2. Cannon A fires a 1.5-kg ball with a muzzle velocity of 550 m/s, while cannon B fires cannon balls with one-third the mass but at twice the muzzle velocity. Which of these two cannons would be more effective in damaging a fortification? Explain why.

3. It is estimated that the meteor that created the crater shown in Figure 6.21 on the previous page had a radius of 40 m, a mass of approximately 2.6×10^8 kg, and struck Earth at a speed of nearly 7.20×10^4 km/h.
   (a) What was the kinetic energy of the meteor at the instant of impact?
   (b) When one tonne (t) of TNT explodes, it releases about 4.6×10^9 J of energy. In terms of tonnes of TNT, how much energy did the meteor have at impact?

Answers

1. (a) 365 J   (b) 87.6 m/s
2. $E_{k_A} : E_{k_B}$ = 3 : 4. Ball B has more energy.
3. (a) 5.2×10^{16} J   (b) 1.1×10^7 t

1. If a force does not act parallel to the resulting displacement, what is the effect on the work done by the force?

2. Describe how a non-zero force can act on an object over a displacement and yet do no work.

3. Explain why the frame of reference affects the calculated value of an object's gravitational potential energy but not the change in its gravitational potential energy.

4. What is meant by elastic potential energy?

5. A force of 1500 N [up] acts to lift an object of 50.0-kg mass to a height of 24.0 m above its original position.

   (a) How much work did the force do on the object?

   (b) What was the gain in the object's gravitational potential energy?

   (c) What might account for the difference in the two answers?

6. A force of 850 N [30°] acts on an object while it undergoes a displacement of 65.0 m [330°]. What is the work the force does on the object?

7. You are working on the 5th floor of a building at a height of 18.0 m above the sidewalk. A construction crane lifts a mass of 350 kg from street level to the 12th floor of the building, 22.0 m above you. Relative to your position, what is the gravitational potential energy of the mass

   (a) at street level?

   (b) when it is on the 12th floor?

   (c) What is its change in gravitational potential energy as it is raised?

8. A spring has an elastic constant of 650 N/m. Initially, the spring is compressed to a length of 0.100 m from its equilibrium position.

   (a) What is the elastic potential energy stored in the spring?

   (b) How much further must the spring be compressed if its potential energy is to be tripled?

9. Two cars (A and B) each have a mass of 1.20×10^3 kg. The initial velocity of car A is 12.0 m/s [180°] while that of car B is 24.0 m/s [180°]. Both cars increase their velocity by 10.0 m/s [180°].

   (a) Calculate the gain in kinetic energy of each car.

   (b) If both cars gain the same amount of velocity, why do they gain different amounts of kinetic energy?

10. A cart with a mass of 3.00 kg rolls from the top of an inclined plane that is 7.50 m long with its upper end at a height of 3.75 m above the ground. The force of friction acting on the cart as it rolls is 4.50 N in magnitude.

    (a) What is the change in gravitational potential energy when the cart arrives at ground level?

    (b) What is the work done by friction?

11. (a) An ideal spring with an elastic constant of 2000 N/m is compressed a distance of 0.400 m. How much elastic potential energy does this compression store in the spring?

    (b) If this spring transfers all of its elastic potential energy into the kinetic energy of a 2.00-kg mass, what speed would that mass have? Assume the initial speed of the mass is zero.

e **TEST**

To check your understanding of potential and kinetic energy, follow the eTest links at www.pearsoned.ca/school/physicssource.

6.2 Mechanical Energy

mechanics: the study of kinematics, statics, and dynamics

mechanical energy: the sum of potential and kinetic energies

In physics, the study of **mechanics** includes kinematics (the study of motion), statics (the study of forces in equilibrium), and dynamics (the study of non-zero forces and the motion that results from them). Gravitational potential energy, elastic potential energy, and kinetic energy form what is called **mechanical energy**. When work is done on a system, there may be changes in the potential and kinetic energies of the system. This relationship is expressed as the work-energy theorem.

The Work-Energy Theorem

A 1.50×10^5-kg jet plane waits at the end of the runway. When the air-traffic controller tells the pilot to take off, the powerful engines can each produce more than 2.5×10^5 N of thrust to accelerate the plane along the runway. In order to produce the speed of about 250 km/h required for takeoff, the engines would need to convert more than 3×10^8 J of chemical energy from the fuel supply into kinetic energy.

info **BIT**

Doubling the speed of a vehicle means quadrupling the necessary stopping distance. This relationship between stopping distance and speed is based on the physics of work and kinetic energy.

▶ **Figure 6.23** The work done by the jet's engines must convert enough chemical energy into kinetic energy to produce a velocity sufficient for takeoff.

 e **LAB**

For a probeware activity, go to www.pearsoned.ca/ school/physicssource.

As explained by Newton's Laws of Motion, the non-zero net force causes the jet plane to accelerate along the runway. Since a change in kinetic energy must involve a change in speed, kinetic energy changes are always the result of the acceleration, which in turn is caused by a non-zero net force. In terms of work and energy, this means that changes in kinetic energy (ΔE_k) are always the result of the work done by a non-zero net force (W_{net}).

$$\Delta E_k = W_{net}$$
$$= (F_{net})(\cos \theta)(\Delta d)$$
$$= (ma)(\cos \theta)(\Delta d)$$

PHYSICS INSIGHT

In the example of the airplane takeoff, θ is the angle between the direction of F_{net} or a, and d.

In all cases, work done by a non-zero net force results in a change in kinetic energy but the applied forces on an object may cause changes in its potential energy, its kinetic energy, or both. For example, once the jet plane is in the air, the thrust produced by its engines must increase its speed (ΔE_k) as well as cause it to gain altitude (ΔE_p).

Zero and Non-zero Net Forces and Effects on Energy

A motor that is pulling a block up a frictionless inclined plane at a constant speed (Figure 6.24) is exerting a force that causes a change in gravitational potential energy but not kinetic energy. The constant speed indicates that the applied force (F_{app}) is exactly balanced by the $F_{g\parallel}$ component of F_g. There is zero net force; $F_{app} = F_{g\parallel}$.

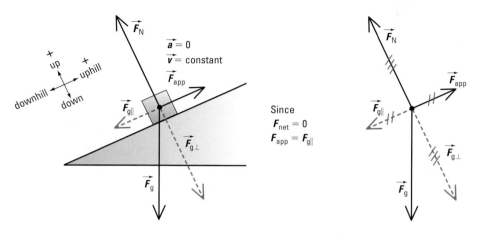

▲ **Figure 6.24** If all the forces acting on a block combine to produce a net force of zero, the block moves up the incline at a constant speed. It increases its gravitational potential energy but not its kinetic energy.

If, however, the force applied is now increased so that there is a non-zero net force and $F_{app} > F_{g\parallel}$ (Figure 6.25), the forces are no longer balanced, the block accelerates up the incline, and both kinetic energy and potential energy change. Now the work done on the block is transferred to both its kinetic energy and its gravitational potential energy. This is expressed mathematically as

$W = \Delta E$ or, in more detail, as

$W = \Delta E_k + \Delta E_p$ This is known as the **work-energy theorem**.

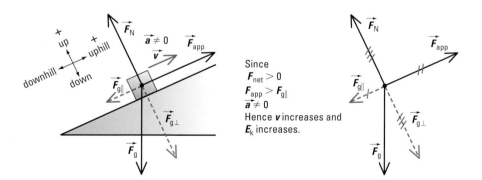

▲ **Figure 6.25** If the forces acting on a block are such that there is a non-zero net force up the plane, then $F_{app} > F_{g\parallel}$. Both the kinetic energy and the gravitational potential energy will increase as the block moves up the incline.

> The work-energy theorem states that the work done on a system is equal to the sum of the changes in the potential and kinetic energies of the system.

Example 6.7

A block is moved up a frictionless inclined plane by a force parallel to the plane. At the foot of the incline, the block is moving at 1.00 m/s. At the top of the incline, 0.850 m above the lower end, the block is moving at 4.00 m/s. The block has a mass of 1.20 kg. What is the work done on the block as it moves up the incline?

Given

$m = 1.20$ kg
$v_1 = 1.00$ m/s
$v_2 = 4.00$ m/s
$\Delta h = 0.850$ m
$g = 9.81$ m/s^2

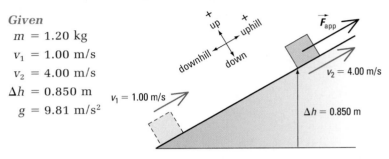

▲ **Figure 6.26**

Required
work done on the block as it moves up the incline (W)

Analysis and Solution
The work-energy theorem states that the work will be equal to the sum of the changes in the kinetic and potential energies. For the change in kinetic energy find the difference in the final and initial kinetic energy using the final and initial speeds. Change in gravitational potential energy can be found from the change in height (Figure 6.26).

$$W = \Delta E_k + \Delta E_p$$
$$= (E_{k_2} - E_{k_1}) + (mg\Delta h)$$
$$= \left(\frac{1}{2}mv_2{}^2 - \frac{1}{2}mv_1{}^2\right) + (mg\Delta h)$$
$$= \left[\frac{1}{2}(1.20\ \text{kg})(4.00\ \text{m/s})^2 - \frac{1}{2}(1.20\ \text{kg})(1.00\ \text{m/s})^2\right]$$
$$+ (1.20\ \text{kg})(9.81\ \text{m/s}^2)(0.850\ \text{m})$$
$$= (9.60\ \text{J} - 0.60\ \text{J}) + (10.01\ \text{J})$$
$$= 19.0\ \text{J}$$

Paraphrase and Verify
The work caused the block to gain a total of 19.0 J, the sum of 9.00 J of kinetic and 10.0 J of potential energy as it moved up the ramp.

Practice Problems

1. A mountain climber rappels down the face of a cliff that is 25.0 m high. When the climber, whose mass is 72.0 kg, reaches the bottom of the cliff he has a speed of 5.00 m/s. What is the work done on the climber by the rope?

2. A force of 150 N [up] acts on a 9.00-kg mass lifting it to a height of 5.00 m.
   (a) What is the work done on the mass by this force?
   (b) What is the change in gravitational potential energy?
   (c) What change in kinetic energy did the mass experience?

3. Draw a free-body diagram for the forces on the mass in question 2.
   (a) Calculate the net force acting on the mass.
   (b) Calculate the work done on the mass by the net force.
   (c) How does this relate to the answer to question 2?

Answers

1. -1.68×10^4 J
2. (a) 750 J
   (b) 441 J
   (c) 309 J
3. (a) 61.7 N [up]
   (b) 309 J
   (c) $\Delta E_k = 309$ J

Calculations of Mechanical Energy

To calculate the mechanical energy of an object is simply to find the total of the kinetic energy and all forms of potential energy.

$$E_m = E_k + E_p$$

Because gravitational potential energy is defined relative to a reference point, mechanical energy will also depend on that reference point.

Example 6.8

A cannon ball is fired from Earth's surface. At the peak of its trajectory, it has a horizontal speed of 160 m/s and is 1.20×10^3 m above the ground. With reference to the ground, what is the mechanical energy of the cannon ball at the highest point on its trajectory, if the mass of the cannon ball is 5.20 kg?

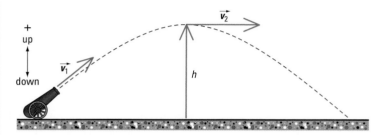

▲ **Figure 6.27**

Given
$m = 5.20$ kg

$v = 160$ m/s

$h = 1.20 \times 10^3$ m

$g = 9.81$ m/s²

Required
mechanical (total) energy of the cannon ball (E_m)

Analysis and Solution
At the top of its trajectory, the cannon ball has kinetic energy due to its horizontal motion, and gravitational potential energy because of its height above the ground.

$$E_m = E_k + E_p$$

$$= \frac{1}{2}mv^2 + mgh$$

$$= \frac{1}{2}(5.20 \text{ kg})\left(160\,\frac{\text{m}}{\text{s}}\right)^2 + (5.20 \text{ kg})\left(9.81\,\frac{\text{m}}{\text{s}^2}\right)(1.20 \times 10^3 \text{ m})$$

$$= 6.656 \times 10^4 \text{ J} + 6.121 \times 10^4 \text{ J}$$

$$= 1.28 \times 10^5 \text{ J}$$

Paraphrase and Verify
The total energy of the cannon ball at the top of the trajectory is 1.28×10^5 J. The gravitational potential energy is positive because the cannonball is higher than the reference point.

Practice Problems

1. A rocket is accelerating upward. When the rocket has reached an altitude of 5.00×10^3 m, it has reached a speed of 5.40×10^3 km/h. Relative to its launch site, what is its mechanical energy, if the mass of the rocket is 6.50×10^4 kg?

2. What is the speed of a 4.50-kg cannon ball if, at a height of 275 m above the ground, its mechanical energy relative to the ground is 6.27×10^4 J?

3. As a roller coaster trolley with a mass of 600 kg coasts down the first hill, it drops a vertical distance of 45.0 m from an initial height of 51.0 m above the ground. If, at the bottom of the hill, its speed is 30.0 m/s:
   (a) what is the trolley's mechanical energy relative to the top of the hill, and
   (b) what is the trolley's mechanical energy relative to the ground?

Answers

1. 7.63×10^{10} J
2. 150 m/s
3. (a) 5.13×10^3 J
   (b) 3.05×10^5 J

Knowledge

1. What are the forms of energy that make up mechanical energy?

2. Why does your choice of a frame of reference affect the calculated value of the mechanical energy?

3. What is the relationship between the net force and kinetic energy?

4. State the work-energy theorem.

Applications

5. A net force of 5.75×10^3 N [180°] acts on a mass of 23.0 kg. If, while the force acts, the mass travels through a displacement of 360 m [210°], what work did the net force do on the object? Into what form of energy was this work transferred?

6. At a height of 75.0 m above the ground, a cannon ball is moving with a velocity of 240 m/s [up]. If the cannon ball has a mass of 12.0 kg, what is its total mechanical energy relative to the ground? What effect would there be on the answer, if the velocity of the cannon ball were downward instead of upward? Explain.

7. A mass of 8.50 kg is travelling 7.50 m/s [up]. It is acted on by a force of 340 N [up] over a displacement of 15.0 m [up].

   (a) What work does the applied force do on the object?

   (b) What is its gain in potential energy?

   (c) What is its change in kinetic energy?

   (d) What is its speed at the end of the 15.0-m displacement?

Extensions

8. The figure below shows the force versus displacement graph for an elastic spring as it is compressed a distance of 0.240 m from its equilibrium position by a force of magnitude 2.40×10^3 N. A 7.00-kg mass is placed at the end of the spring and released. As the spring expands, it accelerates the mass so that when the spring's compression is still 0.180 m from its equilibrium position, the mass has a speed of 6.00 m/s.

   (a) What is the mechanical energy in this system when the spring is compressed to 0.240 m?

   (b) What is the mechanical energy in the system when the spring is compressed to 0.180 m?

   (c) How much work has been done on the mass by this system as the spring expanded from a compression of 0.240 m to 0.180 m?

   (d) How does the work done on the mass by the spring compare to the kinetic energy of the mass?

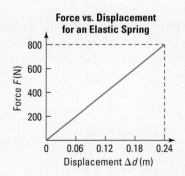

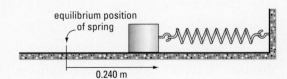

 e **TEST**

To check your understanding of the work–energy theorem and mechanical energy, follow the eTest links at www.pearsoned.ca/school/physicssource.

6.3 Mechanical Energy in Isolated and Non-isolated Systems

Isolated Systems

Imagine two people are in an isolated (sealed) room. They may complete as many money transfers as they like but the total amount of money in the room before and after each transfer will be the same. We can say that the total amount of money in this system is conserved, in that it does not change during transactions.

▲ **Figure 6.28** In an isolated room, the total amount of money in the room, before and after a transaction, is constant.

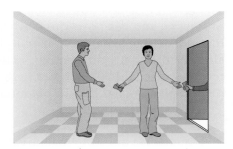

▲ **Figure 6.29** In a non-isolated room, the amount of money in the room may change.

Now imagine that the room is not isolated. In this case, money may be taken out of (or put into) the room so that the total amount of money in the room is not necessarily constant. In this system, it cannot be said that money is conserved. It would be much more complex to keep track of the money transfers that occur in this non-isolated room compared with those occurring in the isolated room.

In physics, when the energy interactions of a group of objects need to be analyzed, we often assume that these objects are isolated from all other objects in the universe. Such a group is called an **isolated system**.

Isolated Systems and Conservation of Energy

While objects within an isolated system are free to interact with each other, they cannot be subjected to unbalanced forces from outside that system. In terms of mechanical energy, that means that no force from outside the system may work to transfer energy to or from any object inside the system. The quantity of energy in the system must be constant. Even though friction may seem like an internal force, its effect is to allow energy to escape from a system as heat. Thus, an isolated system must also be frictionless. These ideas will be further explored later in the chapter.

info **BIT**

In everyday terms, energy conservation means to use as little energy as possible to accomplish a task. In physics, energy conservation refers to systems, such as an ideal pendulum, in which the total amount of energy is constant.

isolated system: a group of objects assumed to be isolated from all other objects in the universe

---

Chapter 6 In an isolated system, energy is transferred from one object to another whenever work is done.   311

Conservation of Mechanical Energy

e **TECH**

Consider the transformation of energy from potential energy to kinetic energy in a falling object, and in a ball bouncing on a trampoline. Follow the eTech links at www.pearsoned.ca/school/physicssource.

Because the mechanical energy (the sum of potential and kinetic energies) for an isolated system must be a constant, it follows that if you calculate the mechanical energy (E_m) at any two randomly chosen times, the answers must be equal. Hence,

$$E_{m_2} = E_{m_1} \qquad (1)$$

> Within an isolated system, energy may be transferred from one object to another or transformed from one form to another, but it cannot be increased or decreased. This is the **law of conservation of energy**.

Relationship between kinetic and potential energy in an isolated system
The law of conservation of energy is one of the fundamental principles of science and is a powerful mathematical model for analysis and prediction of the behaviour of objects within systems. Viewed from a slightly different perspective, conservation of energy states that, in terms of mechanical energy, any gain in kinetic energy must be accompanied by an equal loss in potential energy.

$$\Delta E_k = -\Delta E_p \qquad (2)$$

e **SIM**

Find out more about the mechanical energy, gravitational potential energy, and kinetic energy of a satellite-Earth system or a projectile-Earth system. Go to www.pearsoned.ca/school/physicssource.

Statements (1) and (2) are equivalent. This can be verified as follows. If total energy remains constant regardless of time or position, then

$$E_{m_2} = E_{m_1}.$$

But mechanical energy is the sum of the kinetic and potential energies. Therefore,

$$E_{k_2} + E_{p_2} = E_{k_1} + E_{p_1}$$

Hence,

$$E_{k_2} - E_{k_1} = -E_{p_2} + E_{p_1}$$

$$\Delta E_k = -(E_{p_2} - E_{p_1})$$

Thus,

$$\Delta E_k = -\Delta E_p \text{ is true.}$$

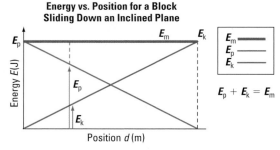

▲ **Figure 6.30** In an isolated system the loss in gravitational potential energy is equal to the gain in kinetic energy.

As a block slides down a frictionless inclined plane, its gravitational potential energy will decrease and its kinetic energy will increase. Figure 6.30 shows the energy-position graph for this isolated system. As the block moves down the plane, the sum of the heights of the potential and kinetic energy curves (value of blue line plus value of red line) at any point is equal to the block's mechanical energy (E_m). The mechanical energy (shown by the purple line) is constant; therefore, energy is conserved. This graph is typical of an isolated system.

Example 6.9

A frictionless roller coaster car has a mass ($m = 8.00 \times 10^2$ kg). At one point on its journey, the car has a speed of 4.00 m/s and is 35.0 m above the ground. Later, its speed is measured to be 20.0 m/s.
(a) Calculate its total initial energy relative to the ground.
(b) What is its gravitational potential energy in the second instance?

Given

$m = 8.00 \times 10^2$ kg

$v_1 = 4.00$ m/s

$h_1 = 35.0$ m

$v_2 = 20.0$ m/s

$g = 9.81$ m/s^2

Required
(a) mechanical energy of the system (E_{m_1})
(b) gravitational potential energy when the speed is 20.0 m/s (E_{p_2})

Analysis and Solution
A frictionless roller coaster can be treated as an isolated system.
(a) The mechanical energy at any point is the sum of its kinetic and potential energies.

$$E_{m_1} = E_{k_1} + E_{p_1}$$

$$E_{m_1} = \frac{1}{2}mv_1^2 + mgh_1$$

$$= \frac{1}{2}(8.00 \times 10^2 \text{ kg})\left(4.00\frac{\text{m}}{\text{s}}\right)^2 +$$

$$(8.00 \times 10^2 \text{ kg})\left(9.81\frac{\text{m}}{\text{s}^2}\right)(35.0 \text{ m})$$

$$= 2.810 \times 10^5 \text{ J}$$

$$= 2.81 \times 10^5 \text{ J}$$

(b) The system is defined as isolated, meaning that energy is conserved. By the law of conservation of energy, the mechanical energy at any two points must be equal. The potential energy at the second point must be equal to the mechanical energy less the kinetic energy at the second point.

$$E_{m_2} = E_{m_1}$$

$$E_{k_2} + E_{p_2} = E_{m_1}$$

$$E_{p_2} = E_{m_1} - E_{k_2}$$

$$= E_{m_1} - \frac{1}{2}mv_2^2$$

$$= 2.810 \times 10^5 \text{ J} - \frac{1}{2}(8.00 \times 10^2 \text{ kg})\left(20.0\frac{\text{m}}{\text{s}}\right)^2$$

$$= 2.810 \times 10^5 \text{ J} - 1.600 \times 10^5 \text{ J}$$

$$= 1.21 \times 10^5 \text{ J}$$

Practice Problems

1. In an isolated system, a crate with an initial kinetic energy of 250 J and gravitational potential energy of 960 J is sliding down a frictionless ramp. If the crate loses 650 J of gravitational potential energy, what will be its final kinetic energy?

2. A mass of 55.0 kg is 225 m above the ground with a velocity of 36.0 m/s [down]. Use conservation of energy to calculate its velocity when it reaches a height of 115 m above the ground. Ignore the effects of air resistance.

3. A human "cannon ball" in the circus is shot at a speed of 21.0 m/s at an angle of 20° above the horizontal from a platform that is 15.0 m above the ground. See Figure 6.31.
   (a) If the acrobat has a mass of 56.0 kg, what is his gravitational potential energy relative to the ground when he is at the highest point of his flight? Ignore the effects of air resistance.
   (b) If the net in which he lands is 2.00 m above the ground, how fast is he travelling when he hits it?

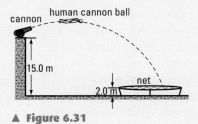

▲ **Figure 6.31**

Answers
1. 900 J
2. 58.8 m/s [down]
3. (a) 9.69 × 10³ J
   (b) 26.4 m/s

Paraphrase and Verify

(a) The total initial energy relative to the ground is 2.81×10^5 J.

(b) The gravitational potential energy at a speed of 20.0 m/s is 1.21×10^5 J. The kinetic energy increased from 6.40×10^3 J to 1.60×10^5 J, while the gravitational potential energy decreased from 2.74×10^5 J to 1.21×10^5 J. As kinetic energy increases, potential energy decreases. When the speed is 20.0 m/s, the car must be below its starting point.

MINDS ON · Energy and Earth's Orbit

At its closest point to the Sun (perihelion), around January 4th, Earth is about 147 million kilometres from the Sun. At its farthest point from the Sun (aphelion), around July 5th, Earth is about 152 million kilometres from the Sun.

- In terms of the conservation of energy, what conclusions can be made about Earth's speed as it moves around the Sun?

- What assumptions must you make to support your conclusions?

A Simple Pendulum

A simple pendulum is an excellent approximation of an isolated system. During its downswing, Earth's gravity does work on the pendulum to transfer gravitational potential energy into kinetic energy. On the upswing, gravity transfers kinetic energy back into gravitational potential energy. The mechanical energy of the pendulum is constant (Figure 6.32).

Newton's third law of motion states that for every action force there is an equal but opposite reaction force. This means that as Earth's gravity acts on the pendulum converting gravitational potential energy into kinetic energy, the pendulum must also act to convert gravitational potential energy to kinetic energy for Earth; Earth must be part of the isolated system that contains the pendulum. Earth's mass compared to that of the pendulum is enormous, so its reaction to the pendulum is immeasurably small. This explains why we can ignore the effects of the pendulum on Earth and analyze the pendulum as if it were an isolated system.

Treating the pendulum as an isolated system greatly simplifies the calculations of the system's mechanical energy. It means that the force of gravity works on the pendulum without changing the energy in the system. In fact, while work done by the force of gravity may transfer energy from one form to another it never causes a change in mechanical energy (Figure 6.33). Forces that act within systems but do not change their mechanical energy are defined as **conservative forces**. This type of force will be discussed in more detail later in this chapter.

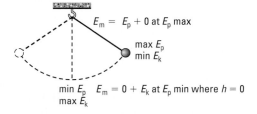

$E_m = E_p + 0$ at E_p max

max E_p
min E_k

min E_p $E_m = 0 + E_k$ at E_p min where $h = 0$
max E_k

▲ **Figure 6.32** As a pendulum swings, gravity acts to convert energy back and forth between gravitational potential energy and kinetic energy.

PHYSICS INSIGHT

If $h = 0$ had been defined to occur at the lowest point of the pendulum's swing, the gravitational potential energy at the lowest point would be zero and the mechanical energy would be equal to the kinetic energy. Then, at the highest point on the swing, where movement stops and kinetic energy is zero, the mechanical energy would be equal to the potential energy.

Because the pendulum acts as an isolated system, energy is conserved. To calculate the mechanical energy of a pendulum it is necessary to know its mass, its height above the reference point, and its speed. If all of those values are known at any one point on its swing, then the mechanical energy of the pendulum is known at all points on its swing. Once the mechanical energy is known, it can be used to predict the pendulum's motion at any instant along its path, and to correlate kinetic and potential energy with the amplitude of the swing.

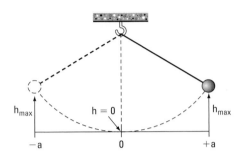

▶ **Figure 6.33** The force of gravity acts to change the gravitational potential energy and kinetic energy of the pendulum so that the mechanical energy remains constant.

Example 6.10

An ideal pendulum, as shown in Figure 6.32, is suspended by a string that is 2.00 m long. It is pulled sideways and released. At the highest point of its swing the pendulum bob is 25.0 cm above the floor. At the lowest point of its swing the pendulum bob is 5.00 cm above the floor. The mass of the pendulum bob is 250 g.

(a) What is the mechanical energy of the pendulum, relative to the floor, when the bob is at its highest point?
(b) What is the mechanical energy of the pendulum when the bob is at its lowest point?
(c) What is the kinetic energy of the bob when it is at its lowest point?
(d) What is the speed of the pendulum bob when the bob is at its lowest point?

Given
$m = 0.250$ kg
$g = 9.81$ m/s^2
$h_1 = 0.250$ m
$h_2 = 0.0500$ m
$v_1 = 0$

Required
(a) sum of gravitational potential and kinetic energies of the pendulum at the highest point (E_{m_1})
(b) mechanical energy of the pendulum at the lowest point (E_{m_2})
(c) kinetic energy of the bob at the lowest point (E_{k_2})
(d) speed of the bob at the lowest point (v_2)

Practice Problems

1. When the pendulum bob in Example 6.10 is 15.0 cm above the floor, calculate:
   (a) its mechanical energy
   (b) its kinetic energy
   (c) its speed

2. A model rocket has a mass of 3.00 kg. It is fired so that when it is 220 m above the ground it is travelling vertically upward at 165 m/s. At that point its fuel runs out so that the rest of its flight is without power. Assume that the effect of air friction is negligible and that all potential energies are measured from the ground.
   (a) What is the mechanical energy of the rocket when it is 220 m above the ground?
   (b) When it reaches the highest point on its trajectory, what will its gravitational potential energy be?
   (c) How far above the ground is the rocket at its highest point?
   (d) When it hits the ground, what is its velocity?

3. A roller coaster trolley and its passengers have a mass of 840 kg. The trolley comes over the top of the first hill with a speed of 0.200 m/s. The hill is 85.0 m above the ground. The trolley goes down the first hill and up to the crest of the second hill 64.0 m above the ground. Ignore the effect of frictional forces. What is the kinetic energy of the trolley at the top of the second hill?

4. A pole-vaulter with a mass of 56.0 kg tries to convert the kinetic energy of her approach into height.
   (a) What is the maximum height she can expect to attain if her approach speed is 8.00 m/s? Assume that the centre of mass of the vaulter is 0.850 m above the ground.
   (b) Describe the energy changes that occur from the time the vaulter starts to run until she reaches the highest point of her jump.

Answers

1. (a) 0.613 J
   (b) 0.245 J
   (c) 1.40 m/s

2. (a) 4.73×10^4 J
   (b) 4.73×10^4 J
   (c) 1.61×10^3 m
   (d) 178 m/s

3. 1.73×10^5 J

4. (a) 4.11 m

Analysis and Solution

(a) At its highest point, the speed of the pendulum is zero. Thus, the mechanical energy at that point is equal to its gravitational potential energy.

$$E_{m_1} = E_{p_1} + E_{k_1}$$

$$E_{m_1} = mgh_1 + \frac{1}{2}mv_1^2$$

$$= (0.250 \text{ kg})\left(9.81 \frac{\text{m}}{\text{s}^2}\right)(0.250 \text{ m}) + \frac{1}{2}(0.250 \text{ kg})(0)^2$$

$$= 0.6131 \frac{\text{kg} \cdot \text{m}^2}{\text{s}^2}$$

$$= 0.613 \text{ J}$$

(b) In an isolated system, the mechanical energy is constant. Thus, by the law of conservation of energy the mechanical energy at its lowest point is equal to the mechanical energy at its highest point.

$$E_{m_2} = E_{m_1}$$

$$\therefore E_{m_2} = 0.613 \text{ J}$$

(c) The kinetic energy at the lowest point is the difference between the mechanical and gravitational potential energies at that point.

$$E_{m_2} = E_{p_2} + E_{k_2}$$

$$E_{k_2} = E_{m_2} - E_{p_2}$$

$$= E_{m_2} - (mgh_2)$$

$$= 0.6131 \text{ J} - (0.250 \text{ kg})\left(9.81\frac{\text{m}}{\text{s}^2}\right)(0.0500 \text{ m})$$

$$= 0.6131 \text{ J} - (0.1226 \text{ J})$$

$$= 0.491 \text{ J}$$

(d) The speed at the lowest point can be found from kinetic energy.

$$E_{k_2} = \frac{1}{2}mv_2^2$$

$$v_2 = \sqrt{\frac{2E_{k_2}}{m}} = \sqrt{\frac{2(0.491 \text{ J})}{0.250 \text{ kg}}}$$

$$= 1.98 \frac{\text{m}}{\text{s}}$$

Paraphrase and Verify

(a) At the highest point, the total energy of the pendulum is 0.613 J.
(b) As the bob swings lower, gravitational potential energy is lost and kinetic energy is gained. The total energy remains 0.613 J.
(c) At the lowest point, the kinetic energy is 0.490 J, the difference between its total energy and its gravitational potential energy.
(d) At the lowest point of its swing, the bob has a speed of 1.98 m/s.

6-2 *Inquiry Lab*

Required Skills
- Initiating and Planning
- Performing and Recording
- Analyzing and Interpreting
- Communication and Teamwork

Conservation of Mechanical Energy

Question

Is energy conserved during the motion of a pendulum?

Hypothesis

State a hypothesis concerning the energy status of a pendulum. Remember to write this in the form of an if/then statement.

Variables

The variables in this lab are the values used to calculate the gravitational potential energy (mass, gravitational acceleration, and height) and the kinetic energy (mass and speed) at various points on the swing of the pendulum. Consider and identify which are controlled variable(s), which manipulated variable(s), and which responding variables.

Materials and Equipment

string (at least 2.0 m long)
pendulum bob (a 1-kg mass or greater)
metre-stick
ticker tape timer
masking tape
stopwatch (for timer calibration)

Procedure

> For some interval timers, the period of the timer varies with the operating voltage. If your timer is of that type, begin by calibrating the timer. This is done by pulling a strip of ticker tape through the timer for a measured time, as set out below.

Calibrate the timer:

1. Start the tape moving steadily through the timer, then connect the timer to the power supply for an exact measure of time (3 to 5 s works well). Be sure the tape does not stop moving while the timer is running.

2. Count the number of intervals between the dots (N) and divide that number into the measured time (t) to determine the time lapse per interval (Δt). Do at least one more calibration trial (without changing the voltage) to check if the time per interval (Δt) remains constant.

(NOTE: The voltage to the timer must not vary from trial to trial. If you are using a variable-voltage power supply, adjust the voltage so that the timer runs smoothly, and leave the power supply untouched for the remainder of the experiment. Stop and start the timer by disconnecting and reconnecting the lead attached to the black post of the power supply rather than turning the power supply off and on.)

3. Record your results in a table of data (Table 6.3).

▼ **Table 6.3** Calibration Data

Test Number	Total Time t (s)	Number of intervals N	Time/Interval t (s)
1			
2			

Set up the apparatus:

4. Suspend the pendulum from a suitable solid point and allow the pendulum bob to come to rest at its lowest point. Place a marker (e.g., a piece of masking tape) on the floor below the centre of mass of the bob to indicate the pendulum's rest position. Measure and record the length (L) of the pendulum, and mass (m) of the pendulum bob.

(NOTE: The length of a pendulum is measured from the point at which it pivots to the centre of mass of the pendulum bob. If the shape of the bob is a symmetrical solid, such as a sphere or a cylinder, the centre of mass is at its geometric centre.)

5. Pull the pendulum sideways so that its horizontal displacement (x) is about one-half its length. Place a marker, such as an iron stand, at this point, which will be x_{max} for the experiment. Ensure the path of the pendulum is clear, then release it to check the path of its swing. One team member should be positioned to catch the pendulum so that it does not swing back.

> ⚠ **CAUTION: Make sure that the path of the pendulum is clear before you allow it to begin its swing.**

6 Position the ticker tape timer at a distance approximately equal to the length of the pendulum from the pendulum's rest position. Locate the timer so that its height is just above the lowest point of the pendulum bob's path. Align the timer so that the tape does not bind as the bob pulls it through the timer. See Figure 6.34. Anchor the timer firmly so that it does not shift during trials.

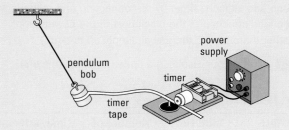

▲ **Figure 6.34**

7 With ticker tape attached to the pendulum but without the timer running, do a trial run of the system. Attach the tape to the pendulum bob at its centre of mass, so that the pull of the tape does not cause the bob to twist. Use a length of ticker tape that will reach from the timer to a point slightly beyond the bob's rest position. Move the pendulum bob sideways to its starting point. Hold the bob in place while you pull the tape tight, then gently allow the tape to take up the weight of the bob. Be sure that the tape is not twisted so that it does not rip as it passes through the timer. Release the tape and allow the pendulum to pull it through the timer.

Collect data:

8 Once the timer is positioned so that the tape moves smoothly through it, you are ready to do a trial with the timer running. First, with the bob at its rest position, have one team member hold the bob stationary and pull the tape through the timer until it is just taut. Place a mark on the tape at the location where the timer records its dots. This mark on the tape records the position of the bob when its horizontal displacement is equal to zero ($x = 0$).

9 Move the pendulum bob sideways to the starting point of its swing (x_{max}). Again hold the bob steady while a team member pulls the tape tight. Gently allow the tape to take up the weight of the pendulum bob. Start the timer, then release the pendulum.

10 Lay the tape out on a table and place a line across the tape through the first dot the timer put on the tape. At that position, the speed is zero ($v = 0$) and the position is the maximum displacement (x_{max}). Measure the length of the tape from $x = 0$ to x_{max}.

11 Locate the two dots that define the interval containing the mark that indicates the position of the bob at its rest position ($x = 0$). Label this interval as interval 1. Measure the length (Δx_1) of this interval (the space between the two dots on either side of the mark) and record it in a data table (Table 6.4). Calculate the speed v of the pendulum for interval 1 by dividing Δx_1 by the interval time Δt.

12 Along the length of the tape, between $x = 0$ and x_{max}, choose at least four more time intervals and draw a line across the tape at the midpoint of each chosen interval. Starting from interval 1, number the selected intervals as 2, 3, etc. For each of the chosen intervals, measure (a) the length of the interval (Δx), and (b) the distance (x) to the midpoint of the interval from the line indicating $x = 0$. Record your measurements in a data table (Table 6.4).

Analysis

1. Use a table similar to Table 6.4 to organize your data.

2. Calculate the height (h) of the pendulum above its rest position by using the relationship $h = L - \sqrt{L^2 - x^2}$. (See the diagram in Figure 6.35.)

3. Calculate the values for the gravitational potential (E_p), the kinetic (E_k) and the mechanical (E_m) energies for each of the intervals you marked on your tape.

4. On the same set of axes, plot graphs for E_p and E_k against the horizontal displacement (x) of the pendulum. Describe the relationship between E_k and the position of the pendulum that is indicated by the graph. Does E_k change uniformly as the pendulum swings? Does E_p change uniformly as the pendulum swings? What relationship does the graph suggest exists between E_p and E_k for the pendulum?

5. On the same set of axes, plot a graph of the total mechanical energy (E_m) of the system against horizontal position (x). What does the graph suggest is the nature of the total mechanical energy for the pendulum? Suggest a reason for this relationship.

6. Within experimental error, can the mechanical energy of the system be considered constant? If the mechanical energy is assumed constant, what value would you choose to be the most representative of this energy? Explain why. For each of the intervals that you chose for analysis, what is the percent error in the mechanical energy at that interval? Does your analysis indicate a systemic error change for the pendulum as it swings? What would be the cause of this error?

7. How is your hypothesis affected by your data? Explain.

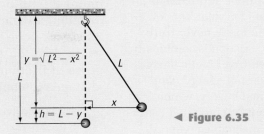

◄ **Figure 6.35**

▼ **Table 6.4** Pendulum Data

Interval Number	Horizontal Displacement x (m)	Height h (m)	E_p (J)	Interval Length Δx (cm)	Interval Speed v (m/s)	E_k (J)	E_m (J) $(E_p + E_k)$
1	0	0	0				
2							

Conservative and Non-conservative Forces

To understand the law of conservation of energy you must understand that some forces, such as gravity and elastic forces, act within systems without affecting the mechanical energy of the system. When such forces operate, energy is conserved. These are called **conservative forces.** Other forces, such as friction, and forces applied from outside a system, cause the energy of the system to change so that energy is not conserved. These are known as **non-conservative forces**.

Figure 6.36 shows a system of two ramps joining point P to point Q. The drop Δh is the same for the two ramps, but ramp A is shorter than ramp B, because of the hills in ramp B. If a frictionless car is released from P and moves down one ramp to Q, the amount of kinetic energy the car gains in moving from P to Q does not depend on which ramp (A or B) the car coasts down. If energy is conserved, the kinetic energy at point Q is equal to the potential energy at point P, so the speed of the car at point Q will be the same whether it comes down ramp A or ramp B.

Since a conservative force does not affect the mechanical energy of a system, the work done by a conservative force to move an object from one point to another within the system is independent of the path the object follows.

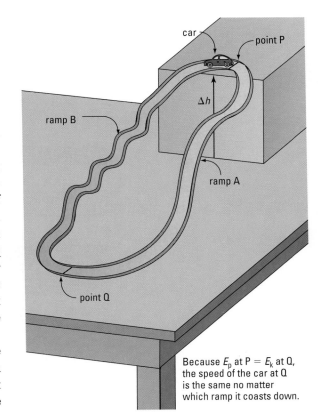

Because E_p at P $= E_k$ at Q, the speed of the car at Q is the same no matter which ramp it coasts down.

▲ **Figure 6.36** If a conservative force acts on an object, then the work it does is independent of the path the object follows between two points.

non-isolated system: a system in which there is an energy exchange with the surroundings

Friction Is a Non-conservative Force

In the absence of friction, the car in Figure 6.36 would return to point P with no change in its mechanical energy. However, if there is friction, any motion of the car will be subject to it. When you analyze the work done by friction, you can see that path length does affect the work done on the car. The term Δd, the distance through which the force of friction acts, is not the displacement, but is always the actual distance the object travels.

W_f is the work done by the force of friction, F_f, on the system. Therefore:

$$W_f = F_f \Delta d$$

but $\Delta d_B > \Delta d_A$,

so $W_{f_B} > W_{f_A}$ and the car on Ramp B would lose more energy.

Since the potential energy at the bottom of the ramp is the same regardless of the route, the loss in mechanical energy must be a loss in kinetic energy. Therefore, friction is not a conservative force. Because thermal energy is being radiated out of the system, the system is, by definition, a **non-isolated system**. The amount of work done by friction will cause the mechanical energy of the system to change so that

$$\Delta E_m = W_f$$

Therefore,

$$E_{m_2} - E_{m_1} = W_f \text{ or}$$

$$E_{m_2} = E_{m_1} + W_f$$

The direction of the force of friction is always exactly opposite to the direction of the motion; therefore, the calculated value of W_f is always negative. Friction always reduces the mechanical energy of a system.

Concept Check

What assumptions must be made if you wish to use the law of conservation of energy to solve a problem in physics?

MINDS ON — That's the Way the Ball Bounces

With each successive bounce, the height attained by a bouncing ball becomes less. Assuming the elastic forces that cause the ball to bounce are conservative in nature, and no outside forces act on the ball, you might expect it to behave as an isolated system. If so, the energy of the ball should be conserved. Use the concept of systems and conservation of energy to explain why the height decreases with each bounce.

Energy Changes in Non-isolated Systems

Not all external forces remove mechanical energy from a system. Motors, in general, are used to add mechanical energy to a system. A ski-lift motor, for example, increases the gravitational potential energy of the skiers. More generally, if several external forces (A, B, C, . . .), as well as friction, act on a system, then the total work done by all of these forces produces the change in mechanical energy.

$$E_{m_2} = E_{m_1} + W$$

$$= E_{m_1} + (W_A + W_B + W_C + \ldots + W_f)$$

This is simply another version of the work–energy theorem.

Comparison of Energy-Position Graphs for Isolated and Non-isolated Systems

Figure 6.37 shows the energy-position graphs for a block sliding down an inclined plane in a non-isolated system. In an energy-position graph, the mechanical energy E_m is the sum of the potential energy E_p and kinetic energy E_k. So, the height of the mechanical energy line above the axis is the sum of the heights of the potential and kinetic energy lines. The purple line is the sum of the values of the red line and the blue line.

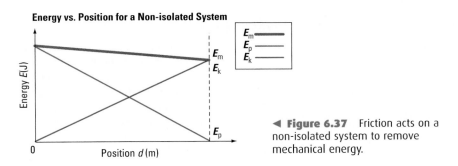

Energy vs. Position for a Non-isolated System

◀ **Figure 6.37** Friction acts on a non-isolated system to remove mechanical energy.

By rearranging the equation for the definition of work,

$$\Delta E = F\Delta d$$

$$\therefore F = \frac{\Delta E}{\Delta d}$$

it can be easily seen that force is equal to the slope of an energy-position graph. The units of the slope are $\frac{N \cdot \cancel{m}}{\cancel{m}}$, or units of force. In particular:

- The component of the force of gravity parallel to the motion can be determined by calculating the slope of the gravitational potential energy-position graph.
- The net force can be determined by calculating the slope of the kinetic energy-position graph.

*e*MATH

To determine the forces along an incline in an isolated system by using an energy-position graph, visit www.pearsoned.ca/physicssource.

For example, in the isolated system in Figure 6.30 on page 312, the slope of the potential energy curve gives the component of gravity parallel to the inclined plane. The slope of the kinetic energy curve gives the net force. The slope of the mechanical energy curve is zero indicating that no outside forces act on this system.

In the non-isolated system shown in Figure 6.37, E_m is not constant so friction is present. The slope of the total energy curve gives the force of friction. As an example of a non-isolated system, imagine a cart accelerating down an inclined plane. The force of friction removes energy from the system, but it is not sufficient to stop the cart from speeding up. The magnitude of the change in kinetic energy is less than the magnitude of the change in gravitational potential energy. In this case, the mechanical energy decreases by the amount of energy that friction removes from the system. The graph would be similar to Figure 6.37.

Project LINK

How will the design of your persuader apparatus allow for the energy changes in a system during a collision?

6-3 Design a Lab

The Energy Involved in a Collision

The Question
What happens to the energy of the system when two carts collide?

Design and Conduct Your Investigation
Design an experiment to investigate the energy of a system in which two carts collide. In one case, compare the energy before and after the collision for **"elastic" collisions** in which the carts interact via a spring bumper. In a second case, compare the energy before and after a collision when the carts stick together in what is called an **"inelastic" collision**. You will need to develop a list of materials and a detailed procedure. Use the work-energy theorem to explain your results and form conclusions.

*e*LAB

If probeware is available, perform *6-3 Design a Lab* using a motion sensor. For a probeware activity, go to www.pearsoned.ca/school/physicssource.

Concept Check

A block slides down an inclined plane, radiating energy out of the system as heat due to friction. Yet when you measure the mechanical energy at the bottom of the ramp, the total energy in the system is unchanged. Explain how this might occur.

Knowledge

1. What is meant by an isolated system?

2. If energy is conserved in a system, how can work be done in the system?

3. Describe the changes in the forms of energy as an acrobat bounces on a trampoline so that she goes higher after each bounce.

4. Can a non-conservative force act in an isolated system? Explain.

5. A golfer drives a golf ball from the top of a cliff. The ball's initial velocity is at an angle above the horizontal. If there were no air friction, describe the energy transformations from the time the golfer starts her swing until the golf ball lands on the ground at a distance from the bottom of the cliff. Include the energy transformation at the point of impact.

6. The pendulum of a clock is given a tiny push at the beginning of each swing. Why?

Applications

7. Two masses are suspended by a light string over a frictionless pulley. Mass A is 2.40 kg, mass B is 1.50 kg. Can this be considered an isolated system? Explain. On release, mass A falls to the tabletop, 1.40 m below. What is the kinetic energy of this system the instant before mass A hits the tabletop?

8. Draw graphs showing the gravitational potential, kinetic, and mechanical energy of the system in question 7 against the change in position of mass A if there is (a) no friction, (b) a force of friction, but mass A still accelerates.

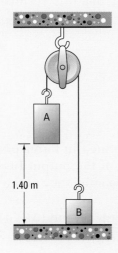

▲ Diagram for questions 7 and 8.

9. The figure below shows the energy-position graphs for two different systems. For each graph, describe what is happening to the object(s) in the system in terms of their energies. Describe for each the nature of the forces acting on the object(s).

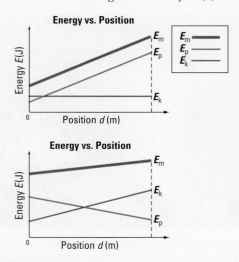

Extensions

10. A 3.60-m-long pendulum with a 1.25-kg bob is pulled sideways until it is displaced 1.80 m horizontally from its rest position.

    (a) Use the Pythagorean theorem to calculate the bob's gain in height. If the pendulum is released, calculate the speed of the bob when it

    (b) passes through its rest position, and

    (c) when it is 0.250 m above its rest position.

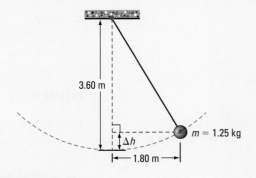

e TEST

To check your understanding of mechanical energy in isolated and non-isolated systems, follow the eTest links at www.pearsoned.ca/school/physicssource.

6.4 Work and Power

Power, Work, and Time

info **BIT**

In metric terms, 1.00 hp = 746 W or about 0.75 kW.

Toward the end of the 18th century, horses were the main source of energy used to drive the pumps that removed water from mines. Thus, when James Watt (1736–1819) wanted to know how his newly improved steam engine compared with existing methods of pumping water out of mines, he compared its effectiveness to that of horses. Today, even though it is a rather awkward unit, we still use his concept of **horsepower (hp)** to identify the power output of motors, especially in the automotive industry.

The high-performance race car in Figure 6.38 accelerates to speeds over 530 km/h in about 4.4 s. A family sedan with a 250-hp engine can accelerate to 100 km/h, from rest, in about 8.0 s. Aside from acceleration, what aspect of a car's performance is affected by the horsepower rating of its motor? On the highway, cars with 100-hp motors and cars with 300-hp motors both easily travel at the speed limit. What factors decide how much power is required to move a car along the highway?

▲ **Figure 6.38** This drag racer's 7000 hp engine burns a special fuel mixture called nitromethane. Each of its eight cylinders generates approximately three times the power of a normal car engine. The distortion of the tires, as seen above, is evidence of the magnitude of the forces exerted during acceleration.

power: the rate of doing work

In physics, **power** (P) is defined as the rate of doing work. Thus, the equation for power is

$$P = \frac{W}{\Delta t} \text{ or } P = \frac{\Delta E}{\Delta t}$$

The unit of power, the watt (W), is named in recognition of James Watt's contributions to physics. Using the equation for power we see that a power output of one watt results when one joule of work is done per second.

$$1 \text{ W} = \frac{1 \text{ J}}{1 \text{ s}}$$
$$= 1 \frac{\text{J}}{\text{s}}$$

Efficiency

efficiency: ratio of the energy output to the energy input of any system

Efficiency may be defined in terms of energy or in terms of power. In both cases, the ratio of the output (useful work) to the input (energy expended) defines the efficiency of the system. Thus, efficiency can be calculated as either,

$$\text{Efficiency} = \frac{\text{Energy output } (\Delta E_{\text{out}})}{\text{Energy input } (\Delta E_{\text{in}})}, \text{ or}$$

$$= \frac{\text{Power output } (P_{\text{out}})}{\text{Power input } (P_{\text{in}})}$$

Concept Check

In terms of kg, m, and s, what is the unit for power?

Example 6.11

An elevator and its occupants have a mass of 1300 kg. The elevator motor lifts the elevator to the 12th floor, a distance of 40.0 m, in 75.0 s. (a) What is the power output of the elevator? (b) What is the efficiency of the system if the motor must generate 9.40 kW of power to do the specified work?

Given

$m = 1.30 \times 10^3$ kg

$g = 9.81$ m/s²

$\Delta h = +40.0$ m

$\Delta t = 75.0$ s

$P_{in} = 9.40 \times 10^3$ W

Required

(a) rate at which the elevator does work

(b) efficiency of the system

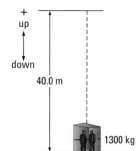

▲ **Figure 6.39**

Analysis and Solution

(a) The work done by the elevator is equal to its gain in gravitational potential energy. The power output of the elevator is the change in potential energy divided by the time.

$$P = \frac{\Delta E_p}{\Delta t}$$

$$= \frac{mg\Delta h}{\Delta t}$$

$$= \frac{(1.30 \times 10^3 \text{ kg})\left(9.81 \dfrac{\text{m}}{\text{s}^2}\right)(40.0 \text{ m})}{75.0 \text{ s}}$$

$$= 6.802 \times 10^3 \frac{\text{J}}{\text{s}}$$

$$= 6.80 \times 10^3 \text{ W}$$

(b) Efficiency is the ratio of the power output to the power input.

$$Efficiency = \frac{P_{out}}{P_{in}}$$

$$= \frac{6.80 \times 10^3 \text{ W}}{9.40 \times 10^3 \text{ W}}$$

$$= 0.723$$

Paraphrase and Verify

(a) The power output of the elevator is 6.80×10^3 W. The answer has the right order of magnitude for the given data. The power output is equivalent to about sixty-eight 100-W light bulbs.

(b) The efficiency of the system is 0.723 (72.3%).

Practice Problems

1. The engine of a crane lifts a mass of 1.50 t to a height of 65.0 m in 3.50 min. What is the power output of the crane? Convert the SI unit answer to hp.

2. If a motor is rated at 5.60 kW, how much work can it do in 20.0 min?

3. A tractor, pulling a plough, exerts a pulling force of 7.50×10^3 N over a distance of 3.20 km. If the tractor's power output is 25.0 kW, how long does it take to do the work?

Answers

1. 4.55 kW (6.10 hp)

2. 6.72×10^6 J

3. 960 s (16.0 min)

Measuring the Power Output of a Motor

The Question

How much power can a small electric motor generate?

The Problem

The problem in the lab is to measure the power output of a motor by timing how long it takes for the motor to do a fixed amount of work.

Variables

The variables for measuring power are the work done against gravity (ΔE_P) and the time (Δt) it takes to do the work. Calculating ΔE_P requires mass (m), gravitational acceleration (g), and change in height (Δh).

Materials

> small dc electric motor
> alligator clip leads
> iron stand
> 1-kg mass
> test-tube clamps
> low-voltage power supply
> dowel (about 3 cm long and 1 cm in diameter)
> thread (about 2.5 m long)
> tape
> paper clip
> washers
> balance scale (sensitive to at least 0.1 g)
> stopwatch
> metre-stick

Procedure

1. Use the balance to determine the mass of the paper clip. Record your measurement.

2. Place 10 washers on the balance scale and determine their mass. Calculate the average mass of the washers. Record your measurement.

3. Assemble the apparatus as shown in Figure 6.40. Set up a measuring scale behind the string holding the washers. The distance between the upper and lower timing marks on the scale may be adjusted if your apparatus permits, but should be 1.5 m or greater.

> ⚠ **CAUTION: Close the test-tube clamp just tight enough to hold the motor in place. If you tighten it too much, it could warp the body of the motor.**

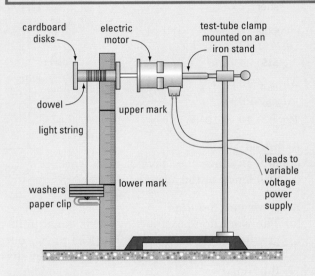

▲ **Figure 6.40**

> ⚠ **CAUTION: Check with your instructor to be sure the connections are correct before you plug in the power supply. If the motor is incorrectly connected, it could be damaged when the current is turned on.**

4. Connect the power supply to the electric motor. Once your instructor has approved your connection, disconnect the lead connected to the red post of the power supply and turn on the power supply.

5. Place five washers on the string, as shown in Figure 6.40. Complete the circuit by holding the insulated alligator clip lead on the red post of the power supply and observe the speed with which the motor lifts the washers. Adjust the number of washers until the motor moves the load upward at a uniform speed. (If the speed is too great, it will be difficult to time the motion of the washers. If the speed is too slow, then the motor may not run smoothly.)

6 Pull the thread to unwind thread from the dowel until the washers rest on the floor. Start the motor. Measure the time the washers take to travel between the lower and upper timing marks.

7 Record your measurements in a table such as Table 6.5.

8 Vary the number of washers on the paper clip and repeat the trial. Do trials with at least three different masses.

9 Calculate the work that the motor did in lifting the washers the measured distance.

10 Calculate the power output for each trial.

Analysis

1. Does the power output of the motor vary with the force it is exerting?

2. Make a graph of the power output versus the mass being lifted.

3. For what mass does the motor produce the most power?

4. What is the advantage of lifting the weights over a long distance?

5. Suggest reasons why the motor might generate more power when different masses are used.

6. Does the motor feel warm after it has done some work? What does that tell you about this system?

7. Would it make sense to use a very large motor to lift very tiny masses? Explain.

8. In terms of car engines, what are the implications for engine size?

▼ **Table 6.5**   Power Output of a Motor

Trial Number	Number of Washers	Mass m (kg)	Time Δt (s)	Change in Potential Energy $\Delta E_p = mg\Delta h$ (J)	Power $P = \Delta E_p/\Delta t$ (W)

Power and Speed

When a motor, such as the electric motor in 6-4 Inquiry Lab, applies a constant force to move an object at a constant speed, the power output of the motor can be shown to be the product of the force and the speed. When the force is constant, the work done can be found by the equation

$$W = F\Delta d$$

Inserting the equation for work into the equation for power gives:

$$P = \frac{F\Delta d}{\Delta t}$$

$$= F\frac{\Delta d}{\Delta t}$$

But the expression $\Delta d/\Delta t$ is just average speed v_{ave}; therefore,

$$P = (F)(v_{ave})$$

e **WEB**

Why is it that if you double the speed of a car, the rate at which it consumes fuel more than doubles? Is lowering the speed limit the most effective way to conserve energy or would design changes (e.g., hybrid fuel systems or fuel cells) be more effective? With a group of classmates, investigate how best to improve the energy efficiency of automobiles. Use your library and the Internet. Present the results of your investigation in a report using presentation software such as PowerPoint ™. Begin your search at www.pearsoned.ca/school/physicssource.

Example 6.12

A car, of mass 2000 kg, is travelling up a hill at a constant speed of 90.0 km/h (25.0 m/s). The force of air resistance, which opposes this motion, is 450 N. The slope of the hill is 6.0° (Figure 6.41).
(a) Draw a free-body diagram to show the external forces acting on the car as it moves up the hill.
(b) Determine the forward force needed to maintain the car's speed.
(c) Assuming that all the power output of the car engine goes into maintaining the car's forward motion, calculate the power output of the engine.

Given

$m = 2.00 \times 10^3$ kg
$\vec{F}_{air} = 4.50 \times 10^2$ N [downhill]
$g = 9.81$ m/s²
$v = 25.0$ m/s
$\theta = 6.0°$

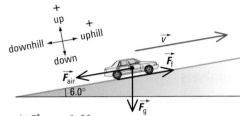

▲ **Figure 6.41**

Required
(a) a free-body diagram for the car
(b) forward force (F_f)
(c) power (p)

Analysis and Solution
(a) Figure 6.42(a) shows the free-body diagram.
(b) Since the car is not accelerating, the net force on the car must be zero, $F_{net} = 0$, both parallel and perpendicular to the incline of the hill. The forward force (F_f) must be equal to the sum of the magnitudes of the force of air resistance (F_{air}) and the component of the gravitational force that acts parallel to the incline ($F_{g\parallel}$).

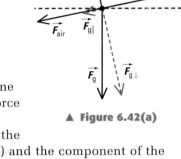

▲ **Figure 6.42(a)**

In the parallel direction

$\vec{F}_{net\parallel} = \vec{F}_f + \vec{F}_{g\parallel} + \vec{F}_{air}$

$F_{net\parallel} = F_f + F_{g\parallel} + F_{air}$

Now,

$F_{g\parallel} = -mg\sin\theta$

$= -(2.00 \times 10^3 \text{ kg})\left(9.81 \dfrac{\text{m}}{\text{s}^2}\right)(\sin 6.0°)$

$= -2.051 \times 10^3$ N

▲ **Figure 6.42(b)**

Therefore,

$0 = F_f + (-2.051 \times 10^3 \text{ N}) + (-4.50 \times 10^2 \text{ N})$

$F_f = 2.051 \times 10^3 \text{ N} + 4.50 \times 10^2 \text{ N}$

$= 2.50 \times 10^3$ N

Practice Problems

1. What is the power output of an electric motor that lifts an elevator with a mass of 1500 kg at a speed of 0.750 m/s?

2. An engine's power is rated at 150 kW. Assume there is no loss of force due to air resistance. What is the greatest average speed at which this engine could lift a mass of 2.00 t?

3. A 1250-kg race car accelerates uniformly from rest to 30.0 m/s in 4.00 s. What must be the average power output of its motor?

4. Each car in a freight train experiences a drag force of 6.00×10^2 N due to air resistance.
   (a) If the engine of the train is to pull a train of 75 cars at a constant speed of 72.0 km/h, what power is required to move the cars?
   (b) If the engine operates at 15.0% efficiency, what must be the power generated by the engine to move these cars?

Answers:

1. 11.0 kW

2. 7.65 m/s

3. 141 kW

4. (a) 900 kW
   (b) 6.00×10^3 kW

(c) Calculate the power output of the engine using the forward force and the speed with which the car moves along the ramp.

$$P = F_f v_{ave}$$
$$= (2.50 \times 10^3 \text{ N})(25.0 \text{ m/s})$$
$$= 6.25 \times 10^4 \text{ W}$$
$$= 62.5 \text{ kW}$$

Paraphrase

(a) The free-body diagram shows the external forces acting on the car.

(b) If the car moves at a constant speed, then the forward force must be a force of 2.5×10^3 N.

(c) The power output of the car is 62.5 kW.

MINDS ON   Power and Dance

At the moment of takeoff, Cossack dancers must generate considerable power to perform their spectacular leaps (Figure 6.43). Discuss techniques you could use to measure the power the dancers must generate to make such a jump. University Faculties of Kinesiology study this and other aspects of how humans move.

1. What factors involved in the jump will you need to determine?

2. What equipment might you require to measure those factors?

3. How would you measure the dancer's maximum power output compared with the power he can generate over a sustained period of time?

▲ **Figure 6.43**

e **WEB**

To learn more about power generated in human activities, follow the links at www.pearsoned.ca/school/physicssource.

THEN, NOW, AND FUTURE   Fuel for the Future?

While the automobile in Figure 6.44 may look like a normal car, nothing could be further from the truth. When this vehicle travels along one of Vancouver's streets, its motor is barely audible. Perhaps even more surprising is the fact that the exhaust this car produces is pure water. While the motor that drives the car is actually an electric motor, it is the source of the electricity that is getting all the attention. The "battery" in this car is called a fuel cell.

At present, fuel cells are not an economically viable replacement for the internal combustion engine although successful trials of fuel-cell buses have been made in several cities around the world.

▲ **Figure 6.44** This car's exhaust is pure water.

The impact of fossil fuel (oil and coal)-burning systems on the environment has made the search for alternative energy sources much more attractive. This search is further enhanced by the realization that the supply of fossil fuels is finite. Even though Canada has, at present, an abundant supply of fossil fuels, it is still a world leader in fuel-cell research.

For further information, go to the Internet. Start your research at www.pearsoned.ca/school/physicssource.

Questions

1. What are the advantages and disadvantages of a fuel-cell-driven motor over an internal combustion engine?

2. Which of the advantages and disadvantages identified above can be further improved on or overcome by scientific and technological research? Explain.

3. What are the limitations of science and technology to finding answers to the problems associated with energy production and use?

6–5 *Problem-Solving Lab*

Required Skills
- Initiating and Planning
- Performing and Recording
- Analyzing and Interpreting
- Communication and Teamwork

Power and Gears

Recognize a Need

Modern bicycles have many gears to enable riders to make best use of their efforts. In the automotive industry, manufacturers use a device called a dynamometer (Prony brake) to measure the power output of the motors they install in their vehicles. A Prony brake for bicycles would be a useful thing.

The Problem

How does the gear used by a cyclist affect the power output at the drive wheel of the bicycle? In which gear do cyclists generate the greatest power?

Criteria for Success

A successful experiment will determine if there is a relationship between the power at the drive wheel of the bicycle and the gear in which the bicycle is being ridden.

Brainstorm Ideas

Investigate the design of a Prony brake, then brainstorm how that design might be adapted to measure the power output of a bicycle. Remember, for your results to be useful

the design must allow a rider to "ride" the bicycle in a normal manner. If a computer and probeware are available, consider using probeware in your experimental design, to measure the speed of the Prony brake.

*e*WEB

 Use the Internet to investigate Prony brake design. Begin your search at www.pearsoned.ca/school/physicssource.

Build a Prototype

Build a Prony brake that can measure the power output of a student riding a bicycle.

Test and Evaluate

Make measurements of the power output of a student riding a bicycle using various gear settings.

Communicate

Prepare a report of your research using a computer spreadsheet program to organize your data and to generate a graph of the power output versus the gear level. Print your graph, in colour if possible, as part of your report.

6.4 *Check and Reflect*

Knowledge

1. What is the relationship between the amount of work that is done and the power output of the machine that does the work?

2. A farmer says, "My tractor with its 60-hp engine easily pulls a plough while my car with a 280-hp engine cannot even budge it." How can you explain this fact?

3. What is the relationship between the speed of an object and the power required to move it?

Applications

4. You lift a 25.0-kg mass to your waist (0.800 m) in 1.20 s. What is your power output?

5. An airplane's engine exerts a thrust of 1.20×10^4 N to maintain a speed of 450 km/h. What power is the engine generating?

6. An electric motor has a power rating of 1.50 kW. If it operates at 75% efficiency, what work can it do in an hour?

7. A motor of a car must generate 9.50 kW to move the car at a constant speed of 25.0 m/s. What is the force of friction on the car?

Extension

8. A cannon fires a ball with a muzzle velocity of 240 m/s. The cannon ball has a mass of 3.60 kg. The barrel of the cannon is 1.20 m long and exerts a force of friction on the cannon ball of 650 N. What is the average power provided to fire the cannon ball?

*e*TEST

 To check your understanding of power, work, and efficiency, follow the eTest links at www.pearsoned.ca/school/physicssource.

Key Terms

energy
work
gravitational potential
  energy

reference point
elastic potential energy
kinetic energy
mechanics

mechanical energy
work-energy theorem
isolated system
non-isolated system

conservation of energy
power
efficiency

Key Equations

$W = (F \cos \theta)\Delta d$

$\Delta E_p = mg\Delta h$

$E_p = mgh$

$E_p = \dfrac{1}{2}kx^2$

$E_k = \dfrac{1}{2}mv^2$

$W = \Delta E_k + \Delta E_p$

$E_m = E_k + E_p$

$P = \dfrac{W}{\Delta t} = \dfrac{\Delta E}{\Delta t}$

Conceptual Overview

The concept map below summarizes many of the concepts and equations in this chapter. Copy and complete the map to produce a full summary of the chapter.

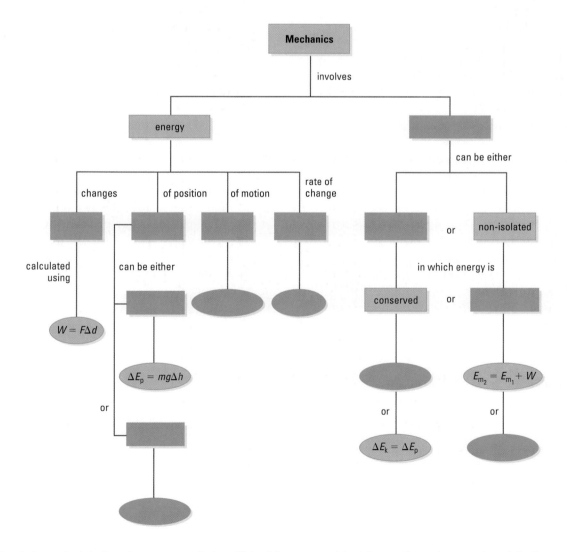

Knowledge

1. (6.1) (a) When a force acts on an object to do work, why do you need to know the angle between the direction of the force and the direction of the displacement?

   (b) If you know how the magnitude of a force changes while it acts over a displacement, how can you find the amount of work it does?

   (c) Describe the nature of the energy transfers for the work done on a bungee jumper from the time he leaps off the platform until his velocity is zero at the lowest point of his jump.

   (d) Two students calculate the gravitational potential energy of a mass resting on a shelf. One student calculates that it has 12.0 J of energy while the other calculates the gravitational potential energy to be 35.0 J. Is it possible that they are both right? Explain.

   (e) Two masses, A and B, are at rest on a horizontal frictionless surface. Mass A is twice as great as mass B. The same force acts on these masses over the same displacement. Which mass will have the greater (i) speed, and (ii) kinetic energy at the end of the displacement? Explain.

   (f) Many fitness facilities have treadmills as exercise machines. Is running on a treadmill work since the runner is not really moving?

   (g) Explain why it takes less force to push a cart up an inclined plane onto a platform than it does to lift the cart straight up from the floor. Assume you are able to move the cart by either method. Does it also take less work to lift it or to roll it up the plane?

   (h) An object sits on a tabletop. In terms of describing the object's gravitational potential energy, which reference point is better: the ground outside the room, the floor of the room, or the tabletop?

2. (6.2) (a) What is the effect of the work done by a net force?

   (b) If a force acts upward on an object, does all the work done by this force become potential energy?

   (c) What forms of energy are considered to be part of mechanical energy?

   (d) Can two people calculate the mechanical energy of an object and get two different correct answers? Explain.

3. (6.3) (a) Explain why the force of gravity but not the force of friction is called a conservative force.

   (b) An ideal spring is one where no energy is lost to internal friction. Is the force exerted by the spring considered a conservative force? Explain. Is a mass that is oscillating up and down on the end of an ideal spring a good approximation of an isolated system?

   (c) Since no system on Earth is truly an isolated system, why is it advantageous to assume that a system is isolated?

   (d) A truly isolated system does not exist on Earth. How does that affect the fundamental principle of conservation of energy?

   (e) If a system is not isolated, how can one calculate the change in mechanical energy in the system?

   (f) The mechanical energy of a system is measured at two different times and is the same each time. Is this an isolated system? Explain.

4. (6.4) (a) An elevator takes 2.50 min to travel from the ground floor to the 10th floor of an apartment block. The tenants want the landlord to increase the speed of the elevator but the landlord argues that speeding up the elevator means that it will need to work harder and that would take more energy. Is he correct? Explain.

   (b) The transmission of an automobile allows the work done in the engine to be transmitted to the wheels. For a given power output by the engine, the wheels are not rotated as fast by a low gear as they are by a high gear. What advantage does having gears give the driver of a car?

Applications

5. What is the change in kinetic energy if a net force of 3.80×10^3 N [0°] acts on a mass while it undergoes a displacement of 95.0 m [335°]?

6. For gravitational potential energy, when the height doubles so does the potential energy. However, for elastic potential energy, if the stretch of the spring doubles, the energy does not.

   (a) How does the stored elastic potential energy change if the stretch doubles?

   (b) Explain in terms of force-position graphs for gravitational and elastic potential energies why this happens.

7. The figure below shows the graph of the force as a function of displacement for an elastic spring stretched horizontally 25.0 cm from its equilibrium position. A mass of 0.400 kg is attached to the spring and released. If the mass is sliding on a horizontal frictionless surface, what is the speed of the mass when the spring has contracted to (a) 10.0 cm from its equilibrium position, and (b) its equilibrium position?

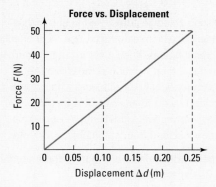

Force vs. Displacement

▲ Graph for question 7

8. A bungee jumper with a mass of 65.0 kg leaps from a bridge. At the lowest point of the jump he is 30.0 m below the point from which the jump began. If, at equilibrium, the bungee cord is 15.0 m long, what is the elastic constant for the cord? **HINT:** Assume an isolated system. At the lowest point the bungee cord must convert all of the jumper's lost gravitational potential energy into elastic potential energy in the cord.

9. A motorcycle stuntman wants to jump over a line of city buses. He builds a takeoff ramp that has a slope of 20°, with its end 3.20 m above the ground. The combined mass of the motorcycle and rider is 185 kg. To clear the buses, the cyclist needs to be travelling 144 km/h when he leaves the end of the ramp. How high above the ground is the motorcycle at its highest point?

10. A skydiver reaches a maximum speed (or terminal velocity) of 36.0 m/s due to the force of air resistance. If the diver has a mass of 65.0 kg, what is the power output of the air resistance acting on him?

Extensions

11. Even when making short flights, jets climb to altitudes of about 10 000 m. Gaining altitude requires a great expenditure of fuel. Prepare a short research report to explain the advantages and disadvantages of travelling at these altitudes.

Consolidate Your Understanding

You have been hired to tutor a student on the topics in this chapter. Describe how you would answer the questions below. In each instance, include an example.

1. What is the difference between work and energy?

2. When an object moves up a hill, how does the length of the hill affect the increase in the gravitational potential energy?

3. If a cart, at rest, is allowed to coast from the top of a hill to the bottom, is the kinetic energy at the bottom of the hill always equal to the loss in gravitational potential energy?

4. A given force is to act on a block to accelerate it from rest as it slides up the length of an inclined plane. Using accurate spring balances and rulers, how could you gather data to enable you to calculate, with reasonable accuracy, the kinetic energy of the block when it reaches the top of the incline? You may not use timing devices.

5. What is the difference between an isolated and a non-isolated system in terms of work and energy?

6. What factor of a car's motion is most directly affected by the power of its engine?

Think About It

Review the answers you gave to the questions in Think About It on page 291. How would you change these answers?

e **TEST**

To check your understanding of energy, work, and power, follow the eTest links at www.pearsoned.ca/school/physicssource.

Building a Persuader Apparatus

Scenario

It is 1965. Seatbelts are oddities used only by airline passengers at takeoff and landings. The term "airbag" hasn't even been invented. Speed limits and traffic deaths are on the rise. Imagine that you are part of a team of engineers who design and build automobiles. Your company challenges you to design and build a model that can be used to convince its shareholders and the public that it is possible to build much safer automobiles. The automobile company has challenged your design team to produce safety features for its vehicles that will allow its passengers to survive crashes under severe conditions. Your team must determine how best to protect the passenger while, at the same time, keeping the size and mass of the car itself to reasonable proportions. Your presentation to the company will be used to persuade them of the benefits of your design. Finally, your report should persuade the public of the advantages of using the safety equipment you recommend for automobiles.

Planning

Your team should consist of three to five members. Your first task is to formulate your research question. This done, you will need to identify the assumptions about the nature of the collisions in which your vehicle may be involved. Since not all collisions may be head-on, your passenger (a fresh raw egg) should survive unscathed from a wide variety of crash scenarios. While all team members should be active participants in all aspects of the project, you should identify and draw on any special talents of your team. Create a team structure that assigns responsibilities such as team manager, data analyst, and record keeper. Begin by brainstorming possible design features and research strategies. Where might you find information on existing safety features? Which features are the most effective? How will you compare results for the various types of crashes? You may wish to draw on information from all topics in this course to improve the safety features of your vehicle. Create timelines for all phases of the project. Create a report that incorporates written, graphic, and photographic analysis of your project.

Materials

- material for construction of the vehicle
- mass-measuring equipment
- equipment to provide known energy crash conditions
- egg passengers
- digital camera
- computer

Assessing Results

Assess the success of your project based on a rubric* designed in class that considers:
- research strategies
- thoroughness of the experimental design
- effectiveness of the experimental technique
- effectiveness of the team's public presentation

Procedure

1. Research existing safety features used in automotive production. Identify which features are the most effective in reducing crash injuries. Keep a record of the sources of your information. If information comes from the Internet, be sure to identify the site, and who sponsors the information. Be alert to Internet sites that may contain biased information. Identify the most common types of injuries resulting from automobile accidents.

2. Design the persuader vehicle and gather the materials required for its construction.

3. Design the experiment that your team will use to test the effectiveness of your vehicle's design. Make sure that your experimental design makes it possible to accurately compare the energy of the vehicle when it is involved in different crash scenarios.

⚠️ **CAUTION: Your vehicle will need to gain considerable energy, which may or may not result in unexpected behaviour when it crashes. Take proper precautions to ensure that the vehicle path is clear during trials.**

4. Test your vehicle's safety features under a variety of crash conditions. Assess how effective your system is when it is involved in crashes happening from different directions.

5. Prepare a report using an audiovisual format that will dramatically emphasize for your audience the value of the safety features that you recommend.

Thinking Further

Write a short appendix to your report (two or three paragraphs) to identify possible directions that future research might take to make automobile travel even safer. Suggest steps that government, technology, and industry should take in making automobile travel safer.

*Note: Your instructor will assess the project using a similar assessment rubric.

Unit Concepts and Skills: Quick Reference

Concepts	Summary	Resources and Skill Building
Chapter 5	**Newton's laws can explain circular motion.**	
	5.1 Defining Circular Motion	
Speed and velocity	The velocity of an object moving with circular motion is tangent to the circle and 90° to the radial line.	Figures 5.3–5.6, 5.8–5.11, 5.13; QuickLab 5-1; Inquiry Lab 5-2
Centripetal acceleration and force	Centripetal acceleration and centripetal force are both directed toward the centre of the circle.	Figures 5.8–5.11; Table 5.2; eSIM
	5.2 Circular Motion and Newton's Laws	
Velocity and circular motion	The velocity of circular motion can be determined by dividing the circumference by the period.	Example 5.2; Minds On
Centripetal acceleration	The centripetal acceleration of an object is determined by the velocity squared divided by the radius.	Figures 5.18–5.20; Example 5.3
Centripetal force — a horizontal system in circular motion	Newton's second law states $F = ma$ and can be applied to centripetal acceleration. A car making a turn experiences a centripetal acceleration and force that is created by the force of friction between the tires and the road.	Inquiry Lab 5-3; eTECH; Example 5.4; Figures 5.24, 5.25
Centripetal force — a vertical system in circular motion	The minimum speed necessary to move an object through a vertical loop equates centripetal force with gravitational force. Centripetal force can be equated to the gravitational force for planetary objects.	Figures 5.27–5.30; eTECH; Example 5.5; eSIM
Centripetal force — acceleration and frequency	Centripetal acceleration and force can be determined using period and frequency instead of speed.	Figures 5.32–5.34; Example 5.7
	5.3 Satellites and Celestial Bodies in Circular Motion	
Kepler's laws	Kepler formulated three laws that explained the motion of planets in the solar system.	Figures 5.36–5.38; Tables 5.4–5.6; Examples 5.8, 5.9; eSIM; Design a Lab 5-4
Newton's version of Kepler's third law	Newton recognized the reason that Kepler's laws were correct: $F_g = F_c$ for Earth–Moon system. He also found a way to determine the mass of an object from the period of a celestial body orbiting it.	Figures 5.41, 5.42; Examples 5.10, 5.11; eTECH
Orbital perturbations	The discovery of Uranus and Pluto occurred because of the apparent disturbances in the orbit of the planets. Extrasolar planets have been discovered by examining perturbations in stars' movements.	Then, Now, and Future; Figures 5.46, 5.47
Artificial satellites	Humans have placed a variety of artificial satellites into orbit to meet society's needs.	5-5 Decision-Making Analysis; Figures 5.48–5.51
Chapter 6	**In an isolated system, energy is transferred from one object to another whenever work is done.**	
	6.1 Work and Energy	
Work	Work is the transfer of energy that occurs when a force acts over a displacement. It is a scalar quantity measured in joules. (1 J = 1 N·m)	Example 6.1
Potential energy	Potential energy is the energy a body has because of its position or configuration. It is a scalar quantity measured in joules.	QuickLab 6-1; Example 6.2; Example 6.3; Example 6.4
Kinetic energy	Kinetic energy is the energy a body has because of its motion. It is a scalar quantity measured in joules.	QuickLab 6-1; Example 6.5; Example 6.6
	6.2 Mechanical Energy	
Work-energy theorem	Work done by a net force causes a change in kinetic energy.	Example 6.7
	The work–energy theorem states that the work done on a system is equal to the sum of the changes in the potential and kinetic energies.	Example 6.7
Mechanical energy	Mechanical energy is the sum of the potential and kinetic energies.	Example 6.8
	6.3 Mechanical Energy in Isolated and Non-isolated Systems	
Isolated systems	The law of conservation of energy states that in an isolated system, the mechanical energy is constant.	Example 6.9; Example 6.10
Conservation of energy	A simple pendulum is a good approximation of an isolated system in which energy is conserved.	Inquiry Lab 6-2
Conservative forces	A conservative force does not affect the mechanical energy of a system.	Example 6.10; Inquiry Lab 6-2
Non-isolated systems	In non-isolated systems, the mechanical energy may change due to the action of non-conservative forces.	Design a Lab 6-3
	6.4 Work and Power	
Power	Power is defined as the rate of doing work. Power is calculated by finding the ratio of the work done to the time required to do the work. It is measured in watts. (1 W = 1 J/s)	Example 6.11; Inquiry Lab 6-4; Example 6.12
	Power may be calculated by taking the product of the force doing the work and the average speed.	Problem-Solving Lab 6-5

Vocabulary

1. Using your own words, define these terms:
   artificial satellite
   axis of rotation
   axle
   centripetal acceleration
   centripetal force
   conservation of energy
   conservative force
   cycle
   eccentricity
   efficiency
   elastic potential energy
   ellipse
   energy
   frequency
   gravitational potential energy
   isolated system
   Kepler's constant
   Kepler's laws
   kinetic energy
   mean orbital radius
   mechanical energy
   non-isolated system
   orbital period
   orbital perturbations
   period
   potential energy
   power
   reference point
   revolution
   rpm
   satellite
   uniform circular motion
   work
   work-energy theorem

Knowledge

CHAPTER 5

2. An object is moving in a circular path with a uniform centripetal acceleration that doesn't change. What will happen to the velocity if the radius is reduced?

3. The centripetal acceleration of a car as it goes around a turn is inward, but the car will not skid in that direction if it is moving too quickly. Explain.

4. A bucket of water is spun in a vertical circle on the end of a rope.
   (a) Explain what force or forces act as the centripetal force when the bucket is in the highest position.
   (b) In which position is the rope most likely to break? Why?

5. Explain why centripetal force is inward when the force acting on your hand as you spin an object in a circular path is outward.

6. Using what you have learned about the force of gravity and circular motion, provide a thorough explanation why centripetal force changes for planets orbiting the Sun.

7. A roller coaster goes around a vertical loop with just enough velocity to keep it on the track.
   (a) In which position or positions is the force of gravity the centripetal force? Explain.
   (b) In which position or positions is there a force exerted on the track by the roller coaster? Explain.
   (c) Using the equation $F_g = mg$ and equation 6 from Chapter 5 on page 256, show why mass does not affect the speed required for the roller coaster to successfully enter and exit the loop as shown in the diagram below.

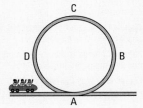

8. What is the relationship between frequency and radius for a rotating disc?

9. The motor of a table saw is rated for its horsepower and rotational frequency. Explain why rotational frequency is used instead of rotational speed.

10. What physical quantities must be known for the mass of Earth to be determined?

11. Kepler showed that planets follow elliptical orbits.
    (a) Which planet has the least elliptical orbit?
    (b) Which planet's semi-major axis is the closest in length to its semi-minor axis?

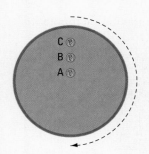

12. Three identical coins are placed on a rotating platter as shown. As the frequency of rotation increases, identify which coin will begin to slide off first. Explain your answer.

13. Briefly explain how Neptune was discovered. Use the terms orbital perturbation, force of gravity, and orbital velocity in your explanation.

14. Your friend argues that Neptune would not have been discovered as soon as it was if Neptune were a much smaller planet and Uranus much bigger. Is she right? Defend your answer.

15. What difficulties do astronomers face when searching for extrasolar planets that might have life as we know it?

CHAPTER 6

16. Express a joule in terms of kilograms, metres, and seconds.

17. If work is a scalar quantity, why is it affected by the directions of the force and displacement?

18. What happens to an object's gravitational potential energy when it is in free fall?

19. Explain why doubling the speed of an object does not result in a doubling of its kinetic energy.

20. A large mass and a small mass with the same kinetic energy are sliding on a horizontal frictionless surface. If forces of equal magnitude act on each of these bodies to bring them to rest, which one will stop in the shorter distance? Explain.

21. Describe the energy changes of a roller coaster car from the time when it is just coming over the crest of one hill until it arrives at the crest of the next hill.

22. A cart is pulled up an inclined plane by a force that is just large enough to keep the cart moving without a change in its speed. Is this an isolated system? Explain why or why not. Is the force used to move the cart up the incline a conservative force?

23. A cart at the top of an inclined plane is allowed to roll down the plane. Under what conditions can this system be considered isolated? If the conditions that make this an isolated system do not exist, is the force that moves the cart down the plane still considered a conservative force? Explain.

24. A slingshot is used to propel a stone vertically upward. Describe the energy changes that are involved from the time the stone is placed in the slingshot until the stone reaches its maximum height.

25. If a force that acts on an object results in a change in the object's kinetic energy, what can be said about the nature of this force?

26. How do you calculate work from a force-displacement graph?

27. According to the work-energy theorem, how much work is done on an isolated system?

28. Does power affect the amount of work you are able to do? Explain why or why not.

Applications

29. Electrons in an electric (AC) circuit vibrate at 60 Hz. What is their period?

30. A cell phone is set to vibrate when it rings. It vibrates with a period of 0.0160 s. What is the frequency of the ring?

31. A toy top spins at 300.0 rpm. What is the frequency (in Hz) and the period of the top?

32. The Moon orbits Earth once every 27.3 days at a mean orbital radius of 3.844×10^5 km. What is its speed?

33. A child sits in a pretend airplane on a ride at an amusement park. The airplane is at the end of a long arm that moves in a circular path with a radius of 4.0 m at a speed of 1.57 m/s. What is the period of the ride?

34. A person sliding down a water slide at a speed of 5.56 m/s encounters a turn with a radius of 10.0 m. Determine the acceleration that he experiences in the turn.

35. A pilot of a jet airplane makes a sharp turn to create an acceleration of 4.00 times the acceleration of gravity. If the turn has a radius of 500.0 m, what is the speed of the plane?

36. A cork (m = 2.88 g) is caught in a small whirlpool created in the basin of a sink. What is the centripetal force acting on the cork, if its speed is 0.314 m/s at a radius of 4.00 cm?

37. When braking to a stop, the maximum force that friction exerts on a 1250-kg auto is 3200 N.
  (a) If the original speed of the auto is 12.0 m/s, what is the minimum stopping distance?
  (b) If the speed of the car were twice as great, how would that affect the minimum stopping distance?

38. A force of 250 N [up] is applied to a mass of 15.0 kg over a displacement of 9.60 m [up].

(a) How much work does the force do on the mass?

(b) What is the change in gravitational potential energy?

(c) If it is an isolated system, explain the difference between the answers for (a) and (b).

39. A car with a mass of 2.00×10^3 kg is travelling at a velocity of 15.0 m/s [0°] on a horizontal stretch of highway. The driver presses on the accelerator so that the force propelling the car forward is increased to 3.30×10^3 N [0°]. The force acts over a displacement of 55.0 m [0°] during which force of friction on the car is 5.00×10^2 N in magnitude.

(a) Draw a free-body diagram to analyze the forces acting on the car. What is the net force on the car?

(b) What is the work done by net force over the displacement?

(c) What is the final kinetic energy of the car?

(d) What is the final speed of the car?

40. A block with a mass of 0.800 kg is initially at rest on a frictionless inclined plane. A force of 5.00 N, applied parallel to the inclined plane, moves the block a distance of 4.50 m up the plane. If, at the end of the effort, the block has a speed of 6.00 m/s up the incline, what is the change in height through which it moved?

41. A varying force acts on a 25.0-kg mass over a displacement as shown in the graph below. The mass has an initial velocity of 12.0 m/s [0°]. Recall that the area of a force-displacement graph is equivalent to the work done by the force.

(a) What is the work that the force did on the mass?

(b) What is the final speed of the mass?

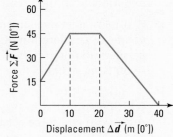

42. In the following diagram, block A is at rest on a frictionless inclined plane. It is attached to block B by a light cord over a frictionless pulley. Block A has a mass of 4.50 kg and B has a mass of 5.50 kg. When they are released, block A moves up the incline so that after it has moved a distance of 1.50 m along the incline it has a speed of 3.00 m/s.

(a) What is the change in gravitational potential energy for block A?

(b) What was the change in height through which block A moved?

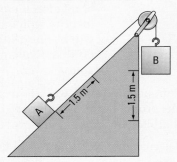

43. For question 42, draw the graph that shows the potential, kinetic, and mechanical energies for the system as a function of the displacement assuming (a) there is no friction, (b) there is friction, but block A still accelerates up the hill.

44. A pendulum bob with a mass of 0.750 kg is initially at rest at its equilibrium position. You give the bob a push so that when it is at a height of 0.150 m above its equilibrium position it is moving at a speed of 2.00 m/s.

(a) How much work did you do on the bob?

(b) If you pushed on the bob with a force of 40.0 N parallel to the displacement, how far did you push it?

45. A billiard ball with a speed of 2.00 m/s strikes a second ball initially at rest. After the collision, the first ball is moving at a speed of 1.50 m/s. If this is an elastic collision (i.e., energy is conserved), what is the speed of the second ball after the collision? Assume that the balls have identical masses of 0.200 kg.

46. A cannon ball ($m = 3.00$ kg) is fired at a velocity of 280 m/s at an angle of 20° above the horizontal. The cannon is on a cliff that is 450 m above the ocean.

(a) What is the mechanical energy of the cannon ball relative to the base of the cliff?

(b) What is the greatest height above the ocean that the cannon ball reaches?

(c) What is the speed of the cannon ball when it lands in the ocean?

47. A Styrofoam™ ball is dropped from a height of 5.00 m. The mass of the ball is 0.200 kg. When the ball hits the ground it has a speed of 3.00 m/s.

(a) What change in mechanical energy does the ball undergo while it falls?

(b) What is the average force that air friction exerted on the falling ball?

48. What is the average power output if an engine lifts a 250-kg mass a distance of 30.0 m in 20.0 s?

49. What is the effective power required to maintain a constant speed of 108 km/h if the force opposing the motion is 540 N in magnitude?

50. An airplane engine has an effective power output of 150 kW. What will be the speed of the plane if the drag (air friction opposing the motion of the plane) exerts a force of 2.50×10^3 N?

Extensions

51. A 90.9-kg gymnast swings around a horizontal bar in a vertical circle. When he is directly over top of the bar, his arms experience a tug of 108.18 N. What is the velocity of his body in this position? (Assume that the gymnast's mass is centred 1.20 m from the bar.)

52. Another solar system, with three planets circling a star, exists in a galaxy far far away. One planet, Tatooine, orbits the star with the period of 6.31×10^7 s and a radius of 3.00×10^{11} m. Tatooine has a moon that orbits it with a period of 1.73×10^6 s at a radius of 6.00×10^8 m.
(a) What is the mass of Tatooine's star?
(b) What is the mass of Tatooine?
(c) What is the speed of Tatooine's moon?

53. A soil-moving machine called a bucket wheel loader has a large metallic wheel with a radius of 3.05 m that has many scoops attached to it. The scoops are designed to dig into the ground and lift soil out as the wheel turns around. If the wheel turns with a frequency of 0.270 Hz, will the soil fall out of a scoop when it gets to the top of the wheel?

54. Three blocks (A, B, and C), with masses 6.00 kg, 4.00 kg, and 2.00 kg, respectively, are initially at rest on a horizontal frictionless surface as shown in diagram (a) on the right. A force of 48.0 N [90°] acts on block A over a displacement of 7.50 m [90°]. Block A is connected to block B by a string that is 1.00 m long and block B is connected to block C by a string that is 1.50 m long. Initially, the three blocks are touching each other. As the blocks move and the strings become taut, they end up as shown in diagram (b). Is this an isolated or a non-isolated system? Explain.
(a) What is the speed of the blocks after the force has acted for the full 7.50 m?
(b) What is the speed of block A when the force has acted over a displacement of 2.00 m?
Hint: Find the work done by the force.

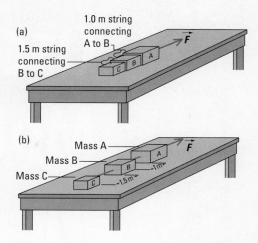

Skills Practice

55. Your cousin doesn't understand how a satellite can stay in orbit without falling toward Earth. Using the knowledge you have gained from this unit, provide a short explanation.

56. Figure 6.21 on page 303 shows the impact crater for a meteor that landed in Arizona. How widespread is the evidence of meteors striking Earth? Where is the impact crater closest to where you live? Do Internet research to identify locations of impact craters in Alberta and Canada. On a map of Alberta, show the location of meteor impacts. What clues on maps show meteor landings? For each crater, identify how much kinetic energy the meteor would have had when it struck Earth.

57. Explain how you would experiment to determine the quantity of external work done on a system for a cart accelerating down an inclined plane. Could you confirm this quantity by measuring forces?

Self-assessment

58. Describe to a classmate one misconception you had about circular motion before studying this unit. Explain what you know about this concept now.

59. Describe to a classmate the relationship between the roles of science and technology in the development of new energy resources.

60. Can science provide solutions to all of the problems associated with the impact of energy consumption on the environment? Give reasons for your answer.

 e **TEST**

To check your understanding of circular motion, work, and energy, follow the eTest links at www.pearsoned.ca/school/physicssource.

UNIT

IV

Oscillatory Motion and Mechanical Waves

An earthquake more than two thousand kilometres away sent this tsunami speeding across the Indian Ocean. Waves, a form of simple harmonic oscillations, can efficiently transport incredible amounts of energy over great distances. How does a wave move through its medium? How does understanding simple harmonic motion help us understand how waves transport energy?

Unit at a Glance

Unit Themes and Emphases

- Change, Energy, and Matter
- Scientific Inquiry
- Nature of Science

Focussing Questions

As you study this unit, consider these questions:
- Where do we observe oscillatory motion?
- How do mechanical waves transmit energy?
- How can an understanding of the natural world improve how society, technology, and the environment interact?

Unit Project

- By the time you complete this unit, you will have the knowledge and skill to research earthquakes, the nature of earthquake shock waves, and the use of the Richter scale to rate earthquake intensity. On completion of your research, you will demonstrate the operation of a seismograph.

e WEB

To learn more about earthquakes and their environmental effects, follow the links at www.pearsoned.ca/school/physicssource.

Oscillatory motion requires a set of conditions.

On October 15, 1997, NASA launched the Cassini-Huygens space probe toward Saturn — a distance of 1 500 000 000 km from Earth. The probe's flight path took it by Venus twice, then Earth, and finally past Jupiter on its way to Saturn. This route was planned so that, as the probe approached each planet, it would be accelerated by the planet's gravitational force. Each time, it picked up more speed that would get it to Saturn more quickly (Figure 7.1). Recall from Chapter 4 that increasing the probe's speed this way is referred to as gravity assist.

The entire journey of 3 500 000 000 km took seven years. For this incredible feat to succeed, scientists had to know where the planets would be seven years in the future. How could they do this? They relied on the fact that planets follow predictable paths around the Sun. Nature is full of examples of repetitive, predictable motion. Water waves, a plucked guitar string, the orbits of planets, and even a bumblebee flapping its wings are just a few.

In this chapter, you will examine oscillatory motion. Oscillatory motion is a slightly different form of motion from the circular motion you studied in Chapter 5. You will better understand why bungee jumpers experience the greatest pull of the bungee cord when they are at the bottom of a fall and why trees sway in the wind. You may notice the physics of many objects that move with oscillatory motion and gain a new insight into the wonders of the natural world.

▲ **Figure 7.1** The Cassini-Huygens probe successfully orbits Saturn after a seven-year journey through the solar system.

Oscillatory Motion of Toys

Problem

What is the time taken by one complete back-and-forth motion of a toy?

Materials

several different wind-up toys, such as:
- swimming frog
- hopping toy
- monkey with cymbals
- walking toy

yo-yo

stopwatch (or wristwatch with a second hand)

▲ **Figure 7.2**

Procedure

1. Fully wind the spring mechanism of one of the toys.

2. Release the winding knob and start your stopwatch.

3. Count the number of complete back-and-forth movements the toy makes in 10 s. These back-and-forth movements are called oscillations.

4. Record the number of oscillations made by the toy.

5. Repeat steps 1 to 4 for each toy. For the yo-yo, first achieve a steady up-and-down rhythm. Then do steps 3 and 4, counting the up-and-down motions. This type of repetitive movement is also an oscillation.

Questions

1. In what ways are the motions of all the toys similar?

2. Divide the number of oscillations of each toy by the time. Be sure to retain the units in your answer. What does this number represent? (Hint: Look at the units of the answer.)

3. Which toy had the most oscillations per second? Which had the least?

4. Divide the time (10 s) by the number of oscillations for each toy. Be sure to retain the units in your answer. How long is the interval of oscillation of each toy?

5. Which toy had the longest time for one oscillation? Which had the shortest time?

Think About It

1. How are the oscillations per second and the time for one oscillation related?

2. What do you think influences the number of oscillations per second of the toys you tested?

Discuss your answers in a small group and record them for later reference. As you complete each section of this chapter, review your answers to these questions. Note any changes to your ideas.

7.1 Period and Frequency

On a warm summer day in your backyard, you can probably hear bees buzzing around, even if they are a few metres away. That distinctive sound is caused by the very fast, repetitive up-and-down motion of the bees' wings (Figure 7.3).

Take a closer look at the bumblebee. The motion of a bee's wings repeats at regular intervals. Imagine that you can examine the bee flying through the air. If you start your observation when its wings are at the highest point (Figure 7.4(a)), you see them move down to their lowest point (Figure 7.4(c)), then back up again. When the wings are in the same position as when they started (Figure 7.4(e)), one complete **oscillation** has occurred. An oscillation is a repetitive back-and-forth motion. One complete oscillation is called a **cycle**.

▲ **Figure 7.3** The wings of a bee in flight make a droning sound because of their motion.

▲ **Figure 7.4** The bee's wings make one full cycle from (a) to (e). The time for this motion is called the period.

The time required for the wings to make one complete oscillation is the period (*T*). If the period of each cycle remains constant, then the wings are moving up and down with **oscillatory motion**. Recall from Chapter 5 that the number of oscillations per second is the frequency (*f*), measured in hertz (Hz). The equation for frequency and period is:

oscillatory motion: motion in which the period of each cycle is constant

$$f = \frac{1}{T} \tag{1}$$

Table 7.1 shows the period of a bee's wings as it hovers, along with other examples of periods.

▼ **Table 7.1** Periods of Common Items

Object	Period
Bumblebee wings	0.00500 s
Hummingbird wings	0.0128 s
Medical ultrasound technology	1×10^{-6} to 5×10^{-8} s
Middle C on a piano	0.0040 s
Electrical current in a house	0.0167 s

A piston in the engine of a car also undergoes oscillatory motion if it is moving up and down in equal intervals of time. The piston shown in Figure 7.5 moves from position (a) (its highest point) through (b) to position (c), where it is at its lowest point. It begins moving back up again through (d) to (e), where it returns to its highest position. The range of movement from (a) to (e) is one cycle. A single piston in a Formula 1 racecar can achieve a frequency of 300 cycles/second or 300 Hz (18 000 rpm). The piston makes 300 complete cycles in only 1 s. Conversely, the period of the piston, which is the time for one complete cycle, is the inverse of the frequency. It is a mere 0.003 s or about 100 times faster than the blink of an eye!

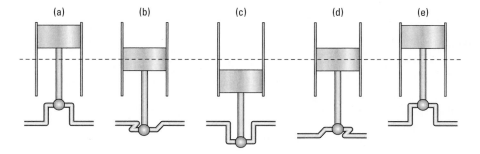

▲ **Figure 7.5**   The piston makes one complete cycle from positions (a) to (e). The time it takes to do this is its period. The number of times it does this in 1 s is its frequency.

Example 7.1

What is the frequency of an automobile engine where the pistons oscillate with a period of 0.0625 s?

Analysis and Solution

$$f = \frac{1}{T}$$

$$= \frac{1}{0.0625 \text{ s}}$$

$$= 16.0 \text{ Hz}$$

The frequency of the engine is 16.0 Hz.

Practice Problems

1. Earthquake waves that travel along Earth's surface can have periods of up to 5.00 minutes. What is their frequency?

2. A hummingbird can hover because it flaps its wings with a frequency of 78 Hz. What is the period of the wing's motion?

Answers

1. 3.33×10^{-3} Hz
2. 0.013 s

MINDS ON   Examples of Oscillatory Motion

Working with a partner or group, make a list of three or four natural or human-made objects that move with the fastest oscillatory motion that you can think of.

Make a similar list of objects that have very long periods of oscillatory motion. Beside each object estimate its period. The lists must not include the examples already mentioned. Be prepared to share your lists with the class.

Relating Period and Frequency

Your teacher may want to do this Inquiry Lab in the gym instead of the science lab.

Question

What is the relationship between the period and the frequency of a bouncing ball?

Hypothesis

Write a hypothesis that relates the period of the ball's bounce to its frequency. Remember to use an "if/then" statement.

Variables

The variables in this lab are the height of the bounce, period, and frequency. Read the procedure, then determine and label the controlled, manipulated, and responding variables.

Materials and Equipment

basketball	stopwatch
metre-stick	chair
tape	

Procedure

1. Copy Table 7.2 into your notes.

▼ **Table 7.2** Bounce, Period, and Frequency

Bounce Height (cm)	Time for 20 Bounces (s)	Period (s/bounce)	Frequency (bounces/s)
50			
75			
100			
125			
150			

2. Find a convenient place to bounce the basketball near the wall. Using the metre-stick, place tape at heights of 50, 75, 100, 125, and 150 cm. Mark the heights on the tape.

3. Using just a flick of the wrist, begin bouncing the ball at the 50-cm mark. The top of the ball should just make it to this height at the top of its bounce. The ball should bounce with a steady rhythm.

4. While one person is bouncing the ball, another person uses the stopwatch to record the time taken for 20 complete bounces. Record this time in Table 7.2.

5. Reset the stopwatch and begin bouncing the ball to the next height up. Record the time for 20 complete bounces as you did in step 4. To achieve the proper height you may have to stand on a chair.

Analysis

1. Using the data for 20 bounces, determine the period and frequency for each height. Record the values in the table.

2. Draw a graph of frequency versus period. What type of relationship is this?

3. What effect did increasing the bounce height have on the period of a bounce?

In 7-2 Inquiry Lab, the ball will bounce much more quickly if it travels a shorter distance than a longer one. Bouncing quickly, it will make many bounces in a certain length of time, and its frequency will be high. By necessity, the amount of time it takes to make one bounce (its period) will be small. The next section explores oscillatory motion by going one step further. You will examine a type of oscillatory motion in which the range of motion is related to the applied force.

7.1 Check and Reflect

Knowledge

1. What conditions are necessary for oscillatory motion?

2. What two units are equivalent to cycles/s?

3. Define period and frequency.

4. How are period and frequency related?

5. Is it possible to increase the period of an oscillatory motion without increasing the frequency? Explain.

6. Give three examples of oscillatory motion that you have observed.

Applications

7. What is the frequency of a swimming water toy that makes 20.0 kicking motions per second?

8. Do the oars on a rowboat move with oscillatory motion? Explain.

9. Determine the frequency of a guitar string that oscillates with a period of 0.004 00 s.

10. A dragonfly beats its wings with the frequency of 38 Hz. What is the period of the wings?

11. A red-capped manakin is a bird that can flap its wings faster than a hummingbird, at 4800 beats per minute. What is the period of its wings?

12. A dog, happy to see its owner, wags its tail 2.50 times a second.

    (a) What is the period of the dog's tail?

    (b) How many wags of its tail will the dog make in 1 min?

Extensions

13. Use your library or the Internet to research the frequency of four to six different types of insect wings. Rank these insect wings from highest to lowest frequency.

14. Which of these motions is oscillatory? Explain.

    (a) a figure skater moving with a constant speed, performing a figure eight

    (b) a racecar racing on an oval track

    (c) your heartbeat

15. Many objects exhibit oscillatory motion. Use your library or the Internet to find the frequency or range of frequencies of the objects below.

    (a) fluorescent light bulbs

    (b) overhead power lines

    (c) human voice range

    (d) FM radio range

    (e) lowest note on a bass guitar

 e TEST

To check your understanding of period and frequency, follow the eTest links at www.pearsoned.ca/school/physicssource.

Simple Harmonic Motion

info **BIT**

A human eardrum can oscillate back and forth up to 20 000 times a second.

Children on swings can rise to heights that make their parents nervous. But to the children, the sensation of flying is thrilling. At what positions on a swing does a child move fastest? When does the child's motion stop?

Many objects that move with oscillatory motion exhibit the same properties that a child on a swing does. A piston moves up and down in the cylinder of an engine. At the extreme of its motion, it stops for a brief instant as it reverses direction and begins to accelerate downward until it reaches the bottom of its stroke. There it stops again and accelerates back, just as the swing does.

In order for the piston or a child on a swing to experience acceleration, it must experience a non-zero net force. This section explores how the net force affects an object's motion in a special type of oscillatory motion called simple harmonic motion.

7-3 QuickLab

Determining the Stiffness of a Spring

Problem

How does the force applied to a spring affect its displacement?

Materials

spring (with loops at each end)
spring scale
metre-stick
tape

Procedure

1 Make a two-column table in your notebook. Write "Displacement (cm)" as the heading of the left column, and "Force (N)" as the heading of the right column.

2 Determine the maximum length the spring can be pulled without permanently deforming it. If you are unsure, ask your instructor what the maximum displacement of the spring is. Divide this length by 5. This will give you an idea of the even increments through which to pull your spring.

3 Lie the spring flat on the surface of the table so that it lies in a straight line. Leave room for it to be stretched. Do not pull on the spring.

4 Fix one end of the spring to the desk by holding the loop at the end of the spring with your hand. Do not let this end of the spring move.

5 Attach the spring scale to the free end of the spring but do not pull on it yet.

6 Align the 0-cm mark of the metre-stick with the other end of the spring at exactly where the spring scale is attached. Tape the stick to the desk (Figure 7.6).

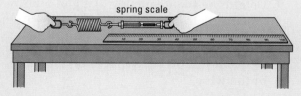
spring scale

▲ **Figure 7.6**

7 Pull the spring, using the spring scale, by the incremental distance determined in step 2. Record the values of the displacement and force in your table.

8 Repeat step 7, until you have five values each for displacement and force in your table.

9 Gently release the tension from the spring. Clean up and put away the equipment at your lab station.

Questions

1. Determine the controlled, manipulated, and responding variables.

2. Plot a graph of force versus displacement. Be sure to use a scale that allows you to use the full graph paper. Draw a line of best fit.

3. What kind of relationship does the line of best fit represent?

4. Determine the slope of the line. What are the units of the slope?

5. Extrapolate where the line intercepts the horizontal axis. Why does it intercept there?

 LAB

For a probeware activity, go to
www.pearsoned.ca/school/physicssource.

Hooke's Law

Robert Hooke (1635–1703) was a British scientist best remembered for using a microscope to discover plant cells, but his talents extended into many areas (Figure 7.7). He is credited with inventing the universal joint, which is used today on many mechanical devices (including cars); the iris diaphragm used to adjust the amount of light that enters a camera lens; the respirator to help people breathe; and the compound microscope, just to name a few of his inventions. In oscillatory motion, he is acknowledged for his work with elastic materials and the laws that apply to them (Figure 7.8).

In 1676, Hooke recognized that the more stress (force) applied to an object, the more strain (deformation) it undergoes. The stress can be applied in many ways. For example, an object can be squeezed, pulled, or twisted. Elastic materials will usually return to their original state after the stress has been removed. This will not occur if too much force is applied or if the force is applied for too long a time. In those cases, the object will become permanently deformed because it was strained beyond the material's ability to withstand the deformation. The point at which the material cannot be stressed farther, without permanent deformation, is called the elastic limit.

A spring is designed to be a very elastic device, and the deformation of a spring (whether it is stretched or compressed) is directly related to the force applied. The deformation of a spring is referred to as its displacement. From his observations, Hooke determined that the deformation (displacement) is proportional to the applied force. This can also be stated as "force varies directly with displacement." It can be written mathematically as:

$$F \propto x$$

This relationship is known as **Hooke's law**, which states:

The deformation of an object is proportional to the force causing the deformation.

▲ **Figure 7.7** Robert Hooke lived at the same time as Sir Isaac Newton.

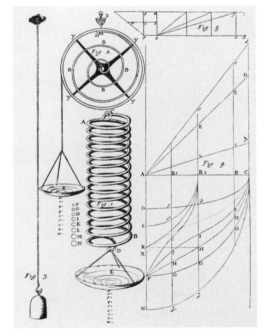

▲ **Figure 7.8** Hooke's notes show the simple devices he used to derive his law.

Figure 7.9(a) shows a spring that conforms to Hooke's law. It experiences a displacement that is proportional to the applied force. When no mass is applied to the spring, it is not compressed, and it is in its equilibrium position. As mass is added in increments of 10 g, the displacement (deformation) of the spring increases proportionally in increments of 5 cm, as shown in Figures 7.9(b), (c), and (d).

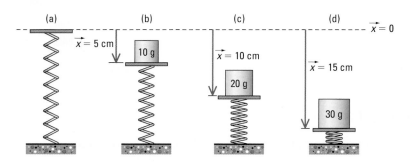

▲ **Figure 7.9** The spring pictured above conforms to Hooke's law. If the mass is doubled, the displacement will also double, as seen in (b) and (c). If the force (mass) is tripled, the displacement will triple, as seen in (b) and (d).

Each spring is different, so the force required to deform it will change from spring to spring. The stiffness of the spring, or **spring constant**, is represented by the letter k. Using k, you can write the equation for Hooke's law as:

$$\vec{F} = k\vec{x}$$

where $\vec{F}$ is the applied force that extends or compresses the spring, k is the spring constant, and $\vec{x}$ is the displacement.

Graphing Hooke's Law

Figure 7.10 shows how you can use a force meter to measure the applied force required to pull the spring from its equilibrium position to successively farther displacements. For simplicity, we'll assume that all the springs used in this text are "ideal" springs, meaning that they have no mass.

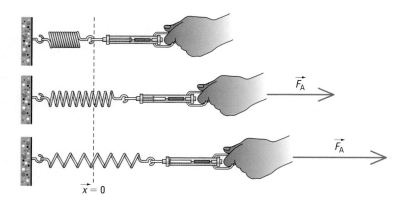

▲ **Figure 7.10** A force meter is attached to a spring that has not been stretched. The spring is then pulled through several displacements. Each time, the force required for the displacement is recorded.

Table 7.3 shows the data collected for this spring and the results plotted on the graph shown in Figure 7.11.

▼ **Table 7.3** Data for Figure 7.11

Displacement (m)	Force (N)
0.00	0.0
0.10	5.0
0.20	10.0
0.30	15.0
0.40	20.0

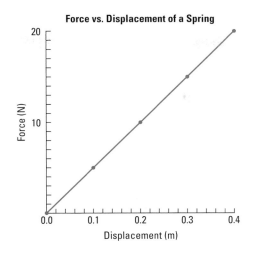

◄ **Figure 7.11** Graph of data from Table 7.3

Notice that the relationship is linear (a straight line), which means force is proportional to the displacement. The slope of the line can be determined by the following calculations:

$$\text{slope} = \frac{\Delta F}{\Delta x}$$

$$= \frac{(20.0 \text{ N} - 0.0 \text{ N})}{(0.40 \text{ m} - 0.00 \text{ m})}$$

$$= 5.0 \times 10^1 \text{ N/m}$$

This slope represents the spring constant k. The variables F and x are vectors but here we are calculating their scalar quantities so no vector arrows are used. In this example, an applied force of 50 N is needed to stretch (or compress) this spring 1 m. Therefore, the units for the spring constant are newtons per metre (N/m). By plotting the force-displacement graph of a spring and finding its slope, you can determine the spring constant of any ideal spring or spring that obeys Hooke's law.

Of the many objects that display elastic properties, springs are arguably the best to examine because they obey Hooke's law over large displacements. Steel cables are also elastic when stretched through relatively small displacements. Even concrete displays elastic properties and obeys Hooke's law through very small displacements.

In simpler terms, the property of elasticity gives a material the ability to absorb stress without breaking. This property is vital to consider when structural engineers and designers build load-bearing structures such as bridges and buildings (Figure 7.12). You will learn more about the factors that must be considered in bridge and building design later in this chapter.

▲ **Figure 7.12** The Jin Mao Tower in Shanghai, China, is 88 storeys high. Skyscrapers are built with elastic materials so they can sway in high winds and withstand the shaking of an earthquake. The main building materials for the Jin Mao Tower are concrete and steel.

Example 7.2

Practice Problems

1. A spring is stretched through several displacements and the force required is recorded. The data are shown below. Determine the spring constant of this spring by plotting a graph and finding the slope.

Displacement (m)	Force (N)
0.00	0.0
0.10	20.0
0.20	50.0
0.30	80.0
0.40	95.0
0.50	130.0
0.60	150.0

2. Determine the spring constant of a spring that has the force-displacement graph shown in Figure 7.15.

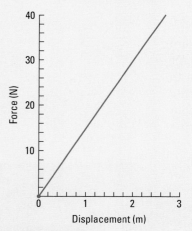

Force vs. Displacement

▲ **Figure 7.15**

Answers

1. 2.5×10^2 N/m
2. 15 N/m

To determine the spring constant of a spring, a student attaches a force meter to one end of the spring, and the other end to a wall as shown in Figure 7.13. She pulls the spring incrementally to successive displacements, and records the values of displacement and force in Table 7.4. Plot the values on a graph of force as a function of displacement. Using a line of best fit, determine the spring constant of the spring.

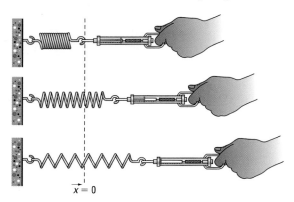

▲ **Figure 7.13**

Given

▼ **Table 7.4**   Data for Figure 7.14

Displacement (m)	Force (N)
0.00	0.00
0.10	0.25
0.20	0.35
0.30	0.55
0.40	0.85

Required

spring constant (k)

Analysis and Solution

Using the values from Table 7.4, plot the graph and draw a line of best fit.

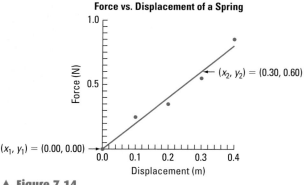

▲ **Figure 7.14**

The slope of the line gives the spring constant (k). Pick two points from the line and solve for the slope using the equation below. Note the points used in the equation are not data points.

$$\text{slope} = k = \frac{\Delta F}{\Delta x}$$

point 1 = (0.00, 0.00)

point 2 = (0.30, 0.60)

$$k = \frac{(0.60 \text{ N} - 0.00 \text{ N})}{(0.30 \text{ m} - 0.00 \text{ m})}$$

$$= 2.0 \text{ N/m}$$

Paraphrase
The spring constant of the spring is 2.0 N/m.

The Restoring Force

Imagine that you have applied a force to pull a spring to a positive displacement $(\vec{x})$ as shown in Figure 7.16. While you hold it there, the spring exerts an equal and opposite force in your hand, as described by Newton's third law in Chapter 3. However, this force is to the left, in the negative direction, and attempts to restore the spring to its equilibrium position. This force is called the **restoring force**.

restoring force: a force acting opposite to the displacement to move the object back to its equilibrium position

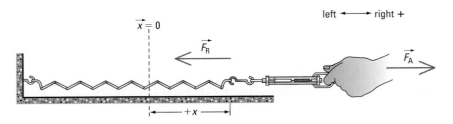

▲ **Figure 7.16** The spring system is pulled from its equilibrium position to displacement $\vec{x}$. The displacement is positive, but the restoring force is negative.

The restoring force always acts in a direction opposite to the displacement. Therefore, Hooke's law is properly written with a negative sign when representing the restoring force.

$$\vec{F} = -k\vec{x} \tag{2}$$

In this case, while the spring is held in this position, the applied force and the restoring force are equal, so the net force on the system is zero. In the next section, a mass will be attached to the spring and it will slide on a frictionless horizontal surface. The restoring force will be the only force in the system and will give rise to a repetitive back-and-forth motion called simple harmonic motion.

Example 7.3

A spring has a spring constant of 30.0 N/m. This spring is pulled to a distance of 1.50 m from equilibrium as shown in Figure 7.17. What is the restoring force?

Practice Problems

1. Determine the restoring force of a spring displaced 55.0 cm. The spring constant is 48.0 N/m.

2. A spring requires a force of 100.0 N to compress it a displacement of 4.0 cm. What is its spring constant?

Answers

1. −26.4 N

2. 2.5×10^3 N/m

Analysis and Solution

Draw a diagram to represent the stretched spring. Displacement to the right is positive, so the restoring force is negative because it is to the left, according to Hooke's law.

$$\vec{F} = -k\vec{x}$$

$$= \left(-30.0 \ \frac{N}{\cancel{m}}\right)(1.50 \ \cancel{m})$$

$$= -45.0 \ N$$

The restoring force is 45.0 N [left].

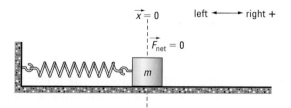

left ◄———► right +

▲ **Figure 7.17**

Simple Harmonic Motion of Horizontal Mass-spring Systems

Figure 7.18 shows a mass attached to an ideal spring on a horizontal frictionless surface. This simple apparatus can help you understand the relationship between the oscillating motion of an object and the effect the restoring force has on it.

◄ **Figure 7.18** The mass is in its equilibrium position ($\vec{x} = 0$) and is at rest. There is no net force acting on it. Any displacement of the mass to the right is positive, and to the left, negative.

e SIM

Observe a simulation of simple harmonic motion in a horizontal mass-spring system. Follow the eSIM links at www.pearsoned.ca/school/physicssource.

The position of the mass is represented by the variable $\vec{x}$ and is measured in metres. In Figure 7.18, there is no tension on the spring nor restoring force acting on the mass, because the mass is in its equilibrium position. Figure 7.19 shows how the restoring force affects the acceleration, displacement, and velocity of the mass when the mass is pulled to a positive displacement and released.

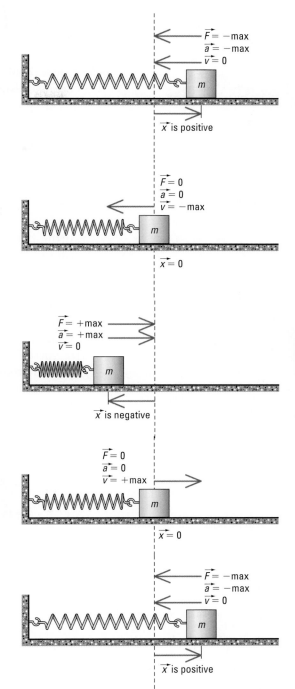

▶ **Figure 7.19(a)**   The mass has been pulled to its maximum displacement, called its **amplitude** (symbol *A*). When the mass is released, it begins oscillating with a displacement that never exceeds this distance. The greater the amplitude, the more energy a system has. In this diagram, $\vec{x} = A$.

At maximum displacement, the restoring force is at a maximum value, and therefore, so is the acceleration of the mass, as explained by Newton's second law ($\vec{F} = m\vec{a}$). When the mass is released, it accelerates from rest ($\vec{v} = 0$) toward its equilibrium position. As the mass approaches this position, its velocity is increasing. But the restoring force is decreasing because the spring is not stretched as much. Remember that force varies directly with displacement.

▶ **Figure 7.19(b)**   As the mass returns to its equilibrium position ($\vec{x} = 0$), it achieves its maximum velocity. It is moving toward the left (the negative direction), but the restoring force acting on it is zero because its displacement is zero.

The mass continues to move through the equilibrium position and begins to compress the spring. As it compresses the spring, the restoring force acts on the mass toward the right (the positive direction) to return it to its equilibrium position. This causes the mass to slow down, and its velocity approaches zero.

▶ **Figure 7.19(c)**   After passing through the equilibrium position, the mass experiences a restoring force that opposes its motion and brings it to a stop in this position. Its amplitude here is equal, but opposite to its amplitude when it started. At maximum displacement, the velocity is zero. The restoring force has reached its maximum value again. The restoring force is positive, and the displacement is negative. The restoring force again accelerates the mass toward equilibrium.

▶ **Figure 7.19(d)**   The mass has accelerated on its way to the equilibrium position where it is now. The restoring force and acceleration are again zero, and the velocity has achieved the maximum value toward the right. At equilibrium, the mass is moving to the right. It has attained the same velocity as in diagram (b), but in the opposite direction.

▶ **Figure 7.19(e)**   The mass has returned to the exact position where it was released. Again the restoring force and acceleration are negative and the velocity is zero. The oscillation will repeat again as it did in diagram (a).

In Figure 7.19(e), the mass has returned to the position where it started, and one full oscillation has occurred. Throughout its entire motion, the mass-spring system obeys Hooke's law. In other words, at any instant, the restoring force is proportional to the displacement of the mass. Any object that obeys Hooke's law undergoes **simple harmonic motion** (SHM). SHM is oscillatory motion where the restoring force is proportional to the displacement of the mass. An object that moves with SHM is called a **simple harmonic oscillator**.

simple harmonic motion:
oscillatory motion where the restoring force is proportional to the displacement of the mass

simple harmonic oscillator:
an object that moves with simple harmonic motion

Simple Harmonic Motion of Vertical Mass-spring Systems

Figure 7.20(a) shows a spring without a mass attached, anchored to a ceiling. Assume that the spring itself is massless, so it will not experience any displacement. When a mass is attached, the spring is pulled down and deforms as predicted by Hooke's law. The mass will come to rest when the downward force of gravity is equal to the upward pull (tension) of the spring (Figure 7.20(b)). The displacement of the spring depends on its spring constant. A weak spring has a small spring constant. It will stretch farther than a spring with a large spring constant.

In Figure 7.20(b), the net force (or restoring force) acting on the mass is zero. It is the result of the upward tension exerted by the spring balancing the downward force of gravity. This position is considered the equilibrium position and the displacement is zero.

If the mass is lifted to the position shown in Figure 7.21(a) and released, it will begin oscillating with simple harmonic motion. Its amplitude will equal its initial displacement. Regardless of the position of the mass, the force of gravity remains constant but the tension of the spring varies. In the position shown in Figures 7.21(b) and (d), the net (restoring) force is zero. This is where the spring's tension is equal and opposite to the force of gravity. In the position shown in Figure 7.21(c), the displacement of the spring is equal to the amplitude, and the tension exerted by the spring is at its maximum. The mass experiences the greatest restoring force, which acts upward.

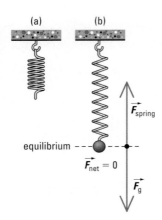

▲ **Figure 7.20** The spring in (a) has no mass attached. In (b), the spring stretches until the force exerted by the mass is equal and opposite to the force of gravity (b), and equilibrium is reached. The net force (or restoring force) is the vector sum of the force of gravity and the tension of the spring. In this case, it is zero.

▶ **Figure 7.21** The net force (the restoring force) is the vector sum of the upward force exerted by the spring and the downward force of gravity. The force of gravity is always negative and constant, but the force exerted by the spring varies according to the displacement, so the net force changes as the position of the mass changes from (a) to (e). The values of $\vec{F}_{net}$, $\vec{a}$, and $\vec{v}$ are identical to the horizontal mass-spring system.

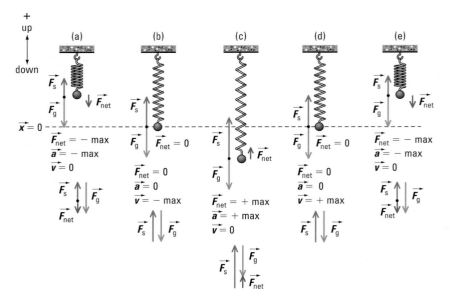

When the mass is below the equilibrium position, the upward force exerted by the tension of the spring is greater than the gravitational force. So the net force — and therefore the restoring force — is upward. Above the equilibrium position, the downward force of gravity exceeds the upward tension of the spring, and the restoring force is downward. The values of velocity, acceleration, and restoring force change in exactly the same way that they do in a horizontal mass-spring system.

Example 7.4

A spring is hung from a hook on a ceiling. When a mass of 510.0 g is attached to the spring, the spring stretches a distance of 0.500 m. What is the spring constant?

Given
$x = 0.500$ m
$m = 0.5100$ kg
$g = 9.81$ m/s²

Required
spring constant (k)

Analysis and Solution
Draw a diagram to show the mass-spring system and the forces acting on the mass.

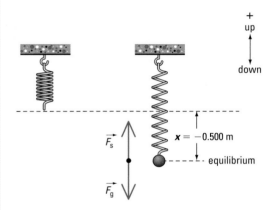

▲ **Figure 7.22**

The mass is not moving so the net force on the mass is zero. $\vec{F}_s$ and $\vec{F}_g$ are therefore equal in magnitude.

$kx = mg$

$k = \dfrac{mg}{x}$

$= \dfrac{(0.510 \text{ kg})\left(9.81 \dfrac{\text{m}}{\text{s}^2}\right)}{0.500 \text{ m}}$

$= 10.0$ N/m

Paraphrase
The spring constant is 10.0 N/m.

Practice Problems

1. Five people with a combined mass of 275.0 kg get into a car. The car's four springs are each compressed a distance of 5.00 cm. Determine the spring constant of the springs. Assume the mass is distributed evenly to each spring.

2. Two springs are hooked together and one end is attached to a ceiling. Spring A has a spring constant (k) of 25 N/m, and spring B has a spring constant (k) of 60 N/m. A mass weighing 40.0 N is attached to the free end of the spring system to pull it downward from the ceiling. What is the total displacement of the mass?

Answers
1. 1.35×10^4 N/m
2. −2.3 m

Examples of Simple Harmonic Motion

Provided the cord doesn't go slack, a person making a bungee jump will bob up and down with SHM, as shown in Figures 7.23 and 7.24. The cord acts as the spring and the person is the mass. The only difference is that the motion is vertical instead of horizontal.

The reeds of woodwind instruments, such as the clarinet, behave as simple harmonic oscillators. As the musician blows through the mouthpiece, the reed vibrates as predicted by the laws of SHM.

▲ **Figure 7.23** A bungee jumper experiences SHM as long as the cord does not go slack.

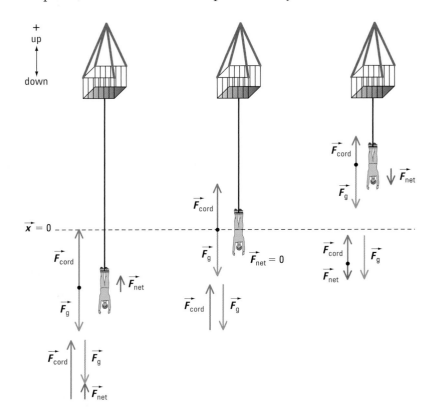

▲ **Figure 7.24** The bungee jumper bouncing up and down on the cord after a jump in (a) is a vertical mass-spring system. The cord acts as a spring and the jumper is the mass. The restoring (net) force acting on the bungee jumper is the same as it was for the vertical mass-spring system. When the oscillating finally stops, the jumper will come to a stop in the equilibrium position.

e WEB

After the first few oscillations following the jump, the bungee jumper oscillates with simple harmonic motion. To learn more about simple harmonic motion in the vertical direction, follow the links at www.pearsoned.ca/school/physicssource.

Once a simple harmonic oscillator is set in motion, it will slowly come to rest because of friction *unless* a force is continually applied. We will examine these conditions in section 7.4 on resonance.

SHM is repetitive and predictable, so we can state the following:

- The restoring force acts in the opposite direction to the displacement.
- At the extremes of SHM, the displacement is at its maximum and is referred to as the amplitude. At this point, force and acceleration are also at their maximum, and the velocity of the object is zero.
- At the equilibrium position, the force and acceleration are zero, and the velocity of the object is at its maximum.

Simple Harmonic Motion of a Pendulum

The Cassini-Huygens space probe featured at the beginning of this chapter is named in honour of two distinguished scientists. Among many other notable accomplishments, the Italian astronomer Giovanni Cassini (1625–1712) observed the planets Mars and Jupiter and measured their periods of rotation. Christiaan Huygens (1629–1695), a Dutch mathematician and astronomer, invented the first accurate clock. It used a swinging pendulum and was a revolution in clock making (Figure 7.25).

For small displacements, a swinging pendulum exhibits SHM. Since SHM is oscillatory, a clock mechanism that uses a pendulum to keep time could be very accurate. Up until Huygens's time, clocks were very inaccurate. Even the best clocks could be out by as much as 15 minutes a day. They used a series of special gears and weights that didn't always produce a uniform rate of rotation — a necessity for an accurate mechanical clock. Huygens recognized that if he could take advantage of the uniform oscillations of a pendulum, he could produce a much better clock. When completed, his pendulum clock was accurate to within one minute a day. This may not be very accurate by today's standards, but was easily the best of its time. Pendulum clocks became the standard in time keeping for the next 300 years.

Let's examine cases where an ideal pendulum swings through a small angle, as explained in Figure 7.26 (a) to (e). In this book, all pendulums are ideal. That is, we assume that the system is frictionless, and the entire mass of the pendulum is concentrated in the weight. While this is not possible in reality, it is reasonable to make these assumptions here because your studies are focussed on the motion of the pendulum.

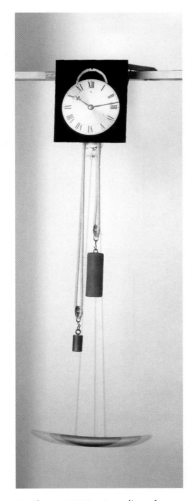

▲ **Figure 7.25** A replica of Huygens's pendulum clock

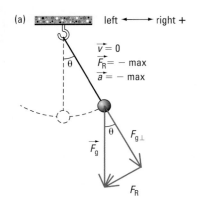

(a)

$\vec{v} = 0$
$\vec{F_R} = -\max$
$\vec{a} = -\max$

◄ **Figure 7.26(a)**   The mass (called a "bob") is attached to the string and has been pulled from its equilibrium (rest) position through a displacement angle of θ. It has a mass m. When the bob's displacement is farthest to the right, the restoring force is a maximum negative value and velocity is zero.

When the pendulum is released, gravity becomes the restoring force. Given the direction of the force of gravity, the acceleration due to gravity is straight down. However, the motion of the pendulum is an arc. A component of gravity acts along this arc to pull the bob back toward equilibrium and is, by definition, the restoring force ($\vec{F_R}$).

We can express F_R in terms of F_g with the following equation: $F_R = F_g(\sin \theta)$

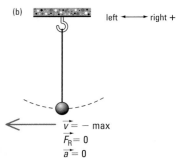

(b)

$\vec{v} = -\max$
$\vec{F_R} = 0$
$\vec{a} = 0$

◄ **Figure 7.26(b)**   As the bob accelerates downward, its velocity begins to increase and the restoring force ($\vec{F_R}$) becomes less and less. When it reaches the equilibrium position, no component of gravity is acting parallel to the motion of the bob, so the restoring force is zero, but the velocity has reached its maximum value.

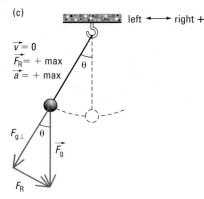

(c)

$\vec{v} = 0$
$\vec{F_R} = +\max$
$\vec{a} = +\max$

◄ **Figure 7.26(c)**   The bob has reached its maximum displacement to the left. The restoring force has also reached a maximum value but it acts toward the right. The bob's velocity is zero again.

The bob passes through the equilibrium position and begins to move upward. As it does so, the restoring force becomes larger as the displacement of the bob increases. But just like the mass-spring system, the restoring force is acting in a direction opposite to the bob's displacement. At the other extreme of the bob's displacement, the restoring force has slowed the bob to an instantaneous stop. In this position, the displacement and restoring force are a maximum, and the bob's velocity is zero.

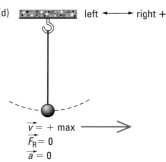

(d)

$\vec{v} = +\max$
$\vec{F_R} = 0$
$\vec{a} = 0$

◄ **Figure 7.26(d)**   The bob's displacement is again zero, and so is the restoring force. The bob has achieved its maximum velocity, but this time it is to the right.

On its back swing, the bob moves through the equilibrium position again, as shown here. The velocity is a maximum value, just as it was in Figure 7.26(b), but now it's in the opposite direction.

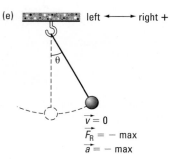

(e)

$\vec{v} = 0$
$\vec{F_R} = -\max$
$\vec{a} = -\max$

◄ **Figure 7.26(e)**   The restoring force once more brings the bob's motion to a stop for an instant at the position farthest to the right. The restoring force is a maximum negative value, and the bob's velocity is zero. The pendulum has made one complete oscillation as shown in diagrams (a) to (e).

Note that the motion of the pendulum bob and the mass-spring systems are similar. Figure 7.19(a–e) on page 355 and Figure 7.26(a–e) on this page are comparable because both systems undergo the same changes to force, velocity, and acceleration at the same displacements.

Motion with Large Amplitudes

Earlier in this chapter, you read that a pendulum acts as a simple harmonic oscillator for small angles. Why is that? How is its motion different from SHM at larger angles?

The best way to answer these questions is to plot a graph of force versus displacement like those done for springs earlier in this chapter (e.g., Figure 7.11 on page 351). The displacement of the pendulum can be measured by its angle from the vertical. If the graph is linear, then the restoring force is proportional to the displacement, and the pendulum has moved in SHM, as described by Hooke's law. To create this graph, use the equation for restoring force that you saw in the explanation of Figure 7.26(a) on the previous page:

$$F_R = F_g(\sin \theta) \tag{3}$$

From this equation, we can plot the values for angles up to 90° for a bob with a mass of 1.0 kg.

As the graph in Figure 7.27 shows, the line is not linear, so the restoring force does not vary proportionally with the displacement. Strictly speaking, a pendulum is not a true simple harmonic oscillator. However, the line is almost linear up to about 20°. At angles of less than 15°, the deviation from a straight line is so small that, for all practical purposes, it is linear.

▼ **Table 7.5** Data for Figure 7.27

Angle (°)	Restoring Force (N)
0	0
10	1.70
20	3.36
30	4.91
40	6.31
50	7.51
60	8.50
70	9.22
80	9.66
90	9.81

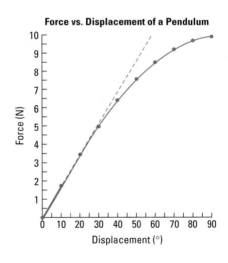

▲ **Figure 7.27** For the pendulum to be a true simple harmonic oscillator, its graph of restoring force versus displacement should be linear, as the dotted line suggests. After 15°, its line departs from the straight line, and its motion can no longer be considered SHM.

Example 7.5

Practice Problems

1. Determine the restoring force of a pendulum that is pulled to an angle of 12.0° left of the vertical. The mass of the bob is 300.0 g.

2. At what angle must a pendulum be displaced to create a restoring force of 4.00 N [left] on a bob with a mass of 500.0 g?

Answers

1. 0.612 N [right]
2. 54.6°

Determine the magnitude of the restoring force for a pendulum bob of mass 100.0 g that has been pulled to an angle of 10.0° from the vertical.

Given

$g = 9.81$ m/s²

Required

restoring force (F_R)

Analysis and Solution

Draw a diagram of the pendulum in its displaced position to show the forces acting on the bob.

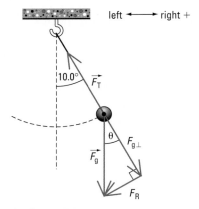

left ◄——► right +

▲ **Figure 7.28**

The restoring force $\vec{F}_R$ is the component of $\vec{F}_g$ that is tangential to the arc path of the pendulum.

$$
\begin{aligned}
F_R &= F_g(\sin \theta) \\
&= mg(\sin \theta) \\
&= (0.1000 \text{ kg})\left(9.81 \ \frac{\text{m}}{\text{s}^2}\right)(\sin 10.0°) \\
&= 0.170 \text{ N}
\end{aligned}
$$

Paraphrase

The magnitude of the restoring force acting on the pendulum is 0.170 N.

When Christiaan Huygens designed the first pendulum clock, his primary concern was to have the clock operate with a very consistent period. For a uniform period, he could use gear ratios in the mechanism to translate the motion of the pendulum to meaningful units of time, such as minutes and hours.

Which factors influence the period of a pendulum, and which do not? To discover how a pendulum's mass, period, and length influence its period, do 7-4 Inquiry Lab.

A Pendulum and Simple Harmonic Motion

Question

What is the relationship between the period of a pendulum and its mass, amplitude, and length?

Materials and Equipment

thermometer clamp
retort stand
40-cm thread (dental floss)
4 masses: 50 g, 100 g, 150 g, 200 g
ruler (30 cm) or metre-stick
protractor
stopwatch or watch with a second hand

Hypothesis

Before you begin parts A, B, and C, state a suitable hypothesis for each part of the lab. Remember to write your hypotheses as "if/then" statements.

Variables

The variables are the length of the pendulum, the mass of the pendulum, elapsed time, and the amplitude of the pendulum. Read the procedure for each part and identify the controlled, manipulated, and responding variables each time.

Part A: Mass and Period

Procedure

1 Copy Table 7.6 into your notebook.

▼ **Table 7.6** Mass and Period

Length of Pendulum =			
Mass (g)	**No. of Cycles/20 s**	**Frequency (Hz)**	**Period (s)**
50			
100			
150			
200			

2 Attach the thermometer clamp to the top of the retort stand. Attach the thread to the thermometer clamp. Make sure the thread is a little shorter than the height of the clamp from the table.

3 Squeeze one end of the thread in the clamp and use a slip knot on the other end to attach the first mass. The mass should hang freely above the table.

4 Measure the length of the thread from the clamp to the middle of the mass. Record this as the length of the pendulum at the top of Table 7.6.

5 Pull the mass on the thread back until it makes an angle of 15° with the vertical, as measured with the protractor.

6 Remove the protractor, and release the mass as you start to time it. Count the number of complete oscillations it makes in 20 s. Record this number in your table.

7 Remove the mass and replace it with the next mass. Loosen the clamp and adjust the length of the thread so that it is the same length as for the previous mass. (Remember to measure length to the middle of the mass.) Repeat steps 5 to 7 until all the masses are used.

Analysis

1. Determine the frequency and period of each mass. Record the numbers in your table.

2. Plot a graph of period versus mass. Remember to place the manipulated variable on the horizontal axis.

3. What conclusion can you draw about the relationship between the mass and the period of a pendulum? Explain your answer and show any relevant calculations.

Part B: Amplitude and Period

Procedure

1 Copy Table 7.7 into your notebook.

▼ **Table 7.7** Amplitude and Period

Length of Pendulum =			
Amplitude (°)	No. of Cycles/20 s	Frequency (Hz)	Period (s)
5			
10			
15			
20			

2 Use the same apparatus as in part A.

3 Attach a 200-g mass to the free end of the thread.

4 Measure the length of the thread from the clamp to the middle of the mass. Record this length at the top of Table 7.7.

5 Pull the mass on the thread back until it makes an angle of 5° with the vertical, as measured with the protractor.

6 Remove the protractor, and release the mass as you start to time it. Count the number of complete oscillations it makes in 20 s. Record this number in Table 7.7.

7 Repeat steps 5 and 6, each time increasing the amplitude by 5°.

Analysis

1. Determine the frequency and period for each amplitude and record the numbers in the appropriate columns in the table.

2. Plot a graph of period versus amplitude. Remember to place the manipulated variable on the horizontal axis.

3. What conclusion can you draw about the relationship between the amplitude and the period of a pendulum? Show any relevant calculations.

Part C: Length and Period

Procedure

1 Copy Table 7.8 into your notebook.

▼ **Table 7.8** Length and Period

Length (m)	No. of Cycles/20 s	Frequency (Hz)	Period (s)

2 Use the same apparatus as in part A. Start with a pendulum length of 40.0 cm.

3 Attach a 200-g mass to the free end of the thread.

4 Measure the length of the thread from the clamp to the middle of the mass. Record this length in Table 7.8.

5 Pull the mass on the thread back until it makes an angle of 15° with the vertical, as measured with the protractor.

6 Remove the protractor, and release the mass as you start to time it. Count the number of complete oscillations it makes in 20 s. Record this number in Table 7.8.

7 Repeat steps 4 to 6, but each time decrease the length of the pendulum by half.

Analysis

1. Determine the frequency and period for each length and record the values in the appropriate column in the table.

2. Plot a graph of period versus length. Remember to place the manipulated variable on the horizontal axis.

3. What conclusion can you draw about the relationship between the length and the period of a pendulum? Show any relevant calculations.

 e **LAB**

For a probeware activity, go to
www.pearsoned.ca/school/physicssource.

Pendulums and mass-spring systems are not the only simple harmonic oscillators. There are many other examples: a plucked guitar string, molecules vibrating within a solid, and water waves are just a few. In section 7.4, you will explore some human-made examples of SHM and learn about an interesting property called resonance.

Knowledge

1. The restoring force of a vertical mass-spring system is determined by the mass attached to the spring and the spring constant k. What two factors determine the restoring force of a pendulum?

2. Copy the following tables into your notes. Then fill in the blanks by using the words, "zero" or "maximum."

Pendulum System	Displace-ment	Acceler-ation	Velocity	Restoring Force
max $\vec{x}$				
max $\vec{a}$				
max $\vec{v}$				
min $\vec{F}$				

Mass-spring System	Displace-ment	Acceler-ation	Velocity	Restoring Force
max $\vec{x}$				
max $\vec{a}$				
max $\vec{v}$				
min $\vec{F}$				

3. Explain why a pendulum is not a true simple harmonic oscillator.

Applications

4. A mass of 2.0 kg is attached to a spring with a spring constant of 40.0 N/m on a horizontal frictionless surface. Determine the restoring force acting on the mass when the spring is compressed to a displacement of −0.15 m.

5. A spring hangs vertically from a ceiling and has a spring constant of 25.0 N/m. How far will the spring be stretched when a 4.0-kg mass is attached to its free end?

6. An applied force of −25.0 N is required to compress a spring −0.20 m. What force will pull it to a displacement of +0.15 m?

7. Two students are given the task of determining the spring constant of a spring as accurately as possible. To do this, they attach a force meter to a spring that is lying on a desk and is anchored at the other end. One student pulls the spring through several displacements, while the other records the force applied, as shown in the table below. Using this table, plot a graph of force versus displacement. Find the spring constant by determining the slope of the line of best fit.

Displacement (m)	Force (N)
0.00	0.00
0.10	0.15
0.20	0.33
0.30	0.42
0.40	0.60

8. Determine the restoring force for a pendulum bob with a mass of 0.400 kg that is pulled to an angle of 5.00° from the vertical.

9. A toy car with a wind-up spring motor on a horizontal table is pulled back to a displacement of 20.0 cm to the left and released. If the 10.0-g car initially accelerates at 0.55 m/s² to the right, what is the spring constant of the car's spring? (Hint: The restoring force is $F = ma$.)

Extension

10. Obtain three different types of rulers: plastic, metal, and wooden. Fix one end of each ruler to the side of a desk so the ruler juts out horizontally a distance of 25 cm from the edge. Hang enough weight on the end that sticks out to make the ruler bend downward by 2 to 3 cm. Record the deflection of the ruler and the mass used in each case. (Note: The deflection does not have to be the same for each ruler.) Use these data to determine the spring constant for each ruler. Rank the rulers from highest spring constant to lowest.

e TEST

To check your understanding of simple harmonic motion, follow the eTest links at www.pearsoned.ca/school/physicssource.

7.3 Position, Velocity, Acceleration, and Time Relationships

One way for ball players to practise their timing is by attempting to throw a ball through a tire swinging on a rope. Someone just beginning this kind of practice might throw too early or too late, missing the tire altogether. Part of the difficulty has to do with the continually changing velocity of the tire.

Choosing the best time to throw the ball is an exercise in physics. With practice, the human brain can learn to calculate the proper time to throw without even being aware that it is doing so.

Throwing the ball through the tire is much more difficult than it sounds because the tire is a simple harmonic oscillator for small amplitudes. Not only is the velocity continually changing, but so is the restoring force and the acceleration. The only constant for a swinging tire is its period.

In this section, you will mathematically analyze acceleration, velocity, and period for SHM in a mass-spring system, and then determine the period of a pendulum.

Both mass-spring systems and pendulums are simple harmonic oscillators, as described in section 7.2, but they are different from each other. The mass-spring system has a spring constant k, but the pendulum does not. For this reason, we will look at each separately, starting with the mass-spring system.

Acceleration of a Mass-spring System

In section 7.2, you learned that two equations can be used to describe force in the mass-spring system: Newton's second law and Hooke's law. They can be written mathematically as:

- Newton's second law: $\vec{F}_{net} = m\vec{a}$
- Hooke's law: $\vec{F} = -k\vec{x}$ (2)

Since both equations refer to the restoring force, you can equate them:

$$\vec{F}_{net} = \vec{F}$$

$$m\vec{a} = -k\vec{x}$$

$$\vec{a} = -\frac{k\vec{x}}{m} \qquad (4)$$

where $\vec{a}$ is the acceleration in metres per second squared; k is the spring constant in newtons per metre; $\vec{x}$ is the displacement in metres; and m is the mass of the oscillator in kilograms.

The acceleration of a horizontal mass-spring simple harmonic oscillator can be determined by its spring constant, displacement, and mass. It's logical that the acceleration of the mass depends on how stiff the spring is and how far it is stretched from its equilibrium position. It is also reasonable to assume that, if the mass is large, then the acceleration will be small. This assumption is based on Newton's second law.

The acceleration depends on the displacement of the mass, so the acceleration changes throughout the entire motion as shown in Figure 7.29. Since acceleration of a simple harmonic oscillator is not uniform, only the instantaneous acceleration of the mass can be determined by equation 4.

 e **MATH**

To see how the spring constant, mass, position and acceleration are related graphically, visit www.pearsoned.ca/school/physicssource.

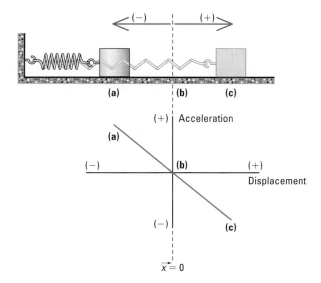

◀ **Figure 7.29** The acceleration of a simple harmonic oscillator depends on its position. In position (a), the oscillator moves from its maximum displacement and maximum positive acceleration through to position (b), where the displacement and acceleration are zero. It then moves to position (c), where the oscillator again experiences a maximum acceleration and displacement in the other direction.

The Relationship Between Acceleration and Velocity of a Mass-spring System

The acceleration of a simple harmonic oscillator is continually changing, so it should come as no surprise that the velocity changes too. As we have just seen, the maximum acceleration occurs when the oscillator is at its maximum displacement.

At this position, it is tempting to think that the velocity will be at its maximum as well, but we know that this is not the case. Remember, the acceleration is at its greatest magnitude at the extremes of the motion, yet the oscillator has actually stopped in these positions! In some ways, a ball thrown vertically into the air is similar (Figure 7.30). The acceleration of gravity acts on the ball to return it to the ground. When the ball reaches its maximum height, it comes to a stop for an instant, just like the mass-spring system you studied earlier in this chapter.

maximum height
$\vec{v} = 0$
$\vec{a} = -9.81 \text{ m/s}^2$

▶ **Figure 7.30** At its maximum height, the ball stops for a brief instant, yet the acceleration of gravity acting on it is not zero. This is similar to the mass-spring system.

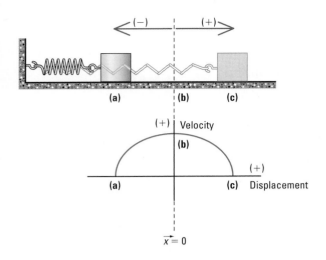

▲ Figure 7.31 The velocity of a simple harmonic oscillator is not uniform. The mass experiences its greatest acceleration at the extremes of its motion where the velocity is zero. Only after the mass accelerates from position (a) to (b) does its velocity reach its maximum value. The mass then decelerates from (b) to (c) where it comes to a stop again.

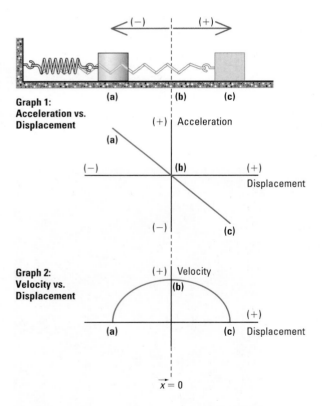

▲ Figure 7.32 The mass-spring system experiences a changing acceleration and velocity as it makes one-half of a full oscillation from position (a) to position (c).

Since the acceleration of the oscillator decreases as it approaches the equilibrium position (Figure 7.31(a)), the velocity does not increase at a uniform rate. The velocity-displacement graph looks like Figure 7.31(b).

Figure 7.32 shows a diagram of a simple harmonic oscillator (a mass-spring system) as it moves through one-half of a complete oscillation from (a) to (b) to (c). Below the diagram are the acceleration-displacement and velocity-displacement graphs. The diagram of the oscillator and the graphs are vertically aligned so the graphs show you what is happening as the mass-spring system moves.

In the diagram at the top of Figure 7.32, you can see the oscillator in position (a). It is at its farthest displacement to the left and the spring is compressed. The velocity-displacement graph shows that the oscillator's velocity in this position is zero (graph 2). You can also see from the acceleration-displacement graph that the acceleration at that moment is positive and a maximum, but the displacement is negative (graph 1).

Acceleration and Displacement — Always Opposite

In fact, if you look closely at graph 1, you might notice how the acceleration and displacement are always opposite to one another, regardless of the position of the mass. The acceleration is positive while the displacement is negative, and vice versa. This isn't surprising, however, because it is what the negative sign in the equation for Hooke's law illustrates: $\vec{F} = -k\vec{x}$.

Look again at Figure 7.32 and follow the mass as it moves from position (a) to positions (b) and (c). As the oscillator accelerates from position (a) to the right, it picks up speed. The velocity-displacement graph (graph 2) shows that the velocity is positive and increasing as the oscillator approaches position (b), yet the acceleration is decreasing, as shown in graph 1. The oscillator goes through the equilibrium position with a maximum positive velocity, but now the acceleration becomes negative as the spring tries to pull the oscillator back (graph 1). This is why the oscillator slows down and the velocity-displacement graph returns to zero in position (c).

Consider a vertical mass-spring system. A bungee jumper will experience a positive acceleration when she is below the equilibrium position and a negative acceleration when above it (Figures 7.33 and 7.34).

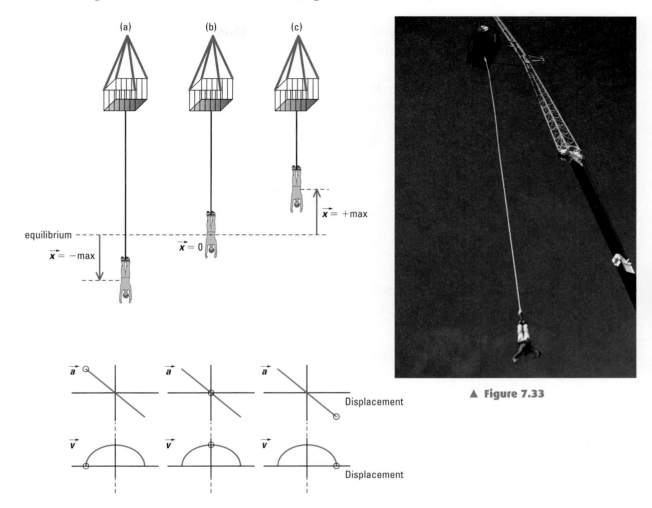

▲ **Figure 7.33**

▲ **Figure 7.34**   After a jump, the bungee jumper is shown in three positions: At the lowest point (a), in the equilibrium position (b), and at her maximum displacement (c). In each case the circled region on the graphs indicates her acceleration and velocity.

Maximum Speed of a Mass-spring System

Now you know that a simple harmonic oscillator will experience its greatest speed at the equilibrium position. What factors influence this speed, and how can we calculate it?

In our examples, the mass-spring system is frictionless, and no external forces act on it. This is referred to as an isolated system and the law of conservation of energy applies. We will use this concept to derive the equation for the maximum speed.

Recall from Chapter 6 that the total mechanical energy in an isolated system remains constant. That means that the kinetic and potential energy of the system may vary, but their sum is always the same.

In other words, at any position in the motion of a mass-spring system, the sum of kinetic and potential energies must be equal to the total energy of the system. Recall that kinetic energy is expressed as:

$$E_k = \frac{1}{2}mv^2$$

Recall that elastic potential energy is expressed as:

$$E_p = \frac{1}{2}kx^2$$

Let's begin by looking at the energy of the system in two positions:
- When the mass is at the maximum displacement (Figure 7.35(a)).
- When the mass is at the minimum displacement (Figure 7.35(b)).

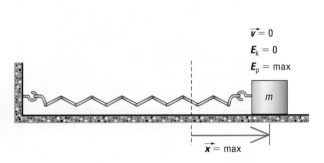

▲ **Figure 7.35(a)** The oscillator at its maximum displacement. Potential energy has reached a maximum value ($E_{p_{max}}$) because the oscillator's displacement is a maximum ($\vec{x} = A$). The kinetic energy is zero ($\vec{v} = 0$).

▲ **Figure 7.35(b)** The oscillator at its minimum displacement ($\vec{x} = 0$). Kinetic energy has reached a maximum value ($E_{k_{max}}$) because the oscillator has a maximum velocity. The potential energy is zero ($\vec{x} = 0$).

Remember that the total energy of the system remains constant regardless of the oscillator's position. The equation for the total energy is:

$$E_T = E_p + E_k$$

The kinetic energy of the oscillator at its maximum displacement is zero so the total energy of the oscillator at that position must be:

$$E_T = E_{p_{max}}$$

The potential energy of the oscillator at its minimum displacement is zero so the total energy of the oscillator at that position must be:

$$E_T = E_{k_{max}}$$

Because the total energy is always the same, we can write:

$$E_{k_{max}} = E_{p_{max}}$$

or

$$\frac{1}{2}mv^2_{max} = \frac{1}{2}kx^2_{max}$$

If we use A to represent x_{max}, we can write:

$$\frac{1}{2}mv_{max}^2 = \frac{1}{2}kA^2$$

We can then simplify this equation to solve for v_{max}:

$$\frac{1}{\cancel{2}}mv^2{}_{max} = \frac{1}{\cancel{2}}kA^2$$

$$mv^2{}_{max} = kA^2$$

$$v^2{}_{max} = \frac{kA^2}{m}$$

Then we take the square root of each side:

$$v_{max} = \sqrt{\frac{kA^2}{m}}$$

or

$$v_{max} = A\sqrt{\frac{k}{m}} \qquad (5)$$

Factors That Influence the Maximum Speed of a Mass-spring System

Three factors influence the maximum speed of a mass-spring system:

- the amplitude of the oscillations: If the oscillator moves through a large amplitude, the restoring force increases in proportion to the amplitude. As the restoring force increases, so does the acceleration, and the oscillator will achieve a greater velocity by the time it reaches the equilibrium position.

- the stiffness of the spring: A stiffer spring with a higher spring constant exerts a stronger restoring force and creates a greater maximum velocity for the same reasons that increasing the amplitude does.

- the mass of the oscillator: Changing the mass of an oscillator has a different effect. If the mass increases, the velocity of the oscillations decreases. This is because the oscillator has more inertia. A larger mass is harder to accelerate so it won't achieve as great a speed as a similar mass-spring system with less mass.

eWEB

To find out how these factors are taken into account in bungee jumping, follow the links at www.pearsoned.ca/school/physicssource.

Concept Check

1. When acceleration is negative, displacement is positive and vice versa. Why?
2. Why is the velocity-time graph of a simple harmonic oscillator a curved line?
3. The acceleration-displacement graph and velocity-displacement graph are shown in Figure 7.32 on page 368 for half of an oscillation only. Sketch three more acceleration-displacement and velocity-displacement graphs for the second half of the oscillation.
4. Suppose the amplitude of an object's oscillation is doubled. How would this affect the object's maximum velocity?

Example 7.6

A 100.0-g mass hangs motionless from a spring attached to the ceiling. The spring constant (k) is 1.014 N/m. The instructor pulls the mass through a displacement of 40.0 cm [down] and releases it. Determine: (a) the acceleration when the mass is at a displacement of 15.0 cm [up], and (b) the maximum speed of the mass.

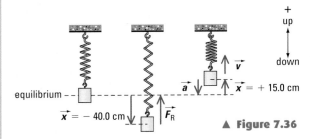

▲ **Figure 7.36**

Given

$m = 100.0$ g
$k = 1.014$ N/m
$\vec{x} = 40.0$ cm [down]

Required

(a) acceleration ($\vec{a}$) when $\vec{x} = 15.0$ cm [up]
(b) maximum speed (v_{max})

Analysis and Solution

(a) The mass will begin to oscillate when released. Acceleration is a vector quantity so direction is important.

$$\vec{F}_{net} = \vec{F}_R$$
$$m\vec{a} = -k\vec{x}$$
$$\vec{a} = \frac{-k\vec{x}}{m}$$
$$= \frac{\left(-1.014 \frac{N}{m}\right)(+0.150 \text{ m})}{0.100 \text{ kg}}$$
$$= -1.52 \text{ m/s}^2$$

(b) The maximum speed occurs when the mass is in the equilibrium position, whether it is moving up or down. The displacement of the mass before it is released is the amplitude (A) of the mass's oscillation.

$$v_{max} = A\sqrt{\frac{k}{m}}$$
$$= 0.400 \text{ m} \sqrt{\frac{1.014 \frac{N}{m}}{0.100 \text{ kg}}}$$
$$= 1.27 \text{ m/s}$$

Paraphrase

(a) The mass has an acceleration of 1.52 m/s² [down] when it is 15.0 cm above the equilibrium position.
(b) The maximum speed of the mass is 1.27 m/s.

Practice Problems

1. A 0.724-kg mass is oscillating on a horizontal frictionless surface attached to a spring (k = 8.21 N/m). What is the mass's displacement when its instantaneous acceleration is 4.11 m/s² [left]?

2. A 50.0-g mass is attached to a spring with a spring constant (k) of 4.00 N/m. The mass oscillates with an amplitude of 1.12 m. What is its maximum speed?

3. An instructor sets up an oscillating vertical mass-spring system (k = 6.05 N/m). The maximum displacement is 81.7 cm and the maximum speed is 2.05 m/s. What is the mass of the oscillator?

Answers

1. 0.362 m [right]
2. 10.0 m/s
3. 0.961 kg

Period of a Mass-spring System

The next time you are travelling in a vehicle at night, watch for bicycles moving in the same direction as your vehicle. Notice the peculiar motion of pedals as they reflect the light from your headlights (Figure 7.37). From a distance, these reflectors don't appear to be moving in a circular path, but seem to be moving up and down. The apparent up-and-down motion of the pedals is the same kind of motion as a mass-spring system oscillating back and forth, so it is simple harmonic motion. This observation proves useful because it is an example of how circular motion can be used to describe simple harmonic motion. The next few pages show how to derive equations for the period and maximum speed of a simple harmonic oscillator.

▲ **Figure 7.37** The reflectors on the bicycle seem to be moving up and down instead of in a circle.

Two conditions are necessary if circular motion is to be used to replicate simple harmonic motion:

1. The period of both the circular motion and the simple harmonic motion must be the same.

2. The radius of the circular motion must match the amplitude of the oscillator.

For example, look at Figure 7.38, where a mass moving in a circular path with a radius r is synchronized with a mass-spring simple harmonic oscillator. This illustration demonstrates how circular motion can be used to describe SHM.

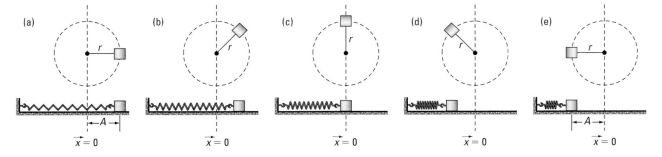

▲ **Figure 7.38** A mass moving in a circle is a simple harmonic oscillator that corresponds to the mass-spring oscillator shown below it. One-half of a complete cycle is shown here.

For our purposes, the following conditions are true:

- The radius of the circular motion is equal to the amplitude of the oscillator ($r = A$, as shown in Figure 7.38(a)).

- The mass in circular motion moves at a constant speed.

- The periods of the mass in circular motion and the oscillator in the mass-spring system are the same.

▲ **Figure 7.39** The strings of a piano all have different masses. Even if they vibrate with the same amplitude they will have a different period of vibration because each string has a different mass. A heavy string will vibrate with a longer period (and lower frequency) than a lighter string.

Deriving the Equation for the Period of a Mass-spring System

Recall that the maximum velocity of a simple harmonic oscillator occurs when it is in its equilibrium position, which is position (c) in Figure 7.38. At the exact moment that the mass in circular motion is in position (c), its velocity is in the same direction as the velocity of the mass-spring system, and they are both moving at the same speed. But if the mass moving in a circular path is moving at a constant speed, then it must always be moving at the maximum speed of the mass-spring oscillator! Therefore, the maximum speed (v_{max}) of the mass-spring system is equal to the speed (v) of the circular mass system.

The speed of an object moving in a circular path was derived in Chapter 5. It is:

$$v = \frac{2\pi r}{T} \qquad (6)$$

The speed of the circular motion (v) matches the maximum speed on the mass-spring oscillator (v_{max}), and the radius of the circle matches its amplitude. Therefore, we can customize the equation for the mass-spring oscillator:

$$v_{max} = \frac{2\pi A}{T} \qquad (7)$$

If we equate equation 5 and equation 7, we get:

$$A\sqrt{\frac{k}{m}} = \frac{2\pi A}{T}$$

We can then solve for T:

$$A\!\!\!\!/\,\sqrt{\frac{k}{m}} = \frac{2\pi A\!\!\!\!/}{T}$$

$$T = \frac{2\pi}{\sqrt{\dfrac{k}{m}}}$$

$$T = 2\pi\sqrt{\frac{m}{k}} \qquad (8)$$

This equation describes the period of a simple harmonic oscillator, where T is the period of the oscillator in seconds; k is the spring constant in newtons per metre; and m is the mass of the oscillator in kilograms. Figure 7.39 is an example of an application of this equation.

PHYSICS INSIGHT

The period of a simple harmonic oscillator does not depend on displacement.

Factors Affecting the Period of an Oscillating Mass

The larger the oscillating mass is, the longer its period of oscillation is. This seems reasonable since a large mass takes longer to speed up or slow down. It would also seem reasonable that the period should be inversely related to the spring constant, as the equation suggests. After all, the stiffer the spring, the more force it exerts over smaller displacements. Therefore, you could expect the mass to oscillate more quickly and have a smaller period.

What is interesting about this equation is not what influences the period but what does not. It may seem odd that the displacement of the mass has no influence on the period of oscillation. This means that if you were to pull a mass-spring system to a displacement $\vec{x}$ and then let go, it would have the same period of oscillation as it would if you pulled it to a displacement of $2\vec{x}$ and released it! The two identical mass-spring systems in Figure 7.40 have different amplitudes. Are their periods different?

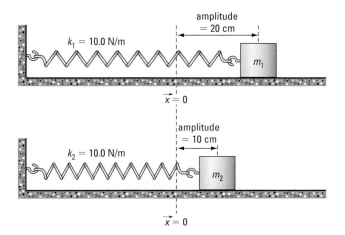

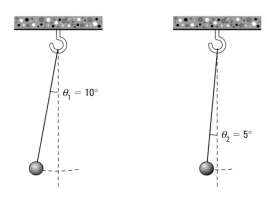

▲ **Figure 7.40** Two identical mass-spring systems have the same spring constant and mass, but different amplitudes. Which has the longest period? They have the same period because displacement doesn't affect period.

▲ **Figure 7.41** Two identical pendulums have the same mass and length, but different amplitudes. Which one has the longest period? They have the same period because displacement doesn't affect the period of a simple harmonic oscillator.

This relationship is true for any simple harmonic oscillator, including a pendulum with a small amplitude. It is easy enough to test. Take two pendulums with the same mass and length (Figure 7.41). Pull both bobs back to different displacements. Remember to keep the displacements small so the pendulums oscillate with SHM. Release them at the same time. You will discover that both make one full oscillation in unison. This means they return to the point of release at exactly the same time. The pendulum that begins with the larger displacement has farther to travel but experiences a larger restoring force that compensates for this.

Example 7.7

What is the period of oscillation of a mass-spring system that is oscillating with an amplitude of 12.25 cm and has a maximum speed of 5.13 m/s? The spring constant (k) is 5.03 N/m.

Given

$A = 12.25$ cm

$k = 5.03$ N/m

$v_{\text{max}} = 5.13$ m/s

Required

period of the oscillations (T)

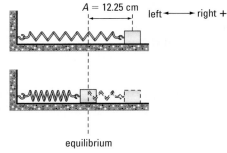

▲ **Figure 7.42**

Analysis and Solution

To determine the period of the oscillator, you need to know the oscillator's mass. Use the maximum speed equation (equation 5) to find the mass:

$$E_{k_{\text{max}}} = E_{P_{\text{max}}}$$

$$\frac{mv_{\text{max}}^2}{2} = \frac{kA^2}{2}$$

$$mv_{\text{max}}^2 = kA^2$$

$$m = \frac{kA^2}{v_{\text{max}}^2}$$

$$m = \frac{kA^2}{v_{\text{max}}^2}$$

$$= \frac{\left(5.03\ \dfrac{\text{N}}{\text{m}}\right)(0.1225\ \text{m})^2}{\left(5.13\ \dfrac{\text{m}}{\text{s}}\right)^2}$$

$$= 0.02868\ \text{kg}$$

Then use equation 8 to determine the period:

$$T = 2\pi\sqrt{\frac{m}{k}}$$

$$= 2\pi\sqrt{\frac{0.02868\ \text{kg}}{5.03\ \dfrac{\text{N}}{\text{m}}}}$$

$$= 0.150\ \text{s}$$

Paraphrase

The period of the mass-spring oscillator is 0.150 s.

1. What effect does doubling the displacement have on the period of oscillation of a simple harmonic oscillator? Explain your answer.
2. In order to compare circular motion to the motion of a simple harmonic oscillator, what two conditions must be satisfied?
3. If the mass and spring constant of a mass-spring oscillator were doubled, what effect would this have on the period of the oscillations?
4. Two mass-spring systems with identical masses are set oscillating side by side. Compare the spring constants of the two systems if the period of one system is twice the other.

The Period of a Pendulum

Christiaan Huygens recognized that a pendulum was ideally suited for measuring time because its period isn't affected by as many of the factors that influence a mass-spring system. A pendulum doesn't have a spring constant, k, like the mass-spring system does, and unlike the mass-spring system, the mass of the pendulum does not affect its period. Because of these factors, a new equation for a pendulum's period must be derived. In doing so, you will discover why its mass is irrelevant and what factors play a role in its period of oscillation.

Take a closer look at the pendulum when it is at a small displacement of 15° or less, as shown in Figure 7.43. For a small angle (θ), the displacement of the bob can be taken as x. The sine of angle θ is expressed as:

$$\sin \theta = \frac{x}{l}$$

Recall that the restoring force for a pendulum is $F_R = F_g \sin \theta$. For simplicity, call the restoring force F so you can make a substitution for $\sin \theta$:

$$F = F_g\left(\frac{x}{l}\right)$$

Recall that in a mass-spring system, the restoring force is $F = -kx$. We want to solve for the period (T), which is a scalar quantity, so the negative sign in Hooke's law can be omitted. The two equations for restoring force can then be equated:

$$k\cancel{x} = (mg)\frac{\cancel{x}}{l}$$

$$k = \frac{mg}{l}$$

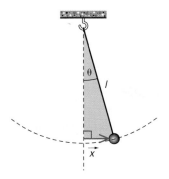

▲ **Figure 7.43** For a pendulum with a small displacement of 15° or less, the displacement is x.

None of the values of mass, acceleration due to gravity, or length change for a pendulum. They are constants, which are represented by k. Substitute them into equation 8:

$$T = 2\pi\sqrt{\frac{m}{k}}$$

$$= 2\pi\sqrt{\frac{\cancel{m}}{\left(\frac{(\cancel{m}g)}{l}\right)}}$$

$$T = 2\pi\sqrt{\frac{l}{g}} \tag{9}$$

where l is the length of the pendulum string in metres; and g is the gravitational field strength in metres per second squared.

Recall that the length of the pendulum is always measured from the point where it is attached at the top, to the centre of mass of the bob, *not* the point at which the string or wire is attached to the bob. Also recall that the period of the pendulum's swing does not depend on the mass of the pendulum bob. This may not seem logical but it is indeed the case — just as the acceleration of an object in free fall doesn't depend on the mass of the object.

The Pendulum and Gravitational Field Strength

Equation 8 is useful when it is manipulated to solve for g, the gravitational field strength. As you learned in section 4.3 of Chapter 4, the gravitational field strength varies with altitude and latitude.

The magnitude of the gravitational field is 9.81 m/s² at any place on Earth's surface that corresponds to the average radius of Earth. However, very few places on the surface of Earth are at exactly the average radius. To determine the exact value of g at any point, you can use a pendulum and manipulate equation 8. If you solve for g, you get:

$$g = \frac{4\pi^2 l}{T^2} \tag{10}$$

Due to the changing nature of Earth's gravity, Christiaan Huygens's pendulum clock (introduced in section 7.2) was only accurate if it was manufactured for a specific place. For example, pendulum clocks designed to operate in London could not be sold in Paris because the accuracy could not be maintained. The difference in gravitational field strength between London and Paris meant that the period of oscillation would be slightly different.

The difference in g between two locations could be quite small, but the cumulative effect on a pendulum clock would be significant. An extreme example of the varying value of g at different geographic locations can be illustrated by using a pendulum to determine the gravitational field strength at the top of Mount Everest.

PHYSICS INSIGHT

The period of a pendulum does not depend on its mass or amplitude.

e **SIM**

Learn more about the motion of a pendulum and the factors that affect it. Follow the eSIM links at www.pearsoned.ca/school/physicssource.

Example 7.8

What is the gravitational field strength at the top of Mount Everest at an altitude of 8954.0 m, if a pendulum with a length of 1.00 m has a period of 2.01 s?

Analysis and Solution

Use equation 10 to determine g. Note that no vector arrow is required with the symbol g because you are calculating a scalar quantity.

$$g = \frac{4\pi^2 l}{T^2}$$

$$= \frac{(4\pi^2)(1.00 \text{ m})}{(2.01 \text{ s})^2}$$

$$= 9.77 \text{ m/s}^2$$

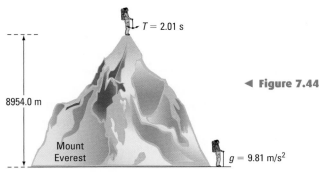

$T = 2.01$ s

8954.0 m

Mount Everest

$g = 9.81$ m/s^2

◀ **Figure 7.44**

The gravitational field strength at the top of Mount Everest is 9.77 m/s², which is very close to the accepted value of 9.81 m/s². The extra height of Mount Everest adds very little to the radius of Earth.

Practice Problems

1. What is the gravitational field strength on Mercury, if a 0.500-m pendulum swings with a period of 2.30 s?

2. A pendulum swings with a period of 5.00 s on the Moon, where the gravitational field strength is 1.62 m/s² [down]. What is the pendulum's length?

3. What period would a 30.0-cm pendulum have on Mars, where the gravitational field strength is 3.69 m/s² [down]?

Answers
1. 3.73 m/s² [down]
2. 1.03 m
3. 1.79 s

At the top of Mount Everest, a pendulum will swing with a slightly different period than at sea level. So a pendulum on Mount Everest, oscillating with a longer period than one at sea level, will report a different time.

Huygens's clocks also suffered from another problem: the pendulum arm would expand or contract in hot or cold weather. Since the length of the arm also determines the period of oscillation, these clocks would speed up or slow down depending on the ambient temperature.

Given their limitations, pendulum clocks were not considered the final solution to accurate timekeeping. Further innovations followed that you may want to research on your own.

e **WEB**

To learn more about pendulum clocks and the evolution of timekeeping, create a timeline of the evolution of clock design. In your timeline include what the innovation was, who invented it, and the year it was introduced. Begin your search at www.pearsoned.ca/school/physicssource.

Concept Check

1. An archer is doing target practice with his bow and arrow. He ties an apple to a string and sets it oscillating left to right, down range. In what position of the apple should he aim so that he increases his chances of hitting it? Explain your answer.

2. What factors affect the accuracy of pendulum clocks? Why?

Knowledge

1. Explain the effect that changing each of the following factors has on the period of a mass-spring system:

   (a) amplitude

   (b) spring constant

   (c) mass

2. Explain what effect changing each of the following factors has on the period of a pendulum:

   (a) amplitude

   (b) gravitational field strength

   (c) mass

3. Describe the positions that a mass-spring system and pendulum are in when:

   (a) acceleration is a maximum

   (b) velocity is a maximum

   (c) restoring force is maximum

4. Why is the acceleration of a simple harmonic oscillator not uniform?

5. A mass-spring system has a negative displacement and a positive restoring force. What direction is the acceleration?

Applications

6. A 60.0-kg boy bungee-jumps using a bungee cord that has a spring constant of 25.0 N/m. If the amplitude of his oscillations is 30.0 m, what is the fastest the jumper will move as he oscillates up and down?

7. What length of pendulum would oscillate with a period of 4.0 s on the surface of Mars ($g = 3.71$ m/s^2)?

8. A mass of 3.08 kg oscillates on the end of a horizontal spring with a period of 0.323 s. What acceleration does the mass experience when its displacement is 2.85 m to the right?

9. A 50.0-kg girl bounces up and down on a pogo stick. The girl has an instantaneous acceleration of 2.0 m/s^2 when the displacement is -8.0 cm. What is the spring constant of the pogo stick's spring?

10. A pendulum bob ($m = 250.0$ g) experiences a restoring force of 0.468 N. Through what angle is it displaced?

11. A 50.0-cm pendulum is placed on the Moon, where g is 1.64 m/s^2. What is the period of the pendulum?

Extensions

12. A horizontal mass-spring system oscillates with an amplitude of 1.50 m. The spring constant is 10.00 N/m. Another mass moving in a circular path with a radius of 1.50 m at a constant speed of 5.00 m/s is synchronized with the mass-spring system. Determine the system's:

    (a) period

    (b) mass

    (c) maximum acceleration

13. A quartz crystal ($m = 0.200$ g) oscillates with simple harmonic motion at a frequency of 10.0 kHz and has an amplitude of 0.0500 mm. What is its maximum speed?

14. A horizontal mass-spring system has a mass of 0.200 kg, a maximum speed of 0.803 m/s, and an amplitude of 0.120 m. What is the mass's position when its acceleration is 3.58 m/s^2 to the west?

15. An inquisitive student brings a pendulum aboard a jet plane. The plane is in level flight at an altitude of 12.31 km. What period do you expect for a 20.0-cm pendulum? (Hint: First determine the gravitational field strength as shown in Chapter 4.)

 e TEST

To check your understanding of position, velocity, acceleration, and time relationships in mass-spring systems and pendulums, follow the eTest links at www.pearsoned.ca/school/physicssource.

7.4 Applications of Simple Harmonic Motion

People's arms swing as they walk. An annoying rattle can develop in a car when it reaches a certain speed. A child can make large waves in the bathtub by sliding back and forth. Many things can be made to vibrate, and when they do, they seem to do it with a period of motion that is unique to them. After all, how often do you think about your arms swinging as you walk? You don't — they seem to swing of their own accord and at their own frequency. The water in the bathtub will form very large waves when the child makes a back-and-forth motion at just the right rate. Any other rate won't create the waves that splash over the edge and soak the floor, which, of course, is the goal.

In all these cases, the object vibrates at a natural frequency. **Resonant frequency** is the natural frequency of vibration of an object. In other words, objects that are caused to vibrate do so at a natural frequency that depends on the physical properties of the object. All objects that can vibrate have a resonant frequency, including a pendulum.

resonant frequency: the natural frequency of vibration of an object

Maintaining a Pendulum's Resonant Frequency

A pendulum swings back and forth at its resonant frequency. Since the acceleration of gravity does not change if we stay in the same place, the only factor that affects the resonant frequency is the pendulum's length. All pendulums of the same length oscillate with the same natural (resonant) frequency.

Huygens made use of this fact when he designed his pendulum clock (Figure 7.45). He knew that all pendulum clocks would keep the same time as long as the length of the pendulum arms was the same. Their resonant frequencies would be identical.

However, Huygens faced some challenges in making a pendulum clock. The arm of the pendulum would expand or contract with temperature, affecting its period. But this was a relatively minor issue compared to another difficulty that had to be overcome — friction. Unless something was done, friction would very quickly stop the pendulum from swinging.

To compensate for the effects of friction, he designed his clocks so that the pendulum was given a small push at just the right moment in its swing. The timing of these pushes coincided with the resonant frequency of the pendulum. By doing this, Huygens could make the pendulum swing for as long as the periodic force was applied.

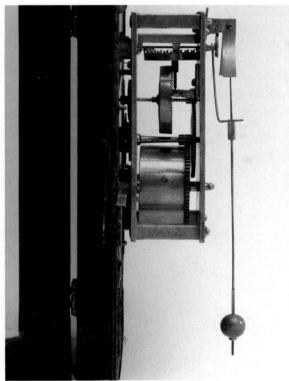

▲ **Figure 7.45** The interior of Huygens's clock

Forced Frequency

To visualize how this works, imagine a child on a swing. A swing is an example of a pendulum, with the child as the bob. The swing moves back and forth at its natural frequency, which depends only on its length. To keep the swing going with the same amplitude, all the parent has to do is push at just the right moment. The timing of the pushes must match the frequency of the swing.

As anyone who has pushed a swing can attest, it takes very little energy to keep a swing swinging to the same height. The frequency at which the force is applied to keep the swing moving is called the **forced frequency**. If the forced frequency matches or is close to the resonant frequency of the object, then very little force is required to keep the object moving. The resonant frequency won't change though, because it depends only on the length of the pendulum. If the parent decides to push a little harder each time the swing returns, then the swing's **amplitude** will increase, but not its frequency. A larger force than is needed to overcome friction will create a larger amplitude of motion. If the forced frequency isn't close to the resonant frequency, then the object will not vibrate very much and will have a small amplitude.

Imagine trying to increase the frequency of a pendulum by increasing the forced frequency. Much of the force won't be transferred to the pendulum because the pendulum won't be in the right position when the force is applied. The pendulum will bounce around but there will be no increase in its amplitude of vibration, and its motion will become harder to predict. The flowchart in Figure 7.46 on the next page summarizes the relationship between forced frequency and resonant frequency.

Mechanical Resonance

A forced frequency that matches the resonant frequency is capable of creating very large amplitudes of oscillation. This is referred to as **mechanical resonance**. This can be a good or bad thing. The larger the amplitude, the more energy the system has. Huygens's pendulum clock didn't need to have large oscillations, so a very small force could keep the pendulum swinging. A small weight-driven mechanism was used to provide the force needed. The force simply had to be applied with the same frequency as the pendulum. Huygens managed to do this without much difficulty.

His pendulum clocks were a great success but weren't completely practical since they had to be placed on solid ground. A pendulum clock would not work aboard a ship because sailing ships of the time were buffeted by the waves more than today's large ocean-going vessels are. The motion of the ship on the waves would disturb a pendulum's SHM, so sailors could not take advantage of the increased accuracy these clocks provided.

forced frequency: the frequency at which an external force is applied to a resonating object

PHYSICS INSIGHT

The forced frequency that is the same as the resonant frequency will increase the amplitude of the SHM, but will not change the resonant frequency.

mechanical resonance: the increase in amplitude of oscillation of a system as a result of a periodic force whose frequency is equal or very close to the resonant frequency of the system

The key to successfully navigating across an ocean (where there are no landmarks) was to use an accurate clock on the ship. This clock could be synchronized to a clock in Greenwich, England, which is situated on the prime meridian of 0° longitude. As the ship travelled east or west, the sailors could compare their local time, using the Sun and a sundial, to the ship's clock, which was still synchronized to the time on the prime meridian. The difference in time between the two clocks could be used to compute their longitudinal position. However, it wasn't until the 1700s that a brilliant clockmaker, John Harrison, successfully made a marine chronometer (ship's clock) that was immune to the buffeting of waves and temperature. It contained several ingenious innovations and, for better or worse, did away with the pendulum.

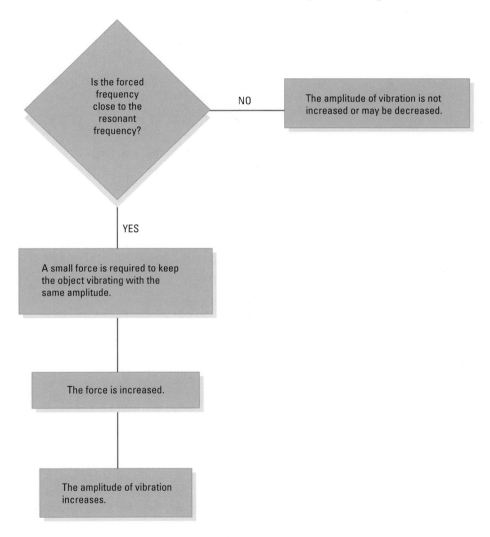

▲ **Figure 7.46** Flowchart of the effect of forced frequency on resonant amplitude

Investigating Mechanical Resonance

Problem

How can we cause a pendulum to begin oscillating at its resonant frequency using a forced frequency?

Materials

retort stands
string
thread
2 identical masses (200 g each)

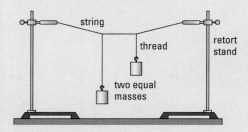

▲ **Figure 7.47**

Procedure

Part A

1 Read the questions in the next column before doing the lab.

2 Set up the two retort stands about 75 cm apart.

3 Tie the string to both retort stands at the same height (50.0 cm) on each stand, as shown in Figure 7.47. Clamp the ends of the string to the retort stands so they don't slip. The string should be taut.

4 Pull the two retort stands farther apart if you need to remove slack from the string.

5 Attach the thread to one mass and tie the other end to the string so that the distance from the mass to the string is 30 cm. This is mass 1.

6 Repeat step 5 for the second mass (mass 2) so that it has a length of 10 cm and is attached to the string about 15 cm from the first.

7 Make sure neither mass is moving, then pull mass 2 back a small distance and release it. Observe the motion of mass 1 as mass 2 oscillates. Make a note of the maximum amplitude that mass 1 achieves.

8 Repeat step 7 three more times. Each time adjust mass 2 so that its length is 10 cm more. For your last trial, mass 2 should have a length of 40.0 cm.

Part B

9 Adjust mass 2 so that it is as close to the length of mass 1 as possible.

10 Make sure both masses are motionless. Pull back and release mass 2. Note the amplitude of vibration that mass 1 achieves.

11 Pull the retort stands farther apart and hold them there so the tension in the string is increased, and the string is almost horizontal.

12 Make sure both masses are motionless, then pull back mass 2 and release it. Note the amplitude of vibration that mass 1 achieves.

Questions

Part A

1. At what length did mass 2 create the maximum oscillation of mass 1? Explain why this happened, in terms of frequency.

2. At what length did mass 2 create the minimum oscillation of mass 1? Explain why this happened, in terms of frequency.

3. Why did mass 1 have a large amplitude of vibration in only one case?

Part B

4. What effect did increasing the tension on the string have on the amplitude achieved by mass 1?

5. Why did increasing the tension alter the maximum oscillation of mass 1?

6. Write a sentence describing the effect that increasing the tension had on the resonant amplitude of mass 1. Use the terms *forced frequency* and *resonant amplitude* in your answer.

e **LAB**

For a probeware lab, go to
www.pearsoned.ca/school/physicssource.

Resonance Effects on Buildings and Bridges

A forced frequency that matches the resonant frequency can create problems for designers of bridges and skyscrapers. A bridge has a resonant frequency that can be amplified by the effect of wind. Air flows around the top and bottom of a bridge and can cause it to flutter just like a flag. The bridge will vibrate at its resonant frequency, with a large amplitude, even though the force applied by the wind may be relatively small. As the bridge vibrates, it may flex more than it is designed to and could conceivably vibrate to pieces.

A skyscraper is also susceptible to forced vibrations caused by the wind. Most skyscrapers have a huge surface area and catch a lot of wind. Even though a building is a rigid structure, the force of the wind can make it sway back and forth. The wind causes a phenomenon called "vortex shedding." It can create a forced vibration that matches the natural frequency of the building's back-and-forth vibration. The unfortunate result is to increase the sway (amplitude) of the building. The occupants on the top floors of the skyscraper will feel the effects the most. Over time, the continual large sway could weaken the building's structural supports and reduce its lifespan.

e WEB

The designers of the Tacoma Narrows Bridge did not anticipate the effect wind-induced resonance would have on the bridge. To learn more about what happened to the Tacoma Narrows Bridge and the causes, follow the links at www.pearsoned.ca/school/physicssource.

Reducing Resonance Effects

To counter resonance effects on bridges and buildings, engineers build them in such a way as to reduce the amplitude of resonance. Bridge designers make bridges more streamlined so that the wind passes over without imparting much energy. They also make bridges stiff, so a larger force is needed to create a large amplitude. The second-largest bridge in the world, the Great Belt East Bridge of Denmark is built with a smooth underside, like an airplane wing, that greatly increases its streamlined shape (Figure 7.48). It is not likely that a forced vibration would cause it to resonate.

Skyscraper designers employ many strategies to lessen resonant vibration. One very effective approach is to use a large mass at the top of the building, called a "tuned mass damper," which is free to oscillate back and forth (Figure 7.49). Controlled by computers, it can be made to vibrate at the resonant frequency of the building. When the building sways left, the mass moves right, and when the building sways right, the mass moves left. This has the effect of cancelling the vibration of the building. Any process that lessens the amplitude of an object's oscillations is referred to as "damping."

▲ **Figure 7.48** The Great Belt East Bridge of Denmark is 6.8 km long and is constructed with a smooth underside. This allows air to flow by without inducing a resonant frequency.

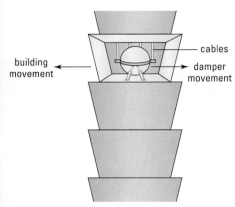

cables

building movement ← → damper movement

▲ **Figure 7.49** The Taipei 101 building in Taiwan was completed in 2004 and stands 101 stories high. The inset shows a tuned mass damper in the building designed by Motioneering Inc. of Guelph, Ontario. It has a huge mass and vibrates opposite to the direction of the building, cancelling much of the amplitude of the resonant vibration.

THEN, NOW, AND FUTURE   Stressed-out Airplanes

Ask any mechanical engineers, and they will tell you the importance of designing equipment to minimize vibration. Vibration causes excess wear on parts and stress on materials. Nowhere is this more evident than on an airplane. Yancey Corden knows this better than most people. Yancey is an aircraft maintenance engineer, and one of his jobs is to inspect aircraft for excess metal fatigue.

Yancey was born on the Pavilion Reserve in south central British Columbia but grew up north of Williams Lake. His father maintained their car, boat, and other equipment around the home. Yancey watched and helped his father, and during this time, his interest in mechanics grew.

Not long after finishing high school, Yancey enrolled in the aircraft maintenance engineer program at the British Columbia Institute of Technology located in Burnaby. He is now qualified with an M1 certification, which allows him to work on planes under 12 500 kg, and an M2 certification, which allows him to work on larger planes.

He received specialized training in structural maintenance. This

▲ **Figure 7.50**   Yancey Corden

involves an in-depth knowledge of the skin and frame of the plane.

In 2003 Yancey moved to Alberta where he works in Red Deer for a company called Air Spray. Air Spray maintains and repairs Lockheed L-188 airplanes. These planes were originally manufactured as passenger craft in the 1950s, but because of their rugged design, they have been converted to firefighting aircraft today. They carry over 10 000 kg of water and fire retardant and are capable of dumping the entire amount in three seconds.

When a dump of water and fire retardant occurs, the wings and airframe of the plane undergo a huge

shift of force. This happens because the airplane springs upward due to the lighter load, and as a result, the wings tend to flutter up and down. This vibration causes stress fractures on the wing, and it is Yancey's job to find them. If a problem is found, Yancey designs the solution. This could involve fabricating a new part or simply fixing the existing one.

He enjoys his job because each day is different and brings new challenges.

He is thankful that he had the foresight to maintain good marks when he went to high school because the physics and science courses he took directly applied to his training. He is very proud of his heritage but he also believes it is important to focus on who you are and where you are going.

Questions

1. What factors contribute to metal fatigue on a firefighting airplane?

2. What steps must be taken to gain a licence as an aircraft maintenance engineer?

3. To what factors does Yancey attribute his success?

Quartz Clocks

The technology of clock design and manufacture has taken huge leaps since the 1600s when Huygens built his first pendulum clock. Today, quartz clocks are the most accurate timepieces commercially available. They have an accuracy of about 1/2000 of a second a day.

A quartz clock works on the principle of resonance. Inside each quartz clock is a tiny crystal of quartz. Quartz is a mineral that naturally grows in crystals. It also has a property unique to just a handful of materials: it will bend when a voltage is applied to it. If a pulse of voltage is applied to it, the crystal will begin to vibrate at its resonant frequency, just as a cymbal vibrates when hit by a drumstick. Once the quartz crystal is set vibrating, the circuitry of the clock times successive voltage pulses to synchronize with the frequency of the crystal. The synchronized voltage provides the forced frequency to keep the crystal oscillating just as the pendulums of Huygens's clocks needed a synchronized forced frequency to keep them from running down.

The difference is that the pendulum clock receives the forced frequency through mechanical means, while the quartz crystal clocks get the forced vibration from electrical means.

Resonant Frequency of a Quartz Crystal

The crystal's resonant frequency depends on its size and shape and is not affected significantly by temperature. This makes it ideal for keeping time. As the crystal gets larger, more voltage is required to make it oscillate, and its resonant frequency decreases. A piece of quartz could be cut to oscillate once every second, but it would be far too large for a wristwatch and would require a large voltage to operate. If the crystal size is decreased, less voltage is required to make it oscillate.

Quartz crystals are cut to a size and shape small enough to fit into a watch and use a small voltage (Figure 7.51). In most of today's quartz watches, the crystal vibrates with a resonant frequency of about 30 kHz and operates at 1.5 V. A small microprocessor in the watch combines these oscillations to make one oscillation per second so the watch can display time in a meaningful way.

The topic of resonant frequencies is large and can't possibly be fully covered in this unit. You will learn more about resonance in musical instruments in Chapter 8.

info **BIT**

A substance that deforms with an applied voltage is called a piezoelectric material. A piezoelectric material will also create a voltage if stressed. Some butane lighters use a piezoelectric material to create a flame. As the lighter trigger is pressed, butane gas is released and the piezoelectric material undergoes stress. The piezoelectric material creates a voltage that causes a spark to jump a very small gap at the end of the lighter, igniting the butane.

e **WEB**

Atomic clocks keep time extremely precisely. Do they use a principle of resonance to keep such accurate time? Begin your search at www.pearsoned.ca/school/physicssource.

▶ **Figure 7.51** The quartz crystal in a wristwatch is enclosed in the small metal cylinder (lower right).

Knowledge

1. What provides the force necessary to start a building or bridge oscillating?

2. What is forced frequency?

3. Explain what engineers use to reduce resonant vibrations of buildings and how these devices or structures work.

4. Explain the effect of applying a force to a vibrating object with the same frequency.

5. Identify two limitations of Huygens's pendulum clock.

6. Can a pendulum clock built to operate at the equator have the same accuracy at the North Pole? Explain.

7. What is damping? Use an example in your explanation.

Applications

8. How could a person walking across a rope bridge prevent resonant vibration from building up in the bridge?

9. An opera singer can shatter a champagne glass by sustaining the right musical note. Explain how this happens.

10. Tuning forks are Y-shaped metal bars not much bigger than a regular fork. They can be made to vibrate at a specific frequency when struck with a rubber hammer. A piano tuner uses tuning forks to tune a piano. Explain, in terms of resonance, how this might be done.

11. Students are asked to find ways to dampen or change the resonant frequency of a pendulum. Here is a list of their suggestions. Identify the ones that would work and those that would not. In each case, justify your answer.

    (a) Apply a forced frequency that is different from the resonant frequency.

    (b) Place the pendulum in water.

    (c) Increase the mass of the pendulum bob.

    (d) Move the pendulum to a higher altitude.

12. What factors affect the resonance of a quartz crystal?

13. (a) What are two advantages of a quartz clock over a pendulum clock?

    (b) Are there any disadvantages of a quartz clock compared with a pendulum clock?

Extensions

14. Use the knowledge you have gained about the design of a pendulum clock and the equation for its period in section 7.3 to answer the following question. What would the length of the pendulum's arm have to be so that it would oscillate with a resonant frequency of 1.00 Hz in Alberta ($g = 9.81$ m/s^2)? Under what conditions would it be most accurate?

15. Use your local library or the Internet to find out what automobile manufacturers do to reduce resonant frequencies in cars.

16. Investigate other methods not mentioned in the text that bridge designers use to lessen resonant vibrations.

17. Tuned mass dampers are not just used on buildings; cruise ships also have them. Explain why a cruise ship might have them and how they would be used.

18. Use your local library or the Internet to explore orbital resonance. In one or two paragraphs, explain how it applies to Saturn's rings.

 e TEST

To check your understanding of applications of simple harmonic motion, follow the eTest links at www.pearsoned.ca/school/physicssource.

Key Terms and Concepts

period	oscillatory motion	simple harmonic	resonant frequency
frequency	Hooke's law	motion	amplitude
oscillation	spring constant	simple harmonic	forced frequency
cycle	restoring force	oscillator	mechanical resonance

Key Equations

$$\vec{F} = -k\vec{x}$$

$$v_{max} = A\sqrt{\frac{k}{m}}$$

$$T = 2\pi\sqrt{\frac{m}{k}}$$

$$T = 2\pi\sqrt{\frac{l}{g}}$$

Conceptual Overview

The concept map below summarizes many of the concepts and equations in this chapter. Copy and complete the map to have a full summary of the chapter.

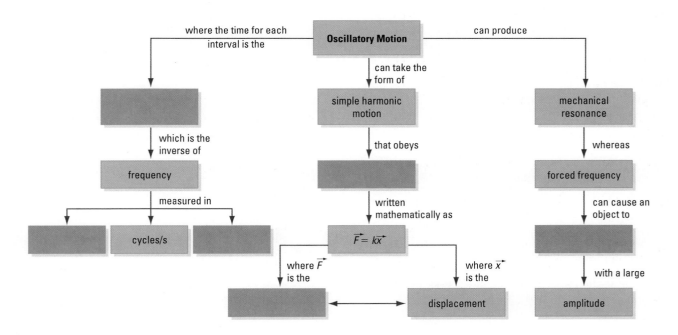

▲ **Figure 7.52**

Knowledge

1. (7.1) What is oscillatory motion? Use an example in your answer.

2. (7.1) Under what conditions must a ball be bounced so it has oscillatory motion?

3. (7.2) What is the defining property of an elastic material?

4. (7.2) What force, or forces, act on an isolated, frictionless simple harmonic oscillator?

5. (7.2) State the directional relationship that exists between the restoring force and displacement of a simple harmonic oscillator.

6. (7.2) What quantity does the slope of a force-displacement graph represent?

7. (7.2) What can be said about a pendulum's position if the restoring force is a non-zero value?

8. (7.3) Why isn't acceleration uniform for a simple harmonic oscillator?

9. (7.3) Why is it acceptable to consider a pendulum a simple harmonic oscillator for small displacements, but not for large displacements?

10. (7.4) What effect does the forced frequency have on the resonant frequency if they are similar?

Applications

11. Determine the restoring force acting on a 1.0-kg pendulum bob when it is displaced:

(a) 15°

(b) 5°

12. Determine the frequency of a guitar string that oscillates with a period of 0.0040 s.

13. What is the period of a ball with a frequency of 0.67 Hz?

14. After a diver jumps off, a diving board vibrates with a period of 0.100 s. What is its frequency?

15. What is the restoring force on a 2.0-kg pendulum bob displaced 15.0°?

16. Determine the spring constant from the following graph:

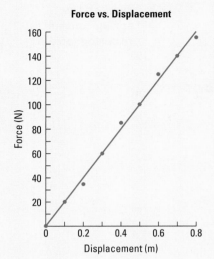

Force vs. Displacement

17. A spring hangs from the ceiling in a physics lab. The bottom of the spring is 1.80 m from the floor. When the teacher hangs a mass of 100 g from the bottom of the spring, the spring stretches 50.0 cm.

(a) What is its spring constant?

(b) What force must a person apply to pull the 100.0-g mass on the bottom of the spring down through a displacement of 20.0 cm?

(c) The 100.0-g mass is removed and a 300.0-g mass is attached. What is the displacement of the mass from the floor?

18. Two different springs, A and B, are attached together at one end. Spring B is fixed to the wall as shown. The spring constant of A is 100.0 N/m and B is 50.0 N/m. What is the combined displacement of the two springs when a force of 25.0 N is applied?

19. Students stretch an elastic band attached to a force meter through several displacements and gather the following data. Use a graphing calculator or another acceptable method to plot the graph of this data and determine if the elastic band moves as predicted by Hooke's law.

Displacement (cm)	Force (N)
0.00	0.00
10.0	3.80
20.0	15.2
30.0	34.2
40.0	60.8
50.0	95.0

20. How long must the arm of a pendulum clock be to swing with a period of 1.00 s, where the gravitational field strength is 9.81 m/s²?

21. What is the period of a 10.0-kg mass attached to a spring with a spring constant of 44.0 N/m?

22. Determine the maximum velocity of a 2.00-t crate suspended from a steel cable (k = 200.0 N/m) that is oscillating up and down with an amplitude of 12.0 cm.

23. A 0.480-g spider is oscillating vertically on the end of its thread with a maximum displacement of 0.040 m and a maximum speed of 0.100 m/s. What acceleration does the spider have if it is displaced 0.0200 m upwards from the equilibrium position?

24. Determine the period of oscillation of a pendulum that has a length of 25.85 cm.

25. An astronaut who has just landed on Pluto wants to determine the gravitational field strength. She uses a pendulum that is 0.50 m long and discovers it has a frequency of vibration of 0.182 Hz. What value will she determine for Pluto's gravity?

26. A student is given the relationship for a pendulum: $T = 2\pi\sqrt{X}$
    (a) What does X represent?
    (b) The student records the period of the pendulum and finds it is 1.79 s. What is the pendulum's length?

Extensions

27. A spring (k = 10.0 N/m) is suspended from the ceiling and a mass of 250.0 g is hanging from the end at rest. The mass is pulled to a displacement of 20.0 cm and released.
    (a) What is the maximum velocity of the mass?
    (b) What is the period of oscillation of the mass if it is displaced 15.0 cm and released?

28. A horizontal mass-spring system has a mass M attached to a spring that oscillates back and forth at a frequency of 0.800 Hz. Determine the frequency in the following cases.
    (a) The mass is doubled.
    (b) The amplitude is tripled.

29. Identify which of the following examples is SHM and which is not. Explain.
    (a) a bouncing ball
    (b) a hockey player moving a puck back and forth with his stick
    (c) a plucked guitar string

Consolidate Your Understanding

Create your own summary of oscillatory motion, simple harmonic motion, restoring force, and mechanical resonance by answering the questions below. If you want to use a graphic organizer, refer to Student References 4: Using Graphic Organizers on pp. 869–871. Use the Key Terms and Concepts listed above and the Learning Outcomes on page 342.

1. Prepare a quick lesson that you could use to explain Hooke's law to a peer using the following terms: restoring force, displacement, linear relationship.

2. Construct a two-column table with the title "Mass-spring System." The first column has the heading, "Factors Affecting Period" and the second column has the heading, "Factors Not Affecting Period." Categorize the following factors into the two columns: mass, spring constant, amplitude, restoring force, velocity.

Think About It

Review your answers to the Think About It questions on page 343. How would you answer each question now?

e **TEST**

To check your understanding of oscillatory motion, follow the eTest links at www.pearsoned.ca/school/physicssource.

Mechanical waves transmit energy in a variety of ways.

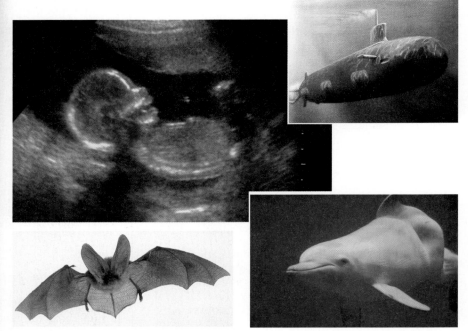

▲ **Figure 8.1**

What do bats and dolphins have in common? The phrase "blind as a bat" states a common fallacy. Bats have some vision using light, but when placed in pitch-black rooms crisscrossed with fine wires, they can easily fly around and unerringly locate tiny flying insects for food. Dolphins have shown that they can quickly locate and retrieve objects even when they are blindfolded. We usually assume that vision requires light but both bats and dolphins have evolved the ability to "see" using sound waves.

Research in science and technology has developed "eyes" that enable humans also to see using sound waves, that is, navigate with senses other than sight. Medicine uses ultrasound (frequencies above the audible range) to look at objects such as a fetus or a tumour inside the body. Submarines can circumnavigate the globe without surfacing by using sound waves to explore their underwater environment.

In Chapter 6, you studied how mass transfers energy when it moves through space. Waves, on the other hand, are able to transmit vast quantities of energy between two places without moving any mass from one location to another. Radio waves carry information, sound waves carry conversations, and light waves provide the stimulus for the cells that enable vision. This chapter introduces you to the nature and properties of waves. By experimenting with various forms of wave motion, you will learn about this common, but often misunderstood method of energy transmission.

Fundamental Properties of Wave Motion

Problem

To determine properties of waves in a ripple tank.

Materials

ripple tank and apparatus for its operation
dowel (~ 1.5 cm in diameter)
2 stopwatches
ruler, two paper clips
light and stand to project waves onto screen
screen (a large sheet of newsprint works well)

Procedure

1 Set up the ripple tank as shown in Figure 8.2. The water should be about 1 cm deep. Make sure that energy-absorbing buffers are placed around the edge of the tank to prevent unwanted reflections. Check your assembly with your instructor.

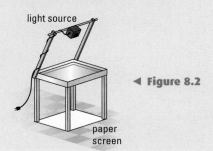

◀ **Figure 8.2**

light source

paper
screen

2 (a) Place a tiny spot of paper in the middle of the ripple tank.

    (b) Dip the end of your finger once into the water about the middle of the ripple tank to create a single, circular, wave front. Observe the speck of paper as the wave front passes it.
Sketch what you observe. Describe the motion.

3 (a) On the screen, place the two paper clips at a measured distance apart, ~ 30–40 cm.

    (b) Position your finger so that its shadow is over one of the paper clips and generate another single wave front.

    (c) Using a stopwatch, measure the time for the wave to travel from one paper clip to the other. Record the distance and time. Calculate the speed of the wave. Do a few trials for accuracy.

4 (a) Place the dowel in the water near one edge of the tank. Tap the dowel gently and observe the wave front. Sketch and describe the motion.

    (b) Position the paper clips in the wave's path and measure the speed of the straight wave front.

> ⚠ **CAUTION: Use care with ripple tanks. It is easy to break the glass bottom or to spill water. This is a serious hazard in an area where electricity is being used. Vibrating the tank will generate unwanted waves.**

Questions

1. When a wave front passes the speck of paper, what motion does the paper make? Does it move in the same or the opposite direction to the motion of the wave front? What does that tell you about the motion of the water as the wave moves through it?

2. On your sketches, draw several vector arrows along the fronts to indicate the direction in which they are moving. What is the angle between the line of the wave front and its motion? In Procedure 4(a), what is the angle between the edge of the dowel and the direction of the motion of the wave front?

3. Which wave front moves faster, the circular wave front or the straight wave front?

---

1. What differences and similarities are there between the ways energy is transmitted by waves and by matter?

2. What assumptions must be made to use water waves as a model for sound waves?

Discuss your answers in a small group and record them. As you complete each section of this chapter, review your answers to these questions. Note any changes in your ideas.

e **SIM**

Find out more about waves in ripple tanks. Go to www.pearsoned.ca/school/physicssource.

8.1 The Properties of Waves

info **BIT**

In December of 2004, an earthquake, near the island of Sumatra, set off a tsunami that is estimated to have had more than 2 petajoules (10^{15} J) of energy. This tsunami, the most powerful in recorded history, took over 225 000 lives and did untold billions of dollars in damage to the economies and the environments of the countries that border on the Indian Ocean.

info **BIT**

On the day of the tsunami of 2004 that devastated Phuket, Thailand, people travelling in a ferry in deep water offshore from Phuket felt only a greater than usual swell as the wave passed them by.

▲ **Figure 8.3** Surfers use a wave's energy to speed their boards across the water.

medium: material, for example, air or water through which waves travel; the medium does not travel with the wave

wave: disturbance that moves outward from its point of origin transferring energy through a medium by means of vibrations

equilibrium position: rest position or position of a medium from which the amplitude of a wave can be measured

crest: region where the medium rises above the equilibrium position

trough: region where the medium is lower than the equilibrium position

When a surfer catches a wave, many people assume that the forward motion of the surfer is the result of the forward motion of the water in the wave. However, experimental evidence indicates that in a deep-water wave the water does not, in general, move in the direction of the wave motion. In fact, the surfer glides down the surface of the wave just as a skier glides down the surface of a ski hill. Like the skier, the surfer can traverse across the face of the hill as well as slide down the hill. But, unlike the ski hill, the water in the wave front is constantly rising. So, even though the surfer is sliding down the front of the wave he never seems to get much closer to the bottom of the wave.

It is a common misconception that the water in a wave moves in the direction in which the waves are travelling. This may be because waves arriving at the shoreline move water to and fro across the sand. As you will see, this movement is a feature of the interaction of the wave with the sloping shoreline rather than the actual motion of the wave itself. In deep water, there is only very limited lateral motion of water when a wave moves past a particular point.

Waves and Wave Trains

When a stone is thrown into a still pond or lake, a ripple moves outward in ever-enlarging concentric circles (Figure 8.4). The water is the transporting **medium** of the **wave** and the undisturbed surface of the water is known as the wave's **equilibrium position**. Regions where the water rises above the equilibrium position are called **crests** and regions where the water is lower than its equilibrium position are called **troughs**. In the crest or trough, the magnitude of greatest displacement from the equilibrium is defined as the waves' **amplitude** (*a*). A complete cycle of a crest followed by a trough is called a **wavelength**; its symbol is λ (Figure 8.5).

▲ **Figure 8.4** Many of the terms used to describe wave motions come from the observation of waves on the surface of water.

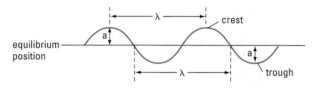

▲ **Figure 8.5** Properties of a wave

A **wave front** moving out from the point of origin toward a barrier is called an **incident wave**. A wave front moving away from the barrier is called a **reflected wave,** while a series of waves linked together is a **wave train**. The concept of a wave train implies a regular repetition of the motion of the medium through which the wave travels. As a result, many parts of the medium are moving in a motion that is identical to the motion of other points on the wave train. At these points, the waves are said to be **in phase** (Figure 8.6).

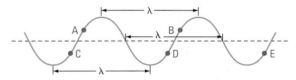

A and B are in phase
C, D, and E are in phase

▲ **Figure 8.6** In-phase points along a wave train have identical status relative to the medium and are separated by one wavelength, λ.

Instead of creating individual pulses by hand in a ripple tank, you may use a wave generator to create a continuous series of crests and troughs forming a wave train. Wave generators can act as a **point source** similar to the tip of a finger, or as a straight line, similar to a dowel. In 8-1 QuickLab you measured the speed of a single pulse by observing its motion. However, because it is impossible to keep track of a single wave in a wave train, to measure the speed of a wave train requires a greater understanding of the properties of waves.

e **WEB**

To learn more about experiments using ripple tanks, follow the links at www.pearsoned.ca/school/ physicssource.

amplitude: the distance from the equilibrium position to the top of a crest or the bottom of a trough

wavelength: the distance between two points on a wave that have identical status. It is usually measured from crest to crest or from trough to trough.

wave front: an imaginary line that joins all points reached by the wave at the same instant

incident wave: a wave front moving from the point of origin toward a barrier

reflected wave: a wave front moving away from a barrier

wave train: a series of waves forming a continuous series of crests and troughs

point source: a single point of disturbance that generates a circular wave

Wave Trains in a Ripple Tank, Part 1: Reflecting Waves

In this ripple tank experiment, the properties of a two-dimensional wave train are analyzed.

Question

How do the incident and reflected wave trains interact when wave trains reflect from a straight barrier?

Materials and Equipment

ripple tank, including the apparatus for its operation
dowel (~ 1.5 cm in diameter)
rectangular wooden bar (~ 2 cm × 2 cm)
wave generators (point-source and straight-line)
light and stand to project waves onto screen
screen (a large sheet of newsprint works well)
two small blocks of wood about 8 mm thick

Variables

In this experiment you are to observe the directions of motion of the incident waves and reflected waves and how these directions are related to each other. Other variables to be observed are the interactions that occur when the incident and reflected wave trains move in different directions through the same point in the ripple tank. As you observe the wave motions you should identify which are the controlled variables, manipulated variables, and responding variables.

General Procedure

1 (a) Set up the ripple tank as shown in Figure 8.7.

(b) When using motorized wave generators, it is important that the generator just barely contacts the surface of the water. It should never touch the tank during operation. Check with your instructor to make sure that your apparatus is properly assembled.

> ⚠ **CAUTION: Use care with ripple tanks. It is easy to break the glass bottom or to spill water. This is a serious hazard in an area where electricity is being used. Vibrating the tank will generate unwanted waves that interfere with the desired observations. The wave generator should never touch the tank during operation.**

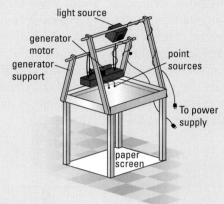

light source
generator motor
generator support
point sources
To power supply
paper screen

▲ **Figure 8.7**

Procedure

1 (a) Place the point-source wave generator at one edge of the ripple tank and the straight barrier at the other edge. The shadow of both the barrier and the source should be visible on the screen.

(b) Use the point-source wave generator to create a continuous wave train in the ripple tank. Observe what happens to the incident wave train when it meets the reflected wave train.

(c) Make a sketch of your observations. Wave trains are a bit tricky to observe at first. Discuss what you see with your team members. When you have reached a consensus, write a brief description of your observations. On your sketch, place vector arrows along an incident and a reflected wave front to indicate the direction and speed of their motions.

2 (a) Set up the straight-line wave generator at one edge of the ripple tank. Place the barrier at the other edge parallel to the generator. The shadows of both the generator and the barrier should be visible on the screen.

(b) Start the generator to create a continuous wave train. Observe what happens when the reflected wave train moves back through the incident wave train. Draw diagrams and write a description of the observations. Again, draw vector arrows along incident and reflected wave fronts to indicate their relative velocities.

③ Move the barrier so that it is at an angle of about 30° to the generator and repeat step 2 (b).

④ Set the barrier so that the angle between it and the generator is about 60° and repeat step 2 (b).

Analysis

1. (a) When the incident wave train created by the point-source generator is passing through the reflected wave train, what happens to the waves in the region where they overlap?

   (b) Can you see the direction of the motion for both the incident and reflected wave trains?

2. (a) When the barrier is parallel to the straight wave generator, what pattern do you observe when the reflected waves are moving back through the incident waves?

   (b) In which direction does the pattern seem to be moving? Can you see the direction of the motion for both the incident and reflected wave trains?

3. Answer question 2 for the set-up when the barrier is at an angle to the straight wave generator.

4. In all cases above, how does the spacing of the waves in the reflected wave train compare to the spacing of the waves in the incident wave train?

Waves and Rays

When waves in a ripple tank are viewed from above (Figure 8.8) the wave fronts appear as a set of bright and dark bands (crests and troughs). When we draw wave trains as seen from above, we use a line to represent a wave front along the top of a crest. The point halfway between two lines is the bottom of a trough. A series of concentric circles represents the wave train generated by a point source.

ray: a line that indicates only the direction of motion of the wave front at any point where the ray and the wave intersect

▲ **Figure 8.8**   View of a ripple tank from above

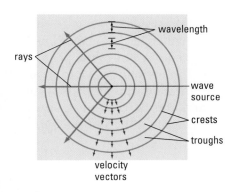

▲ **Figure 8.9**   A point source generates waves that move outward as concentric circles with the source at their centre

Waves are in constant motion. At all points on a wave front, the wave is moving at right angles to the line of the crest. There are two ways to indicate this (Figure 8.9). You could draw a series of vector arrows at right angles to the wave front with their length indicating the speed of the wave. Or, you could draw **rays**, lines indicating only the direction of motion of the wave front at any point where the ray and the wave front intersect. The rays in Figure 8.9 are called **diverging** rays since they spread out as they move away from the origin. When rays diverge, it indicates that the energy given to the wave at its source is being spread over a larger and larger area. This is why, as sound moves away from a point source such as a bell, the volume decreases with the square of the distance.

e **WEB**

To learn more about the mathematical relationship between the volume of sound and the distance from the source, follow the links at www.pearsoned.ca/school/physicssource.

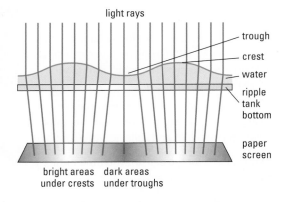

light rays

trough

crest

water

ripple tank bottom

paper screen

bright areas under crests dark areas under troughs

▲ **Figure 8.10** Sketch of a wave showing light refracting through a crest and a trough

When waves in a ripple tank are projected onto a screen below, the wave fronts appear as a set of bright and dark bands. It may seem logical that the light and dark bands seen on the screen below the ripple tank result from the differences in water depth between the crests and the troughs. But that difference is only about a millimetre and cannot account for the high contrast in light seen on the screen. In fact, a crest acts like a converging lens to concentrate the light, creating a bright bar. A trough acts like a diverging lens to spread the light out making the area under the trough darker (Figure 8.10). You will learn more about light refraction in Unit VII of this course.

Reflection of a Wave Front

When a wave front is incident on a straight barrier, it reflects. The direction the wave travels after reflection depends on the angle between the incident wave front and the barrier. A circular wave front, as generated by a point source, S, produces the simplest reflection pattern to explain. In this case, the reflected wave follows a path as if it had been generated by an imaginary point source S′, at a position behind the barrier identical to that of the actual point source in front of the barrier (Figure 8.11).

Now consider an incident wave front created by a straight wave generator (Figure 8.12). The straight wave front also reflects as if the reflected wave had been generated by an imaginary generator located behind the barrier. The position of the imaginary generator behind the barrier is equivalent to the position of the real generator in front of the barrier. The incident wave front and the reflected wave front are travelling in different directions, but the angle θ between the incident wave front and the barrier must be identical to the angle θ between the reflected wave front and the barrier.

 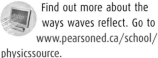
e **SIM**

Find out more about the ways waves reflect. Go to www.pearsoned.ca/school/physicssource.

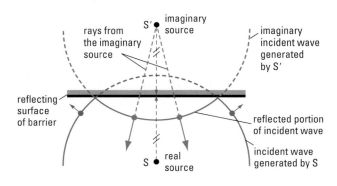

imaginary source

rays from the imaginary source

S′

imaginary incident wave generated by S′

reflecting surface of barrier

reflected portion of incident wave

S real source

incident wave generated by S

▲ **Figure 8.11** When circular waves reflect from a straight barrier, the reflected waves seem to be moving away from an imaginary source.

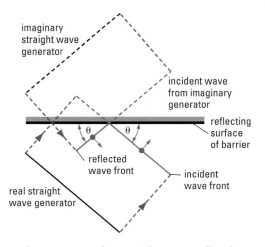

imaginary straight wave generator

incident wave from imaginary generator

reflecting surface of barrier

reflected wave front

incident wave front

real straight wave generator

▲ **Figure 8.12** When straight waves reflect from a straight barrier, the angle between the reflected wave front and the barrier must be equal to the angle between the incident wave front and the barrier.

MINDS ON | Waves Can Have Curls Too

When waves travel in deep water, their shape is similar to the waves in a ripple tank. But as waves near the shoreline they change shape and develop what is known as a curl in which the top of the wave falls in front of the wave. Recall Figure 8.3 on page 394. In terms of the wave's motion, explain the causes of its curl.

8-3 *Inquiry Lab*

Required Skills
■ Initiating and Planning
■ Performing and Recording
■ Analyzing and Interpreting
■ Communication and Teamwork

Wave Trains in a Ripple Tank, Part 2: Wave Speed and Wavelength

In this ripple tank experiment, the properties of a two-dimensional wave train are further analyzed.

Question

What effect does a change in speed have on wave trains?

Materials and Equipment

ripple tank, including the apparatus for its operation
rectangular wooden bar ($\sim$ 2 cm $\times$ 2 cm)
wave generators (point-source and straight-line)
light and stand to project waves onto screen
screen (a large sheet of newsprint works well)
two small blocks of wood about 8 mm thick

Variables

In this lab you will be observing how water depth affects the properties of waves. The variables that might be affected by changes in the depth are speed, frequency, wavelength, and direction. As you make your observations, consider which of the variables are controlled variables, manipulated variables, and responding variables.

General Procedure

1. (a) Set up the ripple tank as shown in Figure 8.7.
   (b) When using motorized wave generators, it is important that the generator just barely contacts the surface of the water. It should never touch the tank during operation. Check with your instructor to make sure that your apparatus is properly assembled.

⚠️ **CAUTION: Use care with ripple tanks. It is easy to break the glass bottom or to spill water. This is a serious hazard in an area where electricity is being used. Vibrating the tank will generate unwanted waves that interfere with the desired observations. The wave generator should never touch the tank during operation.**

Procedure

1. Place small pads (about 8 mm thick) under the legs along one edge of the ripple tank so that the water gets shallower toward that edge. The water should be less than 1 mm deep at the shallow edge.

2. (a) Near the deep edge, create a wave train using the point-source generator.
   (b) Observe what happens to the wave fronts as the wave train moves toward the shallow edge. Discuss your observations with your team members. Sketch and briefly describe your observations.
   (c) Place vector arrows along several of the wave fronts to indicate the direction and speed of the wave fronts as they move into shallow water.

3. (a) Set up the straight-line wave generator at the deep edge of the tank.
   (b) Turn on the generator and observe the wave train as it moves into the shallow water.
   (c) Sketch your observations and describe the motion of the wave train as it moves into shallow water. Use vector arrows along the wave fronts to assist you in your descriptions.

4. (a) Now place the pads under the legs of the ripple tank on an edge that is at a right angle to the position of the straight-line wave generator.
   (b) Use the straight-line wave generator to create a wave train.
   (c) Observe the wave train as it travels across the tank. Discuss your observations with your team members. Sketch and write a brief description of what you saw to accompany your sketch. Use vector arrows drawn along several of the wave fronts to indicate their relative velocity as they move into the shallow water.

Analysis

1. For each of the trials, when the waves moved from deep to shallow edge (or vice versa), comment on the kinds of changes you observed.

   (a) Were the wavelengths of the incident waves affected as they moved into shallow water?

   (b) Was the shape of the wave fronts affected as they entered shallow water?

   (c) If so, how did the shape of the wave fronts change as they changed speed?

2. What do you think causes the observed changes?

3. When the straight wave fronts moved across the tank at right angles to the change in the depth of the water, was the shape of the wave front affected?

4. What wave properties are affected by waves as they move from deep to shallow water?

5. When a water wave moves toward a beach, how would the change in the depth of the water affect the motion of the wave?

8.1 Check and Reflect

Knowledge

1. If a wave pattern is created by a point source, what is the nature of the ray diagram that would represent the wave fronts?

2. When a wave front reflects from a barrier, what is the relationship between the direction of the motions of the incident and reflected wave fronts?

Applications

3. The sketch shows a ray diagram that represents the motion of a set of wave fronts. If you were observing these wave fronts in a ripple tank, describe what you would see.

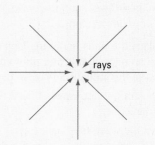

4. Draw a diagram of a set of straight wave fronts that are incident on a straight barrier such that the angle between the wave fronts and the barrier is 40°. Draw the reflected wave fronts resulting from this interaction. How do the properties (speed, wavelength, and amplitude) of the reflected wave compare with the properties of the incident wave? Use a wavelength of about 1 cm in your diagram.

Extensions

5. Reflection of light is the essence of how we use mirrors to see images. What does the reflection of waves in a ripple tank tell you about the formation of images? Hint: Think of where the reflected waves in the ripple tank seem to originate.

6. When a sound travels in water, the speed of the sound depends on the temperature of the water. If the sonar ping emitted by a submarine has a wavelength of 2.50 m, what happens to that wavelength when it enters a region where sound travels faster?

 e **TEST**

To check your understanding of the properties of waves, follow the eTest links at www.pearsoned.ca/school/physicssource.

8.2

Transverse and Longitudinal Waves

Did you ever have a Slinky™ toy when you were a child? When a Slinky™ is stretched out along the floor and oscillated from side to side across its axis (centre line), or forward and back along its axis, mechanical waves are transmitted along its length. The sideways oscillations set up a **transverse wave** while those along the axis set up a **longitudinal wave** as shown in Figure 8.13. In this section we will consider the characteristics of such waves.

Transverse Pulses

A pulse moving through a spring is a good introduction to the way a wave moves through a medium. An ideal spring is one that allows a pulse to travel through it without loss of energy. By definition, a **pulse** is just the crest or the trough of a wave; its length is one-half a wavelength. The spring provides a medium in which the motion of a pulse can be observed from the side. Initially, the spring is in its equilibrium position. When you flip the spring sharply to the side and back, the motion of your hand sets up a series of sequential motions in the coils of the spring. Each coil imitates, in turn, the motion of the hand. This results in a **transverse** pulse (Figure 8.14) that moves along the spring.

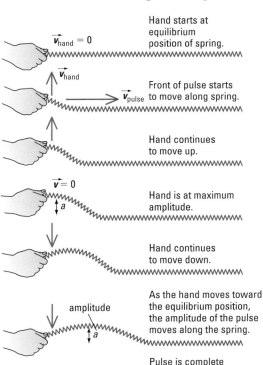

$\vec{v}_{hand} = 0$ — Hand starts at equilibrium position of spring.

$\vec{v}_{hand}$ — $\vec{v}_{pulse}$ — Front of pulse starts to move along spring.

Hand continues to move up.

$\vec{v} = 0$ — a — Hand is at maximum amplitude.

Hand continues to move down.

amplitude — a — As the hand moves toward the equilibrium position, the amplitude of the pulse moves along the spring.

l — Pulse is complete when the hand is at equilibrium position.

$\vec{v}_{hand} = 0$

As a pulse moves along a spring, the coils of the spring move at right angles to the direction of the pulse's motion. Compare $\vec{v}_{hand}$ and $\vec{v}_{pulse}$ in Figure 8.14. At the front of the pulse, the coils are moving away from the spring's equilibrium position toward the point of maximum displacement from the equilibrium. In the trailing edge of the pulse, the coils are moving back toward the equilibrium position.

◀ **Figure 8.14** When you move your hand you set up a sequence in which the coils of the spring imitate the motion of your hand. This creates a moving pulse.

info **BIT**

The ever-popular Slinky™ was invented in 1945 by Richard James, a naval engineer working on tension springs. The name comes from the Swedish for "sleek" or "sinuous." Each Slinky™ is made from 80 feet (24.384 m) of wire.

▲ **Figure 8.13**
(a) A transverse pulse
(b) A longitudinal pulse
Arrows indicate the direction of the medium. The pulses are moving through the springs toward the bottom of the page.

pulse: a disturbance of short duration in a medium; usually seen as the crest or trough of a wave

e **WEB**

To learn more about the forces operating in an oscillating spring, follow the links at www.pearsoned.ca/school/physicssource.

Energy Changes During the Movement of a Pulse

Along the pulse, energy is stored in the form of both elastic potential energy and kinetic energy. As a section of the spring moves from the equilibrium position to the top of the pulse, that section has both kinetic energy (it is moving sideways) and elastic potential energy (it is stretched sideways). At the point on the pulse where the displacement is greatest the coils are, for an instant, motionless. Then, the tension in the spring returns the coils to their equilibrium position.

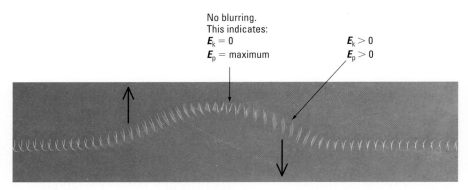

No blurring.
This indicates:
$E_k = 0$
$E_p = $ maximum

$E_k > 0$
$E_p > 0$

▲ **Figure 8.15** A transverse pulse is generated when a spring is given a sharp flip to the side. Arrows indicate the direction of motion of the coils. Can you determine which way the pulse is moving?

In Figure 8.15 the blurring on the front and back segments of the pulse indicates the transverse motion and the presence of kinetic energy as well as elastic potential energy. At the top, there is no blurring as the coils are temporarily motionless. At that instant that segment of the spring has only elastic potential energy. As it returns to its equilibrium position, the segment has, again, both kinetic and potential energies. The energy in a pulse moves along the spring by the sequential transverse motions of the coils.

Recall from section 6.3, that a pendulum, along the arc of its path, has both kinetic and potential energy, but at the point where the pendulum's displacement is greatest, all the energy is in the form of potential energy. Thus, the energy of an oscillating pendulum is equivalent to its potential energy at the point where its displacement is greatest. Similarly, the amplitude of the wave in an experimental spring can be used to determine the quantity of energy that is stored in the pulse.

info **BIT**

When considering sound, amplitude determines loudness.

Concept Check

You generate a pulse in a Slinky™ stretched out on the floor. If you wish to, you could give the next pulse more energy. How would you do that?

Pulses in a Spring, Part 1: Pulses in an Elastic Medium

In this experiment, you will study how a pulse moves through a medium.

Question

What are the mechanics by which pulses move through a medium?

Variables

The measured properties of a pulse include its amplitude (a), pulse length (l), period (Δt), and speed (v).

Materials and Equipment

light spring	stopwatch
metre-stick or measuring tape	masking tape

⚠ **CAUTION: A stretched spring stores consider-able amounts of elastic potential energy. Be careful not to release the end of a spring while it is stretched. When collapsing a spring, have the person holding one end walk the spring slowly toward the other end. If you allow the spring to gently unwind as you are walking you will prevent the spring from tying itself into a knot.**

Procedure

1. Have one team member hold the end of the spring while another stretches it until it is moderately stretched (about 5–6 m).

2. Place strips of masking tape on the floor at either end of the spring to mark this length. Near the middle of the spring, attach a strip of tape about 5 cm long to one of the coils.

3. Have one of the people holding the spring generate a transverse pulse. Generate the pulse by moving your hand sharply to one side (about 60–75 cm) and back to its original position. This is a **transverse pulse** since its amplitude is perpendicular to the direction of its motion.

4. Sketch the pulse. Indicate the motions of the pulse and the coils using vector arrows. Observe the motion of the tape at the middle of the spring to assist in these observations. Generate more pulses until you understand the nature of the motion of the pulse in the spring.

5. On your sketch of the pulse, label the following parts:
   - The amplitude (a) is the perpendicular distance from the equilibrium position of the spring to the top of the pulse.
   - The pulse length (l) is the distance over which the spring is distorted from its equilibrium position.

   NOTE: When you stand at the side of the spring, the pulse seems to move past you very quickly, almost as a blur. Watching from the end of the spring may make it easier to observe the details of the motion.

6. Make a **longitudinal pulse** by moving your hand sharply toward the person holding the spring at the other end, and then back to its original position. This pulse is called a longitudinal pulse, because its amplitude is along the direction of its motion. Repeat the pulse a few times to determine the nature of the motion of the spring as the pulse moves through it. Sketch and describe the motion of the coils as the pulse moves along the spring.

Analysis

1. What decides the amplitude of the transverse pulse? The longitudinal pulse?

2. Does the pulse change shape as it moves along the spring? If so, what causes the change in shape of the pulse? Would you expect the pulse shape to change if this were an isolated system?

3. How is the reflected pulse different from the incident pulse? If this were an isolated system, how would the reflected pulse differ from the incident pulse?

4. Describe the motion of the strip of tape at the middle of the spring as the pulse passes it. Does the tape move in the direction of the pulse?

5. How does the motion of the medium relate to the motion of the pulse?

6. How does the pulse transfer energy from one end of the spring to the other?

7. The motion of a pulse in the spring requires you to make assumptions about the motion of an ideal pulse. What assumptions must you make to create a model of how a transverse pulse moves through an elastic medium?

Longitudinal Waves

e SIM

Find out about similarities and differences between transverse and longitudinal waves. Go to www.pearsoned.ca/school/physicssource.

If, instead of moving your hand across the line of the spring, you give the spring a sharp push along its length, you will observe that a pulse moves along the spring. This pulse is evidence of a **longitudinal wave**. The pulse is seen as a region where the coils are more tightly compressed followed by a region where the coils are more widely spaced. These two regions are called, respectively, a **compression** and a **rarefaction** and correspond to the crest and trough in a transverse wave. In the case of a longitudinal wave, the coils of the spring oscillate back and forth parallel to the direction of the motion of the wave through the medium. But, as with transverse waves, once the wave has passed through, the medium returns to its original place. Once again, energy is transmitted through the medium without the transmission of matter.

▶ **Figure 8.16** Longitudinal waves are formed when the source oscillates parallel to the direction of the wave motion.

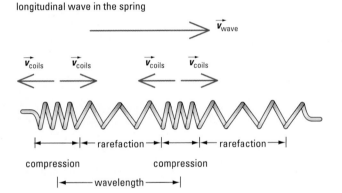

Project LINK

What aspect of your seismograph will relate to the ideas of compression and rarefaction in a longitudinal wave?

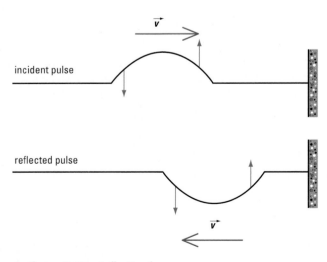

▲ **Figure 8.17** Reflection from the fixed end of a spring causes the pulse to be inverted.

Reflection of Pulses from a Fixed Point

When a pulse (or wave) is generated in a spring it soon arrives at the other end of the spring. If that end is held in place, the total pulse reflects from the end and travels back toward the source. The reflected pulse is always inverted relative to the incident pulse (Figure 8.17).

In an ideal medium, the other properties of the pulse (amplitude, length, and speed) are unaffected by reflection. These properties of the reflected pulse are identical to those of the incident pulse.

When a wave train is generated in the spring, the crests of the incident wave are reflected as troughs while the troughs of the incident wave are reflected as crests.

Pulses in a Spring, Part 2: Speed, Amplitude, and Length

In this experiment, you will study the speed, amplitude, and length of pulses.

Question

What is the relationship between the amplitude, length, and speed of a pulse?

Variables

The measured properties of a pulse include its amplitude (a), pulse length (l), period (Δt), and speed (v).

Materials and Equipment

light spring
stopwatch
metre-stick or measuring tape
masking tape

Procedure

1 (a) Measure the speed of a transverse pulse as it moves along the spring. Have the person creating the pulse "count down" so that team members with stopwatches can time the pulse as it moves toward the other end. Measure the time from the instant the front edge of the pulse leaves the hand of the person generating it until the front edge arrives at the hand at the other end. Do this a few times to establish a consistent value. Record your results. Use the time and the distance between the hands to calculate the speed of the pulse.

(b) Generate pulses by moving your hand to the side and back at different speeds (more quickly or more slowly). Measure the speed of each of these pulses.

2 Have the person holding one end of the spring move so that the spring is stretched about 1 m farther. (Do not overstretch the spring.) Generate a pulse and measure the speed of the pulse in the spring at this higher tension. Carefully walk the spring back to the length used initially.

3 Make a transverse pulse by moving your hand a different distance sideways. Try to keep the time used to make the pulse the same as before. Repeat this a few times to observe changes in the pulse. Record your observations.

4 Now make several transverse pulses by moving your hand to a given amplitude but change the speed at which you move. Repeat a few times and record your observations.

Analysis

1. Does the speed at which you moved your hand to generate a pulse affect the speed of the pulse?

2. When the spring was stretched to a greater length, what happened to the speed of the pulse?

3. What controls the amplitude (a) of the pulse? Can you create pulses with equal lengths but different amplitudes?

4. What controls the length (l) of the pulse? Can pulses of equal amplitudes have different lengths?

5. What is the relationship between the length of the pulse and the speed (v) of the pulse in the medium?

6. Does the length of a pulse affect its larger amplitude or vice versa? Explain why or why not.

7. Does the energy in a pulse seem to depend on its amplitude or its length? Give reasons for your decision. Consider what changes occur as the pulse moves through the spring.

8. What decides the speed, the length, and the amplitude of the pulse?

9. What aspect of wave motion in water can you simulate by changing the tension in a spring?

10. What do your findings for the relationship of the amplitudes and lengths of pulses in springs tell you about the relationship between the amplitudes and wavelengths of waves in water?

11. Sound is often referred to as a wave. What aspect of a sound would relate to (a) the amplitude, and (b) the wavelength of its waves?

Pulse Length and Speed

The speed of the pulse depends on the medium. If you stretch the spring so that the tension increases, then the speed of the pulse increases. Relaxing the tension causes the speed to decrease. The speed of the pulse in the spring also determines the length of the pulse.

The instant you start to move your hand to generate a pulse, the disturbance begins to move along the spring at a constant speed, v. Assume that the time it takes to move your hand to create the complete pulse is Δt. By the time your hand returns the spring to its equilibrium position, the front of the pulse will have travelled a distance Δd, which can be defined as the length l of the pulse (Figure 8.18).

Remember

$$v = \frac{\Delta d}{\Delta t} \quad \text{and, therefore}$$

$$\Delta d = v\Delta t$$

$$\therefore l = v\Delta t$$

▶ **Figure 8.18** The length (*l*) of the pulse depends on the speed (*v*) of the pulse and the time (Δ*t*) taken to complete the pulse.

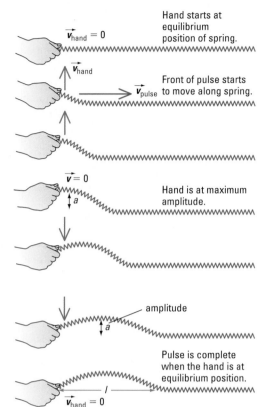

Hand starts at equilibrium position of spring. $\vec{v}_{hand} = 0$

$\vec{v}_{hand}$ Front of pulse starts to move along spring. $\vec{v}_{pulse}$

$\vec{v} = 0$ Hand is at maximum amplitude. a

amplitude a

Pulse is complete when the hand is at equilibrium position. l $\vec{v}_{hand} = 0$

e **WEB**

To learn more about the way the structures of the human ear transfer sound waves, follow the links at www.pearsoned.ca/school/physicssource.

info **BIT**

When a wave moves across the surface of water, the water moves between crests and troughs by localized circular motions. This local circular motion moves water back and forth between a trough and the adjacent crest.

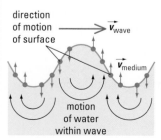

direction of motion of surface $\vec{v}_{wave}$

$\vec{v}_{medium}$

motion of water within wave

◀ **Figure 8.19**

Waves and the Medium

A solid such as a spring is an elastic medium and can store elastic potential energy by stretching longitudinally or transversely. The only way that fluids (liquids and gases) can store elastic potential energy is by being compressed. Therefore, waves within fluids must be longitudinal waves, known as pressure waves. This is the principle used in engines and aerosol sprays. As compressions and rarefactions move through a fluid, the motion of the molecules in the fluid is very similar to the motion of the coils when a longitudinal wave moves through a spring.

For water to transmit energy as a transverse wave, the waves must be displaced vertically, but in liquids the vertical displacement cannot be a form of elastic potential energy. Thus, transverse waves can be transmitted only at the surface of water, or other liquids, where the waves are the result of gravitational potential energy rather than elastic potential energy.

Water can transmit both transverse (surface) waves and longitudinal (internal) waves such as sound. We know that sound waves in gases are longitudinal waves.

Is it possible to create a transverse wave in a gas? Why or why not? Consider how transverse waves are created in liquids.

Example 8.1

To create a pulse in a fixed ideal spring, you move your hand sideways a distance of 45 cm from the equilibrium position. It takes 0.80 s from the time you begin to move your hand until it returns the spring to its equilibrium position. If the pulse moves at a speed of 2.5 m/s, describe the incident pulse and reflected pulse that pass through the midpoint of the spring.

Given
$a = 0.45$ m
$\Delta t = 0.80$ s
$v = 2.5$ m/s

Required
(a) length of the pulse
(b) description of incident pulse passing the midpoint of the spring
(c) description of reflected pulse passing the midpoint of the spring

Analysis and Solution
(a) The length of the pulse can be found using $l = v\Delta t$.
$$l = v\Delta t$$
$$= \left(2.5\ \frac{m}{s}\right)(0.80\ s)$$
$$= 2.0\ m$$
(b) The spring is defined as an ideal spring, so the amplitude of the pulse is constant. The amplitude at all points on the spring will be the same as at the source. Therefore,
$a = 0.45$ m
At the midpoint of the spring, the amplitude of the incident pulse is 0.45 m, its length is 2.0 m, and its speed is 2.50 m/s.
(c) Reflection inverts the pulse but does not change any of its properties. The reflected pulse is identical to the incident pulse except that it is inverted relative to the incident pulse.

Paraphrase and Verify
(a) The pulse length is equal to the distance travelled by the pulse in the time required to generate it.
(b) In an ideal spring the amplitude of the pulse is constant.
(c) When pulses are reflected from a fixed end of a spring they are inverted.

Practice Problems

1. A pulse is generated in a spring where it travels at 5.30 m/s.
   (a) If the time to generate the pulse is 0.640 s, what will be its length?
   (b) How does the speed of the pulse affect its amplitude?

2. A pulse moves along a spring at a speed of 3.60 m/s. If the length of the pulse is 2.50 m, how long did it take to generate the pulse?

3. A pulse that is 1.80 m long with an amplitude of 0.50 m is generated in a period of 0.50 s. If the spring, in which this pulse is travelling, is 5.0 m long, how long does it take the pulse to return to its point of origin?

4. A spring is stretched to a length of 6.0 m. A pulse 1.50 m long travels down the spring and back to its point of origin in 3.6 s. How long did it take to generate the pulse?

Answers

1. (a) 3.39 m (b) It does not; they are independent.

2. 0.694 s

3. 2.8 s

4. 0.45 s

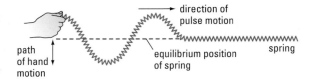

direction of
pulse motion

path
of hand
motion

equilibrium position
of spring

spring

▲ **Figure 8.20** Simple harmonic motion generates a wave train in the form of a sine curve.

Waves Are a Form of Simple Harmonic Motion

If you move your hand from side to side in simple harmonic motion, as indicated in Figure 8.20, transverse waves are generated in the spring. When a transverse wave moves through a medium, the motion of the medium may seem, at first, quite complex. In a transverse wave, each segment of the medium simply oscillates in simple harmonic motion about its equilibrium position in the direction perpendicular to the direction of the wave motion. This simple harmonic motion is transferred sequentially from one segment of the medium to the next to produce the motion of a continuous wave.

Universal Wave Equation

Pulses provide a useful tool to introduce the nature of waves. However, in nature, sound and light are wave phenomena rather than pulses. In this section, we will begin to shift the emphasis to the properties of waves. Whereas the letter *l* is used to indicate the length of a pulse, the Greek letter lambda, λ, is used to indicate wavelength. The terms **crest** and **trough** come from the description of water waves but are used throughout wave studies. For a water wave, the crest occurs where the medium is displaced above the equilibrium position, while a trough is the region displaced below the equilibrium position. However, for media such as springs, the terms crest and trough merely refer to two regions in the medium that are displaced to opposite sides of the equilibrium position (Figure 8.20).

Other variables used in wave studies (**frequency**–*f*, **period**–*T*, **amplitude**–*a*) come from and have the same meanings as in your study of simple harmonic motion in section 7.2. The period (*T*) is the time taken to generate one complete wavelength. Since two pulses join to create one wave, the period for a wave is twice the time required to generate a pulse. Therefore, the wavelength of a wave is twice the length of a pulse.

With this in mind, the relationship between wavelength, speed, and period is the same for waves as it is for pulses. That is,

$$\lambda = vT$$

rather than

$$l = v\Delta t.$$

For periodic motion,

$$T = \frac{1}{f}.$$

The equation for wavelength now can be written as

$$\lambda = \frac{v}{f}$$

or

$$v = f\lambda$$. The latter form is known as the **universal wave equation**.

Constant Frequency, Speed, and Wavelength

In 8-3 Inquiry Lab, you investigated what happened to a wave train as it moved from deep to shallow water. Changes occurred because the speed in shallow water was slower than it was in deep water. Since the frequency of the waves as they moved from deep to shallow water was unchanged, the reduction in speed was, as predicted by the universal wave equation, accompanied by a reduction in wavelength (Figure 8.21). For a constant frequency, the ratio of the velocities is the same as the ratio of the wavelengths.

$$\frac{v_1}{v_2} = \frac{\lambda_1 \not{f}}{\lambda_2 \not{f}}$$

$$= \frac{\lambda_1}{\lambda_2}$$

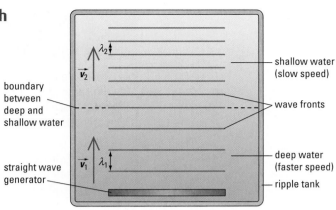

▲ **Figure 8.21** When the frequency is constant, a change in speed results in a change in wavelength.

When waves change speed, they often change direction as well. You will study this phenomenon further in Unit VII.

Example 8.2

To generate waves in a stretched spring, you oscillate your hand back and forth at a frequency of 2.00 Hz. If the speed of the waves in the spring is 5.40 m/s, what is the wavelength?

Given
v = 5.40 m/s
   = 2.00 Hz

Required
wavelength

Analysis and Solution
The variables (v, f, λ) are related by the universal wave equation.

$$v = f\lambda$$

$$\lambda = \frac{v}{f}$$

$$= \frac{5.40 \ \dfrac{m}{s}}{2.00 \ Hz}$$

$$= \frac{5.40 \ \dfrac{m}{\not{s}}}{2.00 \ \dfrac{1}{\not{s}}}$$

$$= 2.70 \ m$$

Paraphrase and Verify
The wavelength is 2.70 m. The period of the wave $\left(\dfrac{1}{f}\right)$ is 0.50 s.

Practice Problems

1. Orchestras use the note ("A" above middle "C") with a frequency of 440 Hz for tuning their instruments. If the speed of sound in an auditorium is 350 m/s, what is the length of the sound wave generated by this frequency?

2. A submarine sonar system sends a burst of sound with a frequency of 325 Hz. The sound wave bounces off an underwater rock face and returns to the submarine in 8.50 s. If the wavelength of the sound is 4.71 m, how far away is the rock face?

3. A fisherman anchors his dinghy in a lake 250 m from shore. The dinghy rises and falls 8.0 times per minute. He finds that it takes a wave 3.00 min to reach the shore. How far apart are the wave crests?

Answers
1. 0.795 m
2. 6.50 km
3. 10 m

- Walk side by side with a partner at the same speed. One student should take long steps while the other takes very short steps.

  1. If the two students maintain their pace, what is the relationship between the frequency and the length of their steps?

- With both students keeping their steps the same length as in the first trial, walk so that your steps are in phase (take steps at the same time).

  2. When the two students walk in phase, what is the effect of taking shorter steps? What is the relationship between speed and step length?

8.2 Check and Reflect

Knowledge

1. Explain the relationship between the motion of a transverse wave and the motion of the medium through which it moves.

2. Explain how the medium moves when a longitudinal wave passes through it.

3. What is the difference between a transverse and a longitudinal wave?

4. What decides the amount of energy stored in a wave?

Applications

5. Sound waves travel through seawater at about 1500 m/s. What frequency would generate a wavelength of 1.25 m in seawater?

6. Temperature changes in seawater affect the speed at which sound moves through it. A wave with a length of 2.00 m, travelling at a speed of 1500 m/s, reaches a section of warm water where the speed is 1550 m/s. What would you expect the wavelength in the warmer water to be?

7. A speaker system generates sound waves at a frequency of 2400 Hz. If the wave speed in air is 325 m/s, what is the wavelength?

8. When you generate a wave in a spring, what is the relationship between the frequency, wavelength, and amplitude?

9. Two tuning forks are generating sound waves with a frequency of 384 Hz. The waves from one tuning fork are generated in air where the speed of sound is 350 m/s. The other tuning fork is generating sound under water where the speed of sound is 1500 m/s. Calculate the wavelength for the sound (a) in air, and (b) in water. (c) Would you hear the same musical note under water as you did in air?

Extensions

10. A radio speaker generates sounds that your eardrum can detect. What does the operation of the speaker and your eardrum suggest about the nature of sound waves? How does the nature of the medium (air) through which sound travels support your assumptions?

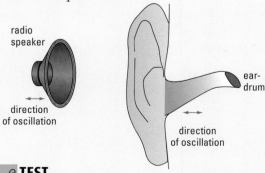

radio speaker

direction of oscillation

ear-drum

direction of oscillation

*e***TEST**

To check your understanding of transverse and longitudinal waves, follow the eTest links at www.pearsoned.ca/school/physicssource.

8.3 Superposition and Interference

Superposition of Pulses and Interference

When waves travel through space it is inevitable that they will cross paths with other waves. In nature, this occurs all the time. Imagine two people who sit facing each other and are speaking at the same time. As each person's sound waves travel toward the other person they must meet and pass simultaneously through the same point in space (Figure 8.22). Still, both people are able to hear quite plainly what the other person is saying. The waves obviously were able to pass through each other so that they reached the other person's ears unchanged.

How waves interact when they cross paths is well understood. When you observe two waves crossing in the ripple tank, things happen so quickly that it is difficult to see what is happening. Still, it is plain that the waves do pass through each other. By sending two pulses toward each other in a spring, it is easier to analyze the events. It is helpful to imagine that the spring in which the pulses are travelling is an ideal, isolated system. The pulses then travel without loss of energy. First, consider two upright pulses moving through each other. When two pulses pass through the same place in the spring at the same time, they are said to **interfere** with each other. In the section of the spring where **interference** occurs, the spring takes on a shape that is different from the shape of either of the pulses individually (Figure 8.23).

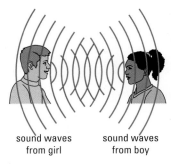

▲ **Figure 8.22** When two people talk simultaneously, each person's sound waves reach the other person's ears in their original form.

sound waves from girl

sound waves from boy

interference: the effect of two pulses (or two waves) crossing within a medium; the medium takes on a shape that is different from the shape of either pulse alone

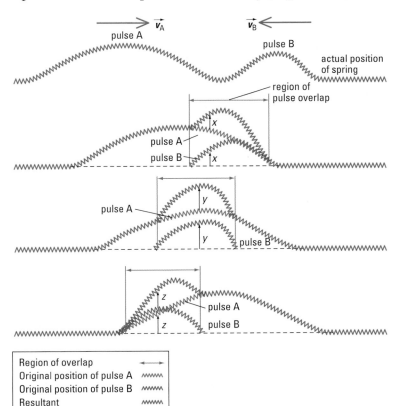

pulse A $\vec{v}_A$

pulse B $\vec{v}_B$

actual position of spring

region of pulse overlap

pulse A
pulse B
x
x

pulse A
pulse B
y
y

z
pulse A
pulse B
z

Region of overlap	←→
Original position of pulse A	‿‿‿
Original position of pulse B	‿‿‿
Resultant	‿‿‿

◀ **Figure 8.23** When two upright pulses move through each other, the displacement of the resultant pulse is the sum of the displacements of pulse A and pulse B. If at any point in the region of overlap, the displacement of one pulse, shown here as x, y, and z, is added to the displacement of the other, the displacement of the resultant pulse is increased. This is called constructive interference.

The new shape that the spring takes on is predicted by the **principle of superposition**. This principle, based on the conservation of energy, makes it quite easy to predict the shape of the spring at any instant during which the pulses overlap.

> The displacement of the combined pulse at each point of interference is the algebraic sum of the displacements of the individual pulses.

In Figure 8.23 the two pulses have different sizes and shapes and are moving in opposite directions. The displacement of a pulse is positive for crests and negative for troughs. Since in Figure 8.23 both displacements are positive, at any point where the two pulses overlap, the displacement of the resultant pulse is greater than the displacements of the individual pulses. When pulses overlap to create a pulse of greater amplitude, the result is **constructive interference** (Figure 8.24).

Now consider the case when an inverted pulse meets an upright pulse. The displacement of the inverted pulse is a negative value. When the displacements of these pulses are added together, the displacement of the resultant pulse is smaller than the displacement of either pulse. When pulses that are inverted with respect to each other overlap to create a pulse of lesser amplitude, the result is **destructive interference** (Figure 8.25).

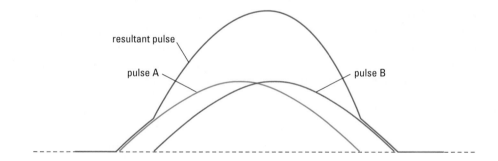

▲ **Figure 8.24**   Constructive interference

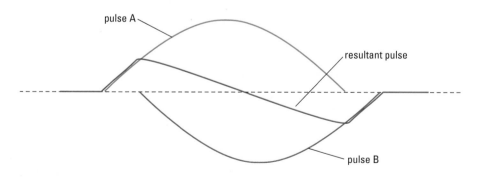

▲ **Figure 8.25**   Destructive interference

Figure 8.26 shows a special case of destructive interference. Two pulses that have the same shape and size are shown passing through each other. Because the pulses are identical in shape and size, their displacements at any position equidistant from the front of each pulse are equal in magnitude but opposite in sign. At the point where the two pulses meet, the sum of their displacements will always be zero. At the instant when these two pulses exactly overlap, the displacement at all points is zero and the pulses disappear. The resultant is a flat line. Immediately following this instant, the pulses reappear as they move on their way.

The Inversion of Reflected Pulses in a Fixed Spring

The principle of superposition explains why pulses are inverted when they reflect from the fixed end of a spring (Figure 8.27). Because the end of the spring is fixed in place, at that point the sum of the displacements of the incident pulse and the reflected pulse must always be zero. Thus, at the point of reflection, the displacement of the reflected pulse must be the negative of the incident pulse. Hence, the reflected pulse must be inverted relative to the incident pulse.

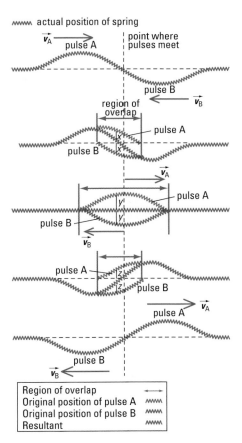

▲ **Figure 8.26** When pulses that are inverted with respect to each other overlap, the displacement of one pulse is reduced by the displacement of the other pulse. At any point in the region of overlap, the displacement of Pulse B, shown here as *x*, *y*, and *z*, reduces the displacement of Pulse A to produce the resultant. This is called destructive interference.

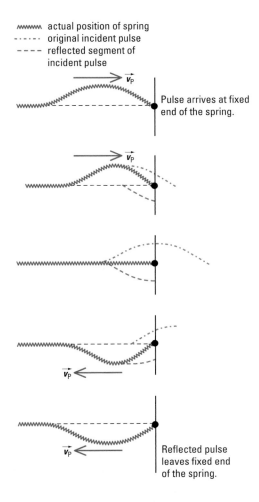

▲ **Figure 8.27** If the end of the spring is fixed, the reflected pulse must be inverted relative to the incident pulse.

Chapter 8 Mechanical waves transmit energy in a variety of ways. 413

Interference of Waves

Questions

1 What happens when two pulses pass through the same point in a medium?

2 How can two waves, moving in opposite directions, exist simultaneously in the same space?

3 What causes a standing wave?

Materials

light spring
heavy spring
masking tape
stopwatch
tape measure or metre-stick

> ⚠ **CAUTION: A stretched spring stores considerable amounts of elastic energy. Be careful not to release the end of a spring while it is stretched. When collapsing a spring, have the person holding one end walk the spring slowly toward the other end. Allow the spring to gently unwind as you are walking to prevent the spring from tying itself into a knot.**

Variables

Part 1: In this part you are concerned with the amplitudes and lengths of the pulses. Observe these variables before, during, and after the period in which they interfere with each other.

Part 2: In this part you will explore the relationship between the frequency and the standing wave pattern generated in a spring. From the structure of the standing wave pattern and the length of the spring, the wavelength and the speed of the standing wave are easily calculated.

For both parts, identify which are the controlled variables, manipulated variables, and responding variables.

Part 1: Superposition and Interference of Pulses

1 (a) Place two parallel strips of tape on the floor about 5 m apart. Measure and record the distance between them. Use these tapes to maintain a constant length for the spring while it is stretched.

(b) Have the team member holding one end of the spring generate a pulse. When this pulse reaches the fixed end of the spring, have the same team member generate a second similar pulse. Try to generate the second incident pulse so that it meets the reflection of the first pulse at the strip of tape near the middle of the spring. Focus on the nature of the spring's motion while the pulses interact. This complex interaction occurs quite quickly and may need to be repeated a few times until you are confident that you can see what is happening. Discuss the observations with your team members.

(c) Record your observations in sketches and writing.

2 (a) Again, have one team member generate two pulses. This time, however, generate the second pulse so that it is on the opposite side of the spring (i.e., inverted) to the first pulse. The second pulse will now be on the same side of the spring as the reflected pulse. Again, time the pulses so that they meet near the centre of the spring.

(b) Observe how these pulses interact when they meet at the centre of the spring. Discuss what you think is happening with the other members of your team.

Analysis

1. When pulses on opposite sides of the spring meet, does the amplitude increase or decrease in the region of overlap?

2. When pulses on the same side of the spring meet, does the amplitude increase or decrease in the overlap region?

Part 2: Standing Waves
Procedure

1 (a) Have a team member at one end of the spring create a double wave (a series of four pulses) by oscillating his or her hand back and forth twice across the spring's equilibrium position.

(b) Observe what happens as this wave travels back and forth along the spring. Pay particular attention to what happens when the reflected portion of the wave is passing through the incident wave. Discuss your observations with your lab team to come to a consensus on what is occurring.

(c) Record your observations. Keep in mind what you observed when the pulses crossed in Part 1 of the lab.

2 (a) Now create a steady wave train by moving your hand back and forth. Try to find the frequency such that the spring oscillates in two segments about its midpoint. If, at first, there are more than two segments, then reduce the frequency slightly. If, at first, the spring is oscillating as only one segment, then increase the frequency until the second segment appears. Once the spring begins to oscillate as two segments, maintain that frequency.

(b) Measure and record the frequency of oscillation by timing ten oscillations. Since you know the length of the spring (the distance between the tapes you placed on the floor), record the length of a wave for this frequency. Each half of the spring is a pulse so that, in this mode, the wavelength is equal to the length of the spring.

(c) Record the data obtained in step 2(b) in a table. Use column headings: trial number, number of segments, frequency, wavelength, and speed.

3 (a) Begin with the frequency at which the spring oscillates in two halves and gradually increase the frequency.

(b) Describe what happens when you try to maintain a slight increase in the frequency. Keep increasing the frequency until a new oscillation pattern is established. Measure the frequency for this pattern. Record your results in your table of data.

(c) Starting from this frequency, gradually increase the frequency until a new pattern of oscillation is found. Once the new wave pattern is established, measure its frequency and record your measurements in your data table.

4 If time permits, change to the heavier spring and repeat steps 2 and 3.

⚠ **CAUTION: Be very careful not to accidentally release the heavy spring while it is stretched. It will contain a large quantity of elastic potential energy and may seriously injure someone. To relax the tension in the spring, walk one end of the spring slowly toward the other end.**

Analysis

1. When you created a sustained wave so that the spring oscillated as a stable pattern, in which direction did the waves move? Why do you think that is the case? Does this tell you why this pattern is known as a **standing wave**?

2. (a) Two segments of a standing wave are equal to one wavelength. For each trial recorded in the table of data, calculate the wavelength of the standing wave.

(b) For each trial, use the universal wave equation to calculate the speed of the waves in the spring.

3. To what does the speed of a standing wave refer?

4. Express the frequencies, for the different trials recorded in your data table, as ratios using simple whole numbers. Compare these ratios to the number of segments in which the spring oscillates for each trial. **NOTE:** The parts of a standing wave that remain motionless are called **nodes** or **nodal points**. The midpoints of the parts that oscillate back and forth are called **antinodes**. Each segment that contains an antinode is simply a pulse or one-half a wavelength. In a standing wave two adjacent segments are required to complete one wavelength.

5. Once a standing wave is established in the spring, what do you notice about the amplitude of the oscillations you use to sustain the wave compared with the amplitude of the antinodes? What explanation might exist for the difference in these two amplitudes?

6. Beginning at the fixed end of the spring, describe the locations of the nodes (points that remain motionless) and antinodes (midpoints of the parts that oscillate back and forth) along the spring in terms of wavelength.

7. How does the principle of superposition explain what must be happening at the antinodes of a standing wave?

8. What relationship exists between the wavelength of a standing wave and the frequency creating the wavelength?

9. Go back to your observations in Part 1 of 8-2 Inquiry Lab. When a train of straight waves parallel to the barrier was reflected back through the incident wave train, did you observe a standing wave?

10. If you could generate a standing wave for sound, what do you think would be the nature of the sound at the location of an antinode? a node?

e **LAB**

For a probeware activity, go to
www.pearsoned.ca/school/physicssource.

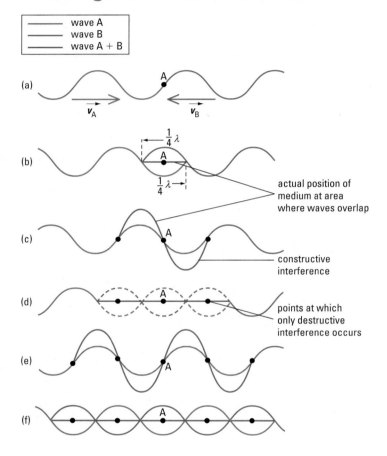

MINDS ON | Total Destruction?

At the instant when two pulses "completely destroy" each other, the spring is in its equilibrium position. How is it possible for the two pulses to reappear as if from nothing?

Where does the energy in the pulses go when the sum of the amplitudes is zero? **Hint:** It might help to think of the spring in terms of a system.

Standing Waves and Resonance

▶ **Figure 8.28** The diagrams show how waves travelling in opposite directions interfere as they move through each other.

e MATH

To graphically analyze the superposition of waves that are in or out of phase, visit www.pearsoned.ca/school/physicssource.

e WEB

Find out more about the superposition of waves. Follow the links at www.pearsoned.ca/school/physicssource.

When two wave trains with identical wavelengths and amplitudes move through each other (Figure 8.28), the resulting interference pattern can be explained by using the principle of superposition. When crests from the two waves or troughs from the two waves occupy the same point in the medium, the waves are **in phase.** Waves that are in phase produce constructive interference. When a crest from one wave occupies the same point in the medium as a trough from a second wave, we say that these waves are **out of phase**. Out-of-phase waves produce destructive interference. As the two wave trains pass through each other in opposite directions, they continually shift in and out of phase to produce a wave that seems to oscillate between fixed nodes, rather than move through the medium.

- (a) Point A is the initial point of contact between the two wave trains shown in blue and purple. The crest from the purple wave train and the trough from the blue wave train arrive at point A at the same instant.
- (b) The two identical waves have moved a distance of $\frac{1}{4}\lambda$ in opposite directions. This overlap results in destructive interference and the spring is flat in the region of overlap. The position of the spring where the two waves overlap, the resultant, is shown in red.
- (c) Each wave has moved a further $\frac{1}{4}\lambda$ along the spring. Now the waves are exactly in phase and constructive interference occurs. The regions to the left and right of point A show a crest and a trough, respectively, with displacement of the resultant being twice that of the blue or purple waves.
- Every time the wave trains move a further $\frac{1}{4}\lambda$ along the spring, the interference changes from constructive to destructive and vice versa.

At point A, only destructive interference occurs. The magnitudes of the displacements of the waves arriving at point A are always equal but opposite in sign. As the waves continue to move in opposite directions, the nature of the interference continually changes. However, at point A and every $\frac{1}{2}\lambda$ from point A, there are points at which only destructive interference occurs. These are called **nodal points** or **nodes**.

Between the nodes, the spring goes into a flip-flop motion as the interference in these areas switches from constructive (crest crossing crest) to destructive (crest crossing trough) and back to constructive interference (trough crossing trough). The midpoints of these regions on the spring are called **antinodes**. The first antinode occurs at a distance of $\frac{1}{4}\lambda$ on either side of A, and then at every $\frac{1}{2}\lambda$ after that point. Because the wave seems to oscillate around stationary nodes along the spring, it is known as a **standing wave**. Standing waves are also seen in nature; an example is shown in Figure 8.29.

Standing Waves in a Fixed Spring

When you generate a wave train in a spring that is fixed at one end, the reflected wave train must pass back through the incident wave train. These two wave trains have identical wavelengths and nearly identical amplitudes. For incident and reflected wave trains, the initial point of contact is by definition the fixed point at which reflection occurs. This means that the endpoint of the spring is always a nodal point and, as shown in Figure 8.30, nodes occur every $\frac{1}{2}\lambda$ from that point with antinodes between them.

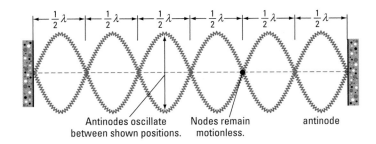

Antinodes oscillate between shown positions.   Nodes remain motionless.   antinode

node: a point on a spring or other medium at which only destructive interference occurs; a point that never vibrates between supercrests and supertroughs; in a standing wave nodes occur at intervals of $\frac{1}{2}\lambda$

antinode: a point in an interference pattern that oscillates with maximum amplitude; in a standing wave antinodes occur at intervals of $\frac{1}{2}\lambda$

standing wave: a condition in a spring or other medium in which a wave seems to oscillate around stationary points called nodes. The wavelength of a standing wave is the distance between alternate nodes or alternate antinodes.

▲ **Figure 8.29** Standing waves occur in nature. This photograph shows a standing wave in a stream crossing a sandy beach in Scotland.

e **WEB**

Find out about the details of a standing wave in a spring. Follow the links at www.pearsoned.ca/school/physicssource.

◀ **Figure 8.30** In a spring with a fixed end, a standing wave must contain a whole number of antinodes. Nodes occur every half-wavelength from the ends.

▲ **Figure 8.31** Resonance, caused by wind, set up a standing wave that destroyed the Tacoma Narrows Bridge.

resonance: an increase in the amplitude of a wave due to a transfer of energy in phase with the natural frequency of the wave

Resonant Frequencies

When you are generating a standing wave in a spring, the wave reflects from both ends of the spring. There must be a nodal point at both ends with an integral number of antinodes in between. The spring "prefers" to oscillate at those frequencies that will produce a standing wave pattern called the **resonant frequencies** for the spring. When the generator is oscillating at a resonant frequency, the energy is added to the spring in phase with existing oscillations. This reinforces and enhances the standing wave pattern. The added energy works to construct waves with ever-larger amplitudes. If the generator is not oscillating at a resonant frequency of the medium, the oscillations tend to destroy the standing wave motion.

Amplitude and Resonance

Perhaps the most impressive display of a standing wave occurred when **resonance** set up a standing wave in the bridge across the Tacoma Narrows in the state of Washington (Figure 8.31). Opened in November 1940, the bridge was in operation only a few months before resonance ripped it apart. More recently, in June 2000, the newly opened Millennium Bridge in London had to be closed for modifications when the footsteps of pedestrians set up resonance patterns.

Anyone who has ever "pumped up" a swing has used the principle of resonance. To increase the amplitude of its motion, the swing must be given a series of nudges in phase with its natural frequency of motion. Each time the swing begins to move forward, you give it a little push. Since these little pushes are produced in resonance with the swing's natural motion, they are added to its energy and the amplitude increases. If you pushed out of phase with its natural motion, the swing would soon come to rest.

> **Concept Check**
>
> Why does it take so little energy to sustain a standing wave in a spring?

▲ **Figure 8.32** The tone produced when you blow across the top of an open bottle depends on the length of the air column.

Resonating Air Columns

All wind instruments use the principle of resonance to produce music. The simplest example of resonance in music is the note produced when you blow over the top of a bottle (Figure 8.32). Blowing across the top of the bottle oscillates the air in the bottle and generates a standing wave. This standing wave is like the waves travelling in a spring, but unlike a spring that is fixed at both ends, the air column is fixed only at the end where reflection occurs and is free to oscillate at the open end. The resonant frequency of the note produced depends on the length of the air column because, to resonate, the standing wave must have a node at the closed end of the bottle and an antinode at the open end (Figure 8.33).

Closed-Pipe or Closed-Tube Resonance

When a wave source is held at the open end of a pipe, it sends down a wave that reflects from the closed end of the pipe and establishes a standing wave pattern. The sound one hears depends on the length of the air column in the pipe relative to the length of the standing wave. If an antinode occurs at the open end of the pipe (Figure 8.33 (a) and (c)), a point of resonance (resulting from constructive interference) occurs at the open end of the pipe and the sound appears to be amplified. This phenomenon is known as **closed-pipe** or **closed-tube** resonance. However, if the open end of the pipe coincides with the position of a node (destructive interference), then almost no sound can be heard because the source (tuning fork) and the standing wave are out of phase (Figure 8.33 (b) and (d)).

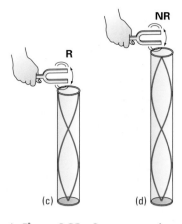

R resonance heard
NR no resonance heard

▲ **Figure 8.33** Resonance series. A tuning fork sets up a standing wave in the air column. The volume of the sound one hears will vary depending on whether there is an antinode (a) and (c), or a node (b) and (d) at the end of the pipe.

Nodes and Antinodes in Closed-Pipe Resonance

In the air column, nodes are located every half-wavelength from the end at which the wave is reflected, just as they are in a standing wave in a spring. If the pipe length is equal to any multiple of $\frac{1}{2}\lambda$, there will be a node at the upper end of the pipe, and destructive interference will occur. Thus, when the air column is $\frac{1}{2}\lambda$, $\frac{2}{2}\lambda$, $\frac{3}{2}\lambda$, $\frac{4}{2}\lambda$, ... in length, little or no sound will be heard.

Antinodes in the air column are located one quarter-wavelength from the end of the pipe where reflection occurs, and then every half-wavelength from that point. Thus, resonance is heard when the pipe is $\frac{1}{4}\lambda$, $\frac{3}{4}\lambda$, $\frac{5}{4}\lambda$, ... long. When resonance is heard for an air column closed at one end, we know that the open end of the column coincides with the location of one of the antinodes. This information can be used to measure the wavelength of sound in gases. If the frequency of the sound is known, then the wavelength can be used to calculate the speed of sound in the gas.

Concept Check

Is the volume of a sound related: to speed, wavelength, amplitude, or frequency of the wave? What evidence is there to support your answer?

Example 8.3

A tuning fork with a frequency of 384 Hz is held above an air column. As the column is lengthened, a closed-pipe resonant point is found when the length of the air column is 67.5 cm. What are possible wavelengths for this data? If the speed of sound is known to be slightly greater than 300 m/s, what is (a) the actual wavelength, and (b) the actual speed of sound?

Practice Problems

1. A tuning fork of frequency 512 Hz is used to generate a standing wave pattern in a closed pipe, 0.850 m long. A strong resonant note is heard indicating that an antinode is located at the open end of the pipe.
   (a) What are the possible wavelengths for this note?
   (b) Which wavelength will give the most reasonable value for the calculation of the speed of sound in air?

2. A tuning fork with a frequency of 256 Hz is held above an air column while the column is gradually increased in length. At what lengths for this air column would the first 4 resonant points be found, if the speed of sound is 330 m/s?

3. A standing wave is generated in a spring that is stretched to a length of 6.00 m. The standing wave pattern consists of three antinodes. If the frequency used to generate this wave is 2.50 Hz, what is the speed of the wave in the spring?

4. When a spring is stretched to a length of 8.00 m, the speed of waves in the spring is 5.00 m/s. The simplest standing wave pattern for this spring is that of a single antinode between two nodes at opposite ends of the spring.
   (a) What is the frequency that produces this standing wave?
   (b) What is the next higher frequency for which a standing wave exists in this spring?

Answers
1. (a) 3.40 m @ 1.74×10^3 m/s; 1.13 m @ 580 m/s; 0.680 m @ 348 m/s; 0.486 m @ 249 m/s
   (b) λ = 0.680 m
2. 0.323 m, 0.968 m, 1.61 m, 2.26 m
3. 10.0 m/s
4. 0.313 Hz, 0.626 Hz

Given
f = 384 Hz
L = 0.675 m

Required
wavelength and speed of sound

Analysis and Solution
The resonant point might represent $\frac{1}{4}\lambda$, $\frac{3}{4}\lambda$, $\frac{5}{4}\lambda$,..., etc., for this tuning fork. Assume that 67.5 cm is the first resonant point; that means 67.5 cm is $\frac{1}{4}\lambda$. Calculate the wavelength and the speed of sound from that data.
Assume that $L = \frac{1}{4}\lambda$. Therefore,

$$\lambda = 4L \qquad\qquad v = f\lambda$$
$$= 4(0.675 \text{ m}) \qquad = (384 \text{ Hz})(2.70 \text{ m})$$
$$= 2.70 \text{ m} \qquad\quad = 1037 \text{ m/s}$$
$$\qquad\qquad\qquad\quad = 1.04 \times 10^3 \text{ m/s}$$

This value is larger than the speed of sound in air.

If the speed of sound is not of the proper order of magnitude, then assume that the resonant point is the second point of resonance and that 67.5 cm is $\frac{3}{4}\lambda$. Calculate the wavelength and the speed of sound from that data.

Assume that $L = \frac{3}{4}\lambda$. Therefore,

$$\lambda = \frac{4L}{3} \qquad\qquad v = f\lambda$$
$$= \frac{4(0.675 \text{ m})}{3} \qquad = (384 \text{Hz})(0.900 \text{ m})$$
$$= 0.900 \text{ m} \qquad\quad = 345.6 \text{ m/s}$$
$$\qquad\qquad\qquad\quad = 346 \text{ m/s}$$

This is a reasonable speed for sound in air.

Complete the analysis by assuming that $L = \frac{5}{4}\lambda$. Therefore,

$$\lambda = \frac{4L}{5} \qquad\qquad v = f\lambda$$
$$= \frac{4(0.675 \text{ m})}{5} \qquad = (384 \text{ Hz})(0.540 \text{ m})$$
$$= 0.540 \text{ m} \qquad\quad = 207.4 \text{ m/s}$$
$$\qquad\qquad\qquad\quad = 207 \text{ m/s}$$

This value is less than the speed of sound in air.

Paraphrase and Verify
The calculations for the speed of sound indicate that the data must have been for the second point of resonance. This assumption gives the speed for sound of 346 m/s. The assumption that the pipe length is for the first resonant point results in a speed about three times that of sound. The assumption that the pipe length is for the third resonant point produces a speed less than 300 m/s.

Measuring the Speed of Sound Using Closed-pipe Resonance

Required Skills
- Initiating and Planning
- Performing and Recording
- Analyzing and Interpreting
- Communication and Teamwork

When a sound wave travels down a closed pipe, the incident wave reflects off the end of the pipe and back toward the source. The interaction of the incident and reflected waves sets up an interference pattern inside the pipe, known as a standing wave. This standing wave can be used to determine the wavelength of the sound.

Problem

What is the speed of sound in air?

Variables

The universal wave equation relates the speed (v) of a wave to its frequency (f) and wavelength (λ). The wavelength is determined from the length of the pipe (L) and the number of the resonant point as counted from the reflecting surface.

Materials and Equipment

tuning forks and tuning fork hammer or an audio
 frequency generator
glass or plastic pipe
tall cylinder

Procedure

1 Assemble the apparatus as shown in Figure 8.34.

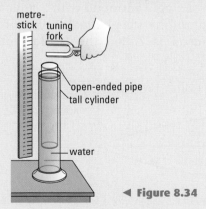

metre-stick tuning fork

open-ended pipe
tall cylinder

water

◀ **Figure 8.34**

2 Place the pipe in the water-filled cylinder so that the column of air in the pipe is quite short.

3 Strike the tuning fork with the hammer.

4 Hold the tuning fork as shown over the end of the pipe and lift the pipe slowly so that the length of the column of air in the pipe increases.

5 As you approach a point where the volume of the sound increases, move the pipe slowly up and down to find the point where the resonance is greatest. Strike the tuning fork as often as necessary to maintain the sound source.

6 Determine the length of the column of air that gives the greatest resonance and record it in a table like Table 8.1. Measure the length from the surface of the water to the location of the tuning fork.

7 Beginning with the column of air at the previously recorded length, gradually increase the length until you have determined the length of the air column that gives the next point of resonance. Record this length.

8 Repeat step 7 to find the length of the column for the third resonant point.

▼ **Table 8.1** Column Length and Resonance

Frequency f (Hz)	Length of column at first resonant point L_1 (m)	Length of column at second resonant point L_2 (m)	Length of column at third resonant point L_3 (m)

Analysis

1. In terms of wavelength, how far is each of the first three resonant points from the reflecting surface of the water at the bottom of the air column?

2. Calculate the wavelength of the sound from the tuning fork for each resonant point. Record your answers in a table similar to Table 8.2. Calculate the speed of sound for each of the wavelengths.

3. When you calculate the wavelength for different resonant points, do the answers agree? If not, what might cause the differences?

4. Why should you start with a short column of air and increase its length if you are to be sure that you have correctly determined the wavelength?

▼ Table 8.2   Resonant Points, Wavelength, and Speed of Sound

Frequency f (Hz)	First Resonant Point		Second Resonant Point		Third Resonant Point	
	Wavelength λ = 4L (m)	Speed v (m/s)	Wavelength λ = 4L/3 (m)	Speed v (m/s)	Wavelength λ = 4L/5 (m)	Speed v (m/s)

5. Why should you measure the length of the column from the reflecting surface to the tuning fork rather than to the top end of the pipe?

6. What is the speed of sound at room temperature?

7. Investigate the effect that air temperature has on the speed of sound. Use hot water or ice water to modify the temperature of the air in the column. Compare the measured speed of sound for at least three temperatures. Suspend a thermometer down the pipe to determine the temperature of the air in the pipe. Plot a graph of the measured speed of sound versus the temperature. Does the graph suggest a linear relationship? Can you use the graph to predict the speed of sound at other temperatures?

8. An alternative technique to determine the speed of sound is to measure the time for an echo to return to you. Stand a measured distance from a wall or other surface that reflects sound. Create an echo by striking together two hard objects, such as metal bars, or, perhaps beating a drum. Listen for the echo. Once you have established an approximate time for the echo to return, strike the bars in a rhythm so that they are in phase with the echo. Have a team member count the number of beats in 1 min. The period of this frequency is the time required for the sound to travel to the wall and back. Use that data to calculate the speed of the sound.

_e_ LAB
For a probeware activity, go to
www.pearsoned.ca/school/physicssource.

fundamental frequency: the lowest frequency produced by a particular instrument; corresponds to the standing wave having a single antinode, with a node at each end of the string

Music and Resonance

Complex modes of vibration give instruments their distinctive sounds and add depth to the musical tones they create. A string of a musical instrument is simply a tightly stretched spring for which the simplest standing wave possible is a single antinode with a node at either end. For this pattern, the length of the string equals one-half a wavelength and the frequency produced is called the **fundamental frequency** (Figure 8.35(a)).

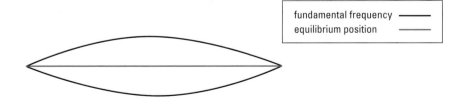

▲ **Figure 8.35 (a)**   The fundamental frequency of a vibrating string oscillates as a standing wave with an antinode at the centre of the string.

This is the lowest frequency produced by a particular instrument. But other standing wave patterns can exist in the string at the same time as it oscillates at its fundamental frequency. By plucking or bowing a string nearer its end than its middle, the string is encouraged to vibrate with multiple frequencies. The frequencies above the fundamental

info **BIT**

Assume that the fundamental frequency is f. In physics and in music, the frequency $2f$ is called the first overtone; $3f$ is the second overtone, and so on. These frequencies are said to form a harmonic series. Thus, physicists may also refer to the fundamental frequency (f) as the first harmonic, the frequency $2f$ as the second harmonic, the frequency $3f$ as the third harmonic, and so on.

frequency that may exist simultaneously with the fundamental frequency are called **overtones.** Figures 8.35 (b) and (c) show the shape of a string vibrating in its first and second overtones, respectively. Figure 8.36 shows a violinist bowing and fingering the strings of her violin to produce notes.

▲ **Figure 8.36** The violinist's fingering technique changes the length of the string and thus changes the fundamental frequency of vibration.

overtone: any frequency of vibration of a string that may exist simultaneously with the fundamental frequency

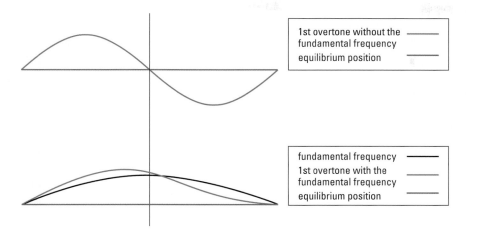

1st overtone without the
fundamental frequency ————
equilibrium position ————

fundamental frequency ————
1st overtone with the
fundamental frequency ————
equilibrium position ————

▲ **Figure 8.35 (b)** The first overtone has the form of a standing wave with two antinodes. A node exists at the midpoint of the string. The lower portion of the diagram shows a string vibrating with both the fundamental frequency and the first overtone simultaneously.

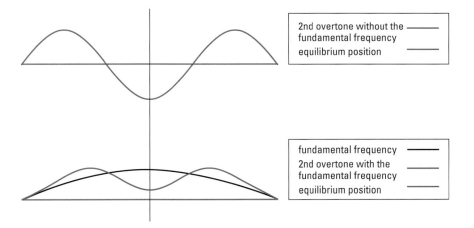

2nd overtone without the ————
fundamental frequency
equilibrium position ————

fundamental frequency ————
2nd overtone with the
fundamental frequency ————
equilibrium position ————

▲ **Figure 8.35(c)** The vibration that produces the second overtone has three antinodes. The lower portion of the diagram shows a string vibrating with both the fundamental frequency and second overtone.

The actual form of a vibrating string can be very complex as many overtones can exist simultaneously with the fundamental frequency. The actual wave form for a vibrating string is the result of the constructive and destructive interference of the fundamental wave with all the existing overtones that occur in the string. For example, Figure 8.37 shows the wave trace on an oscilloscope for the sound of a violin.

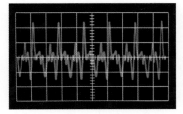

▲ **Figure 8.37** The interference of the fundamental frequency with the overtones produced by a bowed string creates the wave form that gives the violin its unique sound. The wavelength of the fundamental frequency is the distance between the tall sharp crests.

Tuning a Stringed Instrument

Tuning a stringed instrument involves several principles of physics. The universal wave equation, $v = f\lambda$ indicates that the frequency of a sound wave is directly proportional to the speed of the sound and inversely proportional to its wavelength. The wavelength for the fundamental frequency of the standing wave in a string is fixed at twice the length of the string, but the speed of a wave in a string increases with tension. Thus, if the wavelength does not change, the frequency at which a string vibrates must increase with tension. Changing the tension in the string is known as **tuning** (Figure 8.38).

Wind Instruments

Wind instruments produce different musical notes by changing the length of the air columns (Figure 8.39). In 8-7 Inquiry Lab you used a closed pipe and saw that for resonance to occur a node must be present at the closed end while an antinode is created at the open end. For a closed pipe, the longest wavelength that can resonate is four times as long as the pipe (Figure 8.40).

If the pipe is open at both ends, then the wavelengths for which resonance occurs must have antinodes at both ends of the **open pipe** or **open tube** (Figure 8.41). The distance from one antinode to the next is one-half a wavelength; thus, the longest wavelength that can resonate in an open pipe is twice as long as the pipe.

▲ **Figure 8.38**   Tuning a guitar

eLAB

For a probeware activity, go to www.pearsoned.ca/school/physicssource.

▲ **Figure 8.39**   The trumpeter produces different notes by opening valves to change the instrument's overall pipe length.

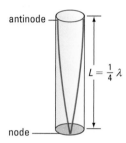

▲ **Figure 8.40**   In a closed pipe, the longest possible resonant wavelength is four times the length of the pipe.

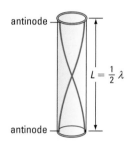

▲ **Figure 8.41**   In an open pipe, the longest possible resonant wavelength is twice the length of the pipe.

Wind instruments are generally open pipes. The wavelength of the resonant frequency will be decided by the length of the pipe (Figure 8.42). In a clarinet or oboe, for example, the length of the pipe is changed by covering or uncovering holes at various lengths down the side of the pipe. The strongest or most resonant frequency will be the wave whose length is twice the distance from the mouthpiece to the first open hole. Overtones are also generated but the note you hear is that with the longest wavelength. As with stringed instruments, the overtones contribute to the wind instrument's characteristic sound.

If the speed of sound in air never varied, then a given wavelength would always be associated with the same frequency. But the speed of sound changes slightly with air temperature and pressure. Thus, in the case of resonance in a pipe, the length of the pipe must be increased or decreased as the speed of sound increases or decreases to ensure that the frequency is that of the desired note.

▲ **Figure 8.42**   A variety of wind instruments

eWEB
To learn how and why wind instruments are affected by temperature, follow the links at www.pearsoned.ca/school/physicssource.

An Interference Pattern from Two In-phase Point Sources

Interference patterns carry information about the waves that create them. For this reason, the patterns are often used to determine the properties of the waves. One of the most interesting interference patterns results from waves generated by two point sources that are in phase. Remember that wave sources are in phase if they generate crests at the same time.

The ripple tank photograph (Figure 8.43) shows the **interference pattern** generated by two **in-phase point sources**. This pattern is the result of constructive and destructive interference as the waves cross. Generally crests appear bright and troughs appear dark. However, in areas where destructive interference occurs, there appear to be fuzzy lines (such as the line indicated by Q_1) that seem to radiate approximately from the midpoint between the sources. While the pattern may appear to be complex, its explanation is fairly simple.

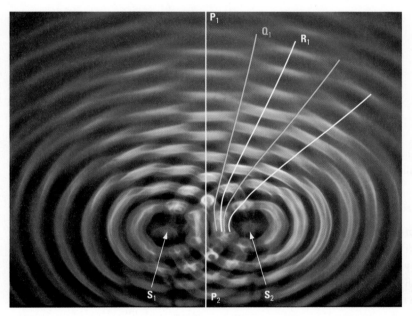

▲ **Figure 8.43**   The interference pattern generated by two in-phase point sources in a ripple tank. The distance between the sources is 3λ.

Individually, point sources generate waves that are sets of expanding concentric circles. As the crests and troughs from each source move outward, they cross through each other. As with all waves, when the crests from one source overlap crests from the other source (or troughs overlap troughs), constructive interference occurs. In these regions there is increased contrast (as indicated by P_1 and R_1). At locations where the crests from one source overlap troughs from the other source, destructive interference occurs. In these regions, contrast is reduced. Because the sources oscillate in phase, the locations where constructive and destructive interference occur are at predictable, fixed points. Like standing waves in a spring, the positions of the nodes and antinodes depend on the wavelength and the distance between the sources. Can you identify the regions of constructive and destructive interference in Figure 8.43 above?

interference pattern: a pattern of maxima and minima resulting from the interaction of waves, as crests and troughs overlap while the waves move through each other

The pattern in Figure 8.43 can be reproduced by drawing sets of concentric circles about two point sources where each circle represents the crest of a wave front (Figure 8.44). In Figure 8.43 the distance (d) between the sources is equal to three wavelengths (3λ). This can be shown by counting the wavelengths between S_1 and S_2 in Figure 8.44.

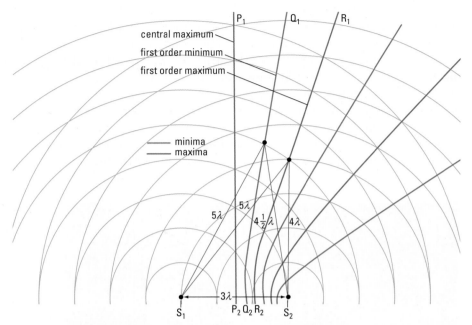

▲ **Figure 8.44** The interference pattern for two in-phase point sources results from the overlap of two sets of concentric circles. In this diagram, the centres of the circles are three wavelengths apart.

Maxima, Minima, and Phase Shifts

The central maximum is a line of antinodes.
In Figure 8.44, the line P_1P_2 is the perpendicular bisector of the line S_1S_2. By definition, every point on P_1P_2 is equidistant from the points S_1 and S_2. Thus, crests (or troughs) generated simultaneously at S_1 and S_2 must arrive at P_1P_2 at the same time, resulting in constructive interference. Along the line P_1P_2 only antinodes are created. The line of antinodes along P_1P_2 is called the central **maximum**.

A nodal line, or minimum, marks locations where waves are exactly out of phase.
A little to the right of the central maximum is the line Q_1Q_2. If you follow this line from one end to the other you will notice that it marks the locations where the crests (lines) from S_1 overlap the troughs (spaces) from S_2 and vice versa. Waves leave the sources in phase, but all points on Q_1Q_2 are a one-half wavelength farther from S_1 than they are from S_2. Thus, at any point on Q_1Q_2, the crests from S_1 arrive one-half a wavelength later than the crests from S_2. This means they arrive at the same time as troughs from S_2. The greater distance travelled by waves from S_1 produces what is called a one-half wavelength **phase shift**. *Waves that began in phase arrive at points on Q_1Q_2 exactly out of phase.* Thus, at every point on Q_1Q_2 destructive interference occurs. The line, Q_1Q_2, is known as a **nodal line** or a **minimum**.

maximum: a line of points linking antinodes that occur as the result of constructive interference between waves

minimum: a line of points linking nodes that occur as the result of destructive interference between waves

phase shift: the result of waves from one source having to travel farther to reach a particular point in the interference pattern than waves from the other source

A first order maximum is the result of a one wavelength phase shift.

Moving farther right, another region of constructive interference occurs. To arrive at any point on R_1R_2, crests from S_1 travel exactly one wavelength farther than crests from S_2. Crests from S_1 arrive at points on R_1R_2 at the same time as crests from S_2 that were generated one cycle later. This one-wavelength phase shift means that all waves arriving at any point on R_1R_2 are still in phase. The line of antinodes resulting from a one-wavelength shift is known as a **first order maximum**. An identical first order maximum exists on the left side. The interference pattern is symmetrical about the central maximum.

Phase shifts equal to whole wavelengths produce maxima.

Moving farther outward from the central maximum, you pass through lines of destructive and constructive interference (minima and maxima). Each region is the result of a phase shift produced when waves travel farther from one source than the other. When the phase shift equals a whole number of wavelengths (0λ, 1λ, 2λ, . . .), the waves arrive in phase, producing antinodes and resulting in the central, first, second, and third order maxima, etc. In Figure 8.44, since the sources are 3λ apart, the greatest phase shift possible is three wavelengths. This produces the third order maximum directly along the line of S_1S_2.

Phase shifts equal to an odd number of half-wavelengths produce minima.

When the phase shift equals an odd number of half-wavelengths $\left(\frac{1}{2}\lambda, \frac{3}{2}\lambda, \frac{5}{2}\lambda, \ldots\right)$ the waves arrive out of phase, producing a nodal line or minimum. In Figure 8.44, the greatest phase shift to produce destructive interference is one-half wavelength less than the three-wavelength separation of the sources, or $\left(3\lambda - \frac{1}{2}\lambda\right) = \frac{5}{2}\lambda$. Because the sources are three wavelengths apart, there are exactly three maxima and three minima to the right and to the left of the central maximum.

e WEB

To learn more about two-point interference systems, follow the links at www.pearsoned.ca/school/physicssource.

8-8 Design a Lab

Interference Patterns and In-phase Sound Sources

The Question

Do interference patterns exist for two in-phase sound sources?

Design and Conduct Your Investigation

An audio frequency generator and two speakers can be used to create an interference pattern for sound. Design a set-up that will enable you to measure the wavelength of sound of known frequencies. If electronic equipment (probeware or waveport) is available, design lab 8-8 to incorporate this equipment. Measure the wavelengths using several maxima and minima to compare measurements. Which type of line gives the best results? How well do the results from this experiment compare with the results from measuring wavelengths using closed-pipe resonance?

8.3 Check and Reflect

Knowledge

1. What is meant by the term interference?

2. For a standing wave, what is the relationship between the amplitude of an antinode and the amplitude of the waves that combine to create the standing wave?

3. In terms of the length of an air column, what is the longest standing wavelength that can exist in an air column that is (a) closed at one end, (b) open at both ends?

4. An air column is said to be closed if it is closed at one end. Consider a pipe of length (L). For a standing wave in this pipe, what are the lengths of the three longest wavelengths for which an antinode exists at the open end of the pipe?

5. What does it mean to say that two wave generators are in phase? What does it mean to say that two waves are in phase?

Applications

6. Two pulses of the same length (l) travel along a spring in opposite directions. The amplitude of the pulse from the right is three units while the amplitude of the pulse from the left is four units. Describe the pulse that would appear at the moment when they exactly overlap if (a) the pulses are on the same side of the spring, (b) the pulses are on opposites sides of the spring.

7. A standing wave is generated in a closed air column by a source that has a frequency of 768 Hz. The speed of sound in air is 325 m/s. What is the shortest column for which resonance will occur at the open end?

8. Draw the interference pattern for two in-phase point sources that are 5λ apart, as follows. Place two points, S_1 and S_2, 5 cm apart near the centre of a sheet of paper. Using each of these points as a centre, draw two sets of concentric circles with increasing radii of 1 cm, 2 cm, 3 cm, . . . , until you reach the edge of the paper. On the diagram, draw solid lines along maxima and dotted lines along minima. Label the maxima according to their order. Explain why there are five minima on either side of the central maximum.

9. An interference pattern from two in-phase point sources is generated in a ripple tank. On the screen, a point on the second order maximum is measured to be 8.0 cm from one point source and 6.8 cm from the other source. What is the wavelength of this pattern?

Extension

10. Do pipe organs, such as those found in churches and concert halls, use closed or open pipes to produce music? What is the advantage of using a real pipe organ as opposed to an electronic organ that synthesizes the sound?

 e TEST

 To check your understanding of superposition and interference of pulses and waves, follow the eTest links at www.pearsoned.ca/school/physicssource.

8.4 The Doppler Effect

Have you ever stood at the side of a road and listened to the cars pass? If you listen carefully, you will detect a very interesting phenomenon. At the instant a car passes you, the sound it makes suddenly becomes lower in pitch. This phenomenon was first explained correctly by an Austrian physicist named Christian Doppler (1803–1853).

Doppler realized that the motion of the source affected the wavelength of the sound. Those waves that moved in the same direction as the source was moving were shortened, making the pitch of the sound higher. Moving in the direction opposite to the motion of the source, the sound waves from the source were lengthened, making the pitch lower.

Wavelength and Frequency of a Source at Rest

Assume that the frequency of a source is 100 Hz and the speed of sound is 350 m/s (Figure 8.46). According to the universal wave equation, if this source is at rest, the wavelength of the sound is 3.5 m.

$$v = f\lambda$$

$$\lambda = \frac{v}{f}$$

$$= \frac{350\,\frac{\text{m}}{\text{s}}}{100\,\frac{1}{\text{s}}}$$

$$= 3.5 \text{ m}$$

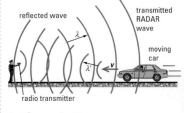

reflected wave
transmitted RADAR wave
moving car
radio transmitter

▲ **Figure 8.45**

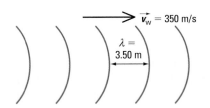

$\vec{v}_w = 350$ m/s

$\lambda = 3.50$ m

◄ **Figure 8.46**   When a wavelength of 3.5 m travels toward you at a speed of 350 m/s, you hear sound that has a frequency of 100 Hz.

You hear the sound at a frequency of 100 Hz because at a speed of 350 m/s, the time lapse between crests that are 3.5 m apart is 1/100 s. If, however, the wavelengths that travel toward you were 7.0 m long, the time lapse between successive crests would be 1/50 s, a frequency equal to 50 Hz.

$$f = \frac{v}{\lambda}$$

$$= \frac{350\,\frac{\text{m}}{\text{s}}}{7.0\,\text{m}}$$

$$= 50\,\frac{1}{\text{s}}$$

$$= 50 \text{ Hz}$$

Wavelength and Frequency of a Moving Source

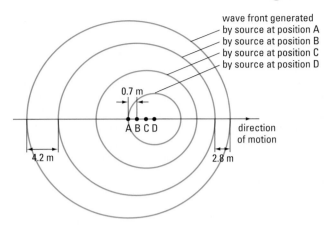

wave front generated
by source at position A
by source at position B
by source at position C
by source at position D

0.7 m

A B C D

direction
of motion

4.2 m

2.8 m

▲ **Figure 8.47** When a sound source moves toward you, the wavelengths in the direction of the motion are decreased.

Imagine that the source generating the 100-Hz sound is moving toward you at a speed of 70 m/s. Assume that the source is at point A (Figure 8.47) when it generates a crest. While the first crest moves a distance of 3.5 m toward you, the source also moves toward you. The distance the source moves while it generates one wavelength is the distance the source travels in 1/100 s at 70 m/s, or 0.7 m. Because of the motion of the source, the next crest is generated (at point B) only 2.8 m behind the first crest. As long as the source continues at the speed of 70 m/s toward you, the crests travelling in your direction will be only 2.8 m apart. Hence, for a car moving toward you, the sound waves emitted by the car will be "squashed together" and thus reach you more frequently than if the car were stationary.

If waves that are 2.8 m long travel toward you at a speed of 350 m/s, then the apparent frequency of the sound arriving at your ear will be 125 Hz. The pitch of the sound that you hear will have been increased because the source is moving toward you.

e SIM

Research examples of shock waves and the variation of wavelength with a moving source. Go to www.pearsoned.ca/school/physicssource.

$$v = f\lambda$$

$$f = \frac{v}{\lambda}$$

$$= \frac{350 \frac{\text{m}}{\text{s}}}{2.80 \text{ m}}$$

$$= 125 \frac{1}{\text{s}}$$

$$= 125 \text{ Hz}$$

At the same time, along a line in the direction opposite to the motion of the source, the wavelengths are increased by the same amount that the waves in front of the source are shortened. For the 100-Hz sound source moving at 70 m/s, the waves behind the source are increased by 0.7 m, to a length of 4.2 m. The time lapse between these crests, which are 4.2 m apart and travelling at 350 m/s, is 0.012 s. Therefore, the perceived frequency in the direction opposite to the motion of the source is about 83 Hz. The pitch of the sound has been lowered.

Analysis of the Doppler Effect

If the velocity of the sound waves in air is v_w, then the wavelength (λ_s) that a stationary source(s) with a frequency of f_s generates is given by

$$\lambda_s = v_w / f_s.$$

The key to this Doppler's analysis is to calculate the distance the source moves in the time required to generate one wavelength (the period (T_s) of the source). If the source is moving at speed v_s, then in the period (T_s) the source moves a distance (Δd_s) that is given by

$\Delta d_s = v_s T_s$. Since, by definition

$T_s = 1/f_s$, then

$$\Delta d_s = v_s/f_s.$$

Sources Moving Toward You

For sources that are moving toward you, Δd_s is the distance by which the wavelengths are shortened. Subtracting Δd_s from λ_s gives the lengths of the waves (λ_d) that reach the listener. Therefore,

$$\lambda_d = \lambda_s - \Delta d_s.$$

Replacing λ_s and Δd_s by their equivalent forms gives

$$\lambda_d = \frac{v_w}{f_s} - \frac{v_s}{f_s}$$

$$\lambda_d = \frac{(v_w - v_s)}{f_s}$$

This is the apparent wavelength (Doppler wavelength) of the sound generated by a source that is moving toward you at a speed v_s. Dividing the speed of the waves (v_w) by the Doppler wavelength (λ_d) produces the Doppler frequency (f_d) of the sound that you hear as the source approaches you. Therefore,

$$f_d = \frac{v_w}{\lambda_d}$$

$$= \frac{v_w}{\left(\dfrac{v_w - v_s}{f_s}\right)}$$

$$= v_w \left(\frac{f_s}{v_w - v_s}\right)$$

$$= \left(\frac{v_w}{v_w - v_s}\right) f_s$$

is the Doppler frequency when the source is approaching the listener.

Sources Moving Away from You

If the source is moving away from the listener, the value of Δd_s is added to the value of λ_s, giving

$$\lambda_d = \lambda_s + \Delta d_s.$$

If you replace λ_s and Δd_s by their equivalent forms and complete the development to find f_d, it is easy to see that the Doppler frequency for a sound where the source moves away from the listener is given by

$$f_d = \left(\frac{v_w}{v_w + v_s}\right) f_s$$

General Form of the Doppler Equation

The equations for the Doppler effect are usually written as a single equation of the form

$$f_d = \left(\frac{v_w}{v_w \mp v_s}\right) f_s$$

PHYSICS INSIGHT

When the distance between you and the source is decreasing, you must subtract to calculate the Doppler effect on frequency and wavelength.

If you are travelling in your car beside a train that is blowing its whistle, is the pitch that you hear for the whistle higher or lower than the true pitch of the whistle? Explain.

Example 8.4

A train is travelling at a speed of 30.0 m/s. Its whistle generates a sound wave with a frequency of 224 Hz. You are standing beside the tracks as the train passes you with its whistle blowing. What change in frequency do you detect for the pitch of the whistle as the train passes, if the speed of sound in air is 330 m/s?

Given

$f_s = 224$ Hz

$v_w = 330$ m/s

$v_s = 30.0$ m/s

Required

(a) Doppler frequency for the whistle as the train approaches
(b) Doppler frequency for the whistle as the train moves away
(c) change in frequency

Analysis and Solution

Use the equations for Doppler shifts to find the Doppler frequencies of the whistle.

(a) For the approaching whistle,   (b) For the receding whistle,

$$f_d = \left(\frac{v_w}{v_w - v_s} \right) f_s \qquad\qquad f_d = \left(\frac{v_w}{v_w + v_s} \right) f_s$$

$$f_d = \left(\frac{330\frac{m}{s}}{330\frac{m}{s} - 30.0\frac{m}{s}} \right) 224 \text{ Hz} \qquad f_d = \left(\frac{330\frac{m}{s}}{330\frac{m}{s} + 30.0\frac{m}{s}} \right) 224 \text{ Hz}$$

$$= \left(\frac{330\frac{m}{s}}{300\frac{m}{s}} \right) 224 \text{ Hz} \qquad\qquad = \left(\frac{330\frac{m}{s}}{360\frac{m}{s}} \right) 224 \text{ Hz}$$

$$= 246.4 \text{ Hz} \qquad\qquad\qquad\qquad = 205.3 \text{ Hz}$$
$$= 246 \text{ Hz} \qquad\qquad\qquad\qquad = 205 \text{ Hz}$$

(c) The change in pitch is the difference in the two frequencies.
Therefore, the pitch change is

$$\Delta f = 246.4 \text{ Hz} - 205.3 \text{ Hz}$$
$$= 41.1 \text{ Hz}$$

Paraphrase and Verify

As the train passes, the pitch of its whistle is lowered by a frequency of about 41 Hz.

Practice Problems

1. You are crossing in a crosswalk when an approaching driver blows his horn. If the true frequency of the horn is 264 Hz and the car is approaching you at a speed of 60.0 km/h, what is the apparent (or Doppler) frequency of the horn? Assume that the speed of sound in air is 340 m/s.

2. An airplane is approaching at a speed of 360 km/h. If you measure the pitch of its approaching engines to be 512 Hz, what must be the actual frequency of the engines? The speed of sound in air is 345 m/s.

3. An automobile is travelling toward you at a speed of 25.0 m/s. When you measure the frequency of its horn, you obtain a value of 260 Hz. If the actual frequency of the horn is known to be 240 Hz, calculate v_w, the speed of sound in air.

4. As a train moves away from you, the frequency of its whistle is determined to be 475 Hz. If the actual frequency of the whistle is 500 Hz and the speed of sound in air is 350 m/s, what is the train's speed?

Answers

1. 278 Hz
2. 364 Hz
3. 325 m/s
4. 18.4 m/s

The Sound Barrier

Jet planes are not allowed to break or exceed the sound barrier in the airspace over most cities. When an object travels at speeds at, or greater than, the speed of sound it creates a sonic boom. The boom is the result of the **shock wave** created by the motion of the object.

e **WEB**

To learn more about possible health effects of sonic booms at close range, and the recent concerns of the Innu Nation, follow the links at www.pearsoned.ca/school/physicssource.

Bow Waves

A boat moving through water produces a bow wave. The crest of the wave moves sideways away from the object, producing the wave's characteristic V-shape. For an airplane moving through the fluid medium of the atmosphere, a V-shaped bow wave, or pressure wave, travels outward at the speed of sound (Figure 8.48). If the speed of the airplane is less than the speed of sound, the bow wave produced at any instant lags behind the bow wave produced just an instant earlier. The bow wave carries energy away from the plane in a continuous stream (Figure 8.49(a)).

Sonic Boom

However, for an airplane travelling at the speed of sound, the bow wave and the airplane travel at the *same* speed. Instant by instant, crests of the bow wave are produced at the same location as the crest of the bow wave produced by the plane an instant earlier (Figure 8.49). The energy stored in the bow wave becomes very intense. To the ear of an observer, crests of successively produced bow waves arrive simultaneously in what is known as a sonic boom. In early attempts to surpass the speed of sound, many airplanes were damaged. At the speed of sound, there is a marked increase in drag and turbulence. This effect damaged planes not designed to withstand it. A reporter assumed the increased drag acted like a barrier to travelling faster than sound and coined the term **sound barrier**.

Mathematically, from the arguments presented above, the Doppler wavelength is given by

$$\lambda_d = \frac{(v_w - v_s)}{f_s}.$$

▲ **Figure 8.48** When conditions are right, the change in pressure produced by the airplane's wings can cause sufficient cooling of the atmosphere so that a cloud forms. The extreme conditions present when a jet is travelling near the speed of sound often result in the type of cloud seen in this photo.

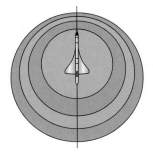

(a) Slower than speed of sound: Pressure waves move out around plane.

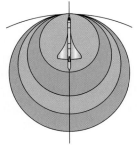

(b) At speed of sound: Pressure waves at nose form a shock wave.

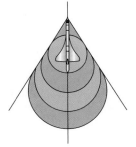

(c) At supersonic speed: Shock waves form a cone, resulting in a sonic boom.

▲ **Figure 8.49** As an airplane accelerates from subsonic to supersonic speeds, the changing relationship between the plane and the bow waves or pressure waves results in a sonic boom.

If a plane is travelling at the speed of sound, then $v_s = v_w$, which means that for any sound produced by the jet, the Doppler wavelength in the direction of the jet's motion is zero. Even if the plane's speed is greater than that of sound, the bow waves still combine to form a shock wave. In this way a sonic boom can be heard for any object, such as a rifle bullet, that has a supersonic speed.

THEN, NOW, AND FUTURE   Ultrasound

While impressive given the technology available at the time, the results of early attempts at using ultrasound in medicine were of poor quality. Initially, ultrasound images from within a body were very blurry and two-dimensional. By today's standards, the technology was extremely crude and there was virtually no scientific understanding of how the sound would behave when it encountered different types of tissue.

Today, computers have made it possible to form three-dimensional images that can be rotated so that you can see all sides. Doppler ultrasound is used to detect blood flow through an organ. Today, 4-D ultrasound (time is the 4th dimension) is a real-time 3-D image that moves.

1. What are the advantages and disadvantages of ultrasound imaging compared with other imaging techniques such as CT scans and MRI?

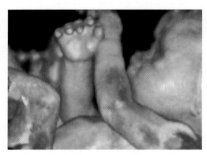
▲ **Figure 8.50**   A 3-D ultrasound picture of a developing fetus

8.4 Check and Reflect

Knowledge

1. What causes the Doppler effect?

2. Two sound sources have the same frequency when at rest. If they are both moving away from you, how could you tell if one was travelling faster than the other?

3. Explain the cause of a sonic boom.

Applications

4. The siren of a police car has a frequency of 660 Hz. If the car is travelling toward you at 40.0 m/s, what do you perceive to be the frequency of the siren? The speed of sound in air is 340 m/s.

5. A police car siren has a frequency of 850 Hz. If you hear this siren to have a frequency that is 40.0 Hz greater than its true frequency, what was the speed of the car? The speed of sound is 350 m/s.

6. A jet, travelling at the speed of sound (Mach 1), emits a sound wave with a frequency of 1000 Hz. Use the Doppler effect equations to calculate the frequency of this sound as the jet first approaches you, then moves away from you. Explain what these answers mean in terms of what you would hear as the jet moved toward, then past, you.

Extensions

7. Astronomers have shown that the colour of light from distant stars is shifted from the blue end toward the red end of the spectrum. This is known as **red shift**. Astronomers realized that since light energy is transmitted as a wave, the red shift was the result of the Doppler effect applied to light. What does the red shift indicate about the motions of the star, which emits light that we see as a red shift? **Hint:** Investigate the relationship between the frequency and colour for light.

e TEST

To check your understanding of the Doppler effect, follow the eTest at www.pearsoned.ca/school/physicssource.

Key Terms and Concepts

medium	incident wave	principle of	closed pipe
wave	reflected wave	superposition	fundamental frequency
equilibrium position	wave train	constructive interference	overtone
crest	point source	destructive interference	open pipe
trough	ray	node	interference pattern
amplitude	pulse	antinode	maximum
wavelength	interference	standing wave	minimum
wave front		resonance	phase shift

Key Equations

$$\lambda = vT \qquad\qquad v = f\lambda \qquad\qquad f_d = \left(\frac{v_w}{v_w \mp v_s}\right)f_s$$

Conceptual Overview

The concept map below summarizes many of the concepts and equations in this chapter. Copy and complete the map to produce a full summary of the chapter.

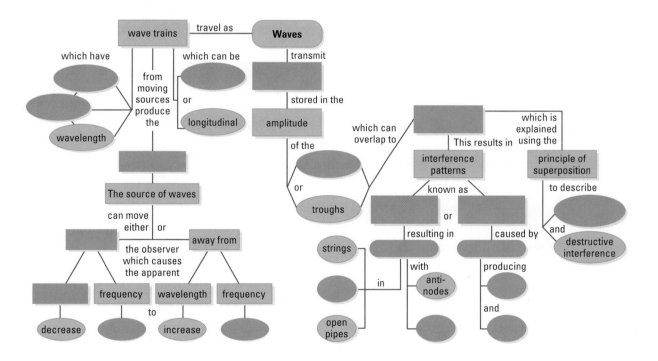

Knowledge

1. (8.1) (a) When a wave moves on water, what is the nature of the motion of the water within the wave?

   (b) What is the relationship between the direction of an incident wave and a reflected wave?

   (c) If you were able see the sound waves emitted when a tuning fork was struck, what would you record as your observation?

2. (8.2) (a) What affects the speed of a water wave?

   (b) What is the nature of the motion of the medium when a longitudinal wave moves through it?

   (c) Describe how the speed of a wave affects its wavelength and its amplitude.

   (d) Explain why waves are considered a form of Simple Harmonic Motion.

   (e) If speed is constant, how does wavelength vary with frequency?

3. (8.3) (a) Describe the conditions required to produce constructive and destructive interference in waves.

   (b) Describe how the principle of superposition applies to what happens when two pulses of identical length and amplitude interfere to produce no apparent pulse.

   (c) Define node, antinode, and standing wave.

   (d) In terms of the wavelength of the waves that have combined to form a standing wave, describe the position of the nodes and antinodes as you move away from the fixed end of a spring.

   (e) Why can a standing wave be generated only by what is defined as resonant frequency?

4. (8.4) (a) Does the Doppler effect apply only to sound or can it apply to any form of wave motion? Explain.

   (b) How are the waves in the direction of a source's motion affected as the speed of the source increases?

Applications

5. The speed of a wave in a spring is 15.0 m/s. If the length of a pulse moving in the spring is 2.00 m, how long did it take to generate the pulse? Why don't we talk about the frequency for a pulse?

6. Waves are generated by a straight wave generator. The waves move toward and reflect from a straight barrier. The angle between the wave front and the barrier is 30°. Draw a diagram that shows what you would observe if this occurred in a ripple tank. Use a line drawn across the middle of a blank sheet of paper to represent the barrier. Draw a series of wave fronts about 1 cm apart intersecting the barrier at 30°. Use a protractor to make sure the angle is correct. Now draw the reflected waves. Draw a ray to indicate the motion of the incident wave front and continue this ray to indicate the motion of the reflected wave front. **Hint:** Draw the reflected ray as if it had a new source.

7. A ripple tank is set up so that the water in it is 0.7 cm deep. In half of the tank, a glass plate is placed on the bottom to make the water in that half shallower. The glass plate is 0.5 cm thick. Thus, the tank has a deep section (0.7 cm) and a shallow section (0.2 cm). In the deep section the wave velocity is 15.0 cm/s while in the shallow section the velocity is 10.0 cm/s. Straight waves, parallel to the edge of the glass, move toward the line between the deep and shallow sections. If the waves have a frequency of 12.0 Hz, what changes in wavelength would you observe as they enter the shallow section? What would happen to the direction of the motion?

8. A ripple tank is set up as described in question 7. For this ripple tank you measure the speed of the waves to be 12.0 cm/s and 9.0 cm/s in the deep and shallow sections, respectively. If waves in the deep section that are 11.5 cm long cross over to the shallow section, what would be the wavelength in the shallow section?

9. The term ultrasound means the frequency is higher than those that our ears can detect (about 12 kHz). Animals can often hear sounds that, to our ears, are ultrasound. For example, a dog whistle has a frequency of 12.8 kHz. If the speed of sound in air is 350 m/s, what is the wavelength of the sound generated by this whistle?

10. A spring is stretched to a length of 7.0 m. A frequency of 2.0 Hz generates a standing wave in the spring that has six nodes.

    (a) Sketch the standing wave pattern for the spring.

    (b) Calculate the velocity of the wave.

11. The figure shows two waves that occupy the same point in space. Copy the sketch onto a sheet of paper using the dimensions indicated. Draw the wave that results from the interference of these two waves.

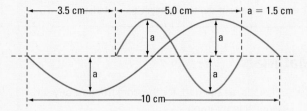

12. If a frequency of 1.5 Hz generates a standing wave in a spring that has three antinodes, (a) what frequency generates a standing wave with five antinodes in the same spring, and (b) what is the fundamental frequency for this spring?

13. A violin string is 33.0 cm long. The thinnest string on the violin is tuned to vibrate at a frequency of 659 Hz.

(a) What is the wave velocity in the string?

(b) If you place your finger on the string so that its length is shortened to 28.0 cm, what is the frequency of the note that the string produces?

14. (a) What is the shortest closed pipe for which resonance is heard when a tuning fork with a frequency of 426 Hz is held at the open end of the pipe? The speed of sound in air is 335 m/s.

(b) What is the length of the next longest pipe that produces resonance?

15. Draw the interference pattern generated by two in-phase point sources that are four wavelengths apart.

16. In the interference pattern for two in-phase point sources, a point on a second order maximum is 2.8 cm farther from one source than the other. What is the wavelength generated by these sources?

17. The horn on a car has a frequency of 290 Hz. If the speed of sound in air is 340 m/s and the car is moving toward you at a speed of 72.0 km/h, what is the apparent frequency of the sound?

18. How fast is a sound source moving toward you if you hear the frequency to be 580 Hz when the true frequency is 540 Hz? The speed of sound in air is 350 m/s. Express your answer in km/h.

19. If the speed of sound in air is 350 m/s, how fast would a sound source need to travel away from you if the frequency that you hear is to be one-half the true frequency? What would you hear if this sound source had been moving toward you?

20. When a police car is at rest, the wavelength of the sound from its siren is 0.550 m. If the car is moving toward you at a speed of 120 km/h, what is the frequency at which you hear the siren? Assume that the speed of sound is 345 m/s.

21. If the speed of sound in air is 350 m/s, how fast must a sound source move toward you if the frequency that you hear is twice the true frequency of the sound? What frequency would you hear if this sound source had been moving away from you?

Extensions

22. Describe an arrangement that you might use if you wanted to create an interference pattern similar to the one in Figure 8.44 on page 426 by using sound waves that have a frequency of 512 Hz. Except for standing waves in strings or pipes, why do you think that we do not often find interference patterns in nature?

23. Explain why the number of maxima and minima in the interference pattern generated by two in-phase point sources depends on the ratio of the distance between the sources to the wavelength.

 _e_ TEST

To check your understanding of waves and wave motion, follow the eTest links at www.pearsoned.ca/school/physicssource.

Consolidate Your Understanding

Answer each of the following questions in your own words. Provide examples to illustrate your explanation.

1. What are the advantages and disadvantages of using a spring as a model for wave motion?

2. What are the conditions for which a standing wave pattern is generated? Why are standing waves not often seen in nature?

3. Explain how the energy in a wave is transmitted from one place to another.

4. Describe what is meant by the principle of superposition. How does this principle explain standing waves?

5. What is meant by resonance?

Think About It

Review your answers to the Think About It questions on page 393. How would you answer each question now?

Earthquakes

Scenario

The tsunami that swept coastal regions of the Indian Ocean on December 26, 2004, was set off by an earthquake centred off the coast of the island of Sumatra in Indonesia. Seismographs around the world identified the location and strength of the earthquake. It was determined that the earthquake rated about 9.0–9.3 on the Richter scale. You have been asked by the government of Alberta to make a presentation on the seismology of earthquakes. Your challenge is threefold.

- First: you are to explain the nature of earthquake shock waves, their movement through Earth, and how the location of the earthquake epicentre is identified by seismographs around the world.
- Second: you are to explain how the intensity of earthquakes is measured. This means that you must explain what the Richter scale is, and how it is used to rate earthquake intensity.
- Third: you are to demonstrate the operation of a seismograph.

Planning

Your team should consist of three to five members. Choose a team manager and a record keeper. Assign other tasks as they arise. The first task is to decide the structure of your presentation and the research questions you will need to investigate. Questions you will need to consider are: How will you present the information to your audience? What are the resources at your disposal? Do you have access to computers and presentation programs such as PowerPoint®? Which team members will design, build, and demonstrate the model seismograph?

Brainstorm strategies for research and create a schedule for meeting the deadlines for all phases of the project. Where is your team going to look for the information necessary to complete the project? What types of graphics will be most effective to assist your presentation? How will you best demonstrate the function of your seismograph? Your final report should include written, graphic, and photographic analyses of your presentation.

Assessing Results

Assess the success of your project based on a rubric* designed in class that considers:
- research strategies
- thoroughness of the experimental design
- effectiveness of the experimental technique
- effectiveness of the team's public presentation

Materials

- materials, as needed, for the construction of your model seismograph

Procedure

1. Research the nature of the shock waves set off by an earthquake. Be alert to Internet sites that may contain unreliable or inaccurate information. Make sure that you evaluate the reliability of the sources of information that you use for your research. If you gather information from the Internet, make sure you identify who sponsors the site and decide whether or not it is a reputable source of information. Maintain a list of your references and include it as an appendix to your report. Use graphics to explain how the shock waves move through Earth, and how seismologists locate the epicentre of an earthquake.

2. Research the history of the Richter scale and its use in identifying the intensity of an earthquake.

3. Design and build your model of a seismograph. Decide how you will demonstrate its use in your presentation.

4. Prepare an audio-visual presentation that would inform your audience on the nature of earthquakes and how they are detected.

Thinking Further

Write a short appendix (three or four paragraphs) to your report to suggest steps that governments might take to make buildings safer in earthquake zones.

Answer questions such as: What types of structures are least susceptible to damage by earthquakes? What types are most susceptible?

*Note: Your instructor will assess the project using a similar assessment rubric.

Unit Concepts and Skills: Quick Reference

Concepts	Summary	Resources and Skill Building
Chapter 7	**Oscillatory motion requires a set of conditions.**	
	7.1 Period and Frequency	
Period	Period is the time for one complete cycle, measured in seconds (s). If the period of each cycle remains constant, the object is moving with oscillatory motion.	QuickLab 7-1; Inquiry Lab 7-2; Minds On; Figures 7.4, 7.5
Frequency	Frequency is the number of cycles per second, measured in Hertz (Hz).	QuickLab 7-1; Inquiry Lab 7-2; Example 7.1; Figure 7.5
	7.2 Simple Harmonic Motion	
Spring constant	The spring constant is the amount of force needed to stretch or compress the spring 1 m and is measured in N/m. It can also be thought of as the stiffness of a spring.	QuickLab 7-3; Examples 7.2–7.4
Hooke's law	Hooke's law states that the deformation of an object is proportional to the force causing it.	Figures 7.9–7.16
Simple harmonic motion	SHM refers to anything that moves with uniform oscillatory motion and conforms to Hooke's law.	Figures 7.19–7.23; eSIM
Pendulum motion	The pendulum is a simple harmonic oscillator for angles less than 15°.	Figures 7.25–7.27; Example 7.5; Inquiry Lab 7-4; Table 7.5
	7.3 Position, Velocity, Acceleration, and Time Relationships	
Acceleration of a mass-spring system	The acceleration of a mass-spring system depends on displacement, mass, and the spring constant, and it varies throughout the motion of the mass-spring system.	Figure 7.28
Relationship between acceleration and velocity of a mass-spring system	The acceleration and velocity of a mass-spring system are continually changing. The velocity of a mass-spring system is determined by its displacement, spring constant, and mass.	Figures 7.29–7.33; Example 7.6
Period of a mass-spring system	The period of a mass-spring oscillator is determined by its mass and spring constant, but not its amplitude.	Figures 7.35–7.37; Example 7.7
Period of a pendulum	A pendulum's period is determined by its length and the acceleration of gravity, but not the mass of the bob.	Figures 7.39, 7.40; eSIM; Example 7.8
	7.4 Applications of Simple Harmonic Motion	
Resonance	Resonance is the natural frequency of vibration of an object.	Figure 7.41; QuickLab 7-5
Forced frequency	Forced frequency is the frequency at which an external force is applied to a resonating object.	Figure 7.41; QuickLab 7-5
Resonance effects on buildings and bridges	Bridges and buildings can resonate due to the force of the wind.	Figures 7.44, 7.45; Then, Now, and Future
Chapter 8	**Mechanical waves transmit energy in a variety of ways.**	
	8.1 The Properties of Waves	
Wave properties may be qualitative or quantitative.	Waves have many properties that can be used to analyze the nature of the wave and the way it behaves as it moves through a medium. Some of these properties are qualitative (crest, trough, wave front, medium, incident wave, reflected wave, wave train) while others are quantitative (amplitude, wavelength, frequency, wave velocity).	QuickLab 8-1; Inquiry Lab 8-2; Inquiry Lab 8-3
	8.2 Transverse and Longitudinal Waves	
Universal wave equation	Waves can move through a medium either as transverse or longitudinal waves. The relationship among the frequency, wavelength, and wave velocity is given by the universal wave equation.	Inquiry Lab 8-4; Inquiry Lab 8-5; Example 8.1; Example 8.2
	8.3 Superposition and Interference	
Interference patterns may result when more than one wave moves through a medium.	When two, or more, waves travel in different directions through the same point in space their amplitudes combine according to the principle of superposition. Depending on the properties of the waves, they may form an interference pattern. Interference patterns can often be used to determine the properties of the waves from which they are formed.	Inquiry Lab 8-6; Example 8.3; Inquiry Lab 8-7; Design a Lab 8-8
	8.4 The Doppler Effect	
Doppler effect	When a sound source moves either toward or away from a sensor (ear or microphone), the frequency of the sound that is detected will be different from the frequency emitted by the source.	Example 8.4
Sonic boom	When an object is travelling at the speed of sound it creates a shock wave known as a sonic boom.	Figure 8.49

Vocabulary

1. Use your own words to define the following terms, concepts, principles, or laws. Give examples where appropriate.

amplitude
antinodes
closed-pipe air column
constructive interference
crest
destructive interference
diverging
Doppler effect
equilibrium
forced frequency
frequency
fundamental frequency
Hooke's law
incident wave
in phase
interference
longitudinal wave
maximum
mechanical resonance
medium
minimum
nodes or nodal points
open-pipe air column
oscillation
oscillatory motion
overtone
period
phase shift
principle of superposition
pulse
ray
reflected wave
resonance
resonant frequency
restoring force
shock wave
simple harmonic motion
simple harmonic oscillator
sonic boom
sound barrier
spring constant
standing waves
transverse wave
trough
two-point-source interference pattern

wave
wave front
wave train
wave velocity
wavelength

Knowledge

CHAPTER 7

2. How are the units of frequency and period similar? How are they different?

3. The SI unit for frequency is Hz. What are two other accepted units?

4. For any simple harmonic oscillator, in what position is
   (a) the velocity zero?
   (b) the restoring force the greatest?

5. Why doesn't a pendulum act like a simple harmonic oscillator for large amplitudes?

6. The equation for Hooke's law uses a negative sign ($F = -kx$). Why is this sign necessary?

7. Aboriginal bows used for hunting were made from wood. Assuming the wood deforms according to Hooke's law, explain how you would go about measuring the spring constant of the wood.

8. Suppose the same pendulum was tested in both Calgary and Jasper. In which location would you expect the pendulum to oscillate more slowly? Explain.

9. Explain why the sound from one tuning fork can make a second tuning fork hum. What conditions must be necessary for this to happen?

10. A pendulum in a clock oscillates with a resonant frequency that depends on several factors. From the list below, indicate what effect (if any) the following variables have on the pendulum's resonant frequency.
    (a) length of pendulum arm
    (b) latitude of clock's position
    (c) longitude of clock's position
    (d) elevation
    (e) restoring force

11. The diagram below shows waves in two springs. For each of the springs, how many wavelengths are shown?

12. Sound waves, travelling through air, are reflected from the wall of a building. Describe how the reflection affects
    (a) the speed,
    (b) the wavelength,
    (c) the amplitude, and
    (d) the direction of a wave train.

13. The energy in a transverse wave is located in the crests and troughs. Where is the energy in a longitudinal wave located?

14. How is the shape of a circular wave front changed when it reflects from a straight barrier?

15. What aspect of a pulse decides the amount of energy it transfers?

16. When water waves enter a region where they travel slower, what happens to the
    (a) frequency,
    (b) wavelength, and
    (c) direction of the waves?

17. In the interference pattern from two in-phase point sources, what name is given to a line along which destructive interference occurs?

18. What decides the speed at which a wave travels through a spring?

19. What causes a standing wave in a spring?

20. Draw a transverse wave train that consists of two wavelengths. On your diagram, label the equilibrium position for the medium, a crest, a trough, the amplitude, a wavelength, and the direction of the wave velocity. Along the wavelength that you identified above, draw several vector arrows to indicate the direction of the motion of the medium.

21. Why does moving your finger along the string of a violin alter the note that it produces?

22. What property of the sound produced by a tuning fork is affected by striking the tuning fork with different forces? What does that tell you about the relationship between the properties of the sound and the sound wave created by striking the tuning fork?

23. When two in-phase point sources generate an interference pattern, what conditions are required to create (a) the central maximum, (b) a second order maximum?

24. In terms of the length of an open pipe, what is the longest wavelength for which resonance can occur?

25. You are walking north along a street when a police car with its siren on comes down a side street (travelling east) and turns northward on the street in front of you. Describe what you would hear, in terms of frequency of the sound of its siren, before and after the police car turns.

26. What is the relationship between frequency, wavelength, and wave velocity?

27. Why does the frequency of a sound source that is moving toward you seem to be higher than it would be if the source were at rest?

Applications

28. Determine the force necessary to stretch a spring ($k = 2.55$ N) to a distance of 1.20 m.

29. A musician plucks a guitar string. The string has a frequency of 400.0 Hz and a spring constant of 5.0×10^4 N/m. What is the mass of the string?

30. When a pendulum is displaced 90.0° from the vertical, what proportion of the force of gravity is the restoring force?

31. While performing a demonstration to determine the spring constant of an elastic band, a student pulls an elastic band to different displacements and measures the applied force. The observations were recorded in the table below. Plot the graph of this data. Can the spring constant be determined? Why or why not?

Displacement (m)	Force (N)
0.1	0.38
0.2	1.52
0.3	3.42
0.4	6.08
0.5	9.5
0.6	13.68

32. A force of 40.0 N is required to move a 10.0-kg horizontal mass-spring system through a displacement of 80.0 cm. Determine the acceleration of the mass when its displacement is −25.0 cm.

33. Use the following table to determine the spring constant of a spring.

Displacement (cm)	Force (mN)
2.5	10.0
5.0	21.0
7.5	31.0
10.0	39.0
12.5	49.0

34. A 50.0-g mass oscillates on the end of a vertical mass-spring system ($k = 25.0$ N/m) with a maximum acceleration of 50.0 m/s^2.

(a) What is its amplitude of vibration?

(b) What is the maximum velocity of the mass?

35. A bee's wing is a simple harmonic oscillator. It has a mass of 1.0×10^{-5} kg and makes one complete oscillation in 4.5×10^{-3} s. What is the maximum wing speed if the amplitude of its motion is 1.10 cm?

36. A skyscraper begins resonating in a strong wind. A tuned mass damper ($m = 10.0$ t) at the top of the building moves through a maximum displacement of 1.50 m in the opposite direction to dampen the oscillations. If the mass damper is attached to a horizontal spring and has a maximum speed of 1.40 m/s, what is the period of its oscillations?

37. A branch at the top of a tree sways with simple harmonic motion. The amplitude of motion is 0.80 m and its speed is 1.5 m/s in the equilibrium position. What is the speed of the branch at the displacement of 0.60 m?

38. A tuned mass damper at the top of a skyscraper is a mass suspended from a thick cable. If the building sways with a frequency of 0.125 Hz, what length must the cable supporting the weight be to create a resonance in the damper?

39. When a wave slows down, what property of the wave is not affected? What effect does this have on the other properties of the wave? Explain.

40. Explain how a wave can transmit energy through a medium without actually transmitting any matter.

41. A light wave is transmitted through space at 3.00×10^8 m/s. If visible light has wavelengths ranging from about 4.30×10^{-7} m to 7.50×10^{-7} m long, what range of frequencies are we able to see?

42. Radio waves travel at the speed of light waves (3.00×10^8 m/s). If your radio is tuned to a station broadcasting at 1250 kHz, what is the length of the waves arriving at the radio antenna?

43. A pendulum oscillates with a period of 0.350 s. Attached to the pendulum is a pen that marks a strip of paper on the table below the pendulum as it oscillates. When the strip of paper is pulled sideways at a steady speed, the pen draws a sine curve on the paper. What will be the wavelength of the sine curve if the speed of the paper is 0.840 m/s?

44. A submarine sends out a sonar wave that has a frequency of 545 Hz. If the wavelength of the sound is 2.60 m, how long does it take for the echo to return when the sound is reflected from a submarine that is 5.50 km away?

45. A wire is stretched between two points that are 3.00 m apart. A generator oscillating at 480 Hz sets up a standing wave in the wire that consists of 24 antinodes. What is the velocity at which waves move in this wire?

46. A spring is stretched to a length of 5.40 m. At that length the speed of waves in the spring is 3.00 m/s.

(a) If a standing wave with a frequency 2.50 Hz were generated in this spring, how many nodes and antinodes would there be along the spring?

(b) What is the next lower frequency for which a standing wave pattern could exist in this spring?

47. The second string on a violin is tuned to the note D with a frequency of 293 Hz. This is the fundamental frequency for the open string, which is 33.0 cm long.

(a) What is the speed of the waves in the string?

(b) If you press on the string with your finger so that the oscillating portion of the string is 2/3 the length of the open string, what is the frequency of the note that is created?

48. An audio frequency generator set at 154 Hz is used to generate a standing wave in a closed-pipe resonator, where the speed of sound is 340 m/s.

(a) What is the shortest air column for which resonance is heard?

(b) What is the next longer column length for which resonance is heard?

49. A submarine's sonar emits a sound with a frequency of 875 Hz. The speed of sound in seawater is about 1500 m/s. If you measure the frequency of the sound to be 870 Hz, what is the velocity of the submarine?

50. A police car is travelling at a speed of 144 km/h. It has a siren with a frequency of 1120 Hz. Assume that the speed of sound in air is 320 m/s.

(a) If the car is moving toward you, what frequency will you hear for the siren?

(b) If the car had been moving away from you at the same speed, what frequency would you have heard?

Extensions

51. What generalization can be made about the frequency of vibration with regard to the mass for a mass-spring system? (Assume all other qualities remain constant.)

52. An alien crash-lands its spaceship on a planet in our solar system. Unfortunately, it is unable to tell which planet it is. From the wreckage of the spaceship the alien constructs a 1.0-m-long pendulum from a piece of wire with four metal nuts on the end. If this pendulum swings with the frequency of 3.27 s, on which planet did the alien land: Mercury, Venus, or Earth?

53. Use a compass to draw a simulation of the wave pattern generated by two in-phase point source generators that are 3.5 wavelengths apart. Near the middle of the page, place two points (S_1 and S_2) 3.5 cm apart to represent the positions of the sources. Draw wavelengths 1.0 cm long by drawing concentric circles that increase in radii by 1.0-cm increments. Locate on the diagram all the maxima and minima that are generated by this set-up and draw lines to indicate their positions. How does this pattern differ from the one in Figure 8.44 on page 426? Explain why these differences occur.

54. In a stereo system, there are two speakers set at some distance apart. Why does a stereo system not result in an interference pattern?

55. If a sound source is at rest, the frequency you hear and the actual frequency are equal. Their ratio equals one ($f_d/f_s = 1$). If the sound source moves toward you at an ever-increasing speed, this frequency ratio also increases. Plot a graph for the ratio of the frequencies vs. the speed of the sound source as the speed of the source increases from zero to Mach 1. What is the value of the ratio when the speed of the source is Mach 1?

Skills Practice

56. Use a graphing calculator or another suitable means to plot a graph of period against frequency. What type of relationship is this?

57. Outline an experimental procedure that you could perform to determine the spring constant of a vertical mass-spring system.

58. Sketch a diagram of a horizontal mass-spring system in three positions: at both extremes of its motion, and in its equilibrium position. In each diagram, draw vector arrows representing the restoring force, velocity, and acceleration. State whether these are at a maximum or a minimum.

59. Outline a procedure that you could use to determine the mass of a horizontal mass-spring system without measuring the mass on a scale.

60. A student wants to determine the mass of the bob on a pendulum but only has access to a stopwatch and a ruler. She decides to pull the pendulum bob back through a displacement of 10° and time 20 complete oscillations. Will it be possible to determine the mass from the data gathered? Explain.

61. Construct a concept map for the simple harmonic motion of a pendulum. Include the following terms: period, displacement, restoring force, velocity, length, and gravitational field strength.

62. In a paragraph, explain why Huygens's pendulum clock was a revolution in clock making and what the limitations were in its design. Be sure to use these terms: pendulum length, resonant frequency, forced frequency, and gravitational field strength.

63. Research the term "red shift" as used in astronomy. Prepare a report on the importance of red shift to our understanding of the nature of the universe.

64. Describe how to use springs to explore what happens to pulses transmitted from one medium to another in which the wave speed is different.

65. Explain to someone who has not studied physics the differences in the ways objects and waves transport energy between points on Earth.

Self-assessment

66. Identify a concept or issue that you studied in this unit and would like to learn more about.

67. Learning often requires that we change the way we think about things. Which concept in this unit required the greatest change in your thinking about it? Explain how your thinking changed.

68. Which of the concepts in this unit was most helpful in explaining to you how objects interact?

e TEST

To check your understanding of oscillatory motion and waves, follow the eTest links at www.pearsoned.ca/school/physicssource.

Momentum and Impulse

Many situations and activities in the real world, such as snowboarding, involve an object gaining speed and momentum as it moves. Sometimes two or more objects collide, such as a hockey stick hitting a puck across the ice. What physics principles apply to the motion of colliding objects? How does the combination of the net force during impact and the interaction time affect an object during a collision?

Unit at a Glance

Unit Themes and Emphases

- Change and Systems
- Science and Technology

Focussing Questions

In this study of momentum and impulse, you will investigate the motion of objects that interact, how the velocity of a system of objects is related before and after collision, and how safety devices incorporate the concepts of momentum and impulse.

As you study this unit, consider these questions:

- What characteristics of an object affect its momentum?
- How are momentum and impulse related?

Unit Project

An Impulsive Water Balloon

- By the time you complete this unit, you will have the skills to design a model of an amusement ride that is suitable for a diverse group of people. You will first need to consider acceptable accelerations that most people can tolerate. To test your model, you will drop a water balloon from a height of 2.4 m to see if it will remain intact.

e **WEB**

Research the physics concepts that apply to collisions in sports. How do athletes apply these concepts when trying to score goals for their team? How do they apply these concepts to minimize injury? Write a summary of your findings. Begin your search at www.pearsoned.ca/school/physicssource.

The momentum of an isolated system of interacting objects is conserved.

Most sports involve objects colliding during the play. Hockey checks, curling takeouts, football tackles, skeet shooting, lacrosse catches, and interceptions of the ball in soccer are examples of collisions in sports action. Players, such as Randy Ferbey, who are able to accurately predict the resulting motion of colliding objects have a better chance of helping their team win (Figure 9.1).

When objects interact during a short period of time, they may experience very large forces. Evidence of these forces is the distortion in shape of an object at the moment of impact. In hockey, the boards become distorted for an instant when a player collides with them. Another evidence of these forces is a change in the motion of an object. If a goalie gloves a shot aimed at the net, you can see how the impact of the puck affects the motion of the goalie's hand.

In this chapter, you will examine how the net force on an object and the time interval during which the force acts affect the motion of the object. Designers of safety equipment for sports and vehicles use this type of analysis when developing new safety devices. In a system of objects, you will also investigate how their respective velocities change when the objects interact with each other.

◀ **Figure 9.1**
Sports such as curling involve applying physics principles to change the score. Randy Ferbey, originally from Edmonton, won the Brier (Canadian) Curling Championship six times, and the World Curling Championship four times.

Predicting Angles After Collisions

Problem

How do the masses of two objects affect the angle between their paths after they collide off centre?

Materials

pennies and nickels with smooth, circular outer edges
marking devices for the paths (paper, tape, pencil, ruler)
stack of books
protractor (optional)

Procedure

1. Set up the books and paper as shown in Figure 9.2. Open the cover of the book at the top of the stack for backing. Tape the paper securely to the lab bench.

2. Position one penny at the bottom of the ramp. Mark its initial position by drawing an outline on the paper.

3. Place the incoming penny at the top of the ramp as shown in Figure 9.2. Mark its initial position.

4. Predict the path each coin will take after they collide off centre. Lightly mark the predicted paths.

5. Send the coin down the ramp and mark the position of each coin after collision. Observe the relative velocities of the coins to each other both before and after collision.

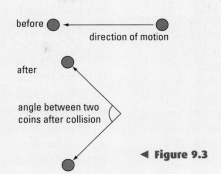

before ●←——————————●
direction of motion

after ●

angle between two
coins after collision

◀ **Figure 9.3**

6. Determine if the angle between the paths after collision is less than 90°, 90°, or greater than 90° (Figure 9.3).

7. Repeat steps 5 and 6, but have the incoming coin collide at a different contact point with the coin at the bottom of the ramp.

8. Repeat steps 2 to 7 using a penny as the incoming coin and a nickel at the bottom of the ramp.

9. Repeat steps 2 to 7 using a nickel as the incoming coin and a penny at the bottom of the ramp.

Questions

1. What was the approximate angle formed by the paths of the two coins after collision when the coins were
   (a) the same mass?
   (b) of different mass?

2. Describe how the speeds of the two coins changed before and after collision.

3. How can you predict which coin will move faster after collision?

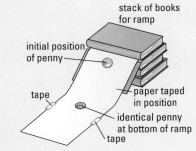

stack of books
for ramp

initial position
of penny

tape

paper taped
in position

identical penny
at bottom of ramp

tape

▶ **Figure 9.2**

Think About It

1. Under what circumstances could an object initially at rest be struck and move at a greater speed after collision than the incoming object?

2. Under what circumstances could a coin in 9-1 QuickLab rebound toward the ramp after collision?

Discuss your answers in a small group and record them for later reference. As you complete each section of this chapter, review your answers to these questions. Note any changes to your ideas.

info BIT

A tragic avalanche occurred during the New Year's Eve party in the Inuit community of Kangiqsualujjuaq, formerly in Quebec and now part of Nunavut. At 1:30 a.m. on January 1, 1999, snow from the nearby 365-m mountain slope came cascading down, knocking out a wall and swamping those inside the gymnasium at the party. The snow on the mountain was initially about 1 m thick. After the avalanche was over, the school was covered with up to 3 m of snow.

info BIT

Most avalanches occur on slopes that form an angle of 30° to 45° with the horizontal, although they can occur on any slope if the right conditions exist. In North America, a large avalanche may release about 230 000 m³ of snow.

9.1 Momentum Is Mass Times Velocity

Snow avalanches sliding down mountains involve large masses in motion. They can be both spectacular and catastrophic (Figure 9.4).

Unbalanced forces affect the motion of all objects. A snow mass on the side of a mountain experiences many forces, such as wind, friction between the snow and the mountain, a normal force exerted by the mountain on the snow, and gravity acting vertically downward. Skiers and animals moving along the mountain slope also apply forces on the snow mass.

When a large mass of snow becomes dislodged and slides down a mountain slope due to gravity, it not only gains speed but also more mass as additional snow becomes dislodged along the downward path.

▶ **Figure 9.4** When the risk of an avalanche seems imminent, ski patrols reduce the mass of snow along a mountain slope by forcing an avalanche to take place. They do this by targeting large masses of snow with guns or explosives to dislodge the snow.

Momentum Is a Vector Quantity

All objects have mass. The **momentum**, $\vec{p}$, of an object is defined as the product of the mass of the object and its velocity. Since momentum is the product of a scalar (mass) and a vector (velocity), momentum is a vector quantity that has the same direction as the velocity.

momentum: product of the mass of an object and its velocity

$$\vec{p} = m\vec{v}$$

Momentum has units of kilogram-metres per second (kg·m/s).

When you compare the momenta of two objects, you need to consider both the mass and the velocity of each object (Figure 9.5). Although two identical bowling balls, A and B, have the same mass, they do not necessarily have the same momentum. If ball A is moving very slowly, it has a very small momentum. If ball B is moving much faster than ball A, ball B's momentum will have a greater magnitude than ball A's because of its greater speed.

▲ **Figure 9.5** The bowling ball in both photos is the same. However, the bowling ball on the left has less momentum than the ball on the right. What evidence suggests this?

In real life, almost no object in motion has constant momentum because its velocity is usually not constant. Friction opposes the motion of all objects and eventually slows them down. In most instances, it is more accurate to state the *instantaneous* momentum of an object if you can measure its instantaneous velocity and mass.

e **WEB**

Switzerland has a long history of studying avalanches. Find out what causes an avalanche. What physical variables do avalanche experts monitor? What models are scientists working on to better predict the likelihood and severity of avalanches? Begin your search at www.pearsoned.ca/school/ physicssource.

Concept Check

How would the momentum of an object change if

(a) the mass is doubled but the velocity remains the same?

(b) the velocity is reduced to $\frac{1}{3}$ of its original magnitude?

(c) the direction of the velocity changes from [E] to [W]?

Relating Momentum to Newton's Second Law

e WEB

Research how momentum applies to cycling and other sports. Write a brief report of your findings. Begin your search at www.pearsoned.ca/school/physicssource.

The concept of momentum can be used to restate Newton's second law. From Unit II, Newton's second law states that an external non-zero net force acting on an object is equal to the product of the mass of the object and its acceleration, $\vec{F}_{net} = m\vec{a}$. Acceleration is defined as the rate of change of velocity. For constant acceleration, $\vec{a} = \dfrac{\Delta \vec{v}}{\Delta t}$ or $\dfrac{\vec{v}_f - \vec{v}_i}{\Delta t}$. If you substitute $\dfrac{\vec{v}_f - \vec{v}_i}{\Delta t}$ for $\vec{a}$ in Newton's second law, you get

$$\vec{F}_{net} = m\vec{a}$$
$$= m\left(\frac{\vec{v}_f - \vec{v}_i}{\Delta t}\right)$$
$$= \frac{m\vec{v}_f - m\vec{v}_i}{\Delta t}$$

The quantity $m\vec{v}$ is momentum. So the equation can be written as

$$\vec{F}_{net} = \frac{\vec{p}_f - \vec{p}_i}{\Delta t}$$

$$= \frac{\Delta \vec{p}}{\Delta t} \text{ where } \vec{F}_{net} \text{ is constant}$$

Written this way, Newton's second law relates the net force acting on an object to its rate of change of momentum. It is interesting to note that Newton stated his second law of motion in terms of the rate of change of momentum. It may be worded as:

> An external non-zero net force acting on an object is equal to the rate of change of momentum of the object.
>
> $$\vec{F}_{net} = \frac{\Delta \vec{p}}{\Delta t} \text{ where } \vec{F}_{net} \text{ is constant}$$

e SIM

For a given net force, learn how the mass of an object affects its momentum and its final velocity. Follow the eSim links at www.pearsoned.ca/school/physicssource.

This form of Newton's law has some major advantages over the way it was written in Unit II. The equation $\vec{F}_{net} = m\vec{a}$ only applies to situations where the mass is constant. However, by using the concept of momentum, it is possible to derive another form for Newton's second law that applies to situations where the mass, the velocity, or both the mass and velocity are changing.

In situations where the net force changes over a time interval, the *average* net force is equal to the rate of change of momentum of the object.

$$\vec{F}_{net_{ave}} = \frac{\Delta \vec{p}}{\Delta t}$$

In Example 9.1, a person in a bumper car is moving at constant velocity. Since both the person and the car move together as a unit, both objects form a system. The momentum of the system is equal to the total mass of the system times the velocity of the system.

Example 9.1

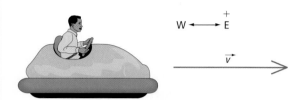

W ⟵ E
+

$\vec{v}$

▲ **Figure 9.6**

A 180-kg bumper car carrying a 70-kg driver has a constant velocity of 3.0 m/s [E]. Calculate the momentum of the car-driver system. Draw both the velocity vector and the momentum vector.

Given

$m_c = 180$ kg $m_d = 70$ kg $\vec{v} = 3.0$ m/s [E]

Required

momentum of system $(\vec{p})$
velocity and momentum vector diagrams

Analysis and Solution

The driver and bumper car are a system because they move together as a unit. Find the total mass of the system.

$m_T = m_c + m_d$

$\quad = 180$ kg $+ 70$ kg

$\quad = 250$ kg

The momentum of the system is in the direction of the velocity of the system. So use the scalar form of $\vec{p} = m\vec{v}$ to find the magnitude of the momentum.

$p = m_T v$

$\quad = (250$ kg$)(3.0$ m/s$)$

$\quad = 7.5 \times 10^2$ kg·m/s

Draw the velocity vector to scale (Figure 9.7).

W ⟵ E
+

|—————|
1.0 m/s

$\vec{v} = 3.0$ m/s

▲ **Figure 9.7**

Practice Problems

1. A 65-kg girl is driving a 535-kg snowmobile at a constant velocity of 11.5 m/s [60.0° N of E].
   (a) Calculate the momentum of the girl-snowmobile system.
   (b) Draw the momentum vector for this situation.

2. The combined mass of a bobsled and two riders is 390 kg. The sled-rider system has a constant momentum of 4.68×10^3 kg·m/s [W]. Calculate the velocity of the sled.

Answers

1. (a) 6.9×10^3 kg·m/s [60.0° N of E]
   (b)

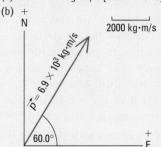

2. 12.0 m/s [W]

Draw the momentum vector to scale (Figure 9.8).

W ◄——► E   ┕———┙ 100 kg·m/s
       +

$\vec{p} = 7.5 \times 10^2$ kg·m/s
——————————————————————————————►

▲ **Figure 9.8**

Paraphrase
The momentum of the car-driver system is 7.5×10^2 kg·m/s [E].

Using Proportionalities to Solve Momentum Problems

Example 9.2 demonstrates how to solve momentum problems using proportionalities. In this example, both the mass and velocity of an object change.

Example 9.2

An object has a constant momentum of 2.45×10^2 kg·m/s [N]. Determine the momentum of the object if its mass decreases to $\frac{1}{3}$ of its original value and an applied force causes the speed to increase by exactly four times. The direction of the velocity remains the same. Explain your reasoning.

Analysis and Solution
From the equation $\vec{p} = m\vec{v}$, $p \propto m$ and $p \propto v$.
Figure 9.9 represents the situation of the problem.

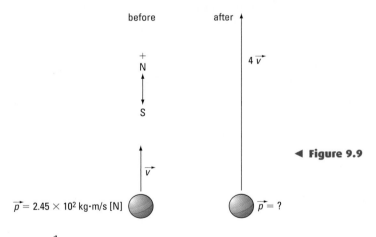

◄ **Figure 9.9**

$$p \propto \frac{1}{3}m \quad \text{and} \quad p \propto 4v$$

Calculate the factor change of p.

$$\frac{1}{3} \times 4 = \frac{4}{3}$$

Calculate p.

$$\frac{4}{3}p = \frac{4}{3} \times (2.45 \times 10^2 \text{ kg·m/s})$$
$$= 3.27 \times 10^2 \text{ kg·m/s}$$

The new momentum will be 3.27×10^2 kg·m/s [N].

Practice Problems

1. Many modern rifles use bullets that have less mass and reach higher speeds than bullets for older rifles, resulting in increased accuracy over longer distances. The momentum of a bullet is initially 8.25 kg·m/s [W]. What is the momentum if the speed of the bullet increases by a factor of $\frac{3}{2}$ and its mass decreases by a factor of $\frac{3}{4}$?

2. During one part of the liftoff of a model rocket, its momentum increases by a factor of four while its mass is halved. The velocity of the rocket is initially 8.5 m/s [up]. What is the final velocity during that time interval?

Answers

1. 9.28 kg·m/s [W]
2. 68 m/s [up]

Knowledge

1. (a) Explain, in your own words, the concept of momentum.

   (b) State the units of momentum.

2. Explain why momentum is a vector quantity.

3. How is momentum related to Newton's second law?

4. Explain why stating Newton's second law in terms of momentum is more useful than stating it in terms of acceleration.

5. Explain, in your own words, the difference between momentum and inertia.

6. Provide three examples of situations in which

   (a) velocity is the dominant factor affecting the momentum of an object, and

   (b) mass is the dominant factor affecting the momentum of an object.

Applications

7. A Mexican jumping bean moves because an insect larva inside the shell wiggles. Would it be an advantage to have the mass of the insect greater or less than the mass of the shell? Explain.

8. What is the momentum of a 6.0-kg bowling ball with a velocity of 2.2 m/s [S]?

9. The momentum of a 75-g bullet is 9.00 kg·m/s [N]. What is the velocity of the bullet?

10. (a) Draw a momentum vector diagram for a 4.6-kg Canada goose flying with a velocity of 8.5 m/s [210°].

    (b) A 10.0-kg bicycle and a 54.0-kg rider both have a velocity of 4.2 m/s [40.0° N of E]. Draw momentum vectors for each mass and for the bicycle-rider system.

11. A hockey puck has a momentum of 3.8 kg·m/s [E]. If its speed is 24 m/s, what is the mass of the puck?

12. Draw a momentum vector diagram to represent a 425-g soccer ball flying at 18.6 m/s [214°].

13. At what velocity does a 0.046-kg golf ball leave the tee if the club has given the ball a momentum of 3.45 kg·m/s [S]?

14. (a) A jet flies west at 190 m/s. What is the momentum of the jet if its total mass is 2250 kg?

    (b) What would be the momentum of the jet if the mass was $\frac{3}{4}$ of its original value and the speed increased to $\frac{6}{5}$ of its original value?

15. The blue whale is the largest mammal ever to inhabit Earth. Calculate the mass of a female blue whale if, when alarmed, it swims at a velocity of 57.0 km/h [E] and has a momentum of 2.15×10^6 kg·m/s [E].

Extensions

16. A loaded transport truck with a mass of 38 000 kg is travelling at 1.20 m/s [W]. What will be the velocity of a 1400-kg car if it has the same momentum?

17. Summarize the concepts and ideas associated with momentum using a graphic organizer of your choice. See Student References 4: Using Graphic Organizers on pp. 869–871 for examples of different graphic organizers. Make sure that the concepts and ideas are clearly presented and appropriately linked.

eTEST

To check your understanding of momentum, follow the eTest links at www.pearsoned.ca/school/physicssource.

9.2 Impulse Is Equivalent to a Change in Momentum

Stunt people take the saying, "It isn't the fall that hurts, it's the sudden stop at the end," very seriously. During the filming of a movie, when a stunt person jumps out of a building, the fall can be very dangerous. To minimize injury, stunt people avoid a sudden stop when landing by using different techniques to slow down more gradually out of sight of the cameras. These techniques involve changing the magnitude and direction of momentum.

Sometimes stunt people jump and land on a net. Other times, they may roll when they land. For more extreme jumps, such as from the roof of a tall building, a huge oversized, but slightly under-inflated, air mattress may be used (Figure 9.10). A hidden parachute may even be used to slow the jumper to a safer speed before impact with the surface below. Despite all these precautions, injuries occur as stunt people push the limits of what is possible in their profession.

Designers of safety equipment know that a cushioned surface can reduce the severity of an impact. Find out how the properties of a landing surface affect the shape of a putty ball that is dropped from a height of 1 m by doing 9-2 QuickLab.

▶ **Figure 9.10** The thick mattress on the ground provides a protective cushion for the stunt person when he lands. Why do you think the hardness of a surface affects the extent of injury upon impact?

Softening the Hit

Problem

How is the change in the shape of a putty ball upon impact related to the structure of the landing surface?

Materials

putty-type material   metre-stick
closed cell foam or felt pad   urethane foam pad or pillow
waxed paper or plastic wrap

Procedure

1 Choose three surfaces of varying softness onto which to drop a putty ball. One of the surfaces should be either a lab bench or the floor. Cover each surface with some waxed paper or plastic wrap to protect it.

2 Knead or work the putty until you can form three pliable balls of equal size.

3 Measure a height of 1 m above the top of each surface. Then drop the balls, one for each surface (Figure 9.11).

4 Draw a side-view sketch of each ball after impact.

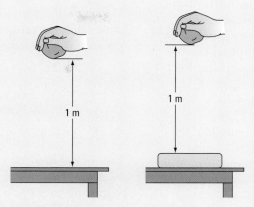

▲ **Figure 9.11**

Questions

1. Describe any differences in the shape of the putty balls after impact.

2. How does the amount of cushioning affect the deformation of the putty?

3. Discuss how the softness of the landing surface might be related to the time required for the putty ball to come to a stop. Justify your answer with an analysis involving the kinematics equations.

Force and Time Affect Momentum

In 9-2 QuickLab, you found that the softer the landing surface, the less the shape of the putty ball changed upon impact. The more cushioned the surface, the more the surface became indented when the putty ball collided with it. In other words, the softer and more cushioned landing surface provided a greater stopping distance for the putty ball.

Suppose you label the speed of the putty ball at the instant it touches the landing surface v_i, and the speed of the putty ball after the impact v_f. For all the landing surfaces, v_i was the same and $v_f = 0$. So the greater the stopping distance, the longer the time required for the putty ball to stop (Figure 9.12). In other words, the deformation of an object is less when the stopping time is increased.

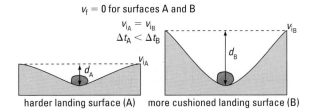

harder landing surface (A)   more cushioned landing surface (B)

◀ **Figure 9.12**   The stopping distance of the putty ball was greater for the more cushioned landing surface (B). So the time interval of interaction was greater on surface B.

Chapter 9 The momentum of an isolated system of interacting objects is conserved.   455

To visualize the effect of how F_{net} and Δt can vary but Δp remains the same, consider the effect of changing two numbers being multiplied together to give the same product.

$3 \times 12 = 36$
$6 \times 6 = 36$
$18 \times 2 = 36$

As the first number increases, the second number decreases in order to get the same product.

Project **LINK**

How will the net force and time interval affect the water balloon when it is brought to a stop?

What types of protective material will you use to surround the water balloon and why?

Apart from the different stopping times, what other differences were there between the drops that would have affected the shape of the putty ball upon impact? The answer to this question requires looking at Newton's second law written in terms of momentum.

From the previous section, the general form of Newton's second law states that the rate of change of momentum is equal to the net force acting on an object.

$$\vec{F}_{net} = \frac{\Delta \vec{p}}{\Delta t}$$

If you multiply both sides of the equation by Δt, you get

$$\vec{F}_{net}\Delta t = \Delta \vec{p}$$

For all the landing surfaces, since m, v_i (at the first instant of impact), and v_f (after the impact is over) of the putty ball were the same, p_i was the same and $p_f = 0$. So $\Delta \vec{p}$ was the same for all drops. But $\vec{F}_{net}\Delta t = \Delta \vec{p}$, so the product of net force and stopping time was the same for all drops.

From Figure 9.12 on page 455, the stopping time varied depending on the amount of cushioning provided by the landing surface. If the stopping time was short, as on a hard landing surface, the magnitude of the net force acting on the putty ball was large. Similarly, if the stopping time was long, as on a very cushioned landing surface, the magnitude of the net force acting on the putty ball was small. This analysis can be used to explain why the putty ball became more deformed when it landed on a hard surface.

To minimize changes to the shape of an object being dropped, it is important to minimize F_{net} required to stop the object, and this happens when you maximize Δt (Figure 9.13). It is also important to note *where* $\vec{F}_{net}$ acts. If $\vec{F}_{net}$ acts on a large area, the result of the impact will have a different effect on the shape of the object than if $\vec{F}_{net}$ acts on only one small part on the surface of the object.

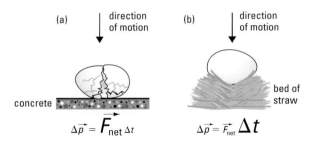

▲ **Figure 9.13** Identical eggs are dropped from a height of 2 m onto a concrete floor or a pile of straw. Although $\Delta \vec{p}$ is the same in both situations, the magnitude of the net force acting on the egg *and* the stopping time determine whether or not the egg will break.

Concept Check

In 9-2 QuickLab, was the momentum of the putty ball at the first instant of impact zero? Explain your reasoning.

Impulse Is the Product of Net Force and Interaction Time

In the equation $\vec{F}_{net}\Delta t = \Delta \vec{p}$, the product of net force and interaction time is called **impulse**. Impulse is equivalent to the change in momentum that an object experiences during an interaction. Every time a net force acts on an object, the object is provided with an impulse because the force is applied for a specific length of time.

If you substitute the definition of momentum, $\vec{p} = m\vec{v}$, the equation $\vec{F}_{net}\Delta t = \Delta \vec{p}$ becomes

$$\vec{F}_{net}\Delta t = \Delta(m\vec{v})$$

If m is constant, then the only quantity changing on the right-hand side of the equation is $\vec{v}$. So the equation becomes

$$\vec{F}_{net}\Delta t = m\Delta \vec{v}$$

So impulse can be calculated using either equation:

$$\vec{F}_{net}\Delta t = \Delta \vec{p} \qquad \text{or}$$

$$\vec{F}_{net}\Delta t = m\Delta \vec{v}$$

The unit of impulse is the newton-second (N·s). From Unit II, a newton is defined as 1 N = 1 kg·m/s². If you substitute the definition of a newton in the unit newton-seconds, you get

$$1\ \text{N·s} = 1 \left(\frac{\text{kg·m}}{\cancel{\text{s}^2}}\right)(\cancel{\text{s}})$$

$$= 1\ \frac{\text{kg·m}}{\text{s}}$$

which are the units for momentum. So the units on both sides of the impulse equation are equivalent. Since force is a vector quantity, impulse is also a vector quantity, and the impulse is in the same direction as the net force.

To better understand how net force and interaction time affect the change in momentum of an object, do 9-3 Design a Lab.

impulse: product of the net force on an object and the time interval during an interaction

e SIM

Learn how the mass and acceleration of an object affect its change in momentum. Follow the eSim links at www.pearsoned.ca/school/physicssource.

9-3 *Design a Lab*

Providing Impulse

The Question

What is the effect of varying either the net force or the interaction time on the momentum of an object?

Design and Conduct Your Investigation

State a hypothesis to answer the question using an "if/then" statement. Then design an experiment to measure the change in momentum of an object. First vary F_{net}, then repeat the experiment and vary Δt instead. List the materials you will use, as well as a detailed procedure. Check the procedure with your teacher and then do the investigation.

To find the net force, you may need to find the force of friction and add it, using vectors, to the applied force. The force of kinetic friction is the minimum force needed to keep an object moving at constant velocity once the object is in motion. Analyze your data and form conclusions. How well did your results agree with your hypothesis? Compare your results with those of other groups in your class. Account for any discrepancies.

e LAB

For a probeware activity, go to www.pearsoned.ca/school/physicssource.

Example 9.3 demonstrates how, for the same impulse, varying the interaction time affects the average net force on a car during a front-end collision (the net force on the car is not constant).

Example 9.3

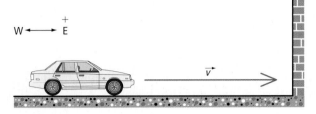

▲ **Figure 9.14**

To improve the safety of motorists, modern cars are built so the front end crumples upon impact. A 1200-kg car is travelling at a constant velocity of 8.0 m/s [E] (Figure 9.14). It hits an immovable wall and comes to a complete stop in 0.25 s.
(a) Calculate the impulse provided to the car.
(b) What is the average net force exerted on the car?
(c) For the same impulse, what would be the average net force exerted on the car if it had a rigid bumper and frame that stopped the car in 0.040 s?

Given
$m = 1200$ kg $\vec{v}_i = 8.0$ m/s [E]
(a) and (b) $\Delta t = 0.25$ s
(c) $\Delta t = 0.040$ s

Required
(a) impulse provided to car
(b) and (c) average net force on car ($\vec{F}_{net_{ave}}$)

Analysis and Solution
When the car hits the wall, the final velocity of the car is zero.
$$\vec{v}_f = 0 \text{ m/s}$$

During each collision with the wall, the net force on the car is not constant, but the mass of the car remains constant.
(a) Use the equation of impulse to calculate the impulse provided to the car.

$$\vec{F}_{net_{ave}}\Delta t = m\Delta\vec{v}$$
$$= m(\vec{v}_f - \vec{v}_i)$$
$$= (1200 \text{ kg})\{0 - (+8.0 \text{ m/s})\}$$
$$= (1200 \text{ kg})(-8.0 \text{ m/s})$$
$$= -9.6 \times 10^3 \text{ kg·m/s}$$

impulse $= 9.6 \times 10^3$ N·s [W]

info **BIT**

Some early cars were built with spring bumpers that tended to bounce off whatever they hit. These bumpers were used at a time when people generally travelled at much slower speeds. For safety reasons, cars today are built to crumple upon impact, not bounce. This results in a smaller change in momentum and a reduced average net force on motorists. The crushing also increases the time interval during the impulse, further decreasing the net force on motorists.

For (b) and (c), substitute the impulse from part (a) and solve for $\vec{F}_{net_{ave}}$.

$$\vec{F}_{net_{ave}}\Delta t = -9.6 \times 10^3 \text{ N} \cdot \text{s}$$

$$\vec{F}_{net_{ave}} = \frac{-9.6 \times 10^3 \text{ N} \cdot \text{s}}{\Delta t}$$

(b) $\vec{F}_{net_{ave}} = \dfrac{-9.6 \times 10^3 \text{ N} \cdot \text{s}}{0.25 \text{ s}}$

$= -3.8 \times 10^4 \dfrac{\text{kg} \cdot \text{m}}{\text{s}^2}$

$= -3.8 \times 10^4 \text{ N}$

$\vec{F}_{net_{ave}} = 3.8 \times 10^4 \text{ N [W]}$

(c) $\vec{F}_{net_{ave}} = \dfrac{-9.6 \times 10^3 \text{ N} \cdot \text{s}}{0.040 \text{ s}}$

$= -2.4 \times 10^5 \dfrac{\text{kg} \cdot \text{m}}{\text{s}^2}$

$= -2.4 \times 10^5 \text{ N}$

$\vec{F}_{net_{ave}} = 2.4 \times 10^5 \text{ N [W]}$

PHYSICS INSIGHT

$\vec{F}_{net_{ave}}$ is in the *opposite* direction to the initial momentum of the car, because from Newton's third law, the wall is exerting a force directed west on the car.

Paraphrase and Verify

(a) The impulse provided to the car is 9.6×10^3 N·s [W].

The average net force exerted by the wall on the car is (b) 3.8×10^4 N [W] when it crumples, and (c) 2.4×10^5 N [W] when it is rigid.

The change in momentum is the same in parts (b) and (c), but the time intervals are different. So the average net force is different in both situations. The magnitude of $\vec{F}_{net_{ave}}$ on the car with the rigid frame is more than 6 times greater than when the car crumples.

Impulse Can Be Calculated Using a Net Force-Time Graph

One way to calculate the impulse provided to an object is to graph the net force acting on the object as a function of the interaction time. Suppose a net force of magnitude 30 N acts on a model rocket for 0.60 s during liftoff (Figure 9.15). From the net force-time graph in Figure 9.16, the product $F_{net}\Delta t$ is equal to the magnitude of the impulse. But this product is also the area under the graph.

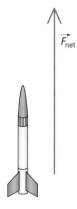

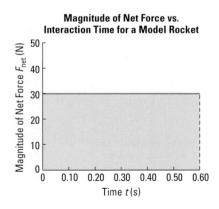

▲ **Figure 9.15** What forces act on the rocket during liftoff?

▲ **Figure 9.16** Magnitude of net force as a function of interaction time for a model rocket. The area under the graph is equal to the magnitude of the impulse provided to the rocket.

The magnitude of the impulse provided to the rocket is

$$\text{magnitude of impulse} = F_{net}\Delta t$$
$$= (30 \text{ N})(0.60 \text{ s})$$
$$= 18 \text{ N} \cdot \text{s}$$

In other words, the area under a net force-time graph gives the magnitude of the impulse. Note that a net force acting over a period of time *causes* a change in momentum.

When F_{net} is not constant, you can still calculate the impulse by finding the area under a net force-time graph. Figure 9.17 shows the magnitude of the net force exerted by a bow on an arrow during the first part of its release. The magnitude of the net force is greatest at the beginning and decreases linearly with time.

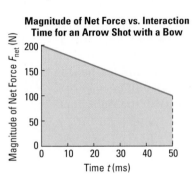

Magnitude of Net Force vs. Interaction Time for an Arrow Shot with a Bow

◀ **Figure 9.17** Magnitude of net force as a function of interaction time for an arrow shot with a bow.

info **BIT**

The area of a trapezoid is equal to $\frac{1}{2}(a + b)(h)$.

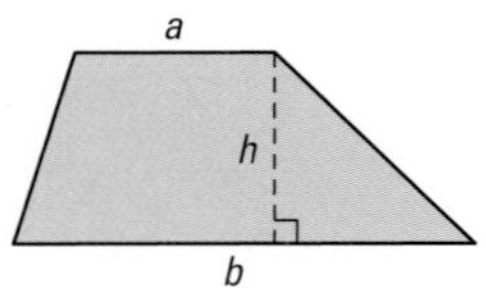

▲ **Figure 9.18**

In this case, the area under the graph could be divided into a rectangle and a triangle or left as a trapezoid (Figure 9.18). So the magnitude of the impulse provided to the arrow is

$$\text{magnitude of impulse} = \frac{1}{2}(a + b)(h)$$
$$= \frac{1}{2}(100 \text{ N} + 200 \text{ N})(0.050 \text{ s})$$
$$= 7.5 \text{ N} \cdot \text{s}$$

Sometimes two net force-time graphs may appear different but the magnitude of the impulse is the same in both cases. Figure 9.19 (a) shows a graph where F_{net} is much smaller than in Figure 9.19 (b). The value of Δt is different in each case, but the *area* under both graphs is the same. So the magnitude of the impulse is the same in both situations.

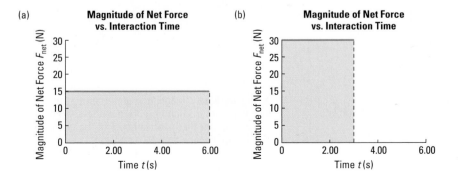

(a) **Magnitude of Net Force vs. Interaction Time**

(b) **Magnitude of Net Force vs. Interaction Time**

▲ **Figure 9.19** What other graph could you draw that has the same magnitude of impulse?

Effect of a Non-linear Net Force on Momentum

In real life, many interactions occur during very short time intervals (Figure 9.20). If you tried to accurately measure the net force, you would find that it is difficult, if not impossible, to do. In addition, the relationship between F_{net} and Δt is usually non-linear, because F_{net} increases from zero to a very large value in a short period of time (Figure 9.21).

Magnitude of Net Force vs. Interaction Time

Magnitude of Net Force F_{net} (N)

$F_{net_{ave}}$

Δt

Time t (s)

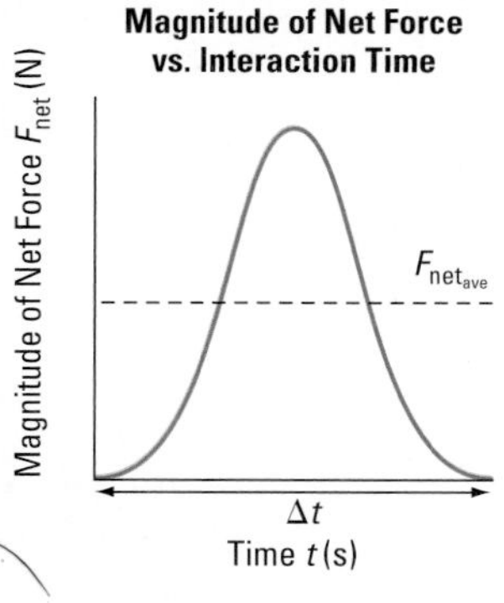

▲ **Figure 9.21**
The average net force gives some idea of the net force that an object actually experienced during impact.

▲ **Figure 9.20**   When a baseball bat hits a ball, what evidence demonstrates that the force during the interaction is very large? What evidence demonstrates that the force on the ball changes at the instant the ball and bat separate?

From a practical point of view, it is much easier to measure the interaction time and the overall change in momentum of an object during an interaction, rather than F_{net}. In this case, the equation of Newton's second law expressed in terms of momentum is

$$\vec{F}_{net_{ave}} = \frac{\Delta \vec{p}}{\Delta t}$$

and the equation of impulse is

$$\vec{F}_{net_{ave}} \Delta t = \Delta \vec{p} \qquad \text{or}$$

$$\vec{F}_{net_{ave}} \Delta t = m \Delta \vec{v}$$

In all the above equations, $\vec{F}_{net_{ave}}$ represents the average net force that acted on the object during the interaction.

In Example 9.4, a golf club strikes a golf ball and an approximation of the net force-time graph is used to simplify the calculations for impulse. In reality, the net force-time graph for such a situation would be similar to that shown in Figure 9.21.

Example 9.4

A golfer hits a long drive sending a 45.9-g golf ball due east. Figure 9.22 shows an approximation of the net force as a function of time for the collision between the golf club and the ball.

(a) What is the impulse provided to the ball?

(b) What is the velocity of the ball at the moment the golf club and ball separate?

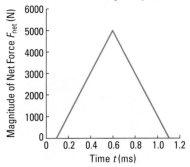

Magnitude of Net Force vs. Interaction Time for a Golf Ball Being Hit by a Golf Club

▲ **Figure 9.22**

Given

$$m = 45.9 \text{ g} \qquad t_i = 0.1 \text{ ms}$$
$$t_f = 1.1 \text{ ms} \qquad F_{net_i} = 0 \text{ N}$$
$$F_{net_{max}} = 5000 \text{ N} \qquad F_{net_f} = 0 \text{ N}$$

Required

(a) impulse provided to ball

(b) velocity of ball after impact $(\vec{v}_f)$

Analysis and Solution

The impulse and velocity after impact are in the east direction since the golfer hits the ball due east.

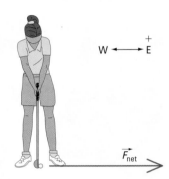

W ←———→ E +

$\vec{F}_{net}$ →

▲ **Figure 9.23**

(a) $\Delta t = t_f - t_i$

$\quad\quad = 1.1 \text{ ms} - 0.1 \text{ ms}$

$\quad\quad = 1.0 \text{ ms or } 1.0 \times 10^{-3} \text{ s}$

magnitude of impulse = area under net force-time graph

$$= \frac{1}{2}(\Delta t)(F_{net_{max}})$$

$$= \frac{1}{2}(1.0 \times 10^{-3} \text{ s})(5000 \text{ N})$$

$$= 2.5 \text{ N·s}$$

impulse = 2.5 N·s [E]

(b) Impulse is numerically equal to $m\Delta\vec{v}$ or $m(\vec{v}_f - \vec{v}_i)$.

But $\vec{v}_i = 0$ m/s

So, impulse $= m(\vec{v}_f - 0)$

$+2.5$ N·s $= m\vec{v}_f$

$$\vec{v}_f = \frac{+2.5 \text{ N·s}}{m}$$

$$= \frac{+2.50\left(\dfrac{kg·m}{s^2}\right)·s}{(45.9 \text{ g})\left(\dfrac{1 \text{ kg}}{1000 \text{ g}}\right)}$$

$$= +54 \text{ m/s}$$

Paraphrase

(a) The impulse provided to the ball is 2.5 N·s [E].

(b) The velocity of the ball after impact is 54 m/s [E].

Practice Problems

1. (a) Draw a graph of net force as a function of time for a 0.650-kg basketball being shot. During the first 0.15 s, F_{net} increases linearly from 0 N to 22 N. During the next 0.25 s, F_{net} decreases linearly to 0 N.

   (b) Using the graph, calculate the magnitude of the impulse provided to the basketball.

   (c) What is the speed of the ball when it leaves the shooter's hands?

2. (a) A soccer player heads the ball with an average net force of 21 N [W] for 0.12 s. Draw a graph of the average net force on the ball as a function of time. Assume that $F_{net_{ave}}$ is constant during the interaction.

   (b) Calculate the impulse provided to the soccer ball.

   (c) The impulse changes the velocity of the ball from 4.0 m/s [E] to 2.0 m/s [W]. What is the mass of the ball?

Answers

1. (a)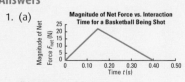

   (b) 4.4 N·s, (c) 6.8 m/s

2. (a)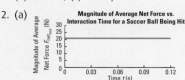

   (b) 2.5 N·s [W], (c) 0.42 kg

The Design of Safety Devices Involves Varying $F_{net_{ave}}$ and Δt

Many safety devices are based on varying both the average net force acting on an object and the interaction time for a given impulse. Suppose you attached a sled to a snowmobile with a rope hitch. As long as the sled is accelerating along a horizontal surface or is being pulled uphill, there is tension in the rope because the snowmobile applies a force on the sled (Figure 9.24).

If the driver in Figure 9.24 (a) brakes suddenly to slow down, the momentum of the snowmobile changes suddenly. However, the sled continues to move in a straight line until friction eventually slows it down to a stop. In other words, the only way that the momentum of the sled changes noticeably is if $\vec{F}_f$ acts for a long enough period of time.

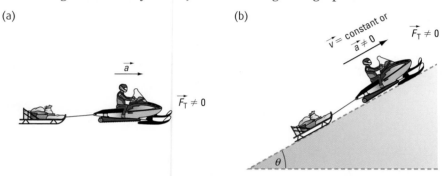

▲ **Figure 9.24** (a) A snowmobile accelerating along a horizontal surface, and (b) the same snowmobile either moving at constant speed or accelerating uphill. In both (a) and (b), the tension in the rope is not zero.

Suppose the snowmobile driver is heading downhill and applies the brakes suddenly as in Figure 9.25 (a). $\vec{F}_{g\parallel}$ will cause the sled to accelerate downhill as shown in Figure 9.25 (b). The speed of the sled could become large enough to overtake the snowmobile, bump into it, or tangle the rope.

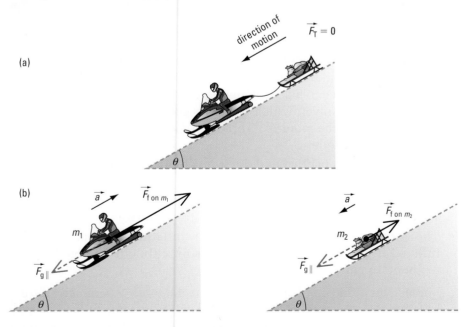

▲ **Figure 9.25** (a) The snowmobile is braking rapidly, and the tension in the rope is zero. (b) The free-body diagrams for the snowmobile and sled only show forces parallel to the incline.

The driver can change the momentum of the snowmobile suddenly by using the brakes. But, as before, the only way that the momentum of the sled can eventually become zero is if $\vec{F}_\mathrm{f}$ acts for a long enough time interval. With experience, a driver learns to slow down gradually so that a towed sled remains in its proper position.

Some sleds are attached to snowmobiles using a metal tow bar, which alleviates this problem (Figure 9.26). Since the tow bar can never become slack like a rope, the sled always remains a fixed distance from the snowmobile.

Tow bars usually have a spring mechanism that increases the time during which a force can be exerted. So if the driver brakes or changes direction suddenly, the force exerted by the snowmobile on the sled acts for a longer period of time. Compared to a towrope, the spring mechanism in the tow bar can safely cause the momentum of the sled to decrease in a shorter period of time.

▶ **Figure 9.26** A rigid tow bar with a spring mechanism provides the impulse necessary to increase or decrease the momentum of a towed sled.

e **WEB**

During takeoff, the magnitude of Earth's gravitational field changes as a rocket moves farther away from Earth's surface. The mass of a rocket also changes because it is burning fuel to move upward. Research how impulse and momentum apply to the design and function of rockets and thrust systems. Write a brief report of your findings, including diagrams where appropriate. Begin your search at www.pearsoned.ca/school/physicssource.

Safety devices in vehicles are designed so that, for a given impulse such as in a collision, the interaction time is increased, thereby reducing the average net force. This is achieved by providing motorists with a greater distance to travel, which increases the time interval required to stop the motion of the motorist. Three methods are used to provide this extra distance and time:

• The dashboard is padded and the front end of the vehicle is designed to crumple.
• The steering column telescopes to collapse, providing an additional 15–20 cm of distance for the driver to travel forward.
• The airbag is designed to leak after inflation so that the fully inflated bag can decrease in thickness over time from about 30 cm to about 10 cm.

In fact, an inflated airbag distributes the net force experienced during a collision over the motorist's chest and head. By spreading the force over a greater area, the magnitude of the average net force at any one point on the motorist's body is reduced, lowering the risk of a major injury.

A similar reasoning applies to the cushioning in running shoes and the padding in helmets and body pads used in sports (Figure 9.27). For a given impulse, all these pieces of equipment increase the interaction time and decrease the average net force.

(a)   (b)

▲ **Figure 9.27** Padding in sports equipment helps reduce the risk of major injuries, because for a given impulse, the interaction time is increased and the average net force on the body part is reduced. (a) Team Canada in the World Women's hockey tournament in Sweden, 2005. (b) Calgary Stampeders (in red) playing against the B.C. Lions in 2005.

The effect of varying the average net force and the interaction time can be seen with projectiles. A bullet fired from a pistol with a short barrel does not gain the same momentum as another identical bullet fired from a rifle with a long barrel, assuming that each bullet experiences the same average net force (Figure 9.28). In the gun with the shorter barrel, the force from the expanding gases acts for a shorter period of time. So the change in momentum of the bullet is less.

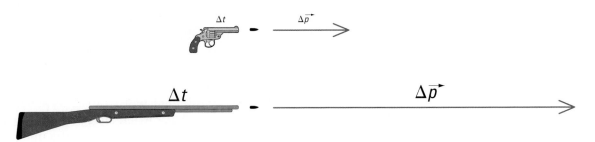

▲ **Figure 9.28** For the same average net force on a bullet, a gun with a longer barrel increases the time during which this force acts. So the change in momentum is greater for a bullet fired from a long-barrelled gun.

Improved Sports Performance Involves Varying $F_{net_{ave}}$ and Δt

In baseball, a skilled pitcher knows how to vary both the net force acting on the ball and the interaction time, so that the ball acquires maximum velocity before it leaves the pitcher's hand (Figure 9.29). To exert the maximum possible force on the ball, a pitcher uses his arms, torso, and legs to propel the ball forward. To maximize the time he can exert that force, the pitcher leans back using a windup and then takes a long step forward. This way, his hand can be in contact with the ball for a longer period of time. The combination of the greater net force and the longer interaction time increases the change in momentum of the ball.

► **Figure 9.29** When a pitcher exerts a force on the ball during a longer time interval, the momentum of a fastball increases even more.

In sports such as hockey, golf, and tennis, coaches emphasize proper "follow through." The reason is that it increases the time during which the puck or ball is in contact with the player's stick, club, or racquet. So the change in momentum of the object being propelled increases.

A similar reasoning applies when a person catches a ball. In this case, a baseball catcher should decrease the net force on the ball so that the ball doesn't cause injury and is easier to hold onto. Players soon learn to do this by letting their hands move with the ball. For the same impulse, the extra movement with the hands results in an increased interaction time, which reduces the net force.

This intentional flexibility when catching is sometimes referred to as having "soft hands," and it is a great compliment to a football receiver. Hockey goalies allow their glove hand to fly back when snagging a puck to reduce the impact and allow them a better chance of keeping the puck in their glove. Boxers are also taught to "roll with the punch," because if they move backward when hit, it increases the interaction time and decreases the average net force of an opponent's blow.

Knowledge

1. (a) What quantities are used to calculate impulse?

   (b) State the units of impulse.

2. How are impulse and momentum related?

3. What graph could you use to determine the impulse provided to an object? Explain how to calculate the impulse using the graph.

4. What is the effect on impulse if

   (a) the time interval is doubled?

   (b) the net force is reduced to $\frac{1}{3}$ of its original magnitude?

5. Even though your mass is much greater than that of a curling stone, it is dangerous for a moving stone to hit your feet. Explain why.

Applications

6. Using the concept of impulse, explain how a karate expert can break a board.

7. (a) From the graph below, what is the magnitude of the impulse provided to a 48-g tennis ball that is served due south?

   (b) What is the velocity of the ball when the racquet and ball separate?

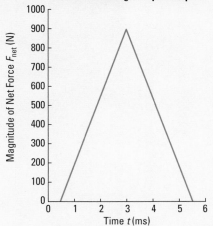

Magnitude of Net Force vs. Interaction Time for a Tennis Ball Being Hit by a Racquet

8. What impulse is generated by a slapshot when an average net force of magnitude 520 N is applied to a puck for 0.012 s?

9. During competitive world-class events, a four-person bobsled experiences an average net force of magnitude 1390 N during the first 5.0 s of a run.

   (a) What is the impulse provided to the bobsled?

   (b) If the sled has the maximum mass of 630 kg, what will be the velocity of the sled?

10. An advertisement for a battery-powered 25-kg skateboard says that it can carry an 80-kg person at a speed of 8.5 m/s. If the skateboard motor can exert a net force of magnitude 75 N, how long will it take to attain that speed?

11. Whiplash occurs when a car is rear-ended and either there is no headrest or the headrest is not properly adjusted. The torso of the motorist is accelerated by the seat, but the head is jerked forward only by the neck, causing injury to the joints and soft tissue. What is the average net force on a motorist's neck if the torso is accelerated from 0 to 14.0 m/s [W] in 0.135 s? The mass of the motorist's head is 5.40 kg. Assume that the force acting on the head is the same magnitude as the force on the torso.

12. What will be the change in momentum of a shoulder-launched rocket that experiences a thrust of 2.67 kN [W] for 0.204 s?

Extensions

13. Experienced curlers know how to safely stop a moving stone. What do they do and why?

14. Research one safety device used in sports that applies the concept of varying $F_{net_{ave}}$ and Δt for a given impulse to prevent injury. Explain how the variables that affect impulse are changed by using this device. Begin your search at www.pearsoned.ca/school/physicssource.

 e TEST

To check your understanding of impulse, follow the eTest links at www.pearsoned.ca/school/physicssource.

9.3 Collisions in One Dimension

During mating season each fall, adult bighorn rams compete for supremacy in an interesting contest. Two rams will face each other, rear up, and then charge, leaping into the air to butt heads with tremendous force (Figure 9.30). Without being consciously aware of it, each ram attempts to achieve maximum momentum before the collision, because herd structure is determined by the outcome of the contest. Often, rams will repeat the head-butting interaction until a clear winner is determined. While most other mammals would be permanently injured by the force experienced during such a collision, the skull and brain structure of bighorn sheep enables them to emerge relatively undamaged from such interactions.

In the previous section, many situations involved an object experiencing a change in momentum, or impulse, because of a collision with another object. When two objects such as bighorn rams collide, what relationship exists among the momenta of the objects both before and after collision? In order to answer this question, first consider one-dimensional collisions involving spheres in 9-4 QuickLab.

▲ **Figure 9.30** By lunging toward each other, these bighorn rams will eventually collide head-on. During the collision, each ram will be provided with an impulse.

Observing Collinear Collisions

Problem

What happens when spheres collide in one dimension?

Materials

one set of four identical ball bearings or marbles (set A)

a second set of four identical ball bearings or marbles of double the mass (set B)

a third set of four identical ball bearings or marbles of half the mass (set C)

1-m length of an I-beam curtain rod or two metre-sticks with smooth edges

masking tape

Procedure

① Lay the curtain rod flat on a bench to provide a horizontal track for the spheres. Tape the ends of the rod securely. If you are using metre-sticks, tape them 5 mm apart to form a uniform straight horizontal track.

② Using set A, place three of the spheres tightly together at the centre of the track.

③ Predict what will happen when one sphere of set A moves along the track and collides with the three stationary spheres.

before   after

direction of motion

▲ **Figure 9.31**

④ Test your prediction. Ensure that the spheres remain on the track after collision. Record your observations using diagrams similar to Figure 9.31.

⑤ Repeat steps 2 to 4, but this time use set B, spheres of greater mass.

⑥ Repeat steps 2 to 4, but this time use set C, spheres of lesser mass.

⑦ Repeat steps 2 to 4 using different numbers of stationary spheres. The stationary spheres should all be the same mass, but the moving sphere should be of a different mass in some of the trials.

Questions

1. Describe the motion of the spheres in steps 4 to 6.

2. Explain what happened when

   (a) a sphere of lesser mass collided with a number of spheres of greater mass, and

   (b) a sphere of greater mass collided with a number of spheres of lesser mass.

In 9-4 QuickLab, for each set of spheres A to C, when one sphere hit a row of three stationary ones from the same set, the last sphere in the row moved outward at about the same speed as the incoming sphere. But when one sphere from set A hit a row of spheres from set B, the last sphere in the row moved outward at a much *slower* speed than the incoming sphere, and the incoming sphere may even have rebounded. When one sphere from set A hit a row of spheres from set C, the last sphere in the row moved outward at a *greater* speed than the incoming sphere, and the incoming sphere continued moving forward.

To analyze these observations, it is important to first understand what a collision is. A **collision** is an interaction between two objects in which a very large force acts on each object for a very short time. In other words, the collision provides an impulse to each object in which F_{net} is large and Δt is very short.

e **MATH**

Explore how the masses of two colliding objects affect their velocities just after collision. Follow the eMath links at www.pearsoned.ca/school/ physicssource.

collision: an interaction between two objects involving an impulse with a large F_{net} and a very short Δt

Systems of Objects in Collisions

system: two or more objects that interact with each other

Each trial in 9-4 QuickLab involved two or more spheres colliding with each other. A group of two or more objects that interact is called a **system**. You encountered the concept of a system in Unit III in the context of energy.

For each system in 9-4 QuickLab, the total mass remained constant because the mass of each sphere did not change as a result of the interaction. However, friction was an external force that acted on the system. For example, in steps 4 to 6 of 9-4 QuickLab, you likely observed that the speed of the sphere moving outward was a little less than the speed of the incoming sphere.

In real life, a system of colliding objects is provided with two impulses: one due to external friction and the other due to the actual collision (Figure 9.32). External friction acts before, during, and after collision. The second impulse is only present *during the actual collision*. Since the actual collision time is very short, the impulse due to external friction *during* the collision is relatively small.

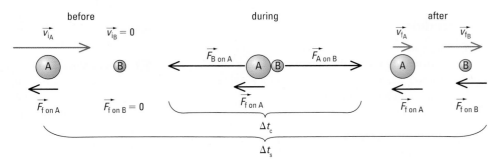

▲ **Figure 9.32** External friction acts throughout the entire time interval of the interaction Δt_s. But the action-reaction forces due to the objects only exist when the objects actually collide, and these forces only act for time interval Δt_c.

If you apply the form of Newton's second law that relates net force to momentum to analyze the motion of a system of objects, you get

$$(\vec{F}_{\text{net}})_{\text{sys}} = \frac{\Delta \vec{p}_{\text{sys}}}{\Delta t} \text{ where } \vec{p}_{\text{sys}} \text{ is the momentum of the system}$$

The **momentum of a system** is defined as the sum of the momenta of all the objects in the system. So if objects A, B, and C form a system, the momentum of the system is

$$\vec{p}_{\text{sys}} = \vec{p}_A + \vec{p}_B + \vec{p}_C$$

In the context of momentum, when the mass of a system is constant and no external net force acts on the system, the system is **isolated**. So $(\vec{F}_{\text{net}})_{\text{sys}} = 0$. In 9-5 Inquiry Lab, an isolated system of objects is involved in a one-dimensional collision. Find a quantitative relationship for the momentum of such a system in terms of momenta before and after collision.

Relating Momentum Just Before and Just After a Collision

Question

How does the momentum of a system consisting of two objects compare just before and just after a collision?

Hypothesis

State a hypothesis relating the momentum of a system immediately before and immediately after collision. Remember to write an "if/then" statement.

Variables

Read the procedure carefully and identify the manipulated variables, the responding variables, and the controlled variables.

Materials and Equipment

one of these set-ups: air track, dynamics carts, Fletcher's trolley, bead table or air table with linear guides
colliding objects for the set-up chosen: gliders, carts, discs, blocks, etc.
objects of different mass
fastening material (Velcro™ strips, tape, Plasticine™, magnets, etc.)
balance
timing device (stopwatch, spark-timer, ticker-tape timer, electronic speed-timing device, or time-lapse camera)
metre-sticks

Procedure

1 Copy Tables 9.1 and 9.2 on page 472 into your notebook.

2 Set up the equipment in such a way that friction is minimized and the two colliding objects travel in the same straight line.

3 Attach some fastening material to the colliding objects, so that the two objects remain together after impact.

4 Measure and record the masses of the two objects. If necessary, change the mass of one object so that the two objects have significantly different masses.

5 Set up the timing device to measure the velocity of object 1 just before and just after collision. Object 2 will be stationary before collision. The velocities of both objects will be the same after collision because they will stick together.

6 Send object 1 at a moderate speed on a collision course with object 2. Ensure that both objects will stick together and that the timing device is working properly. Make adjustments if needed.

7 Send object 1 at a moderate speed on a collision course with stationary object 2, recording the velocities and the masses as trial 1.

8 Send object 1 at a different speed on a collision course with stationary object 2, recording the velocities and the masses as trial 2.

9 Change the mass of one of the objects and again send object 1 at a moderate speed on a collision course with stationary object 2, recording the velocities and the masses as trial 3.

10 If you can simultaneously measure the speed of two objects, run trials where both objects are in motion before the collision. Do one trial in which they begin moving toward each other and stick together upon impact, and another trial where they move apart after impact. If you remove the fastening material, you will have to remeasure the masses of the objects. Include the direction of motion for both objects before and after collision.

11 If you did not do step 10, do two more trials, changing the mass of one of the objects each time. Include the direction of motion for both objects before and after collision.

e LAB

For a probeware activity, go to
www.pearsoned.ca/school/physicsource.

Analysis

1. Determine the velocities for each colliding object in each trial, and record them in your data table. Show your calculations.

2. For each trial, calculate the momentum of each object just before and just after collision. Show your calculations. Record the values in your data table.

3. Calculate the momentum of the system just before and just after collision for each trial. Show your calculations. Record the values in your data table.

4. Calculate the difference between the momentum of the system just before and just after collision. Show your calculations. Record the values in your data table.

5. What is the relationship between the momentum of the system just before and just after collision? Does this relationship agree with your hypothesis?

6. What effect did friction have on your results? Explain.

7. Check your results with other groups. Account for any discrepancies.

▼ **Table 9.1**   Mass and Velocity

Trial	Before and After for Object 1			Before and After for Object 2		
	Mass m_1 (g)	Initial Velocity $\vec{v}_{1_i}$ (m/s)	Final Velocity $\vec{v}_{1_f}$ (m/s)	Mass m_2 (g)	Initial Velocity $\vec{v}_{2_i}$ (m/s)	Final Velocity $\vec{v}_{2_f}$ (m/s)
1						
2						
3						
4						
5						

▼ **Table 9.2**   Momentum

Trial	Before and After for Object 1		Before and After for Object 2		Before and After for System		
	Initial Momentum $\vec{p}_{1_i}\left(g\cdot\dfrac{m}{s}\right)$	Final Momentum $\vec{p}_{1_f}\left(g\cdot\dfrac{m}{s}\right)$	Initial Momentum $\vec{p}_{2_i}\left(g\cdot\dfrac{m}{s}\right)$	Final Momentum $\vec{p}_{2_f}\left(g\cdot\dfrac{m}{s}\right)$	Initial Momentum of System $\vec{p}_{sys_i}\left(g\cdot\dfrac{m}{s}\right)$	Final Momentum of System $\vec{p}_{sys_f}\left(g\cdot\dfrac{m}{s}\right)$	Change in Momentum of System $\Delta\vec{p}_{sys}\left(g\cdot\dfrac{m}{s}\right)$
1							
2							
3							
4							
5							

Momentum Is Conserved in One-dimensional Collisions

In 9-5 Inquiry Lab, you discovered that, in one-dimensional collisions, the momentum of a system immediately before collision is about the same as the momentum of the system immediately after collision.

If the external force of friction acting on the system is negligible, the momentum of the system is constant. This result is true no matter how many objects are in the system, how many of those objects collide, how massive the objects are, or how fast they are moving.

The general form of Newton's second law for a system is

$$(\vec{F}_{net})_{sys} = \frac{\Delta \vec{p}_{sys}}{\Delta t}$$

In an isolated system, the external net force on the system is zero, $(\vec{F}_{net})_{sys} = 0$. So

$$0 = \frac{\Delta \vec{p}_{sys}}{\Delta t}$$

In order for $\frac{\Delta \vec{p}_{sys}}{\Delta t}$ to be zero, the change in momentum of the system must be zero.

$$\Delta \vec{p}_{sys} = 0$$
$$\vec{p}_{sys_f} - \vec{p}_{sys_i} = 0$$
$$\vec{p}_{sys_i} = \vec{p}_{sys_f}$$

In other words, $\vec{p}_{sys}$ = constant.

This is a statement of the **law of conservation of momentum**. In Unit III, you encountered another conservation law, that is, in an isolated system the total energy of the system is conserved. Conservation laws always have one quantity that remains unchanged. In the law of conservation of momentum, it is momentum that remains unchanged.

law of conservation of momentum: momentum of an isolated system is constant

When no external net force acts on a system, the momentum of the system remains constant.

$$\vec{p}_{sys_i} = \vec{p}_{sys_f} \text{ where } (\vec{F}_{net})_{sys} = 0$$

Concept Check

Why did cannons on 16th- to 19th-century warships need a rope around the back, tying them to the side of the ship (Figure 9.33)?

◀ **Figure 9.33**

$$\overleftarrow{F_{\text{reaction}}}\ \text{(A) (B)}\ \overrightarrow{F_{\text{action}}}$$
$$\overleftarrow{F_{\text{B on A}}} \qquad \overrightarrow{F_{\text{A on B}}}$$

▲ **Figure 9.34**
The action-reaction forces when two objects collide

eSIM

Learn how the momentum of a system just before and just after a one-dimensional collision are related. Vary the ratio of the mass of two pucks. Follow the eSim links at www.pearsoned.ca/school/physicssource.

Writing the Conservation of Momentum in Terms of Mass and Velocity

Suppose a system consists of two objects, A and B. If the system is isolated, $(\vec{F}_{\text{net}})_{\text{sys}} = 0$. Consider the internal forces of the system. At collision time, object A exerts a force on object B and object B exerts a force on object A (Figure 9.34). From Newton's third law, these action-reaction forces are related by the equation

$$\vec{F}_{\text{A on B}} = -\vec{F}_{\text{B on A}}$$

Objects A and B interact for the same time interval Δt. If you multiply both sides of the equation by Δt, you get an equation in terms of impulse:

$$\vec{F}_{\text{A on B}}\,\Delta t = -\vec{F}_{\text{B on A}}\,\Delta t$$

Since impulse is equivalent to a change in momentum, the equation can be rewritten in terms of the momenta of each object:

$$\Delta\vec{p}_{\text{B}} = -\Delta\vec{p}_{\text{A}}$$
$$\Delta\vec{p}_{\text{A}} + \Delta\vec{p}_{\text{B}} = 0$$
$$\vec{p}_{\text{A}_f} - \vec{p}_{\text{A}_i} + \vec{p}_{\text{B}_f} - \vec{p}_{\text{B}_i} = 0$$
$$\vec{p}_{\text{A}_i} + \vec{p}_{\text{B}_i} = \vec{p}_{\text{A}_f} + \vec{p}_{\text{B}_f}$$

If the mass of each object is constant during the interaction, the equation can be written in terms of m and $\vec{v}$:

$$m_{\text{A}}\vec{v}_{\text{A}_i} + m_{\text{B}}\vec{v}_{\text{B}_i} = m_{\text{A}}\vec{v}_{\text{A}_f} + m_{\text{B}}\vec{v}_{\text{B}_f}$$

This equation is the law of conservation of momentum in terms of the momenta of objects A and B. So if two bighorn rams head-butt each other, the sum of the momenta of both rams is constant during the collision, even though the momentum of each ram changes. The law of conservation of momentum has no known exceptions, and holds even when particles are travelling close to the speed of light, or when the mass of the colliding particles is very small, as in the case of electrons.

In real life, when objects collide, external friction acts on nearly all systems and the instantaneous forces acting on each object are usually not known (Figure 9.35). Often, the details of the interaction are also unknown.

However, you do not require such information to apply the law of conservation of momentum. Instead, it is the mass and instantaneous velocity of the objects immediately before and immediately after collision that are important, so that the effects of external friction do not change the conditions of the system.

▲ **Figure 9.35** During a vehicle collision, many forces cause a change in the velocity and shape of each vehicle.

Conservation of Momentum Applied to Rockets

In Unit II, the motion of a rocket was explained using Newton's third law. However, the conservation of momentum can be used to explain why a rocket can accelerate even in a vacuum. When the engines of a rocket burn fuel, the escaping exhaust gas has mass and considerable speed.

When a rocket is in outer space, external friction is negligible. So the rocket-exhaust gas system is an isolated system. For a two-object system, the equation for the conservation of momentum is

$$\Delta \vec{p}_{rocket} + \Delta \vec{p}_{gas} = 0$$

$$\Delta \vec{p}_{rocket} = -\Delta \vec{p}_{gas}$$

where, during time interval Δt, $\Delta \vec{p}_{rocket}$ is the change in momentum of the rocket including any unspent fuel and $\Delta \vec{p}_{gas}$ is the change in momentum of the fuel that is expelled in the form of exhaust gas. It is the change in momentum of the exhaust gas that enables a rocket to accelerate (Figure 9.36). In the case of a very large rocket, such as a Saturn V, the magnitude of $\Delta \vec{p}_{gas}$ would be very large (Figure 9.37).

▲ **Figure 9.36** With a height of about 112 m, the Saturn V rocket was the largest and most powerful rocket ever built.

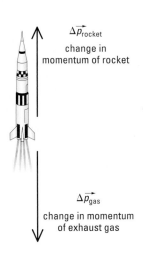

$\Delta \vec{p}_{rocket}$
change in momentum of rocket

$\Delta \vec{p}_{gas}$
change in momentum of exhaust gas

▲ **Figure 9.37** From the law of conservation of momentum, the magnitude of $\Delta \vec{p}_{gas}$ is equal to the magnitude of $\Delta \vec{p}_{rocket}$. That is why a rocket can accelerate on Earth or in outer space.

Concept Check

(a) Refer to the second infoBIT on this page. Why is less thrust needed by the second-stage engines of a rocket?

(b) Why is even less thrust needed by the third-stage engine?

In Example 9.5, the conservation of momentum is applied to a system of objects that are initially stationary. This type of interaction is called an explosion.

Example 9.5

A 75-kg hunter in a stationary kayak throws a 0.72-kg harpoon at 12 m/s [right]. The mass of the kayak is 10 kg. What will be the velocity of the kayak and hunter immediately after the harpoon is released?

Given

$m_p = 75$ kg $m_k = 10$ kg $m_h = 0.72$ kg

$\vec{v}_{p_i} = 0$ m/s $\vec{v}_{k_i} = 0$ m/s $\vec{v}_{h_i} = 0$ m/s

$\vec{v}_{h_f} = 12$ m/s [right]

before   +   after

 left ←——→ right

 $\vec{v}_{T_f} = ?$  $\vec{v}_{h_f} = 12$ m/s

▲ **Figure 9.38**

Required

final velocity of hunter and kayak

Analysis and Solution

Choose the kayak, hunter, and harpoon as an isolated system. The hunter and kayak move together as a unit after the harpoon is released. So find the total mass of the hunter and kayak.

$$m_T = m_p + m_k$$
$$= 75 \text{ kg} + 10 \text{ kg}$$
$$= 85 \text{ kg}$$

The hunter, kayak, and harpoon each have an initial velocity of zero. So the system has an initial momentum of zero.

$$\vec{p}_{sys_i} = 0$$

Apply the law of conservation of momentum.

$$\vec{p}_{sys_i} = \vec{p}_{sys_f}$$
$$\vec{p}_{sys_i} = \vec{p}_{T_f} + \vec{p}_{h_f}$$
$$0 = m_T \vec{v}_{T_f} + m_h \vec{v}_{h_f}$$
$$\vec{v}_{T_f} = -\left(\frac{m_h}{m_T}\right)\vec{v}_{h_f}$$
$$= -\left(\frac{0.72 \text{ kg}}{85 \text{ kg}}\right)(+12 \text{ m/s})$$
$$= -0.10 \text{ m/s}$$
$$\vec{v}_{T_f} = 0.10 \text{ m/s [left]}$$

Practice Problems

1. A 110-kg astronaut and a 4000-kg spacecraft are attached by a tethering cable. Both masses are motionless relative to an observer a slight distance away from the spacecraft. The astronaut wants to return to the spacecraft, so he pulls on the cable until his velocity changes to 0.80 m/s [toward the spacecraft] relative to the observer. What will be the change in velocity of the spacecraft?

2. A student is standing on a stationary 2.3-kg skateboard. If the student jumps at a velocity of 0.37 m/s [forward], the velocity of the skateboard becomes 8.9 m/s [backward]. What is the mass of the student?

Answers

1. 0.022 m/s [toward the astronaut]
2. 55 kg

Paraphrase and Verify

The velocity of the kayak and hunter will be 0.10 m/s [left] immediately after the harpoon is released. Since the harpoon is thrown right, from Newton's third law, you would expect the hunter and kayak to move left after the throw. So the answer is reasonable.

In Example 9.6, a dart is fired at a stationary block sitting on a glider. This situation involves two objects (dart and block) that join together and move as a unit after interaction. This type of interaction is called a hit-and-stick interaction.

Example 9.6

A wooden block attached to a glider has a combined mass of 0.200 kg. Both the block and glider are at rest on a frictionless air track. A dart gun shoots a 0.012-kg dart into the block. The velocity of the block-dart system after collision is 0.78 m/s [right]. What was the velocity of the dart just before it hit the block?

Given

$m_b = 0.200$ kg $m_d = 0.012$ kg

$\vec{v}_{b_i} = 0$ m/s $\vec{v}_f = 0.78$ m/s [right]

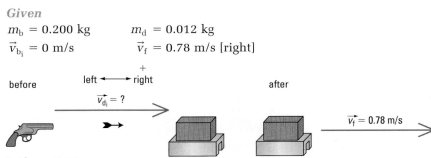

▲ **Figure 9.39**

Required

initial velocity of dart ($\vec{v}_{d_i}$)

Analysis and Solution

Choose the block, glider, and dart as an isolated system. The dart, block, and glider move together as a unit after collision. The block-glider unit has an initial velocity of zero. So its initial momentum is zero.

$$\vec{p}_{b_i} = 0$$

Apply the law of conservation of momentum.

$$\vec{p}_{sys_i} = \vec{p}_{sys_f}$$
$$\vec{p}_{b_i} + \vec{p}_{d_i} = \vec{p}_{sys_f}$$
$$0 + m_d\vec{v}_{d_i} = (m_b + m_d)\vec{v}_f$$
$$\vec{v}_{d_i} = \left(\frac{m_b + m_d}{m_d}\right)\vec{v}_f$$
$$= \left(\frac{0.200 \text{ kg} + 0.012 \text{ kg}}{0.012 \text{ kg}}\right)(+0.78 \text{ m/s})$$
$$= \left(\frac{0.212 \text{ kg}}{0.012 \text{ kg}}\right)(+0.78 \text{ m/s})$$
$$= +14 \text{ m/s}$$
$$\vec{v}_{d_i} = 14 \text{ m/s [right]}$$

Practice Problems

1. A student on a skateboard, with a combined mass of 78.2 kg, is moving east at 1.60 m/s. As he goes by, the student skilfully scoops his 6.4-kg backpack from the bench where he had left it. What will be the velocity of the student immediately after the pickup?

2. A 1050-kg car at an intersection has a velocity of 2.65 m/s [N]. The car hits the rear of a stationary truck, and their bumpers lock together. The velocity of the car-truck system immediately after collision is 0.78 m/s [N]. What is the mass of the truck?

Answers

1. 1.5 m/s [E]

2. 2.5 × 10³ kg

Paraphrase

The dart had a velocity of 14 m/s [right] just before it hit the block.

Example 9.7 involves a basketball player, initially moving with some velocity, colliding with a stationary player. After the interaction, both players move in different directions.

Example 9.7

A basketball player and her wheelchair (player A) have a combined mass of 58 kg. She moves at 0.60 m/s [E] and pushes off a stationary player (player B) while jockeying for a position near the basket. Player A ends up moving at 0.20 m/s [W]. The combined mass of player B and her wheelchair is 85 kg. What will be player B's velocity immediately after the interaction?

Given

$m_A = 58$ kg $\qquad m_B = 85$ kg

$\vec{v}_{A_i} = 0.60$ m/s [E] $\quad \vec{v}_{B_i} = 0$ m/s

$\vec{v}_{A_f} = 0.20$ m/s [W]

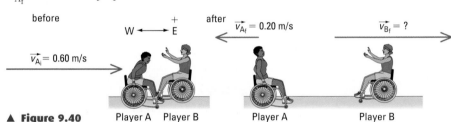

▲ **Figure 9.40**

Player A   Player B   Player A   Player B

Required

final velocity of player B ($\vec{v}_{B_f}$)

Analysis and Solution

Choose players A and B as an isolated system.
Player B has an initial velocity of zero. So her initial momentum is zero.

$$\vec{p}_{B_i} = 0$$

Apply the law of conservation of momentum.

$$\vec{p}_{sys_i} = \vec{p}_{sys_f}$$
$$\vec{p}_{A_i} + \vec{p}_{B_i} = \vec{p}_{A_f} + \vec{p}_{B_f}$$
$$m_A\vec{v}_{A_i} + 0 = m_A\vec{v}_{A_f} + m_B\vec{v}_{B_f}$$
$$\vec{v}_{B_f} = \left(\frac{m_A}{m_B}\right)(\vec{v}_{A_i} - \vec{v}_{A_f})$$
$$= \left(\frac{58 \text{ kg}}{85 \text{ kg}}\right)\{+0.60 \text{ m/s} - (-0.20 \text{ m/s})\}$$
$$= \left(\frac{58}{85}\right)(0.60 \text{ m/s} + 0.20 \text{ m/s})$$
$$= +0.55 \text{ m/s}$$
$$\vec{v}_{B_f} = 0.55 \text{ m/s [E]}$$

Practice Problems

1. A 0.25-kg volleyball is flying west at 2.0 m/s when it strikes a stationary 0.58-kg basketball dead centre. The volleyball rebounds east at 0.79 m/s. What will be the velocity of the basketball immediately after impact?

2. A 9500-kg rail flatcar moving forward at 0.70 m/s strikes a stationary 18 000-kg boxcar, causing it to move forward at 0.42 m/s. What will be the velocity of the flatcar immediately after collision if they fail to connect?

Answers

1. 1.2 m/s [W]
2. 0.096 m/s [backward]

In Example 9.8, two football players in motion collide with each other. After the interaction, the players bounce apart.

Example 9.8

A 110-kg Stampeders football fullback moving east at 1.80 m/s on a snowy playing field is struck by a 140-kg Eskimos defensive lineman moving west at 1.50 m/s. The fullback is bounced west at 0.250 m/s. What will be the velocity of the Eskimos defensive lineman just after impact?

Given

$m_S = 110$ kg $\qquad m_E = 140$ kg
$\vec{v}_{S_i} = 1.80$ m/s [E] $\quad \vec{v}_{E_i} = 1.50$ m/s [W]
$\vec{v}_{S_f} = 0.250$ m/s [W]

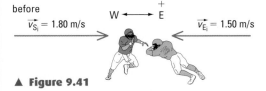

▲ **Figure 9.41**

Required
final velocity of Eskimos lineman ($\vec{v}_{E_f}$)

Analysis and Solution
Choose the fullback and lineman as an isolated system. Apply the law of conservation of momentum.

$$\vec{p}_{sys_i} = \vec{p}_{sys_f}$$
$$\vec{p}_{S_i} + \vec{p}_{E_i} = \vec{p}_{S_f} + \vec{p}_{E_f}$$
$$m_S\vec{v}_{S_i} + m_E\vec{v}_{E_i} = m_S\vec{v}_{S_f} + m_E\vec{v}_{E_f}$$
$$m_E\vec{v}_{E_f} = m_S\vec{v}_{S_i} + m_E\vec{v}_{E_i} - m_S\vec{v}_{S_f}$$
$$\vec{v}_{E_f} = \left(\frac{m_S}{m_E}\right)\vec{v}_{S_i} + \vec{v}_{E_i} - \left(\frac{m_S}{m_E}\right)\vec{v}_{S_f}$$
$$= \left(\frac{m_S}{m_E}\right)(\vec{v}_{S_i} - \vec{v}_{S_f}) + \vec{v}_{E_i}$$
$$= \left(\frac{110 \text{ kg}}{140 \text{ kg}}\right)\{(+1.80 \text{ m/s})$$
$$- (-0.250 \text{ m/s})\} + (-1.50 \text{ m/s})$$
$$= \left(\frac{110}{140}\right)(1.80 \text{ m/s} + 0.250 \text{ m/s})$$
$$- 1.50 \text{ m/s}$$
$$= +0.111 \text{ m/s}$$
$$\vec{v}_{E_f} = 0.111 \text{ m/s [E]}$$

Paraphrase
The velocity of the Eskimos defensive lineman immediately after impact is 0.111 m/s [E].

Practice Problems

1. A 72-kg snowboarder gliding at 1.6 m/s [E] bounces west at 0.84 m/s immediately after colliding with an 87-kg skier travelling at 1.4 m/s [W]. What will be the velocity of the skier just after impact?

2. A 125-kg bighorn ram butts heads with a younger 122-kg ram during mating season. The older ram is rushing north at 8.50 m/s immediately before collision, and bounces back at 0.11 m/s [S]. If the younger ram moves at 0.22 m/s [N] immediately after collision, what was its velocity just before impact?

Answers
1. 0.62 m/s [E]
2. 8.6 m/s [S]

Elastic and Inelastic Collisions in One Dimension

PHYSICS INSIGHT

The law of conservation of energy states that the *total* energy of an isolated system remains constant. The energy may change into several different forms. This law has no known exceptions.

In Examples 9.3 to 9.8, some of the collisions involved hard objects, such as the golf club hitting the golf ball. Other collisions, such as the block and dart, involved a dart that became embedded in a softer material (a block of wood). In all these collisions, it was possible to choose an isolated system so that the total momentum of the system was conserved.

When objects collide, they sometimes deform, make a sound, give off light, or heat up a little at the moment of impact. Any of these observations indicate that the kinetic energy of the system before collision is not the same as after collision. However, the total energy of the system is constant.

Concept Check

(a) Is it possible for an object to have energy and no momentum? Explain, using an example.

(b) Is it possible for an object to have momentum and no energy? Explain, using an example.

*e***SIM**

Predict the speed of two pucks just after a one-dimensional collision using momentum and energy concepts. Follow the eSim links at www.pearsoned.ca/school/physicssource.

Elastic Collisions

Suppose you hit a stationary pool ball dead centre with another pool ball so that the collision is collinear and the balls move without spinning immediately after impact. What will be the resulting motion of both balls (Figure 9.42)?

The ball that was initially moving will become stationary upon impact, while the other ball will start moving in the same direction as the incoming ball. If you measure the speed of both balls just before and just after collision, you will find that the speed of the incoming ball is almost the same as that of the outgoing ball. Since $E_k = \frac{1}{2}mv^2$, the final kinetic energy of the system is almost the same as the initial kinetic energy of the system.

▶ **Figure 9.42** Many collisions take place during a game of pool. What evidence suggests that momentum is conserved during the collision shown in the photo? What evidence suggests that energy is conserved?

If the initial kinetic energy of a system is equal to the final kinetic energy of the system after collision, the collision is **elastic**.

elastic collision: a collision in which $E_{k_i} = E_{k_f}$

In an elastic collision, the total kinetic energy of the system is conserved.

$$E_{k_i} = E_{k_f}$$

Most macroscopic interactions in the real world involve some of the initial kinetic energy of the system being converted to sound, light, or deformation (Figure 9.43). When deformation occurs, some of the initial kinetic energy of the system is converted to heat because friction acts on objects in almost all situations. These factors make it difficult to achieve an elastic collision.

Even if two colliding objects are hard and do not appear to deform, energy is still lost in the form of sound, light, and/or heat due to friction. Usually, the measured speed of an object after interaction is a little less than the predicted speed, which indicates that the collision is inelastic.

Example 9.9 demonstrates how to determine if the collision between a golf club and a golf ball is elastic.

Project **LINK**

How will you apply the concepts of conservation of momentum and conservation of energy to the design of the water balloon protection?

info **BIT**

A steel sphere will bounce as high on a steel anvil as a rubber ball will on concrete. However, when a steel sphere is dropped on linoleum or hardwood, the collision is not elastic because the sphere hardly bounces at all. The kinetic energy of the sphere is converted to sound, heat, and the deformation of the floor surface. To try this, use flooring samples. Do not try this on floors at home or at school.

◄ **Figure 9.43** Was the collision that occurred just before this photo was taken elastic? What evidence do you have to support your answer?

Example 9.9

A 0.160-kg billiard ball travelling at 0.500 m/s [N] strikes a stationary 0.180-kg snooker ball and rebounds at 0.0290 m/s [S]. The snooker ball moves off at 0.471 m/s [N]. Ignore possible rotational effects. Determine if the collision is elastic.

Practice Problems

1. A 45.9-g golf ball is stationary on the green when a 185-g golf club face travelling horizontally at 1.24 m/s [E] strikes it. After impact, the club face continues moving at 0.760 m/s [E] while the ball moves at 1.94 m/s [E]. Assume that the club face is vertical at the moment of impact so that the ball does not spin. Determine if the collision is elastic.

2. An argon atom with a mass of 6.63×10^{-23} kg travels at 17 m/s [right] and strikes another identical argon atom dead centre travelling at 20 m/s [left]. The first atom rebounds at 20 m/s [left], while the second atom moves at 17 m/s [right]. Determine if the collision is elastic.

Answers

1. inelastic
2. elastic

Given

$m_b = 0.160$ kg
$m_s = 0.180$ kg
$\vec{v}_{b_i} = 0.500$ m/s [N]
$\vec{v}_{s_i} = 0$ m/s
$\vec{v}_{b_f} = 0.0290$ m/s [S]
$\vec{v}_{s_f} = 0.471$ m/s [N]

Required
determine if the collision is elastic

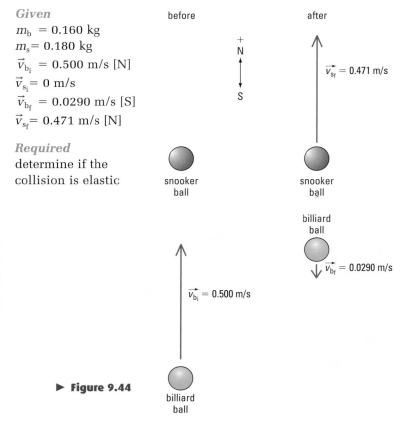

► **Figure 9.44**

Analysis and Solution

Choose the billiard ball and the snooker ball as an isolated system. Calculate the total initial kinetic energy and the total final kinetic energy of the system.

$$E_{k_i} = \frac{1}{2}m_b(v_{b_i})^2 + \frac{1}{2}m_s(v_{s_i})^2 \qquad E_{k_f} = \frac{1}{2}m_b(v_{b_f})^2 + \frac{1}{2}m_s(v_{s_f})^2$$

$$= \frac{1}{2}(0.160 \text{ kg})(0.500 \text{ m/s})^2 + 0 \qquad = \frac{1}{2}(0.160 \text{ kg})(0.0290 \text{ m/s})^2$$

$$= 0.0200 \text{ kg} \cdot \text{m}^2/\text{s}^2 \qquad\qquad\qquad + \frac{1}{2}(0.180 \text{ kg})(0.471 \text{ m/s})^2$$

$$= 0.0200 \text{ J} \qquad\qquad\qquad\qquad = 0.0200 \text{ kg} \cdot \text{m}^2/\text{s}^2$$

$$= 0.0200 \text{ J}$$

Since $E_{k_i} = E_{k_f}$, the collision is elastic.

Paraphrase

The collision between the billiard ball and the snooker ball is elastic.

Inelastic Collisions

In 9-2 QuickLab on page 455, after the putty ball collided with a hard surface, the putty ball became stationary and had no kinetic energy. Upon impact, the putty ball deformed and the kinetic energy of the putty ball was converted mostly to thermal energy.

Although the *total* energy of the system was conserved, the total initial kinetic energy of the system was not equal to the total final kinetic energy of the system after collision. This type of collision is **inelastic**.

> In an inelastic collision, the total kinetic energy of the system is *not* conserved.

$$E_{k_i} \neq E_{k_f}$$

Whenever two objects stick together after collision, the collision is inelastic. However, this type of interaction does not necessarily mean that the final kinetic energy of the system is zero. For example, consider a **ballistic pendulum**, a type of pendulum used to determine the speed of bullets before electronic timing devices were invented (Figure 9.45).

*e***WEB**

Research examples of elastic and inelastic one-dimensional collisions. Then analyze how the momentum and energy change in those collisions. Begin your search at www.pearsoned.ca/ school/physicssource.

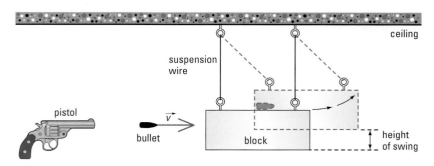

▲ **Figure 9.45** When a bullet is fired into the block, both the block and bullet move together as a unit after impact.

The pendulum consists of a stationary block of wood suspended from the ceiling by light ropes or cables. When a bullet is fired at the block, the bullet becomes embedded in the wood upon impact. The kinetic energy of the bullet is converted to sound, thermal energy, deformation of the wood and bullet, and the kinetic energy of the pendulum-bullet system.

The initial momentum of the bullet causes the pendulum to move upon impact, but since the pendulum is suspended by cables, it swings upward just after the bullet becomes embedded in the block. As the pendulum-bullet system swings upward, its kinetic energy is converted to gravitational potential energy.

Example 9.10 involves a ballistic pendulum. By using the conservation of energy, it is possible to determine the speed of the pendulum-bullet system immediately after impact. By applying the conservation of momentum to the collision, it is possible to determine the initial speed of the bullet.

Example 9.10

A 0.0149-kg bullet from a pistol strikes a 2.0000-kg ballistic pendulum. Upon impact, the pendulum swings forward and rises to a height of 0.219 m. What was the velocity of the bullet immediately before impact?

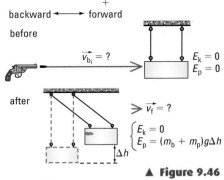

▲ **Figure 9.46**

Given

$m_b = 0.0149$ kg $m_p = 2.0000$ kg $\Delta h = 0.219$ m

Required

initial velocity of bullet ($\vec{v}_{b_i}$)

Analysis and Solution

Choose the pendulum and the bullet as an isolated system. Since the pendulum is stationary before impact, its initial velocity is zero. So its initial momentum is zero.

$$\vec{p}_{p_i} = 0$$

Immediately after collision, the bullet and pendulum move together as a unit. The kinetic energy of the pendulum-bullet system just after impact is converted to gravitational potential energy.

$$E_k = E_p$$

Apply the law of conservation of energy to find the speed of the pendulum-bullet system just after impact.

$$E_k = E_p$$
$$\frac{1}{2}\cancel{(m_b + m_p)}\,(v_f)^2 = \cancel{(m_b + m_p)}\,g(\Delta h)$$
$$(v_f)^2 = 2g(\Delta h)$$
$$v_f = \sqrt{2g(\Delta h)}$$
$$= \sqrt{2\left(9.81\,\frac{m}{s^2}\right)(0.219\ m)}$$
$$= 2.073\ m/s$$
$$\vec{v}_f = 2.073\ m/s\ [forward]$$

Apply the law of conservation of momentum to find the initial velocity of the bullet.

$$\vec{p}_{sys_i} = \vec{p}_{sys_f}$$
$$\vec{p}_{b_i} + \vec{p}_{p_i} = \vec{p}_{sys_f}$$
$$m_b\vec{v}_{b_i} + 0 = (m_b + m_p)\vec{v}_f$$
$$\vec{v}_{b_i} = \left(\frac{m_b + m_p}{m_b}\right)\vec{v}_f$$
$$= \left(\frac{0.0149\ kg + 2.0000\ kg}{0.0149\ kg}\right)(+2.073\ m/s)$$
$$= \left(\frac{2.0149\ \cancel{kg}}{0.0149\ \cancel{kg}}\right)(+2.073\ m/s)$$
$$= +280\ m/s$$
$$\vec{v}_{b_i} = 280\ m/s\ [forward]$$

Practice Problems

1. A 2.59-g bullet strikes a stationary 1.00-kg ballistic pendulum, causing the pendulum to swing up to 5.20 cm from its initial position. What was the speed of the bullet immediately before impact?

2. A 7.75-g bullet travels at 351 m/s before striking a stationary 2.5-kg ballistic pendulum. How high will the pendulum swing?

Answers

1. 391 m/s

2. 6.0 cm

Paraphrase
The initial velocity of the bullet immediately before impact was
280 m/s [forward].

Example 9.11 demonstrates how to determine if the collision in
Example 9.10 is elastic or inelastic by comparing the kinetic energy of
the system just before and just after collision.

Example 9.11

Determine if the collision in Example 9.10 is elastic or inelastic.

Given

$m_b = 0.0149$ kg $\vec{v}_{b_i} = 280$ m/s [forward] from Example 9.10
$m_p = 2.0000$ kg $\vec{v}_f = 2.073$ m/s [forward] from Example 9.10

Required

initial and final kinetic energies (E_{k_i} and E_{k_f}) to find if the collision
is elastic

Analysis and Solution

Choose the pendulum and the bullet as an isolated system.
Calculate the total initial kinetic energy and the total final kinetic energy
of the system.

$$E_{k_i} = \frac{1}{2}m_b(v_{b_i})^2 + \frac{1}{2}m_p(v_{p_i})^2 \qquad E_{k_f} = \frac{1}{2}(m_b + m_p)(v_f)^2$$

$$= \frac{1}{2}(0.0149 \text{ kg})(280 \text{ m/s})^2 + 0 \qquad = \frac{1}{2}(0.0149 \text{ kg} + 2.0000 \text{ kg})(2.073 \text{ m/s})^2$$

$$= 585 \text{ kg·m}^2/\text{s}^2 \qquad\qquad = 4.33 \text{ kg·m}^2/\text{s}^2$$

$$= 585 \text{ J} \qquad\qquad\qquad = 4.33 \text{ J}$$

Since $E_{k_i} \neq E_{k_f}$, the collision is inelastic.

Paraphrase and Verify

Since the kinetic energy of the system just before impact is
much greater than the kinetic energy of the system just after
impact, the collision is inelastic. This result makes sense since
the bullet became embedded in the pendulum upon impact.

Practice Problems

1. In Example 9.6 on pages 477 and
   478, how much kinetic energy is lost
   immediately after the interaction?

2. (a) Determine if the interaction
   in Example 9.8 on page 479
   is elastic.
   (b) What percent of kinetic energy
   is lost?

Answers

1. 1.1 J
2. (a) inelastic
   (b) 98.7%

Knowledge

1. In your own words, state the law of conservation of momentum.

2. (a) In the context of momentum, what is an isolated system?

   (b) Why is it necessary to choose an isolated system when solving a momentum problem?

3. Explain the difference between an elastic and an inelastic collision. Include an example of each type of collision in your answer.

4. What evidence suggests that a collision is

   (a) elastic?

   (b) inelastic?

Applications

5. Give two examples, other than those in the text, of possible collinear collisions between two identical masses. Include a sketch of each situation showing the velocity of each object immediately before and immediately after collision.

6. A student is sitting in a chair with nearly frictionless rollers. Her homework bag is in an identical chair right beside her. The chair and bag have a combined mass of 20 kg. The student and her chair have a combined mass of 65 kg. If she pushes her homework bag away from her at 0.060 m/s relative to the floor, what will be the student's velocity immediately after the interaction?

7. At liftoff, a space shuttle has a mass of 2.04×10^6 kg. The rocket engines expel 3.7×10^3 kg of exhaust gas during the first second of liftoff, giving the rocket a velocity of 5.7 m/s [up]. At what velocity is the exhaust gas leaving the rocket engines? Ignore the change in mass due to the fuel being consumed. The exhaust gas needed to counteract the force of gravity has already been accounted for and should not be part of this calculation.

8. A 60.0-kg student on a 4.2-kg skateboard is travelling south at 1.35 m/s. A friend throws a 0.585-kg basketball to him with a velocity of 12.6 m/s [N]. What will be the velocity of the student and skateboard immediately after he catches the ball?

9. A hockey forward with a mass of 95 kg skates in front of the net at 2.3 m/s [E]. He is met by a 104-kg defenceman skating at 1.2 m/s [W]. What will be the velocity of the resulting tangle of players if they stay together immediately after impact?

10. A 75.6-kg volleyball player leaps toward the net at 1.18 m/s [right], and blocks a 0.275-kg volleyball moving at 12.5 m/s [left]. The volleyball rebounds at 6.85 m/s [right].

    (a) What will be the horizontal velocity of the player immediately after the block?

    (b) Determine if the collision is elastic.

11. A 220-kg bumper car (A) going north at 0.565 m/s hits another bumper car (B) and rebounds at 0.482 m/s [S]. Bumper car B was initially travelling south at 0.447 m/s, and after collision moved north at 0.395 m/s.

    (a) What is the mass of bumper car B?

    (b) Determine if the collision is elastic.

Extension

12. Summarize the concepts and ideas associated with one-dimensional collisions using a graphic organizer of your choice. See Student References 4: Using Graphic Organizers on pp. 869–871 for examples of different graphic organizers. Make sure that the concepts and ideas are clearly presented and appropriately linked.

e TEST

To check your understanding of the conservation of momentum and one-dimensional collisions, follow the eTest links at www.pearsoned.ca/school/physicssource.

9.4 Collisions in Two Dimensions

Many interactions in the universe involve collisions. Comets, asteroids, and meteors sometimes collide with celestial bodies. Molecules and atoms are constantly colliding during chemical reactions throughout the universe: in stars, in Earth's atmosphere, and even within your body.

An interesting collision in recent history occurred on June 30, 1908, at Tunguska, Siberia, between a cosmic object and Earth (Figure 9.47). Eyewitnesses reported seeing a giant fireball that moved rapidly across the sky and eventually collided with the ground. Upon impact, a tremendous explosion occurred producing an atmospheric shock wave that circled Earth twice. About 2000 km^2 of forest were levelled and thousands of trees were burned. In fact, there was so much fine dust in the atmosphere that people in London, England, could read a newspaper at night just from the scattered light.

info **BIT**

Scientists speculate that the cosmic object that hit Tunguska was about 100 m across and had a mass of about 1×10^6 t. The estimated speed of the object was about 30 km/s, which is 1.1×10^5 km/h. After the collision at Tunguska, a large number of diamonds were found scattered all over the impact site. So the cosmic object contained diamonds as well as other materials.

◄ **Figure 9.47** The levelled trees and charred remnants of a forest at Tunguska, Siberia, after a cosmic object collided with Earth in 1908. Although the chance that a similar collision with Earth during your lifetime may seem remote, such collisions have happened throughout Earth's history.

In real life, most collisions occur in three dimensions. Only in certain situations, such as those you studied in section 9.3, does the motion of the interacting objects lie along a straight line. In this section, you will examine collisions that occur in two dimensions. These interactions occur when objects in a plane collide off centre. In 9-1 QuickLab on page 447, you found that when two coins collide off centre, the resulting path of each coin is in a different direction from its initial path. You may have noticed that certain soccer or hockey players seem to be at the right place at the right time whenever there is a rebound from the goalie. How do these players know where to position themselves so that they can score on the rebound? Find out by doing 9-6 Inquiry Lab.

Analyzing Collisions in Two Dimensions

Question

How does the momentum of a two-body system in the x and y directions compare just before and just after a collision?

Hypothesis

State a hypothesis relating the momentum of a system in each direction immediately before and immediately after collision. Remember to write an "if/then" statement.

Variables

Read the procedure and identify the controlled, manipulated, and responding variables in the experiment.

Materials and Equipment

air table or bead table
pucks
spark-timer or camera set-up to measure velocities
rulers or metre-sticks
protractors

Procedure

1. Copy Tables 9.3 and 9.4 on page 489 into your notebook.

2. Label the pucks as "puck 1" and "puck 2" respectively. Measure the mass of each puck and record it in Table 9.3.

3. Set up the apparatus so that puck 2 is at rest near the centre of the table.

4. Have each person in your group do one trial. Each time, send puck 1 aimed at the left side of puck 2, recording the paths of both pucks. Make sure the recording tracks of both pucks can be used to accurately measure their velocities before and after collision.

5. Have each person in your group measure and analyze one trial. Help each other as needed to ensure the measurements and calculations for each trial are accurate.

6. Find a suitable point on the recorded tracks to be the impact location.

7. On the path of puck 1 before collision, choose an interval where the speed is constant. Choose the positive x-axis to be in the initial direction of puck 1.

8. Using either the physical centre of the puck, or the leading or trailing edge, measure the distance and the time interval. Record those values in Table 9.3.

9. On the path of each puck after collision, choose an interval where the speed is constant. Measure the distance, direction of motion relative to the positive x-axis, and time interval. Record those values in Table 9.3.

Analysis

1. Calculate the initial velocity and initial momentum of puck 1. Record the values in Table 9.4.

2. Calculate the velocity of puck 1 after collision. Resolve the velocity into x and y components. Record the values in Table 9.4.

3. Use the results of question 2 to calculate the x and y components of the final momentum of puck 1. Record the values in Table 9.4.

4. Repeat questions 2 and 3 but this time use the data for puck 2. Explain why the y component of the momentum of puck 2 is negative.

5. Record the calculated values from each member of your group as a different trial in Table 9.4.

6. For each trial, state the relationship between the initial momentum of the system in the x direction and the final momentum of the system in the x direction. Remember to consider measurement errors. Write this result as a mathematical statement.

7. The initial momentum of the system in the y direction was zero. For each trial, what was the final momentum of the system in the y direction? Remember to consider measurement errors. Write this result as a mathematical statement.

8. Compare your answers to questions 6 and 7 with other groups. Does this relationship agree with your hypothesis? Account for any discrepancies.

For a probeware activity, go to
www.pearsoned.ca/school/physicssource.

▼ **Table 9.3** Mass, Distance, Time Elapsed, and Angle

Trial	Before and After for Puck 1						After for Puck 2			
	Mass m_1 (g)	Initial Distance d_{1_i} (m)	Initial Time Elapsed Δt_{1_i} (s)	Final Distance d_{1_f} (m)	Final Time Elapsed Δt_{1_f} (s)	Final Angle θ_{1_f} (°)	Mass m_2 (g)	Final Distance d_{2_f} (m)	Final Time Elapsed Δt_{2_f} (s)	Final Angle θ_{2_f} (°)
1										
2										
3										
4										
5										

▼ **Table 9.4** Velocity and Momentum

Trial	Before and After for Puck 1						After for Puck 2			
	Initial x Velocity v_{1ix} (m/s)	Initial x Momentum $p_{1ix}\left(g\cdot\dfrac{m}{s}\right)$	Final x Velocity v_{1fx} (m/s)	Final y Velocity v_{1fy} (m/s)	Final x Momentum $p_{1fx}\left(g\cdot\dfrac{m}{s}\right)$	Final y Momentum $p_{1fy}\left(g\cdot\dfrac{m}{s}\right)$	Final x Velocity v_{2fx} (m/s)	Final y Velocity v_{2fy} (m/s)	Final x Momentum $p_{2fx}\left(g\cdot\dfrac{m}{s}\right)$	Final y Momentum $p_{2fy}\left(g\cdot\dfrac{m}{s}\right)$
1										
2										
3										
4										
5										

Momentum Is Conserved in Two-dimensional Collisions

In 9-6 Inquiry Lab, you found that along each direction, x and y, the momentum of the system before collision is about the same as the momentum of the system immediately after collision. In other words, momentum is conserved in two-dimensional collisions. This result agrees with what you saw in 9-5 Inquiry Lab, where only one-dimensional collisions were examined.

As in one-dimensional collisions, the law of conservation of momentum is valid only when no external net force acts on the system. In two dimensions, the motion of each object in the system must be analyzed in terms of two perpendicular axes. To do this, you can either use a vector addition diagram drawn to scale or vector components.

The law of conservation of momentum can be stated using components in the x and y directions.

In two-dimensional collisions where no external net force acts on the system, the momentum of the system in both the x and y directions remains constant.

$$p_{sys_{ix}} = p_{sys_{fx}} \text{ and } p_{sys_{iy}} = p_{sys_{fy}} \text{ where } (\vec{F}_{net})_{sys} = 0$$

e **SIM**

Apply the law of conservation of momentum to two-dimensional collisions. Go to www.pearsoned.ca/school/physicssource.

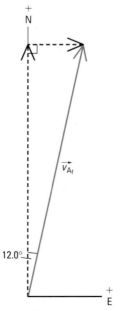

info **BIT**

In championship curling, rebound angles and conservation of momentum are crucial for placing stones in counting position behind guards. Just nudging a stone several centimetres can make all the difference.

Concept Check

(a) Will the magnitude of the momentum of an object always increase if a non-zero net force acts on it? Explain, using an example.

(b) How can the momentum of an object change but its speed remain the same? Explain, using an example.

Example 9.12 involves a curling stone colliding off centre with an identical stone that is at rest. The momentum of each stone is analyzed in two perpendicular directions.

Example 9.12

A 19.6-kg curling stone (A) moving at 1.20 m/s [N] strikes another identical stationary stone (B) off centre, and moves off with a velocity of 1.17 m/s [12.0° E of N]. What will be the velocity of stone B after the collision? Ignore frictional and rotational effects.

Given

$m_A = 19.6$ kg $m_B = 19.6$ kg $\vec{v}_{A_i} = 1.20$ m/s [N]

$\vec{v}_{B_i} = 0$ m/s $\vec{v}_{A_f} = 1.17$ m/s [12.0° E of N]

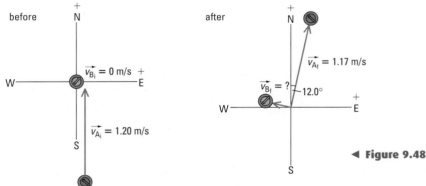

◄ **Figure 9.48**

Required

final velocity of stone B ($\vec{v}_{B_f}$)

Analysis and Solution

Choose both curling stones as an isolated system. Stone B has an initial velocity of zero. So its initial momentum is zero.

$$\vec{p}_{B_i} = 0$$

Resolve all velocities into east and north components (Figure 9.49).

Vector	East component	North component
$\vec{v}_{A_i}$	0	1.20 m/s
$\vec{v}_{B_i}$	0	0
$\vec{v}_{A_f}$	(1.17 m/s)(sin 12.0°)	(1.17 m/s)(cos 12.0°)

▲ **Figure 9.49**

Apply the law of conservation of momentum to the system in the east and north directions.

E direction

$$p_{\text{sys}_{iE}} = p_{\text{sys}_{fE}}$$
$$p_{A_{iE}} + p_{B_{iE}} = p_{A_{fE}} + p_{B_{fE}}$$
$$m_A v_{A_{iE}} + 0 = m_A v_{A_{fE}} + m_B v_{B_{fE}}$$
$$0 + 0 = m_A v_{A_{fE}} + m_B v_{B_{fE}}$$
$$m_B v_{B_{fE}} = -m_A v_{A_{fE}}$$
$$v_{B_{fE}} = -\left(\frac{m_A}{m_B}\right) v_{A_{fE}}$$
$$= -\left(\frac{19.6 \ \text{kg}}{19.6 \ \text{kg}}\right)(1.17 \ \text{m/s})(\sin 12.0°)$$
$$= -0.2433 \ \text{m/s}$$

N direction

$$p_{\text{sys}_{iN}} = p_{\text{sys}_{fN}}$$
$$p_{A_{iN}} + p_{B_{iN}} = p_{A_{fN}} + p_{B_{fN}}$$
$$m_A v_{A_{iN}} + 0 = m_A v_{A_{fN}} + m_B v_{B_{fN}}$$
$$m_B v_{B_{fN}} = m_A v_{A_{iN}} - m_A v_{A_{fN}}$$
$$v_{B_{fN}} = \left(\frac{m_A}{m_B}\right)(v_{A_{iN}} - v_{A_{fN}})$$
$$= \left(\frac{19.6 \ \text{kg}}{19.6 \ \text{kg}}\right)\{1.20 \ \text{m/s} - (1.17 \ \text{m/s})(\cos 12.0°)\}$$
$$= 0.05557 \ \text{m/s}$$

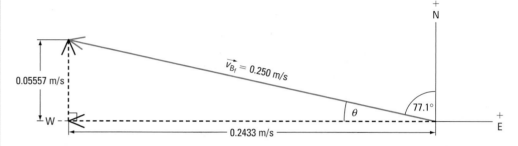

▲ **Figure 9.50**

Use the Pythagorean theorem to find the magnitude of $\vec{v}_{B_f}$.

$$v_{B_f} = \sqrt{(v_{B_{fE}})^2 + (v_{B_{fN}})^2}$$
$$= \sqrt{(-0.2433 \ \text{m/s})^2 + (0.05557 \ \text{m/s})^2}$$
$$= 0.250 \ \text{m/s}$$

Use the tangent function to find the direction of $\vec{v}_{B_f}$.

$$\tan \theta = \frac{\text{opposite}}{\text{adjacent}}$$
$$= \frac{0.05557 \ \text{m/s}}{0.2433 \ \text{m/s}}$$
$$= 0.2284$$
$$\theta = \tan^{-1}(0.2284)$$
$$= 12.9°$$

From Figure 9.50, θ is between $\vec{v}_{B_f}$ and the west direction. So the direction of $\vec{v}_{B_f}$ measured from north is $90.0° - 12.9° = 77.1°$.

$$\vec{v}_{B_f} = 0.250 \ \text{m/s} \ [77.1° \ \text{W of N}]$$

Paraphrase

The final velocity of the second stone is 0.250 m/s [77.1° W of N].

Practice Problems

1. A 97.0-kg hockey centre stops momentarily in front of the net. He is checked from the side by a 104-kg defenceman skating at 1.82 m/s [E], and bounces at 0.940 m/s [18.5° S of E]. What is the velocity of the defenceman immediately after the check?

2. A 1200-kg car, attempting to run a red light, strikes a stationary 1350-kg vehicle waiting to make a turn. Skid marks show that after the collision, the 1350-kg vehicle moved at 8.30 m/s [55.2° E of N], and the other vehicle at 12.8 m/s [36.8° W of N]. What was the velocity of the 1200-kg vehicle just before collision? Note this type of calculation is part of many vehicle collision investigations where charges may be pending.

Answers

1. 1.03 m/s [15.7° N of E]

2. 15.6 m/s [N]

Example 9.13 involves a football tackle with two players. Each player has an initial velocity, but when they collide, both players move together as a unit. To analyze the motion, the centre of mass of the combination of both players must be used.

The **centre of mass** is a point that serves as an average location of the total mass of an object or system. Depending on the distribution of mass, the centre of mass may be located even *outside* the object. Generally, momentum calculations are made using the centre of mass of an object.

No matter where any external forces are acting on an object, whether the object is rotating or not, or whether the object is deformable or rigid, the translational motion of the object can be easily analyzed in terms of its centre of mass.

centre of mass: point where the total mass of an object can be assumed to be concentrated

info **BIT**

When an object is symmetric and has uniform density, its centre of mass is in the same location as the physical centre of the object.

Example 9.13

A 90-kg quarterback moving at 7.0 m/s [270°] is tackled by a 110-kg linebacker running at 8.0 m/s [0°]. What will be the velocity of the centre of mass of the combination of both players after impact?

Given

$m_q = 90$ kg $\qquad m_l = 110$ kg
$\vec{v}_{q_i} = 7.0$ m/s [270°] $\qquad \vec{v}_{l_i} = 8.0$ m/s [0°]

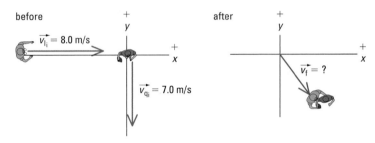

▲ **Figure 9.51**

Required
final velocity of centre of mass of both players $(\vec{v}_f)$

Analysis and Solution
Choose the quarterback and the linebacker as an isolated system. The linebacker tackled the quarterback. So both players have the same final velocity.
Resolve all velocities into x and y components.

Vector	*x* component	*y* component
$\vec{v}_{q_i}$	0	−7.0 m/s
$\vec{v}_{l_i}$	8.0 m/s	0

Apply the law of conservation of momentum to the system in the x and y directions.

Practice Problems

1. A 2000-kg car travelling at 20.0 m/s [90.0°] is struck at an intersection by a 2500-kg pickup truck travelling at 14.0 m/s [180°]. If the vehicles stick together upon impact, what will be the velocity of the centre of mass of the car-truck combination immediately after the collision?

2. A 100-kg hockey centre is moving at 1.50 m/s [W] in front of the net. He is checked by a 108-kg defenceman skating at 4.20 m/s [S]. Both players move off together after collision. What will be the velocity of the centre of mass of the combination of both players immediately after the check?

Answers
1. 11.8 m/s [131°]
2. 2.30 m/s [71.7° S of W]

x direction

$$p_{\text{sys}_{ix}} = p_{\text{sys}_{fx}}$$
$$p_{q_{ix}} + p_{l_{ix}} = p_{\text{sys}_{fx}}$$
$$m_q v_{q_{ix}} + m_l v_{l_{ix}} = (m_q + m_l)v_{f_x}$$
$$0 + m_l v_{l_{ix}} = (m_q + m_l)v_{f_x}$$
$$(m_q + m_l)v_{f_x} = m_l v_{l_{ix}}$$
$$v_{f_x} = \left(\frac{m_l}{m_q + m_l}\right)v_{l_{ix}}$$
$$= \left(\frac{110 \text{ kg}}{90 \text{ kg} + 110 \text{ kg}}\right)(8.0 \text{ m/s})$$
$$= \left(\frac{110 \text{ kg}}{200 \text{ kg}}\right)(8.0 \text{ m/s})$$
$$= 4.40 \text{ m/s}$$

y direction

$$p_{\text{sys}_{iy}} = p_{\text{sys}_{fy}}$$
$$p_{q_{iy}} + p_{l_{iy}} = p_{\text{sys}_{fy}}$$
$$m_q v_{q_{iy}} + m_l v_{l_{iy}} = (m_q + m_l)v_{fy}$$
$$m_q v_{q_{iy}} + 0 = (m_q + m_l)v_{fy}$$
$$(m_q + m_l)v_{f_y} = m_q v_{q_{iy}}$$
$$v_{f_y} = \left(\frac{m_q}{m_q + m_l}\right)v_{q_{iy}}$$
$$= \left(\frac{90 \text{ kg}}{90 \text{ kg} + 110 \text{ kg}}\right)(-7.0 \text{ m/s})$$
$$= \left(\frac{90 \text{ kg}}{200 \text{ kg}}\right)(-7.0 \text{ m/s})$$
$$= -3.15 \text{ m/s}$$

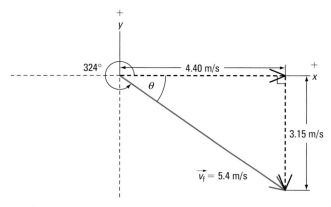

▲ **Figure 9.52**

Use the Pythagorean theorem to find the magnitude of $\vec{v}_f$.
$$v_f = \sqrt{(v_{f_x})^2 + (v_{f_y})^2}$$
$$= \sqrt{(4.40 \text{ m/s})^2 + (-3.15 \text{ m/s})^2}$$
$$= 5.4 \text{ m/s}$$

Use the tangent function to find the direction of $\vec{v}_f$.
$$\tan \theta = \frac{\text{opposite}}{\text{adjacent}}$$
$$= \frac{3.15 \text{ m/s}}{4.40 \text{ m/s}}$$
$$= 0.7159$$
$$\theta = \tan^{-1}(0.7159)$$
$$= 35.6°$$

From Figure 9.52, θ is between $\vec{v}_f$ and the positive x-axis. So the direction of $\vec{v}_f$ measured *counterclockwise* from the positive x-axis is $360° - 35.6° = 324.4°$.
$$\vec{v}_f = 5.4 \text{ m/s } [324°]$$

Paraphrase

The final velocity of both players is 5.4 m/s [324°].

Example 9.14 deals with a fireworks bundle that is initially stationary. After it explodes, three fragments (A, B, and C) fly in different directions in a plane. A vector addition diagram is used to determine the momentum of fragment C. This quantity is then used to calculate its final velocity.

Example 9.14

A 0.600-kg fireworks bundle is at rest just before it explodes into three fragments. A 0.200-kg fragment (A) flies at 14.6 m/s [W], and a 0.180-kg fragment (B) moves at 19.2 m/s [S]. What is the velocity of the third fragment (C) just after the explosion? Assume that no mass is lost, and that the motion of the fragments lies in a plane.

Given

$m_T = 0.600$ kg $m_A = 0.200$ kg $m_B = 0.180$ kg

$\vec{v}_i = 0$ m/s $\vec{v}_{A_f} = 14.6$ m/s [W] $\vec{v}_{B_f} = 19.2$ m/s [S]

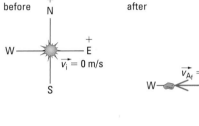
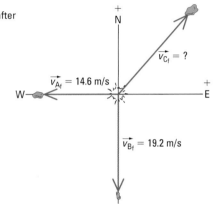

▲ **Figure 9.53**

Required
final velocity of fragment C ($\vec{v}_{C_f}$)

Analysis and Solution
Choose fragments A, B, and C as an isolated system. Since no mass is lost, find the mass of fragment C.

$$m_C = m_T - (m_A + m_B)$$
$$= 0.600 \text{ kg} - (0.200 \text{ kg} + 0.180 \text{ kg})$$
$$= 0.220 \text{ kg}$$

The original firework has an initial velocity of zero. So the system has an initial momentum of zero.

$$\vec{p}_{sys_i} = 0$$

The momentum of each fragment is in the same direction as its velocity. Calculate the momentum of fragments A and B.

$p_{A_f} = m_A v_{A_f}$ $p_{B_f} = m_B v_{B_f}$

$\quad = (0.200 \text{ kg})(14.6 \text{ m/s})$ $\quad = (0.180 \text{ kg})(19.2 \text{ m/s})$

$\quad = 2.92 \text{ kg·m/s}$ $\quad = 3.46 \text{ kg·m/s}$

$\vec{p}_{A_f} = 2.92 \text{ kg·m/s [W]}$ $\vec{p}_{B_f} = 3.46 \text{ kg·m/s [S]}$

Practice Problems

1. A 0.058-kg firecracker that is at rest explodes into three fragments. A 0.018-kg fragment moves at 2.40 m/s [N] while a 0.021-kg fragment moves at 1.60 m/s [E]. What will be the velocity of the third fragment? Assume that no mass is lost, and that the motion of the fragments lies in a plane.

2. A 65.2-kg student on a 2.50-kg skateboard moves at 0.40 m/s [W]. He jumps off the skateboard with a velocity of 0.38 m/s [30.0° S of W]. What will be the velocity of the skateboard immediately after he jumps? Ignore friction between the skateboard and the ground.

Answers

1. 2.9 m/s [52.1° S of W]
2. 5.4 m/s [65.6° N of W]

Apply the law of conservation of momentum to the system.

$$\vec{p}_{\text{sys}_i} = \vec{p}_{\text{sys}_f}$$

$$0 = \vec{p}_{A_f} + \vec{p}_{B_f} + \vec{p}_{C_f}$$

Use a vector addition diagram to determine the momentum of fragment C.

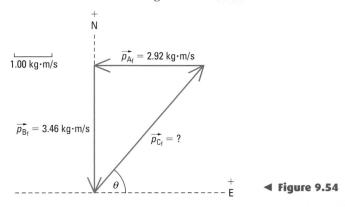

◀ **Figure 9.54**

From Figure 9.54, careful measurements give $p_{C_f} = 4.53$ kg·m/s and $\theta = 49.8°$ N of E.

Divide the momentum of fragment C by its mass to find the velocity.

$$p_{C_f} = m_C v_{C_f}$$

$$v_{C_f} = \frac{p_{C_f}}{m_C}$$

$$= \frac{4.53 \text{ kg} \cdot \dfrac{\text{m}}{\text{s}}}{0.220 \text{ kg}}$$

$$= 20.6 \text{ m/s}$$

$$\vec{v}_{C_f} = 20.6 \text{ m/s } [49.8° \text{ N of E}]$$

Paraphrase
The velocity of the third fragment just after the explosion is 20.6 m/s [49.8° N of E].

Elastic and Inelastic Collisions in Two Dimensions

As with one-dimensional collisions, collisions in two dimensions may be either elastic or inelastic. The condition for an elastic two-dimensional collision is the same as for an elastic one-dimensional collision, $E_{k_i} = E_{k_f}$. To determine if a collision is elastic, the kinetic energy values before and after collision must be compared.

The kinetic energy of an object only depends on the *magnitude* of the velocity vector. So it does not matter if the velocity vector has only an x component, only a y component, or both x and y components. If you can determine the magnitude of the velocity vector, it is possible to calculate the kinetic energy.

An example of an inelastic collision occurs when two objects join together and move as a unit immediately after impact. If two objects bounce apart after impact, the collision may be either elastic or inelastic, depending on the initial and final kinetic energy of the system. Usually, if one or both colliding objects deform upon impact, the collision is inelastic.

e SIM

Predict v_{f_x} and v_{f_y} for an object just after a two-dimensional collision using momentum and energy concepts. Follow the eSim links at www.pearsoned.ca/school/physicssource.

In track sports, the material used for the track has a profound effect on the elasticity of the collision between a runner's foot and the running surface (Figure 9.55). If a track is made of a very hard material such as concrete, it experiences very little deformation when a runner's foot comes in contact with it. The collision is more elastic than if the track were made of a more compressible material such as cork. So less kinetic energy of the runner is converted to other forms of energy upon impact.

However, running on harder tracks results in a decreased interaction time and an increase in the net force acting on each foot, which could result in more injuries to joints, bones, and tendons. But a track that is extremely compressible is not desirable either, because it slows runners down. With all the pressure to achieve faster times in Olympic and world competitions, researchers and engineers continue to search for the optimum balance between resilience and safety in track construction.

Example 9.15 involves determining if the collision between two curling stones is elastic.

▶ **Figure 9.55** Canadian runner Diane Cummins (far right) competing in the 2003 World Championships. The material of a running surface affects the interaction time and the net force acting on a runner's feet. How would the net force change if the track were made of a soft material that deforms easily?

Example 9.15

Determine if the collision in Example 9.12 on pages 490 and 491 is elastic. If it is not, what percent of the kinetic energy is retained?

Given

$m_A = 19.6$ kg $\qquad m_B = 19.6$ kg $\qquad \vec{v}_{A_i} = 1.20$ m/s [N]

$\vec{v}_{B_i} = 0$ m/s $\qquad \vec{v}_{A_f} = 1.17$ m/s [12.0° E of N]

$\vec{v}_{B_f} = 0.2495$ m/s [77.1° W of N]

Required

determine if the collision is elastic

Analysis and Solution

Choose the two curling stones as an isolated system.

Calculate the total initial kinetic energy and the total final kinetic energy of the system.

$$E_{k_i} = \frac{1}{2}m_A(v_{A_i})^2 + \frac{1}{2}m_B(v_{B_i})^2$$

$$= \frac{1}{2}(19.6 \text{ kg})(1.20 \text{ m/s})^2 + 0$$

$$= 14.11 \text{ kg·m}^2/\text{s}^2$$

$$= 14.11 \text{ J}$$

$$E_{k_f} = \frac{1}{2}m_A(v_{A_f})^2 + \frac{1}{2}m_B(v_{B_f})^2$$

$$= \frac{1}{2}(19.6 \text{ kg})(1.17 \text{ m/s})^2 + \frac{1}{2}(19.6 \text{ kg})(0.2495 \text{ m/s})^2$$

$$= 14.03 \text{ kg·m}^2/\text{s}^2$$

$$= 14.03 \text{ J}$$

Since $E_{k_i} \neq E_{k_f}$, the collision is inelastic.
Find the percent of E_k retained.

$$\% E_k \text{ retained} = \frac{E_{k_f}}{E_{k_i}} \times 100\%$$

$$= \frac{14.03 \text{ J}}{14.11 \text{ J}} \times 100\%$$

$$= 99.4\%$$

Paraphrase
The collision is inelastic, and 99.4% of the kinetic energy is retained.

Conservation Laws and the Discovery of Subatomic Particles

Based on the results of experiments, scientists have gained great confidence in the laws of conservation of momentum and of conservation of energy, and have predicted that there are no known exceptions. This confidence has enabled scientists to make discoveries about the existence of particles within atoms as well. You will learn more about subatomic particles in Units VII and VIII.

In 1930, German scientists Walther Bothe and Wilhelm Becker produced a very penetrating ray of unknown particles when they bombarded the element beryllium with alpha particles (Figure 9.56). An **alpha particle** is two protons and two neutrons bound together to form a stable particle.

In 1932, British scientist James Chadwick (1891–1974) directed rays of these unknown particles at a thin paraffin strip and found that protons were emitted from the paraffin. He analyzed the speeds and angles of the emitted protons and, by using the conservation of momentum, he showed that the protons were being hit by particles of approximately the same mass. In other related experiments, Chadwick was able to determine the mass of these unknown particles very accurately using the conservation of momentum.

Earlier experiments had shown that the unknown particles were neutral because they were unaffected by electric or magnetic fields. You will learn about electric and magnetic fields in Unit VI. Chadwick had attempted for several years to find evidence of a suggested neutral particle that was believed to be located in the nucleus of an atom. The discovery of these neutral particles, now called neutrons, resulted in Chadwick winning the Nobel Prize for Physics in 1935.

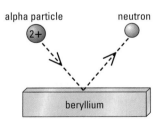

▲ **Figure 9.56** The experiment of Bothe and Becker using beryllium paved the way for Chadwick who later discovered the existence of neutrons by creating an experiment where he could detect them.

eSIM

Practise solving problems involving two-dimensional collisions. Follow the eSim links at www.pearsoned.ca/school/physicssource.

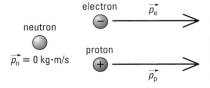

▲ **Figure 9.57** If a neutron is initially stationary, $\vec{p}_{sys_i} = 0$. If the neutron becomes transformed into a proton and an electron moving in the same direction, the momentum of the system is no longer zero.

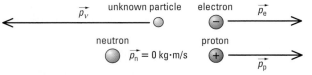

▲ **Figure 9.58** The existence of another particle accounted for the missing momentum and missing energy observed when a neutron transforms itself into a proton and an electron.

Scientists later found that the neutron, when isolated, soon became transformed into a proton and an electron. Sometimes the electron and proton were both ejected in the same direction, which seemed to contradict the law of conservation of momentum (Figure 9.57). Furthermore, other experiments showed that the total energy of the neutron before transformation was greater than the total energy of both the proton and electron. It seemed as if the law of conservation of energy was not valid either.

Austrian physicist Wolfgang Pauli (1900–1958) insisted that the conservation laws of momentum and of energy were still valid, and in 1930, he proposed that an extremely tiny neutral particle produced during the transformation must be moving in the opposite direction at an incredibly high speed. This new particle accounted for the missing momentum and missing energy (Figure 9.58).

Many other scientists accepted Pauli's explanation because they were convinced that the conservation laws of momentum and of energy were valid. For 25 years, they held their belief in the existence of this tiny particle, later called a neutrino, with no other evidence. Then in 1956, the existence of neutrinos was finally confirmed experimentally, further strengthening the universal validity of conservation laws.

THEN, NOW, AND FUTURE   Neutrino Research in Canada

Canada is a world leader in neutrino research. The SNO project (Sudbury Neutrino Observatory) is a special facility that allows scientists to gather data about these extremely tiny particles that are difficult to detect.

The observatory is located in INCO's Creighton Mine near Sudbury, Ontario, 2 km below Earth's surface. Bedrock above the mine shields the facility from cosmic rays that might interfere with the observation of neutrinos.

The experimental apparatus consists of 1000 t of heavy water encased in an acrylic vessel shaped like a 12-m diameter boiling flask (Figure 9.59). The vessel is surrounded by an array of about 1000 photo detectors, all immersed in a 10-storey chamber of purified water.

When a neutrino collides with a heavy water molecule, a tiny burst of light is emitted, which the photo detectors pick up.

Despite all that equipment, scientists only detect an average of about 10 neutrinos a day. So experiments

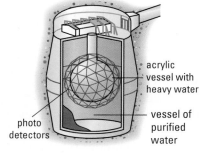

▲ **Figure 9.59** The Sudbury Neutrino Observatory is a collaborative effort among 130 scientists from Canada, the U.S., and the U.K.

must run for a long time in order to collect enough useful data.

Scientists are interested in neutrinos originating from the Sun and other distant parts of the universe. At first, it seemed that the Sun was not emitting as many neutrinos as expected. Scientists thought they would have to modify their theories about the reactions taking place within the core of the Sun.

Tripling the sensitivity of the detection process, by adding 2 t

of salt to the heavy water, showed that $\frac{2}{3}$ of the neutrinos from the Sun were being transformed into different types of neutrinos as they travelled. This discovery has important implications about the basic properties of a neutrino, including its mass.

It now appears that scientists' theories about the reactions within the core of the Sun are very accurate. Continued research at this facility will help answer fundamental questions about matter and the universe.

Questions

1. Why was Sudbury chosen as the site for this type of observatory?

2. Explain why, at first, it appeared that the Sun was not emitting the expected number of neutrinos.

3. If a neutrino has a very small mass and travels very fast, why doesn't it run out of energy?

Knowledge

1. How is a two-dimensional collision different from a one-dimensional collision? Explain, using examples.

2. In your own words, state the law of conservation of momentum for two-dimensional collisions. Show how the law relates to x and y components by using an example.

3. In your own words, define the centre of mass of an object.

4. Explain why scientists accepted the existence of the neutrino for so long when there was no direct evidence for it.

Applications

5. A cue ball travelling at 0.785 m/s [270°] strikes a stationary five-ball, causing it to move at 0.601 m/s [230°]. The cue ball and the five-ball each have a mass of 160 g. What will be the velocity of the cue ball immediately after impact? Ignore frictional and rotational effects.

6. A stationary 230-kg bumper car in a carnival is struck off centre from behind by a 255-kg bumper car moving at 0.843 m/s [W]. The more massive car bounces off at 0.627 m/s [42.0° S of W]. What will be the velocity of the other bumper car immediately after collision?

7. A 0.25-kg synthetic rubber ball bounces to a height of 46 cm when dropped from a height of 50 cm. Determine if this collision is elastic. If not, how much kinetic energy is lost?

8. A football halfback carrying the ball, with a combined mass of 95 kg, leaps toward the goal line at 4.8 m/s [S]. In the air at the goal line, he collides with a 115-kg linebacker travelling at 4.1 m/s [N]. If the players move together after impact, will the ball cross the goal line?

9. A 0.160-kg pool ball moving at 0.563 m/s [67.0° S of W] strikes a 0.180-kg snooker ball moving at 0.274 m/s [39.0° S of E]. The pool ball glances off at 0.499 m/s [23.0° S of E]. What will be the velocity of the snooker ball immediately after collision?

10. A 4.00-kg cannon ball is flying at 18.5 m/s [0°] when it explodes into two fragments. One 2.37-kg fragment (A) goes off at 19.7 m/s [325°]. What will be the velocity of the second fragment (B) immediately after the explosion? Assume that no mass is lost during the explosion, and that the motion of the fragments lies in the xy plane.

11. A 0.952-kg baseball bat moving at 35.2 m/s [0°] strikes a 0.145-kg baseball moving at 40.8 m/s [180°]. The baseball rebounds at 37.6 m/s [64.2°]. What will be the velocity of the centre of mass of the bat immediately after collision if the batter exerts no force on the bat during and after the instant of impact?

Extensions

12. Some running shoe designs contain springs. Research these types of shoes and the controversy surrounding them. How do momentum and impulse apply to these shoes? Write a brief report of your findings. Include diagrams where appropriate. Begin your search at www.pearsoned.ca/school/physicssource.

13. Italian physicist Enrico Fermi gave the name "neutrino" to the elusive particle that scientists were at first unable to detect. Research Fermi's contributions to physics. Write a brief report of your findings. Begin your search at www.pearsoned.ca/school/physicssource.

 e TEST

To check your understanding of two-dimensional collisions, follow the eTest links at www.pearsoned.ca/school/physicssource.

Key Terms and Concepts

momentum	collision	law of conservation	elastic collision
impulse	system	of momentum	inelastic collision
			centre of mass

Key Equations

Momentum: $\vec{p} = m\vec{v}$

Impulse: $\vec{F}_{net}\Delta t = \Delta\vec{p}$ or $\vec{F}_{net}\Delta t = m\Delta\vec{v}$

$\vec{F}_{net_{ave}}\Delta t = \Delta\vec{p}$ or $\vec{F}_{net_{ave}}\Delta t = m\Delta\vec{v}$

Conservation of momentum: $\vec{p}_{sys_i} = \vec{p}_{sys_f}$

Elastic collisions: $E_{k_i} = E_{k_f}$

Conceptual Overview

The concept map below summarizes many of the concepts and equations in this chapter.
Copy and complete the map to have a full summary of the chapter.

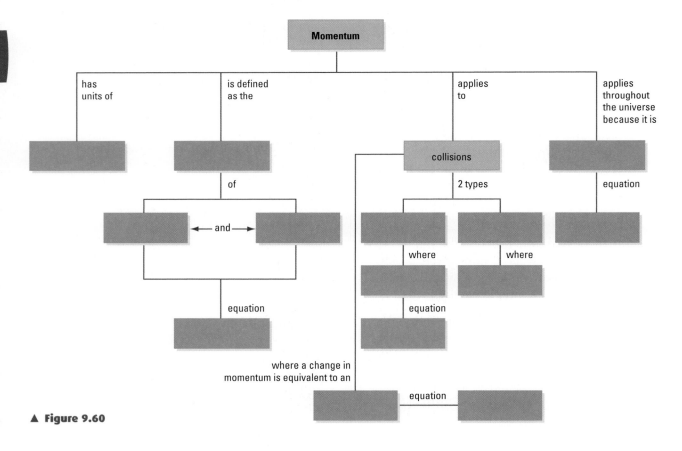

▲ **Figure 9.60**

An Impulsive Water Balloon

Scenario

Imagine you are part of a creative engineering design team commissioned to design and build an amusement ride that will make the West Edmonton Mall 14-storey "Space Shot" obsolete. The ride must allow patrons to experience the thrill of free fall in a safe environment. Accelerations have to remain within appropriate limits during a required change from vertical to horizontal motion, and as the people are brought to rest. A model must be constructed for sales demonstrations using a water balloon that experiences a minimum 2.4-m drop, where the impulse changes the magnitude and direction of the momentum while maintaining the integrity of the balloon. The water balloon must begin with a vertical drop equivalent to eight storeys. Then for the equivalent height of six storeys, the balloon must change direction and come to a stop horizontally.

Planning

Form a design team of three to five members. Plan and assign roles so that each team member has at least one major task. Roles may include researcher, engineer to perform mathematical calculations, creative designer, construction engineer, materials acquisition officer, and writer, among others. One person may need to perform several roles in turn. Ensure that all team members help along the way. Prepare a time schedule for each task, and for group planning and reporting sessions.

Materials

- small balloon filled with water
- plastic zip-closing bag to contain the water balloon
- cardboard and/or wooden frame for apparatus
- vehicle or container for balloon
- cushioning material
- braking device
- art materials

> ⚠ **CAUTION: Test your design in an appropriate area. Make sure no one is in the way during the drop.**

Assessing Results
After completing the project, assess its success based on a rubric designed in class* that considers
- research strategies
- experiment and construction techniques
- clarity and thoroughness of the written report
- effectiveness of the team's presentation
- quality and fairness of the teamwork

Procedure

1. Research the range of acceptable accelerations that most people can tolerate.

2. Calculate the maximum speed obtained when an object is dropped from an eight-storey building (equivalent to 24.6 m).

3. Calculate the impulse necessary to change the direction of motion of a 75.0-kg person from vertical to horizontal in the remaining height of six storeys (equivalent to 18.4 m). The person must come to a stop at the end. Assume that the motion follows the arc of a circle.

4. Determine the time required so that the change in the direction of motion and stopping the person meets the maximum acceptable acceleration in step 1.

5. Include your calculations in a report that shows your design and method of changing the motion.

6. Build a working model and test it. Make modifications as necessary to keep the water balloon intact for a fall. Present the project to your teacher and the class.

Thinking Further

1. Explain why eight storeys was used in the calculation in step 2, instead of 14 storeys.

2. What other amusement rides has your team thought of while working on this project? What would make each of these rides thrilling and appealing?

3. In what ways could your ideas have a practical use, such as getting people off a high oil derrick or out of a high-rise building quickly and safely?

4. What conditions would cause a person to be an unacceptable candidate for your ride? Write out a list of rules or requirements that would need to be posted.

*Note: Your instructor will assess the project using a similar assessment rubric.

Unit Concepts and Skills: Quick Reference

Concepts	Summary	Resources and Skill Building
CHAPTER 9	**The momentum of an isolated system of interacting objects is conserved.**	
	9.1 Momentum Is Mass Times Velocity	
Momentum	Momentum is the product of the mass of an object and its velocity. Momentum is a vector quantity measured in kilogram-metres per second (kg·m/s).	Examples 9.1 & 9.2
Newton's second law	Newton's second law states that the net force on an object is equal to the rate of change of its momentum.	
	9.2 Impulse Is Equivalent to a Change in Momentum	
Impulse	The impulse provided to an object is defined as the product of the net force (or average net force if $\vec{F}_{net} \neq$ constant) acting on the object during an interaction and the interaction time. Impulse is equivalent to the change in momentum of the object.	9-2 QuickLab
Effects of varying the net force and time interval for a given impulse	The magnitude of the net force during an interaction and the interaction time determine whether or not injuries or damage to an object occurs.	Figures 9.12 & 9.13 9-3 Design a Lab Example 9.3
Net force-time graph	Impulse can be determined by calculating the area under a net force-time graph.	Example 9.4
	9.3 Collisions in One Dimension	
Conservation of momentum in one dimension	Momentum is conserved when objects in an isolated system interact in one dimension. A system is the group of objects that interact with each other, and it is isolated if no external net force acts on these objects.	9-4 QuickLab 9-5 Inquiry Lab Examples 9.5–9.8, 9.10
Elastic collisions	Elastic collisions are collisions in which a system of objects has the same initial and final kinetic energy. So both the momentum and kinetic energy of the system are conserved.	Example 9.9
Inelastic collisions	Inelastic collisions are collisions in which a system of objects has different initial and final kinetic energy values.	Example 9.11
	9.4 Collisions in Two Dimensions	
Conservation of momentum in two dimensions	Momentum is conserved when objects in an isolated system interact in two dimensions. An isolated system has no external net force acting on it.	9-6 Inquiry Lab Examples 9.12–9.14
Elastic and inelastic collisions	Elastic collisions in two dimensions satisfy the same conditions as one-dimensional elastic collisions, that is, $E_{k_i} = E_{k_f}$.	Example 9.15

Vocabulary

1. Using your own words, define these terms, concepts, principles, or laws.
   momentum
   impulse
   one-dimensional collisions
   conservation of momentum
   conservation of energy
   elastic collisions
   inelastic collisions
   two-dimensional collisions
   centre of mass

Knowledge

CHAPTER 9

2. Compare and contrast momentum and impulse.

3. Explain the relationship between the units in which momentum and impulse are measured.

4. A student calculated the answer to a problem and got 40 kg·m/s [W]. Which quantities could the student have calculated?

5. In your own words, restate Newton's second law in terms of momentum.

6. What difference does it make that momentum is a vector quantity rather than a scalar quantity?

7. Compare and contrast a net force and an average net force acting on an object during an interaction.

8. Statistics show that less massive vehicles tend to have fewer accidents than more massive vehicles. However, the survival rate for accidents in more massive vehicles is much greater than for less massive ones. How could momentum be used to explain these findings?

9. Using the concept of impulse, explain how the shocks on a high-end mountain bike reduce the chance of strain injuries to the rider.

10. State the quantities, including units, you would need to measure to determine the momentum of an object.

11. State the quantities that are conserved in one- and two-dimensional collisions. Give an example of each type of collision.

12. How do internal forces affect the momentum of a system?

13. What instructions would you give a young gymnast so that she avoids injury when landing on a hard surface?

14. Will the magnitude of the momentum of an object always increase if a net force acts on it? Explain, using an example.

15. What quantity do you get when $\Delta \vec{p}$ is divided by mass?

16. For a given impulse, what is the effect of
    (a) increasing the time interval?
    (b) decreasing the net force during interaction?

17. For each situation, explain how you would effectively provide the required impulse.
    - to catch a water balloon tossed from some distance
    - to design a hiking boot for back-country hiking on rough ground
    - to shoot an arrow with maximum velocity using a bow
    - for an athlete to win the gold medal in the javelin event with the longest throw
    - for a car to accelerate on an icy road

18. Why does a hunter always press the butt of a shotgun tight against the shoulder before firing?

19. Describe a method to find the components of a momentum vector.

20. Explain why the conservation of momentum and the conservation of energy are universal laws.

21. Why does the law of conservation of momentum require an isolated system?

22. Suppose a problem involves a two-dimensional collision between two objects, and the initial momentum of one object is unknown. Explain how to solve this problem using
    (a) a vector addition diagram drawn to scale
    (b) vector components

23. Explain, in terms of momentum, why a rocket does not need an atmosphere to push against when it accelerates.

24. If a firecracker explodes into two fragments of unequal mass, which fragment will have the greater speed? Why?

25. When applying the conservation of momentum to a situation, why is it advisable to find the velocities of all objects in the system immediately after collision, instead of several seconds later?

26. Which physics quantities are conserved in a collision?

27. A curling stone hits another stationary stone off centre. Draw possible momentum vectors for each stone immediately before and immediately after collision, showing both the magnitude and direction of each vector.

28. A Superball™ of rubber-like plastic hits a wall perpendicularly and rebounds elastically. Explain how momentum is conserved.

29. What two subatomic particles were discovered using the conservation of momentum and the conservation of energy?

30. Explain how an inelastic collision does not violate the law of conservation of energy.

31. If a system is made up of only one object, show how the law of conservation of momentum can be used to derive Newton's first law.

32. A Calgary company, Cerpro, is a world leader in ceramic armour plating for military protection. The ceramic structure of the plate transmits the kinetic energy of an armour-piercing bullet throughout the plate, reducing its penetrating power. Explain if this type of collision is elastic or inelastic.

33. A compact car and a heavy van travelling at approximately the same speed perpendicular to each other collide and stick together. Which vehicle will experience the greatest change in its direction of motion just after impact? Why?

34. Is it possible for the conservation of momentum to be valid if two objects move faster just before, than just after, collision? Explain, using an example.

35. Fighter pilots have reported that immediately after a burst of gunfire from their jet fighter, the speed of their aircraft decreased by 50–65 km/h. Explain the reason for this change in motion.

36. A cannon ball explodes into three fragments. One fragment goes north and another fragment goes east. Draw the approximate direction of the third fragment. What scientific law did you use to arrive at your answer?

Applications

37. Calculate the momentum of a 1600-kg car travelling north at 8.5 m/s.

38. Draw a momentum vector diagram to represent a 575-g basketball flying at 12.4 m/s [26.0° S of E].

39. Calculate the momentum of a 1250-kg car travelling south at 14.8 m/s.

40. A bowling ball has a momentum of 28 kg·m/s [E]. If its speed is 4.5 m/s, what is the mass of the ball?

41. A curling stone has a momentum of 32 kg·m/s [W]. What would be the momentum if the mass of the stone decreased by a factor of $\frac{7}{8}$ and its speed increased by a factor of $\frac{4}{3}$?

42. A soccer ball has a momentum of 2.8 kg·m/s [W]. What would be the momentum if its mass decreased by a factor of $\frac{3}{4}$ and its speed increased by a factor of $\frac{9}{8}$?

43. The graph below shows the magnitude of the net force as a function of interaction time for a volleyball being blocked. The velocity of the ball changes from 18 m/s [N] to 11 m/s [S].

    (a) Using the graph, calculate the impulse on the volleyball.

    (b) What is the mass of the ball?

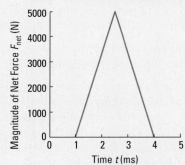

Magnitude of Net Force vs. Interaction Time for a Volleyball Block

44. (a) Calculate the impulse on a soccer ball if a player heads the ball with an average net force of 120 N [210°] for 0.0252 s.

    (b) If the mass of the soccer ball is 0.44 kg, calculate the change in velocity of the ball.

45. At a buffalo jump, a 900-kg bison is running at 6.0 m/s toward the drop-off ahead when it senses danger. What horizontal force must the bison exert to stop itself in 2.0 s?

46. (a) What is the minimum impulse needed to give a 275-kg motorcycle and rider a velocity of 20.0 m/s [W] if the motorcycle is initially at rest?

(b) If the wheels exert an average force of 710 N [E] to the road, what is the minimum time needed to reach a velocity of 20.0 m/s [W]?

(c) Explain how the force directed east causes the motorcycle to accelerate westward.

(d) Why is it necessary to specify a minimum impulse and a minimum time?

47. A 1.15-kg peregrine falcon flying at 15.4 m/s [W] captures a 0.423-kg pigeon flying at 4.68 m/s [S]. What will be the velocity of their centre of mass immediately after the interaction?

48. A 275-kg snowmobile exerts a net force of magnitude 508 N on the snow and a 75-kg driver for 15.0 s.

(a) What impulse will the snow provide to the snowmobile and driver?

(b) Calculate the change in velocity of the snowmobile.

49. The graph below shows the magnitude of the net force as a function of time for a 275-g volleyball being spiked. Assume the ball is motionless the instant before it is struck.

(a) Using the graph, calculate the magnitude of the impulse on the volleyball.

(b) What is the speed of the ball when it leaves the player's hand?

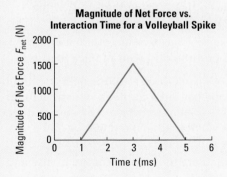

Magnitude of Net Force vs. Interaction Time for a Volleyball Spike

50. A Centaur rocket engine expels 520 kg of exhaust gas at 5.0×10^4 m/s in 0.40 s. What net force on the rocket will that generate?

51. An elevator with passengers has a total mass of 1700 kg. What is the net force on the cable needed to give the elevator a velocity of 4.5 m/s [up] in 8.8 s if it is starting from rest?

52. A 0.146-kg baseball pitched at 40 m/s is hit back toward the pitcher at a speed of 45 m/s.

(a) What is the impulse provided to the ball?

(b) The bat is in contact with the ball for 8.0 ms. What is the average net force that the bat exerts on the ball?

53. An ice dancer and her 80-kg partner are both gliding at 2.5 m/s [225°]. They push apart, giving the 45-kg dancer a velocity of 3.2 m/s [225°]. What will be the velocity of her partner immediately after the interaction?

54. Two students at a barbecue party put on inflatable Sumo-wrestling outfits and take a run at each other. The 87.0-kg student (A) runs at 1.21 m/s [N] and the 73.9-kg student (B) runs at 1.51 m/s [S]. The students are knocked off their feet by the collision. Immediately after impact, student B rebounds at 1.43 m/s [N].

(a) If the collision is completely elastic, calculate the velocity of student A immediately after impact using energy considerations.

(b) How different would your answer be if only conservation of momentum were used? Calculate to check.

(c) How valid is your answer to part (a)?

55. A cannon mounted on wheels has a mass of 1380 kg. It shoots a 5.45-kg projectile at 190 m/s [forward]. What will be the velocity of the cannon immediately after firing the projectile?

56. A 3650-kg space probe travelling at 1272 m/s [0°] has a directional thruster rocket exerting a force of 1.80×10^4 N [90.0°] for 15.6 s. What will be the newly adjusted velocity of the probe?

57. In a movie stunt, a 1.60-kg pistol is struck by a 15-g bullet travelling at 280 m/s [50.0°]. If the bullet moves at 130 m/s [280°] after the interaction, what will be the velocity of the pistol? Assume that no external force acts on the pistol.

58. A 52.5-kg snowboarder, travelling at 1.24 m/s [N] at the end of her run, jumps and kicks off her 4.06-kg snowboard. The snowboard leaves her at 2.63 m/s [62.5° W of N]. What is her velocity just after she kicks off the snowboard?

59. A 1.26-kg brown bocce ball travelling at 1.8 m/s [N] collides with a stationary 0.145-kg white ball, driving it off at 0.485 m/s [84.0° W of N].

(a) What will be the velocity of the brown ball immediately after impact? Ignore friction and rotational effects.

(b) Determine if the collision is elastic.

60. Two people with a combined mass of 128 kg are sliding downhill on a 2.0-kg toboggan at 1.9 m/s. A third person of mass 60 kg inadvertently stands in front and upon impact is swept along with the toboggan. If all three people remain on the toboggan after impact, what will be its velocity after impact?

61. An aerosol paint can is accidentally put in a fire pit. After the fire is lit, the can is heated and explodes into two fragments. A 0.0958-kg fragment (A) flies off at 8.46 m/s [E]. The other fragment (B) has a mass of 0.0627 kg. The 0.0562-kg of gas inside bursts out at 9.76 m/s [N]. What will be the velocity of fragment B immediately after the explosion? Assume that no mass is lost during the explosion, and that the motion of the fragments lies in a plane.

62. A 0.185-kg golf club head travelling horizontally at 28.5 m/s hits a 0.046-kg golf ball, driving it straight off at 45.7 m/s.
   (a) Suppose the golfer does not exert an external force on the golf club after initial contact with the ball. If the collision between the golf club and the ball is elastic, what will be the speed of the club head immediately after impact?
   (b) Show that the law of conservation of momentum is valid in this interaction.

63. A student on a skateboard is travelling at 4.84 m/s [0°], carrying a 0.600-kg basketball. The combined mass of the student and skateboard is 50.2 kg. He throws the basketball to a friend at a velocity of 14.2 m/s [270°]. What is the resulting velocity of the centre of mass of the student-skateboard combination immediately after the throw? Ignore frictional effects.

64. An oxygen molecule of mass 5.316×10^{-23} kg with a velocity of 43.0 m/s [0°] collides head-on with a 7.311×10^{-23}-kg carbon dioxide molecule with initial velocity of 36.0 m/s [180°]. After collision, the oxygen molecule has a velocity of 24.9 m/s [180°].
   (a) Calculate the velocity of the carbon dioxide molecule immediately after collision.
   (b) Determine if the collision is elastic using calculations.

65. An isolated stationary neutron is transformed into a 9.11×10^{-31}-kg electron travelling at 4.35×10^5 m/s [E] and a 1.67×10^{-27}-kg proton travelling at 14.8 m/s [E]. What is the momentum of the neutrino that is released?

66. An 8.95-kg bowling ball moving at 3.62 m/s [N] hits a 0.856-kg bowling pin, sending it off at 3.50 m/s [58.6° E of N].
   (a) What will be the velocity of the bowling ball immediately after collision?
   (b) Determine if the collision is elastic.

67. A wooden crate sitting in the back of a pickup truck travelling at 50.4 km/h [S] has a momentum of magnitude 560 kg·m/s.
   (a) What is the mass of the crate?
   (b) What impulse would the driver have to apply with the brakes to stop the vehicle in 5.25 s at an amber traffic light?
   (c) If the coefficient of friction between the crate and the truck bed is 0.30, will the crate slide forward as the truck stops? Justify your answer with calculations.

68. A firecracker bursts into three fragments. An 8.5-g fragment (A) flies away at 25 m/s [S]. A 5.6-g fragment (B) goes east at 12 m/s. Calculate the velocity of the 6.7-g fragment (C). Assume that no mass is lost during the explosion, and that the motion of the fragments lies in a plane.

69. A spherical molecule of 60 carbon atoms arranged like a geodesic dome is called a buckyball and has a mass of 1.2×10^{-21} kg. One buckyball (A) travelling at 9.2 m/s [E] collides with another buckyball (B) initially moving at 8.5 m/s [N] in a laboratory container. Buckyball A bounces away at a velocity of 3.3 m/s [45.0° W of N].
   (a) What is the speed of buckyball B after the collision using the fact that the collision is elastic?
   (b) Use the conservation of momentum to find the direction of buckyball B.

70. A moose carcass on a sled is being pulled by a tow rope behind a hunter's snowmobile on a horizontal snowy surface. The sled and moose have a combined mass of 650 kg and a momentum of 3.87×10^3 kg·m/s [E].
   (a) Calculate the velocity of the moose and sled.
   (b) The magnitude of the force of friction between the sled and the snow is 1400 N. As the hunter uniformly slows the snowmobile, what minimum length of time is needed for him to stop and keep the sled from running into the snowmobile (i.e., keep the same distance between the sled and the snowmobile)?

71. A 940-kg car is travelling at 15 m/s [W] when it is struck by a 1680-kg van moving at 20 m/s [50.0° N of E]. If both vehicles join together after impact, what will be the velocity of their centre of mass immediately after impact?

72. A 0.450-kg soccer ball is kicked parallel to the floor at 3.24 m/s [E]. It strikes a basketball sitting on a bench, driving it at 2.177 m/s [30.0° S of E]. The soccer ball goes off at 1.62 m/s [60.0° N of E]. What is the mass of the basketball?

73. A cue ball moving at 2.00 m/s [0°] hits a stationary three-ball, sending it away at 1.58 m/s [36.0°]. The cue ball and three-ball each have a mass of 0.160 kg. Calculate the velocity of the cue ball immediately after collision. Ignore friction and rotational effects.

74. A hunter claims to have shot a charging bear through the heart and "dropped him in his tracks." To immediately stop the bear, the momentum of the bullet would have to be as great as the momentum of the charging bear. Suppose the hunter was shooting one of the largest hunting rifles ever sold, a 0.50 caliber Sharps rifle, which delivers a 2.27×10^{-2} kg bullet at 376 m/s. Evaluate the hunter's claim by calculating the velocity of a 250-kg bear after impact if he was initially moving directly toward the hunter at a slow 0.675 m/s [S].

75. An object explodes into three fragments (A, B, and C) of equal mass. What will be the approximate direction of fragment C if
    (a) both fragments A and B move north?
    (b) fragment A moves east and fragment B moves south?
    (c) fragment A moves [15.0°] and fragment B moves [121°]?

Extensions

76. Research the physics principles behind the design of a Pelton wheel. Explain why it is more efficient than a standard water wheel. Begin your search at www.pearsoned.ca/school/physicssource.

77. A fireworks bundle is moving upward at 2.80 m/s when it bursts into three fragments. A 0.210-kg fragment (A) moves at 4.52 m/s [E]. A 0.195-kg fragment (B) flies at 4.63 m/s [N]. What will be the velocity of the third fragment (C) immediately after the explosion if its mass is 0.205 kg? Assume that no mass is lost during the explosion.

78. Research the types of rockets being used in NASA's current launchings. What is their thrust and time of firing? If possible, obtain data to calculate the impulse on the rocket. How much does the mass of a rocket change over time as it accelerates?

79. Two billiard balls collide off centre and move at right angles to each other after collision. In what directions did the impulsive forces involved in the collision act? Include a diagram in your answer.

80. A 2200-kg car travelling west is struck by a 2500-kg truck travelling north. The vehicles stick together upon impact and skid for 20 m [48.0° N of W]. The coefficient of friction for the tires on the road surface is 0.78. Both drivers claim to have been travelling at 90 km/h before the crash. Determine the truth of their statements.

81. Research the developments in running shoes that help prevent injuries. Interview running consultants, and consult sales literature and the Internet. How does overpronation or underpronation affect your body's ability to soften the road shock on your knees and other joints? Write a brief report of your findings. Begin your search at www.pearsoned.ca/school/physicssource.

82. A 3.5-kg block of wood is at rest on a 1.75-m high fencepost. When a 12-g bullet is fired horizontally into the block, the block topples off the post and lands 1.25 m away. What was the speed of the bullet immediately before collision?

Consolidate Your Understanding

83. Write a paragraph describing the differences between momentum and impulse. Include an example for each concept.

84. Write a paragraph describing how momentum and energy concepts can be used to analyze the motion of colliding objects. Include two examples: One is a one-dimensional collision and the other is a two-dimensional collision. Include appropriate diagrams.

Think About It

Review your answers to the Think About It questions on page 447. How would you answer each question now?

 e **TEST**

To check your understanding of momentum and impulse, follow the eTest links at www.pearsoned.ca/school/physicssource.

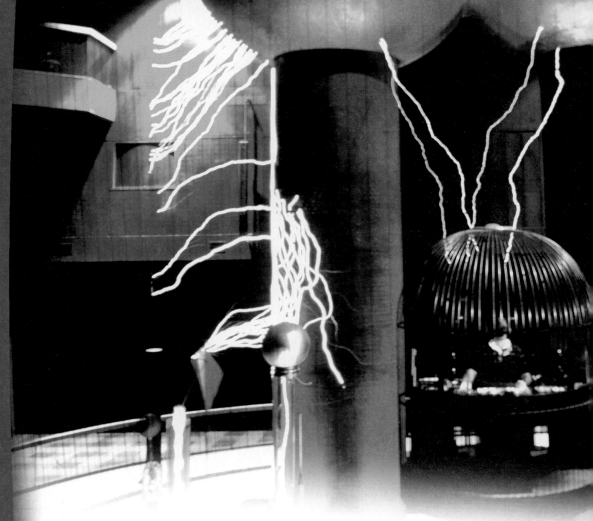

UNIT
VI

Forces and Fields

On huge metal domes, giant electrostatic charge generators can create voltages of 5 000 000 V, compared with 110 V in most of your household circuits. How are electrostatic charges produced? What is voltage? What happens when electric charges interact?

*e*WEB

The person in this photo is standing inside a Faraday cage. To find out how the Faraday cage protects her from the huge electrical discharges, follow the links at www.pearsoned.ca/school/physicssource.

Unit at a Glance

Unit Themes and Emphases

- Energy and Matter
- Nature of Science
- Scientific Inquiry

Focussing Questions

While studying this unit, you will investigate how the science of electricity, magnetism, and electromagnetism evolved and its corresponding effect on technology. As you work through this unit, consider these questions.

- How is the value of the elementary charge determined?
- What is the relationship between electricity and magnetism?
- How does magnetism assist in the understanding of fundamental particles?

Unit Project

Building a Model of a Direct Current Generator

- By the time you complete this unit, you will have the knowledge and skills to build a model of a direct current generator. For this task, you will research wind power and design and build a model of an electric generator that uses wind energy.

Physics laws can explain the behaviour of electric charges.

▲ **Figure 10.1** A thunderbird on a totem pole in Vancouver

A bolt of lightning flashing across dark cloudy skies, followed a few moments later by the deafening sound of thunder, is still one of the most awe-inspiring physical events unleashed by nature. So powerful is this display that many civilizations reasoned these events must be the actions of gods. To the Romans, lightning was the sign that Jove, the king of the gods, was angry at his enemies. In some First Nations traditions, lightning flashes from the eyes of the enormous thunderbird, while thunder booms from the flapping of its huge wings (Figure 10.1).

What is the cause of lightning? Why is it so dangerous?

In this chapter, you will learn how relating lightning to simpler phenomena, such as the sparking observed as you stroke a cat, initially revealed the electrical nature of matter. Further studies of the nature of electric charges and the electrical interactions between them will enable you to understand laws that describe their behaviour. Finally, you will investigate the force acting on electric charges by studying the variables that determine this force and the law that describes how to calculate such forces.

Charging Objects Using a Van de Graaff Generator

Problem

What can demonstrations on the Van de Graaff generator reveal about the behaviour and interactions of electric charges?

Materials and Equipment

Van de Graaff generator and grounding rod
small piece of animal fur (approximately 15 cm x 15 cm)
5 aluminium pie plates
small foam-plastic cup with confetti
soap bubble dispenser and soap

> ⚠ **CAUTION! Follow your teacher's instructions to avoid getting an electric shock.**

Procedure

1 Copy Table 10.1 into your notebook. Make the table the full width of your page so you have room to write in your observations and explanations.

▼ **Table 10.1** Observations and Explanations from Using a Van de Graaff Generator

Demonstration	Observation	Explanation
Animal Fur		
Aluminium Pie Plates		
Foam-plastic Cup and Confetti		
Stream of Soap Bubbles		

2 Watch or perform each of the demonstrations in steps 3 to 9.

3 Place a piece of animal fur, with the fur side up, on the top of the charging sphere of the Van de Graaff generator.

4 Turn on the generator and let it run.

5 Record your observations in Table 10.1, making sure that your description is precise.

6 Ground the sphere with the grounding rod, and turn off the generator.

7 Repeat steps 3 to 6, replacing the animal fur with the aluminium pie plates (stacked upside down), and then the foam-plastic cup with confetti.

8 Turn on the Van de Graaff generator and let it run.

9 Dip the soap bubble dispenser into the soap and blow a stream of bubbles toward the charging sphere of the Van de Graaff generator.

10 Record your detailed observations in Table 10.1.

11 Ground the sphere with the grounding rod, and turn off the generator.

Question

1. Using your knowledge of electricity, provide a possible explanation of the events that occurred during each demonstration.

Think About It

1. How does the sphere of the Van de Graaff generator become charged?

2. Describe a situation during the demonstrations where the forces of interaction between the sphere of the generator and the various objects were:
   (a) attractive
   (b) repulsive

3. How does touching the sphere with a grounding rod ground the sphere?

Discuss your answers in a small group and record them for later reference. As you complete each section of this chapter, review your answers to these questions. Note any changes to your ideas.

10.1 Electrical Interactions

Your world runs on electricity. The music you listen to, the movies you watch, the video games you play—all require electricity to run. Today, electricity is so familiar that you probably don't even think about it when you turn on a light, pop a piece of bread into the toaster, or switch off the TV.

Try to imagine a time before electricity was even named. People had noticed interesting effects in certain situations that seemed almost magical. The Greek philosopher Thales (624–546 BCE) recorded that when he rubbed amber (a hard fossilized form of tree resin), it could attract small pieces of straw or thread. This effect was called "electricity," after the Greek word for amber, "elektron."

The ancient Greeks observed two important properties of electricity:

- Charged objects could either attract or repel each other. These two types of interactions suggested that there must be two different types of charge.
- Repulsion occurred when two similarly charged objects were placed near each other, and attraction occurred when two oppositely charged objects were placed near each other.

These observations can be summarized as the law of charges:

Like charges repel and unlike charges attract.

MINDS ON   Electrical Attraction

Rub an ebonite rod with fur and hold the rod close to a fine stream of water from a faucet. Then rub a glass rod with silk and hold this rod close to a fine stream of water.

Observe what happens in each case. Using your knowledge of charging objects, explain why the ebonite rod or the glass rod affects the water.

There was little progress in understanding the nature of electricity until the 1600s, when the English scientist William Gilbert (1544–1603) performed extensive investigations. In *De Magnete,* his book on magnetism, Gilbert compared the effects of electricity and magnetism. He concluded that:

1. Objects only exhibit electrical effects when recently rubbed; magnetic objects do not need to be rubbed.

2. Electrified objects can attract small pieces of many types of objects; magnetic objects can attract only a few types of objects.

3. Electrified objects attract objects toward one central region; magnetic objects appear to have two poles.

Although Gilbert was able to describe certain effects of electricity, he still did not know the origins of electric charges.

In the 1700s, the American scientist and inventor Benjamin Franklin (1706–1790) attempted to prove that lightning in the sky was the same electricity as the spark observed when you reach for a metal door handle after shuffling across a carpet. He performed his famous kite experiment to explore whether lightning was a form of electricity (Figure 10.2). Luckily, he did not get killed, and he succeeded in drawing electricity from the clouds. He observed that lightning behaves the same way that electricity produced in the laboratory does. Through further investigations, he identified and named the two different types of electric charges as positive and negative charges.

It soon became apparent that electricity is in all substances. This idea caught the imagination of many different people. Scientists studied electricity's intriguing effects (Figure 10.3), and entrepreneurs exploited it. Magicians and carnivals featured the "mysterious" effects of electricity.

▲ **Figure 10.2** This figure is an artist's representation of Benjamin Franklin's famous kite experiment.

▲ **Figure 10.3** Boys were sometimes used in experiments such as this one in the early 1700s. The boy was suspended over the floor and electrostatically charged. His positive electric charge would attract pieces of paper.

Studies to determine the nature of electricity continued. These studies were the beginning of the science of **electrostatics**, which is the study of electric charges at rest. It involves electric charges, the forces acting on them, and their behaviour in substances.

electrostatics: the study of electric charges at rest

The Modern Theory of Electrostatics

Today's theory of electrostatics and the nature of electric charges is based on the models of the atom that Ernest Rutherford (1871–1937) and Niels Bohr (1885–1962) proposed in the early 1900s. In their theories, an atom is composed of two types of charges: positively charged protons in a nucleus surrounded by negatively charged electrons. In nature, atoms have equal numbers of electrons and protons so that each atom is electrically neutral.

Just as some materials are good thermal conductors or insulators, there are also good conductors and insulators of electric charges. Electrical conductivity depends on how tightly the electrons are bound to the nucleus of the atom. Some materials have electrons that are tightly bound to the nucleus and are not free to travel within the substance. These materials are called **insulators**. Materials that have electrons in the outermost regions of the atom that are free to travel are called **conductors**.

insulator: material in which the electrons are tightly bound to the nucleus and are not free to move within the substance

conductor: material in which electrons in the outermost regions of the atom are free to move

Figure 10.4 shows some examples of good conductors and insulators. Note that metals are usually good conductors. It is also interesting to note that a good conductor, such as silver, can have a conductivity 10^{23} times greater than that of a good insulator, such as rubber.

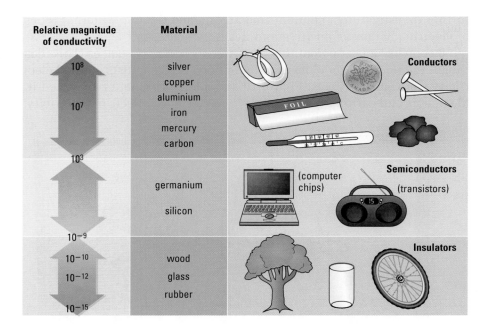

► **Figure 10.4** Relative electrical conductivity of some materials

Semiconductors

Materials that lie in the middle, between good conductors and good insulators, are called **semiconductors**. Because of their nature, they are good conductors in certain situations, and good insulators in other situations. Selenium, for example, is an insulator in the dark, but in the presence of light, it becomes a good conductor. Because of this property, selenium is very useful in the operation of photocopiers (Figure 10.5).

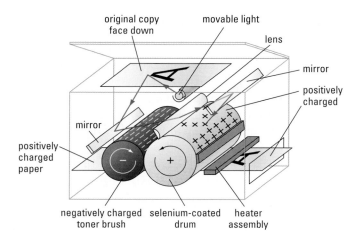

▲ **Figure 10.5** Photocopiers use the semiconductor selenium in the copying process.

The selenium-coated drum in the photocopier is initially given a positive charge and kept in the dark to retain the charge. When a flash of light shines on a document to be copied, an image of the document is transferred to the drum. Where the document is light-coloured, the selenium is illuminated, causing it to be conductive. The positive charge is neutralized, leaving the selenium uncharged at these points. The page remains light-coloured or white. Where the document is dark-coloured, the selenium remains non-conductive, and the positive charge remains. Negatively charged "toner" powder is sprinkled on the drum and attaches to the positively charged portions of the drum. When a sheet of paper is passed over the drum, the toner transfers to the paper and an image of the document is created. This toner image is then fused on the paper with heat, and the copying process is complete.

Silicon and germanium are also semiconductors. They become conductors when atoms such as gallium or arsenic are added to them. This process is called "doping" with impurities. The field of solid-state electronics, which includes components such as transistors, diodes, and silicon chips, is based on this type of semiconductor.

Superconductors

Recall from earlier science studies that resistance is a measure of how difficult it is for electrons to flow through a material. Materials with a low electrical resistance are better conductors because very little energy is lost to heat in the conduction of electricity.

Early attempts at conducting electricity efficiently used conducting materials with low electrical resistance, such as silver, copper, and gold. Researchers soon discovered that the electrical resistance of any material tends to decrease as its temperature decreases. Could the temperature of a material be lowered to the point that it loses all its resistive nature, creating the ideal conductor? This property of materials would have an enormous range of applications. Once a current is established in such a conductor, it should persist indefinitely with no energy loss.

In the early 20th century, a class of materials called **superconductors** was developed. These conductors have no measurable resistance at very low temperatures. The Dutch physicist Heike Kammerlingh Onnes (1853–1926) discovered this effect in 1911 when he observed that solid mercury lost its electrical resistance when cooled to a temperature of $-269\ °C$. Although this discovery was significant, the usefulness of superconductors was limited because of the extremely low temperatures necessary for their operation.

It was not until 1986 that materials were developed that were superconductors at much higher temperatures. These materials are ceramic alloys of rare earth elements, such as lanthanum and yttrium. As an example, one such alloy was made by grinding yttrium, barium, and copper oxide into a mixture and heating the mixture to form the alloy $YBa_2Cu_3O_7$. This substance became a superconductor at $-216\ °C$. In 1987, another alloy was developed that displayed superconductivity at $-175\ °C$. More recent discoveries have reported copper oxide alloys that are superconductors at temperatures as high as $-123\ °C$. The ultimate goal is to develop superconductors that operate at room temperature, thus creating a whole new era of useful applications in technology.

e **WEB**

Find out what research is being done on super-conductors today. How soon will you be seeing superconductors in use around the house? Write a brief summary of what you discover. To learn more about superconductors, follow the links at www.pearsoned.ca/school/physicssource.

Charging Objects

Question

How can objects become electrically charged?

Materials and Equipment

2 white plastic polyethylene strips (or ebonite rods)
fur (approximately 15 cm x 15 cm)
2 clear plastic acetate strips (or glass rods)
silk (approximately 15 cm x 15 cm)
electroscope
silk thread
2 retort stands

Procedure
Part A: Charging by Friction

1 Copy Table 10.2 into your notebook.

▼ **Table 10.2** Observations for Charging by Friction

	White Polyethylene Strip Rubbed with Fur	Clear Acetate Strip Rubbed with Silk
Hanging White Polyethylene Strip		
Hanging Clear Acetate Strip		

2 Hang a white polyethylene strip from one retort stand and a clear acetate strip from another retort stand.

3 While holding the hanging white polyethylene strip in the middle, rub both ends of it with the fur. While holding the hanging clear acetate strip in the middle, rub both ends of it with the silk.

4 Rub the other white polyethylene strip with the fur.

5 Carefully bring this second polyethylene strip close to one end of the hanging white polyethylene strip. Do not allow the two plastic strips to touch each other.

6 Carefully bring the second polyethylene strip close to one end of the hanging clear acetate strip. Do not allow the two plastic strips to touch each other.

7 Observe what happens in each situation and record your observations in Table 10.2.

8 Rub a clear acetate strip with the silk.

9 Carefully bring this strip close to the hanging clear acetate strip. Do not allow the two plastic strips to touch each other. Observe what happens and record your observations in Table 10.2.

10 Carefully bring this clear acetate strip close to one end of the hanging white polyethylene strip. Do not allow the two plastic strips to touch each other. Observe what happens and record your observations in Table 10.2.

Part B: Charging by Conduction

11 Copy Table 10.3 into your notebook.

▼ **Table 10.3** Observations for Charging by Conduction

	Electroscope Charged with the White Polyethylene Strip Rubbed with Fur	Electroscope Charged with the Clear Acetate Strip Rubbed with Silk
Hanging White Polyethylene Strip		
Hanging Clear Acetate Strip		

12 Rub the unattached white polyethylene strip with the fur. Touch this white strip to the knob of the electroscope.

13 Carefully bring the electroscope close to one end of the hanging white polyethylene strip. Observe what happens to the leaves in the electroscope. Record your observations in Table 10.3.

14 Now bring the electroscope near one end of the hanging clear acetate strip. Observe what happens to the leaves in the electroscope. Record your observations in Table 10.3.

15 Ground the electroscope by touching the knob of the electroscope with your finger.

16 Rub a clear acetate strip with the silk and touch the strip to the knob of the grounded electroscope.

17 Repeat steps 13 and 14.

Part C: Charging by Induction

18 Copy Table 10.4 into your notebook.

▼ **Table 10.4** Observations for Charging by Induction

	Grounded Electroscope
Hanging White Polyethylene Strip	
Hanging Clear Acetate Strip	

19 Bring a grounded electroscope near one end of the hanging white polyethylene strip. Observe what happens to the leaves of the electroscope, and record your observations in Table 10.4.

20 Bring a grounded electroscope near one end of the hanging clear acetate strip. Observe what happens to the leaves of the electroscope, and record your observations in Table 10.4.

Analysis

1. What effect did you observe when two similarly charged white polyethylene strips were held near each other or when two similarly charged clear acetate strips were held near each other?

2. What effect did you observe when a charged white polyethylene strip was held near an oppositely charged hanging clear acetate strip or when a charged clear acetate strip was held near an oppositely charged hanging white polyethylene strip?

3. Based on your observations, what charge did the electroscope acquire when it was touched by the charged white polyethylene strip? when it was touched by the charged acetate strip?

4. What evidence is there to show that the electroscope is acquiring a charge when it is held near a charged object?

5. From your observations in Table 10.2, what general rule can you formulate about attraction and repulsion of charged objects?

6. From your observations in Table 10.3, what general rule can you formulate about the charge received by an object when it is touched by another charged object?

7. From your observations in Table 10.4, what general rule can you formulate about the charge received by an object when it is held near another charged object?

8. Does the electroscope acquire a net electrical charge during the process of charging by induction? Justify your answer.

9. What evidence is there from this investigation to prove that there are two types of electrical charges?

10. From the investigation, is there any evidence to prove which type of charge was developed on the white polyethylene strip and on the clear acetate strip?

*e***LAB**

For a probeware activity, go to www.pearsoned.ca/school/physicssource.

Methods of Charging Objects

According to the modern theory of electrostatics, objects can become charged through a transfer of electrons. Electron transfer can occur in three ways: by friction, by conduction, and by induction.

Law of Conservation of Charge

During any charging procedure, it is important to keep in mind that new charges are not being created. The charges existing in materials are merely being rearranged between the materials, as the **law of conservation of charge** states:

> The net charge of an isolated system is conserved.

Net charge is the sum of all electric charge in the system. For example, if a system contains +3 C of charge and −5 C of charge, the system's net charge is -2 C. Suppose you have a system that initially consists of two electrically neutral objects, and there is a transfer of electrons from one object to the other. One object will lose electrons and become positively charged while the other object will gain these electrons and become equally negatively charged. However, the net charge of the system is still zero. Charges have not been created, they have only been rearranged.

Charging Objects by Friction

The most common method of charging objects is by rubbing or friction. You have probably had the unpleasant experience of receiving a shock when you touched a door handle after walking across a carpeted floor. Similarly, gently stroking a cat can result in the generation of small sparks, which are very uncomfortable for the cat.

Charging by this method involves separating electrons from the atoms in one object through rubbing or friction, and then transferring and depositing these electrons to the atoms of another object. The object whose atoms lose electrons then possesses positively charged ions. The object whose atoms gain electrons possesses negatively charged ions.

As shown in Figure 10.6, rubbing the ebonite rod with fur transferred some of the electrons in the fur to the rod. The fur becomes positively charged, and the rod becomes negatively charged.

▲ **Figure 10.6** (a) A neutral ebonite rod and a neutral piece of fur have equal amounts of negative and positive charge. When the fur is rubbed against the rod, a transfer of electrons occurs. (b) After rubbing, the ebonite has gained electrons and has a net negative charge. The fur has lost electrons and has a net positive charge.

Whether an object gains or loses electrons when rubbed by another object depends on how tightly the material holds onto its electrons. Figure 10.7 shows the electrostatic series, in which substances are listed according to how tightly they hold their electrons. Substances at the top have a strong hold on their electrons and do not lose electrons easily. Substances near the bottom have a weak hold on their electrons and lose them easily.

hold electrons tightly

sulfur
brass
copper
ebonite
paraffin wax
silk
lead
fur
wool
glass

hold electrons loosely

▲ **Figure 10.7** The electrostatic or triboelectric series

Concept Check

1. Using information from Figure 10.7, explain why ebonite acquires a stronger charge when rubbed with fur rather than silk.
2. What type of charge does ebonite acquire when rubbed with fur?

Charging objects by friction can also occur during collisions. The collisions of water vapour molecules in rain clouds, for example, cause the separation and transfer of electrons. The result is that vapour molecules become positively or negatively charged, eventually resulting in lightning. You will learn more about lightning later in this chapter. This process of charging objects was also observed by the *Voyageur* spacecraft on its mission to Saturn. Colliding particles in the rings of Saturn create electrical discharges within the rings, similar to lightning on Earth.

Charging Objects by Conduction

Objects can become charged by the transfer of electrons from a charged object to an uncharged object by simply touching the objects together (Figure 10.8). This process is called charging by **conduction**.

conduction: process of charging an object through the direct transfer of electrons when a charged object touches a neutral object

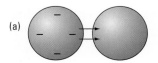 

▲ **Figure 10.8**   (a) During charging by conduction, electrons from a negatively charged metal conducting sphere transfer to a neutral metal conducting sphere, upon contact. (b) The neutral sphere gains electrons and is said to have been charged by conduction.

The quantity of charge that transfers from one object to another depends on the size and shape of the two objects. If both objects are roughly the same size and shape, the charge transferred will be such that both objects are approximately equally charged (Figure 10.9(a)). If one sphere is larger than the other, then the larger sphere will receive more of the charge (Figure 10.9(b)). In the final stage of charging a sphere, the excess charges move to become equidistant from each other because of the forces of repulsion between like charges. Charging by conduction is similar to charging by friction because there is contact between two objects. The process of charging by friction involves more area of contact between the two objects.

▲ **Figure 10.9**   Electrostatic repulsion of like charges forces excess charges within objects to redistribute so that the distances between charges are equal. (a) If two objects are the same size, the charges redistribute equally. (b) If the two objects are different sizes, the object with a larger surface area has more charges.

Once the charge has transferred to another object, it will either be distributed over the surface of the object, if the object is a conductor, or remain on the surface at the point of contact, if the object is an insulator.

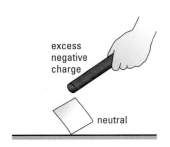

excess
negative
charge

neutral

▲ **Figure 10.10** A piece of paper appears to be attracted to a charged ebonite rod, even before they touch.

induction: movement of charge caused by an external charged object

Charging Objects by Induction

If you bring a negatively charged ebonite rod slowly toward a small piece of uncharged paper, the rod will attract the piece of paper, as shown in Figure 10.10. In fact, the piece of paper would begin to jiggle and move toward the rod even before the rod touches it. This reaction is a result of the forces acting on electrostatic charges. You know that electrostatic attraction can occur only between oppositely charged objects, but how can a charged object attract a neutral or uncharged object? And why is there never a force of repulsion between a charged object and a neutral object?

The answers to these questions are revealed in the third method of charging objects, which involves two processes: induction and charging by induction.

Induction

Induction is a process in which charges in a neutral object shift or migrate because of the presence of an external charged object. This temporary charge separation polarizes the neutral object. One side of the object becomes positively charged and the other side is equally negatively charged. Although the object now behaves as if it is charged, it is still electrically neutral. The charging object and the neutral object do not touch each other, so there is no actual transfer of charge.

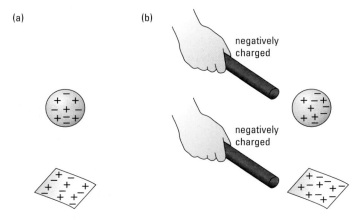

(a)   (b)

negatively charged

negatively charged

▲ **Figure 10.11** (a) A neutral metal sphere and a neutral piece of paper (b) The influence of the large negative charge of a rod causes *charge migration* within the conducting sphere, which polarizes the sphere. The influence of the rod causes *charge shift* within the atoms of the insulating paper. The atoms in the paper become polarized. Because of induction, the sides of the sphere and the atoms in the paper that are positively charged are closer to the negatively charged rod than their negatively charged sides are. The net result is attraction.

charge migration: movement of electrons in a neutral object where one side of the object becomes positive and the other side becomes negative

The process of induction varies slightly, depending on whether the charging object is approaching a substance that is an insulator or a conductor. Figure 10.11(a) depicts a neutral metal sphere (conductor) and a neutral piece of paper (insulator). Figure 10.11(b) shows a negatively charged rod approaching each neutral object. The electrons in the two neutral objects are repelled by the negative charge of an ebonite rod.

The metal sphere is a conductor, so the electrons can move easily through it to its other side. This process of **charge migration** causes the sphere to become polarized, where one side of the sphere is positive and the other side is negative.

Since the paper is an insulator, its electrons cannot move easily through it, so they just shift slightly relative to the nuclei. This process of **charge shift** causes the atoms to become polarized, where one side of an atom becomes positive and the other side becomes negative.

In both cases, the distances from the negatively charged rod to positive charges in the neutral object are less than the distances to negative charges in the object. Therefore, the attraction of the opposite charges is greater than repulsion of like charges, and the net force is attractive.

Charge separation by induction, which results in polarization of objects, explains electrostatic situations such as the initial attraction of a neutral piece of paper to a negatively charged rod without contact, as you saw in Figure 10.10.

Charging by Induction
In the situation shown in Figure 10.11, the electrons in the metal sphere and the paper return to their original positions when the negatively charged rod is removed. The objects lose their polarity and remain electrically neutral. For conductors, like the metal sphere, it is possible to maintain a residual charge by adding a grounding step. **Grounding** involves neutralizing an object by touching or connecting a wire from the object to the ground, as shown in Figure 10.12(a). The grounding path is then removed while the source charge is still present. The grounding step allows the conductor to maintain a charge (Figure 10.12(b)). The complete process of **charging by induction** includes grounding.

charge shift: movement of electrons in an atom where one side of an atom becomes positive and the other side becomes negative

grounding: the process of transferring charge to and from Earth

charging by induction: the process of charging an object by first polarizing it by induction and then retaining the charge by grounding

(a)

(b)

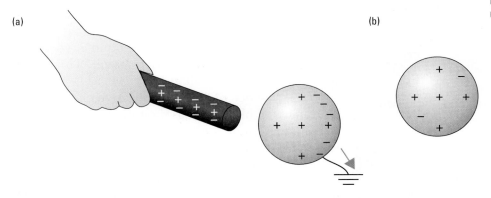

▲ **Figure 10.12** (a) While the charged rod is held near the metal sphere, the sphere remains polarized by induction. Grounding the sphere removes excess charge. In this situation, the sphere appears to have excess electrons on one side, which are removed. The positive charges cannot move because they represent the fixed nuclei of atoms. (b) After the ground and charged rod are removed, the sphere retains a net positive charge because of the loss of electrons. It has been charged by induction.

PHYSICS INSIGHT

The symbol for ground is

A grounded conductor that is polarized by the presence of a charged object will always retain a charge that is opposite to that of the charged object if the ground is removed before the charged object is removed. The conductor has been charged by induction.

How Lightning Gets Its Charge

Many theories attempt to explain the formation of lightning. One theory relates the cause to the processes of evaporation and condensation of water in the clouds and different methods of charging objects. Under the right conditions, a churning cloud formation causes water vapour molecules to collide, resulting in a transfer of electrons between these molecules. The water molecules become oppositely charged by the friction of the collisions.

plasma: highly ionized gas containing nearly equal numbers of free electrons and positive ions

▲ **Figure 10.13** Lightning forms when the bottom of the cloud becomes negatively charged and Earth's surface becomes positively charged.

▲ **Figure 10.14** A streamer moving up from Earth's surface meets a step leader coming down from the clouds and lightning lights up the sky.

Cooling causes water vapour molecules to condense into water droplets. The atoms in these droplets hold onto electrons more readily than atoms in water vapour, and thus the droplets become negatively charged. Being heavier, these negatively charged water droplets accumulate at the bottom of the cloud, causing the bottom of the cloud to become negatively charged (Figure 10.13). The top of the cloud, containing the rising water vapour, becomes positively charged. The increasing polarization of the cloud ionizes the surrounding air, forming a conductive **plasma**. Excess electrons on the bottom of the cloud begin a zigzag journey through this plasma toward the ground at speeds of up to 120 km/s, creating a *step leader*. This is not the actual lightning strike.

The presence of the large negative charge at the bottom of the cloud causes the separation of charges at that location on Earth's surface. Earth's surface at that spot becomes positively charged, and the area below the surface becomes negatively charged. Charge separation has polarized Earth's surface, and it has acquired a charge by induction. Air molecules near Earth's surface become ionized and begin to drift upward. This rising positive charge is called a *streamer*. When the rising positive streamer meets the step leader from the clouds, at an altitude of about 100 m, a complete pathway is formed and the lightning begins. A transfer of negative charge in the form of a lightning strike from the cloud travels to Earth's surface at speeds of up to 100 000 km/s (Figure 10.14).

Knowledge

1. What is the science of electrostatics?

2. Describe a simple experiment that enabled early scientists to determine that there were two different types of charges.

3. In the 1600s, William Gilbert compared the effects of electricity and magnetism.

   (a) Describe two similarities between these effects.

   (b) Describe two differences between these effects.

4. In the classification of substances by electrical conductivity, a substance may be a conductor, insulator, semiconductor, or superconductor.

   (a) What property of matter determines the electrical conductivity of a substance?

   (b) List the classifications given above in order of increasing electrical conductivity.

   (c) Give an example of a substance in each classification.

   (d) Describe the conditions when the semiconductor selenium becomes a conductor or an insulator.

Applications

5. (a) An ebonite rod is rubbed with fur. How can the electrostatic series chart in Figure 10.7 on page 518 help you determine which object will become negatively charged?

   (b) Why is it better to rub an ebonite rod with fur rather than silk?

6. Describe how you could charge a glass sphere positively using the following methods:

   (a) friction

   (b) conduction

   (c) induction

7. Describe how you would charge the sphere in Figure 10.12 negatively by induction.

8. A negatively charged ebonite rod is brought near a neutral pith ball that is hanging by an insulating thread from a support. Describe what happens

   (a) before they touch

   (b) after they touch

9. Compare the distribution of charge

   (a) on hanging aluminium and glass rods if both are touched at one end by a negatively charged ebonite rod

   (b) after a small negatively charged metal sphere momentarily touches a larger neutral metal sphere

10. A negatively charged ebonite rod is held near the knob of a neutral electroscope.

    (a) Explain what happens to the leaves of the electroscope.

    (b) Explain what happens to the leaves of the electroscope if the other side of the knob is now grounded, while the rod is still in place, and then the ground and rod are removed.

    (c) Why is it necessary to remove the ground first and then the rod if the electroscope is to maintain a charge?

Extensions

11. You are given an ebonite rod, fur, an electroscope, and a sphere of unknown charge. Describe an experimental procedure that you could use to determine the charge on the sphere.

12. If a glass rod becomes positively charged when rubbed with silk, how does the law of conservation of charge prove that the silk must be negatively charged?

e TEST

To check your understanding of electrical interactions, follow the eTest links at www.pearsoned.ca/school/physicssource.

10.2 Coulomb's Law

In Chapter 4, you studied Newton's law of universal gravitation and learned that any two objects in the universe exert a gravitational force on each other ($\vec{F}_g$). The magnitude of this force of gravitational attraction is directly proportional to the product of the two masses (m_1 and m_2):

$$|\vec{F}_g| \propto m_1 m_2$$

and inversely proportional to the square of the distance between their centres (r):

$$|\vec{F}_g| \propto \frac{1}{r^2}$$

These relationships can be summarized in the following equation:

$$|\vec{F}_g| = G\frac{m_1 m_2}{r^2}$$

where G is the universal gravitational constant in newton-metres squared per kilogram squared.

Charles de Coulomb suspected that the gravitational force that one mass exerts on another is similar to the electrostatic force that one charge exerts on another. To verify his suspicions, he constructed an apparatus called a torsion balance to measure the forces of electrostatics. Although it could not be used to determine the quantity of charge on an object, Coulomb devised an ingenious method to vary the quantity of charge in a systematic manner. This method is revealed in the 10-3 Inquiry Lab.

PHYSICS INSIGHT

Newton's law of gravitation is called an inverse square law because the gravitational force acting on any two masses is *inversely* proportional to the *square* of the distance between their centres.

10-3 Inquiry Lab

Required Skills
- Initiating and Planning
- Performing and Recording
- Analyzing and Interpreting
- Communication and Teamwork

Investigating the Variables in Coulomb's Law

Question

Two charged objects exert electrostatic forces of magnitude F_e on each other. How does F_e depend on the charges carried by the objects and on the separation between the objects?

Hypothesis

State a hypothesis relating the electrostatic force and each of the variables. Remember to write an "if/then" statement.

Variables

Read the procedure for each part of the inquiry and identify the manipulated variable, the responding variable, and the controlled variables in each one.

Materials and Equipment

Van de Graaff generator or ebonite rod and fur
3 small Styrofoam™ or pith spheres, about 1 cm in
    diameter, coated with aluminium or graphite paint
sewing needle
about 65 cm of thread
3 drinking straws
2 retort stands and 2 clamps
balance
ruler
tape
small mirror (about 10 cm long and 5 cm wide)
marking pen

Procedure

1. Determine the mass of one sphere (sphere 1) and record this mass in kilograms in your notebook.

2. Using the sewing needle, draw the thread through the centre of this sphere and attach both ends of the thread, with tape, to both ends of a drinking straw so that the sphere is suspended in the centre with the thread forming a V pattern. Clamp this straw, horizontally, to a retort stand, as shown in Figure 10.15.

3. Carefully insert the second drinking straw into the second sphere (sphere 2). Then fasten this drinking straw, horizontally, to the clamp on the other retort stand.

4. Adjust the clamps so that both spheres are at the exact same height, and they are touching each other.

5. Carefully insert the third drinking straw into the third sphere (sphere 3). (This sphere will be the grounding sphere that will be used to change the charges on spheres 1 and 2.)

6. Tape sheets of white paper to the wall. Slide the retort stand with sphere 1 close to the wall, about 5 cm away, so that the centre of the sphere aligns with the centre of the paper. Using a ruler, draw a horizontal line on the paper indicating the top position of the string attached to the straw.

7. Tape the mirror onto the centre of the paper so that the image of sphere 1 aligns with the centre of the mirror. Carefully tape the ruler onto the face of the mirror such that the image of sphere 1 appears just above the centre of the ruler. Using the marking pen, mark the position of the centre of the image of sphere 1 on the mirror.

8. Do part A of the activity, which begins below, followed by part B.

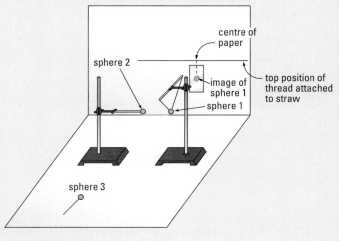

▲ **Figure 10.15**

Part A: The relationship between the quantity of charge on each object and the electrostatic force

In this part of the lab, the distance between the spheres is held constant while the charges on the spheres are varied.

9. Copy Table 10.5 into your notebook, leaving out the numbers in parentheses in the first three columns. Use these numbers only if you are unable to measure the distances accurately. They are hypothetical values that you can use to complete the rest of the activity.

▼ **Table 10.5** Data and Calculations for Part A

Magnitude of Weight of Sphere 1 $\|\vec{F}_g\|$ (10^{-3} N) $\|\vec{F}_g\| = mg$	Vertical Height of Sphere 1 Δd_y (m)	Horizontal Distance to Centre of Sphere 1 from the Centre Mark Δd_x (m)	Product of Charges of Spheres 1 and 2 (q^2)	Magnitude of Force of Electrostatic Repulsion Acting on Spheres 1 and 2 $\|\vec{F}_e\|$ (N)
(1.28)	(0.300)	(0.0500)	$\frac{1}{2}q\frac{1}{2}q = \frac{1}{4}$	
(1.28)	(0.300)	(0.0250)	$\frac{1}{4}q\frac{1}{2}q = \frac{1}{8}$	
(1.28)	(0.300)	(0.0130)	$\frac{1}{4}q\frac{1}{4}q = \frac{1}{16}$	
(1.28)	(0.300)	(0.0062)	$\frac{1}{8}q\frac{1}{4}q = \frac{1}{32}$	
(1.28)	(0.300)	(0.0030)	$\frac{1}{8}q\frac{1}{8}q = \frac{1}{64}$	

10 Rub the ebonite rod with the fur or charge the Van de Graaff generator.

11 Carefully touch sphere 2 to the charged rod or generator to charge the sphere by conduction. Since it is nearly impossible to measure the quantity of charge transferred to sphere 2, assume that the quantity of charge on the sphere is q.

12 Slide the stand holding charged sphere 2 toward sphere 1 on the other stand and momentarily touch the two spheres together. The charge on each object can be assumed to be $\frac{1}{2}q$ because, on contact, the charge is equally divided between two similar spheres. The charge product in this first situation is $\frac{1}{4}q^2$.

13 Slide sphere 2 away from sphere 1 to a position so that the centre of its image is 1.0 cm away from the original centre mark on the mirror.

14 Mark the new position of the centre of the image of sphere 1 on the mirror. Label it position 1.

15 To obtain more data, the charge on each sphere can be varied using sphere 3. Gently touch sphere 3 to sphere 1. Since the charge on each sphere should be shared equally, the new charge on sphere 1 is $\frac{1}{4}q$. The charge product on spheres 1 and 2 is now $\frac{1}{4}q\frac{1}{2}q = \frac{1}{8}q$. Label the new position of sphere 1 as position 2.

16 Remove sphere 3 to a safe distance and ground it by gently touching it with your hand.

17 Repeat steps 14 to 16, alternately touching spheres 1 and 2 with sphere 3 to obtain three more readings. Label these positions 3, 4, and 5.

18 With the ruler, accurately measure the vertical distance from the centre of the image of sphere 1 to the top horizontal line. Record this vertical distance (Δd_y) in metres in the appropriate column of Table 10.5.

19 Measure the distance from the original centre mark on the paper to the centre of the image of sphere 1 in its new position for each trial. Record this distance (Δd_x) in metres in the appropriate column of Table 10.5.

Part B: The relationship between the distance between two charges and the electrostatic force

In this part of the lab, the charges on the spheres are fixed while the distances are varied.

20 Copy Table 10.6 into your notebook, leaving out the numbers in parentheses in the first three columns. Use these numbers only if you are unable to measure the distances accurately. They are hypothetical values that you can use to complete the rest of the activity.

▼ **Table 10.6** Data and Calculations for Part B

Magnitude of Weight of Sphere 1 $\lvert \vec{F}_g \rvert$ $(10^{-3}$ N) $\lvert \vec{F}_g \rvert = mg$	Vertical Height of Sphere 1 Δd_y (m)	Horizontal Distance to Centre of Sphere 1 from the Centre Mark Δd_x (m)	Distance Between the Centres of Spheres 1 and 2 r (m)	Magnitude of Force of Electrostatic Repulsion Acting on Spheres 1 and 2 $\lvert \vec{F}_e \rvert$ (N)
(1.28)	(0.300)	(0.0500)	(0.0600)	
(1.28)	(0.300)	(0.0467)	(0.0617)	
(1.28)	(0.300)	(0.0438)	(0.0638)	
(1.28)	(0.300)	(0.0409)	(0.0659)	
(1.28)	(0.300)	(0.0383)	(0.0683)	

21 Rub the ebonite rod with the fur or charge the Van de Graaff generator.

22 Carefully touch sphere 2 to the rod or the generator to give it a charge.

23 Slide the stand holding charged sphere 2 toward sphere 1 on the other stand and momentarily touch the two spheres together.

24 Slide sphere 2 to a position so that the centre of its image is 0.5 cm away from the original centre mark on the mirror.

25 Mark the new position of the image of sphere 1 on the paper and label it position 1.

26 Repeat steps 24 and 25, sliding sphere 2 to positions 1.0 cm, 1.5 cm, 2.0 cm, and 2.5 cm away, to obtain four more readings. Label these positions 2, 3, 4, and 5.

27 With the ruler, accurately measure the vertical distance from the centre of the image of sphere 1 to the horizontal line representing the top position of the string. Record this vertical distance (Δd_y) in metres in the appropriate column of Table 10.6.

28 Measure the distance from the original centre mark on the mirror to the centre of the image of sphere 1 in its new position. For each trial, record this distance (Δd_x) in metres in the appropriate column of Table 10.6.

29 Measure the distance between the centres of the two spheres. For each trial, record this distance (r) in metres in the appropriate column of Table 10.6.

Analysis

1. Although the force of electrostatic repulsion $|\vec{F}_e|$ acting on two similarly charged spheres cannot be measured directly, it can be calculated as shown in Figure 10.16. Complete the calculations as indicated in Table 10.5.

2. Construct a graph of the force of electrostatic repulsion on the y-axis as a function of the charge product on the x-axis.

3. What does the shape of the graph indicate about the relationship between the force of electrostatic repulsion and the charge product?

4. Complete the calculations as indicated in Table 10.6.

5. Construct a graph of the force of electrostatic repulsion on the y-axis as a function of the distance between the charges on the x-axis.

6. What does the shape of the graph indicate about the relationship between the force of electrostatic repulsion and the distance between the two charges?

7. From the investigation, identify the two variables that affect the force of electrostatic repulsion acting on two charges.

8. Using a variation statement, describe the relationship between these two variables and the force of electrostatic repulsion.

9. Does your investigation confirm your hypotheses about the relationship between the variables and the electrostatic force? Why or why not?

10. How does the relationship between the variables affecting the electrostatic force in this investigation compare with that of the variables affecting the force of gravitational attraction in Newton's law of gravitation?

11. (a) What sources of error could have led to inaccuracy in the investigation?

    (b) What modifications to the investigation would you recommend?

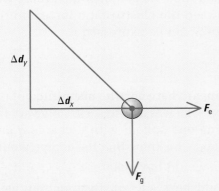

▲ **Figure 10.16(a)**   Use the concept of similar triangles:
$$\frac{\Delta d_y}{\Delta d_x} = \frac{|\vec{F}_g|}{|\vec{F}_e|} \qquad |\vec{F}_e| = \frac{|\vec{F}_g|\Delta d_x}{\Delta d_y}$$

(b)

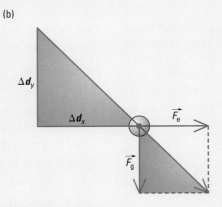

▲ **Figure 10.16(b)**   The shaded triangles are similar.

The Force of Electrostatic Repulsion or Attraction

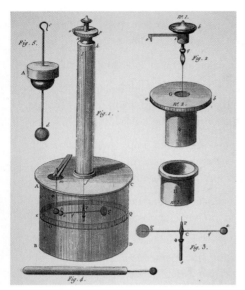

▲ **Figure 10.17**
Coulomb's apparatus

e MATH

In 10-3 Inquiry Lab,
Investigating the Variables
in Coulomb's Law, you
learned how separation and the
magnitude of electric charges affect
the electrostatic force. To graph the
electrostatic force as a function
of separation, and to analyze this
relationship in more depth, visit
www.pearsoned.ca/school/
physicssource.

e SIM

Explore the inverse square
relationship through a
simulation using a sphere
of uniform charge density. Follow
the eSim links at www.pearsoned.ca/
school/physicssource.

Coulomb correctly hypothesized that the two factors influencing the magnitude of the electrostatic force that one charge exerts on another were the magnitudes of the charges on each object and their separation distance. To experimentally derive the relationships between the two factors and the electrostatic force, Coulomb used a procedure similar to that used in the 10-3 Inquiry Lab but with a different apparatus—the torsion balance (Figure 10.17).

To determine the force of electrostatic attraction or repulsion acting on two charged objects, a charged ball on a rod is brought near a charged object on the axle of the torsion balance. Repulsion or attraction causes the ball on the axle to move, causing the axle to rotate. As the axle rotates, a sensitive spring either tightens or loosens, causing the needle to move a proportional angle. This movement of the needle can be measured on a scale. The amount of movement is related to a measure of the force of electrical attraction or repulsion.

Determining Relative Charge

Realizing that there was not yet any way of measuring charge, Coulomb devised a method of accurately determining the relative magnitude of a charge. He knew that if a charged object with a charge of q touches a similar uncharged object, then the charge would be shared equally so that each object would have a charge of $\frac{1}{2}q$. Using this assumption, he was able to do his experiment.

Investigating the relationship between the electrostatic force and the distance between the centres of the spheres, he first charged a sphere with a charge q and touched it momentarily to the sphere on the torsion balance. Each sphere would then have a similar and equal charge of $\frac{1}{2}q$ and $\frac{1}{2}q$. Then, holding the first sphere a measured distance from the sphere in the torsion balance, he was able to measure the electrostatic force acting on the two spheres by the movement of the needle on the calibrated scale. Changing the distance between the spheres and measuring the force each time, he demonstrated there was an inverse square relationship between the electrostatic force and the separation distance. This relationship can be expressed as

$$|\vec{F}_e| \propto \frac{1}{r^2}$$

Investigating further the relationship between the magnitude of the force and the magnitudes of the charges, he was able to accurately vary the charges on each sphere. By charging one sphere with a charge q and touching it to the sphere on the balance, he knew that the charge would be shared equally. The two spheres would have charges of $\frac{1}{2}q$ and $\frac{1}{2}q$ each, and the charge product would be $(\frac{1}{2}q)(\frac{1}{2}q)$. By touching each charged sphere alternately with a third neutral and similar sphere, he could vary the charge products as $(\frac{1}{4}q)(\frac{1}{2}q)$, then $(\frac{1}{4}q)(\frac{1}{4}q)$, and so on.

By varying the charges on both objects and measuring the electrostatic force acting on them, he demonstrated that the magnitude of the electrostatic force is proportional to the product of the two charges:

$$|\vec{F}_e| \propto q_1 q_2$$

In 1785, using the results from his experimentation on charged objects, Charles de Coulomb summarized his conclusions about the electrostatic force. This force is also known as Coulomb's force. His summary of his conclusions is called **Coulomb's law**.

The magnitude of the force of electrostatic attraction or repulsion ($|\vec{F}_e|$) is:
- directly proportional to the product of the two charges q_1 and q_2:

$$|\vec{F}_e| \propto q_1 q_2$$

- inversely proportional to the square of the distance between their centres r:

$$|\vec{F}_e| \propto \frac{1}{r^2}$$

If these are the only variables that determine the electrostatic force, then

$$|\vec{F}_e| \propto \frac{q_1 q_2}{r^2}$$

The beautiful fact about Coulomb's law and Newton's law of gravitation is that they have exactly the same form even though they arise from different sets of operations and apply to completely different kinds of phenomena. The fact that they match so exactly is a fascinating aspect of nature.

Although Coulomb was able to identify and determine the relationships of the variables that affect the electrostatic force acting on two charges, he was unable to calculate the actual force. To do so, the variation statement must be converted to an equation by determining a proportionality constant (k), whose value depends on the units of the charge, the distance, and the force. At the time, however, it was impossible to measure the exact quantity of charge on an object.

The Magnitude of Charges

The SI unit for electric charge is the **coulomb (C)**. A bolt of lightning might transfer 1 C of charge to the ground, while rubbing an ebonite rod with fur typically separates a few microcoulombs (μC). It is difficult to build up larger quantities of charge on small objects because of the tremendous repulsive forces between the like charges.

As you will see in section 15.2, experiments at the beginning of the 20th century showed that an electron has a charge of about -1.60×10^{-19} C. So, 1 C of negative charge corresponds to 6.25×10^{18} electrons, or 6.25 billion billion electrons. Similarly, the charge on a proton is about $+1.60 \times 10^{-19}$ C.

Given these values, physicists were able to calculate the constant of proportionality for Coulomb's law. With this constant, Coulomb's law becomes:

$$|\vec{F}_e| = k\frac{q_1 q_2}{r^2}$$

where $|\vec{F}_e|$ is the magnitude of the force of electrostatic attraction or repulsion in newtons; q_1 and q_2 are the magnitudes of the two charges in coulombs; r is the distance between the centres of the charges in metres; k is the proportionality constant called Coulomb's constant and is equal to 8.99×10^9 N·m²/C². This electrostatic force is attractive if the two objects have opposite charges and repulsive if the two objects have like charges.

This equation is used to determine electrostatic forces in many different types of problems involving charges and the electrostatic forces acting on them. Examples 10.1 and 10.2 show how to calculate the electrostatic force of attraction or repulsion acting on two charges in a one-dimensional situation.

Example 10.1

A small metal sphere with a negative charge of 2.10×10^{-6} C is brought near an identical sphere with a positive charge of 1.50×10^{-6} C so that the distance between the centres of the two spheres is 3.30 cm (Figure 10.18). Calculate the magnitude and type (attraction or repulsion) of the force of one charge acting on another.

Given

$q_1 = -2.10 \times 10^{-6}$ C

$q_2 = +1.50 \times 10^{-6}$ C

$r = 3.30 \times 10^{-2}$ m

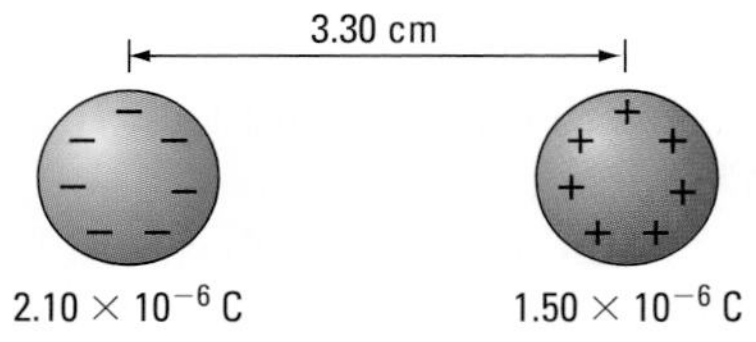

▲ **Figure 10.18**

Required

magnitude and type of the electrostatic force acting on the two charges ($|\vec{F}_e|$)

Analysis and Solution

According to Newton's third law, the electrostatic forces acting on the two spheres are the same in magnitude but opposite in direction. The magnitude of the electrostatic force is

$$|\vec{F}_e| = k\frac{q_1 q_2}{r^2}$$

$$= \frac{\left(8.99 \times 10^9 \, \frac{N \cdot m^2}{C^2}\right)(2.10 \times 10^{-6} \, C)(1.50 \times 10^{-6} \, C)}{(3.30 \times 10^{-2} \, m)^2}$$

$$= 26.0 \text{ N}$$

The magnitude calculation does not use the positive and negative signs for the charges. However, you can use these signs to determine whether the electrostatic force is attractive or repulsive. In this example, the charges have opposite signs, so the force is attractive.

In the next example, the two spheres touch and the charge is distributed between them.

Example 10.2

The two spheres in Example 10.1 are momentarily brought together and then returned to their original separation distance. Determine the electrostatic force now exerted by one charge on the other.

Given
initial magnitude of the charges:

$q_1 = 2.10 \times 10^{-6}$ C
$q_2 = 1.50 \times 10^{-6}$ C
$r = 3.30 \times 10^{-2}$ m

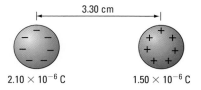

3.30 cm

2.10×10^{-6} C 1.50×10^{-6} C

▲ **Figure 10.19**

Required
magnitude and type of the electrostatic force acting on the two charges ($\vec{F}_e$)

Analysis and Solution
When a sphere with a negative charge of 2.10×10^{-6} C momentarily touches a sphere with a positive charge of 1.50×10^{-6} C, then -1.50×10^{-6} C of charge from the first sphere neutralizes the $+1.50 \times 10^{-6}$ C of charge on the second sphere. The remaining charge of -0.60×10^{-6} C from the first sphere then divides equally between the two identical spheres. Each sphere now has a charge of -3.0×10^{-7} C.

   The magnitude of the electrostatic force is now

$$|\vec{F}_e| = k\frac{q_1 q_2}{r^2}$$

$$= \frac{\left(8.99 \times 10^9 \, \frac{\text{N} \cdot \text{m}^2}{\text{C}^2}\right)(3.0 \times 10^{-7} \, \text{C})(3.0 \times 10^{-7} \, \text{C})}{(3.30 \times 10^{-2} \, \text{m})^2}$$

$$= 0.743 \, \text{N}$$

Since both spheres have a negative charge, the electrostatic force is repulsive.

Paraphrase
The electrostatic force is one of repulsion, with a magnitude of 0.743 N.

Practice Problem

1. A metal sphere with a negative charge of 3.00 μC is placed 12.0 cm from another similar metal sphere with a positive charge of 2.00 μC. The two spheres momentarily touch, then return to their original positions. Calculate the electrostatic force acting on the two metal spheres.

Answer

1. 1.56×10^{-1} N [repulsion]

Vector Analysis of Electrostatic Forces

So far in this section, you have studied Coulomb's law and applied the equation to calculate the magnitude of the electrostatic force that one charged particle exerts on another. However, many situations involve more than two charges. The rest of this section illustrates how to use Coulomb's law to analyze the vector nature of electrostatic forces by determining the electrostatic forces of more than two charges in one-dimensional and two-dimensional situations.

Examples 10.3 and 10.4 illustrate how to apply Coulomb's law to three or more collinear charges. Recall from unit I that *collinear* entities lie along the same straight line.

Example 10.3

A small metal sphere (B) with a negative charge of 2.0×10^{-6} C is placed midway between two similar spheres (A and C) with positive charges of 1.5×10^{-6} C that are 3.0 cm apart (Figure 10.20). Use a vector diagram to find the net electrostatic force acting on sphere B.

Analysis and Solution

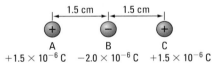

▲ **Figure 10.20**

As shown in Figure 10.21, the vectors are equal in length and opposite in direction.

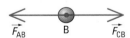

▲ **Figure 10.21**

$$|\vec{F}_{net}| = |\vec{F}_{CB}| - |\vec{F}_{AB}|$$
$$|\vec{F}_{AB}| = |\vec{F}_{CB}|, \text{ so } \vec{F}_{net} = 0.$$

Since the forces are equal in magnitude and opposite in direction, the net electrostatic force on charge B is 0.

Practice Problems

1. Three small, hollow, metallic spheres hang from insulated threads as shown in the figure below. Draw a free-body diagram showing the electrostatic forces acting on sphere B.

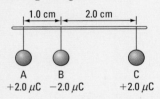

2. For the figure in problem 1 above, draw a vector for the net electrostatic force on sphere B.

Answers

1. ![answer 1 vector diagram]
   $\vec{F}_{AB}$ B $\vec{F}_{CB}$

2. ![answer 2 vector diagram]
   $\vec{F}_{net}$

Example 10.4

A small metal sphere (B) with a negative charge of 2.10×10^{-6} C is placed midway between two similar spheres (A and C) 3.30 cm apart with positive charges of 1.00×10^{-6} C and 1.50×10^{-6} C, respectively, as shown in Figure 10.22. If the three charges are along the same line, calculate the net electrostatic force on the negative charge.

Given

$q_A = +1.00 \times 10^{-6}$ C
$q_B = -2.10 \times 10^{-6}$ C
$q_C = +1.50 \times 10^{-6}$ C
$r_{AC} = 3.30 \times 10^{-2}$ m
$r_{AB} = r_{BC} = \dfrac{1}{2} r_{AC}$

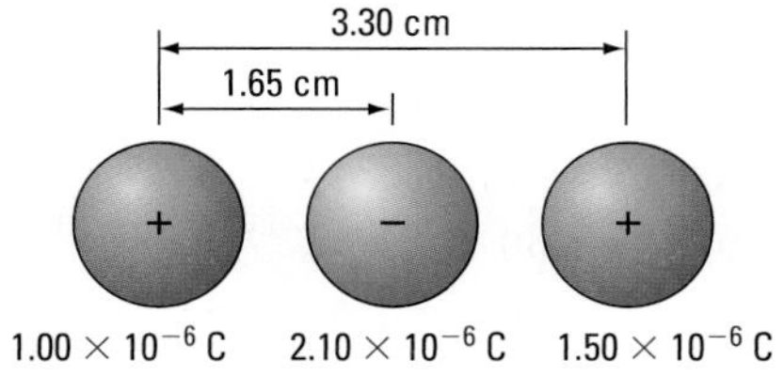

3.30 cm
1.65 cm

+   −   +

1.00×10^{-6} C 2.10×10^{-6} C 1.50×10^{-6} C

▲ **Figure 10.22**

Required

net electrostatic force on q_B ($\vec{F}_{net}$)

Analysis and Solution

The charge on sphere B is negative and the charge on sphere A is positive, so the electrostatic force of q_A on q_B, $\vec{F}_{AB}$, is an attractive force to the left. Similarly, the electrostatic force of q_C on q_B, $\vec{F}_{CB}$, is an attractive force to the right (Figure 10.23). Consider right to be positive.

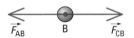

$\vec{F}_{AB}$ B $\vec{F}_{CB}$

▲ **Figure 10.23**

The sum of these two force vectors is the net force on q_B:

$\vec{F}_{net} = \vec{F}_{AB} + \vec{F}_{CB}$

Applying $|\vec{F}_e| = k\dfrac{q_1 q_2}{r^2}$ gives

$$|\vec{F}_{net}| = -\frac{\left(8.99 \times 10^9\ \frac{\text{N·m}^2}{\text{C}^2}\right)(1.00 \times 10^{-6}\ \text{C})(2.10 \times 10^{-6}\ \text{C})}{\left(\dfrac{3.30 \times 10^{-2}\ \text{m}}{2}\right)^2}$$

$$+ \frac{\left(8.99 \times 10^9\ \frac{\text{N·m}^2}{\text{C}^2}\right)(1.50 \times 10^{-6}\ \text{C})(2.10 \times 10^{-6}\ \text{C})}{\left(\dfrac{3.30 \times 10^{-2}\ \text{m}}{2}\right)^2}$$

$= -(69.34\ \text{N}) + (104.0\ \text{N})$
$= 34.7\ \text{N}$

Paraphrase

The net electrostatic force on charge B is 34.7 N to the right.

Practice Problems

1. A metal sphere with a charge of -2.50×10^{-9} C is 1.50 cm to the left of a second metal sphere with a charge of $+1.50 \times 10^{-9}$ C. A third metal sphere of -1.00×10^{-9} C is situated 2.00 cm to the right of the second charged sphere. If all three charges form a line, determine the net electrostatic force on the second sphere.

2. In the situation described above, where should the second sphere be situated so that the net electrostatic force on it would be zero?

Answers

1. 1.16×10^{-4} N [to the left]

2. 2.14×10^{-2} m [to the right of the -2.50×10^{-9} C charge]

In Examples 10.3 and 10.4, the forces act along the same line, so the calculations involve only a single dimension. Examples 10.5 and 10.6 demonstrate how to calculate net electrostatic forces in two dimensions.

Example 10.5

Practice Problems

1. A small metal sphere X with a negative charge of -2.50 C is 1.20 cm directly to the left of another similar sphere Y with a charge of $+3.00$ C. A third sphere Z with a charge of $+4.00$ C is 1.20 cm directly below sphere Y. The three spheres are at the vertices of a right triangle, with sphere Y at the right angle. Calculate the net electrostatic force on sphere Y, sketching diagrams as necessary.

2. Calculate the net electrostatic force on charge B shown in the figure below.

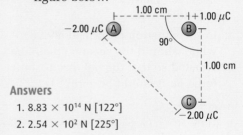

Answers

1. 8.83×10^{14} N [122°]
2. 2.54×10^2 N [225°]

A small metal sphere A with a negative charge of 2.10×10^{-6} C is 2.00×10^{-2} m to the left of another similar sphere B with a positive charge of 1.50×10^{-6} C. A third sphere C with a positive charge of 1.80×10^{-6} C is situated 3.00×10^{-2} m directly below sphere B (Figure 10.24). Calculate the net electrostatic force on sphere B.

Given

$q_A = -2.10 \times 10^{-6}$ C

$q_B = +1.50 \times 10^{-6}$ C

$q_C = +1.80 \times 10^{-6}$ C

$r_{AB} = 2.00 \times 10^{-2}$ m

$r_{BC} = 3.00 \times 10^{-2}$ m

Required

net electrostatic force on sphere B ($\vec{F}_{net}$)

Analysis and Solution

The electrostatic force of q_A on q_B, $\vec{F}_{AB}$, is a force of attraction directed from charge B toward charge A (left). The electrostatic force of q_C on q_B, $\vec{F}_{CB}$, is a force of repulsion directly upward (Figure 10.25).

[Figure 10.24 description — spheres A, B, C with charges 2.10×10^{-6} C, 1.50×10^{-6} C, 1.80×10^{-6} C, distances 2.00×10^{-2} m and 3.00×10^{-2} m]

▲ **Figure 10.24**

▲ **Figure 10.25**

Applying $|\vec{F}_e| = k\dfrac{q_1 q_2}{r^2}$ gives

$$|\vec{F}_{AB}| = k\frac{q_A q_B}{r_{AB}^2}$$

$$= \frac{\left(8.99 \times 10^9 \; \dfrac{\text{N} \cdot \text{m}^2}{\cancel{C}^2}\right)(2.10 \times 10^{-6} \; \cancel{C})(1.50 \times 10^{-6} \; \cancel{C})}{(2.00 \times 10^{-2} \; \text{m})^2}$$

$$= 70.80 \; \text{N}$$

Similarly,

$$|\vec{F}_{CB}| = k\frac{q_B q_C}{r_{BC}^2}$$

$$= \frac{\left(8.99 \times 10^9 \; \dfrac{\text{N} \cdot \text{m}^2}{\cancel{C}^2}\right)(1.50 \times 10^{-6} \; \cancel{C})(1.80 \times 10^{-6} \; \cancel{C})}{(3.00 \times 10^{-2} \; \text{m})^2}$$

$$= 26.97 \; \text{N}$$

Use trigonometry to find the net electrostatic force on charge B, as shown in Figure 10.26.

Use the Pythagorean theorem to find the magnitude of the net force:

$$|\vec{F}_{net}| = \sqrt{(70.80 \text{ N})^2 + (26.97 \text{ N})^2}$$
$$= 75.76 \text{ N}$$
$$= 75.8 \text{ N}$$

Determine the angle θ:

$$\tan \theta = \frac{26.97 \text{ N}}{70.80 \text{ N}}$$
$$\theta = 20.9°$$

▲ **Figure 10.26**

The direction of the net force is [20.9° N of W] or [159°].

Paraphrase

The net electrostatic force on charge B is 75.8 N [20.9° N of W], or 75.8 N [159°].

Example 10.6

A small metal sphere A with a charge of -2.10×10^{-6} C is 2.00×10^{-2} m to the left of a second sphere B with a charge of $+1.50 \times 10^{-6}$ C. A third sphere C with a charge of $+1.80 \times 10^{-6}$ C is situated 3.00×10^{-2} m directly below sphere B. Calculate the net electrostatic force on sphere C.

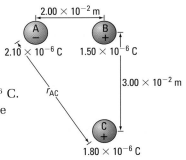

▲ **Figure 10.27**

Given

$q_A = -2.10 \times 10^{-6}$ C

$q_B = +1.50 \times 10^{-6}$ C

$q_C = +1.80 \times 10^{-6}$ C

$r_{AB} = 2.00 \times 10^{-2}$ m

$r_{BC} = 3.00 \times 10^{-2}$ m

Required

net electrostatic force on sphere C ($\vec{F}_{net}$)

Analysis and Solution

The electrostatic force of q_A on q_C, $\vec{F}_{AC}$, is an attractive force directed from charge C toward charge A. The electrostatic force of q_B on q_C, $\vec{F}_{BC}$, is a repulsive force directed downward (Figure 10.28).

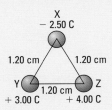

▲ **Figure 10.28**

Practice Problems

1. Three metal spheres are situated in positions forming an equilateral triangle with sides of 1.20 cm, as shown below. X has a charge of -2.50 C; Y has a charge of $+3.00$ C; and Z has a charge of $+4.00$ C. Calculate the net electrostatic force on the Y charge.

   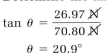

2. Four charged spheres, with equal charges of $+2.20$ C, are situated in positions forming a rectangle, as shown in the figure below. Determine the net electrostatic force on the charge in the top right corner of the rectangle.

   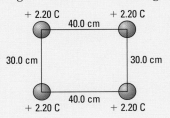

Answers

1. 6.56×10^{14} N [142°]
2. 7.17×10^{11} N [55.0°]

Determine the distance between charges A and C by using the Pythagorean theorem (Figure 10.29):

$$\begin{aligned} r_{AC} &= \sqrt{(2.00 \times 10^{-2}\ m)^2 + (3.00 \times 10^{-2}\ m)^2} \\ &= 3.606 \times 10^{-2}\ m \\ &= 3.61 \times 10^{-2}\ m \end{aligned}$$

▲ **Figure 10.29**

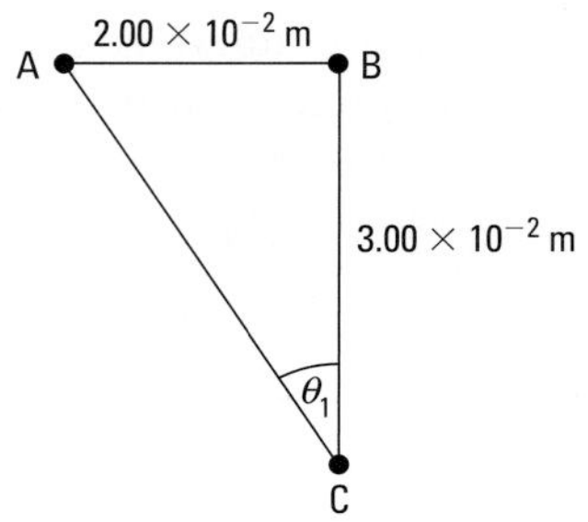

Applying $|\vec{F}_e| = k\dfrac{q_1 q_2}{r^2}$ gives

$$\begin{aligned} |\vec{F}_{AC}| &= k\frac{q_A q_C}{r^2_{AC}} \\ &= \frac{\left(8.99 \times 10^9 \dfrac{N{\cdot}m^2}{\not{C}^2}\right)(2.10 \times 10^{-6}\ \not{C})(1.80 \times 10^{-6}\ \not{C})}{(3.61 \times 10^{-2}\ m)^2} \\ &= 26.13\ N \end{aligned}$$

Similarly,

$$\begin{aligned} |\vec{F}_{BC}| &= k\frac{q_B q_C}{r^2_{BC}} \\ &= \frac{\left(8.99 \times 10^9 \dfrac{N{\cdot}m^2}{\not{C}^2}\right)(1.50 \times 10^{-6}\ \not{C})(1.80 \times 10^{-6}\ \not{C})}{(3.00 \times 10^{-2}\ m)^2} \\ &= 26.97\ N \end{aligned}$$

Use the component method to find the sum of the two force vectors.

Use trigonometry to determine the angle θ_1 for the direction of $\vec{F}_{AC}$ (Figure 10.29):

$$\begin{aligned} \tan\theta_1 &= \frac{2.00 \times 10^{-2}\ \not{m}}{3.00 \times 10^{-2}\ \not{m}} \\ \theta_1 &= 33.69^\circ \end{aligned}$$

▲ **Figure 10.30**

Then resolve $\vec{F}_{AC}$ into x and y components, as shown in Figure 10.30:

$$\begin{aligned} F_{AC_x} &= -(26.13\ N)(\sin 33.69^\circ) \\ &= -14.49\ N \\ F_{AC_y} &= (26.13\ N)(\cos 33.69^\circ) \\ &= 21.74\ N \end{aligned}$$

The electrostatic force of charge B on charge C has only a y component (see Figure 10.28).
So, the x component of $\vec{F}_{BC}$ is 0 N and the y component is −26.97 N.

Now find the sum of the x and y components of $\vec{F}_{net}$.

$$\vec{F}_{net} = \vec{F}_{AC} + \vec{F}_{BC}$$

$$\begin{aligned} F_{net_x} &= F_{AC_x} + F_{BC_x} \\ &= -14.49\ N + 0\ N \\ &= -14.49\ N \end{aligned} \qquad \begin{aligned} F_{net_y} &= F_{AC_y} + F_{BC_y} \\ &= 21.74\ N + (-26.97\ N) \\ &= -5.23\ N \end{aligned}$$

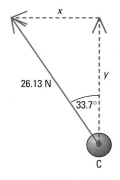

Use trigonometry to determine the magnitude and direction of the net electrostatic force on charge C, as shown in Figure 10.31. Determine the magnitude of the net force using the Pythagorean theorem:

▲ **Figure 10.31**

$$|\vec{F}_{net}| = \sqrt{(14.49 \text{ N})^2 + (5.23 \text{ N})^2}$$
$$= 15.4 \text{ N}$$

To determine the angle θ_2, use the tangent function:

$$\tan \theta_2 = \frac{5.23 \text{ N}}{14.49 \text{ N}}$$
$$\theta_2 = 19.8°$$

The direction of the net force is [19.8° S of W] or [200°].

Paraphrase

The net electrostatic force on charge C is 15.4 N [19.8° S of W] or 15.4 N [200°].

THEN, NOW, AND FUTURE   ESD Control Manager

Since the early 1970s, electrostatic discharge (ESD) has evolved from an interesting, but generally harmless, phenomenon to one of the most rapidly expanding fields of research in science today.

As electronic devices have become smaller and smaller, ESD has become a major cause of failure. Each year, billions of dollars' worth of electronic devices and systems are destroyed or degraded by electrical stress caused by ESD.

A dangerous property of ESD is its ability to cause fires in a flammable atmosphere. Property loss, injuries, and fatalities due to the accidental ignition of petrochemical vapours, dusts, and fuels by ESD are on the rise. ESD has been the proven ignition source in many fires. However, research into the fire-sparking nature of ESD is still in its infancy.

Today, electronics manufacturers have ESD awareness and control programs, ESD control program managers, and, in some cases, entire departments dedicated to preventing the damaging effects of ESD.

Ron Zezulka (Figure 10.32) is the chief technical officer of TB&S Consultants and has specialized in the science of ESD for over 30 years. He graduated from the Southern Alberta Institute of Technology with a diploma as a telecommunications technician and began his career as a failure analyst specializing in the science of ESD for Alberta Government Telephones.

Ron completed many courses to become a control program manager. Because of the newness of the industry, there are no specific quali-

▲ **Figure 10.32** Ron Zezulka

fications for becoming a control program manager in the field of ESD.

An ESD control program manager might have a technical diploma and related job experience, a Master's degree, or a Ph.D. in physics.

In 2001, Ron formed TB&S Consultants and has developed and delivered over 25 different training programs and management systems for the awareness and control of ESD in industry. He has written on the topic and lectured in industry, universities, and colleges on awareness and control of ESD.

Static electricity is now tied to almost every aspect of the physical sciences. As technology advances, so does our need for a greater understanding of ESD phenomena.

Questions

1. Describe two hazards associated with ESD.

2. How could ESD have damaging and harmful effects in your home?

3. How are ESD control program managers employed in industry?

Knowledge

1. Identify the two factors that influence the force of electrostatic attraction or repulsion acting on two charges. Write a mathematical expression to describe the relationship.

2. Describe how the inverse square law, first proposed by Newton for gravitational forces, was applied to electrostatic forces by Coulomb.

3. What is the smallest unit of electric charge and who first discovered the existence of this charge experimentally?

4. Coulomb could not measure the amount of charge on his spheres, but he could vary the amount of charge on each sphere. Describe the procedure he used to do so.

Applications

5. An electrostatic force of 10 N acts on two charged spheres, separated by a certain distance. What will be the new force in the following situations?

   (a) The charge on one sphere is doubled.

   (b) The charge on both spheres is doubled.

6. (a) Why is it difficult to attain a large charge on objects?

   (b) During the rubbing process, an object acquires a charge of -5.0×10^{-9} C. How many electrons did the object gain?

7. Two identical conducting spheres have charges of 5.00×10^{-5} C and 6.00×10^{-5} C and are in fixed positions, 2.00 m apart.

   (a) Calculate the electrostatic force acting on the two charges.

   (b) The spheres are touched together and returned to their original positions. Calculate the new electrostatic force acting on them.

8. Three charges are placed in a line, as shown in the diagram below.

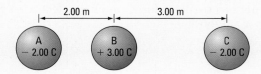

   (a) What is the net electrostatic force on charge A?

   (b) What is the net electrostatic force on charge B?

Extensions

9. A helium nucleus has a positive charge with a magnitude twice that of the negative charge on an electron. Is the electrostatic force of attraction on an electron in a helium atom equal to the force acting on the nucleus? Justify your answer.

10. Electrical forces are so strong that the combined electrostatic forces of attraction acting on all the negative electrons and positive protons in your body could crush you to a thickness thinner than a piece of paper. Why don't you compress?

e TEST

To check your understanding of Coulomb's law, follow the eTest links at
www.pearsoned.ca/school/physicssource.

Key Terms and Concepts

electrostatics
insulator
conductor
semiconductor
superconductor

law of conservation
　of charge
net charge
conduction

induction
charge migration
charge shift
grounding

charging by induction
plasma
Coulomb's law
coulomb (C)

Key Equation

$$|\vec{F}_e| = k\frac{q_1 q_2}{r^2}$$

Conceptual Overview

The concept map below summarizes many of the concepts and equations in this chapter.
Copy and complete the map to have a full summary of the chapter.

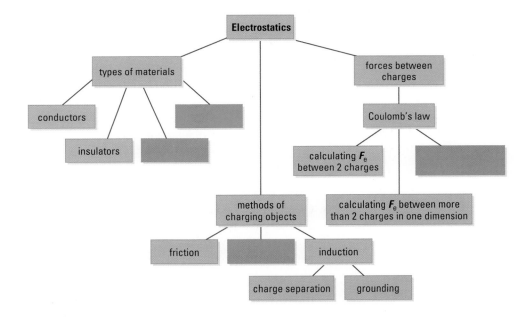

Knowledge

1. (10.1) What is an electrostatic charge?

2. (10.1) On what property of materials does thermal and electrical conductivity depend?

3. (10.1) Under what conditions does selenium become a good conductor or a good insulator? What are materials with this property called?

4. (10.1) What are three methods of charging objects?

5. (10.1) During the process of charging objects by friction, what determines which object becomes negatively or positively charged?

6. (10.1) How are the processes of charging objects by conduction and friction alike? How are they different?

7. (10.1) State the law of charges.

8. (10.1) Who is credited with first naming the two types of charges as negative and positive charges?

9. (10.1) State the law of conservation of charge.

10. (10.1) Selenium and germanium are both semiconductors. Explain why selenium is used in photocopiers rather than germanium.

11. (10.2) Calculate the electrostatic force acting on two charged spheres of $-3.00\ \mu C$ and $-2.50\ \mu C$ if they are separated by a distance of 0.200 m.

12. (10.2) What is the distance between two charges of -5.00 C each if the force of electrostatic repulsion acting on them is 5.00×10^3 N?

13. (10.2) Charge A has a charge of -2.50 C and is 1.50 m to the left of charge B, which has a charge of $+3.20$ C. Charge B is 1.70 m to the left of a third charge C, which has a charge of -1.60 C. If all three charges are collinear, what is the net electrostatic force on each of the following?
    (a) charge B
    (b) charge C

Applications

14. Why does dust settle on the front of a TV screen?

15. Why is it desirable to develop materials with low electrical resistance?

16. Explain why a charged ebonite rod can be discharged by passing a flame over its surface.

17. Explain why repulsion between two objects is the only evidence that both objects are charged.

18. Why do experiments on electrostatics not work well on humid days?

19. Why does a charged pith ball initially attract another neutral pith ball, then repel it?

20. Why can you not charge a copper rod while holding one end with one hand and rubbing the other end with a piece of fur?

21. A person standing on an insulated chair touches a charged sphere. Is the person able to discharge the sphere and effectively ground it?

22. Two charged spheres, separated by a certain distance, attract each other with an electrostatic force of 10 N. What will be the new force in each of the following situations?
    (a) The charge on both spheres is doubled and the separation distance is halved.
    (b) The charge on one sphere is doubled while the charge on the other sphere is tripled and the separation distance is tripled.

23. Calculate and compare the electrical and gravitational forces acting on an electron and a proton in the hydrogen atom when the distance between their centres is 5.29×10^{-11} m.

24. An equilateral triangle with sides of 0.200 m has three charges of -2.50 C each, situated on the vertices of the triangle. Calculate the net electrostatic force on each charge. What assumption did you have to make to complete the calculation?

25. In a Coulomb-type experiment, students were investigating the relationship between the force of electrostatic repulsion acting on two charged spheres and their separation distance. The results of their investigation yielded the results shown in the table below.

Separation Distance (r) (× 10⁻² m)	Magnitude of Force of Repulsion |$\vec{F}$| (N)
1.00	360.0
2.00	89.9
3.00	40.0
4.00	27.5
5.00	14.4

(a) Draw a graph of the results shown in the table.

(b) From the shape of the graph, what is the relationship between the electrostatic force and the separation distance between two charges?

(c) Make a new table of values to obtain data to straighten the graph.

(d) Draw a graph of the data in your new table of values.

(e) Determine the slope of the graph.

(f) What value does the slope of this graph represent?

(g) If the charges of the two spheres are the same, what is the value of the charge on each sphere?

Extensions

26. Does a neutral object contain no charges? Explain.

27. Is it possible for a single negative or a single positive charge to exist in nature under normal conditions? Explain your answer.

28. Explain why it is impossible to charge a coin by rubbing it between your fingers.

29. Compare the production of lightning on Earth with the lightning between the rings of Saturn observed by the *Voyager* spacecraft on its mission to Saturn.

30. You are given two equally sized metal spheres on insulated stands, a piece of wire, a glass rod, and some silk. Devise and describe a method to do the following without touching the rod to the spheres:

(a) give the spheres equal and opposite charges

(b) give the spheres equal and like charges

31. Using the principles of electrostatics, explain the causes and effects of the following demonstrations:

(a) Two strips of clear adhesive tape are stuck together and then carefully separated. When the two strips are brought close to each other, attraction occurs.

(b) Two strips of clear adhesive tape are stuck onto a desktop and then carefully removed. When the two strips are held close to each other, repulsion occurs.

Consolidate Your Understanding

Create your own summary of the behaviour of electric charges and the laws that govern electrical interactions by answering the questions below. If you want to use a graphic organizer, refer to Student Reference 3: Using Graphic Organizers. Use the Key Terms and Concepts listed on page 539 and the Learning Outcomes on page 510.

1. Create a flowchart to describe how to calculate the electrostatic forces between two or more charged objects in one- or two-dimensional situations.

2. Write a paragraph explaining the three methods of charging objects. Share your report with a classmate.

Think About It

Review your answers to the Think About It questions on page 511. How would you answer each question now?

 e **TEST**

To check your understanding of the behaviour of electric charges, follow the eTest links at www.pearsoned.ca/school/physicssource.

Electric field theory describes electrical phenomena.

▲ **Figure 11.1** The eerie glow of St. Elmo's fire on the masts of a ship

On Christopher Columbus's second voyage to the Americas, his ships headed into stormy weather, and the tips of the ships' masts began to glow with a ghostly bluish flame. Sailors of the time believed that this bluish glow was a good sign that the ship was under the protection of St. Elmo, the patron saint of sailors, so they called the blue "flames" St. Elmo's fire (Figure 11.1).

People throughout history have written about this strange glow. Julius Caesar reported that "in the month of February, about the second watch of the night, there suddenly arose a thick cloud followed by a shower of hail, and the same night the points of the spears belonging to the Fifth Legion seemed to take fire." Astronauts have seen similar glows on spacecraft.

What is the cause of this eerie phenomenon? Why does it most often appear during thunderstorms?

You will discover the answers to these questions as you continue to study the phenomena associated with electric charges. In this chapter, you will begin by learning how knowledge of the forces related to electric charges led to the idea of fields, and you will compare different types of electric fields. Then you will learn how force is used to define the strength of electric fields. Finally, you will study the motion of charges in electric fields and explain electrical interactions using the law of conservation of energy.

Shielding of Cellular Phones

Electronic equipment usually contains material that is used as "shielding." In this activity, you will discover what this shielding material does.

Problem

How does the shielding of electronic equipment, such as a cellular phone, affect its operation?

Materials

2 cellular phones
sheets (about 20 cm × 20 cm) of various materials, such as aluminium foil, plastic wrap, wax paper, paper, cloth, fur
1 short length of coaxial cable

Procedure

Part A

1 Wrap the sheet of aluminium foil around one of the cellular phones.

2 With the other cellular phone, dial the number of the wrapped cellular phone and record any response.

3 Remove the aluminium foil and again dial the number of the cellular phone.

4 Repeat steps 1 to 3 using the sheets of other materials.

Part B

5 Carefully remove the outer strip of insulated plastic around one end of the coaxial cable and examine the inner coaxial cable wires.

Questions

1. What effect did wrapping a cellular phone with the various materials have on the operation of the cellular phone?

2. Cellular phones receive communication transmissions that are electrical in nature. Speculate why the transmissions are shielded by certain materials. Which materials are most effective for shielding?

3. What material forms the protective wrapping around the inner coaxial transmission wires? Explain the purpose of this protective wrapping.

Think About It

1. Desktop computers or computers in vehicles have sensitive electronic components that must be protected from outside electrical interference. Identify a possible source of outside electrical interference. Describe how computer components may be protected from this interference and explain why this protection is necessary.

2. Sometimes, if your debit card fails to scan, the clerk wraps the card with a plastic bag and re-scans it. Explain why a plastic bag wrapped around a card would allow the card to scan properly. Why do clerks not wrap the card with aluminium foil for re-scanning?

Discuss and compare your answers in a small group and record them for later reference. As you complete each section of this chapter, review your answers to these questions. Note any changes to your ideas.

11.1 Forces and Fields

▲ **Figure 11.2**   Forces exerted by the horses attached to the chariot cause the "violent" motion of the chariot.

▲ **Figure 11.3**   To return to its natural element, a rock falls with "natural" motion to Earth's surface.

The ancient Greek philosophers explained most types of motion as being the result of either "violent" or "natural" forces. They thought that violent forces cause motion as the result of a force exerted by one object in contact with another (Figure 11.2). They thought that natural forces cause the motion of objects toward their "natural element" (Figure 11.3). However, the Greeks found another kind of motion more difficult to explain. You will observe this kind of motion in the following Minds On activity.

MINDS ON   Action at a Distance

Charge a rubber rod by rubbing it with fur and slowly bring it close to the hairs on your forearm. Do not touch the hairs or your arm. Observe what happens.

1. What evidence is there that the charged rod affects the hairs on your arm without actual contact?
2. Is the force exerted by the rod on the hairs of your arm attractive or repulsive?

info BIT

A new theory in physics, called string theory, proposes that contact between objects is through "strings" that transmit the forces between objects. This new theory has a striking similarity to the effluvium theory proposed 2500 years ago.

The rubber rod seems to be able to exert a type of violent force on the hairs of your arm without visible contact. This type of force was classified as "action at a distance," where one object could exert a force on another object without contact. To explain "action at a distance," the Greeks proposed the effluvium theory.

According to this theory, all objects are surrounded by an effluvium. This invisible substance is made up of minute string-like atoms emitted by the object that pulsate back and forth. As the effluvium extends out to other bodies, the atoms of the different objects become entangled. Their effluvium eventually draws them toward each other. The effluvium theory helped to explain what seemed to be "action at a distance." Although the effluvium was invisible, there was still a form of contact between the objects.

Fields

In the 17th century, scientists, including Newton, tried to determine why one object can exert a force on another object without touching it. These scientists attempted to explain "action at a distance," such as the curved path of a thrown ball or the effect of a charged piece of amber on the hair on a person's arm. Finding that "natural" or "violent" forces and "effluvium" could not explain gravity or electrical forces, scientists developed the concept of fields to describe these forces.

A **field** is defined as a region of influence surrounding an object. The concept of fields helped Newton postulate his laws of universal gravitation, which you studied in Chapter 4.

Consider a space module on its way to the Moon (Figure 11.4). Nearing its lunar destination, the module begins to experience the increasing influence of the Moon. As a result, the module's motion begins to follow a curved path, similar to the projectile motion of an object thrown horizontally through the air near Earth's surface.

As Newton's laws state, the motion of any object can follow a curved path only when acted on by a non-zero force that has a perpendicular component. In space, this happens to the space module when it is near the Moon, so the space near the Moon must be different from the space where no large objects like the Moon are present. From this, we can infer that a field exists around a large object, such as the Moon. When other objects enter this field, they interact with the Moon. Similarly, Earth has a field. Gravitational force acts on other objects that enter this field. Recall from Chapter 4 that this field around objects is called a gravitational field.

Michael Faraday (1791–1867) applied the idea of fields to electrostatic phenomena. He determined that the space around a rubber rod must be different when the rubber rod is charged than when it is not. The charges on the rod create an electric field around the rod. An electrostatic force acts on another charged object when it is placed in this field. An electric field exists around every charge or charged object. It can exist in empty space, whether or not another charge or charged object is in the field.

Although field theory is a powerful tool for describing phenomena and predicting forces, physicists are still debating how objects can actually exert forces at a distance. Chapter 17 describes how quantum theory provides an extremely accurate model for describing such forces.

field: a region of influence surrounding an object

▲ **Figure 11.4** A space module passing near a large planet or the Moon follows a curved path.

Concept Check

Use field theory to explain the path of a baseball thrown from outfield to home plate.

Observing Electric Fields — Demonstration

Question

What is the shape of the electric field around various charged objects?

Materials and Equipment

plastic platform with 2 electrode holders
overhead projector
petri dish
canola or olive oil
lawn seeds
single-point electrode
two-point (oppositely charged) electrodes
parallel copper plates about 4 cm × 4 cm
hollow sphere conductor 4–6 cm in diameter
2 Wimshurst generators
connecting wires

Procedure

1. Pour some of the canola or olive oil into the petri dish so the dish is about three-quarters full.

2. Place the petri dish with the oil on the plastic platform on the overhead projector. Carefully sprinkle the lawn seeds evenly over the surface of the oil.

3. Attach the single-point electrode, with a connecting wire, to one contact of the Wimshurst generator. Immerse the electrode in the oil in the centre of the dish.

4. Crank the Wimshurst generator several times and carefully observe the pattern of the seeds in the oil.

5. Remove the electrode and allow sufficient time for the lawn seeds to redistribute on the surface. (Gentle stirring with a pencil might be required.)

6. Repeat steps 3 to 5 with each of the following:

   (a) two electrodes connected to similar contacts on two Wimshurst machines

   (b) two electrodes connected to opposite contacts on one Wimshurst machine

   (c) two parallel copper plates connected to opposite contacts on one Wimshurst machine

   (d) one hollow sphere connected to one contact of one Wimshurst machine

Analysis

1. Describe and analyze the pattern of the lawn seeds created by each of the charged objects immersed in the oil in step 6 of the procedure by answering the following questions:

   (a) Where does the density of the lawn seeds appear to be the greatest? the least?

   (b) Does there appear to be a starting point and an endpoint in the pattern created by the lawn seeds?

2. Are there any situations where there appears to be no observable effect on the lawn seeds?

3. Based on your observations of the patterns created by the lawn seeds on the surface of the oil, what conclusion can you make about the space around charged objects?

Magnitude and Direction of an Electric Field

The electric field that surrounds a charged object has both magnitude and direction. Therefore, an electric field is classified as a vector field. At any point around a charge, the field can be represented by a vector arrow. The arrow's length represents the magnitude of the electric field and the arrowhead indicates direction at that point.

By definition, the direction of the electric field around a charge is the direction of the force experienced by a small positive **test charge** placed in the electric field (Figure 11.5). A test charge is a charge with a magnitude small enough so that it does not disturb the charge on the **source charge** and thus change its electric field.

test charge: charge with a magnitude small enough that it does not disturb the charge on the source charge and thus change its electric field

source charge: charge that produces an electric field

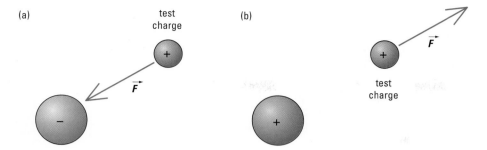

(a)   test charge   (b)   test charge

▲ **Figure 11.5**   The direction of the electric field at a point is the direction of the electric force exerted on a positive test charge at that point. (a) If the source charge is negative, the field is directed toward the source. (b) If the source charge is positive, the field is directed away from the source.

Concept Check

Identify the difference in the electric field at points I and II as represented by the vector arrows in Figure 11.6.

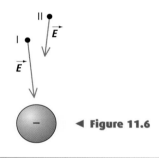

◄ **Figure 11.6**

You can determine the magnitude of the electric field around a point charge from the effect on another charge placed in it. If a small positive test charge is placed in the field, this charge will experience a greater force when it is near the charge producing the field than when it is farther away from it.

By definition, the electric field ($\vec{E}$) at a given point is the ratio of the electric force ($\vec{F_e}$) exerted on a charge (q) placed at that point to the magnitude of that charge. The electric field can be calculated using the equation

$$\vec{E} = \frac{\vec{F_e}}{q}$$

where q is the charge in the electric field in coulombs (C); $\vec{F_e}$ is the electric force on the charge in newtons (N); and $\vec{E}$ is the strength of the electric field at that point in newtons per coulomb (N/C), in the direction as defined previously.

info **BIT**

A tremendous range of field strengths occurs in nature. For example, the electric field 30 cm away from a light bulb is roughly 5 N/C, whereas the electron in a hydrogen atom experiences an electric field in the order of 10^{11} N/C from the atom's nucleus.

Example 11.1

A sphere with a negative charge of 2.10×10^{-6} C experiences an electrostatic force of repulsion of 5.60×10^{-2} N when it is placed in the electric field produced by a source charge (Figure 11.7). Determine the magnitude of the electric field the source charge produces at the sphere.

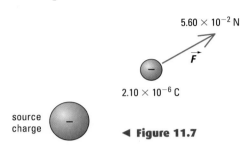

◀ **Figure 11.7**

Given
$q = -2.10 \times 10^{-6}$ C
$\vec{F}_e = 5.60 \times 10^{-2}$ N [repulsion]

Required
magnitude of the electric field ($|\vec{E}|$)

Analysis and Solution

Since $\vec{E} = \dfrac{\vec{F}_e}{q}$,

$$|\vec{E}| = \frac{|\vec{F}_e|}{q}$$

$$= \frac{5.60 \times 10^{-2} \text{ N}}{2.10 \times 10^{-6} \text{ C}}$$

$$= 2.67 \times 10^4 \text{ N/C}$$

Paraphrase
The magnitude of the electric field is 2.67×10^4 N/C at the given point.

The equation for determining the magnitude of the electric field around a point charge, like that shown in Figure 11.8, can be derived mathematically as follows:

If $|\vec{E}| = \dfrac{|\vec{F}_e|}{q_2}$ and $|\vec{F}_e| = \dfrac{kq_1q_2}{r^2}$, then

$$|\vec{E}| = \frac{\dfrac{kq_1\cancel{q_2}}{r^2}}{\cancel{q_2}}$$

$$|\vec{E}| = \frac{kq}{r^2}$$

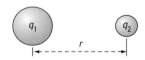

▲ **Figure 11.8** A test charge (q_2) is placed in the electric field of a source charge (q_1). The distance between their centres is r.

PHYSICS INSIGHT

Equations based on Coulomb's law only work for point charges.

where q is the magnitude of the source charge producing the electric field in coulombs (ignore the sign of the charge); r is the distance from the centre of the source charge to a specific point in space in metres; k is Coulomb's constant (8.99×10^9 N·m²/C²); and $|\vec{E}|$ is the magnitude of the electric field in newtons per coulomb.

Example 11.2

Determine the electric field at a position P that is 2.20×10^{-2} m from the centre of a negative point charge of 1.70×10^{-6} C.

Given
$q = -1.70 \times 10^{-6}$ C
$r = 2.20 \times 10^{-2}$ m

Required
electric field $\left(\vec{E} \right)$

Analysis and Solution
The source charge producing the electric field is q. So,

$$|\vec{E}| = \frac{kq}{r^2}$$

$$= \frac{\left(8.99 \times 10^9 \, \frac{\text{N·m}^2}{\text{C}^2} \right)(1.70 \times 10^{-6} \, \text{C})}{(2.20 \times 10^{-2} \, \text{m})^2}$$

$$= 3.16 \times 10^7 \, \text{N/C}$$

The source charge is negative, so the electric field is toward the source.

Paraphrase
The electric field at point P is 3.16×10^7 N/C [toward the source].

Practice Problems

1. The electric field at a position 2.00 cm from a charge is 40.0 N/C directed away from the charge. Determine the charge producing the electric field.

2. An electron has a charge of 1.60×10^{-19} C. At what distance from the electron would the magnitude of the electric field be 5.14×10^{11} N/C?

Answers

1. $+1.78 \times 10^{-12}$ C
2. 5.29×10^{-11} m

Concept Check

Compare gravitational fields and electrostatic fields by listing two similarities and two differences between the two types of fields.

Often, more than one charge creates an electric field at a particular point in space. In earlier studies, you learned the superposition principle for vectors. According to the superposition principle, fields set up by many sources superpose to form a single net field. The vector specifying the net field at any point is simply the vector sum of the fields of all the individual sources, as shown in the following examples. Example 11.3 shows how to calculate the net electric field at a point in one-dimensional situations.

e **MATH**

The nucleus of an atom exhibits both electric and gravitational fields. To study their similarities and differences graphically, visit www.pearsoned.ca/school/ physicssource.

Example 11.3

Practice Problems

1. Calculate the net electric field at a point 2.10×10^{-2} m to the left of the 1.50×10^{-6} C charge in Figure 11.9.

2. An electron and a proton are 5.29×10^{-11} m apart in a hydrogen atom. Determine the net electric field at a point midway between the two charges.

Answers

1. 3.67×10^7 N/C [left]
2. 4.11×10^{12} N/C [toward the electron]

▲ **Figure 11.10**

Two positively charged spheres, A and B, with charges of 1.50×10^{-6} C and 2.00×10^{-6} C, respectively, are 3.30×10^{-2} m apart. Determine the net electric field at a point P located midway between the centres of the two spheres (Figure 11.9).

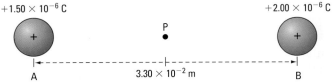

▲ **Figure 11.9**

Given
$q_A = +1.50 \times 10^{-6}$ C
$q_B = +2.00 \times 10^{-6}$ C
$r = 3.30 \times 10^{-2}$ m

Required
net electric field at point P ($\vec{E}_{net}$)

Analysis and Solution
As shown in Figure 11.10, the electric field created by q_A at point P is directed to the right, while the electric field at point P created by q_B is directed to the left. Consider right to be positive.
The distance between q_A and point P is:

$$r_{q_A \text{ to P}} = \frac{3.30 \times 10^{-2} \text{ m}}{2} = 1.65 \times 10^{-2} \text{ m}$$

To calculate the electric field at point P created by q_A, use:

$$|\vec{E}_{q_A}| = k\frac{q_A}{r^2_{q_A \text{ to P}}} = \frac{\left(8.99 \times 10^9 \, \frac{\text{N·m}^2}{\text{C}^{\cancel{2}}}\right)(1.50 \times 10^{-6} \, \cancel{C})}{(1.65 \times 10^{-2} \text{ m})^2}$$

To calculate the electric field at point P created by q_B, use:

$$|\vec{E}_{q_B}| = k\frac{q_B}{r^2_{q_B \text{ to P}}} = \frac{\left(8.99 \times 10^9 \, \frac{\text{N·m}^2}{\text{C}^{\cancel{2}}}\right)(2.00 \times 10^{-6} \, \cancel{C})}{(1.65 \times 10^{-2} \text{ m})^2}$$

Use vector addition to determine the net electric field at point P:
$$\vec{E}_{net} = \vec{E}_{q_A} + \vec{E}_{q_B}$$

$$= \left(\frac{\left(8.99 \times 10^9 \, \frac{\text{N·m}^2}{\text{C}^{\cancel{2}}}\right)(1.50 \times 10^{-6} \, \cancel{C})}{(1.65 \times 10^{-2} \text{ m})^2}\right) +$$

$$\left(-\frac{\left(8.99 \times 10^9 \, \frac{\text{N·m}^2}{\text{C}^{\cancel{2}}}\right)(2.00 \times 10^{-6} \, \cancel{C})}{(1.65 \times 10^{-2} \text{ m})^2}\right)$$

$$= (4.953 \times 10^7 \text{ N/C}) + (-6.604 \times 10^7 \text{ N/C})$$

$$= -1.65 \times 10^7 \text{ N/C}$$

Paraphrase
The net electric field at point P is 1.65×10^7 N/C [left].

Example 11.4 demonstrates how to determine the net electric field at a point due to two charges in a two-dimensional situation.

Example 11.4

Calculate the net electric field at a point P that is 4.00×10^{-2} m from a small metal sphere A with a negative charge of 2.10×10^{-6} C and 3.00×10^{-2} m from another similar sphere B with a positive charge of 1.50×10^{-6} C (Figure 11.11).

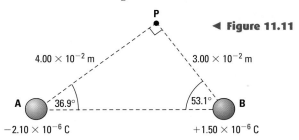

◄ **Figure 11.11**

Given

$$q_A = -2.10 \times 10^{-6} \text{ C} \qquad q_B = +1.50 \times 10^{-6} \text{ C}$$
$$r_{A \text{ to } P} = 4.00 \times 10^{-2} \text{ m} \qquad r_{B \text{ to } P} = 3.00 \times 10^{-2} \text{ m}$$
$$\theta_A = 36.9° \text{ to the horizontal} \qquad \theta_B = 53.1° \text{ to the horizontal}$$

Required
net electric field at point P ($\vec{E}_{\text{net}}$)

Analysis and Solution
Since q_A is a negative charge, the electric field created by q_A at point P is directed toward q_A from point P.
Since q_B is a positive charge, the electric field created by q_B at point P is directed away from q_B toward point P.
Determine the electric field created by q_A at point P:

$$|\vec{E}_A| = \frac{kq_A}{r_{A \text{ to } P}^2}$$

$$= \frac{\left(8.99 \times 10^9 \dfrac{\text{N·m}^2}{\text{C}^2}\right)(2.10 \times 10^{-6} \text{ C})}{(4.00 \times 10^{-2} \text{ m})^2}$$

$$= 1.180 \times 10^7 \text{ N/C}$$

Determine the electric field created by q_B at point P:

$$|\vec{E}_B| = \frac{kq_B}{r_{B \text{ to } P}^2}$$

$$= \frac{\left(8.99 \times 10^9 \dfrac{\text{N·m}^2}{\text{C}^2}\right)(1.50 \times 10^{-6} \text{ C})}{(3.00 \times 10^{-2} \text{ m})^2}$$

$$= 1.498 \times 10^7 \text{ N/C}$$

Practice Problems

1. Calculate the net electric field at point P, which is 0.100 m from two similar spheres with positive charges of 2.00 C and separated by a distance of 0.0600 m, as shown in the figure below.

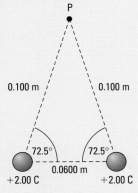

2. Two charges of +4.00 C are placed at the vertices of an equilateral triangle with sides of 2.00 cm, as shown in the figure below. Determine the net electric field at the third vertex of the triangle.

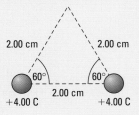

Answers
1. 3.43×10^{12} N/C [90.0°]
2. 1.56×10^{14} N/C [90.0°]

Chapter 11 Electric field theory describes electrical phenomena.   551

The directions of $\vec{E}_A$ and $\vec{E}_B$ are shown in Figure 11.12.

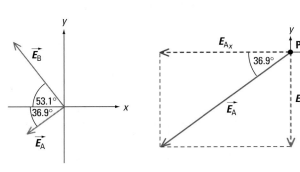

▲ Figure 11.12   ▲ Figure 11.13   ▲ Figure 11.14

Resolve each electric field into x and y components (see Figures 11.13 and 11.14). Use vector addition to determine the resultant electric field.

$E_{A_x} = -(1.180 \times 10^7 \text{ N/C})(\cos 36.9°)$ $E_{A_y} = -(1.180 \times 10^7 \text{ N/C})(\sin 36.9°)$
$\quad = -9.436 \times 10^6 \text{ N/C}$ $\quad = -7.085 \times 10^6 \text{ N/C}$

$E_{B_x} = -(1.498 \times 10^7 \text{ N/C})(\cos 53.1°)$ $E_{B_y} = (1.498 \times 10^7 \text{ N/C})(\sin 53.1°)$
$\quad = -8.994 \times 10^6 \text{ N/C}$ $\quad = 1.198 \times 10^7 \text{ N/C}$

Add the x components:
$E_{net_x} = E_{A_x} + E_{B_x}$
$\quad = (-9.436 \times 10^6 \text{ N/C}) + (-8.994 \times 10^6 \text{ N/C})$
$\quad = -1.843 \times 10^7 \text{ N/C}$

Add the y components:
$E_{net_y} = E_{A_y} + E_{B_y}$
$\quad = (-7.085 \times 10^6 \text{ N/C}) + (1.198 \times 10^7 \text{ N/C})$
$\quad = 4.895 \times 10^6 \text{ N/C}$

Use the Pythagorean theorem to solve for the magnitude of the electric field:

$|\vec{E}_{net}| = \sqrt{(1.843 \times 10^7 \text{ N/C})^2 + (4.895 \times 10^6 \text{ N/C})^2}$
$\quad = 1.91 \times 10^7 \text{ N/C}$

Use the tangent function to determine the direction of the net electric field at point P (Figure 11.15).

$\tan \theta = \dfrac{4.895 \times 10^6 \text{ N/C}}{1.843 \times 10^7 \text{ N/C}}$

$\theta = 14.9°$

The direction of the net field is

$180.0° - 14.9° = 165°$

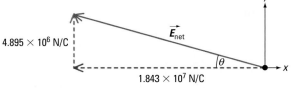

▲ Figure 11.15

Paraphrase

The net electric field at point P is 1.91×10^7 N/C [165°].

In chapter 10, you learned that there are two types of electric charges that interact and are affected by electrostatic forces. In this section, you have learned that these charges are surrounded by electric fields—regions of electric influence around every charge. Electrostatic forces affect charges placed in these fields. Fields explain how two charges can interact, even though there is no contact between them. Since electric fields are vector fields, you can use vector addition to determine a net electric field at a point in the presence of more than one charge in one-dimensional and two-dimensional situations.

11.1 Check and Reflect

Knowledge

1. What is the difference between an electric force and an electric field?

2. Why was it necessary to introduce a "field theory"?

3. What is one important property of the test charge placed in an electric field produced by a larger source charge?

4. Why is an electric field classified as a vector field?

5. If vector arrows can represent an electric field at a point surrounding a charge, identify the two ways that the vector arrows, shown below, represent differences in the electric fields around the two source charges.

6. Describe the effect on the electric field at a point
   (a) if the magnitude of the charge producing the field is halved
   (b) if the sign of the charge producing the field is changed
   (c) if the magnitude of the test charge in the field is halved

Applications

7. Given a small sphere with a charge of magnitude 4.50×10^{-6} C, determine:

(a) the magnitude and direction of the electric field at a point 0.300 m to the right of the charge

(b) the magnitude and direction of the electric force exerted by this electric field on a charge of magnitude 2.00×10^{-8} C placed at the point in (a)

8. A small test sphere with a negative charge of 2.50 μC experiences an electrostatic attractive force of magnitude 5.10×10^{-2} N when it is placed at a point 0.0400 m from another larger charged sphere. Calculate

(a) the magnitude and direction of the electric field at this point

(b) the magnitude and the sign of charge on the larger charged sphere

9. A negative charge of 3.00 C is 1.20 m to the right of another negative charge of 2.00 C. Calculate

(a) the net electric field at a point along the same line and midway between the two charges

(b) the point along the same line between the two charges where the net electric field will be zero

Extension

10. Four similarly charged spheres of -5.00 C are placed at the corners of a square with sides of 1.20 m. Determine the electric field at the point of intersection of the two diagonals of the square.

e TEST
To check your understanding of forces and fields, follow the eTest links at www.pearsoned.ca/school/physicssource.

11.2 Electric Field Lines and Electric Potential

In section 11.1, you learned that the electric field from a charge q at a point P can be represented by a vector arrow, as shown in Figure 11.16. The length and direction of the vector arrow represent the magnitude and direction of the electric field ($\vec{E}$) at that point. By measuring the electric force exerted on a test charge at an infinite number of points around a source charge, a vector value of the electric field can be assigned to every point in space around the source charge. This creates a three-dimensional map of the electric field around the source charge (Figure 11.16).

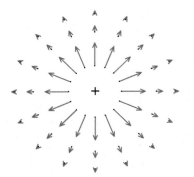

▲ **Figure 11.16** A three-dimensional map of the electric field around a source charge

info **BIT**

A lightning rod works because of the concentration of charges on the point of a conductor. This concentration of charge creates an electric field that ionizes air molecules around the point. The ionized region either makes contact with an upward streamer to a cloud, thus preventing the formation of a damaging return lightning stroke, or intercepts a downward leader from the clouds and provides a path for the lightning to the ground to prevent damage to the structure.

e **SIM**

 Explore the electric fields around a point charge and two charges. Follow the eSim links at www.pearsoned.ca/school/physicssource.

Electric Field Lines

For many applications, however, a much simpler method is used to represent electric fields. Instead of drawing an infinite number of vector arrows, you can draw lines, called **electric field lines,** to represent the electric field. Field lines are drawn so that exactly one field line goes through any given point within the field, and the tangent to the field line at the point is in the direction of the electric field vector at that point. You can give the field lines a direction such that the direction of the field line through a given point agrees with the direction of the electric field at that point.

Use the following rules when you draw electric field lines around a point charge:

- Electric field lines due to a positive source charge start from the charge and extend radially away from the charge to infinity.
- Electric field lines due to a negative source charge come from infinity radially into and terminate at the negative source charge.
- The density of lines represents the magnitude of the electric field. In other words, the more closely spaced and the greater the number of lines, the stronger is the electric field.

Figure 11.17 shows how to draw electric field lines around one and two negative point charges.

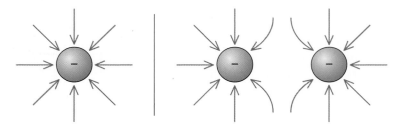

▲ **Figure 11.17** The field lines around these charges were drawn using the rules given above.

Rarely is the electric field at a point in space influenced by a single charge. Often, you need to determine the electric field for a complicated arrangement of charges. Electric field lines can be used to display these electric fields.

In Figure 11.18, lawn seeds have been sprinkled on the surface of a container of cooking oil. In each case, a different charged object has been put into the oil.

- On a sheet of paper, sketch the electric field lines in each situation using the rules for drawing electric field lines given on page 554.

- Use concise statements to justify the pattern you drew in each of the sketches.

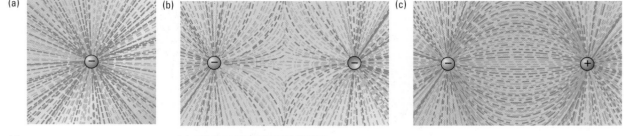

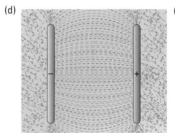

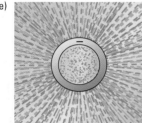

Figure 11.18   (a) one negative charge, (b) two negative charges, (c) one negative and one positive charge, (d) two oppositely charged plates, (e) one negatively charged cylindrical ring

Conductors and Electric Field Lines

In a conductor, electrons move freely until they reach a state of static equilibrium. For static equilibrium to exist, all charges must be at rest and thus must experience no net force. Achieving static equilibrium creates interesting situations that occur only in conducting objects and not in non-conducting objects. These situations occur only for brief intervals of time. Following are five different situations involving charge distribution on conductors and their corresponding electric field lines.

Solid Conducting Sphere

When a solid metal sphere is charged, either negatively or positively, does the charge distribute evenly throughout the sphere?

To achieve static equilibrium, all excess charges move as far apart as possible because of electrostatic forces of repulsion. A charge on the sphere at position A in Figure 11.19(a), for example, would experience a net force of electrostatic repulsion from the other charges. Consequently, all excess charges on a solid conducting sphere are repelled. These excess charges eventually distribute evenly on the surface of the metal conducting sphere.

Figure 11.19(b) shows the corresponding electric field lines created by the distribution of charge on the outer surface of a solid conducting sphere. Because electric field lines cannot have a component tangential to the surface, the lines at the outer surface must always be perpendicular to the outer surface.

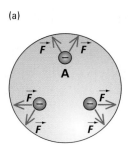
(a)

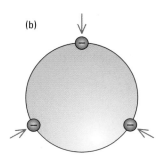
(b)

▲ **Figure 11.19(a)** Charges on a solid sphere

▲ **Figure 11.19(b)** Electric field lines for a charged solid sphere

Solid, Flat, Conducting Plate

How do excess charges, either positive or negative, distribute on a solid, flat, conducting plate like the one in Figure 11.20(a)?

On a flat surface, the forces of repulsion are similarly parallel or tangential to the surface. Thus, electrostatic forces of repulsion acting on charges cause the charges to spread and distribute evenly along the outer surface of a charged plate, as shown in Figure 11.20(b).

Electric field lines extend perpendicularly toward a negatively charged plate. The electric field lines are uniform and parallel, as shown in Figure 11.20(c).

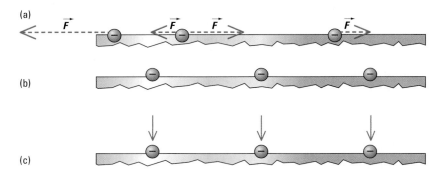

▲ **Figure 11.20**
(a) Forces among three charges on the top surface of a flat, conducting plate
(b) Uniform distribution of charges on a charged, flat, conducting plate
(c) Uniform distribution of charges, shown with electric field lines

Irregularly Shaped Solid Conducting Object

For an irregularly shaped solid conductor, the charges are still repelled and accumulate on the outer surface. But do the charges distribute evenly on the outer surface? Figure 11.21(a) is an example of a charged, irregularly shaped object.

On a flatter part of the surface, the forces of repulsion are nearly parallel or tangential to the surface, causing the charges to spread out more, as shown in Figure 11.21(b). At a pointed part of a convex surface, the forces are directed at an angle to the surface, so a smaller component of the forces is parallel or tangential to the surface. With less repulsion along the surface, more charge can accumulate closer together. As a rule, the net electrostatic forces on charges cause the charges to accumulate at the points of an irregularly shaped convex conducting object. Conversely, the charges will spread out on an irregularly shaped concave conducting object.

On irregularly shaped conductors, the charge density is greatest where the surface curves most sharply (Figure 11.21(c)). The density of electric field lines is also greatest at these points.

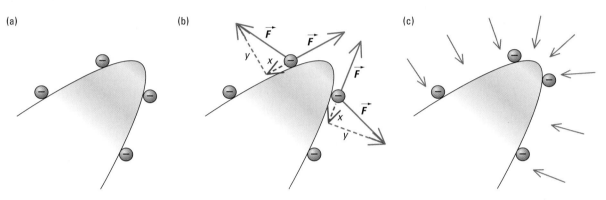

▲ **Figure 11.21(a)** A charged, irregularly shaped convex object

▲ **Figure 11.21(b)** Forces affecting charges on the surface of an irregularly shaped convex object

▲ **Figure 11.21(c)** Electric field lines around a charged irregularly shaped convex object

Hollow Conducting Object

When a hollow conducting object is charged, either negatively or positively, does the charge distribute evenly throughout the inner and outer surfaces of the object?

As you saw in Figures 11.19, 11.20, and 11.21, excess charges move to achieve static equilibrium, and they move as far apart as possible because of electrostatic forces of repulsion. In a hollow conducting object, all excess charges are still repelled outward, as shown in Figure 11.22(a). However, they distribute evenly only on the outer surface of the conducting object. There is no excess charge on the inner surface of the hollow object, no matter what the shape of the object is. The corresponding electric field lines created by the distribution of charge on the outer surface of a hollow object are shown in Figure 11.22(b). The electric field lines at the outer surface must always be perpendicular to the outer surface.

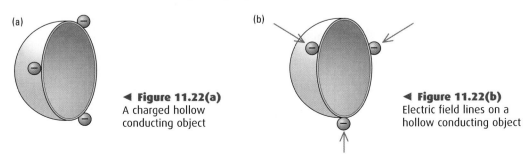

◄ **Figure 11.22(a)**
A charged hollow conducting object

◄ **Figure 11.22(b)**
Electric field lines on a hollow conducting object

Chapter 11 Electric field theory describes electrical phenomena. 557

info BIT

Coaxial cable wires are used to transmit electric signals such as cable TV to your home. To prevent electric and magnetic interference from outside, a covering of conducting material surrounds the coaxial wires. Any charge applied to the conducting layer accumulates on the outside of the covering. No electric field is created inside a hollow conductor, so there is no influence on the signals transmitted in the wires.

Most surprisingly, the electric field is zero everywhere inside the conductor, so there are no electric field lines anywhere inside a hollow conductor. As previously described, this effect can be explained using the superposition principle. Fields set up by many sources superpose, forming a single net field. The vector specifying the magnitude of the net field at any point is simply the vector sum of the fields of each individual source. Anywhere within the interior of a hollow conducting object, the vector sum of all the individual electric fields is zero. For this reason, the person inside the Faraday cage, shown in the photograph on the first page of the unit opener, is not affected by the tremendous charges on the outside surface of the cage.

Parallel Plates

If two parallel metal plates, such as those in Figure 11.23(a), are oppositely charged, how are the charges distributed? Electrostatic forces of repulsion of like charges, within each plate, cause the charges to distribute evenly within each plate, and electrostatic forces of attraction of opposite charges on the two plates cause the charges to accumulate on the inner surfaces. Thus, the charges spread and distribute evenly on the inner surfaces of the charged plates.

(a)

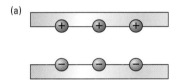

▲ **Figure 11.23(a)**
The distribution of charges on oppositely charged parallel plates

(b)

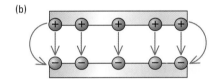

▲ **Figure 11.23(b)**
Electric field lines between two oppositely charged parallel plates

e WEB

Research the operation of an ink-jet printer. What is the function of charged plates in these printers? Begin your search at www.pearsoned.ca/school/physicssource.

The magnitude of the resulting electric field can be shown to be the vector sum of each individual field, so it can be shown that the electric field anywhere between the plates is uniform. Thus, between two oppositely charged and parallel plates, electric field lines exist only between the charged plates. These lines extend perpendicularly from the plates, starting at the positively charged plate and terminating at the negatively charged plate. The electric field lines are uniform in both direction and density between the two oppositely charged plates, and the electric field is zero outside the plates. Such a system is called a parallel-plate capacitor. This type of capacitor is found in many different types of electrical equipment, including printers and televisions (where it is part of the "instant on" feature). It is also used in particle accelerators, such as cathode-ray tubes and mass spectrometers. You will learn about mass spectrometers in Unit VIII.

During a heart attack, the upper and lower parts of the heart can begin contracting at different rates. Often these contractions are extremely rapid. This fluttery unsynchronized beating, called *fibrillation*, pumps little or no blood and can damage the heart. A defibrillator uses a jolt of electricity to momentarily stop the heart so that it can return to a normal beat (Figure 11.24).

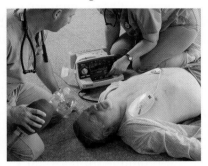

▲ **Figure 11.24** A defibrillator stops the fibrillation of the heart muscle by applying an electric shock.

A defibrillator consists of two parallel charged plates (see Figure 11.23(b)), called a parallel-plate capacitor, connected to a power supply and discharging pads. A typical defibrillator stores about 0.4 C on the plates, creating a potential difference of approximately 2 kV between the plates.

When discharged through conductive pads placed on the patient's chest, the capacitor delivers about 0.4 kJ of electrical energy in 0.002 s. Roughly 200 J of this energy passes through the patient's chest.

A defibrillator uses a high-voltage capacitor to help save lives. Such capacitors have many other applications in other electrical and electronic devices, such as the high-voltage power supplies for cathode-ray tubes in older televisions and computer monitors.

The charge stored in such capacitors can be dangerous. Products containing such high-voltage capacitors are designed to protect the users from any dangerous voltages. However, service technicians must be careful when working on these devices. Since the capacitors store charge, they can deliver a nasty shock even after the device is unplugged.

Questions

1. How does the magnitude of the power delivered by the plates compare with the actual power delivered to the chest by the jolt?

2. Identify a feature of televisions that demonstrates an important application of parallel-plate capacitors.

3. If a defibrillator can store 0.392 C of charge in 30 s, how many electrons are stored in this time period?

In the early 1800s, Michael Faraday performed an experiment to investigate the electric fields inside a hollow metal container. He used ice pails, so this experiment is often called "Faraday's ice pail experiment."

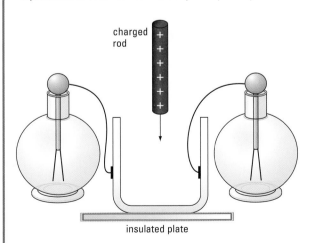

▲ **Figure 11.25** An ice pail is a metal container. It is placed on an insulated surface, and electroscopes are attached to the inside and outside surfaces of the metal container.

This activity is called a conceptual experiment because you will not perform the experiment. Instead, you will predict and justify the results of an experimental procedure that duplicates Faraday's investigation.

The purpose of the experiment is to determine what type of electric field exists on the inside and the outside of a hollow metal container.

A positively charged rod is placed into position inside the metal container, near the centre, as shown in Figure 11.25. The rod is then moved to a position inside the metal container, near one of the inner surfaces.

- Which of the electroscopes would show a deflection when the rod is near the centre of the metal container?

- Clearly explain your reasoning and the physical principles you used in determining your answers to these questions.

Electric Potential Energy and Electric Potential

A Van de Graaff generator can generate up to 250 000 V. Touching the dome not only produces the spectacular results shown in Figure 11.26, it can also cause a mild, harmless shock. On the other hand, touching the exposed wires of a wall socket, which has a voltage of 120 V, can be fatal.

An understanding of this dramatic difference between the magnitude of the voltage and its corresponding effect requires a study of the concepts of electric potential energy and electric potential. These concepts are important in the study of electric fields. Even though the terms seem similar, they are very different. To explain the difference, you will study these concepts in two types of electric fields: non-uniform electric fields around point charges, and uniform electric fields between parallel charged plates.

▲ **Figure 11.26** The charged dome of a Van de Graaff generator exposes a person to very large voltages.

Electric Potential Energy

In previous grades, you learned about the relationship between work and potential energy. Work is done when a force moves an object in the direction of the force such that:

$$W = \vec{F} \Delta \vec{d}$$

where W is work; $\vec{F}$ is the force; and $\Delta \vec{d}$ is the displacement of the object.

In a gravitational system, lifting a mass a vertical distance against Earth's gravitational field requires work to stretch an imaginary "gravitational spring" connecting the mass and Earth, as shown in Figure 11.27(a). Further, because the force required to do the work is a conservative force, the work done against the gravitational field increases the gravitational potential energy of the system by an amount equal to the work done. Therefore:

gravitational potential energy gain = work done

$$\Delta E_p = W$$

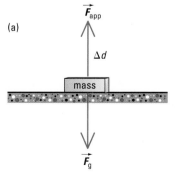

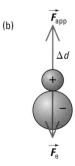

▲ **Figure 11.27(a)** Work is required to lift a mass to a certain position above Earth's surface.

▲ **Figure 11.27(b)** Work is required to move a small positive charge away from a larger negative charge.

Similarly, in an electrostatic system, moving a small charge through a certain distance in a non-uniform electric field produced by another larger point charge requires work to either compress or stretch an imaginary "electrostatic spring" connecting the two charges, as shown in Figure 11.27(b). Since the force required to do this work is also a conservative force, the work done in the electric field must increase the electric potential energy of the system.

Electric potential energy is the energy stored in the system of two charges a certain distance apart (Figure 11.28). Electric potential energy change equals work done to move a small charge:

$$\Delta E_p = W$$

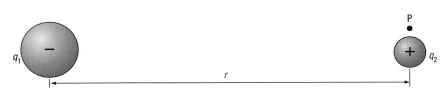

▲ **Figure 11.28** Electric potential energy is the energy stored in the system of two charges a certain distance apart.

Example 11.5

Moving a small charge from one position in an electric field to another position requires 3.2×10^{-19} J of work. How much electric potential energy will be gained by the charge?

Analysis and Solution
The work done against the electrostatic forces is W.
The electric potential energy gain is ΔE_p.
In a conservative system,
$\Delta E_p = W$

So,
$\Delta E_p = W$
$\quad = 3.2 \times 10^{-19}$ J

The electric potential energy gain of the charge is 3.2×10^{-19} J.

Practice Problems

1. A small charge gains 1.60×10^{-19} J of electric potential energy when it is moved to a point in an electric field. Determine the work done on the charge.

2. A charge moves from one position in an electric field, where it had an electric potential energy of 6.40×10^{-19} J, to another position where it has an electric potential energy of 8.00×10^{-19} J. Determine the work necessary to move the charge.

Answers
1. 1.60×10^{-19} J
2. 1.60×10^{-19} J

Choosing a Reference Point

In Chapter 7, you learned that the reference point for zero gravitational potential energy could be chosen as either Earth's surface or infinity. Choosing a zero reference point is necessary so you can analyze the relationship between work and gravitational potential energy.

Consider a zero reference point at Earth's surface. An object at rest on Earth's surface would have zero gravitational potential energy relative to Earth's surface. If the object is lifted upward, opposite to the direction of the gravitational force it experiences, then work is being done on the object. The object thus gains gravitational potential energy. If the object falls back to the surface in the same direction as the gravitational force, then the object loses gravitational potential energy.

As with gravitational potential energy, the value of electric potential energy at a certain position is meaningless unless it is compared to a reference point where the electric potential energy is zero. The choice of a zero reference point for electric potential energy is arbitrary and may be made at two different positions. For example, suppose an electric field is being produced by a large negative charge. A small positive charge would be attracted and come to rest on the surface of the larger negative charge, where it would have zero electric potential energy. This position could be defined as a zero electric potential energy reference point (Figure 11.29(a)).

Alternatively, the small positive test charge may be moved to another position so far away from the larger negative charge that it is no longer attracted to it. This position would be an infinite distance away. This point, at infinity, may be chosen as the other zero electric potential energy reference point. Thus, the zero electric potential energy reference point could be at a position on the surface of the charge producing the field, or it could be at infinity. This text uses *infinity* as the zero electric potential energy reference point for point charges in all calculations (Figure 11.29(b)).

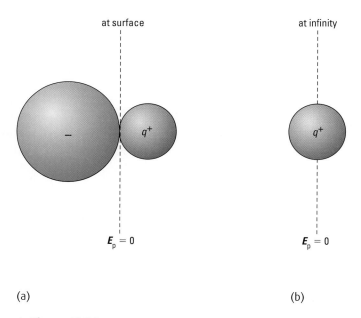

(a)

(b)

▲ **Figure 11.29**
(a) The test charge has zero electric potential energy at the surface of the source charge.
(b) The test charge has zero electric potential energy at infinity.

Work and Electric Potential Energy

The relationship between work and electric potential energy relative to this zero reference point involves understanding that two different types of charges produce two different electric fields. Whenever work is done on a charge to move it against the electric force caused by the electric field, the charge gains electric potential energy. The following examples illustrate the relationship between work and electric potential energy.

Electric Potential Energy Between Parallel Charged Plates

Except at the edges, the electric field between two oppositely charged plates is uniform in magnitude and direction. Suppose a small positive charge between the plates in the field moves from the negative plate to the positive plate with a constant velocity. This motion requires an external force to overcome the electrostatic forces the charged plates exert on the positive charge. The work done on the charge increases the system's electric potential energy:

$$\Delta E_p = W = \vec{F}\Delta\vec{d}$$

Example 11.6

When a small positive charge moves from a negative plate to a positive plate, 2.3×10^{-19} J of work is done. How much electric potential energy will the charge gain?

Analysis and Solution
In a conservative system, $\Delta E_p = W$.

$\Delta E_p = W$

$= 2.3 \times 10^{-19}$ J

Paraphrase
The electric potential energy gain of the charge is 2.3×10^{-19} J.

Practice Problem

1. A charge gained 4.00×10^5 J of electric potential energy when it was moved between two oppositely charged plates. How much work was done on the charge?

Answer

1. 4.00×10^5 J

Electric Potential

Suppose two positive charges are pushed toward a positive plate. In this case, twice as much work is done, and twice as much electric potential energy is stored in the system. However, just as much electric potential energy is still stored per charge. Storing 20 J of energy in two charges is the same as storing 10 J of energy in each charge.

At times, it is necessary to determine the total electric potential energy at a certain location in an electric field. At other times, it is convenient to consider just the electric potential energy *per unit charge* at a location. The electric potential energy stored per unit charge is the

electric potential or **voltage:** the change in electric potential energy stored per unit charge

amount of work required to move a unit charge to a point in the electric field and has a special name: **electric potential**, or **voltage**. To determine the electric potential at a location, use this equation:

$$\text{electric potential} = \frac{\text{change in electric potential energy}}{\text{charge}}$$

$$V = \frac{\Delta E_p}{q}$$

where V is in volts, ΔE_p is in joules, and q is in coulombs.

Since electric potential energy is measured in joules and charge is measured in coulombs,

$$1 \text{ volt} = \frac{1 \text{ joule}}{1 \text{ coulomb}}$$

info **BIT**

The SI unit of electric potential is the volt, named in honour of the Italian physicist Count Alessandro Volta (1745–1827), who developed the first electric battery in the early 1800s.

Thus, if the electric potential or voltage at a certain location is 10 V, then a charge of 1 C will possess 10 J of electric potential energy, a charge of 2 C will possess 20 J of electric potential energy, and so on. Even if the total electric potential energy (E_p) at a location changes, depending on the amount of charge placed in the electric field, the electric potential (V) at that location remains the same.

A balloon can be used as an example to help explain the difference between the concepts of electric potential energy and electric potential. Suppose you rub a balloon with fur. The balloon acquires an electric potential of a few thousand volts. In other words, the electric energy stored *per coulomb of charge* on the balloon is a few thousand volts. Written as an equation,

$$V = \frac{\Delta E_p}{q}$$

Now suppose the balloon were to gain a large charge of 1 C during the rubbing process. In order for the voltage to stay the same, a few thousand joules of work would be needed to produce the electrical energy that would allow the balloon to maintain that voltage. However, the amount of charge a balloon acquires during rubbing is usually only in the order of a few microcoulombs. So, acquiring this voltage requires a small amount of work to produce the energy needed. Even though the electric potential or voltage is high, the electric potential energy is low because of the extremely small charge.

electron volt: the change in energy of an electron when it moves through a potential difference of 1 V

An **electron volt (eV)** is the quantity of energy an electron gains or loses when passing through a potential difference of exactly 1 V. An electron volt is vastly less than a joule:

$$1 \text{ eV} = 1.60 \times 10^{-19} \text{ J}$$

Although not an SI unit, the electron volt is sometimes convenient for expressing tiny quantities of energy, especially in situations involving a single charged particle such as an electron or a proton. The energy difference in Example 11.6 could be given as

$$(2.3 \times 10^{-19} \text{ J}) \left(\frac{1 \text{ eV}}{1.60 \times 10^{-19} \text{ J}} \right) = 1.4 \text{ eV}$$

Example 11.7

Moving a small charge of 1.6×10^{-19} C between two parallel plates increases its electric potential energy by 3.2×10^{-16} J. Determine the electric potential between the two parallel plates.

Analysis and Solution

To determine the electric potential between the plates, use the equation

$$V = \frac{\Delta E_p}{q}$$

$$= \frac{3.2 \times 10^{-16}\,\text{J}}{1.6 \times 10^{-19}\,\text{C}}$$

$$= 2.0 \times 10^3 \text{ V}$$

The electric potential between the plates is 2.0×10^3 V.

Practice Problems

1. In moving a charge of 5.0 C from one terminal to the other, a battery raises the electric potential energy of the charge by 60 J. Determine the potential difference between the battery terminals.

2. A charge of 2.00×10^{-2} C moves from one charged plate to an oppositely charged plate. The potential difference between the plates is 500 V. How much electric potential energy will the charge gain?

Answers

1. 12 V
2. 10.0 J

Electric Potential Difference

When a charge moves from one location to another, it experiences a change in electric potential between the two points. This change or difference is commonly referred to as, simply, **electric potential difference**, potential difference, or voltage difference, ΔV, where

$$\Delta V = V_{\text{final}} - V_{\text{initial}}$$

The potential difference depends only on the two locations. It does not depend on the charge or the path taken by the charge as it moves from one location to another.

electric potential difference: change in electric potential experienced by a charge moving between two points in an electric field

Example 11.8

A small charge of 3.2×10^{-19} C is moved between two parallel plates from a position with an electric potential of 2.0×10^3 V to another position with an electric potential of 4.0×10^3 V (Figure 11.30).

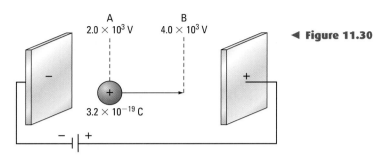

◄ **Figure 11.30**

Determine:
(a) the potential difference between the two positions
(b) the electric potential energy gained by moving the charge, in joules (J) and electron volts (eV)

Given

$V_{\text{initial}} = 2.0 \times 10^3$ V
$V_{\text{final}} = 4.0 \times 10^3$ V
$q = 3.2 \times 10^{-19}$ C

Required
(a) potential difference between two positions (ΔV)
(b) electric potential energy gained by the charge (ΔE_{p})

Analysis and Solution
(a) The voltage is the electric potential difference between the two positions. So,

$$\Delta V = V_{\text{final}} - V_{\text{initial}}$$
$$= (4.0 \times 10^3 \text{ V}) - (2.0 \times 10^3 \text{ V})$$
$$= 2.0 \times 10^3 \text{ V}$$

(b) To calculate the electric potential energy, use the equation

$$V = \frac{\Delta E_{\text{p}}}{q}.$$
$$\Delta E_{\text{p}} = Vq$$
$$= (2.0 \times 10^3 \text{ V})(3.2 \times 10^{-19} \text{ C})$$
$$= 6.4 \times 10^{-16} \text{ J}$$

Since 1 eV = 1.60×10^{-19} J,

$$\Delta E_{\text{p}} = (6.4 \times 10^{-16} \text{ J})\left(\frac{1 \text{ eV}}{1.60 \times 10^{-19} \text{ J}}\right)$$

$$= 4.0 \times 10^3 \text{ eV}$$
$$= 4.0 \text{ keV}$$

Paraphrase
(a) The potential difference between the two positions is 2.0×10^3 V.
(b) The energy gained by moving the charge between the two positions is 6.4×10^{-16} J or 4.0×10^3 eV.

Practice Problems

1. A sphere with a charge of magnitude 2.00 C is moved between two positions between oppositely charged plates. It gains 160 J of electric potential energy. What is the potential difference between the two positions?

2. An electron moves between two positions with a potential difference of 4.00×10^4 V. Determine the electric potential energy gained by the electron, in joules (J) and electron volts (eV).

Answers

1. 80.0 V
2. 6.40×10^{-15} J or 4.00×10^4 eV

The Electric Field Between Charged Plates

Earlier in this section, you determined the electric field strength surrounding a point charge using the following equations:

$$|\vec{E}| = \frac{kq}{r^2} \ \text{ or } \ |\vec{E}| = \frac{|\vec{F}_e|}{q}$$

You also learned that the electric field around a point charge is a non-uniform electric field. Its magnitude depends on the distance from the charge. Later, you learned that a special type of electric field exists between two charged parallel plates. The magnitude of the electric field between the plates is uniform anywhere between the plates and it can be determined using the general equation for an electric field, $|\vec{E}| = \frac{|\vec{F}_e|}{q}$. You cannot use the equation $|\vec{E}| = \frac{kq}{r^2}$ because it is used only for point charges.

Now, after studying electric potential difference, you can see how another equation for determining the electric field strength between plates arises from an important relationship between the uniform electric field and the electric potential difference between two charged parallel plates (Figure 11.31).

If a small positively charged particle (q) is moved through the uniform electric field ($\vec{E}$), a force is required, where $\vec{F} = \vec{E}q$. This force is the force exerted on the particle due to the presence of the electric field. If this force moves the charged particle a distance (Δd) between the plates, then the work done is:

$$W = |\vec{F}|\Delta d$$

$$\text{or } W = |\vec{E}|q\Delta d$$

Since this system is conservative, the work done is stored in the charge as electric potential energy:

$$W = \Delta E_p = |\vec{E}|q\Delta d$$

Since $V = \dfrac{\Delta E_p}{q}$ and the charge moves through an electric potential difference, the electric potential difference between the plates is:

$$\Delta V = \frac{|\vec{E}|q\Delta d}{q}$$

$$= |\vec{E}|\Delta d$$

To calculate the magnitude of the uniform electric field between charged plates, use the equation

$$|\vec{E}| = \frac{\Delta V}{\Delta d}$$

where ΔV is the electric potential difference between two charged plates in volts; Δd is the distance in metres between the plates; and $|\vec{E}|$ is the magnitude of the electric field in volts per metre.

e **WEB**

One of the newest technological applications of parallel-plate capacitors is in disposable cameras. Research the role of capacitors in these cameras. Begin your search at www.pearsoned.ca/school/physicssource.

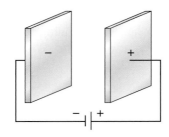

▲ **Figure 11.31** Electrically charged parallel plates

Note that 1 V/m equals 1 N/C because

$$1 \text{ V/m} = \frac{1 \text{ J/C}}{1 \text{ m}}$$

$$= \frac{\dfrac{1 \text{ N·m}}{1 \text{ C}}}{1 \text{ m}}$$

$$= 1 \text{ N/C}$$

Example 11.9

Practice Problems

1. Two charged parallel plates, separated by 5.0×10^{-4} m, have an electric field of 2.2×10^4 V/m between them. What is the voltage between the plates?

2. Spark plugs in a car have electrodes whose faces can be considered to be parallel plates. These plates are separated by a gap of 5.00×10^{-3} m. If the electric field between the electrodes is 3.00×10^6 V/m, calculate the voltage between the electrode faces.

Answers

1. 11 V
2. 1.50×10^4 V

A CRT computer monitor accelerates electrons between charged parallel plates (Figure 11.32). These electrons are then directed toward a screen to create an image. If the plates are 1.2×10^{-2} m apart and have a potential difference of 2.5×10^4 V between them, determine the magnitude of the electric field between the plates.

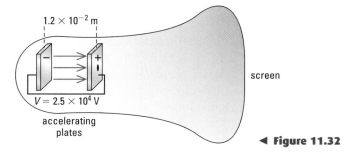

◄ **Figure 11.32**

Given

$$\Delta V = 2.5 \times 10^4 \text{ V}$$

$$\Delta d = 1.2 \times 10^{-2} \text{ m}$$

Required

magnitude of the electric field between the plates ($|\vec{E}|$)

Analysis and Solution

To calculate the magnitude of the electric field between the plates, use the equation

$$|\vec{E}| = \frac{\Delta V}{\Delta d}$$

$$= \frac{2.5 \times 10^4 \text{ V}}{1.2 \times 10^{-2} \text{ m}}$$

$$= 2.1 \times 10^6 \text{ V/m}$$

Paraphrase

The magnitude of the electric field between the plates is 2.1×10^6 V/m.

Knowledge

1. Describe the difference between an electric field vector and an electric field line.

2. Sketch electric field lines around the following charges:

   (a) a positive charge

   (b) a negative charge

   (c) two positive charges

   (d) two negative charges

   (e) a positive charge and a negative charge

3. Describe the difference between electric potential and electric potential energy.

Applications

4. At a point in Earth's atmosphere, the electric field is 150 N/C downward and the gravitational field is 9.80 N/kg downward.

   (a) Determine the electric force on a proton (p^+) placed at this point.

   (b) Determine the gravitational force on the proton at this point. The proton has a mass of 1.67×10^{-27} kg.

5. A box with metal sides is charged with a negatively charged object.

   (a) Compare the distribution of charge at the corners of the box with the faces of the box.

   (b) Draw the electric field lines inside and surrounding the box.

6. What is the electric field intensity 0.300 m away from a small sphere that has a charge of 1.60×10^{-8} C?

7. Calculate the electric field intensity midway between two negative charges of 3.2 μC and 6.4 μC separated by 0.40 m.

8. A 2.00-C charge jumps across a spark gap in a spark plug across which the voltage is 1.00×10^3 V. How much energy is gained by the charge?

9. Determine the magnitude and direction of the net electric field at point P shown in the diagram below.

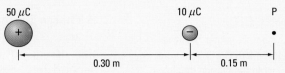

10. A uniform electric field exists between two oppositely charged parallel plates connected to a 12.0-V battery. The plates are separated by 6.00×10^{-4} m.

    (a) Determine the magnitude of the electric field between the plates.

    (b) If a charge of -3.22×10^{-6} C moves from one plate to another, calculate the change in electric potential energy of the charge.

Extensions

11. A metal car is charged by a charged object. Compare the charge distribution on the outside and the inside of the metal car body. Why is this property useful to the occupants of the car if the car is struck by lightning?

12. Which electroscope in the illustration below indicates the presence of a charge? Explain your answer.

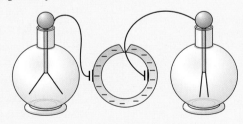

13. Two points at different positions in an electric field have the same electric potential. Would any work be required to move a test charge from one point to another? Explain your answer.

 e **TEST**

To check your understanding of electric field lines, follow the eTest links at www.pearsoned.ca/school/physicssource.

11.3 Electrical Interactions and the Law of Conservation of Energy

info **BIT**

Living cells "pump" positive sodium ions (Na$^+$) from inside a cell to the outside through a membrane that is 0.10 μm thick. The electric potential is 0.70 V higher outside the cell than inside it. To move the sodium ions, work must be done. It is estimated that 20% of the energy consumed by the body in a resting state is used to operate these "pumps."

A charge in an electric field experiences an electrostatic force. If the charge is free to move, it will accelerate from its original position in the direction of the electrostatic force, as described by Newton's second law. The accelerated motion of the charge in the non-uniform electric field of a point charge is different from the accelerated motion of a charge in a uniform electric field between charged plates.

Figure 11.33 shows a charge in the non-uniform field of a point charge. The electrostatic force on a charge placed in the field varies inversely as the square of the distance between the charges. A varying force causes non-uniform acceleration. Describing the motion of the charge in this type of situation requires applying calculus to Newton's laws of motion, which is beyond the scope of this text. However, to determine the particle's speed at a given point, you can use the law of conservation of energy.

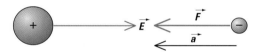

▲ **Figure 11.33** The electrostatic force on a point charge in a non-uniform electric field causes non-uniform acceleration of the charge.

If the forces acting on an object are conservative forces, then the work done on a system changes the potential energy of the system. Electric potential energy, like gravitational potential energy, can be converted to kinetic energy. A charged particle placed in an electric field will accelerate from a region of high potential energy to a region of low potential energy. According to the law of conservation of energy, the moving charge gains kinetic energy at the expense of potential energy. If you assume that no energy is lost to friction and the forces are conservative, the kinetic energy gained equals the potential energy lost, so the sums of the two energies are always equal:

$$E_{p_i} + E_{k_i} = E_{p_f} + E_{k_f}$$

Example 11.10

A pith ball of mass 2.4×10^{-4} kg with a positive charge of 1.2×10^{-8} C is initially at rest at location A in the electric field of a larger charge (Figure 11.34). At this location, the charge on the pith ball has 3.0×10^{-7} J of electric potential energy. When released, the ball accelerates toward the larger charge. At position B, the ball has 1.5×10^{-8} J of electric potential energy. Find the speed of the pith ball when it reaches position B.

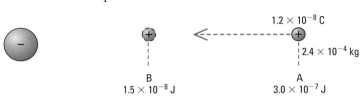

▲ **Figure 11.34**

Given

$m = 2.4 \times 10^{-4}$ kg $q = +1.2 \times 10^{-8}$ C

$E_{p_i} = 3.0 \times 10^{-7}$ J $E_{p_f} = 1.5 \times 10^{-8}$ J

Required

speed of the ball at position B (v)

Analysis and Solution

The pith ball is at rest at A, so its initial kinetic energy is zero. Its electric potential energy at B is lower than at A. Since this system is conservative, the loss of electric potential energy when the ball moves from A to B is equal to a gain in kinetic energy, according to the law of conservation of energy:

$$E_{p_i} + E_{k_i} = E_{p_f} + E_{k_f}$$

Substitute the given values and solve for E_{k_f}.

$$(3.0 \times 10^{-7} \text{ J}) + 0 = (1.5 \times 10^{-8} \text{ J}) + E_{k_f}$$

$$E_{k_f} = 2.85 \times 10^{-7} \text{ J}$$

Since the kinetic energy of an object is $E_k = \dfrac{1}{2}mv^2$,

$$v^2 = \frac{2E_k}{m}$$

$$v = \sqrt{\frac{2E_k}{m}}$$

$$= \sqrt{\frac{2(2.85 \times 10^{-7} \text{ J})}{2.4 \times 10^{-4} \text{ kg}}}$$

$$= 4.9 \times 10^{-2} \text{ m/s}$$

Paraphrase

The speed of the pith ball at position B is 4.9×10^{-2} m/s.

Practice Problems

1. A negative charge of 3.00×10^{-9} C is at rest at a position in the electric field of a larger positive charge and has 3.20×10^{-12} J of electric potential energy at this position. When released, the negative charge accelerates toward the positive charge. Determine the kinetic energy of the negative charge just before it strikes the larger positive charge.

2. A small sphere with a charge of -2.00 μC and a mass of 1.70×10^{-3} kg accelerates from rest toward a larger positive charge. If the speed of the sphere just before it strikes the positive charge is 5.20×10^4 m/s, how much electric potential energy did the negative charge lose?

Answers

1. 3.20×10^{-12} J
2. 2.30×10^6 J

It is easier to describe the motion of a charge in a uniform electric field between two parallel plates, as shown in Figure 11.35. In this case, the acceleration is constant because of the constant force, so either the work–energy theorem or the laws of dynamics can be used. (Because the electric field is constant (uniform), the force acting on a charge q is also constant because $\vec{F}_e = q\vec{E}$.)

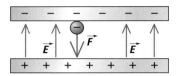

▲ **Figure 11.35** In a uniform electric field between two parallel plates, the acceleration of a charge is constant.

Concept Check

Electrostatic forces and gravitational forces are similar, so the motion of objects due to these forces should be similar. Consider a charge in an electric field between two parallel plates. Sketch the direction of the motion of the charge when its initial motion is:
- perpendicular to the plates (the electrostatic force is similar to the gravitational force on falling masses)
- parallel to the plates (the electrostatic force is similar to the gravitational force that causes the parabolic projectile motion of a mass close to the surface of a large planet or moon)

Example 11.11

Two vertical parallel plates are connected to a DC power supply, as shown in Figure 11.36. The electric potential between the plates is 2.0×10^3 V. A sphere of mass 3.0×10^{-15} kg with a positive charge of 2.6×10^{-12} C is placed at the positive plate and released. It accelerates toward the negative plate. Determine the speed of the sphere at the instant before it strikes the negative plate. Ignore any gravitational effects.

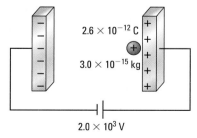

▲ **Figure 11.36**

Given

$q = +2.6 \times 10^{-12}$ C

$V = 2.0 \times 10^3$ V

$m = 3.0 \times 10^{-15}$ kg

Required

speed of the sphere at the negative plate (v)

Analysis and Solution

This system is conservative. You can use kinetic energy of the charge to find its speed.

The initial electric potential energy of the sphere at the positive plate is $E_{P_i} = Vq$. Since the sphere was at rest, its initial kinetic energy, E_{k_i}, is 0 J.

The final electric potential energy of the sphere at the negative plate is $E_{P_f} = 0$ J.

According to the law of conservation of energy,

$$E_{P_i} + E_{k_i} = E_{P_f} + E_{k_f}$$
$$Vq + 0 \text{ J} = 0 \text{ J} + E_{k_f}$$
$$(2.0 \times 10^3 \text{ V})(2.6 \times 10^{-12} \text{ C}) + 0 \text{ J} = 0 \text{ J} + E_{k_f}$$
$$E_{k_f} = 5.2 \times 10^{-9} \text{ J}$$

Since $E_k = \dfrac{1}{2}mv^2$,

$$v = \sqrt{\frac{2E_k}{m}}$$
$$= \sqrt{\frac{2(5.2 \times 10^{-9} \text{ J})}{3.0 \times 10^{-15} \text{ kg}}}$$
$$= 1.9 \times 10^3 \text{ m/s}$$

Paraphrase

The speed of the sphere at the negative plate is 1.9×10^3 m/s.

Practice Problems

1. An alpha particle with a charge of $+3.20 \times 10^{-19}$ C and a mass of 6.65×10^{-27} kg is placed between two oppositely charged parallel plates with a voltage of 4.00×10^4 V. The alpha particle is injected at the positive plate with an initial speed of zero, and it accelerates toward the negative plate. Determine the final speed of the alpha particle just before it strikes the oppositely charged negative plate.

2. If a charge of -6.00×10^{-6} C gains 3.20×10^{-4} J of kinetic energy as it accelerates between two oppositely charged plates, what was the voltage difference between the two parallel plates?

Answers

1. 1.96×10^6 m/s

2. 53.3 V

Example 11.12

An electron enters a parallel-plate capacitor, as shown in Figure 11.37.

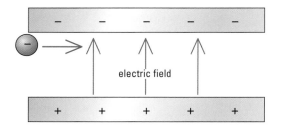

Practice Problems

1. Two horizontal parallel plates, 1.2×10^{-2} m apart, are connected to a DC power supply, as shown in the figure below. The electric field between the plates is 1.7×10^5 V/m. A sphere of mass 3.0×10^{-15} kg with a positive charge of 2.6×10^{-12} C is injected into the region between the plates, with an initial speed of 3.3×10^3 m/s, as shown. It accelerates toward the negative plate. Copy the diagram into your notebook, sketch the motion of the positive charge through the region between the plates, and determine the distance the positive charge moves toward the negative plate after 6.0×10^{-6} s have elapsed. Gravitational effects may be ignored in this case.

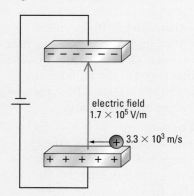

2. An electron, travelling at 2.3×10^3 m/s, enters perpendicular to the region between two horizontal charged parallel plates. If the electric field is 1.5×10^2 V/m, calculate the time taken for the electron to fall a distance of 1.0×10^{-2} m toward the positive plate below. Ignore gravitational effects.

Answers
1. 2.6×10^{-3} m
2. 2.8×10^{-8} s

▲ **Figure 11.37**

(a) Copy Figure 11.37 into your notebook and sketch the motion of the electron through the capacitor.
(b) If the electron experiences a downward acceleration of 2.00×10^{17} m/s² due to the electric field between the plates, determine the time taken for the electron to travel 0.0100 m to the positive plate.

Given
$\vec{a} = 2.00 \times 10^{17}$ m/s² [down]

$\Delta d = 0.0100$ m

Required
(a) sketch of the electron's motion
(b) time (Δt)

Analysis and Solution
(a) The electron's acceleration is downward, so the motion of the electron through the capacitor will follow a parabolic path to the positive plate (Figure 11.38), similar to the projectile motion of an object travelling horizontally to the surface of Earth and experiencing downward acceleration due to gravity.

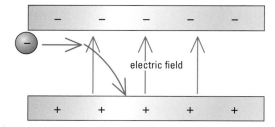

▲ **Figure 11.38**

(b) Use the equation $\Delta d = v_i \Delta t + \dfrac{1}{2}a(\Delta t)^2$ to determine the time it takes the electron to fall to the positive plate. Since $v_i = 0$,

$$\Delta d = \frac{1}{2}a(\Delta t)^2$$

$$\Delta t = \sqrt{\frac{2\Delta d}{a}}$$

$$= \sqrt{\frac{2(0.0100 \text{ m})}{2.00 \times 10^{-17} \dfrac{\text{m}}{\text{s}^2}}}$$

$$= 3.16 \times 10^{-10} \text{ s}$$

Paraphrase

(a) The path of the electron through the capacitor is parabolic.

(b) The time taken for the electron to fall to the positive plate is 3.16×10^{-10} s.

11.3 Check and Reflect

Knowledge

1. A charged particle is placed in an electric field. In what direction will the charged particle always travel?

2. Electric potential energy exists only where a charge is present at a point in an electric field. Must a charge also be present at that point for there to be electric potential?

3. Two charges are at the same position in an electric field produced by a larger third charge, as shown in the diagram below. If charge B is greater than charge A, explain which charge has more electric potential and which has more electric potential energy.

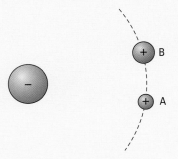

Applications

4. Calculate the speed of an electron and a proton after each has accelerated from rest through an electric potential of 220 V.

5. Electrons in a TV picture tube are accelerated by 25 kV. What is the maximum speed they can acquire?

6. A charge gains 1.92×10^{-14} J of electric potential energy when it moves through a potential difference of 3.20×10^4 V. What is the magnitude of the charge?

7. How much work must be done to increase the electric potential of a charge of 2.00×10^{-6} C by 120 V?

8. A deuterium ion (H^{1+}), a heavy isotope of hydrogen, has a charge of 1.60×10^{-19} C and a mass of 3.34×10^{-27} kg. It is placed between two oppositely charged plates with a voltage of 2.00×10^4 V. Find the final maximum speed of the ion if it is initially placed at rest

   (a) at the positive plate

   (b) midway between the two plates

9. A small charge of $+3.0 \times 10^{-8}$ C with a mass of 3.0×10^{-5} kg is slowly pulled through a potential difference of 6.0×10^2 V. It is then released and allowed to accelerate toward its starting position. Calculate

   (a) the initial work done to move the charge

   (b) the maximum kinetic energy of the returning charge

   (c) the final speed of the returning charge

10. An electron, travelling horizontally at a speed of 5.45×10^6 m/s, enters a parallel-plate capacitor with an electric field of 125 N/C between the plates, as shown in the figure below.

5.45 × 10⁶ m/s

   (a) Copy the diagram into your notebook and sketch

   (i) the electric field lines between the plates

   (ii) the motion of the electron through the capacitor

   (b) Determine the force due to the electric field on the electron.

   (c) Ignoring gravitational effects, calculate the acceleration of the electron.

   (d) If the electron falls a vertical distance of 6.20×10^{-3} m toward the positive plate, how far will the electron travel horizontally between the plates?

Extensions

11. An electron and a proton are located midway between two oppositely charged plates with a voltage of 4.00×10^4 V. Determine which particle will reach its respective plate first.

12. How can the electric potential at a point in an electric field be high when the electric potential energy is low?

13. In question 10, explain why the resulting motion of an electron, initially travelling perpendicular to the uniform electric field between the two charged parallel plates, will be parabolic and not circular.

e TEST

To check your understanding of electrical interactions and the law of conservation of energy, follow the eTest links at www.pearsoned.ca/school/physicssource.

Key Terms and Concepts

field
test charge
source charge
electric field line

electric potential energy
electric potential (voltage)
electron volt
electric potential difference

Key Equations

$$\vec{E} = \frac{\vec{F_e}}{q}$$

$$|\vec{E}| = \frac{kq}{r^2}$$

$$\Delta E_p = W$$

$$\Delta E_p = W = \vec{F}\Delta\vec{d}$$

$$V = \frac{\Delta E_p}{q}$$

$$\Delta V = V_{final} - V_{initial}$$

$$|\vec{E}| = \frac{\Delta V}{\Delta d}$$

$$E_{p_i} + E_{k_i} = E_{p_f} + E_{k_f}$$

Conceptual Overview

The concept map below summarizes many of the concepts and equations in this chapter.
Copy and complete the map to have a full summary of the chapter.

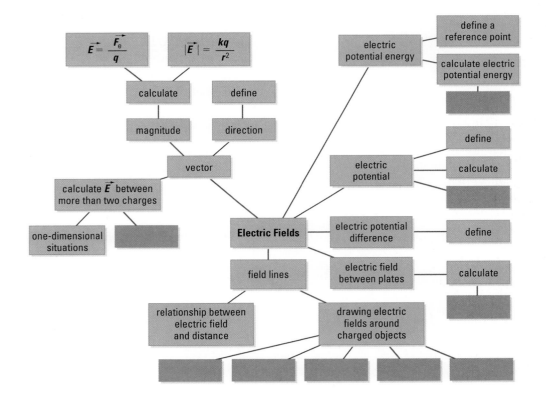

Knowledge

1. (11.1) Identify the three theories that attempt to explain "action at a distance."

2. (11.1) How can it be demonstrated that the space around a charged object is different from the space around an uncharged object?

3. (11.1) How does a vector arrow represent both the magnitude and direction of a vector quantity?

4. (11.2) What is the difference between an electric field vector and an electric field line?

5. (11.2) Two hollow metal objects, with shapes shown below, are charged with a negatively charged object. In your notebook, sketch the distribution of charge on both objects and the electric field lines surrounding both objects.

| cross-section of hollow sphere | cross-section of hollow oval object |

6. (11.2) How do electric field lines represent the magnitude of an electric field?

7. (11.2) Where do electric field lines originate for
   (a) a negative point charge?
   (b) a positive point charge?

8. (11.2) Identify two equations that can be used to calculate the magnitude of an electric field around a point charge.

9. (11.2) When do electric charges achieve static equilibrium in a charged object?

10. (11.2) Why do electric charges accumulate at a point in an irregularly shaped object?

11. (11.2) What is the zero reference point for electric potential energy
    (a) around a point charge?
    (b) between two oppositely charged parallel plates?

12. (11.2) What equation would you use to calculate the electric potential energy at a certain position around a point charge?

13. (11.3) How is the electrostatic force acting on a charged object in the electric field surrounding a point charge different from the electrostatic force acting on a charged object in the electric field between charged plates?

14. (11.3) Assuming forces in a system are conservative, explain how
    (a) work done in the system is related to potential energy of the system
    (b) kinetic energy is related to potential energy

Applications

15. Compare the electric potential energy at points A and B near a charged sphere, as shown below.

   A   B

16. A large hollow metal coffee can is charged with a charging object. An electroscope is then touched to the inside and outside surfaces of the can. Compare the results.

17. A point charge has a charge of $+2.30\ \mu C$. Calculate
    (a) the electric field at a position 2.00 m from the charge
    (b) the electric force on a charge of $-2.00\ \mu C$ placed at this point

18. A charge of -5.00 C is separated from another charge of -2.00 C by a distance of 1.20 m. Calculate
    (a) the net electric field midway between the two charges
    (b) the position where the net electric field is zero

19. Find the net electric field intensity at point C in the diagram below.

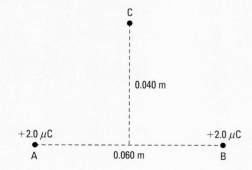

20. A force of 15.0 N is required to move a charge of $-2.0\ \mu C$ through a distance of 0.20 m in a uniform electric field.

 (a) How much work is done on the charge?

 (b) How much electric potential energy does the charge gain in joules?

21. A charge of $-2.50\ \mu C$ is moved from the surface of another point charge of $+3.00$ C a distance of 1.20 m. How much electric potential energy will be gained by the smaller charge?

22. Two parallel plates are separated by a distance of 3.75 cm. Two points, A and B, lie along a perpendicular line between the parallel plates and are 1.10 cm apart. They have a difference in electric potential of 6.00 V.

 (a) Calculate the magnitude of the electric field between the plates.

 (b) Determine the electric potential between the parallel plates.

23. How much work is required to move a charge perpendicular to the electric field between two oppositely charged parallel plates?

24. A cell membrane is 1.0×10^{-7} m thick and has an electric potential difference between its surfaces of 0.070 V. What is the electric field within the membrane?

25. A lithium nucleus (Li^{+3}) that has a charge of 4.80×10^{-19} C is accelerated by a voltage of 6.00×10^5 V between two oppositely charged plates. Calculate the energy, in joules (J) and electron volts (eV), gained by the nucleus.

26. How much electric potential energy, in joules (J) and electron volts (eV), does an alpha particle gain when it moves between two oppositely charged parallel plates with a voltage of 20 000 V?

27. Describe a simple experiment using only a sphere with a known charge and a sensitive meter to measure forces to determine the strength of an electric field at a point away from a larger unknown charge. What would happen to the electric field at a point if

 (a) the magnitude of the test charge were doubled?

 (b) the magnitude of the charge producing the field were doubled?

 (c) the sign of the charge producing the field were changed?

Extensions

28. Explain why electric field lines can never cross.

29. A bird is inside a metal birdcage that is hanging by an insulated rope. If the birdcage is struck by lightning, will the bird be harmed? Explain.

30. Explain why charge redistributes evenly on the outside surface of a spherical charged object and accumulates at a point on an irregularly shaped charged object.

31. Why can there never be excess charges inside a charged sphere?

32. Describe a simple experiment to demonstrate that there are no excess charges on the inside of a hollow charged sphere.

33. Identify a technology that uses the principle that electric charges accumulate at the point of an irregularly shaped object. Describe how the technology applies this principle.

Consolidate Your Understanding

Create your own summary of electric field theory by answering the questions below. If you want to use a graphic organizer, refer to Student Reference 3: Using Graphic Organizers. Use the Key Terms and Concepts listed on page 577 and the Learning Outcomes on page 542.

1. Create a flowchart to describe the differences between electric fields, electric potential energy, and electric potential, using non-uniform and uniform electric fields.

2. Write a paragraph comparing the electric fields around various objects and surfaces. Include diagrams in your comparisons. Share your report with a classmate.

Think About It

Review your answers to the Think About It questions on page 543. How would you answer each question now?

e TEST

To check your understanding of concepts presented in Chapter 11, follow the eTest links at www.pearsoned.ca/school/physicssource.

Properties of electric and magnetic fields apply in nature and technology.

▲ **Figure 12.1** Aurora borealis or northern lights

The spectacular aurora borealis paints the night sky with shimmering colours in northern latitudes (Figure 12.1). Frequently seen above 60° north, its scientific name translates from Latin into "dawn of the north." In southern latitudes, where it is seen mainly above 60° south, it is called the aurora australis — "dawn of the south."

Many ancient civilizations created stories to explain these dancing lights in the sky. Some Inuit peoples of northern Canada believed that the sky was a hard dome that arched over Earth. Spirits could pass through a hole in the dome to the heavens, where they would light torches to guide new arrivals. People still on Earth could whistle to attract the spirits' attention. Tradition still holds that if you whistle while the northern lights dance in the sky, they will move toward you. Other Aboriginal traditions speak of the creator of Earth travelling to the north when he finished his task of creation. There he remained, building large fires to remind his people that he still thinks of them. The northern lights are reflections of these fires.

What are the auroras and what causes them? Why can they be observed only in the far northern or southern latitudes? Is there a relationship between the auroras and surface activity on the Sun, called solar flares? Are they related to other physical phenomena observed on Earth? Finally, how can an understanding of the science of the auroras aid in the development of new technologies? Your studies in this chapter will help answer these questions.

Magnetic Fields in a Bottle

Problem

What is the shape of a magnetic field?

Materials

50 mL of iron filings
450 mL of light cooking oil
1 clear plastic 591-mL pop bottle
string
1 cylindrical cow magnet (must be able
    to fit in the bottle)
tape

Procedure

1 Pour 50 mL of iron filings into the bottle.

2 Pour cooking oil into the bottle until it is about three-quarters full.

3 Replace the cap on the bottle securely and shake the bottle several times so that the iron filings disperse throughout the oil. Remove the cap.

4 Attach the string to one end of the cow magnet and insert the magnet in the bottle. Make sure the magnet is suspended vertically in the middle of the bottle. Tape the other end of the string to the top of the bottle.

5 Replace the cap on the bottle and place the bottle on a table to allow the mixture to settle. Observe the pattern produced by the iron filings.

Questions

1. In your notebook, draw a diagram of the pattern created by the iron filings.

2. Is the pattern created by the iron filings one-, two-, or three-dimensional? Explain your answer.

3. Identify where the density of the iron filings is the greatest and the least. Explain why the filings are distributed this way.

4. From the pattern of the iron filings, is it possible to determine the strength and the direction of the magnetic influence around the magnet? Explain your answer.

Think About It

1. Describe a probable cause of the pattern of the iron filings in 12-1 QuickLab.

2. What types of substances produce this influence?

3. What types of objects are affected by this magnetic influence?

Discuss and compare your answers in a small group and record them for later reference. As you complete each section of this chapter, review your answers to these questions. Note any changes to your ideas.

12.1 Magnetic Forces and Fields

▲ **Figure 12.2** The magnetic effects of certain materials were observed by ancient Greeks as early as 800 BCE

An ancient Greek legend from about 800 BCE describes how the shepherd Magnes, while tending his flock, noticed that pieces of a certain type of rock were attracted to the nails on his shoes and to his metal staff (Figure 12.2). This phenomenon was called magnetism and, as time passed, further studies of the behaviour of this rock revealed several curious effects.

For example, a piece of this rock could either attract or repel another similar piece (Figure 12.3). This effect seemed to result from two different magnetic effects, so investigators thought that there must be two different types of "magnetic ends" on the rock. This observation led to the **law of magnetism**, which states:

Like magnetic ends repel and unlike ends attract each other.

(a)

(b)

▲ **Figure 12.3** A piece of magnetic rock, held near one end of a similar piece of magnetic rock, would attract at one end (a) and repel at the other end (b).

In 1269, Pierre de Maricourt was mapping the position of a magnetized needle placed at various positions on the surface of a spherical piece of this rock. He observed that the directions of the needle formed a pattern that encircled the rock, like meridian lines, and converged at two points on opposite ends of the rock. When this rock was then suspended by a string, the two converging points tended to align along Earth's north–south axis. This property of the rock earned it the name "lodestone" or "leading stone." Maricourt called the end pointing northward the north-seeking or north pole and the end pointing southward the south-seeking or south pole. All magnets have both poles. Lodestone, which contains the mineral magnetite (Fe_3O_4), was later used in the development of compass technology.

Concept Check

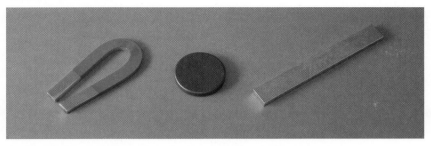

▲ **Figure 12.4**   A U-magnet, a circular magnet, and a bar magnet

Copy the picture of each magnet in Figure 12.4 into your notebook. Since each magnet must have two poles, label the possible positions of the north and south poles of each magnet.

The next big advance in knowledge about magnetism came from the work of William Gilbert. In his book *De Magnete*, published in 1600, he not only reviewed and criticized past explanations of magnetism but he also presented many important new hypotheses.

He compared the orientation of magnetized needles on the surface of a spherical piece of lodestone with the north–south orientation of a compass needle at various locations on Earth's surface. From this study, he proposed that Earth itself is a lodestone with north and south magnetic poles.

Concept Check

How does the north–south alignment of a compass needle suggest that Earth's magnetic north is really a south magnetic pole?

Gilbert was also intrigued by the forces that magnets could exert on other magnetic objects. If you suspend a magnet on a string and bring another magnet close to one of its poles, the suspended magnet will rotate, even though there is no visible contact between the two magnets. Magnets appeared to have the ability to exert forces that seemed to originate from the magnetic poles, and they could affect another magnetic object even without contact. The ancient Greeks called this effect "action at a distance." Recall from chapter 11 that they used the same terminology to describe the effects of electric charges.

In attempting to explain the action at a distance caused by a magnet, Gilbert suggested that an invisible "orb of virtue" surrounds a magnet and extends in all directions around it. Other magnetic substances react to a force created by this orb of virtue and move or rotate in response. His orbs of virtue were the beginnings of the idea of "fields" that would revolutionize physics.

magnetic field: a three-dimensional region of influence surrounding a magnet, in which other magnets or magnetic substances are affected by magnetic forces

Michael Faraday (1791–1867) further developed this concept. He defined a **magnetic field** as a three-dimensional region of magnetic influence surrounding a magnet, in which other magnets or magnetic substances are affected by magnetic forces.

12-2 *QuickLab*

Observing Magnetic Fields

Problem

How can the magnitude and direction of magnetic fields be observed and analyzed?

Materials

1 bar magnet
1 sheet of paper (216 mm × 279 mm)
25 mL of iron filings
1 compass

Procedure

1. Lay the bar magnet on a table and place the paper over the magnet. Trace the shape of the magnet on the paper and label the poles.

2. Carefully sprinkle the iron filings onto the surface of the paper.

3. Tap the paper lightly to reinforce the alignment of the iron filings on the sheet. Draw the pattern of the iron filings around the magnet.

4. Clean the iron filings from the paper and replace the paper over the magnet.

5. Place the compass at several positions around the magnet and trace the direction of the compass needle.

Questions

1. Describe the cause of the pattern produced by the iron filings.

2. Is the pattern created by the iron filings one-, two-, or three-dimensional? Explain.

3. Identify where the density of the iron filings is the greatest and the least. Explain why the filings are distributed this way.

4. Is it possible to determine the strength and direction of the magnetic field surrounding the magnet from the pattern of the iron filings alone? Explain your answer.

5. From your investigation of the effect of a magnetic field on a compass, what appears to be the direction of the magnetic field around a magnet?

Magnetic Fields

The magnetic field surrounding a magnet is represented by the symbol $\vec{B}$ and is measured in teslas (T). A typical bar magnet in the classroom can have a magnetic field of approximately 1×10^{-2} T, whereas Earth's magnetic field is about 5×10^{-5} T. The magnetic field is a vector quantity, so it is represented by a vector arrow. In diagrams, the length of the vector arrow represents the magnitude of the field, and the direction of the arrow represents the direction of the field at a point. You can also use compasses to show the direction of the magnetic field at any position surrounding a magnet, as illustrated in Figure 12.5. The direction of the magnetic field at a given location is defined as the direction in which the north pole of the compass needle points at that location. Figure 12.5 shows that, in general, this direction is from the north to the south pole of the magnet.

info **BIT**

Magnetic field lines run parallel to Earth's surface only at the equator. As they reach the magnetic poles, they gradually dip toward the surface. At the poles, the magnetic field lines point perpendicular to Earth's surface. Navigators in the far north or south must be aware that the magnetic compasses are not useful for navigational purposes in those areas.

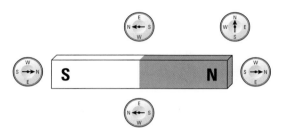

▲ **Figure 12.5**   The direction of a magnetic field is the direction of the force on the north pole of a compass placed in the field.

To represent the entire magnetic field surrounding a magnet, it would be necessary to draw arrows at an infinite number of points around the magnet. This is impractical. Instead, you can draw a few magnetic field lines with a single arrow head indicating the direction of the magnetic field. To find the field direction at a given point, move the arrow head along the field line through that point so that it keeps pointing in the direction of the tangent to the field line. The field lines in Figure 12.6 are a map of the magnetic field with the following features:

e **LAB**

For a probeware activity where you use a magnetic field sensor to determine the relationship between the distance from a magnet and the intensity of the field, go to www.pearsoned.ca/school/physicssource.

- Outside a magnet, the magnetic field lines point away from the north pole of a magnet and toward the south pole.
- The closeness of the lines represents the magnitude of the magnetic field.

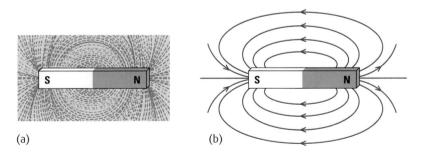

(a)   (b)

▲ **Figure 12.6**   (a) The pattern of iron filings surrounding a bar magnet outlines the magnetic field. (b) Magnetic field lines, representing the direction and magnitude of the magnetic field, can replace the iron filings. The number of magnetic field lines that exit a magnetic material is equal to the number of magnetic field lines that enter the magnetic material, forming closed loops.

Table 12.1 shows some examples of magnetic field strengths.

▼ **Table 12.1**   Magnetic Field Strengths

Physical System	Magnetic field (T)
Earth	5×10^{-5}
Bar magnet	1×10^{-2}
Sunspots	1×10^{-1}
High field magnetic resonance imaging device (MRI)	15
Strongest humanmade magnetic field	40
Magnetar (magnetic neutron star)	1×10^{11}

PHYSICS **INSIGHT**

Before the adoption of SI units, magnetic fields were sometimes measured in a CGS unit called the gauss (G). You might see this unit in some older books. $1 \text{ T} = 10^4 \text{ G}$.

Concept Check

Figure 12.7 shows the patterns produced by iron filings that are influenced by the magnetic fields of one or two magnets. Sketch the magnetic field lines in each case.

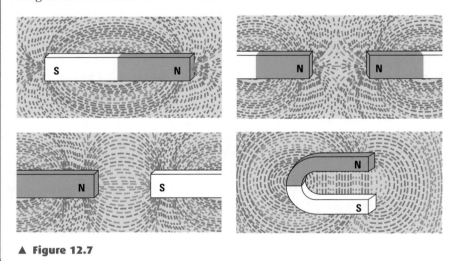

▲ **Figure 12.7**

Concept Check

List at least two similarities and two differences between gravitational, electric, and magnetic fields.

Cause of Magnetism

The force of magnetic repulsion between like poles of magnets is the same force that causes the almost frictionless ride of the Maglev (**mag**netically **lev**itated) train (Figure 12.8). What is the source of this "magnetic levitation" on the train?

(a)   (b)

▲ **Figure 12.8** (a) The force of magnetic repulsion between like poles can cause one magnet to levitate over another. (b) The Maglev train, developed in Japan, floats several centimetres above the guideway, providing a smooth and almost frictionless ride.

Experiments by early investigators revealed many facts about the magnetic fields surrounding magnets and their effects on magnetic objects. However, the actual cause of magnetism eluded scientists until 1820. While demonstrating to students that the current passing through a wire produces heat, Danish professor Hans Christian Oersted (1777–1851) noticed that the needle of a nearby compass deflected each time the circuit was switched on.

This experiment led Oersted to the important conclusion that there is a relationship between electricity and magnetism, at a time when electricity and magnetism were considered separate phenomena. He proved that electric current was a cause of magnetism. Following his initial observations, it was later shown that if electric current was in a straight line, the magnetic field formed a circular pattern (Figure 12.9(a)), and if the electric current was circular, the magnetic field was straight within the coil (Figure 12.9(b)).

info **BIT**

Oersted was among the first to recognize the talent of the writer Hans Christian Andersen and encouraged him when he began writing his now famous fairy tales.

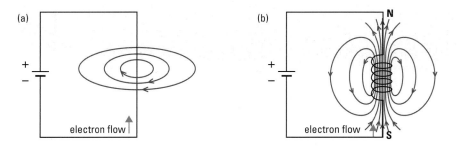

▲ **Figure 12.9** (a) A current passing through a straight conducting wire produces a magnetic field, represented by concentric red circular lines around the wire. (b) A current passing through a coil produces a magnetic field, represented by red circular lines, with poles similar to those of a bar magnet.

PHYSICS INSIGHT

The observation of a magnetic field produced by a moving charge depends on the frame of reference of the observer. If you are stationary and the charge moves past you, you observe a magnetic field. However, if you are moving along with the charge, the charge is stationary relative to you, so you do not observe a magnetic field.

Left-hand Rules for Magnetic Fields

A useful left-hand rule to determine the direction of the magnetic field is the wire-grasp rule described in Figure 12.10. To determine the direction of the magnetic field produced by a moving charge, *use the left-hand wire-grasp rule if the moving charge is negative.* (If the moving charge is positive, then use the right-hand wire-grasp rule.)

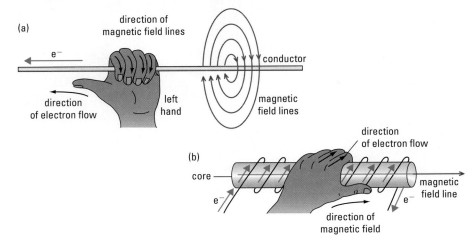

▲ **Figure 12.10** Left-hand rule for direction of a magnetic field due to moving charges: (a) If the conducting wire is straight, then the thumb indicates the direction of the straight current and the cupped fingers indicate the direction of the circular magnetic field. (b) If the current is in a coil of conducting wire, the cupped fingers indicate the circular current and the straight thumb indicates the direction of the straight magnetic field within the coil.

SKILLS PRACTICE   Using the Wire-grasp Rule

1. Sketch the following diagrams into your notebook. Indicate the direction of the magnetic field lines and the direction of current in the wire, as required.

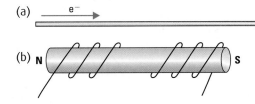

Electromagnets

electromagnet: a magnet having its magnetic field produced by electric current flowing through a coil of wire

As shown in Figure 12.9(b), current in a circular loop or coil of wire produces a magnetic field like that of a bar magnet. An **electromagnet** uses a current-carrying coil of wire to generate a magnetic field that is easy to switch on and off. The strength of an electromagnet can be influenced by:
- increasing the current through the wire
- increasing the number of loops in the coil
- increasing the size of the loops in the coil
- changing the core of the coil

Powerful electromagnets have many industrial uses, such as lifting steel parts, machinery, or scrap iron. Electromagnets are widely used to remotely operate switches or valves. Often, a valve is activated by a metal rod that is drawn into the core of the electromagnet when current flows through the coil. Such mechanisms, called **solenoids**, are common in washing machines, dishwashers, furnaces, and industrial machinery. Figure 12.11 shows two applications of electromagnets.

solenoid: an electromagnet that operates a mechanical device

(a)

(b)

▲ **Figure 12.11**   (a) A lifting magnet (b) An appliance solenoid

Domain Theory and Magnetization

In some atoms, the configuration of the electrons is such that their movement generates a tiny magnetic field. In **ferromagnetic** materials, such as iron, nickel, and cobalt, the magnetic fields of adjacent atoms can align to reinforce each other, forming small regions, or **domains**, with intense magnetic fields. Domains generally range from 0.001 mm to 1 mm across, and may contain billions of atoms.

The orientations of the magnetic fields of the various domains are normally random, so their magnetic fields largely balance each other, leaving the material with little or no overall magnetization. However, size of a domain and the direction of its magnetic field are relatively easy to change. An external magnetic field can cause the domains to align, thus magnetizing the material (Figure 12.12).

The small black arrows in Figure 12.12 indicate the orientation of the magnetic field of an individual domain.

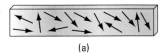
(a)

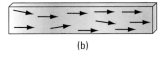
(b)

▲ **Figure 12.12**   (a) When the magnetic fields of atoms in a region line up, they create a magnetic domain in the substance. (b) The final lining up of domains produces a magnet. A typical ferromagnetic object has vastly more domains than the diagrams can show.

If you hang an iron nail by a string and bring a magnet close to the nail, the nail will rotate toward the magnet, even before they touch. The nail is not a magnet with distinct poles, yet a magnetic attraction exists between it and the magnet. When the magnet is close to the nail, the domains in the nail that are oriented for attraction to the magnet increase in size while the other domains shrink. When the magnet is moved away again, the domains in the nail tend to return to random

info **BIT**
Geophysicists theorize that circulating currents of ions in the molten core of Earth produce its magnetic field.

ferromagnetic: having magnetic properties, such as those of iron

domain: a region of a material in which the magnetic fields of most of the atoms are aligned

e **WEB**

All magnetic substances can be classified as one of the following:
• ferromagnetic
• antiferromagnetic
• ferrimagnetic
• paramagnetic
• diamagnetic
Find out what distinguishes one type of magnetic substance from another. Begin your search at www.pearsoned.ca/ school/physicssource.

orientations and the nail loses most of its magnetization. This example illustrates induced magnetization.

The nail will be much more strongly magnetized if it is stroked with a pole of the magnet. The magnetic fields of many of the domains in the nail will align along the direction of motion of the magnet. This magnetization is strong enough that the nail will remain somewhat magnetized when the magnet is removed.

Concept Check

A filing cabinet has been in one position for a long time. It is made of ferromagnetic material, so it can become a permanent magnet. If you hold a compass near the top of the filing cabinet, the compass needle points toward the filing cabinet. If you hold the compass near the bottom of the filing cabinet, the opposite end of the compass points toward the cabinet. Has the cabinet become a permanent magnet through the process of magnetization by contact because it is in Earth's magnetic field? Or has it become a temporary magnet through magnetization by induction caused by the influence of the magnetic compass? Explain your answer.

Magnetism in Nature

The effects of magnetism have been known since early civilizations, but the causes of magnetic behaviour are only now being revealed. A modern understanding of magnetic phenomena began with the development of field theory to replace "action at a distance." Later, the symmetry of nature enabled scientists to use the same field theory that was introduced to describe the gravitational field surrounding any mass and the electric field surrounding any charge to describe the magnetic field surrounding any magnet.

Oersted's investigations, which revealed a relationship between electricity and magnetism, ultimately led to the domain theory to explain a cause of magnetism. As scientists probed deeper into the mysteries of magnetism, many more answers were found. However, the tremendous significance of magnetism has only recently been understood in explaining phenomena and producing technological applications. In the field of biology, for example, researchers have found that certain organisms have ferromagnetic crystals consisting of magnetite in their bodies. Some bacteria use these magnetite crystals to help orient themselves within Earth's magnetic field. Bees and pigeons have magnetite crystals within their brains to help with navigation. The human brain also has these magnetite crystals, but their function is not clear. It is known that an external magnetic field can disrupt the neural activity in the parietal lobe on one side of the human brain.

Understanding magnetism has also led to important technological advancements. These advancements range from simple applications, such as refrigerator magnets, magnetic stripes on cards, and magnetic audiocassette or VCR tapes, to more complicated applications involving magnetic levitation, such as the Maglev train and magnetic resonance imaging (MRI) machines used as a diagnostic tool in health care. Although much has been achieved, there are still many secrets of magnetism to uncover.

THEN, NOW, AND FUTURE   Earth's Magnetic Field

William Gilbert's "Terrella" experiment in the 1500s compared the magnetic field of Earth to that of a bar magnet. From that time, Earth has been considered to be a huge magnet, with similar magnetic properties to a much smaller, ordinary magnet.

This observation was successful in explaining many phenomena. However, care must be taken in comparing the causes of magnetic behaviour in Earth and in a bar magnet. If the cause of magnetism in substances is the motion of charges, scientists are not quite convinced that the motion of charges within Earth's molten core is responsible for Earth's magnetism. They know that Earth's molten core is simply too hot for atoms to remain aligned and exhibit any magnetic properties.

Other probable causes of Earth's magnetic field could be convection currents rising to the cooler surface of Earth, or the motion of charges in the upper ionosphere. The most acceptable and probable cause, though, is the motion of charges in the molten part of Earth, just beneath the crust (Figure 12.13).

Whatever the cause of Earth's magnetic behaviour, it is known that the magnetic field of Earth is not stable. Molten rock within the interior of Earth has no magnetic properties.

However, when molten rock rises to the surface, it cools and solidifies, and its domains orient themselves in line with Earth's magnetic field at the time.

When samples of rock from different strata formed throughout geological times are tested, evidence shows that there are times when not only the magnitude of Earth's magnetic field changed, but also its direction. In the past five million years, more than 20 reversals have occurred, the last one about 700 000 years ago. Coincidentally, modern humans emerged during this time period.

One possible effect of a zero magnetic field, during a reversal, would be an increase in the cosmic ray intensity at Earth's surface. Normally, the magnetic field shields Earth from harmful radiation from space. Fossil evidence indicates that periods of no protective magnetic field have been effective in changing life forms. Evidence that these types of changes could have occurred also comes from heredity studies of fruit flies when exposed to X rays.

We cannot know precisely when the next reversal will occur. However, evidence from recent measurements indicates a decrease in the magnitude of Earth's magnetic field of about 5% in the last 100 years. Based on this evidence,

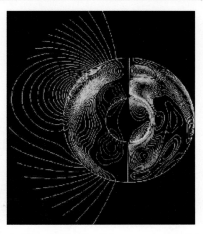

▲ **Figure 12.13** This computer model of Earth shows the molten outer core surrounding the inner core (the small circle). The right side shows the molten currents. The left side shows the magnetic field lines that extend outward through the rest of Earth's interior.

another reversal of Earth's magnetic field may occur within the next 2000 years.

Questions

1. Can the motion of charges in Earth's core create domains? Explain your answer.

2. What is the most probable cause of Earth's magnetic behaviour?

3. What evidence is there on Earth that its magnetic field is not stable?

Knowledge

1. What is the law of magnetism?

2. Explain your answers to the following:

    (a) Does every magnet have a north and a south pole?

    (b) Does every charged object have positive and negative charges?

3. How did William Gilbert determine that Earth was a magnet?

4. What is the most probable cause of magnetism in

    (a) a bar magnet?

    (b) Earth?

5. What accidental discovery did Oersted make?

6. What is the shape of the magnetic field

    (a) around a straight current-carrying conductor?

    (b) within a coil of conducting wire carrying a current?

Applications

7. What would happen to a magnet if you broke it into two pieces?

8. A negatively charged sphere is approaching you. Describe the magnetic field surrounding the sphere and its direction. What would happen if the sphere were positively charged?

9. A spinning top is charged negatively and is spinning clockwise, as observed from above. Describe the magnetic field created by the spinning top and its direction.

10. List at least two differences and two similarities between

    (a) gravitational and electric fields

    (b) gravitational and magnetic fields

    (c) electric and magnetic fields

11. Using the domain theory, explain the following observations:

    (a) A magnet attracts an unmagnetized ferromagnetic material.

    (b) Stroking a nail with a magnet magnetizes the nail.

    (c) A metal table leg affects a compass.

12. Why does dropping or heating a bar magnet decrease its magnetic properties?

13. Consider a bar magnet and Earth, as shown below. Describe the similarities and the differences of their magnetic fields.

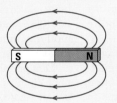
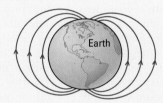

Extensions

14. Why is it difficult to get an accurate bearing with a magnetic compass near the poles?

15. Do magnetic field lines always run parallel to the surface of Earth? Explain your answer.

16. If a current-carrying wire is bent into a loop, why is the magnetic field stronger inside the loop than outside?

*e*TEST

To check your understanding of magnetic forces and fields, follow the eTest links at www.pearsoned.ca/school/physicssource.

12.2 Moving Charges and Magnetic Fields

Near the end of the 1800s, researchers were fascinated by a new technology called the cathode-ray tube (CRT), shown in Figure 12.14. It consisted of a glass tube from which air had been evacuated, and it had positive and negative plates at either end. These new tubes used electric fields to accelerate a beam called a cathode ray through a large potential difference. The beam would "light up" the fluorescent screen at the end of the tube. Scientists were unsure whether this beam was a type of electromagnetic radiation (similar to light), a neutral particle, or a charged particle. They initially called it a cathode ray because it appeared to originate from the cathode plate.

This technology not only enabled J. J. Thomson's discovery of the electron in 1897, but it also led to the later development of many other technologies, one of which was television. The picture tube of a standard TV is a CRT that produces an electron beam. The electron beam is deflected and strikes a fluorescent screen to produce an image.

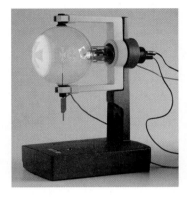

▲ **Figure 12.14** A fluorescent screen detects the production of a cathode ray in an early cathode-ray tube.

The Motor Effect

Deflecting charged particles involves an interaction of two magnetic fields. A charged particle in uniform motion produces a circular magnetic field around it (the wire-grasp rule). Now suppose this charged particle enters an external magnetic field, produced between the faces of two opposite magnetic poles. The interaction of the circular magnetic field of the charge and the external magnetic field produces a magnetic *force* that acts on the particle to deflect it, as shown in Figure 12.15. This magnetic force is also called the **motor effect force** ($\vec{F}_m$) because it causes the rotation of a loop of current-carrying wire. This rotation is fundamental in the operation of an electric motor.

motor effect force: the deflecting force acting on a charged particle moving in a magnetic field

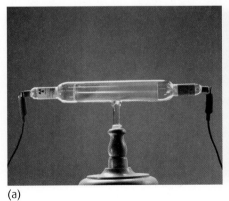

(a)

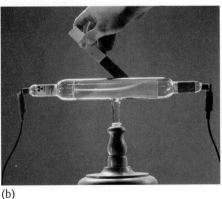

(b)

◀ **Figure 12.15** (a) The cathode ray accelerates in a straight line when it is only influenced by the electric field produced between the cathode and anode plates in a vacuum tube connected to a high-voltage source. (b) A cathode ray will deflect as shown when it is also under the influence of an external magnetic field.

In Figure 12.16, the straight, horizontal lines represent the external magnetic field of the magnetic poles, and the dashed lines represent the magnetic field surrounding the moving charge (using the left-hand rule). In the "replacement magnet" method of illustration, tiny magnets are drawn along the field lines to reinforce the idea of the direction and the effects of the interaction of the two magnetic fields. The × represents negative charge moving into the page. In Figure 12.16, below the moving charge, the external magnetic field and the magnetic field surrounding the charge are in the same direction. Above the moving charge, the two magnetic fields are in opposite directions.

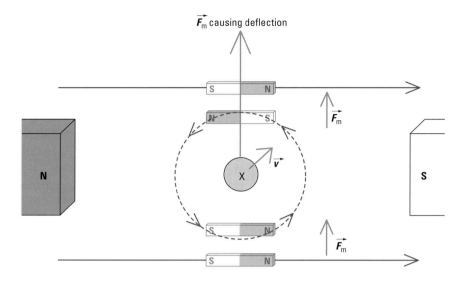

▲ **Figure 12.16** The combined magnetic forces due to the two magnetic fields cause the moving charge to deflect ($\vec{F}_m$) in a direction perpendicular to its direction of motion and perpendicular to the direction of the external magnetic field.

Since the external magnetic field is fixed, the combined effect of the two magnetic fields produces a net magnetic force ($\vec{F}_m$) on the moving charge. As a result, the moving charge deflects in the direction shown, or upward. The deflecting force is always perpendicular to the direction of both the external magnetic field and the motion of the moving charge, as shown in Figure 12.16.

This property distinguishes a magnetic field from electric or gravitational fields. Since the direction of the electric force or gravitational force can be parallel to their respective fields, these fields can be used to change the speed of a charged particle. The magnetic force, on the other hand, is always perpendicular to the velocity of the charged particle. A magnetic force can never do any work on a charged particle, nor can it change the speed or kinetic energy of a charged particle. Since force is not in the direction of the displacement, then there can be no work done on the object. Only the direction of the charged particle's path may be changed.

Left-hand Rule for Deflection

Consider a charged particle travelling perpendicular to an external magnetic field. When it enters the region of a uniform magnetic field, it is deflected in a direction perpendicular to both the original direction of charge movement and the direction of the external magnetic field. A useful hand rule to determine the direction of deflection is the left-hand rule shown in Figure 12.17:

- The thumb indicates the direction of the initial charge movement.
- The extended fingers indicate the direction of the external magnetic field, from north to south.
- The palm faces in the direction of the magnetic force.

(Remember to use the left hand if the moving charges are negative, and the right hand if the charges are positive.)

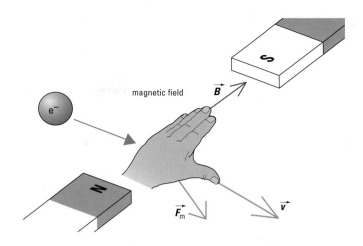

▲ **Figure 12.17** How to use the left-hand rule to determine the deflection of a charged particle

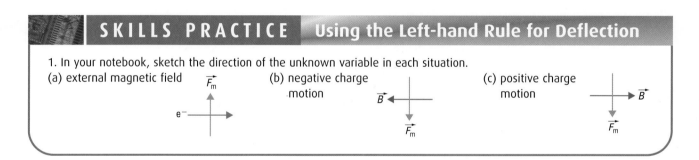

SKILLS PRACTICE **Using the Left-hand Rule for Deflection**

1. In your notebook, sketch the direction of the unknown variable in each situation.
(a) external magnetic field   (b) negative charge motion   (c) positive charge motion

---

12-3 Inquiry Lab

Required Skills
- Initiating and Planning
- Performing and Recording
- Analyzing and Interpreting
- Communication and Teamwork

Using Hand Rules with a Cathode-ray Tube — Demonstration

Question

How can the hand rules be used to determine the deflection of a cathode beam in an external magnetic field?

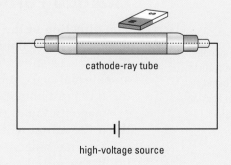

cathode-ray tube

high-voltage source

▲ **Figure 12.18**

Materials and Equipment

1 cathode-ray tube
1 high-voltage source
1 strong bar magnet

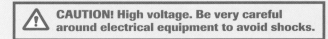

⚠ **CAUTION! High voltage. Be very careful around electrical equipment to avoid shocks.**

Procedure

① Connect the cathode-ray tube to the high-voltage source, as shown in Figure 12.18. Identify the cathode and anode.

② Turn on the current supply. Observe the cathode ray that is produced and its origin.

③ Carefully hold the north pole of a bar magnet near one side of the centre of the cathode tube, in the horizontal plane. Observe the deflection of the cathode ray.

④ Use either the left- or right-hand rule to verify the direction of the deflection of the cathode ray.

⑤ Repeat the procedure in steps 3 and 4 with the south pole of the bar magnet.

⑥ Repeat steps 3 and 4 by holding the magnet on the other side of the cathode tube, in the horizontal plane and then in the vertical plane. Observe the deflection of the beam in each case and use the hand rules to verify the deflection of the cathode ray in each procedure.

Analysis

1. In each case, does the left-hand rule or the right-hand rule verify the direction of the deflection of the cathode ray under the influence of an external magnetic field?

2. How can the hand rules verify whether the cathode ray is a beam of negatively or positively charged particles?

3. Draw the magnetic field lines of the magnet and the moving charges to verify the direction of deflection of the cathode ray.

4. Is the hand rule a valid method of determining the deflection of the cathode ray in all your procedures?

5. How does the deflection of the cathode ray prove that the cathode ray is a beam of charged particles?

Concept Check

Compare the magnetic force of an external magnetic field on a moving charged particle with:
- the gravitational force of Earth on the mass of the charged particle
- the electric force due to another nearby charged particle

---

e SIM

Explore the motion of a charged particle in a uniform magnetic field. Follow the eSim links at www.pearsoned.ca/school/physicssource.

Charged Particle Motion in a Magnetic Field

The direction of the initial motion of a charged particle in an external magnetic field determines how the charged particle will deflect. Figure 12.19 shows what can happen to a charged particle as it enters an external magnetic field:

(a) If the initial motion of the charged particle is parallel to the external magnetic field, then there is no effect.

(b) If the initial motion of the charged particle is perpendicular to the external magnetic field, the charge is deflected in a circular arc.

(c) If the initial motion of the charged particle is at an angle to an external magnetic field, the charge deflects in a circular motion that will form a helical path.

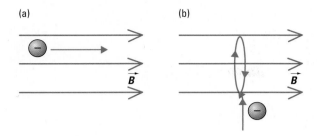

(a)

(b)

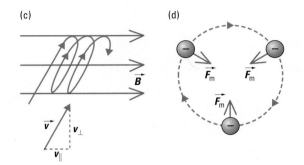

(c)

(d)

◀ **Figure 12.19** (a) When the charged particle's velocity is parallel to the external magnetic field ($\vec{B}$), the charged particle's path is a straight line. (b) The charged particle's motion is perpendicular to the magnetic field, so the particle is deflected in a circular arc. (c) The charged particle's motion is at an angle to the magnetic field, so the particle follows a helical path. (d) This side view from the left shows the magnetic force acting as the centripetal force that causes the charge to follow a circular path.

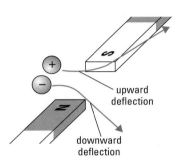

▲ **Figure 12.20** A magnetic field deflects moving oppositely charged particles in opposite directions, as shown.

Oppositely charged particles deflect in opposite directions in a magnetic field (Figure 12.20). If the magnitude of the external magnetic field is large enough, the field can cause circular motion that remains contained in the magnetic field. In this circular motion, the centripetal force is the magnetic force.

Magnetic deflection of charged particles is the underlying principle for useful powerful analytical and research tools such as mass spectrometers and particle accelerators. Unit VIII presents these devices and their applications in science, medicine, and industry.

Auroras

Tremendous expulsions of magnetic energy from the solar atmosphere, called solar flares, expel streams of charged particles at speeds around 10% of the speed of light (Figure 12.21). When some of these particles strike Earth's magnetic field, they are deflected by the magnetic force and spiral in a helical path along Earth's magnetic field lines. These particles enter the atmosphere as they approach Earth's magnetic poles, and collide with air molecules.

These collisions excite the atoms of the air molecules, in a process that will be described in Chapter 15, causing them to emit visible light that we see as the aurora. The process repeats because Earth's non-uniform magnetic field produces a magnetic force component that causes the charged particles to reverse their direction of motion, travelling to Earth's opposite pole. The same auroral effect is produced at this pole, and the process continues to repeat as the charged particles oscillate back and forth between the poles, trapped in a type of "magnetic bottle" called the Van Allen belt.

e **WEB**

Research the formation of the Van Allen belts. Consider the shape of the Van Allen belt on the side of Earth facing the Sun and on the side of Earth away from the Sun. What is the cause of this difference in shape? Begin your search at www.pearsoned.ca/school/physicssource.

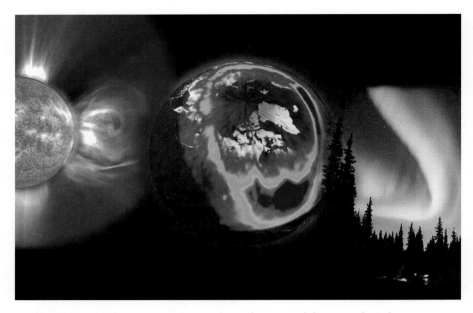

▲ **Figure 12.21** This composite image shows the cause of the aurora borealis. Streams of high-energy charged particles erupt from the Sun (far left). They are deflected by Earth's magnetic field toward the poles, creating the bright ring shown in the satellite image of Earth (centre). There they interact with air molecules in the atmosphere to produce the aurora (far right).

Calculating the Magnetic Force

By studying the different types of deflections, scientists can also explain the complex deflection of charged particles entering a magnetic field at an angle, such as the particles that cause the auroras.

The magnitude of the deflecting force ($|\vec{F}_m|$) depends on all of the following:

- the magnitude of the moving charge (q)
- the magnitude of the perpendicular velocity component ($v_\perp$)
- the magnitude of the external magnetic field (B)

The magnitude of the deflecting force can be calculated using this equation:

$$|\vec{F}_m| = qv_\perp B$$

where q is the magnitude of moving charge in coulombs (C); $v_\perp$ is the component of the speed perpendicular to the magnetic field in metres per second (m/s); and B is the magnitude of the external magnetic field in teslas (T). Example 12.1 describes how to calculate the magnetic force on a charge moving perpendicular to an external magnetic field.

When the velocity of the charge is not perpendicular to the magnetic field, you can use trigonometry to find the perpendicular component:

$$v_\perp = v \sin \theta$$

where θ is the angle between the charge's velocity, $\vec{v}$, and the magnetic field, $\vec{B}$.

Example 12.1

An electron is travelling at 3.20×10^5 m/s perpendicular to an external magnetic field of magnitude 2.20×10^{-1} T (Figure 12.22). Calculate the magnetic force acting on the electron.

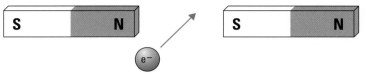

▲ **Figure 12.22**

Given

$q = 1$ electron or -1.60×10^{-19} C

$B = 2.20 \times 10^{-1}$ T

$v_{\perp} = 3.20 \times 10^5$ m/s

Required

magnetic force ($\vec{F}_{\mathrm{m}}$)

Analysis and Solution

Determine the magnitude of the magnetic deflecting force:

$|\vec{F}_{\mathrm{m}}| = qv_{\perp}B$

$\qquad = (1.60 \times 10^{-19}\ \mathrm{C})(3.20 \times 10^5\ \frac{\mathrm{m}}{\mathrm{s}})(2.20 \times 10^{-1}\ \mathrm{T})$

$\qquad = 1.13 \times 10^{-14}$ N

Since the charge is negative, use the left-hand rule to determine the direction of the magnetic force.

- Thumb points in the direction of the charged particle's movement, into the page.

- Extended fingers point in the direction of the external magnetic field, to the right of the page (north to south).

- Palm points in the direction of the magnetic deflecting force, toward the top of the page.

Paraphrase

The magnetic force is 1.13×10^{-14} N [upward].

Practice Problems

1. A proton with a charge of 1.60×10^{-19} C is travelling with a speed of 3.50×10^4 m/s perpendicularly through an external magnetic field of magnitude 4.20×10^{-4} T. Determine the magnitude of the magnetic deflecting force on the proton.

2. An ion with a charge of $+3.20 \times 10^{-19}$ C and a speed of 2.30×10^5 m/s enters an external magnetic field of 2.20×10^{-1} T, at an angle of $30°$, as shown in the figure below. Calculate the magnitude of the magnetic deflecting force on the ion.

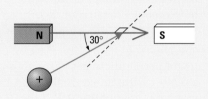

3. A negatively charged sphere travels from west to east along Earth's surface at the equator. What is the direction of the magnetic deflecting force on the sphere?

Answers

1. 2.35×10^{-18} N
2. 8.10×10^{-15} N
3. Downward toward Earth's surface

Often, a charged particle may be influenced by a combination of two fields, such as a magnetic field and a gravitational field, or a magnetic field and an electric field. "Crossed-field" devices are technologies that use both magnetic and electric fields. An example is the magnetron, which produces microwaves in microwave ovens.

Example 12.2

A carbon ion, with a mass of 2.01×10^{-26} kg and a positive charge of magnitude 1.60×10^{-19} C, enters the region of an external magnetic field of magnitude 6.32×10^{-5} T, as shown in Figure 12.23. Find the perpendicular speed at which the magnetic deflecting force will balance the gravitational force such that the carbon ion will travel in a straight line.

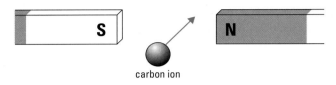

carbon ion

▲ **Figure 12.23**

Given

$m = 2.01 \times 10^{-26}$ kg

$|\vec{B}| = 6.32 \times 10^{-5}$ T

$q = +1.60 \times 10^{-19}$ C

$g = 9.81$ N/kg

Required

speed (v) at which the magnitudes of the magnetic force, $|\vec{F}_m|$, and the gravitational force, $|\vec{F}_g|$, are equal

Analysis and Solution

The gravitational force on the carbon ion has a magnitude of $|\vec{F}_g| = mg$ and is directed downward.

The magnetic force on the carbon ion has a magnitude of $|\vec{F}_m| = qv_\perp B$ and must be directed upward.

$$|\vec{F}_{net}| = |\vec{F}_m| - |\vec{F}_g|$$

But the magnetic deflecting force and the gravitational force balance (Figure 12.24), so $|\vec{F}_{net}| = 0$. Therefore,

$$|\vec{F}_m| = |\vec{F}_g|$$

$$qv_\perp B = mg$$

$$v_\perp = \frac{mg}{Bq}$$

$$= \frac{(2.01 \times 10^{-26} \, \text{kg})\left(9.81 \, \frac{\text{N}}{\text{kg}}\right)}{(6.32 \times 10^{-5} \, \text{T})(1.60 \times 10^{-19} \, \text{C})}$$

$$= 1.95 \times 10^{-2} \, \text{m/s}$$

Paraphrase

The carbon atom will travel in a straight line if its speed is 1.95×10^{-2} m/s.

▲ **Figure 12.24**

$\vec{F}_m$

$\vec{F}_g$

Practice Problems

1. An electron, with a charge of magnitude 1.60×10^{-19} C and a mass of 9.11×10^{-31} kg, is travelling west along the surface of Earth at the equator. If the magnitude of the magnetic field at this location is 5.00×10^{-5} T, what minimum speed must the electron maintain to remain at the same height above Earth's surface?

2. Ions, with a charge of 1.60×10^{-19} C and a mass of 8.12×10^{-26} kg, travel perpendicularly through a region with an external magnetic field of 0.150 T. If the perpendicular speed of the ions is 8.00×10^4 m/s, determine
   (a) the magnitude of the deflecting force on the ion
   (b) the radius of curvature of the motion of the deflected ion

Hint: The magnetic deflecting force is the centripetal force.

$$|\vec{F}_m| = |\vec{F}_c|$$

$$qv_\perp B = \frac{mv^2}{r}$$

Answers

1. 1.12×10^{-6} m/s
2. (a) 1.92×10^{-15} N
   (b) 0.271 m

In this section, you have studied the deflection of a moving charged particle in a magnetic field. Applying this science, you learned not only the importance of this phenomenon in technologies, such as a television and a magnetron, but also the significance of this phenomenon in protecting Earth from harmful cosmic radiations. The magnetic field of Earth, in deflecting dangerous charged particles from striking Earth's surface, also produces one of the most beautiful and spectacular natural light shows—the aurora.

12.2 Check and Reflect

Knowledge

1. Why is a cathode ray called a cathode ray?

2. What is the difference between a magnetic field vector arrow and a magnetic field line?

3. An electron and a proton, both with the same perpendicular velocity, enter a region with a uniform external magnetic field. What can you state about the deflections of both particles?

4. How can the motion of a moving charged particle distinguish between a magnetic field and an electric field?

Applications

5. A positively charged lithium ion is travelling horizontally along Earth's surface. Describe the deflection due to the magnetic force if the ion travels

   (a) south to north

   (b) east to west

   (c) upward into the atmosphere

6. A proton with a speed of 2.00×10^5 m/s enters an external magnetic field of magnitude 0.200 T. Calculate the magnitude of the deflecting force if the proton enters

   (a) perpendicular to the magnetic field

   (b) at an angle of 35.0° to the field

7. A 0.020-g metal ball with a charge of $-3.0\ \mu C$ is thrown horizontally along Earth's equator. How fast must the ball be thrown so that it maintains the same height, during its motion tangential to Earth's surface, if the magnitude of Earth's magnetic field is 5.0×10^{-5} T?

8. An alpha particle, with a charge of $2 \times 1.60 \times 10^{-19}$ C, is travelling perpendicularly through a magnetic field of magnitude 2.00×10^{-2} T at a speed of 1.02×10^{-5} m/s. What minimum gravitational force is required to suspend the alpha particle at the same position above Earth's surface?

9. Electrons in the picture tube of a television are accelerated to a speed of 1.30×10^6 m/s. As they travel through the tube, they experience a perpendicular magnetic field of magnitude 0.0700 T. What is the radius of deflection of the electrons in the tube?

10. A cosmic ray proton travelling through space at 4.38×10^6 m/s deflects in a circular arc with a radius of 5.50×10^6 m. What is the magnitude of the magnetic field at that point in space?

Extensions

11. Explain why a magnetic force can never do work on a moving charge.

12. Why are auroras seen only at higher latitudes?

e TEST

To check your understanding of moving charges and magnetic fields, follow the eTest links at www.pearsoned.ca/school/physicssource.

12.3 Current-carrying Conductors and Magnetic Fields

▲ **Figure 12.25** A galvanometer and an electric motor, like the one in this lawn mower, apply magnetic fields produced by a flow of charge.

Two of the most common applications of magnetic fields acting on moving charged particles are meters (such as ammeters, voltmeters, and galvanometers) and electric motors (Figure 12.25). Although these technologies appear to be different from the technology of the television, the basic operating principle of all these technologies is similar. Recall from earlier science studies that a galvanometer is a device for detecting and measuring small electric currents. How does a galvanometer operate? How is its operation similar to the technologies of the electric motor and television?

Electric Current

current: the quantity of charge that flows through a wire in a given unit of time

ampere: the flow of 1 C of charge past a point in a conductor in 1 s

Recall from earlier science courses that electric **current** is the movement of charged particles. It can be defined more precisely as the quantity of charge that flows through a wire in a given unit of time.

The unit for current, the **ampere** (A), is a measure of the rate of current. The ampere is an SI base unit. A current of 1 A is equivalent to the flow of 1 C of charge past a point in a conductor in 1 s. In other words, 1 A = 1 C/s. For example, the effective value of the current through a 100-W light bulb is about one ampere (1 A) of current. The ampere is named in honour of the French scientist André-Marie Ampère (1775–1836), who is renowned for his analysis of the relationship between current and magnetic force.

This equation shows the relationship between current and charge:

$$I = \frac{q}{t}$$

where I is the current in amperes, q is the magnitude of charge in coulombs, and t is the time elapsed in seconds.

Example 12.3

Calculate the current in a wire through which 20.0 C of charge passes in 4.00 s.

Given
$q = 20.0$ C
$t = 4.00$ s

Required
current (I)

Analysis and Solution
To calculate the current, use the equation

$$I = \frac{q}{t}$$

$$= \frac{20.0 \text{ C}}{4.00 \text{ s}}$$

$$= 5.00 \frac{\text{C}}{\text{s}}$$

$$= 5.00 \text{ A}$$

Paraphrase
The current in the conducting wire is 5.00 A.

Practice Problems

1. A lightning strike transfers 20.0 C of charge to the ground in 1.00 ms. Calculate the current during this lightning strike.

2. If the current in a household appliance is 5.00 A, calculate the amount of charge that passes through the appliance in 10.0 s.

Answers

1. 2.00×10^4 A

2. 50.0 C

Magnetic Force on a Current-carrying Conductor

In a television picture tube, powerful external magnetic fields are used to deflect moving electrons to produce an image on a screen. To analyze the operation of a galvanometer or electric motor, and to reveal the similarity of their operation to that of a television, consider the movement of electrons as a current in a wire conductor. When there is an electric current in a wire that is perpendicular to an external magnetic field, each electron experiences a magnetic force caused by the interactions of its own magnetic field and the external magnetic field (Figure 12.26). You can observe the effect of this force. The magnetic force causes the electrons to deflect upward. However, the electrons cannot escape the wire, so if the magnetic force on the electrons is great enough, the whole wire will rise upward, opposite to the force of gravity. The magnetic force on a conducting wire is the same as the magnetic deflecting force on a moving charge ($\vec{F}_m$) that you studied in section 12.2.

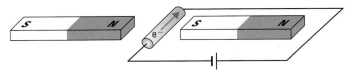

▲ **Figure 12.26** A current of electrons passes through a conducting wire lying perpendicular to an external magnetic field.

Left-hand Rule for Magnetic Force

To determine the direction of the magnetic force, you can use the left-hand rule, as shown in Figure 12.27:

- Your thumb indicates the direction of electron flow in the conductor.
- Your extended fingers point in the direction of the external magnetic field.
- Your palm indicates the direction of the magnetic deflecting force on the wire.

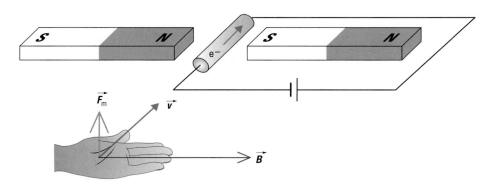

▲ **Figure 12.27** The left-hand rule for determining the direction of magnetic force

To calculate the magnitude of the magnetic force for a length of current-carrying conducting wire, use the equation

$$|\vec{F}_m| = Il_\perp B$$

where I is the current measured in amperes; $l_\perp$ is the length of the wire perpendicular to the magnetic field in metres; B is the magnitude of the external magnetic field in teslas; and $|\vec{F}_m|$ is the magnitude of the magnetic force in newtons.

The Galvanometer

In the operation of the galvanometer, a coil of wire is mounted to allow for movement within the strong magnetic field of the permanent magnet (Figure 12.28). The coil turns against a spring with an attached needle pointing to a calibrated scale. When there is a current in the coil, the magnetic forces cause the coil to rotate. The greater the current, the greater the rotation, as registered on the scale by the needle. The galvanometer, which measures very small currents, can be made to measure larger currents (ammeter) by combining it with small resistors in parallel, and to measure larger potential differences (voltmeter) by combining it with large resistors in series. The magnetic force produced on a current-carrying wire can be demonstrated in the 12-4 QuickLab on page 606.

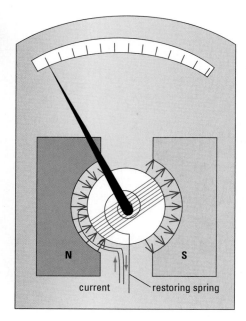

▲ **Figure 12.28** A schematic diagram of a galvanometer reveals all the essential components in its operation.

Example 12.4

An 8.50-cm length of conducting wire lies perpendicular to an external magnetic field of magnitude 4.20 T, as shown in Figure 12.29. If there is a negative charge flow of 2.10 A in the conductor, calculate the magnitude and determine the direction of the magnetic force on the wire.

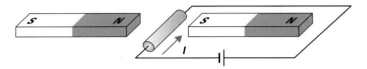

▲ **Figure 12.29**

Given

$l_\perp = 8.50 \times 10^{-2}$ m

$B = 4.20$ T

$I = 2.10$ A

Required

magnitude and direction of the magnetic force on the wire $(\vec{F}_m)$

Analysis and Solution

Determine the magnitude of the magnetic force:

$|\vec{F}_m| = Il_\perp B$

$= (2.10 \text{ A})(8.50 \times 10^{-2} \text{ m})(4.20 \text{ T})$

$= 0.750$ N

Use the left-hand rule to determine the direction of the magnetic force, because the moving charges are negative:

- Thumb points in the direction of the charge movement or current, into the page.
- Extended fingers point in the direction of the external magnetic field, to the right of the page (north to south).
- Palm points in the direction of the magnetic force, to the top of the page.

Paraphrase

The magnetic force is 0.750 N [upward].

Practice Problems

1. A 0.500-m length of conducting wire carrying a current of 10.0 A is perpendicular to an external magnetic field of magnitude 0.200 T. Determine the magnitude of the magnetic force on this wire.

2. A thin conducting wire 0.75 m long has a mass of 0.060 kg. What is the minimum current required in the wire to make it "float" in a magnetic field of magnitude 0.15 T?

Answers

1. 1.00 N

2. 5.2 A

Demonstration of a Current-carrying Conductor in a Uniform Magnetic Field

Problem

How does a uniform magnetic field affect a current-carrying conductor?

Materials

1 piece of stiff insulated conducting wire (6–8 cm long)
2 alligator clips
1 U-shaped magnet
thread or light string
retort stand and clamp
variable low-voltage DC power supply with ammeter

Procedure

1 Set up the apparatus as shown in Figure 12.30.

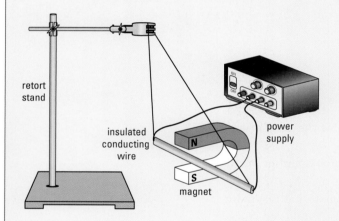

retort stand

insulated conducting wire

power supply

N

S

magnet

▲ **Figure 12.30**

2 Carefully increase the current (amperage) from the power supply.

3 Observe any effects on the current-carrying conductor.

Questions

1. Describe any effects on the current-carrying conductor that occurred as the current through the conducting wire increased.

2. Does the hand rule verify the direction of the movement of the conducting wire? Explain which hand rule must be used.

3. What is the effect of an external magnetic field on a current-carrying conductor?

4. Based on what you have just observed, design a lab that would demonstrate the effects of a uniform magnetic field on a current-carrying conductor.

Magnetic Forces Between Two Current-carrying Conductors

After Oersted demonstrated that a current-carrying conductor creates a magnetic field around a conductor, the French scientist André-Marie Ampère performed extensive studies to determine the magnitude of the magnetic field at any point surrounding a current-carrying conductor. In addition to his mathematical analysis of magnetic fields, he is also noted for determining that two current-carrying conductors exert magnetic forces on each other. The charged particles in one wire are affected by magnetic forces when placed in the magnetic field of another current-carrying wire. Currents in the same direction attract each other (Figure 12.31(a)), and currents in opposite directions repel each other (Figure 12.31(b)).

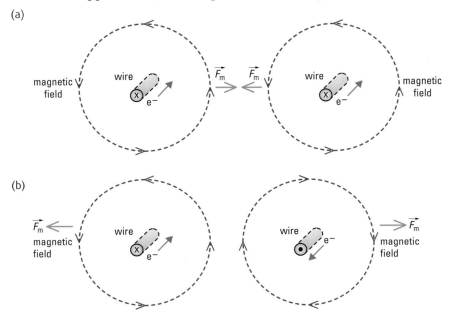

▲ **Figure 12.31** From the left-hand rule for magnetic fields, the red dashed arrows indicate the orientation of the magnetic field around each wire. Use the left-hand rule for magnetic force to determine how the wires will move relative to each other. (a) When currents are in the same direction, the wires attract each other. (b) When currents are in opposite directions, the wires repel each other.

Through careful experimentation and measurement, Ampère was able to determine that the magnetic force between two current-carrying conductors depends on all of the following:

- the length of the conducting wire
- the distance between the two conducting wires
- the amount of current in each wire

The SI unit for current is named in honour of Ampère's work. This unit, the ampere, is now defined as the current required in each of two current-carrying wires, 1 m long and separated by 1 m in air, to produce a force of 2.00×10^{-7} N of magnetic attraction or repulsion. As you learned at the beginning of this section, an ampere is equivalent to the flow of 1 C of charge in 1 s. So, 1 A = 1 C/s, and 1 C = 1 A·s.

In intricate electrical circuits, two conducting wires carrying currents in opposite directions are usually crossed. What is the purpose of this crossing procedure?

12-5 Design a Lab

Using the Current Balance to Measure the Magnetic Force Between Two Current-carrying Conducting Wires

The Question

How can you use a current balance to investigate the factors that influence the magnetic force acting on two current-carrying conducting wires?

Design and Conduct Your Investigation

Study the operation of the current balance in your laboratory and design an experimental procedure to investigate the factors that determine the magnetic force acting on two current-carrying conducting wires. In your experimental design:

- Identify the factors that determine the magnetic force acting on two current-carrying conductors.
- Write an "if/then" hypothesis statement that predicts how changes in the variable affect the magnetic force.
- Clearly outline the procedure you will perform to investigate the relationship of each factor on the magnetic force.
- Describe what you will measure and how the data will be recorded and analyzed.
- Explain how the data will be used to answer the question.

As a group, identify and designate tasks. Prepare a report that describes your experimental design and present it to your teacher. After approval, conduct the investigation and answer the question. How well did your results agree with your hypothesis?

info **BIT**

With advancements in technology, the size of electric motors has become increasingly smaller. Today, 1000 of the smallest electric motors could fit in the period at the end of this sentence.

commutator: a mechanism for maintaining a properly polarized connection to the moving coil in a motor or generator

The Electric Motor

The most important application of the effect of an external magnetic field on current-carrying conductors is the electric motor. Figure 12.32 illustrates a simple electric motor that works with a current-carrying wire loop between two magnetic poles. The current is in one direction. Recall from earlier science studies that current in one direction is called a direct current (DC).

A simple DC electric motor consists of three fundamental components:

- a **stator**—a frame with a coil or permanent magnet to provide a magnetic field
- an **armature** or **rotor**—a rotating loop of conducting wire on a shaft
- a **commutator**—a split metal ring

As electrons in the current pass through the loop of wire in the armature in a clockwise direction (as seen from above in Figure 12.32), they experience a motor effect deflecting force. When you apply the left-hand rule for magnetic force, electrons on the left side of the loop experience a deflecting force upward, and electrons on the right side of the loop experience a deflecting force downward. The combined effect of both forces results in a rotation of the loop in a clockwise direction.

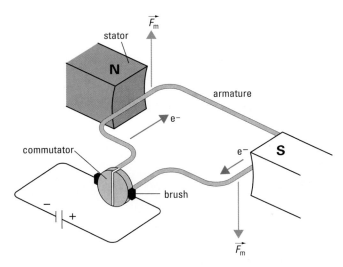

▲ **Figure 12.32** In a simple DC electric motor, the brushes provide a sliding contact between the wires from the battery and the armature. The magnetic field exerts an upward force on the left side of the wire loop and a downward force on the right side, causing the armature to rotate clockwise.

Concept Check

Describe the changes that must be made to the apparatus, shown in Figure 12.32, to cause the armature to rotate counterclockwise.

If the rotation of the loop is to continue, the direction of the motion of the electrons in the loop must change every half-rotation. To accomplish this, the armature is connected to a commutator. A commutator is a split metal ring that is fastened to both ends of the loop of wire in the armature. Each half of the metal ring acts as a contact to the terminals of a power supply. Every half-rotation, the leads of each side of the armature contact a different terminal, changing the direction of the electron movement. Once connected to a steady supply of moving electrons, the armature continues to rotate in one direction. This is the principle of a simple electric motor.

The Generator Effect (Electromagnetic Induction)

In 1996, NASA did an experiment that involved a satellite attached by a conducting tether wire to a NASA space shuttle orbiting in space around Earth (Figure 12.33). Researchers found that the combination generated a current of about 1 A through the wire. The experiment was of particular significance for space scientists because it showed that

▲ **Figure 12.33** A satellite tethered to a NASA space shuttle

this procedure could provide a method of generating the electric energy necessary to power all the electrical components on a space vehicle.

This example is a useful and important application of a scientific phenomenon, but this phenomenon can also produce harmful effects in some situations. For example, engineers constructing the 1280-km north–south gas pipeline from Prudhoe Bay to Valdez in Alaska (Figure 12.34(a)) had to take precautions to eliminate the currents of electricity, called telluric currents, in the pipeline. These currents are caused by fluctuations in Earth's magnetic field. Special magnesium anodes were installed underground along the pipeline to ground it and eliminate the possibility of electrical sparks.

(a)

(b)

▲ **Figure 12.34**   (a) A pipeline in Alaska; (b) An airplane in flight

Similarly, certain grounding conditions must be incorporated in the construction of an airplane to eliminate the current generated by the wings of an airplane in flight through Earth's magnetic field. These currents could affect the operation of all electrical components on the aircraft (Figure 12.34(b)). How are these examples related? What physical phenomenon is generating the current?

The examples described above all involve conductors moving through magnetic fields. The scientific explanation of how they generate electricity began with investigations over 200 years ago.

Faraday's and Henry's Discoveries

Most scientific discoveries are the result of many years of research and investigations. The process is often convoluted and results are often accidental. However, as you have learned, some scientific discoveries are a result of the symmetry of nature. This symmetry led Coulomb and Faraday to conclude that electrical and magnetic forces could be determined using the same mathematical relationships stated by Newton in his universal law of gravitation. Similarly, this symmetry in nature, and Oersted's discovery that electricity could produce magnetism, led scientists to predict that magnetism could produce electricity. Experiments conducted in 1831 by Michael Faraday in England and Joseph Henry (1797–1878) in the United States demonstrated this effect.

*e***LAB**

For a probeware activity that demonstrates the principle of electromagnetic induction, go to www.pearsoned.ca/school/physicssource.

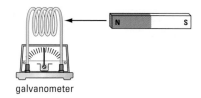

galvanometer

In a simplified version of their experiment, shown in Figure 12.35, a magnet is moved toward a coil of conducting wire connected to a sensitive galvanometer. When the magnet approaches the coil, the galvanometer's needle deflects in one direction, indicating that a current is being produced in the coil of wire. This current is called an induced current, which is produced by a generated voltage. When the magnet is pulled away from the coil, the galvanometer deflects in the opposite direction, indicating that the induced current in the coil is in the opposite direction. When the magnet is stationary, no current is induced. If the magnet were held stationary while the coil of wire was moved back and forth, similar induced currents would be produced. Evidently, it does not matter whether the magnet or the coil of wire moves, as long as there is relative motion between a coil of conducting wire and an external magnetic field.

In their conclusions, Faraday and Henry stated that when a piece of conducting wire cuts through magnetic field lines, an induced current is produced. The production of electricity by magnetism is called the **generator effect** or **electromagnetic induction**. Figure 12.36(a) shows a piece of conducting wire being moved perpendicularly upward through an external magnetic field. As a result, electrons in the wire also move perpendicularly upward. Use the left-hand rule for magnetic force: If the wire is moving upward (thumb) through the external magnetic field (fingers), then each electron experiences a motor effect force (palm). Electrons will gather at one end of the wire with stored electric energy from the work done on the system in moving the wire. Thus, one end of the wire has an accumulation of electrons with stored electric energy while the other end has a deficiency of electrons (Figure 12.36(a)).

If this wire were part of an external circuit, (Figure 12.36(b)) the induced voltage would provide the necessary electromotive force to drive an induced current through the external wire. An electromotive force is created by a difference in electric potential and drives electrons through an external circuit, from a region of high electric potential to a region of lower electric potential.

▲ **Figure 12.35** When a magnet is moved toward a loop of wire connected to a galvanometer, the galvanometer needle deflects. This indicates that an induced current is being produced in the coil of wire.

generator effect or **electromagnetic induction:** production of electricity by magnetism

Project **LINK**

How would you apply the principle of electromagnetic induction and the operation of commutators to construct a DC generator?

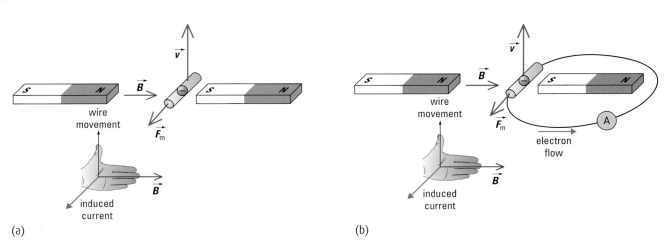

(a)

(b)

▲ **Figure 12.36** A current can be induced in a wire by moving the wire through a magnetic field.

12-6 Inquiry Lab

Required Skills
- Initiating and Planning
- Performing and Recording
- Analyzing and Interpreting
- Communication and Teamwork

Magnetic Fields and Moving Conductors — Demonstration

Question

What factors influence the effect produced when there is relative motion between an external magnetic field and a conducting wire?

Materials and Equipment

2 bar magnets

3 different sizes of coils of conducting wire (the diameter of the coils should allow a bar magnet to be inserted)

galvanometer that can be projected onto a screen using an overhead projector

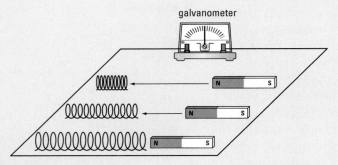

▲ **Figure 12.37**

Procedure

1 Set up the apparatus as shown in Figure 12.37.

2 Slowly push one bar magnet at a uniform speed into the largest coil. Then pull the bar magnet out in the opposite direction at the same speed. Observe the deflection of the galvanometer's needle in both cases.

3 Repeat step 2 with the other end of the magnet. Observe the deflection of the galvanometer's needle in both cases.

4 Repeat step 2, using two bar magnets. Observe the magnitude and direction of the galvanometer's deflection.

5 Repeat step 2, using two bar magnets at a faster speed through the largest coil. Observe the magnitude and direction of the galvanometer's deflection.

6 Repeat step 2, using two bar magnets at the same constant speed through the medium and the smaller coils of conducting wire. Observe the magnitude and direction of the galvanometer's deflection.

Analysis

1. How does the direction of the movement of the magnet affect the direction of the deflection of the galvanometer?

2. How does the polarity of the magnet affect the direction of the deflection?

3. Describe how each of the following factors influences the magnitude of the deflection of the galvanometer and use a mathematical expression to state the relationship:

   (a) speed of the magnets through the conducting wire

   (b) strength of the external magnetic field

   (c) number of loops in the coil of conducting wire

4. What is the effect of relative motion between a conducting wire and a magnetic field?

5. Does it make any difference if the magnet or the conducting wire is moved?

6. What are the factors that determine the magnitude and direction of the induced current when there is relative motion between a conducting wire and an external magnetic field?

7. Based on your observations from this activity, design an experiment that demonstrates the effect of a uniform magnetic field on a moving conductor.

Knowledge

1. What are the factors that affect the magnetic force on a moving charge through an external magnetic field?

2. What are the factors that affect the magnetic force on a charge moving through a conducting wire in an external magnetic field?

3. What is the relationship between amperes and coulombs?

4. In the operation of a simple electric motor and simple electric generator, identify

   (a) a similarity

   (b) a difference

5. What symmetry in nature did Faraday and Henry apply in their discovery of electromagnetic induction?

6. What is the function of a split-ring commutator in the operation of a simple DC motor?

7. How do the electrons in a loop of wire in a generator gain energy?

Applications

8. A wire lying perpendicular to an external magnetic field carries a current in the direction shown in the diagram below. In what direction will the wire move due to the resulting magnetic force?

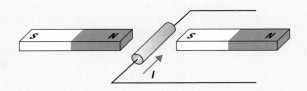

9. A battery supplies a current of 5.20 mA to a circuit. Determine the quantity of charge that flows through the circuit in 2.00 s.

10. Two conducting wires parallel to each other carry currents in opposite directions. Using the appropriate hand rule, determine whether the wires will attract or repel each other.

11. A wire 50 cm long and carrying a current of 0.56 A is perpendicular to an external magnetic field of 0.30 T. Determine the magnitude of the magnetic force on the wire.

12. The north pole of a magnet is pulled away from a copper ring, as shown in the diagram below. What is the direction of the induced current in the ring?

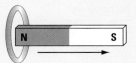

Extension

13. Could a simple electric generator be converted to a simple electric motor? Suggest any alterations that must be made in the design.

 eTEST

To check your understanding of current-carrying conductors and magnetic fields, follow the eTest links at www.pearsoned.ca/school/physicssource.

12.4 Magnetic Fields, Moving Charges, and New and Old Technologies

info BIT

Michael Faraday built the first electric motor in 1821. This motor had a stiff wire hanging from a stand. The lower end of the wire was immersed in a cup of mercury with a bar magnet upright in the middle. When current from a battery flowed through the wire, it rotated around the magnet.

From the old technologies of the simple beginnings of electric motors, electric meters (such as galvanometers and ammeters), loudspeakers, and sucking magnets to the new technologies of magnetohydrodynamic (MHD) propulsion systems and magnetic resonance imaging (MRI), the science of the production of magnetism by electricity plays a significant role in our everyday lives. Although examples of some of these technologies have been described in previous sections, following are other examples of old and new technological applications of this principle. Table 12.2 describes old and new technologies that use moving charges or current-carrying conductors to produce magnetic fields that can interact with external magnetic fields to produce powerful magnetic forces.

▼ **Table 12.2** Loudspeakers and MHD Propulsion

Old Technology	New Technology
Loudspeakers 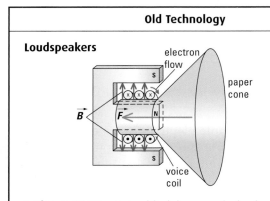 ▲ **Figure 12.38** A simplified diagram of a loudspeaker	**Magnetohydrodynamic (MHD) Propulsion** 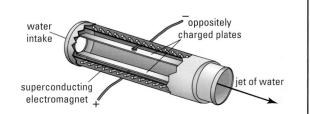 ▲ **Figure 12.39** MHD uses magnetic fields as a propulsion system for seagoing vessels.
The operating principle of most loudspeakers is that current-carrying wires produce magnetic fields that can exert magnetic forces. In the design of the loudspeaker shown in Figure 12.38, a coil of wire, called a voice coil, surrounds the north pole of a very powerful external magnet at the back of the speaker. When your sound system sends an electric signal to the coil, a current is produced in the coil, which produces a magnetic field. As a result, the coil experiences a magnetic force due to the interaction of its magnetic field with the external magnetic field.	The MHD propulsion system is an experimental system for seagoing vessels to replace conventional propeller systems.
Depending on the direction of the current in the coil, the magnetic force of attraction or repulsion causes the coil to slide to the left or right. The direction of the current is determined by the electric signal produced by the sound system. As the voice coil slides back and forth, it causes the paper cone to vibrate in or out, creating sound waves as it pushes on the air in front of the cone. The electric signal from the sound system is thus converted to a mechanical sound wave in air.	MHD uses magnetic fields to produce a jet of water for propulsion. Figure 12.39 is a simplified diagram of this type of system. A powerful superconducting magnet surrounds a thruster tube containing seawater. This magnet produces a magnetic field perpendicular to the tube's length. Inside the tube, electrodes produce a current of ions, perpendicular to the magnetic field, across the tube from the dissolved salts in seawater. As a result of the perpendicular movement of the ions through an external magnetic field, a magnetic force is exerted on the ions, causing them to deflect along the length of the tube. This movement of the water through the tube provides the necessary thrust to propel the vessel. An advantage of MHD propulsion systems is that they have no mechanical moving parts and thus require minimal maintenance.

Generator Effect Applications

The discovery that moving a conducting wire through an external magnetic field generates an induced current in the conductor (generator effect) also led to many important technological applications. From the old technologies of the simple generators, induction coils, and transformers to the new technologies of infant breathing monitors and others, applications of the scientific principle of the production of electricity from magnetism are found everywhere in our lives. Table 12.3 describes two of these applications.

▼ **Table 12.3**   Induction Coils, Transformers, and SIDS Monitors

Old Technology	New Technology
Induction Coils	**SIDS Monitors**
▲ **Figure 12.40** A simplified diagram of Faraday's induction coil	▲ **Figure 12.41** Monitors are designed to detect changes in a baby's breathing.
A change in the current in the primary coil produces a changing magnetic field around the coil. This changing magnetic field produces an induced current in the secondary coil, causing the needle on the galvanometer to deflect. Such coils can induce current in a wire that has no direct connection to the power supply. Figure 12.40 shows a simplified version of Michael Faraday's original induction coil.	In sudden infant death syndrome (SIDS), an infant stops breathing with no apparent cause. One type of SIDS monitor uses induced currents to measure an infant's breathing (Figure 12.41).
	A coil of wire attached to one side of the infant's chest carries an alternating current, which produces a magnetic field. This alternating field cuts another coil taped to the other side of the chest and induces an alternating current in this other coil. As the chest moves up and down, the strength of the induced current varies. These variations are monitored.

A Motor Is Really a Generator, Which Is Really a Motor

You have analyzed and studied the motor effect and the generator effect as separate phenomena in this chapter. However, the symmetry of nature suggests that related phenomena are really variations of the same effect. Since electricity can produce magnetism and magnetism can produce electricity, then perhaps the technologies that are derived from these phenomena are also similar. Is a motor really that different from a generator?

The Curious Relationship Between Motors and Generators

Question

What is the relationship between the motor effect and the generator effect?

Materials and Equipment

1 100-cm length of copper pipe (internal diameter approximately 1.4 cm)
1 cylindrical rare earth magnet (less than 1.4 cm in diameter)
1 metre-stick
1 stopwatch
1 scale

Procedure

1 Copy Table 12.4 into your notebook.

▼ **Table 12.4** Data for *12-7 Inquiry Lab*

Mass of Magnet (m)(kg)	Length of Copper Pipe (Δd)(m)	Average Time Taken for the Magnet to Fall Through the Pipe (t)(s)

2 Measure the mass of the magnet on the scale, and record it in Table 12.4.

3 Measure the length of the copper pipe, and record it in Table 12.4.

4 Holding the pipe in a vertical position, drop the magnet from the exact top of the pipe. Measure the time for the magnet to reappear out the bottom. Record this time in the table.

5 Repeat the procedure in step 4 several times to obtain an average value for the time taken for the magnet to drop the length of the pipe.

Analysis

1. Copy Table 12.5 into your notebook. Use the data from Table 12.4 to complete the calculations in Table 12.5.

▼ **Table 12.5** Calculations for *12-7 Inquiry Lab*

Magnitude of the Weight of the Magnet ($F_g = mg$) (N)	Magnitude of Acceleration of the Magnet Through the Copper Pipe $\left(a = \dfrac{2\Delta d}{t^2}\right)$ (m/s^2)	Magnitude of Net Force Causing the Downward Acceleration of the Magnet ($F_a = ma$) (N)

2. What is the magnitude of the upward force on the falling magnet?

3. Identify and explain where the generator effect is occurring in this experiment.

4. Identify and explain where the motor effect is occurring in this experiment.

5. Do the generator effect and the motor effect complement each other as the magnet falls through the copper pipe? Explain your answer.

An Accidental Discovery

Simple DC electric motors and electric generators have three similar components:

- an external magnetic field
- a loop of conducting wire
- a commutator

At the 1873 Vienna Exhibition, the Belgian inventor Zénoble Théopile Gramme (1826–1901) demonstrated a compact and efficient generator that he had designed. A steam engine provided the power to run the generator. A workman mistakenly connected the output of the generator to a second generator in the display. The shaft of the second generator began spinning even though it was not connected to the steam engine. Gramme immediately realized that the second generator was operating as a motor powered by the first generator.

Gramme and his colleagues then moved the generators several hundred metres apart and connected them with long wires. The American writer Henry Adams (1838–1918) described the importance of Gramme's demonstration: "Suddenly it became clear that ELECTRICITY could now do heavy work, transporting power through wires from place to place."

MINDS ON   Perpetual Motion?

Suppose that a motor and generator are connected to the same shaft and wired such that the output of the generator powers the motor. If you spin the shaft, the generator supplies energy to the motor, which turns the shaft. The generator then produces more energy to run the motor. Explain why this process cannot continue indefinitely.

Lenz's Law

If you did the 12-7 Inquiry Lab, you discovered what happens when you drop a magnet down a metal tube. When a conductor cuts the magnetic field lines of a falling magnet, it generates an induced current in the conducting pipe (the generator effect). However, the induced current moves in a circular motion around the circular pipe, so it creates its own vertical magnetic field, inside the metal tube (the motor effect). The direction of the magnetic field can be directed either upward or downward. The direction of the magnetic field that is produced by the circular induced current in the pipe can have one of the following orientations:

- It will attract the magnet and cause it to fall faster, thus generating a greater induced current.

- It will repel and oppose the motion of the magnet, causing it to fall much slower.

The law of conservation of energy requires that you can never get more out of a system than you put into it. So, the direction of the new magnetic field will always oppose the motion of the magnetic field of the original magnet. This is the principle of **Lenz's law**, which states:

> The direction of a magnetically induced current is such as to oppose the cause of the current.

For example, if a magnet falls with its north pole directed downward, then the magnetic field produced by the induced current in the conducting pipe will have its north pole pointing upward to repel and oppose this motion.

▲ **Figure 12.42** Dropping a magnet down a metal tube induces a current in the tube.

Concept Check

Copy Figure 12.42 into your notebook. Apply Lenz's law by sketching the direction of the induced current in the metal tube and the resulting orientation of the magnetic field in the tube. How would the induced current and magnetic field directions change if the falling magnet's south pole were directed downward?

Figure 12.43 shows a similar situation. As the north pole of a magnet approaches a coil of wire, the induced current generated in the coil produces a north pole to repel and oppose the approaching magnet.

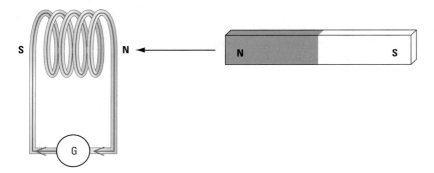

▲ **Figure 12.43** Lenz's law helps us explain that the direction of current induced in the coil has a magnetic field that exerts a force on the bar magnet that opposes the magnet's motion.

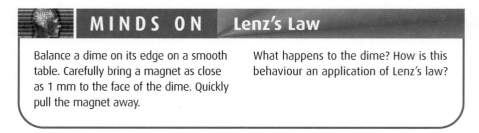

MINDS ON   Lenz's Law

Balance a dime on its edge on a smooth table. Carefully bring a magnet as close as 1 mm to the face of the dime. Quickly pull the magnet away.

What happens to the dime? How is this behaviour an application of Lenz's law?

The principle behind Lenz's law also hinders the operation of electric motors and generators. For an electric motor to operate, an electric current must first be supplied through a conducting loop of wire in a magnetic field, causing the motor effect, so the loop will rotate.

However, as the loop rotates, the conducting wire cuts the magnetic field lines, causing the generator effect. The generator effect induces a current in the loop of wire. The direction of the induced current must be in an opposing direction to the direction of the original current that was supplied. Similarly, to operate a generator, movement of a conducting wire in a magnetic field must be supplied, which will induce a current. However, as soon as the induced current moves through a conductor in a magnetic field, a force on the conducting wire will be produced that opposes the original force and hinders the movement of the conducting wire.

*e*WEB

Research the relationship between Lenz's law and the operation of most vending machines. Write a short report analyzing the operation of vending machines, and describe whether they operate on the principles of Lenz's law and the generator effect or Lenz's law and the motor effect. In your description, include the term "eddy currents." Begin your search at www.pearsoned.ca/school/physicssource.

THEN, NOW, AND FUTURE   Nanotechnology

Since the start of the Industrial Revolution and with advances in technology, machines have become increasingly smaller.

Scientists at University of California's Berkeley National Laboratory have developed the smallest synthetic electric motor ever made. Essentially, it is an electric rotor spinning on an axle 2000 times smaller than the width of a human hair. Imagine tiny electric motors so small that one motor could ride on the back of a virus, or thousands could fit in the period at the end of this sentence. This is the world of nanotechnology, which is an umbrella word that covers many areas of research and deals with objects that are measured in nanometres, or a billionth of a metre.

How do nanomachines work? As you have learned, conventional electric motors use electromagnets or strong external magnets to spin rotors made of loops of wire. The spinning of a rotor provides mechanical energy to do work. In the electric motor of nanotechnology, transistors act as switches to move negative and positive charges around a circle of electrodes. The charges jump around the stator electrodes,

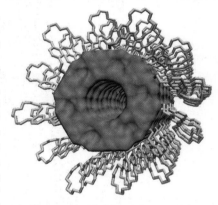

▲ **Figure 12.44** A rosette nanotube

causing an electrically charged rotor to spin around and rotate a nanotube shaft. This spinning rotor provides mechanical energy, similar to a conventional electric motor.

The nanomotor can perform only small functions, such as moving a second hand on a watch, but it has many advantages: It spins without gears or bearings; it is unaffected by gravity or inertia; and it can run for a long time with no breakdowns.

Another application of nanotechnology is the rosette nanotube, like the one shown in Figure 12.44. This type of tube was developed at the National Institute of Nanotechnology

of the National Research Council, located at the University of Alberta. The nanotube is made of molecules that assemble themselves into this distinctive shape.

Possible future applications of these tubes include: nanowires in molecular electronics, drug delivery systems within the body, and environmentally friendly oil sands upgrading additives.

The potential of nanotechnology in electronics is now beginning to be realized and applied to many different fields. Imagine, for example, nanorobots that can be injected into the body to attack viruses and cancer cells.

In the future, it may even be possible to construct molecules of oil and gas, reducing our reliance on fossil fuels. The science of nanotechnology is the science of the future.

Questions

1. What are some advantages of nanotechnology?

2. Describe how a nanomotor works.

3. What could nanotubes be used for?

Knowledge

1. Identify two technological applications that employ

   (a) the motor effect

   (b) the generator effect

2. What are the three basic components of an electric motor and generator?

3. What is Lenz's law?

Applications

4. For an electric motor:

   (a) Describe what you must supply to start the operation of the device.

   (b) Describe what you get out of the operation of the device (motor effect).

   (c) Using Lenz's law, explain how the operation of the motor also produces the generator effect to hinder its own operation.

5. For an electric generator:

   (a) Describe what you must supply to start the operation of the device.

   (b) Describe what you get out of the operation of the device (generator effect).

   (c) Using Lenz's law, explain how the operation of the generator also produces the motor effect to hinder its own operation.

6. Explain why you will feel a force of repulsion if you attempt to move a magnet into a coil of wire.

Extensions

7. An electric motor requires a current in a loop of wire. However, as the loop rotates, it generates a current which, according to Lenz's law, must be in an opposing direction. Why must the induced current be in an opposing direction?

8. A hair dryer operates on a very small current. If the electric motor in the hair dryer is suddenly prevented from rotating, the dryer overheats. Why?

e TEST

To check your understanding of magnetic fields, moving charges, and new and old technologies, follow the eTest links at www.pearsoned.ca/school/physicssource.

Key Terms and Concepts

law of magnetism   ferromagnetic   ampere   electromagnetic induction
magnetic field   domain   commutator   Lenz's law
electromagnet   motor effect force   generator effect
solenoid   current

Key Equations

$$|\vec{F}_\mathrm{m}| = qv_\perp B$$

$$|\vec{F}_\mathrm{m}| = Il_\perp B$$

Conceptual Overview

The concept map below summarizes many of the concepts and equations in this chapter.
Copy and complete the map to have a full summary of the chapter.

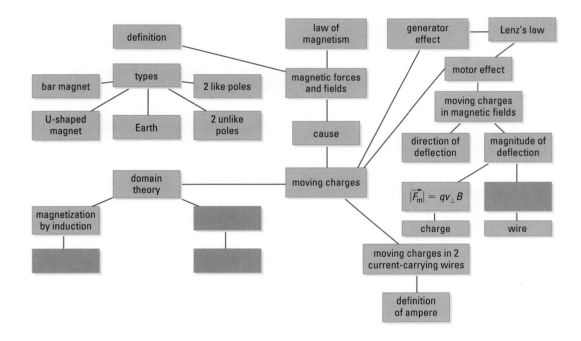

Knowledge

1. (12.1) State the major contribution of each of the following scientists to the study of magnetism:
   (a) William Gilbert
   (b) Hans Christian Oersted
   (c) André Ampère
   (d) Michael Faraday

2. (12.1) State the definition of
   (a) a magnetic field
   (b) the direction of a magnetic field

3. (12.1) Compare a magnetic vector arrow at a point near a magnet and a magnetic field line around a magnet.

4. (12.1) How was it determined that there had to be two different types of magnetic poles?

5. (12.1) Sketch the magnetic field lines around each of the following objects and describe the differences in the magnetic fields of
   (a) a bar magnet and Earth
   (b) a current-carrying straight piece of conducting wire and a current-carrying coil of conducting wire

6. (12.2) Identify the sources of the two magnetic fields required to produce the motor effect force on a moving charge.

7. (12.2) Describe the deflection of a moving charge, through an external magnetic field, if the direction of the initial motion of the charge is
   (a) parallel to the external magnetic field lines
   (b) perpendicular to the external magnetic field lines
   (c) at an angle to the external magnetic field lines

8. (12.2) Where is a magnetic bottle formed?

9. (12.3) Describe a difference between a galvanometer and an ammeter.

10. (12.3) State two definitions for a current of one ampere.

11. (12.4) Identify two technologies that use the principles of
    (a) the motor effect
    (b) the generator effect

12. (12.4) What is the principle of Lenz's law?

Applications

13. Does every charged object necessarily have a positive and a negative charge? Does every magnetized object necessarily have a north and a south pole? Justify your answers.

14. If the direction of the magnetic field outside a magnet is from the north to the south pole, what is the direction of the magnetic field within the magnet?

15. Using domain theory, describe how an iron nail can become magnetic by
    (a) the process of magnetization by induction
    (b) the process of magnetization by contact

16. How will the magnetic force on a moving charged particle change if
    (a) only the charge is doubled?
    (b) the magnetic field is doubled and the speed is halved?
    (c) the mass of the charge is doubled?

17. Use domain theory to explain the difference between a permanent and a temporary magnet.

18. You are told that a straight piece of copper wire has a steady current in it. Given only a compass, describe how you can find the direction of the current in the wire.

19. A drinking straw with a green grape at one end is suspended by a string from a hanging support. When either end of a magnet is brought close to the grape, repulsion occurs. Describe a possible reason for this effect.

20. An electron in a TV tube is moving at 7.00×10^6 m/s perpendicular to a magnetic field of magnitude 0.0880 T in the tube. What is the magnetic deflecting force on the electron?

21. A proton travelling at 35° to an external magnetic field of magnitude 0.0260 T experiences a force of magnitude 5.50×10^{-17} N.
    (a) Calculate the speed of the proton.
    (b) Calculate the kinetic energy of the proton in joules (J) and electron volts (eV).

22. What speed must an alpha particle maintain if it is to remain suspended, relative to Earth's surface, as it travels on a tangent to Earth's surface and perpendicularly through Earth's magnetic field of 50.0 μT?

23. An alpha particle travelling with a speed of 4.30×10^4 m/s enters a uniform magnetic field of 0.0300 T. Determine the magnetic force on the particle if it enters the field at an angle

(a) perpendicular to the magnetic field

(b) 30.0° to the magnetic field

(c) parallel to the magnetic field

24. A magnetic field is used to bend a beam of electrons. What uniform magnetic field is required to bend a beam of electrons moving at 1.2×10^6 m/s in a circular arc of 0.25 m?

25. Two parallel current-carrying wires are observed to attract each other. What is the source of the force of attraction? How could you demonstrate that the force of attraction is not electrostatic attraction?

26. The magnetic force between two magnets was measured as the distance between the magnets was varied. The following information was obtained:

Separation, r ($\times 10^{-2}$ m)	Magnitude of Force, F (N)
5.00	4.02
10.00	1.01
15.00	0.45
20.00	0.25
25.00	0.16

(a) Draw a graph of the magnetic force as a function of separation distance.

(b) From the shape of the graph, what is the relationship between force and separation?

27. An airplane is flying east over Earth's magnetic north pole. As a result of its motion, one wing was detected as having more electrons than the other. Explain why this phenomenon occurs. Identify which wing will have more electrons.

28. A power line carries a current of 5.00×10^3 A. Find the magnetic force on a 100-m length of wire lying perpendicular to Earth's magnetic field of 50.0 μT.

Extensions

29. A magnet is dropped through two similar vertical tubes of copper and glass. Which tube will allow the magnet to fall faster? Explain your answer.

30. A disk magnet on a table has two steel balls in contact with it on either side. The steel balls are slowly moved toward each other while still in contact with the disk magnet. As they move, they repel each other. Describe why the steel balls are attracted to the disk magnet, but repel each other.

Consolidate Your Understanding

Create your own summary of properties of magnetic and electric fields by answering the questions below. If you want to use a graphic organizer, refer to Student Reference 3: Using Graphic Organizers. Use the Key Terms and Concepts listed on page 621 and the Learning Outcomes on page 580.

1. Create a flowchart to identify technological devices that use electric fields, magnetic fields, or a combination of the two fields to control moving charges.

2. Write a paragraph comparing the effects of electric or magnetic fields on moving charges. Share your report with a classmate.

Think About It

Review your answers to the Think About It questions on page 581. How would you answer each question now?

e **TEST**

To check your understanding of the properties of electric and magnetic fields, follow the eTest links at www.pearsoned.ca/school/physicssource.

Building a Model of a Direct Current Generator

Scenario

The search for better electrical energy production began with the pioneering work of Faraday and Henry in the 1800s and continues today. Over half of the energy consumed in our world is electrical energy and the average consumption per person is increasing every year, so more efficient methods of electrical energy production are being sought all the time.

All DC electrical generators consist of three major parts: coils of wire wrapped around a core to make the armature, a commutator, and an external magnetic field. As you learned in this unit, the operating principle behind generators is the movement of a conducting wire through external magnetic field lines so that a voltage is generated in the wire. This in turn induces a current in an external line. All DC generators operate in this fashion.

The only difference among generators is the source of the mechanical energy required to turn the turbines that rotate the coil of wires in the magnetic field. In some places, this is the energy of falling water or tides, while in others it is the energy of moving steam from the combustion of fossil fuels or nuclear reactions. Recently, interest has grown in using wind energy to turn the turbines that operate a generator. A single wind generator can produce about 10 MW of electrical power, which is sufficient for a single small farm.

The purpose of this project is to research and investigate the operation of a wind-powered electrical generator and to build a model of a wind-powered DC generator capable of generating enough electricity to operate a mini-bulb.

Planning

Form a team of four or five members, and decide on and plan the required tasks to complete the project. These tasks may include researching the design of a simple generator, obtaining the necessary materials, constructing the model of the generator, preparing a written report, and presenting the project to the entire class.

Materials

- insulated copper wire
- iron core
- split-ring commutator
- external magnets
- connecting wires
- mini-bulb with support base
- stiff paper to construct a turbine
- balsa wood for the axle
- household fan to produce wind

Procedure

1 Using the Internet, library, or other resources, research the operation of a simple DC electrical generator and create a design of the model that you will construct. Pay special attention to the commutator required for DC generation.

2 Construct a working model of the generator that can provide the electrical energy to light a mini-bulb. In your model, investigate the factors that determine the magnitude of the generated voltage.

3 Prepare a report explaining the design and the specific functions of all the components.

Thinking Further

1 What modifications did you make in the construction of your model of a generator that affected the magnitude of the generated voltage?

2 What other type of commutator could you have used in the design of your generator? What type of current would be induced by this commutator?

3 Identify at least three risks and three benefits of a wind-powered electrical generator.

4 Is wind-powered electrical generation a viable and desirable method of electrical energy generation for the future? Explain your answer.

*Note: Your instructor will assess the project using a similar assessment rubric.

Unit Concepts and Skills: Quick Reference

Concepts	Summary	Resources and Skill Building
Chapter 10	**Physics laws can explain the behaviour of electric charges.**	
	10.1 Electrical Interactions	
Modern theory of electrostatics	Substances can be classified as conductors, insulators, semiconductors, and superconductors. Objects may be charged through the processes of friction, conduction, and induction.	10-1 QuickLab 10-2 Inquiry Lab
	10.2 Coulomb's Law	
Coulomb's law	Coulomb's law states that the electrical force acting on charged objects depends on the charges and the distance between the charges.	10-3 Inquiry Lab Examples 10.1, 10.2
Vector analysis	Electrostatic forces can be solved in one- and two-dimensional situations using vector analysis.	Examples 10.3–10.6
Chapter 11	**Electric field theory describes electrical phenomena.**	
	11.1 Forces and Fields	
Fields	Fields are used to explain action at a distance.	11-1 QuickLab, 11-2 Inquiry Lab
Electric field	An electric field is a three-dimensional region of influence surrounding every charge. Electrostatic force affects another charge placed in the field. The electric field is a vector quantity that has magnitude and direction.	Examples 11.1–11.4
	11.2 Electric Field Lines and Electric Potential	
Electric field lines	Electric field lines can depict the electric fields around different types of charged objects.	Minds On activities, eSIM
Electric potential energy	Electric potential energy is the amount of work done on a charged object to move it from infinity to a position in an electric field. Electric potential energy can be calculated.	Examples 11.5, 11.6
Electric potential	Electric potential is the amount of electric potential energy stored per unit charge and can be calculated.	Example 11.7
Electric potential difference	When a charge moves from a location where it has one electric potential to a location where it has another electric potential, the charge experiences an electric potential difference.	Example 11.8
	11.3 Electrical Interactions and the Law of Conservation of Energy	
Motion of a charge in an electric field	When a charge is placed in an electric field, it experiences a force that causes it to accelerate in the direction of the field. The acceleration of the charge is different in a non-uniform field surrounding a point charge than the acceleration of the charge in the uniform field between charged plates. Work done by the system on the charge increases the charge's potential energy, which can be converted to other forms of energy.	Examples 11.10–11.12
Chapter 12	**Properties of electric and magnetic fields apply in nature and technology.**	
	12.1 Magnetic Forces and Fields	
Magnetic fields	Magnetic fields are three-dimensional regions of magnetic influence surrounding every magnet in which other magnets or magnetic substances are affected by magnetic forces. Magnetic fields are vector fields and can be depicted by magnetic field lines.	12-1 QuickLab, 12-2 QuickLab
Cause of magnetism	The cause of magnetism is motion of charges and can be explained using the domain theory. If the motion of charges is straight, the magnetic field is circular. If the motion of charges is circular, the magnetic field is straight within the loop. The direction of the magnetic field lines can be described using hand rules.	Figure 12.10
Magnetizing objects	Objects can be magnetized through contact or induction.	Concept Check
	12.2 Moving Charges and Magnetic Fields	
Motor effect on a moving charge	A charge moving perpendicularly through an external magnetic field experiences a magnetic force due to two magnetic fields, which can be calculated. This motor effect force can explain the operation of electric motors and other technologies. The magnitude of the motor effect force can be calculated and its direction can be determined using hand rules.	12-3 Inquiry Lab Examples 12.1, 12.2
	12.3 Current-carrying Conductors and Magnetic Fields	
Motor effect on two current-carrying wires	A current-carrying conductor that is perpendicular to an external magnetic field experiences a magnetic force that can be calculated.	Example 12.4 12-4 QuickLab 12-5 Design a Lab
Generator effect	A conductor moving perpendicular to an external magnetic field can produce electricity.	12-6 Inquiry Lab
	12.4 Magnetic Fields, Moving Charges, and New and Old Technologies	
Applications of the generator effect and the motor effect	The generator effect and the motor effect are used in many technologies.	12-7 Inquiry Lab
Lenz's law	Lenz's law explains how a motor is really a generator and a generator is really a motor.	Minds On

Vocabulary

1. Use your own words to define the following terms, concepts, principles, or laws. Give examples where appropriate.

ampere
charge migration
charge shift
charging by induction
commutator
conduction
conductor
coulomb
Coulomb's law
current
domain
electric field line
electric potential (voltage)
electric potential difference
electric potential energy
electromagnet
electromagnetic induction
electron volt
electrostatics
ferromagnetic
field
generator effect
grounding
induction
insulator
law of conservation of charge
law of magnetism
Lenz's law
magnetic field
motor effect force
net charge
plasma
semiconductor
solenoid
source charge
superconductor
test charge

Knowledge

CHAPTER 10

2. Explain why silver is a better conductor of electricity than rubber.

3. State a technological advantage of developing materials that are superconductors.

4. A negatively charged rubber rod is brought near a small metal ball hanging from an insulated thread. The metal ball is momentarily grounded, and then the ground and the rubber rod are removed. Identify the procedure used to charge the metal ball, and determine the final charge on the metal ball.

5. Describe a similarity and a difference between
   (a) charging by friction and charging by conduction
   (b) charge shift and charge migration

6. In each of the following examples, identify the charge on each object and state the method of charging the object.
   (a) An ebonite rod is rubbed with fur and then is held near a neutral metal sphere.
   (b) A glass rod is rubbed with silk and then is touched to a neutral metal sphere.

7. During the rubbing process of charging objects, one object gains a net negative charge. What can you conclude about the charge on the other object?

8. How do the following factors affect the electrostatic force of attraction between two charged objects?
   (a) amount of charge on each object
   (b) distance between the centres of the two objects
   (c) sign of the charge on each object

CHAPTER 11

9. State the superposition principle as it applies to vector fields.

10. Why must a test charge be small when it is used to determine the direction of an electric field around a larger primary charge?

11. Draw the electric field lines around

   (a) a negative point charge

   (b) a positive charge and a negative point charge in the same region

   (c) a negatively charged cone-shaped object

12. Why is there no net electric field inside a charged hollow sphere?

13. Explain the following statement: "It is impossible to shield against gravitational fields, but it is possible to shield against electric fields."

14. Why is the magnitude of a gravitational field so small compared to the magnitude of an electric field?

15. Draw a diagram showing two small, equally charged, positive spheres a small distance apart. On your diagram, identify a point A where the electric field is zero and a point B where the electric potential is zero.

16. Where is the zero electric potential energy reference point around any charge? Describe how electric potential energy changes for a positive or a negative charge, relative to the reference point.

17. Two oppositely charged parallel plates are connected to a 120-V DC supply. What happens to the magnitude of the electric field between the plates if the distance between the plates decreases?

18. Describe the following for a point a small distance from a positively charged sphere:

   (a) the magnitude and direction of the electric field at this point

   (b) the electric potential energy of another small positive charge placed at this point

   (c) the electric potential at this point

19. Describe the relationship between the work done in moving a charge from one region in an electric field to another region, and the energy gained by the charge. What law governs this relationship?

CHAPTER 12

20. Draw a diagram of the magnetic field around a bar magnet and Earth.

   (a) List the similarities between the two fields.

   (b) List the differences between the two fields.

21. Explain why a single magnetic pole cannot exist by itself.

22. Describe two simple demonstration techniques used to outline the magnetic field around a magnet.

23. Justify the following statement: "A charge moving perpendicular to a uniform external magnetic field experiences a force but does not change its speed."

24. Show how a charge moving through an external magnetic field experiences a deflecting force because of the interaction of two magnetic fields.

25. A positively charged disk is spinning in a clockwise direction as seen from above. What is the direction of the magnetic field? Use a diagram to help you describe its shape.

26. Describe the shape and direction of the magnetic field around a negatively charged dart as it travels directly away from you toward a target on a wall.

27. What factors affect the magnetic force on a charge moving through an external magnetic field?

28. State a difference and a similarity between the motor effect and the generator effect.

29. Describe how Lenz's law affects the operation of

   (a) a motor

   (b) a generator

Applications

30. An insulator and a conductor are each contacted by a negatively charged rubber rod. Describe the distribution of charge on each object.

31. Describe how Earth's surface can become positively charged during a thunderstorm. In your description, include the terms "charging by friction" and "charging by conduction."

32. Assume you have only a negatively charged ebonite rod. Describe a procedure for charging a neutral electroscope

   (a) positively

   (b) negatively

33. Why does a negatively charged ebonite rod initially attract a piece of thread and then eventually push it away?

34. When you touch a Van de Graaff generator, your hair stands on end. Explain your answers to the following questions:

   (a) Are you being charged by friction, conduction, or induction?

   (b) Will the same effect occur if you are grounded?

35. A negatively charged ebonite rod is brought near a neutral pith ball hanging on an insulating thread. Describe what happens to the charges in the pith ball and the resulting effect
    (a) before the rod and the pith ball touch
    (b) after the rod and the pith ball touch

36. A straight length of conducting wire, lying horizontal to the surface of Earth, delivers a current in a direction from south to north. Describe the deflection of a compass needle held directly over the conducting wire.

37. A negatively charged Styrofoam™ ball is hanging from an insulated thread. Another negatively charged ball is brought near, on the same horizontal plane, and the hanging ball swings away so that the supporting thread makes an angle of 30° to the vertical.
    (a) Draw a free-body diagram depicting the tension force by the string, the force of gravitational attraction, and the electrical force of repulsion on the hanging ball.
    (b) If the system is in equilibrium, identify the force that balances the gravitational force on the hanging ball and the force that balances the electrostatic force of repulsion on the hanging ball.

38. Explain how the properties of selenium are essential in the operation of a photocopier.

39. Explain the difference between charge shift and charge migration during the process of charging by induction.

40. The cell membrane of a neuron may be thought of as charged parallel plates. The electric potential difference between the outside and the inside of the membrane is about 0.70 V. If the thickness of the membrane is 5.0×10^{-9} m, calculate
    (a) the magnitude of the electric field between the outside and the inside of the membrane
    (b) the amount of work necessary to move a single sodium ion, Na^{+1}, with a charge of 1.6×10^{-19} C, across the membrane

41. In a chart, compare the similarities and differences between Newton's law of universal gravitation and Coulomb's law of electrostatics.

42. Determine the distance between two electrons if the mutual force of repulsion acting on them is 3.50×10^{-11} N.

43. A neutral small hollow metal sphere is touched to another metal sphere with a charge of -3.00×10^{-2} C. If the two charges are then placed 0.200 m apart, calculate the electrostatic force acting on the two spheres after they touch.

44. A football-shaped hollow conducting object is charged negatively.
    (a) Draw the object and then draw the charge distribution on the surface of the object.
    (b) Draw the electric field lines surrounding the object.
    (c) Where will the intensity of the electric field appear to be the greatest?
    (d) Explain how this effect can be used to describe the operation of a lightning rod.

45. A car with a vertical antenna is driven in an easterly direction along the equator of Earth.
    (a) Describe how a current is induced in the antenna.
    (b) Determine the direction of the induced current.

46. A small charge of -2.0 μC experiences an electric force of 3.0×10^{-5} N to the left when it is placed in the electric field of another larger source charge. Determine the strength of the electric field at this point.

47. Calculate the kinetic energy gained by a proton that is allowed to move between two charged parallel plates with a potential difference of 2.0×10^4 V. What maximum speed could the proton acquire?

48. Two spheres with charges of $+4.00$ C and $+3.00$ C are placed 0.500 m apart. At what point between the two charges must a third charge of -2.00 C be placed so that the net electrostatic force acting on this charge is zero?

49. Two oppositely charged parallel plates have a voltage of 2.5×10^4 V between them. If 1.24 J of work is required to move a small charge from one plate to the other, calculate the magnitude of the charge.

50. A wire that is 0.30 m long, lying perpendicular to an external magnetic field of magnitude 0.50 T, experiences a magnetic force of 0.11 N. Determine the current in the wire.

51. A charge of $+3.0 \times 10^{-6}$ C is placed 0.50 m to the right of another charge of -1.5×10^{-5} C. Determine
    (a) the net electric field at a point midway between the two charges
    (b) the electrostatic force of attraction acting on the two charges

52. Touching a Van de Graaff generator can result in a painful shock. If a small length of conducting wire is bent into an L-shape and taped to the ball of the generator, so that a shaft of wire projects outward, you will not get a shock when you touch the ball.

(a) How does the ball of the generator initially acquire a negative charge?

(b) What process of charging objects is involved in the painful shock you receive initially?

(c) How does the shaft of wire that is taped to the ball prevent a shock?

(d) What is the function of the conducting strips projecting from the airplane wing tip shown in the photo below?

53. A small Styrofoam™ ball with a mass of 0.015 kg and coated with a conducting material is suspended by a string 0.75 m long. If the ball is initially given a charge of magnitude 1.5×10^{-8} C, and another charged ball with a charge of magnitude 2.5×10^{-8} C is brought near, the hanging ball swings to a position 1.0 cm from its equilibrium position. Calculate the electrostatic force of repulsion acting on the two charges. Draw a free-body diagram.

54. The largest electric field that can exist between two oppositely charged plates with an air gap between them is 3.00×10^6 N/C. If this electric field limit is exceeded, then a discharge of charge occurs between the plates, resulting in a spark. If the voltage between the plates is 500 V, what is the minimum distance between the plates before a spark occurs?

55. An electron with a mass of 9.11×10^{-31} kg and a charge of magnitude 1.60×10^{-19} C is 5.29×10^{-11} m from a proton with a mass of 1.67×10^{-27} kg and a charge of magnitude 1.60×10^{-19} C. Calculate

(a) the gravitational force of attraction between the two masses

(b) the electrical force of attraction between the two charges

(c) how many times greater the electrical force is than the gravitational force

56. An alpha particle, a proton, and an electron, travelling at the same speed, enter regions with external fields. Describe the motion of each particle as it travels perpendicularly through the same

(a) magnetic field

(b) electric field

(c) gravitational field

57. Given ebonite and glass rods and strips of fur and silk, describe the procedure to charge an electroscope negatively by

(a) conduction

(b) induction (include the grounding step)

58. A particle with a mass of 2.00×10^{-26} kg and a charge of magnitude 6.40×10^{-19} C is fired horizontally along the surface of Earth in an easterly direction. If the particle passes through a metal detector with a magnetic field of 2.00×10^{-4} T in a northerly direction, at what speed must the charged particle be travelling so that the magnetic force counteracts the gravitational force of Earth on the particle at this position? What is the charge of the particle?

59. A helium ion (He^{+2}) with a charge of 3.20×10^{-19} C and a mass of 6.65×10^{-27} kg is injected with a speed of 3.00×10^6 m/s perpendicularly into a region with a uniform magnetic field of 3.30 T.

(a) Calculate the magnitude of the deflecting force on the helium ion.

(b) If this deflecting force causes the helium ion to travel in a circular arc, what is the radius of the arc?

60. Sphere A, with a charge of $+3.50$ μC, is 4.35 cm to the left of sphere B, with a charge of -2.44 μC. Calculate the net electrostatic force on a third sphere C, with a charge of $+1.00$ μC, if this sphere is placed

(a) midway on a line joining charges A and B

(b) at a point 2.50 cm to the right of charge B

(c) at a point 2.50 cm directly down from charge B

61. Calculate the potential difference required to accelerate a deuteron with a mass of 3.3×10^{-27} kg and a charge of magnitude 1.6×10^{-19} C from rest to a speed of 8.0×10^5 m/s.

62. A uniform electric field of 7.81×10^6 N/C exists between two oppositely charged parallel plates, separated by a distance of 3.20 mm. An electron, initially at rest and with a mass of 9.11×10^{-31} kg, is injected into the electric field near the negative plate and accelerates toward the positive plate. The electron passes through a "hole" in the positive plate and then travels perpendicularly through an external magnetic field with a magnitude of 1.50 T.

(a) What is the voltage between the oppositely charged plates?

(b) Calculate the maximum speed acquired by the electron between the plates.

(c) Determine the magnetic force on the electron as it passes through the magnetic field.

(d) Describe the motion of the electron through the electric field and then through the magnetic field.

63. A bar magnet is moved toward a coil of wire that is connected to a sensitive galvanometer, as shown in the figure below.

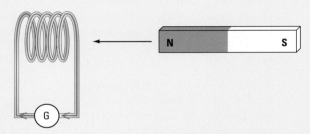

(a) Explain what happens to the galvanometer readings as the north pole of the bar magnet approaches the coil of wire.

(b) Describe how Lenz's law influences the movement of the magnet toward the coil of wire.

(c) Explain what happens to the galvanometer readings as the north pole of the magnet is pulled out of the coil of wire.

(d) Describe how Lenz's law influences the movement of the magnet away from the coil of wire.

Extensions

64. Explain why computer hard disks are encased in metal.

65. Explain why it is safe to remain inside a vehicle during a lightning storm.

66. Are gravitational, electrical, or magnetic forces responsible for the formation of a black hole in space? Explain your answer.

67. Why must technicians who work on very sensitive electronic equipment be grounded?

68. Describe why Earth's magnetic field creates a "magnetic bottle."

69. Charged particles in cosmic rays from the Sun are trapped in Earth's magnetic field in two major radiation belts, called Van Allen radiation belts. The first belt is about 25 500 km and the other is about 12 500 km above the surface of Earth. Explain why spacecraft must avoid these radiation belts.

70. Compare the motion of a negatively charged particle as it travels through a gravitational, electric, or magnetic field in a direction

(a) perpendicular to the field

(b) parallel to and in the same direction as the field

71. Why is lightning more likely to strike pointed objects than rounded objects on the ground?

72. Describe the process by which the steel beams in a high-rise building can become magnetized. Why does this effect not happen in homes built with wood beams?

73. High-voltage power lines operate with voltages as high as a million volts. Explain why a bird can perch on a power line with no effect, but must be careful not to touch two nearby power lines.

74. Explain the difference between the dip angle and the angle of declination of Earth's magnetic field. How do these two angles affect the operation of a directional compass in Alberta?

75. An electron is at rest. Can this electron be set in motion by a magnetic field? Explain your answer.

76. Given only a loop of wire connected to a sensitive galvanometer, describe a simple experiment that could be conducted to prove the existence of a changing magnetic field near a high-voltage power line.

77. The image of the magnetotactic bacterium, as seen under a microscope, reveals a row of magnetite crystals within its cellular structure. Make a hypothesis regarding the purpose of this row of magnetite crystals, and design and describe an experiment to test your hypothesis.

Skills Practice

78. Draw a Venn diagram to review the similarities and differences between electric and magnetic fields.

79. Design an experiment to determine the direction of gravitational, magnetic, and electric fields.

80. Construct a concept map for solving a two-dimensional electrostatic force problem involving three charges at the corners of a triangle.

81. Design an experiment to show that electrostatic forces vary with the inverse square law.

82. A current-carrying wire has a magnetic field surrounding it. The strength of this magnetic field can be found using the formula $|\vec{B}| = \dfrac{\mu I}{2\pi r}$, where $|\vec{B}|$ is the magnitude of the magnetic field surrounding the wire, in teslas, μ is the constant of permeability for space, in T·m/A, I is the current in the wire, in amperes, and r is the distance to the wire, in metres. An experiment is performed to establish the value of the constant, μ. The current was constant through the wire at 5.00 A, and the strength of the magnetic field was measured at various distances from the wire. The data recorded are given in the table below.

Distance from the wire, r (m)	Magnitude of the magnetic field, $|\vec{B}|$ (T)
0.100	6.28
0.200	3.14
0.300	2.09
0.400	1.57
0.500	1.26

(a) Plot a graph to determine the relationship between $|\vec{B}|$ and r.

(b) What is the relationship between $|\vec{B}|$ and r?

(c) What quantities need to be graphed in order to straighten the graph?

(d) Complete a new table of values to straighten the graph.

(e) Plot a new graph with the variables needed to straighten the graph.

(f) Use the graph-slope method and the data from the graph to determine the value of μ.

(g) Use the formula-data substitution method to determine the value of μ.

Self-assessment

83. Describe to a classmate which field concepts and laws you found most interesting when studying this unit. Give reasons for your choices.

84. Identify one topic pertaining to fields studied in this unit that you would like to investigate in greater detail.

85. What concept in this unit did you find most difficult? What steps could you take to improve your understanding?

86. Assess how well you are able to explain electric potential energy and electric potential. Explain to a classmate how you determine a reference point.

 e **TEST**

To check your understanding of forces and fields, follow the eTest links at www.pearsoned.ca/school/physicssource.

UNIT VII

Electromagnetic Radiation

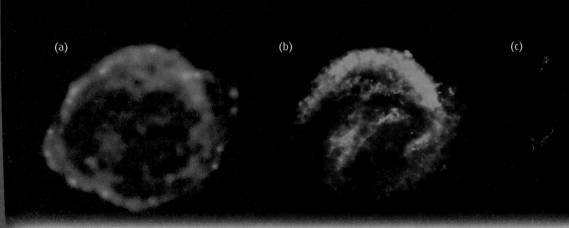

(a)   (b)   (c)

This series of photos of a supernova remnant shows the various types of electromagnetic radiation that are being emitted from the supernova remnant. The large image is a composite. Images (a) and (b) were taken by the Chandra space telescope (high-energy and low-energy X ray), image (c) was taken by the Hubble space telescope (visible part of the spectrum), and image (d) by the Spitzer space telescope (infrared).

(d)

Unit at a Glance

Unit Themes and Emphases

- Diversity and Matter
- Nature of Science
- Scientific Inquiry

Focussing Questions

The study of electromagnetic radiation and its behaviour requires interpretation of evidence to form theories and models. As you study this unit, consider these questions:

- What roles do electricity and magnetism play in electromagnetic radiation?
- Does electromagnetic radiation have a wave or a particle nature?
- What experimental evidence is required to decide whether electromagnetic radiation has a wave or a particle nature?

Unit Project

From Particle to Quantum

- When you have finished this unit you will be able to use experimental evidence concerning electromagnetic radiation to describe our current understanding of light. You will be able to craft a multi-media presentation of highlights in the development of this understanding.

The wave model can be used to describe the characteristics of electromagnetic radiation.

▲ **Figure 13.1**   A Fresnel lens captures light from a lamp and redirects it into a concentrated beam. This 19th-century lens technology used many prisms to produce a light that could be seen for great distances.

When you open your eyes in the morning, the first thing you see is light. In fact, it is the only thing you see. In general, what we perceive with our eyes is a combination of many colours, each with varying brightness, but all coming together through the optical system of our eye. It is light or, more broadly speaking, a form of electromagnetic radiation (EMR), which produces an image in the human eye. But what is EMR? How is it produced? How is it transmitted and at what speed? These questions are historically significant, guiding the direction of research and debate over the ages. Finding answers has helped us understand the fundamental principles of our universe and has enabled advances in technology in areas such as lenses (Figure 13.1), fibre optics, and digital devices. Radios, lasers, global positioning systems, and compact discs (CDs) are examples of devices that depend on an understanding of EMR.

The nature of light has long been a topic of intrigue and debate. Early Greek scientific thought was based on the work of Aristotle and Euclid, who concerned themselves with the physical and geometric mechanisms of visual perception. A more modern debate ensued as detailed evidence began to be collected about the wave and/or particle nature of light. Isaac Newton (1642–1727) and Christiaan Huygens (1629–1695) defined this debate with evidence from early experiments. Newton put forward the particle or corpuscular theory, while Huygens supported the wave model. Today, both the particle and wave models of light have some validity and contribute to our present understanding, described by the quantum model of light.

In this chapter, you will see that visible light is only one form of EMR. You will also discover that the concepts of electrical charge and magnetic fields, explored in Chapters 10–12, come together when you consider EMR. You will investigate the generation, speed, and propagation of EMR, and see how light can be reflected, refracted, diffracted, and polarized. In each instance, the wave and particle nature of light is revealed, helping us to understand these complex phenomena and apply them in new technologies.

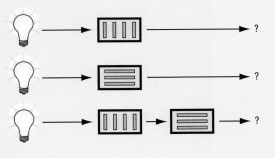

13.1 What Is Electromagnetic Radiation?

electromagnetic radiation: radiant energy in the form of a wave produced by the acceleration of electrons or other charged particles. EMR does not require a material medium; can travel through a vacuum.

frequency: the number of cycles per unit of time

wavelength: the distance between adjacent points that vibrate in phase with one another in a wave

info BIT

Seeing is a photochemical process that is sensitive to certain wavelengths of electromagnetic radiation. When EMR is absorbed by the tissues in the human eye, a compound called *retinal* changes in physical form from bent to straight. The retinal molecule, in turn, is connected to a membrane-bound protein called *opsin* forming the complex molecule called *rhodopsin*. When the retinal molecule changes its form, it separates from the rhodopsin and the opsin triggers a nerve cell to signal the brain that light has been seen.

Electromagnetic radiation (EMR) is radiant energy, energy that travels outward in all directions from its source. There are different types of EMR, some very familiar, and others rarely mentioned outside scientific discussions. Electromagnetic radiation includes AM/FM radio waves, microwaves, heat, visible light (red to violet), ultraviolet radiation, X rays, and gamma rays.

Electromagnetic radiation types are identified based on their **frequency, wavelength**, and source. The energy sources that produce EMR vary greatly, from nuclear reactions in the Sun, which generate gamma radiation, to chemical reactions in the human body that generate infrared radiation (heat).

EMR is produced by the acceleration of charged particles resulting in transverse waves of changing electric and magnetic fields that can travel through space without the need of a material medium. All forms of EMR travel at the same speed, commonly referred to as the speed of light (c, in a vacuum), equal to 3.00×10^8 m/s.

EMR does not always travel directly from the source to the observer. As a result, it can be observed in one of two ways:

directly from the source

indirectly, as reflected or transmitted radiation

Burning magnesium (Figure 13.3) allows both methods of observing radiation. Other objects, such as the text you are reading now, do not produce radiation. You are able to read the text because it is reflecting radiation (light) from another source. If you are wearing glasses, this radiation is transmitted through your lenses.

The evidence obtained in 13-1 QuickLab indicates one unique characteristic of electromagnetic radiation. However, visible light, radiant energy that the eye can detect, only makes up a small portion of the spectrum of EMR present in our universe.

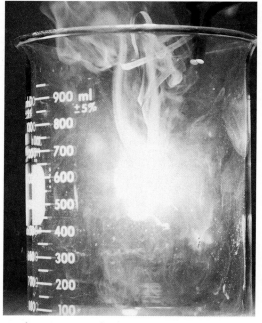

▲ **Figure 13.3** When magnesium burns, you can observe radiation directly from the reaction and indirectly from the radiation that is reflected from the smoke.

Concept Check

Can infrared radiation reflect off objects and be observed by the human body? Explain and give examples.

Types of Electromagnetic Radiation

The **electromagnetic spectrum** is the term applied to all the types of EMR considered together in terms of frequency, wavelength, or energy. All parts of the spectrum are found, with varying intensity, in our natural environment. We are most familiar with the visible spectrum since we sense it directly with our eyes. The infrared spectrum is sensed as heat and the ultraviolet spectrum includes radiation that can damage living cells, often causing a physiological response such as sunburn. Other parts of the spectrum may be present as background radiation. Natural background radiation originates from two primary sources: cosmic radiation and terrestrial sources. Cosmic radiation from deep space interacts with atoms in the atmosphere producing X rays and unstable isotopes. Terrestrial sources of gamma radiation include radioactive isotopes of uranium, radon, potassium, and carbon. Also, aboveground nuclear tests of the 1940s–1960s combined with nuclear accidents such as Chernoybl have scattered a substantial amount of radioactive material within our environment. Figure 13.4 shows the overlap of frequencies and wavelengths among the different forms of EMR in the electromagnetic radiation spectrum.

electromagnetic spectrum: all types of EMR considered in terms of frequency, wavelength, or energy

e **WEB**

To learn more about the different types of EMR and the trends seen across the spectrum, follow the links at www.pearsoned.ca/school/ physicssource.

a) Electromagnetic spectrum

b) Visible spectrum

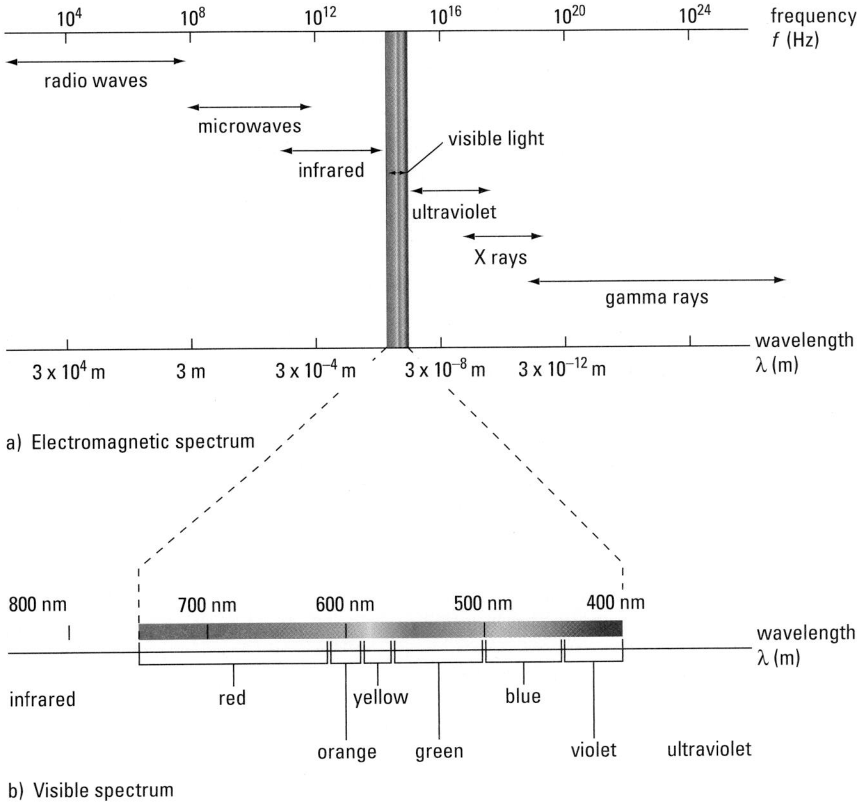

▲ **Figure 13.4** The electromagnetic radiation spectrum showing the visible range

The relative energy of the different types of EMR varies with frequency across the spectrum. Table 13.1 compares the various sources and characteristics of the radiation found in the EMR spectrum.

e **WEB**

To learn more about the medical uses of different types of EMR, follow the links at www.pearsoned.ca/school/ physicssource.

Chapter 13 The wave model can be used to describe the characteristics of electromagnetic radiation. 637

▼ **Table 13.1** The Electromagnetic Spectrum: Characteristics

Type of Electromagnetic Radiation	Method of Production	Characteristics	Problems
Alternating Current Power $f = 60$ Hz $\lambda = 5.0 \times 10^6$ m relative energy: insignificant	oscillation of electrons in alternating current	extremely long wavelength; while the AC power has many familiar uses, the 60-Hz wave emitted has no known uses at present	interference with other local EMR waves
Radio and Radar $f = 10^4 - 10^{10}$ Hz $\lambda = 10^4 - 10^{-2}$ m relative energy: very low	oscillation of electrons in an electric circuit like an antenna	long wavelength allows a large amount of diffraction making it useful for long-distance communication, e.g., cell phones, PC broadband	requires government regulations to control transmission and avoid interference
Microwaves $f = 10^9 - 10^{12}$ Hz $\lambda = 10^{-1} - 10^{-4}$ m relative energy: low	oscillation of electrons in special tubes and solid state devices	shorter wavelength reduces diffraction for short-distance communication; frequency matches the natural resonant frequency of water molecules; used in microwave ovens	may be linked to some forms of cancer; causes damage to living tissue due to heating of water molecules within tissues
Infrared $f = 10^{11} - 4.0 \times 10^{14}$ Hz $\lambda = 10^{-3} - 7.5 \times 10^{-7}$ m relative energy: low	transitions of valence shell electrons in atoms and molecules	causes object absorbing it to become warm; used for remote sensing, night vision scopes, and identification of sources of heat	significant exposure can burn tissue
Visible $f = 4.0 \times 10^{14} - 7.5 \times 10^{14}$ Hz $\lambda = 7.5 \times 10^{-7} - 4.0 \times 10^{-7}$ m relative energy: medium	higher-energy transitions involving valence electrons in atoms	reflects off small objects, making them visible; diffracts around very small objects, making them invisible	limits the size of objects that can be seen
Ultraviolet $f = 7.5 \times 10^{14} - 10^{17}$ Hz $\lambda = 4.0 \times 10^{-7} - 10^{-9}$ m relative energy: high	even higher-energy transitions involving valence electrons in atoms	easily absorbed by objects; causes fluorescence of some materials, tanning in humans; kills bacteria	may cause sunburn; prolonged exposure can cause mutations and cancer in humans
X ray $f = 10^{17} - 10^{20}$ Hz $\lambda = 10^{-9} - 10^{-12}$ m relative energy: very high	transitions of electrons in an atom or the sudden acceleration of high-energy free electrons	penetrates most matter and is absorbed by denser material (like bone or metal); destroys carcinogenic or mutant cells; used for medical imaging in humans and in industry	can cause mutations and cancer in humans
Gamma $f = 10^{19} - 10^{24}$ Hz $\lambda = 10^{-11} - 10^{-16}$ m relative energy: extremely high	decomposition of unstable nuclei, either spontaneously or by the sudden negative accelerations from high-energy particle accelerators	penetrates matter very deeply; destroys carcinogenic or mutant cells on a local scale; used to probe the structure of matter and in industrial imaging	can cause radiation sickness and death
Cosmic $f = 10^{24}$ Hz and greater $\lambda = 10^{-16}$ m and less relative energy: extremely high	bombardment of Earth's atmosphere by extremely high-energy particles from space	penetrates matter very deeply; study of cosmic rays allows investigators to formulate ideas about the universe	can cause radiation sickness and death

Competing Models of Electromagnetic Radiation

Historically, investigators have tried to explain transmission, reflection, refraction, and absorption, and the other characteristics common to all types of EMR by using models. The historical **particle model** describes EMR as a stream of tiny particles radiating outward from a source. A **particle** is a discrete unit of matter having mass, momentum (and thus kinetic energy), and the ability to carry an electric charge. The particle model of EMR is the most simplistic of all the models. It is supported by the facts that EMR propagates in straight lines, can be reflected, and can be absorbed. The pool ball (particle) in Figure 13.5 exhibits particle characteristics. It can travel in a straight line, obey the law of reflection when it bounces off a side rail, and be absorbed by the table when it drops into a pocket.

info **BIT**

The Particle Theory of Light, also known as the Corpuscular Theory of Light, was put forward in Newton's *Opticks*, published in 1704.

particle model: describes EMR as a stream of tiny particles radiating out from a source

wave model: describes EMR as a stream of transverse waves radiating out from a source

▲ **Figure 13.5** A pool ball on a pool table exhibits the particle characteristics of linear movement, reflection, and absorption.

▲ **Figure 13.6** A water wave is a transverse wave that transfers energy in the form of a disturbance.

A second model, the **wave model,** describes EMR as a stream of transverse **waves** radiating outward from a source. As you learned in Chapter 8, a wave is a transfer of **energy** in the form of a disturbance. The energy transfer usually occurs in, but is not limited to, a material medium like water. A water wave travels in a straight line, reflects from surfaces, and can be absorbed (Figure 13.6). For example, water waves, which continually reflect inside a waterbed, transfer unwanted energy that can be absorbed by a sponge (Figure 13.7). EMR, however, does not require the presence of a medium.

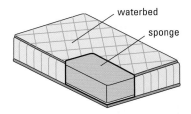

waterbed

sponge

▲ **Figure 13.7** Waves in a waterbed exhibit the wave characteristics of linear movement, reflection, and absorption.

The modern wave model of light has its origins in the 17th century when the Dutch mathematician and scientist, Christiaan Huygens argued that light consisted of waves. He suggested light waves could interfere to produce a wave front, travelling outward in a straight line. At the time, however, Huygens' wave theory was overshadowed by the immense scientific popularity of Newton's particle theories. The wave model gained further support from evidence produced by the work of Thomas Young (Figure 13.8) and his now-famous two-slit experiment of 1801. The details and implication of the experiment are set out in section 13.5, but in general, Young was able to show that a beam of light, when split into two beams and then recombined, shows interference effects that can *only* be explained by assuming that light has wavelike properties.

▲ **Figure 13.8** Thomas Young (1773–1829)

If light behaves as a particle, then one would expect to observe a bright region wherever the light emanating from the slits reaches a distant screen (Figure 13.9(a)). But Young obtained a result similar to that shown in Figure 13.9(b), where a pattern of light of varying intensity is observed after the light passes through the two slits. This pattern is similar to two-source interference patterns in water waves, as seen in section 8.3. Young's experiment thus presented strong evidence for the wave model of light.

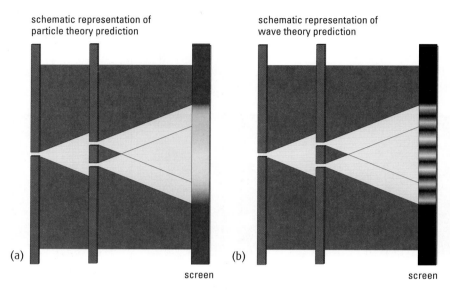

schematic representation of particle theory prediction

schematic representation of wave theory prediction

(a)

(b)

screen

screen

▲ **Figure 13.9** When light is incident on two small slits, it is diffracted as it passes through each slit and an interference pattern is observed that supports the wave model of light.
a) A schematic representation of the particle theory prediction
b) A schematic representation of the wave theory prediction

photon: (from the Greek word meaning "light"); a discrete packet of energy associated with an electromagnetic field

quantum model: a combination of the particle and wave models. It describes light and all other EMR as discrete bundles of energy, each of which is a massless particle that has wavelike characteristics.

Planck and Einstein

By the end of the 19th century, both the particle and wave models of EMR were supported by scientific evidence. In 1900, Max Planck (1858–1947) proposed a radically new model to explain the spectrum of radiation emitted from a perfectly black object. In a mathematical derivation Planck assumed that all of the vibrating molecules, "oscillators," in the black body could vibrate with only specific, discrete amounts of energy. In doing so, he had to ignore the continuous distribution of energy of classical physics and introduce the concept of **quanta,** or discrete packets of energy. Planck was awarded the Nobel Prize for Physics in 1918, "in recognition of the services he rendered to the advancement of Physics by his discovery of energy quanta."

In 1905 Einstein extended this quantum theory by proposing that light is emitted in quantized, tiny, *massless* particles, which are now called **photons.** Planck's original theory thus evolved into the currently accepted **quantum model** of light, which is a combination of both the particle and wave models. This model describes light and all other electromagnetic radiation as discrete bundles or "packets" of energy. Each packet, or photon, is a particle that has wave characteristics. In the quantum model, EMR has two aspects of behaviour, one being wavelike and the other being particle-like. Quantum theory reconciled these two types of behaviour while, at the same time, challenging both the classical wave and particle models.

Planck's quantum idea challenged the wave model by proposing that EMR does not deliver energy in a continuous form as a wave would, but rather, it delivers energy in small bundles. At the same time, his idea challenged the particle model by limiting the energy of the particles to certain discrete values, a condition not possible for a Newtonian particle.

e **WEB**

To learn more about Max Planck, begin your search at www.pearsoned.ca/ school/physicssource.

Concept Check

Consider the wave model of light and the particle model of light.
1. Which of the following best describes the word "model"?
   (a) simplified description of a complex entity or process;
   (b) a representation of something on a smaller scale;
   (c) both a and b.
2. Explain your answer from part 1 and provide several examples of models that are used in a similar way.
3. The EMR spectrum includes many classes of radiation. Describe the wave characteristics used to classify each type of radiation on the spectrum. How are these characteristics related to the energy of the radiation?

Project **LINK**

How will you present the observations and theoretical concepts that culminated in the ideas of Planck and Einstein?

Maxwell's Electromagnetic Theory, 1865

In 1865, James Clerk Maxwell (1831–1879) proposed his Electromagnetic Theory, which synthesized earlier ideas and theories with the results of experiments to provide a theoretical framework for future studies. Maxwell proposed the idea that a changing **electric field** produces a changing **magnetic field** and that the interaction between these fields propagates as a wave through space. In his theory Maxwell linked concepts of electricity and magnetism so that we now call them "electromagnetic."

Maxwell based his theory on key phenomena observed by earlier investigators of electricity and magnetism. You have already met these ideas in Unit 6, but we will restate them here to appreciate the importance of Maxwell's contribution.

electric field: a three-dimensional region of electrostatic influence surrounding a charged object

magnetic field: a three-dimensional region of magnetic influence surrounding a magnet

The Concept of the Electric Field

As Faraday had proposed and as you saw in Chapter 11, an electric field surrounds any charged particle and an electrostatic force will act on another charged particle when it is placed in that field. The electric field strength can be calculated and electric field lines drawn to illustrate the region of influence. Electric field lines begin and end at a charge (Figure 13.10) and the number of field lines passing through any closed surface is determined by the total charge enclosed by the surface. This concept allows the idea of interaction between particles at a distance, even though there is no contact between them.

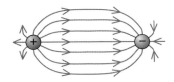

▲ **Figure 13.10** Electric field lines are used to illustrate the region of influence between two oppositely charged particles.

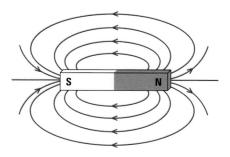

▲ **Figure 13.11** The number of magnetic field lines that exit a magnetic material is equal to the number of magnetic field lines that enter a magnetic material — forming a closed loop.

capacitor: two conductors, holding equal amounts of opposite charges, placed near one another without touching

Maxwell's Equations: a series of equations that summarized the relationships between electricity and magnetism and predicted the existence of electromagnetic waves and their propagation through space

info **BIT**

Maxwell was working with a system of units for electromagnetic theory, referred to as the CGS system. This system was derived from the base units of centimetre, gram, and second. The CGS system has largely been replaced by the SI system, based on the metre, kilogram, and second.

The Concept of the Magnetic Field

A magnetic field (as discussed in Section 12.1) is a three-dimensional region of magnetic influence surrounding a magnet. Magnetic field lines form a closed loop and represent the direction and magnitude of the magnetic field (Figure 13.11).

Relationships Between Electricity and Magnetism

Electrical current in a conductor *produces* a magnetic field perpendicular to the current (Oersted, Unit VI, page 587) and the strength of the magnetic field depends on the magnitude of the current (Ampere, Unit VI, page 607). This relationship is known as Ampere's Law.

Inversely, moving a conductor connected in a circuit through a magnetic field *induces* an electric current. The magnitude of the electrical current is directly related to the rate of change in the magnetic field (Faraday and Henry, Unit VI, page 611). This relationship is known as Faraday's Law.

Putting the Laws of Electromagnetism Together

From this basis and through his work with capacitors, Maxwell developed the laws of electromagnetism. Maxwell's work with capacitors showed that the electric field produced by a **capacitor** could have the same effect as a moving charge. In other words, a changing electric *field* will produce a changing magnetic field in the same manner as a changing electric current can produce a changing magnetic field. This information was extremely important because it showed that a conductor is not necessary for an electromagnetic wave to exist.

Maxwell put these ideas together with incredible ingenuity using calculus, which is beyond the scope of this text. His theory is embodied in a series of equations known as **Maxwell's Equations.**

To visualise the relationship between the electric and magnetic fields, we will proceed stepwise. Begin with a plane transverse wave that shows an electric field of varying strength (Figure 13.12). Next, consider two of the electric field lines on the transverse wave, an upward one at one location and the corresponding downward one at another. Imagine a path connecting the tips of these two electric field vectors, as shown by the dotted line in Figure 13.13. You can see that the electric field changes direction continuously from one direction to the opposite direction along a "closed path."

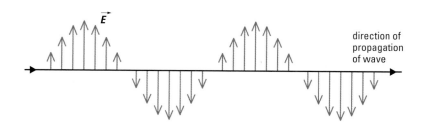

▲ **Figure 13.12** Plane transverse wave showing the electric field lines.

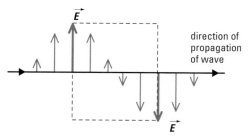

▲ **Figure 13.13** A path connecting two oppositely directed electric field lines on the transverse wave shows the change in the electric field.

Now, consider the magnetic field that exists perpendicular to the electric field along this closed path. When the electric field is set in motion, the magnetic field will change along with the electric field, and similarly along a closed path. An electromagnetic wave will propagate in a direction perpendicular to both fields (Figure 13.14).

The changing electric and magnetic fields will propagate, or radiate, through space in the form of a wave — an **electromagnetic wave** (Figure 13.15). Maxwell proposed that the electromagnetic wave consists of periodic variations in the electric and magnetic field strengths and that these variations occur at right angles to one another as the wave propagates.

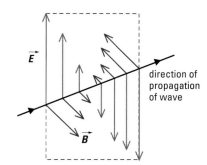

▲ **Figure 13.14** The magnetic field lines (in red) allow us to visualize the magnetic field that exists perpendicular to both the electric field and the direction of the wave.

electromagnetic wave: periodic variation in perpendicular electric and magnetic fields, propagating at right angles to both fields

▲ **Figure 13.15** Three-dimensional view of an electromagnetic wave

Maxwell's Predictions

Maxwell's equations not only correctly predicted the existence of electromagnetic waves, but also allowed him to make some predictions about the waves' properties.

1. Electromagnetic waves are produced whenever an electric charge is accelerating. Therefore, as an electric charge oscillates, electrical energy will be lost, and an equivalent amount of energy will be radiated outward in the form of oscillating electric and magnetic fields.

2. When the electric charge is accelerated in periodic motion, the frequency of oscillation of the charge will correspond exactly to the frequency of the electromagnetic wave that is produced.

3. All electromagnetic waves will travel at a speed of 310 740 000 m/s and obey the universal wave equation ($c = f\lambda$) relating speed, frequency, and wavelength. (Note that Maxwell's theoretical prediction was not far from today's currently accepted value of 3.00×10^8 m/s for the speed of light in a vacuum.)

4. The oscillating electric and magnetic fields will always be perpendicular to each other and perpendicular to the direction of propagation of the wave.

5. Electromagnetic waves should show all the phenomena associated with transverse waves: interference, diffraction, refraction, and polarization.

It is Maxwell's last prediction that supports the wave model of EMR and relates his predictions to experimental evidence. Interference, diffraction, polarization, and refraction, as they relate to the wave model of EMR, will be explored in sections 13.4 and 13.5.

e **WEB**

To learn more about ways of representing the relation between electric and magnetic fields, follow the links at www.pearsoned.ca/school/physicssource. Compare and contrast the representations you find.

Producing Electromagnetic Radiation —
The Story of Accelerating Charge

In 1887, the German physicist Heinrich Hertz (1857–1894) set up an experiment designed both to produce and to detect EMR. In his experimental apparatus, Hertz used a radiator, consisting of a pair of wires attached to both a high-voltage induction coil and a pair of capacity spheres. The wires were separated by a small gap and, given a sufficient quantity of opposite charge on each wire, a current would oscillate back and forth across the gap at a frequency of 10^9 Hz. With each oscillation a spark was produced when the moving charge ionized the air molecules on its way from one wire to the other.

From Maxwell's equations Hertz knew theoretically that this rapidly-moving electric charge should produce EMR. A short distance away from the radiator a collector plate containing a small loop of wire, the antenna, was observed to detect the effect of EMR. While the radiator was in operation and when the radiator and the antenna were tuned to the same frequency, a spark was observed at the antenna indicating a potential difference and an electric current (Figure 13.16).

*e*WEB

To learn more about details of Hertz's experiment, follow the links at www.pearsoned.ca/school/physicssource.

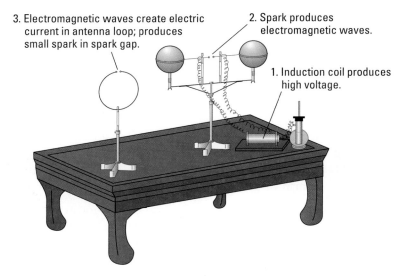

3. Electromagnetic waves create electric current in antenna loop; produces small spark in spark gap.

2. Spark produces electromagnetic waves.

1. Induction coil produces high voltage.

▲ **Figure 13.16** Hertz's apparatus consisted of a high-voltage induction coil, a radiator that produces sparks, and an antenna loop.

Relating Theory and Practice in Hertz's Experiment

The word "changing" appears a number of times in Maxwell's original proposal. As Maxwell understood it, a "changing" electric field was crucial to creating an electromagnetic wave. This is where the induction coil was important in Hertz's experimental design. The induction coil rapidly changed the electric field across the spark gap. When this electric field reached a sufficiently high value, the electrons in the wire "jumped" from one electrode to the other. As the charge was rapidly transferred, the electric field underwent a rapid change that caused a changing magnetic field, which then caused a changing electric field, and so on. An electromagnetic wave was produced and it radiated outward in all directions.

In Hertz's experiment, when the receiver was tuned to the same frequency as the radiator, the induced current flow in the antenna oscillated at a frequency identical to that of the changing electric field in the radiator. This was conclusive evidence that Hertz's device had indeed produced the EMR that was being observed at his antenna. Furthermore, he was able to measure the velocity of the waves by using a zinc reflector plate to produce a standing wave and moving a ring antenna within the standing wave. He could determine the magnitude and direction of the wave's components and therefore the wavelength. Given the frequency of the radiator, the velocity of the wave could be calculated using the universal wave equation ($v = f\lambda$).

Hertz had produced and measured the wavelength and velocity of *non-visible* EMR for the first time. Two years later, in 1889, radio pioneers used this method to transmit the first radio waves across the English Channel. By 1901, the first radio waves were transmitted across the Atlantic Ocean from Cornwall, England to St. John's, Newfoundland and a new age of technology had dawned. The production of EMR was one of the greatest scientific achievements of the 19th century, ushering in new possibilities and technologies that are commonplace today.

e **WEB**

To learn more about Marconi and details of the first trans-Atlantic radio transmission, follow the links at www.pearsoned.ca/school/physicssource.

MINDS ON   Going Wireless

Wireless communication systems that transmit data are commonplace today.

1. Create a list of wireless data transmission technologies.
2. What process must be common to all wireless transmission devices?
3. What variable is used to control the acceleration, and hence the energy, of the accelerating electrons in a wireless device?
4. One radio transmission tower transmits at 5.0 kV. Another transmits at 10.0 kV. Which tower has a greater signal strength and why?

5. Cell phones communicate with cell towers that are dispersed throughout urban cities and transportation corridors. Explain the relationship between the distance that separates a cell phone from the nearest cell tower and the operating power of the cell phone.
6. Many studies have been conducted to investigate and determine if there is a relationship between brain cancer and cell phone usage. Why would one suspect a relationship between cell phone use and brain cancer?

Although modern radio signals are generated without a spark, the technology operates in a way similar to Hertz's original experiment. Radio waves are generated by rapidly changing the electric potential, or voltage, in the radiator tower. The oscillating voltage produces an oscillating electric field in the radiator tower (Figure 13.17).

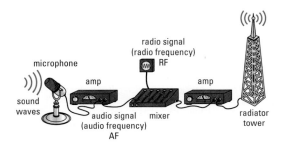

▲ **Figure 13.17**   Schematic of a simple radio transmitter

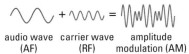

▲ **Figure 13.18**   Amplitude modulation. The audio signal and the carrier signal are mixed by modifying the amplitude of the carrier signal.

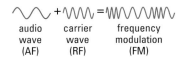

▲ **Figure 13.19**   Frequency modulation

Analog Radio Technology

The first application of Hertz's discovery was made by Guglielmo Marconi (1874–1937). He recognized the potential for transmitting information using electromagnetic waves, by coding the information into dots and dashes, like the Morse code already used in telegraphy. Today, the dots and dashes have been replaced by an analog signal, which uses a continuous spectrum of values.

In radio, sound waves in the range of 20–20 000 Hz (audible to humans) are converted into a weak electrical signal in an analog form. This wave is called the audio frequency signal (AF). The weak audio frequency is then amplified and sent to a mixer. In the mixer, a radio frequency (RF) called a carrier signal, is added to the audio signal to produce an analog wave that contains two sets of information: the audio signal and the carrier signal. The carrier signal frequency is determined by the government and is unique to that station for that broadcast area. It is the carrier signal that you select when you tune your radio to the station.

Finally, the mixed signal is amplified and delivered to the radiator tower, where the movement of electrons through the radiator wire will produce the corresponding form of electromagnetic wave (Figure 13.17). Television signals follow the same process, except that the video and audio portions are transmitted separately.

Radio reception is accomplished by tuning the radio to the carrier signal and then removing, or demodulating, the wave. This reveals the audio signal, which is amplified and delivered to the speakers.

AM or FM Radio?

The mixing of the audio signal and the carrier signal occurs in one of two ways. The first is called amplitude modulation or AM (Figure 13.18). The second method is called frequency modulation or FM. The audio signal and the carrier signal are mixed by modifying the frequency of the carrier signal (Figure 13.19).

▲ **Figure 13.20**

Digital Wireless Cell Phones

The cell phone and text messaging technology of today operates on a very different set of principles.

When a cell phone is switched on it registers with the mobile telephone exchange using a unique digital identifier. Once it has been identified it stays connected to a cellular network of ground-based stations, commonly referred to as cellular tower base stations, which can be found on radio towers, buildings, in church steeples, or any location which is free of physical obstacles and interference. Figure 13.20 shows one such cellular tower base station.

A cell phone communicates with the cell tower base station using radio waves. In turn the base station relays all information to and from the cell phone to another subscriber of the same cell phone network or through an interconnected public switched telephone network that uses fibre optic and copper land lines to transmit the data.

When in use, a cell phone converts the analog voice signal of the person talking into a stream of digital data, which is received by the nearest cell tower base station that may be anywhere from 0.8 –13 km away.

Each cell tower site has a low-power radio broadcast which can be picked up by cell phones. As the user moves, the cell phone constantly monitors the signals being received from various nearby cell tower sta-

tions, switching from one tower to another in such a way that the signal strength remains as high as possible.

The stream of digital data is unique to each type of network technology and each operator is assigned a different radio frequency so that several networks can operate simultaneously at the same location and they will not interfere with one another.

Wireless Technology for the Future

Future uses of cellular phone technology are emerging in the market place as the networks evolve and consume broadcast frequencies formerly occupied by some television channels. New entertainment features will include:

streaming video;

music downloads;

podcasts;

smooth speech recognition and language translations;

ebook features that use projection;

barcode readers that direct users to Internet urls;

global positioning systems and mapping combined with accelerometers to measure position and movements of the cell phone user.

Questions

1. Explain how cell phone user data, including geographical position and movement, could be considered an invasion of privacy.

2. How can multiple cell phone networks and traditional radio broadcasts all exist in the same geographical location and not interfere with one another?

3. Compare the carrier frequency of radio broadcasts with the unique digital identifier of a cell phone. What common purpose do they both serve?

4. Explain why a cell phone only works in certain areas and how changes in the signal strength will be observed by the cell phone user as he or she moves.

1. Consider two electric field lines on a transverse electromagnetic wave. Explain how a changing electric field will produce a changing magnetic field.

2. Why can electromagnetic radiation propagate through empty space, in the absence of a conductor?

3. An electromagnetic wave is produced if an electric charge accelerates. Explain how these two phenomena are linked.

13.1 Check and Reflect

Knowledge

1. List two ways that electromagnetic radiation is detected.

2. List the different types of EMR in the spectrum and the ways in which they are classified.

3. Define EMR using the

   (a) particle model

   (b) wave model

   (c) quantum model

4. Describe the evidence that Thomas Young obtained from the two-slit experiment and explain how it supported the wave model of light.

5. Explain how the observations made by Hertz support the electromagnetic theories of Maxwell.

6. How did Maxwell's study of capacitors add to his theories?

7. Why is the process of "changing" critical to the production of EMR?

Applications

8. A high-voltage spark gap produced sparks with a frequency of 2.5×10^3 Hz. What is the frequency of the EMR observed at an antenna located nearby?

9. What properties need to be considered when choosing the material to build an antenna for a radio receiver?

10. If the magnetic field lines held within a closed path are constant and unchanging, will there be an electric field along the closed path? Explain.

11. If an electric charge is not moving, will it produce a magnetic field? Explain.

12. Explain why it is necessary for the technician to leave the room or wear protective clothing when a patient is being X rayed.

13. Describe how an antenna is affected by an electromagnetic wave.

14. Describe one method used to produce EMR with a known frequency.

Extensions

15. Explain, with the aid of a transverse standing wave diagram, how the current in a ring antenna (such as the one used by Hertz) will be affected as the antenna is moved along the axis of the standing wave. How could this data be used to determine the wavelength of the standing wave?

16. Draw a schematic that shows, in general terms, the role of a satellite in delivering digital, high-definition, television signals between the signal provider and the customer's home receiver.

 e **TEST**

To check your understanding of the nature and production of electromagnetic radiation, follow the eTest links at www.pearsoned.ca/school/physicssource.

13.2 The Speed of Electromagnetic Radiation

info BIT

Maxwell predicted the speed of EMR before Hertz experimentally verified it. Maxwell knew that electric and magnetic fields are not independent of one another and predicted a speed of propagation by dividing the constants, k_e and k_m, which describe electric and magnetic forces between moving charged particles. Using today's currently accepted values of k_e and k_m, we can show that the magnetic field and the electrical field are related by a particular speed.

$$\frac{k_e}{k_m} = \frac{8.99 \times 10^9 \frac{N \cdot m^2}{C^2}}{1.00 \times 10^{-7} \frac{N \cdot s^2}{C^2}}$$

$$= 8.99 \times 10^{16} \frac{m^2}{s^2}$$

$$\sqrt{8.99 \times 10^{16} \frac{m^2}{s^2}} = 2.99 \times 10^8 \frac{m}{s}$$

In addition to producing and detecting electromagnetic radiation in his 1887 experiment, Hertz was able to show that the radiation was travelling at approximately 3.0×10^8 m/s. This was an empirical verification of a theoretical speed predicted by Maxwell years earlier, as described on page 643: All electromagnetic waves will travel at a speed of 310 740 000 m/s and obey the universal wave equation ($c = f\lambda$) relating speed, frequency, and wavelength.

Empirical Determination of the Speed of Electromagnetic Radiation

Light travels so quickly that there is no apparent time difference between turning on a light and the light reaching your eyes — even when the light source is many kilometres away. Galileo (1564–1642) found this out in his attempt to measure the speed of light. His experiment was very basic: Galileo and an assistant stood, each with a covered lantern, on adjacent hills separated by about a kilometre. Galileo would uncover his lantern and as soon as his assistant observed Galileo's lantern, he would uncover the second lantern so that Galileo would see it. Galileo used his pulse rate to measure the time difference. The time interval is actually extremely small — Galileo didn't know it at the time, but light could travel 2 km in about 0.000 066 67 s, a time you couldn't even measure with a digital stopwatch. Galileo realized that using his pulse as a timepiece was not appropriate.

Olaus Roemer (1644–1710) and Christiaan Huygens used one of the four easily visible moons of Jupiter to calculate the speed of light. The period of revolution for Io (Jupiter's brightest moon) had been accurately determined using large amounts of astronomical data collected over many years. Roemer knew that the moon Io should be eclipsed and disappear behind Jupiter at regular, periodic intervals (every 42.5 h). However, he discovered that Io appeared to be eclipsed later than scheduled when Earth was farther away from Jupiter and earlier than scheduled when Earth was closer to Jupiter. The time difference between the longest and shortest periods was 22 min (Figure 13.21).

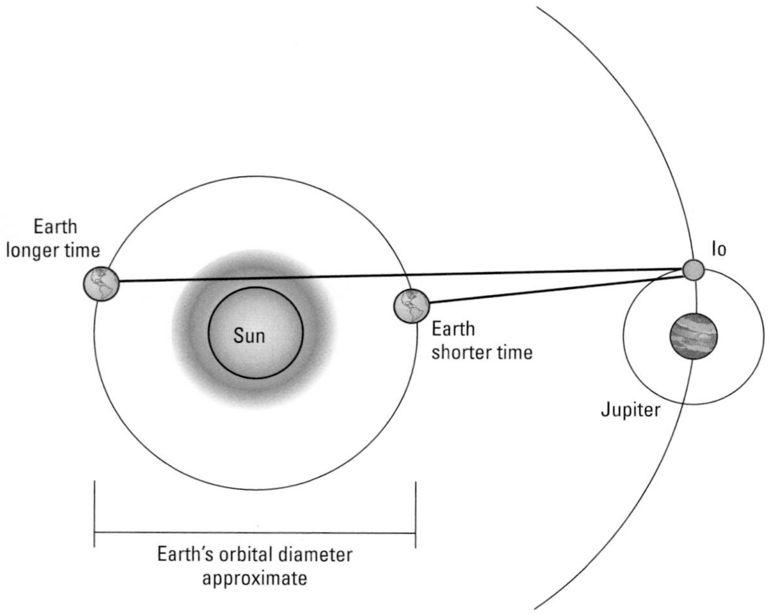

▲ **Figure 13.21** Earth's orbital diameter causes the eclipse of Io to occur at different times because of the extra distance the light must travel when Earth is farthest from Jupiter.

Huygens reasoned that this discrepant behaviour could be due to the difference in the time taken for the light to travel from Jupiter to Earth. Following this reasoning, he estimated Earth's orbital diameter and then determined the speed of light based on the following calculations.

Orbital diameter = 3.0×10^{11} m $\qquad v = \dfrac{\Delta d}{\Delta t}$

Time difference = 22 min = 1320 s $\qquad v = \dfrac{3.0 \times 10^{11} \text{ m}}{1320 \text{ s}}$

$$v = 2.3 \times 10^{8} \text{ m/s}$$

His calculations produced a value of 2.3×10^{8} m/s — astoundingly close to the currently accepted value of 3.0×10^{8} m/s. The value was so large it was rejected by the scientific community of the time and was not accepted until after both Huygens and Roemer were dead.

In 1848, Armand Fizeau became the first person to successfully measure the speed of light at the surface of the planet. His apparatus consisted of a rotating toothed wheel, a light source, some lenses, and a mirror. In his experiment, light was allowed to pass through one of the gaps on the toothed wheel and travel toward the mirror (located on an adjacent hilltop 8.63 km away) where it was reflected back toward the spinning wheel (Figure 13.22). The toothed wheel was rotated such that the reflected light was blocked by a tooth in the wheel as it turned, and the observer would not be able to see the source light. Using the rotational frequency of the spinning wheel, Fizeau was able to determine the time it took the light to travel 8.63 km and back (17.26 km round trip) and therefore to determine the speed at which the light was travelling to the distant mirror and back. His experimentally determined value for the speed of light was 3.15×10^{8} m/s — only 5% more than the currently accepted value.

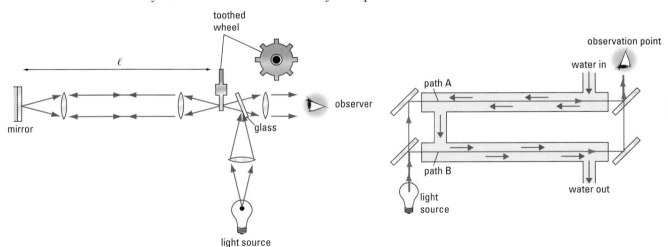

▲ **Figure 13.22** Fizeau's original apparatus for measuring the time it takes light to travel the distance ℓ (8.63 km) and back

▲ **Figure 13.23** Fizeau's apparatus for measuring the speed of light in water

Three years later Fizeau conducted an investigation to determine if the speed of light was affected by a moving medium such as water. In this experiment, water was pumped in opposite directions through two parallel tubes (Figure 13.23). Light from a single source was directed through both tubes, following paths A and B, of identical lengths, to an

Chapter 13 The wave model can be used to describe the characteristics of electromagnetic radiation. 649

observation point. Fizeau argued that if the speed of the light waves changed as a result of travelling through the water tubes, the waves arriving from path A and B would produce an interference pattern at the observation point. A device called an interferometer was used to observe this interference. The experiment proved that light would travel at different speeds in different media. The interference pattern produced was also very strong evidence that light was a wave.

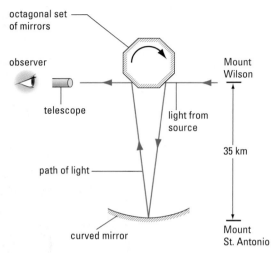

▲ **Figure 13.24** Michelson's experimental apparatus to measure the speed of light

Michelson's Experiment

Building on Fizeau's 1848 experimental design and the work of others, Albert Michelson performed an experiment in 1905, using a rotating set of mirrors instead of a toothed wheel. A very intense light source was directed at an 8-sided, rotating set of mirrors, which reflected the light toward a curved mirror located 35 km away. After travelling 35 km, the light was reflected back toward the rotating mirrors. If the rotating mirrors had made 1/8th of a rotation just as the light returned, the returning light could be observed in a telescope (Figure 13.24).

For the returning light to be observed in the telescope, the rotating mirrors had to turn at a very precise frequency. Michelson knew the light had to travel a round trip distance of 70 km, and if the rotating mirrors had made 1/8th of a rotation (or a multiple of an 1/8th rotation) between the time the light left and then returned, the light could be observed in the telescope. All Michelson needed to measure was the frequency of rotation and he could determine the time required for 1/8th of a rotation. When his mirror rotated at 32 000 rpm (533 Hz), he could observe the light in the telescope.

Practice Problems

1. Students using a 12-sided set of rotating mirrors in an experiment similar to Michelson's determine the speed of light to be 2.88×10^8 m/s. The mirrors are located 30.0 km from the fixed mirror. What is the frequency of rotation?

2. Light reflected from an 8-sided rotating set of mirrors travels 15.0 km to a distant fixed mirror and back. At what frequency is the set rotating if it has turned 1/8th of a rotation before the light returns?

3. An 8-sided set of mirrors, similar to Michelson's, rotating with a frequency of 500 Hz, is located 36.0 km away from a fixed mirror. If the returning light is observed in the system, at what speed is the light travelling?

Answers

1. 400 Hz

2. 1.25×10^3 Hz

3. 2.88×10^8 m/s

Example 13.1

The set of rotating mirrors in Michelson's experiment was rotating at 533 Hz and the reflecting mirror was located 35.0 km away. Show how Michelson determined the speed of light from these data.

Given
$\Delta d = 35.0 \text{ km} \times 2 = 70.0 \text{ km}$, round-trip distance for light path
$\Delta d = 7.00 \times 10^4 \text{ m}$
$f = 533 \text{ Hz}$

Required
speed of light (c)

Analysis and Solution
$$c = \frac{\Delta d}{\Delta t}$$

The light must travel from the set of mirrors to the curved mirror and back again, so the round-trip distance is twice the given distance. $(3.50 \times 10^4 \text{ m})(2) = 7.00 \times 10^4 \text{ m}$.

For the light to follow the path illustrated in Figure 13.24, the rotating set of mirrors must complete a minimum of 1/8th of a rotation while the light is travelling between the rotating mirror and the curved mirror. Therefore, the minimum travel time (Δt) is equal to 1/8th of the period of rotation.

$$T = \frac{1}{f} \qquad\qquad \Delta t = \frac{1}{8}T \qquad\qquad c = \frac{\Delta d}{\Delta t}$$

$$T = \frac{1}{533 \text{ Hz}} \qquad \Delta t = \frac{1}{8}(1.876 \times 10^{-3}\text{ s}) \quad c = \frac{7.00 \times 10^4\text{ m}}{2.345 \times 10^{-4}\text{ s}}$$

$$T = 1.876 \times 10^{-3}\text{ s} \qquad \Delta t = 2.345 \times 10^{-4}\text{ s} \qquad c = 2.98 \times 10^8\text{ m/s}$$

Paraphrase

According to Michelson's observations, the speed of light in air was found to be 2.98×10^8 m/s.

13-2 QuickLab

Measuring the Speed of EMR

Problem

Microwaves are a type of electromagnetic radiation and travel at the speed of light. They have a defined wavelength and frequency when they travel in a vacuum or in air. The universal wave equation $v = f\lambda$ relates the speed of the wave to its frequency and wavelength, where f is the frequency of the radiation, and λ is the wavelength. Each microwave oven generates microwaves at a given frequency, usually 2450 MHz. If the wavelength of the microwave can be measured, its speed can be determined using the universal wave equation.

Materials

microwave oven
microwave-safe dish
marshmallows

Procedure

1. Pack a solid layer of marshmallows in a casserole or microwave-safe dish.

2. Remove the turntable from the microwave oven.

3. Place the dish in the oven and cook until the marshmallows begin to melt in four or five locations.

4. Remove the dish from the oven and measure the distance between adjacent soft spots.

5. Determine the average separation distance between several soft spots. This distance is equal to half the wavelength of a microwave.

6. Calculate the wavelength by multiplying the average separation distance by two.

7. Record the frequency of the microwave, which will be indicated on the back of the microwave oven.

Questions

Use the wavelength and frequency of the microwave to answer the following questions.

1. What is the speed of the microwaves?

2. What is the percent error of your calculated value, when compared with the currently accepted value for the speed of light (3.00×10^8 m/s)?

3. What are several possible sources of error that could affect your calculation?

4. Compare the wavelength of microwaves with that of radio waves and visible light waves. Why are they called microwaves?

Knowledge

1. Why was Galileo's original experiment to determine the speed of light unsuccessful?

2. Explain why, in a Michelson-type experiment, the rotating mirrors have to turn at a very precise frequency in order for light to reach a stationary observer.

3. Explain why the periodic motion of Jupiter's moon Io appears to be constantly changing when observed from Earth.

Applications

4. In measuring the speed of light, the difference in eclipse times for Jupiter's moon Io, is measured. If eclipse occurs 24 min later than expected, and Earth's orbital diameter is 3.0×10^{11} m, calculate the speed of light.

5. A communications satellite is in orbit around Earth at an altitude of 2.00×10^4 km. If the satellite is directly above a ground-based station, how long does it take a signal to travel between the satellite and the station?

6. Using a similar approach to Michelson, a student sets up a 64-sided rotating mirror, 8.00 km away from a fixed mirror. What frequency of rotation would be required to successfully measure the speed of light?

7. A 16-sided rotating mirror is used to measure the time it takes light to travel a certain distance. At what frequency does the mirror need to rotate such that it makes 1/16th of a rotation in the time it takes light to travel 3.5 km and back again?

8. An 8-sided mirror rotates at 545 Hz in an experiment similar to that of Michelson. How far away should the fixed mirror be placed in order to correctly measure the speed of light?

9. The speed of light was measured to be 2.97×10^8 m/s using a 16-sided rotating mirror and a fixed mirror separated by 5.00×10^3 m. At what frequency was the mirror rotating?

10. Students who measure the speed of light using an experimental design similar to that of Michelson, make the following observations when light passes through the apparatus:

    (a) rotating mirror frequency
        $= 1.00 \times 10^3$ Hz

    (b) distance between fixed and rotating mirror = 17.5 km

    Determine the speed of light based on the students' recorded observations.

11. A 64-sided rotating mirror is turning at 340 Hz. If a fixed mirror is located 6.55 km away from the rotating mirror and the light is reflected correctly, what value for the speed of light would be obtained?

Extensions

12. Global positioning satellites (GPS) are used to pinpoint individual locations on the surface of Earth. A minimum of three GPS satellites are required, each with synchronized atomic clocks. Each satellite simultaneously sends a time signal to a GPS receiver on the surface. The time signal of each satellite is compared with the time on the receiver's clock.

    (a) Explain how the exact distance between each satellite and the receiver can be determined.

    (b) Explain how the receiver's location relative to all three satellites indicates an exact coordinate on Earth's surface.

 e **TEST**

To check your understanding of speed and propagation of electromagnetic radiation, follow the eTest links at www.pearsoned.ca/school/physicssource.

13.3 Reflection

On a windless day, the smooth surface of a lake will reflect light and produce stunning images of the surrounding landscape and sky. But introduce the slightest disturbance, a gust of wind or a morning rain shower, and the image becomes distorted and blurred. With enough disturbance, the image on the surface of the water completely disappears.

▲ **Figure 13.25**   a) Reflection in a smooth lake   b) Diffuse reflection due to windy conditions

How do the images in Figure 13.25 form? Light travels in straight lines through a medium that is uniform. This characteristic is termed **rectilinear propagation.** The light falling on a flat, smooth, reflecting surface, such as a mirror, undergoes **specular** or **regular reflection.**

In the case of the smooth lake, the crisp, clear images that form are the result of many parallel incident rays that reflect as parallel reflected rays (Figure 13.26). In the case of the rough lake, the blurred images that form are the result of many parallel incident rays that are scattered after reflecting in many different directions. This behaviour is called **diffuse** or **irregular** reflection (Figure 13.27).

rectilinear propagation: movement of light in straight lines through a uniform medium

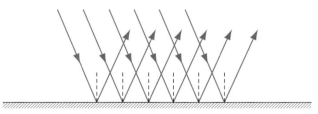

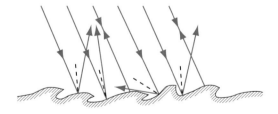

▲ **Figure 13.26**   Ray diagram of specular (regular) reflection   ▲ **Figure 13.27**   Ray diagram of diffuse (irregular) reflection

The Law of Reflection

Particular terms are used to describe reflection. These terms are illustrated in the **ray diagram** shown in Figure 13.28 below. Regular reflection will occur when an **incident light** ray contacts a polished, reflecting surface. The incident ray makes contact at the **point of incidence** and then it leaves the reflecting surface and becomes the **reflected ray.** If, at the point of incidence, an imaginary line, called the **normal line (N),**

ray diagram: a diagram to show a result of a light ray interacting with a surface

plane mirror: a smooth, flat, reflecting surface

law of reflection: the angle of reflection is equal to the angle of incidence and is in the same plane

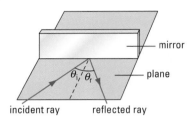

▲ **Figure 13.29**
The Law of Reflection

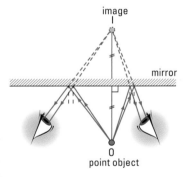

▲ **Figure 13.30** How two different observers see the image of an object located in front of a plane mirror

virtual image: an image from which light rays appear to come; cannot be formed on a non-reflective surface or screen

real image: an image from which light rays come; can be formed on a diffusely reflecting surface or screen

is drawn perpendicular to the surface, then the angle formed between the incident ray and the normal line is called the **angle of incidence.** The angle formed between the reflected ray and the normal line is called the **angle of reflection.**

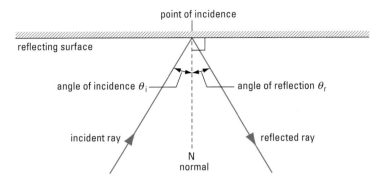

▲ **Figure 13.28** Ray diagram and terminology for regular reflection

Light rays that are incident upon a **plane mirror** at 90° will be reflected directly back to the source. In this case, the incident and reflected rays are parallel to the normal line so that the angle of incidence and the angle of reflection are both zero. In a similar way, when a light ray contacts a mirror at an angle of 25° relative to the normal line, it will reflect at an angle of 25° relative to the normal line. In all cases, the angle of incidence will be equal to the angle of reflection. This is called the **law of reflection** (Figure 13.29).

The angle of reflection is equal to the angle of incidence and is in the same plane.

Image Formation in a Plane Mirror

Look at the image of an object formed in a plane, flat mirror in Figure 13.30. What do the dashed lines represent? Are they real rays coming from a real object? The dashed lines are an extension of the reflected rays, causing your eyes to "believe" that they are rays, originating from an object that is located behind the mirror. But this cannot be so. The light rays appear to be coming from an image, but this image is not real. The image formed in a plane mirror in this fashion is therefore called a **virtual image**. For example, if you were to hold a piece of paper behind the mirror where the image appears to be, you would not see the image on the paper. By contrast, a **real image** is one that can be formed on a diffusely reflecting surface, such as a piece of paper. A projector is a familiar device that produces real images on a screen. Ray diagrams can be used to show how images form with a reflecting surface, such as a mirror.

Drawing a Ray Diagram

Problem

To construct a ray diagram of an image formed in a plane, flat mirror.

Materials

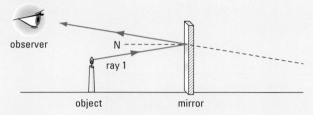

▲ **Figure 13.31**

Procedure

1 Choose one point on the object, such as the tip of the candle flame, in Figure 13.31.

2 Draw an incident ray from the selected point on the object (adding a small normal line where the ray is incident on the surface of the mirror) (Figure 13.31).

3 Based on the law of reflection, the reflected ray leaves the mirror surface such that the angle of incidence is equal to the angle of reflection. Draw the reflected ray.

4 Use a dashed line to extend the reflected ray beyond the back surface of the mirror.

5 On your diagram, repeat steps 2 to 4 for a ray originating from the same location on the object, but at a slightly different angle.

6 Note that the viewer must be located where both reflected rays would enter the eye.

7 Repeat steps 2 to 6 and locate the point where the two dashed lines converge (meet). This is the image location for the first selected point on the object.

Questions

1. How could you test whether the image formed in the mirror was real or virtual?

2. Is the image magnified or the same size as the object?

3. Will the image appear right side up (erect) or upside down (inverted)?

4. Could you use a ray diagram to determine if the word "HELP" would appear backwards in a mirror? Explain.

 MINDS ON | **Image in a Mirror**

Figure 13.32 shows a woman looking in a mirror.

1. How far behind the mirror does her image form, if she is standing 50.0 cm in front of the mirror? Explain how the ray diagram is used to determine this distance.
2. Is the image real or virtual?
3. According to the ray diagram, two sections of the mirror could be removed and her entire face would still be visible. Which two sections are not needed? Explain your reasoning.

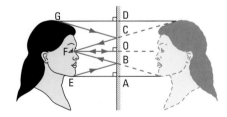

▲ **Figure 13.32** Woman in a Mirror

Image Characteristics

magnification: the relationship of the size of the image to the size of the object

image attitude: the orientation characteristic of an image, whether erect or inverted

When an object is placed in front of a mirror, the image can be described by four general characteristics (Table 13.2). The **magnification** relates the size of the image to the size of the object. The image can be enlarged, diminished, or the same size as the object. The **image attitude** describes the image as being either erect (upright) or inverted (upside down) relative to the object. This is termed vertical inversion. Horizontal, or left/right, inversion can also occur. The **position** describes where the image forms relative to the surface of the mirror. The **type** of image distinguishes between real and virtual images. A real image is one that can be caught or projected on a screen or surface, and a virtual image is one that can only be seen, or photographed.

▼ **Table 13.2** Image Characteristics

Image Characteristic	Description
magnification	same size, enlarged, diminished
attitude	erect or inverted
position	displacement from mirror surface
type	real or virtual

Image characteristics are important for the proper application of signage and warning labels. For example, the word "ambulance" is written in reverse on the front of the vehicle so that other drivers will be able to read the writing in their rear-view mirrors when the ambulance is approaching.

MINDS ON | **Image Characteristics**

Figure 13.33 shows (a) an image of an ambulance and (b) its image in a rear-view mirror.

1. What image characteristic is addressed by printing the word "ambulance" in reverse?
2. While standing in front of a plane, flat mirror, raise your right hand. Which hand in your image was raised?
3. In a plane, flat mirror, do images appear backwards horizontally or upside down vertically or both? Explain.
4. Can an image in a plane mirror ever appear "upside down"?

▲ **Figure 13.33** (a) The front of an ambulance (b) The image it makes in a rear-view mirror

Image Formation in a Curved Mirror

Curved mirrors come in a variety of shapes, the most common being spherical. Spherical mirrors, like the ones used for store security, have a unique geometrical shape (Figure 13.34). This shape is derived from a sphere. Imagine a hollow sphere, with a polished mirror surface on the inside and out.

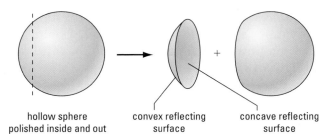

hollow sphere polished inside and out — convex reflecting surface + concave reflecting surface

▲ **Figure 13.34** A spherical store security mirror

◄ **Figure 13.35** A curved mirror can be formed from a hollow sphere.

By removing a section of the sphere, you produce a double-sided spherical mirror with a concave reflecting surface on one side and a convex reflecting surface on the other (Figure 13.35). The concave reflecting surface is curved inwards. This surface is also referred to as a **converging mirror** since it causes parallel light rays to converge after being reflected. The convex reflecting surface is curved outwards. This surface is also referred to as a **diverging mirror** since it causes parallel light rays to spread out or diverge after being reflected.

As with plane-mirror image formation, ray diagrams are useful to determine how images form from curved surfaces. Ray diagrams for curved surfaces, as in Figure 13.36 for example, are more complex and involve an expanded set of terminology.

1. **centre of curvature (C)** – the point in space that would represent the centre of the sphere from which the curved mirror was cut

2. **radius of curvature (r)** – the distance from the centre of curvature to the mirror surface

3. **vertex (V)** – the geometric centre of the curved mirror surface

4. **principal axis (PA)** – an imaginary line drawn through the vertex, perpendicular to the surface of the curved mirror at this point

5. **principal focal point (F)** – the point where light rays that are parallel to and close to the principal axis converge, or appear to diverge from, after being reflected

converging mirror: a concave reflecting surface that causes parallel light rays to converge after being reflected

diverging mirror: a convex reflecting surface that causes parallel light rays to spread out after being reflected

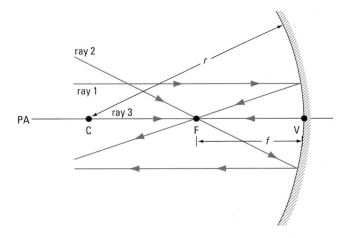

▲ **Figure 13.36** A ray diagram for a converging mirror

6. **focal length (f)** – the distance from the vertex to the focal point, measured along the principal axis. The focal length is related to the radius of curvature by $f = r/2$. This means that as the radius of curvature is reduced, so too is the focal length of the reflecting surface.

Drawing Ray Diagrams for Curved Mirrors

The four general image characteristics of magnification, attitude, position, and type, which were applied to plane mirrors, can also be applied to curved mirrors. For curved mirrors, the normal line at the point of incidence is the same as the radius of the spherical surface. The law of reflection still describes how all the rays will be reflected. To understand and predict how images are produced from curved mirrors, we will need to use three light rays, the law of reflection, and the mirror's focal point, centre of curvature, and vertex. Two rays from a point on an object locate the corresponding point on the image and the third ray will verify its location (Figure 13.37).

Consider each of the three rays:

Incident Ray 1 travels from a point on the object parallel to the principal axis. Any ray that is parallel to the principal axis will reflect through the focal point on a converging mirror, or appear to have originated from the focal point on a diverging mirror.

Incident Ray 2 travels from a point on the object toward the focal point. Any ray that passes through the focal point on a converging mirror, or is directed at the focal point on a diverging mirror, will be reflected back parallel to the principal axis.

Incident Ray 3 travels from a point on the object toward the centre of curvature. Any ray that passes through the centre of curvature on a converging mirror, or is directed at the centre of curvature on a diverging mirror, will be reflected directly back along the incident path. At what incident angle must this light ray hit the mirror surface in order to be reflected straight back along the original path?

These three rays alone will allow you to predict and verify the location and characteristics of the image. Notice that some conventions are used when drawing these ray diagrams:

1. objects are often drawn as erect arrows

2. real rays are drawn as solid lines

3. virtual rays (that only appear to exist behind the mirror) are drawn as dashed lines

Figure 13.38 (a) shows that the converging mirror produces a real image that is inverted and diminished. Figure 13.38 (b) shows that the diverging mirror produces a virtual image that is erect and diminished. Why is one image real and the other virtual? For curved mirrors, a real image is formed where the reflected light rays converge or meet. At this location, a focussed image would appear on a sheet of paper or a screen if it were located in the exact location where the light rays meet. If the screen were to be moved slightly, the image would appear

▼ **Figure 13.37** Reflection of three rays from spherical mirrors

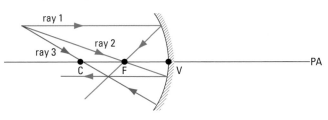

a) A concave, converging mirror

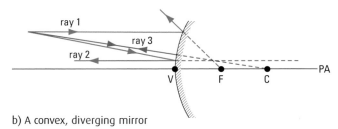

b) A convex, diverging mirror

PHYSICS INSIGHT

All three incident rays obey the Law of Reflection. The resulting rules for drawing ray diagrams are just the application of geometry.

blurred because the reflected rays would not be converging perfectly at the screen's new location. For the diverging mirror, the reflected rays appear to be originating from behind the mirror, but if a screen were located there, the incident light rays would not reach it (the rays would be blocked by the mirror).

WEB

To learn more about ray diagrams for curved mirrors and lenses, follow the links at www.pearsoned.ca/school/physicssource.

▼ **Figure 13.38** Steps for drawing a ray diagram in converging and diverging spherical mirrors

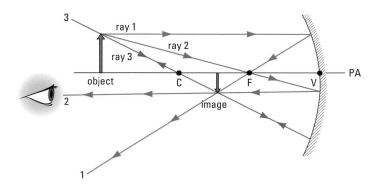

a) A concave, converging mirror

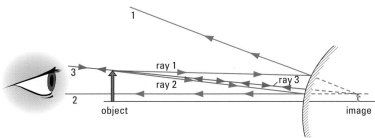

b) A convex, diverging mirror

Characteristics of an Image in a Curved Mirror

If you look at the image of your face in a polished spoon and bring the spoon closer and closer to your nose, you will demonstrate that with curved mirrors, the object's distance from the mirror's vertex has an effect on the characteristics of the image produced. For example, what happens to an image as the object is brought closer to a converging mirror surface? In Figure 13.39(a), the object is located outside the centre of curvature, and a real, inverted, and diminished image appears. If the object is brought closer to the vertex of the mirror, such that it is inside the focal length, as in Figure 13.39(b), then the image becomes virtual, erect, and enlarged.

▼ **Figure 13.39** Object location affects image characteristics.

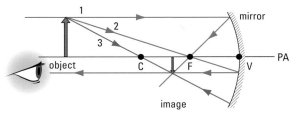

a) A converging mirror with object located outside C (real, inverted, diminished)

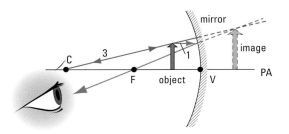

b) A converging mirror with object located inside F (virtual, erect, enlarged)

▼ **Table 13.3** Image Characteristics for Converging Mirrors

Object Position	Image Characteristic
distant	real, inverted, and diminished, close to F
outside centre of curvature	real, inverted, and diminished, between F and C
at the centre of curvature, C	real, inverted, and same size, at C
between focal point and centre of curvature	real, inverted, and enlarged, beyond C
at focal point, F	undefined (no image forms), at infinity
between focal point and vertex	virtual, erect, and enlarged, behind mirror

Table 13.3 summarizes the image characteristics for a concave, converging mirror. You can verify the characteristics by placing the concave side of a spoon in front of your nose and slowly moving it outward. Note that your image will disappear briefly just as the distance between your nose and the spoon reaches the focal point of the spoon. In a similar way, the image characteristics produced by a convex, diverging mirror can be investigated by using the other surface of the spoon.

13-4 *QuickLab*

Converging and Diverging Mirrors

Problem

How do image characteristics in converging and diverging mirrors change as you change the object distance?

Materials

polished spoon
drawing materials

Procedure

❶ Place a polished metal spoon on your nose and slowly pull it away from your face while watching the image.

❷ Complete ray diagrams for the image of your nose inside F, at F, at C, and at a distance, with respect to the spoon as a converging mirror. (Use a small upright arrow to represent your nose in the ray diagram.)

❸ Reverse the spoon so that you are looking at the other side and move it away from your nose again.

❹ Complete ray diagrams for the image of your nose inside F, at F, at C, and at a distance, with respect to the spoon as a diverging mirror. (Remember that a diverging mirror has a virtual focal length, so F and C are located on the opposite side of the spoon to your face.)

Questions

1. What happens to the image as the object is brought closer to the surface of a converging mirror?

2. What happens to the image as the object is brought closer to the surface of a diverging mirror?

3. What characteristics do all images formed in a diverging mirror share?

4. Your image disappears when your face is at the focal point of the mirror. Sketch a ray diagram for a converging mirror with the object located at the focal point to explain why an image should not appear when the object is located at the focal point.

5. Why is it not possible to put an object at F for a convex mirror?

MINDS ON   Seeing Is Believing—Or Is It?

A parabolic mirror is shaped so that incident light rays that travel parallel to the principal axis will be reflected to a central point, or focus. Optical illusions can be produced by arranging two parabolic mirrors facing one another. Use a ray diagram to explain how a three-dimensional, real image, is produced in Figure 13.40.

Hint: The object is located at the focal point of the top mirror. Therefore, all rays that originate from the object will be reflected straight down from the top mirror. Assume the bottom mirror has the same focal length as the top mirror.

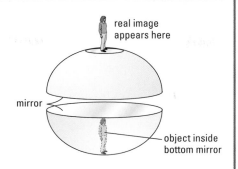

▲ **Figure 13.40** Two parabolic mirrors facing one another, with a hole cut around the vertex of one mirror

Equations for Curved Mirrors

The general rules for drawing ray diagrams of curved mirrors, in combination with the law of reflection, allow us to generate several equations for use with curved mirrors. These equations can be used to determine the characteristics of the image.

In any ray diagram, two rays can be used to determine the image characteristics. In Figure 13.41, there are two similar triangles (AOV, above, and DIV, below). Both triangles have an identical angle (θ) and right angles at the principal axis. Thus,

$$\frac{\text{DI}}{\text{AO}} = \frac{\text{DV}}{\text{AV}}$$

This translates into $\dfrac{h_i}{h_o} = \dfrac{d_i}{d_o}$ where

h_o is the height of the object,
h_i is the height of the image,
d_o is the distance between the mirror vertex and the object, and
d_i is the distance between the mirror vertex and the image.

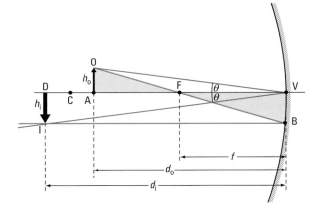

▲ **Figure 13.41** Triangles AOV and DIV are similar triangles; triangles FVB and FAO are also similar triangles.

When we use the ray OFB, the triangles FVB and FAO (shaded light blue) are also similar. Therefore,

$$\frac{\text{AO}}{\text{VB}} = \frac{\text{AF}}{\text{VF}}$$

Since
- AO $= h_o$
- VB $= h_i$
- AF $= d_o - f$
- VF $= f$

Chapter 13 The wave model can be used to describe the characteristics of electromagnetic radiation.   661

We can write this relationship as:

$$\frac{h_o}{h_i} = \frac{d_o - f}{f}$$

Since $\dfrac{h_i}{h_o} = \dfrac{d_i}{d_o}$ the inverse is also true:

$$\frac{h_o}{h_i} = \frac{d_o}{d_i}$$

Combining the equations gives:

$$\frac{d_o}{d_i} = \frac{d_o - f}{f}$$

Dividing both sides by d_o and rearranging:

$$\frac{d_o}{d_i d_o} = \frac{d_o}{d_o f} - \frac{1}{d_o}$$

We obtain this equation:

$$\frac{1}{d_o} + \frac{1}{d_i} = \frac{1}{f}$$

This is the **mirror equation**, which relates the focal length of a curved mirror to the image and object distances.

mirror equation: the equation that relates the focal length of a curved mirror to the image and object distances

> ### Sign Conventions for Use with the Mirror Equation
> As we have seen previously, there are real and virtual images, which can form either in front of or behind the curved mirror. When using the mirror equation, it is therefore necessary to follow a sign convention, which can distinguish the type of image formed.
> - Real objects and images have positive distances (measured from vertex).
> - Virtual objects and images have negative distances (measured from vertex).
> - Erect images and objects have a positive height.
> - Inverted images and objects have a negative height.
> - Converging mirrors have a real principal focal point and the focal length is positive.
> - Diverging mirrors have a virtual principal focal point and the focal length is negative.

With this sign convention, a real image formed by a converging mirror will have a negative height (inverted attitude) while the object height is positive (erect attitude). Both the object and image distances will be positive. Magnification (m) is the ratio of the image height to the object height. A negative sign must be added to the equation for magnification to agree with the sign convention above.

$$m = \frac{h_i}{h_o} = -\frac{d_i}{d_o}$$

An erect image has a positive magnification and an inverted image has a negative magnification.

Concept Check

1. If the object distance is extremely large, approaching infinity, $\dfrac{1}{d_o}$ becomes zero. Based on the mirror equation, where will the image form in relation to the focal length of the mirror?
2. For a plane, flat mirror, $\dfrac{1}{f}$ approaches zero. Based on the mirror equation, where will the image form in relation to the object?

Using a Converging Mirror to Heat Water (Determining the Focal Length of a Converging Mirror)

Recognize a Need

A converging mirror can be used to focus the radiant energy of the Sun onto a specific point to capture energy, to heat water, or to generate electrical energy using a photovoltaic cell.

The Problem

Design an efficient apparatus that uses radiation to heat water.

Criterion for Success

Observing the maximum increase in water temperature in a given time period.

Brainstorm Ideas

To design an efficient water heater that uses sunlight for energy, you will need to consider the following questions:

- Where would a water tank be placed in relation to a converging mirror in order to maximize the amount of radiation that it could absorb?
- What colour should the water tank be?
- What effect will the size of the mirror have on the water temperature?
- What positive and negative effects would result from insulating the water tank?

Build a Prototype

Construct a miniature version of your water heater using a 50-mL volumetric flask, a thermometer, and a converging mirror mounted on a base of clay.

Test and Evaluate

Determine the focal length of the converging mirror using a heat lamp, a metre-stick, and a sheet of paper (Figure 13.42). Recall that rays that travel parallel to the principal axis will be reflected back through the focal point.

1. Place the heat lamp a great distance away so that most of the incident rays travel parallel to the principal axis. Adjust the position of the paper until the light is focussed into a small region. Be careful not to block the light from reaching the mirror. You may need to adjust the position of the mirror to avoid this — try tilting it slightly downward and turning the room lights off to see the image clearly.

2. Record the distance between the paper and the vertex of the mirror. This is the approximate focal length of the mirror and it is also the image distance.

3. Measure the distance between the lamp and the mirror. This is the object distance. Using the mirror equation, with the image and object distances, calculate and verify the approximate focal length of the mirror.

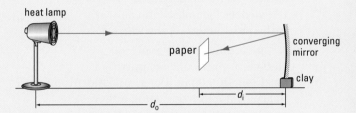

▲ **Figure 13.42** Locating the focal point

4. Using the heat lamp in place of sunlight, measure the increase in water temperature for a given time period when the water tank is located beyond the focal point, at the focal point, and inside the focal point of the mirror.

5. Determine which position results in the greatest increase in water temperature and explain why.

Communicate

Using presentation software, create a brochure that outlines the basic operating principles of your water heater and explains the role of radiant energy in its operation.

Example 13.2

An object is located 20.0 cm from a converging mirror that has a focal length of 15.0 cm.

(a) Where will the image form relative to the mirror vertex?
(b) If the object is 5.00 cm high, determine the attitude, height, and magnification of the image.

Given

$d_o = +20.0$ cm
$f = +15.0$ cm (converging mirror has a positive focal length)
$h_o = +5.00$ cm (assume that the object is erect)

Required

image distance (d_i)
image height (h_i)
magnification (m)

Analysis and Solution

(a) To locate the image, use the relationship between focal length and object distance, the mirror equation:

$$\frac{1}{f} = \frac{1}{d_o} + \frac{1}{d_i}$$

$$\frac{1}{d_i} = \frac{1}{f} - \frac{1}{d_o}$$

Now, solve for d_i:

$$\frac{1}{d_i} = \frac{1}{+15.0 \text{ cm}} - \frac{1}{+20.0 \text{ cm}}$$

$$d_i = +60.0 \text{ cm}$$

or

$$d_i = \frac{d_o f}{d_o - f}$$

$$d_i = \frac{(+20.0 \text{ cm})(+15.0 \text{ cm})}{(+20.0 \text{ cm}) - (+15.0 \text{ cm})}$$

$$d_i = +60.0 \text{ cm}$$

(b) To determine the attitude, height, and magnification, use the equation for magnification:

$$m = \frac{h_i}{h_o} = -\frac{d_i}{d_o}$$

Now, solve for m:

$$m = -\frac{60.0 \text{ cm}}{20.0 \text{ cm}} = -3.0 \times$$

Practice Problems

1. A diverging mirror of focal length 10.0 cm produces an image of an object located 20.0 cm from the mirror. Determine the image distance and the magnification. Is the image real or virtual?

2. Determine the image distance, magnification, and attributes for the following:
   (a) a converging mirror with a focal length of 12.0 cm with an object 6.0 cm from the mirror
   (b) a diverging mirror of focal length 5.00 cm with an object 10.0 cm from the mirror
   (c) a diverging mirror of focal length 10.0 cm with an object 2.0 cm from the mirror

3. A 5.0-cm-high object is placed 2.0 cm in front of a converging mirror and the image is magnified $-4\times$. Where does the image form and what is the focal length of the mirror?

4. A 4.0-cm-high object is placed 15.0 cm from a concave mirror of focal length 5.0 cm. Determine the image characteristics using a ray diagram and the mirror equation.

5. Light from a distant planet is incident on a converging mirror. The image of the planet forms on a screen 45.0 cm from the vertex of the mirror. Find the focal length of the mirror and the image characteristics.

Answers

1. $d_i = -6.67$ cm; $m = 0.333 \times$, virtual

2. (a) $d_i = -12$ cm; $m = 2.0 \times$, virtual, erect, enlarged
   (b) $d_i = -3.33$ cm; $m = 0.333 \times$, virtual, erect, diminished
   (c) $d_i = -1.7$ cm; $m = 0.83 \times$, virtual, erect, diminished

3. $d_i = 8$ cm; $f = 1.6$ cm

4. $d_i = 7.5$ cm; $m = -0.50 \times$;
   $h_i = -2.0$ cm; real, inverted, diminished

5. $f = 45.0$ cm; real, inverted, diminished

Then solve for h_i:

$$h_i = -\frac{d_i h_o}{d_o}$$

$$h_i = -\frac{(60.0 \text{ cm})(+5.00 \text{ cm})}{(+20.0 \text{ cm})}$$

$$h_i = -15.0 \text{ cm}$$

Paraphrase

(a) The real image forms 60.0 cm in front of the mirror vertex.

(b) It is inverted and magnified -3 times to a height of -15.0 cm.

13.3 Check and Reflect

Knowledge

1. Explain why the normal lines in Figure 13.27 are drawn in a variety of directions.

2. Create a concept map using ray diagram terminology including: principal axis, focal point, centre of curvature, and vertex.

3. Explain the difference between "specular" and "diffuse" reflection.

4. Compare "virtual" images with "real" images.

5. Compare "converging" and "diverging" mirrors.

6. Describe the path of the three rays that can be used to determine the characteristics of an image formed in a curved mirror.

7. Why does a diverging, convex mirror have a "virtual" focal point and not a "real" focal point?

Applications

8. An object 4.0 cm high is located 10.0 cm in front of a concave mirror. If the image produced is 5.0 cm high, what is the focal length of the mirror?

9. Draw a ray diagram for a converging mirror and determine the image characteristics when the object is located at:

    (a) 2.0 f (b) 0.50 f (c) 3.0 f

10. Draw a ray diagram for a diverging mirror and determine the image characteristics when the object is located at:

    (a) 0.50 f (b) 1.0 f (c) 1.5 f

11. Some flashlights and headlights use concave mirrors to help generate a light beam. If the light source is positioned at the focal point of the mirror, would all the reflected rays travel outward, parallel to the principal axis? Explain your answer. Include a ray diagram.

Extension

12. A reflecting telescope uses a curved mirror to produce the image at the eyepiece. Research the telescope's design and function. Sketch a ray diagram to explain how the converging mirror is used in the telescope design.

e TEST

To check your understanding of reflection in plane and curved mirrors, follow the eTest links at www.pearsoned.ca/school/physicssource.

13.4 Refraction

▲ **Figure 13.43** A paddle as it appears partially submerged in water

refraction: a change in the direction of a light wave due to a change in its speed as it passes from one medium to another

refractive index: a ratio comparing the speed of light in a vacuum to the measured speed of light in a given material

A paddle appears bent when you put it in water (Figure 13.43); the Sun changes shape when it sets; a rainbow appears when it rains; and a mirage occurs over the hot desert sand, or even over a hot Alberta highway during the day. These are all visual effects created by **refraction**, a change in the direction of a light wave due to a change in its speed as it passes from one medium to another.

When light rays pass at an angle from air to water, they immediately change direction. However, not all of the light will be refracted. Light rays are **partially reflected** and **partially refracted** when they pass from one medium to the next. Figure 13.44 illustrates this phenomenon.

The process of refraction is described by an **incident ray** and a **refracted ray**. The angle between the normal line (drawn perpendicular to the medium interface) and the incident ray is called the **angle of incidence**. The angle between the normal line and the refracted ray is called the **angle of refraction**. When the light ray passes from air to water, it is bent or refracted toward the normal line. And conversely, if a light ray travels from water into air, it is bent away from the normal line. The bending of the light ray depends on the **refractive index** of the medium in which the light travels.

The refractive index of a medium is related to the effect on the speed of light when it travels within that medium. A vacuum does not impede or slow down light travelling through it and therefore, the speed of light (c) is defined as its speed in a vacuum. Air slows the light down a small amount and thus has a slightly greater refractive index than a vacuum. Water slows the light down to a greater extent and has a greater refractive index than air. This retarding effect was observed in Fizeau's experiment on the speed of light in water (page 649). The amount of refraction is related to the magnitude of the change in the speed of light as it passes from one medium to another; the greater the change in speed, the greater the amount of refraction.

Mathematically, the refractive index of a medium (n) can be described as a ratio that compares the speed of light in a vacuum (c) to the measured speed of light in the medium (v).

$$n = \frac{c}{v}$$

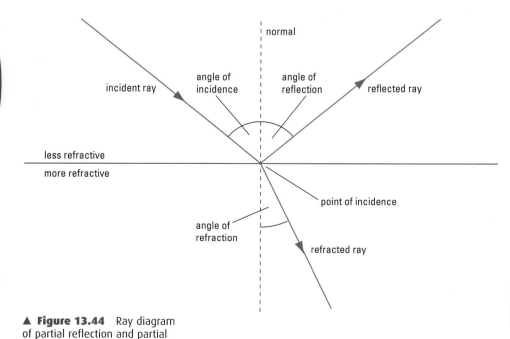

▲ **Figure 13.44** Ray diagram of partial reflection and partial refraction

Table 13.4 lists the refractive indexes for some common substances. Since the speed of light in air is very close to the speed of light in a vacuum, the refractive indexes for a vacuum and for air are considered to be the same.

The following general rules are based on refractive indexes:
- When light passes from a medium with a high refractive index to one with a low refractive index, it is refracted away from the normal line.
- When light passes from a medium with a low refractive index to one with a high refractive index, it is refracted toward the normal line.

▼ **Table 13.4** Absolute Refractive Indexes (for Sodium Yellow Light, $\lambda = 589$ nm)

Medium	Index of Refraction
vacuum	1.0000
air	1.0003
ice	1.31
water	1.33
ethanol	1.37
glycerin	1.47
quartz glass	1.47
crown glass	1.52
light flint glass	1.58
Lucite (plexiglass)	1.52
ruby	1.54
zircon	1.92
diamond	2.42

PHYSICS INSIGHT

On passing through a medium, each wavelength of EMR has a unique refractive index. For this reason, Absolute Refractive Indexes must be quoted for a specific wavelength, as in Table 13.4.

Snell's Law of Refraction

Although the phenomenon of refraction had been observed for centuries, it was not until 1621 that the Dutch mathematician, Willebrord Snell (1580–1626), identified the exact relationship between the angle of incidence and the angle of refraction. **Snell's Law** states that:

$$\frac{\sin \theta_i}{\sin \theta_r} = \text{a constant}$$

This relationship indicates that for any angle of incidence greater than zero, the ratio $\sin \theta_i / \sin \theta_r$ will be constant for any light ray that passes through the boundary between the two media. In the case of an air-water interface, the constant is 1.33, which corresponds to the refractive index of water. In fact, for any ray that passes from air (θ_{air}) into a second medium (θ_r, refractive index n), Snell's Law may also be written in a simple form as:

$$\frac{\sin \theta_{air}}{\sin \theta_r} = n$$

As long as the first medium is air, the Snell's constant and the index of refraction for the second medium are one and the same thing.

If the first medium is not air, then the general form of Snell's Law applies. In the general form, the angle of incidence (θ_i) is replaced with θ_1 and the angle of refraction (θ_r) is replaced with θ_2. The index of refraction for the first medium is denoted as n_1 and the index of refraction

Snell's Law: For any angle of incidence greater than zero, the ratio $\sin \theta_i / \sin \theta_r$ is a constant for any light ray passing through the boundary between two media.

info **BIT**

A mirage (derived from the Latin term "mirari," meaning "to be astonished") is a naturally occurring phenomenon caused by refraction. Often, mirages appear as large bodies of water on hot desert sand, or small puddles on highways. What appears as water is actually an image of the sky being refracted back up from the hot air just above the road surface.

▲ **Figure 13.45**

for the second medium is denoted as n_2. In all cases, the subscript "1" refers to the incident medium and the subscript "2" is reserved for the refracting medium. The general form of Snell's Law is written as:

$$\frac{\sin \theta_1}{\sin \theta_2} = \frac{n_2}{n_1}$$

$$n_1 \sin \theta_1 = n_2 \sin \theta_2$$

The general form of Snell's Law applies in all cases, regardless of the indexes of refraction of the media and/or the direction in which the light travels. Compare the general form with the simple form above. If the first medium is air, or a vacuum, so that n_1 is 1.00, substituting this value into the general form results in the simple form of Snell's Law.

Example 13.3

Practice Problems

1. Light passes from a diamond into air. The angle of refraction as the light emerges from the diamond is 25°. What was the angle of incidence?

2. Light travelling from air into a transparent material is incident at an angle of 20° and refracted at an angle of 17°. Determine the index of refraction for the transparent material.

3. A ray of light passes from air into ruby at an incident angle of 15°. Calculate the angle of refraction.

4. A ray of light, travelling in air, is incident on an unknown sample at an angle of 20°. If the angle of refraction is 15°, determine the index of refraction for the unknown sample.

Answers
1. 10°
2. 1.2
3. 9.7°
4. 1.3

Yellow light travels from water into crown glass. The light rays are incident on the crown glass at an angle of 35°. Calculate the angle of refraction as the light enters the crown glass.

Given
$\theta_1 = 35°$

Required
the angle of refraction (θ_2)

Analysis and Solution
From Table 13.4,
- Index of refraction of water, the first medium, is $n_1 = 1.33$
- Index of refraction of crown glass, the second medium, is $n_2 = 1.52$

Therefore, the general form of Snell's Law applies.

$$n_1 \sin \theta_1 = n_2 \sin \theta_2$$
$$\sin \theta_2 = \frac{n_1 \sin \theta_1}{n_2}$$
$$\theta_2 = \sin^{-1}\left(\frac{(1.33)(\sin 35°)}{1.52}\right)$$
$$\theta_2 = 30°$$

Paraphrase
The angle of refraction for the light travelling from water into crown glass is 30°, when the angle of incidence is 35°.

Snell's Law, Refraction, and Wavelength

Can we explain the phenomenon of refraction, and by association, Snell's Law, by considering light as a wave? Recall that the wave model describes light as a stream of transverse waves radiating outward from a source. Let us assume that the light waves are indeed transverse waves of electromagnetic radiation. As each wave front moves from one medium to the next the wavelength changes, as illustrated by Figure 13.46, but there is *no change* in frequency. In other words, the wave fronts do not "pile up" at the boundary between the two media. The number of waves arriving at the boundary is equal to the number of waves leaving the boundary for any given time interval, so the incident and refracted waves have the same frequency. However, the wavelength changes at the boundary. According to the universal wave equation ($v = f\lambda$), if the wavelength changes and the frequency remains constant, then the speed must change as well. To visualize this, consider light waves travelling from air into water as illustrated in Figure 13.46:

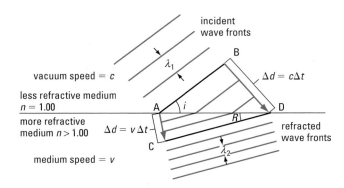

▲ **Figure 13.46** Wave fronts are refracted as they pass from air into water.

The wavelength in air is given by $\lambda_1 = v_1/f$;

The wavelength in water is given by $\lambda_2 = v_2/f$.

Since λ_1 is greater than λ_2, v_1 will be greater than v_2. This means the wave fronts in air travel faster than they do in water, as illustrated in Figure 13.46 and by Fizeau's experiment to measure the speed of light in water, page 649.

An enlarged view of two wave fronts, as shown in Figure 13.47, reveals another relationship. When we use similar triangles, the angle of incidence, θ_1 and the angle of refraction, θ_2 are shown within the coloured right triangles and they share the same hypotenuse, x.

Therefore, the trigonometric ratio for the sine of an angle when applied to each triangle gives:

$$\sin \theta_1 = \frac{\text{opposite}}{\text{hypotenuse}} = \frac{\lambda_1}{x}$$

$$\sin \theta_2 = \frac{\text{opposite}}{\text{hypotenuse}} = \frac{\lambda_2}{x}$$

Since

$$x = \frac{\lambda_1}{\sin \theta_1} \text{ and also } x = \frac{\lambda_2}{\sin \theta_2}$$

therefore

$$\frac{\lambda_1}{\sin \theta_1} = \frac{\lambda_2}{\sin \theta_2}$$

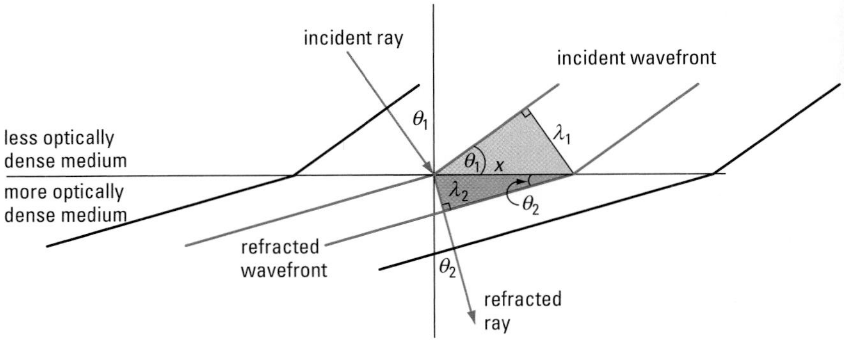

▲ **Figure 13.47** Enlarged view of two wave fronts

This equation can also be written as:

$$\frac{\sin \theta_1}{\sin \theta_2} = \frac{\lambda_1}{\lambda_2}$$

When the universal wave equation is used, the wavelength can also be written in terms of the wave speed as follows.

$$\frac{\sin \theta_1}{\sin \theta_2} = \frac{\dfrac{v_1}{\cancel{f}}}{\dfrac{v_2}{\cancel{f}}}$$

$$\frac{\sin \theta_1}{\sin \theta_2} = \frac{v_1}{v_2}$$

Therefore, Snell's Law can be expanded to read:

$$\frac{\sin \theta_1}{\sin \theta_2} = \frac{v_1}{v_2} = \frac{\lambda_1}{\lambda_2} = \frac{n_2}{n_1}$$

By measuring the incident and refracted angles, velocity, and wavelength, this relationship can be tested.

Example 13.4

A ray of yellow light with a wavelength of 570 nm travels from air into diamond at an angle of 30°. Determine the following:

(a) the speed of light in the diamond
(b) the wavelength of the light as it travels in the diamond

Given
$\lambda_1 = 5.70 \times 10^{-7}$ m

Required
the speed of light in diamond (v_2)
the wavelength of light travelling in diamond (θ_2)

Analysis and Solution
v_1, the speed of light in air $= 3.00 \times 10^8$ m/s

From Table 13.4,
- Index of refraction of air, the first medium, is $n_1 = 1.00$
- Index of refraction of diamond, the second medium, is $n_2 = 2.42$

The general form of Snell's Law applies: $\dfrac{\sin \theta_1}{\sin \theta_2} = \dfrac{v_1}{v_2} = \dfrac{\lambda_1}{\lambda_2} = \dfrac{n_2}{n_1}$

Therefore,

$$v_2 = \frac{n_1 v_1}{n_2} \qquad \lambda_2 = \frac{n_1 \lambda_1}{n_2}$$

$v_2 = 1.24 \times 10^8$ m/s $\qquad \lambda_2 = 2.36 \times 10^{-9}$ m *or* 236 nm

Paraphrase
(a) The speed of light in the diamond is 1.24×10^8 m/s.
(b) The wavelength of light in the diamond is 236 nm.

Practice Problems

1. Determine the speed of light in the following materials:
   (a) water
   (b) ethanol
   (c) ruby
   (d) crown glass

2. Light with a wavelength of 737 nm enters quartz glass at an angle of 25.0°. Determine the angle of refraction and the wavelength of the light in the quartz glass.

3. Light enters an unknown crystal from air with a wavelength of 500 nm. If the wavelength of the light in the crystal is found to be 450 nm, what is the refractive index of the crystal?

Answers

1. (a) 2.26×10^8 m/s
   (b) 2.19×10^8 m/s
   (c) 1.95×10^8 m/s
   (d) 1.97×10^8 m/s

2. 16.7°, 501 nm

3. 1.11

Determining the Refractive Index of a Variety of Materials

In this experiment, known values of the refractive indexes of water and ethanol are verified.

Question

What are the refractive indexes of water and alcohol (ethanol)?

Variables

Manipulated variable: angle of incidence
Responding variable: angle of refraction
Controlled variables: refracting substance, wavelength of light

Materials and Equipment

polar coordinate paper
graphing paper
water
ethanol
single-slit ray box or laser
semicircular plastic dish

Procedure

1 Design a data table or spreadsheet with the headings: angle of incidence (i), angle of refraction (r), sin angle of incidence (sin i), sin angle of refraction (sin r), and ratio sin i / sin r.

2 Fill the semicircular dish with water and place it on the polar coordinate paper such that the 0–180° line is perpendicular to the centre of the flat side of the dish. This will make the 0–180° line the normal line (Figure 13.48).

3 Direct a single ray of light along the normal line (0°). Record the angle of refraction. (This should be zero if the apparatus is set up correctly.)

4 Record the angles of refraction for 10° to 70°, increasing the angle by 10° for each step.

5 Complete the data table or spreadsheet calculations and plot a graph of sin angle of incidence vs. sin angle of refraction. Calculate the slope of this graph.

6 Repeat steps 2 to 5 using ethanol instead of water in the semicircular dish.

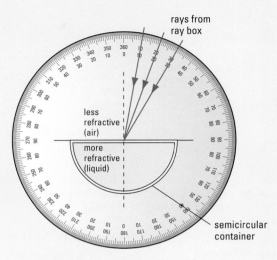

rays from ray box

less refractive (air)

more refractive (liquid)

semicircular container

▲ **Figure 13.48** Semicircular dish on polar coordinate paper with several incident ray angles shown

Analysis

1. (a) What is the value of the slope for the graph when water was used as the refracting substance?

   (b) What is the value of the slope when ethanol was used as the refracting substance?

2. According to your slope calculations, which material, water or ethanol, has a higher index of refraction?

3. Calculate the percent error for each index of refraction using the absolute index of refraction given for each substance in Table 13.4.

4. Comment on the sources of error that could have occurred in this experiment.

5. Why is it important that the incident light ray contacts the semicircular dish at the centre?

6. Why is it important that a "semicircular" dish is used, instead of a rectangular dish?

7. Which material is more effective in changing the direction of light when light enters it?

8. Predict what would happen if the semicircular dish were replaced with a semicircular block of glass or Lucite®. If you have time, test your prediction.

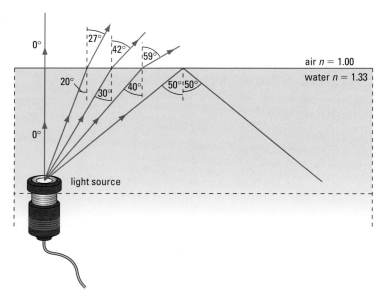

Total Internal Reflection

If you look down a long straight tube, you should be able to see what is at the other end. If the tube has a bend in it, a set of mirrors could be used to reflect the light through to your eye. This is how the periscope on a submarine works. But what if the tube has multiple bends in it? What could be done to ensure the light is able to travel through the entire length of the tube? Could you line the inside walls with mirrors and angle the light so that it reflects from side to side all along the tube, entering at one end and emerging at the opposite end?

In theory, this is exactly what happens in the optical fibres that facilitate the data and telephone communication of computer networks. The process is based on **total internal reflection.** Recall that when light travels from one medium to another, some of the light is partially reflected and some is partially refracted. When light travels from a medium with a high refractive index, like glass, to a medium with a low refractive index, like air, more of the light is reflected than it would be at an interface where its speed decreases.

As illustrated by Figure 13.49, when light travels from the water with a high refractive index to the air with a low refractive index, it bends away from the normal line. As the angle of incidence is increased, the angle of refraction also increases, bending farther and farther from the normal line, and eventually reaching the maximum angle of 90°. Beyond this angle, refraction ceases and all incident light will be reflected back into the high-index medium (in this case, the water). Therefore, not all the light that approaches a water-air boundary will be refracted. The light approaching the boundary at large angles will be reflected back into the water. This is why underwater pool lights, for example, are not visible at all angles from above. At particular angles, they cannot be seen.

When the angle of refraction is 90°, the incident angle will have a value unique to the two media that form the interface. This unique angle of incidence is called the **critical angle.** For light travelling from a medium with a high refractive index to a medium with a low refractive index, the critical angle is determined by assuming that the angle of refraction is 90°.

▲ **Figure 13.49** Increasing the incident angle for light leaving a water-air interface leads to total internal reflection.

total internal reflection: reflection of all incident light back into a medium of higher refractive index due to the inability to refract light beyond the maximum angle of 90°

critical angle: for any two media, the size of the incident angle for which the angle of refraction is 90°

info BIT

The sparkle and glitter associated with diamonds is caused by total internal reflection. The high index of refraction of the diamond and the skill of the jeweller in cutting and finishing are used to trap and focus light, which we observe as sparkles. Polar Bear Diamonds™, mined, cut, and polished in the Northwest Territories, are recognized for their quality worldwide.

▲ **Figure 13.50**

Concept Check

1. Is light refracted toward or away from the normal line when passing from a medium with a low refractive index like air, into a medium with a high refractive index like water?
2. Based on your answer above, can total internal reflection occur when light travels from a low-index medium like air, into a high-index medium like water? Explain why or why not.

Example 13.5

What is the critical angle for the quartz glass-air interface?

Given

The angle of refraction at the critical angle is defined to be $\theta_r = 90°$.

Required

the critical angle for this interface ($\theta_{critical}$)

Analysis and Solution

From Table 13.4,

- Index of refraction of air, the first medium, is $n_1 = 1.00$
- Index of refraction of quartz glass, the second medium, is $n_2 = 1.47$

Use the form of Snell's law for the critical angle:

$$n_2 \sin \theta_{critical} = n_1 \sin 90°$$

$$\sin \theta_{critical} = \frac{n_1 \sin 90°}{n_2}$$

$$\theta_{critical} = \sin^{-1}\left(\frac{n_1 \sin 90°}{n_2}\right)$$

$$\theta_{critical} = \sin^{-1}\left(\frac{1.00 \sin 90°}{1.47}\right)$$

$$\theta_{critical} = 42.9°$$

Paraphrase

Light at an incident angle of 42.9° or greater will be internally reflected at the quartz glass-air interface.

Practice Problem

1. Determine the critical angle for the following interfaces:
   (a) water and air
   (b) diamond and air
   (c) diamond and water

Answer

1. (a) 48.8°
   (b) 24.4°
   (c) 33.3°

e MATH

To investigate Snell's Law, refraction, and the concept of the critical angle, using a graphing calculator or a spreadsheet program, visit www.pearson.ca/school/physicssource.

Total internal reflection has many applications. Most notable are **optical fibres** (Figure 13.51). An optical fibre consists of a central core of glass with a refractive index of approximately 1.5, surrounded by a cladding material of a slightly lower refractive index. Such fibres are used to transmit data on computer and communication networks. The data are transmitted via the modulation of laser light travelling through a glass fibre, with virtually none of the energy loss associated with electrical transmission. Some of the advantages of fibre-optic networks include:

- economically less expensive than copper wire of equivalent length
- thinner, more flexible, and made of non-flammable materials
- able to handle a higher data-carrying capacity based on the fibre bundle diameter
- less signal degradation and interference between multiple signals on the same fibre as compared with copper networks
- the glass fibres are highly transparent so that repeaters (amplifiers) can be many kilometres apart, as opposed to coaxial cable repeaters that must be less than 1 km apart

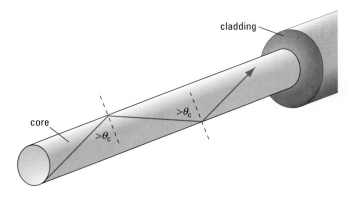

▲ **Figure 13.51** An optical fibre showing cladding, core, axis, and critical angle

e WEB

To learn more about fibre optics including applications in audiovisual equipment and in nanotechnology, begin your search at www.pearsoned.ca/school/physicssource.

info BIT

Buckyballs, also called C_{60} or buckminsterfullarenes, are soccer-ball-shaped molecules made of 60 linked carbon atoms. These carbon molecules may be formed into nanotubes to transmit data using light.

info BIT

Binoculars consist of two identical telescopes mounted side by side and aligned to point in the same direction. When the images from each side of the binoculars are viewed simultaneously, the user is able to sense depth and distance that is not possible with a single telescope view.

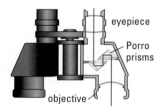

▲ **Figure 13.52**
The light path in binoculars

The Porro prisms in the binoculars use total internal reflection to direct light through the compact, short body of the binoculars with minimal absorption, producing a high-quality image.

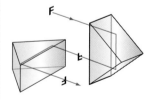

▲ **Figure 13.53**
A double Porro prism

A double Porro-prism system is used in binoculars to reorient an inverted image while at the same time producing a longer, folded pathway for the light to travel between the objective lens and the eyepiece, producing a greater magnification.

Fibre-optic systems also have drawbacks. The complex design of the fibres makes the fibre-optic system relatively expensive to set up and the fibres are also subject to wear and breakage.

13-7 *Decision-Making Analysis*

Fibre Optics: Endless Light

The Issue

The new knowledge society of today has emerged as a result of our ability to communicate and transmit data on a large scale. And to a very large extent, the infrastructure that supports our communication is based on the principles of total internal reflection and its application in fibre-optic systems. New and innovative advances are being made with fibre optics every day – from nanotechnology to entertainment services.

Background Information

The flexibility of fibre optics has allowed for applications in a variety of industries. For example, telephone, television, and data networks, originally all separate industries, are merging into one large application, which is supported by a fibre-optic backbone.

In medicine, applications include the use of a fibrescope to both illuminate internal organs and capture images of them. For example, to see inside the small intestine, an endoscope, a small, flexible bundle of fibres is inserted down the patient's throat and through the stomach. Once the fibres reach the small intestine, images can be transmitted through individual fibres while others are simultaneously used to illuminate the tissue. This application prevents the need for more-invasive, risky procedures that can leave the patient with a higher risk of infection and perhaps result in a prolonged hospital stay.

Other applications include mechanical imaging. For example, fibre-optic bundles can be used to inspect the interior of long pipes, vessels, and hard-to-reach locations, such as bore holes for oil and water wells, pipelines, and hazardous goods containers. With proper instrumentation devices attached, fibre-optic bundles can be used in dangerous conditions to identify gases, pressures, temperatures, and concentrations.

Nanotechnology is an emerging application for fibre optics. In this industry, new nanomaterials, such as C_{60} (buckyballs), are being investigated to expand the power and application of data transmission using light.

Analyze and Evaluate

1. Research applications of fibre optics using the Internet, research journals, and periodicals.

2. Group all the applications by industry and identify what you believe to be the most important applications in each industry.

3. For each of the most important applications, identify the social, political, economic, and environmental impact of the technology.

4. New applications of fibre optics are emerging in nanotechnology. Identify these applications and describe what technological advances could be expected as a result of merging nanotechnology with fibre-optic technology.

5. Prepare a multimedia presentation that demonstrates advances that have been made in a number of industries as a result of fibre-optic applications. Predict what future applications and social issues will evolve as new technologies begin to merge with fibre optics.

Prisms — Dispersion of White Light

Where have you seen a rainbow? Everyone has seen one in the sky, but what about in a diamond, or perhaps on the wall near a hanging crystal in a window. There are many items that produce a rainbow of colours, but all the rainbows have something in common. They all originate from white light.

The investigation of such effects was undertaken by Newton in 1666. He placed a transparent prism in a beam of sunlight passing through his window shutter at Cambridge University. On the opposite wall, an elongated band of colours appeared and he called this a **spectrum** (Figure 13.54). In this spectrum, Newton noted the colours red, orange, yellow, green, blue, indigo, and violet, in the order in which they appeared.

spectrum: the bands of colours making up white light; in order, red, orange, yellow, green, blue, violet

dispersion: separation of white light into its components

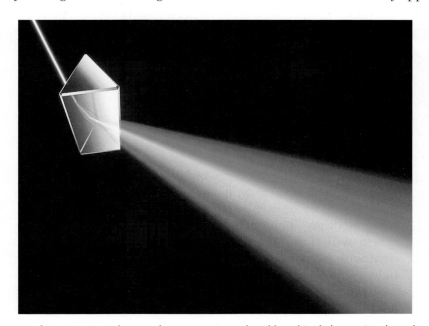

▲ **Figure 13.54** The complete spectrum produced by white light passing through a prism

Newton set out to determine which of two things was true: either the colours of the spectrum are added to the white light by the prism, or the prism separates all the colours from the white light. To test this, Newton set up two prisms, the first one exposed to white light, producing a spectrum of colours (Figure 13.55), and the second one, only exposed to the red (monochromatic) light coming from the first prism. The second prism did not produce any more colours; only the red light emerged. As a second test, Newton placed a converging lens into the path of the spectrum of light and observed the resulting white light as an image on a sheet of white paper.

Based on his observations, Newton concluded that white light is made up of all the colours in the spectrum and the prism was simply separating the colours from on another. The separation of white light into its components is called **dispersion.**

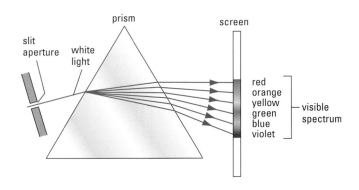

▲ **Figure 13.55** Dispersion of white light by a prism

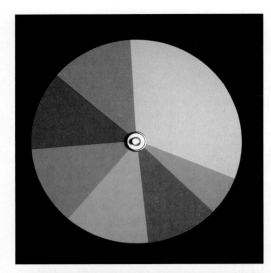

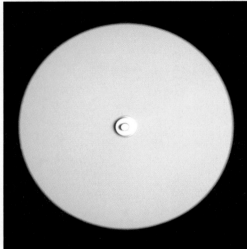

▲ **Figure 13.56** Recomposition of the spectrum using a high-speed disc

e SIM

To learn more about the effects of prisms through the use of simulations, follow the eSim links at www.pearsoned.ca/school/physicssource.

The **recomposition** of the spectrum, therefore, should produce white light, as Newton was able to demonstrate in his second experiment. Recomposition can also be demonstrated by painting all the colours of the spectrum in certain proportions on a disc and spinning the disc at a very high speed (Figure 13.56). At sufficient speed, the disc appears white.

Is dispersion consistent with the wave model of light? If we consider light as a wave, each of the colours in the spectrum has a unique wavelength, as listed in Table 13.5. As light enters a medium with a high refractive index, the wavelength is reduced but the frequency is unchanged. The speed of a wave is the product of its frequency and wavelength as described by the universal wave equation ($v = f\lambda$). Therefore, the light must slow down as it enters the high-index medium. Because the refractive index is related to the speed of a wave, it is therefore also related to the wavelength of the wave when the frequency is constant.

$$n = \frac{\lambda_o}{\lambda}$$

λ_o = wavelength in vacuum

λ = wavelength in medium

This relationship between refractive index and wavelength, for a constant frequency, means that the refractive index is different for each wavelength of light that passes through the same medium. Incident light with a smaller, shorter wavelength will slow down and refract to a greater extent than light with a larger, longer wavelength. As each wavelength of light refracts at a slightly different angle, the wavelengths will separate, producing a continuous spectrum. The wave model of light, therefore, is consistent with the phenomenon of dispersion.

▼ **Table 13.5** Wavelength of each colour in the spectrum

Colour	Wavelength λ (nm)
ultraviolet B	208-320
ultraviolet A	320-400
violet	400-450
blue	450-500
green	500-570
yellow	570-590
orange	590-610
red	610-750
infrared	>750

Dispersion Using a Prism

Problem

Is white light made up of all the colours we can see?

Materials

2 identical prisms
convex lens
intense light source (flashlight or white light ray box)
white paper

Procedure

1 Using one prism, observe the colour spectrum on a piece of white paper. A dark room and a very intense white light source will work best. The convex lens may be placed between the light source and prism to intensify the beam of white light if the spectrum is not immediately clear and visible.

2 Position the second prism in the spectrum produced by the first one. Rotate the second prism and position the white paper so that you can observe the light that emerges from the second prism.

3 Explore a variety of positions and orientations with both prisms.

Questions

1. What is the best way to make a colour spectrum using a single prism? Draw a picture showing the flashlight, prism, convex lens, paper, and the colour spectrum.

2. List the colours of the spectrum from most refracted to least refracted.

3. Compare the wavelengths of each colour to the amount of refraction observed. Describe the relationship between wavelength and amount of refraction.

4. Are the colours of the spectrum added to, or separated from, white light when white light passes through a prism? Support your answer with observations made using two prisms.

5. The spectrum produced by a prism is similar to that observed as a rainbow. Research and explore the similarities between the spectrum produced by a prism and that which is observed as a rainbow.

Thin Lenses

Projection systems connected with computers and movie players, and optical systems including microscopes and telescopes, use lenses that refract light in order to generate images. A typical thin lens is a circular piece of transparent material with a spherically shaped surface that refracts, or changes the direction of light that passes through it. The uniformly curved surface will refract light rays to varying extents depending on where they contact the lens. Rays that are incident near the edge of the lens will be refracted at larger angles than those that are incident near the centre, where the two faces of the lens are almost parallel.

For a **converging lens,** rays that travel parallel to the principal axis will be refracted inward, intersecting at the principal focus, F. For a **diverging lens**, rays that travel parallel to the principal axis will be refracted outward, appearing as though they have originated at a virtual principal focus, F. The distance from each lens to F is the focal length, f (Figure 13.57). Each type of lens has a secondary focus, F′ at a distance of f, on the opposite side of the lens. Each lens also has two centres of curvature (C and C′). The distance from a centre of curvature to the lens represents the radius of the sphere from which the lens surface is made.

PHYSICS INSIGHT

A converging lens has a convex surface while a diverging lens has concave surfaces. Other lenses, including those used in eyeglasses, can have both convex and concave surfaces; it is therefore more useful to refer to a lens by what it does rather than the types of surfaces that are found on it.

converging lens: a lens that refracts rays travelling parallel to the principal axis inward to intersect at the principal focus

diverging lens: a lens that refracts rays travelling parallel to the principal axis outward to appear as though they have originated at a virtual principal focus

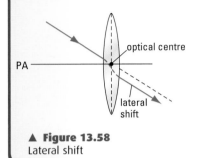
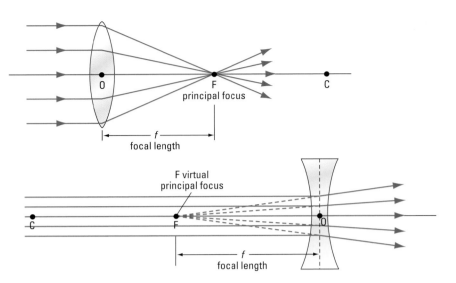

▲ **Figure 13.57**   Converging and diverging lenses

Drawing Ray Diagrams for Thin Lenses

A ray diagram is a useful tool for predicting and understanding how images form as a result of light rays emerging from a curved lens. Ray diagrams for lenses are similar to the ray diagrams used with curved mirrors; only two rays are needed to predict the image location, and a third is used as verification (Figure 13.59).

Ray 1 travels parallel to the principal axis and is refracted such that it emerges and passes through (or appears to have originated from) the principal focus, F.

Ray 2 travels through (or appears to have originated from) the secondary focus, F′, and is refracted such that it emerges and travels parallel to the principal axis.

Ray 3 travels straight through the optical centre of the lens and is not bent.

The ray diagram is not only used to identify the location of an image relative to the lens, but it can also illustrate the other three image attributes of type, attitude, and magnification, that have previously been described for curved mirrors. Relative to the object, the image produced by a curved lens can be real or virtual, inverted or erect, and enlarged or diminished.

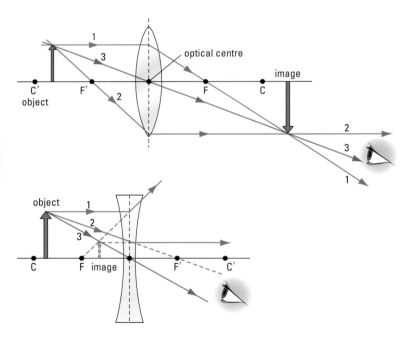

▲ **Figure 13.59**   Ray diagrams for (a) converging, and (b) diverging lenses

Example 13.6

Draw a diagram to determine the image attributes for an object located at the following positions relative to a converging lens.
a) beyond the center of curvature C′ (or 2*f*)
b) at F′
c) between the lens and F′

Given
Object position relative to the converging lens

Required
Ray diagram showing image location and attributes

Analysis and Solution
Construct a ray diagram and visually inspect the image location relative to the converging lens and the image attributes.

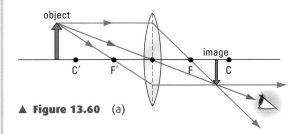

▲ **Figure 13.60** (a)

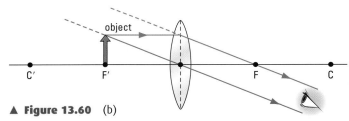

▲ **Figure 13.60** (b)

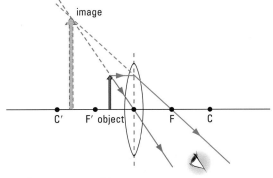

▲ **Figure 13.60** (c)

Paraphrase
(a) The image is located between F and C, and is real, inverted, and diminished.
(b) No image is formed.
(c) The image is located between F′ and C′, and is virtual, erect, and enlarged.

Practice Problems

1. Using a ray diagram, determine the image attributes for the following:
   (a) an object located between C′ and F′ relative to a converging lens
   (b) an object located between C′ and F′ relative to a diverging lens
   (c) an object located between F′ and a converging lens
   (d) an object located between F′ and a diverging lens

Answers
1. (a) Image is beyond C, real, inverted, and enlarged.
   (b) Image is between the lens and F ′, virtual, erect, and diminished.
   (c) Image is between F′ and C′, virtual, erect, and enlarged.
   (d) Image is between the lens and F′, virtual, erect, and diminished.

e **WEB**

To learn more about thin lenses, follow the links at www.pearsoned.ca/school/physicssource.

Equations for Thin Lenses

An equation relating object distance, image distance, and the focal length of a curved lens can be derived using an analysis nearly identical to that for curved mirrors. In Figure 13.61, the green triangle XOF and the blue triangle ZYF are similar. Therefore,

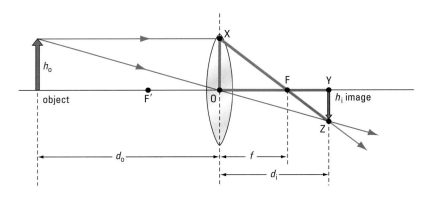

▲ **Figure 13.61**   Thin lens ray diagram

$$\frac{OX}{OF} = \frac{YZ}{YF}$$

$$\frac{h_o}{f} = \frac{h_i}{d_i - f}$$

$$\frac{h_i}{h_o} = \frac{d_i - f}{f}$$

$$\frac{h_i}{h_o} = \frac{d_i}{d_o}$$

$$\frac{d_i}{d_o} = \frac{d_i - f}{f}$$

$$\frac{d_i}{d_o} = \frac{d_i}{f} - \frac{\cancel{f}}{\cancel{f}}$$

Dividing both sides by d_i, and simplifying, gives the **thin lens equation**.

thin lens equation: the equation that relates object distance, image distance, and focal length of a curved lens

$$\frac{\cancel{d_i}}{\cancel{d_i}d_o} = \frac{\cancel{d_i}}{\cancel{d_i}f} - \frac{1}{d_i}$$

$$\frac{1}{d_o} + \frac{1}{d_i} = \frac{1}{f}$$

Notice that this equation is identical to the mirror equation. A sign convention will be used here also, to distinguish between real and virtual distances as well as to identify erect and inverted images.

PHYSICS INSIGHT

Although a converging lens can cause an image to be vertically inverted, this does not mean that it will be horizontally inverted as well. In fact, if an object is located at the centre of curvature for a thin convex lens, the image will be vertically inverted, but not horizontally inverted.

> ### Sign Conventions for the Thin Lens Equation
>
> - All distance measurements are relative to the optical centre of the lens.
> - Positive distances are used for real objects and images.
> - Negative distances are used for virtual images.
> - Positive image and object heights are upward relative to the principal axis.
> - Negative image and object heights are downward relative to the principal axis.
> - Converging lenses have a positive focal length.
> - Diverging lenses have a negative focal length.

Results with a thin lens are similar to those with a curved mirror in that an erect image has a positive magnification and an inverted image has a negative magnification. Therefore, the same magnification equation that is used for curved mirrors is also used for thin lenses.

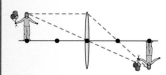

▲ **Figure 13.62**
A vertically, but not horizontally, inverted object

$$m = \frac{h_i}{h_o} = -\frac{d_i}{d_o}$$

Example 13.7

A 2.5-cm-high object is placed 10.0 cm from a diverging lens of focal length 5.0 cm. Determine the image distance, height, and attributes using the thin lens equation. Verify your answer with a ray diagram.

Given

$h_o = +2.5$ cm

$d_o = +10.0$ cm

$f = -5.0$ cm (The lens is a diverging lens.)

Required

image distance (d_i)

height (h_i)

image characteristics

Analysis and Solution

The thin lens equation can be used to determine the image distance, image height, and attributes. A ray diagram can verify the answer.

$$\frac{1}{d_o} + \frac{1}{d_i} = \frac{1}{f} \qquad\qquad \frac{h_i}{h_o} = -\frac{d_i}{d_o}$$

$$\frac{1}{d_i} = \frac{1}{f} - \frac{1}{d_o} \qquad\qquad h_i = -\frac{d_i h_o}{d_o}$$

$$\frac{1}{d_i} = \frac{1}{-5.0 \text{ cm}} - \frac{1}{+2.5 \text{ cm}} \qquad h_i = -\frac{(-1.6667 \text{ cm})(+2.5 \text{ cm})}{+10.0 \text{ cm}}$$

$$\frac{1}{d_i} = \frac{1}{-5.0 \text{ cm}} - \frac{1}{+2.5 \text{ cm}} \qquad h_i = +0.42 \text{ cm}$$

$$\frac{1}{d_i} = -1.7 \text{ cm}$$

Paraphrase

The image distance is −1.7 cm and height is +0.42 cm, indicating the image is virtual, erect, and diminished. The answers are verified by the ray diagram in Figure 13.63.

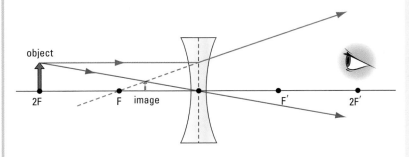

▲ **Figure 13.63**

Practice Problems

1. A 3.00-cm-high object is located 15.0 cm from a converging lens with a focal length of 10.0 cm.
   (a) How far is the image from the lens?
   (b) How high is the image?
   (c) Describe the image characteristics and verify them using a ray diagram.

2. A 10.0-cm-high candle is placed 100.0 cm from a diverging lens with a focal length of 25.0 cm. Determine the following using a ray diagram and the thin lens equation:
   (a) the image location from the lens
   (b) the image height
   (c) the type of image formed

3. A projector uses a converging lens to create a focussed image on a screen located 5.00 m away. The image is generated from a slide located 7.50 cm from the lens.
   (a) What is the focal length of the lens?
   (b) Determine the magnification of the image.

Answers

1. (a) $d_i = 30.0$ cm
   (b) $h_i = -6.00$ cm
   (c) image is real, inverted, enlarged

2. (a) $d_i = -20.0$ cm
   (b) $h_i = 2.00$ cm
   (c) image is virtual

3. (a) $f = 7.39$ cm
   (b) $m = -66.7$ X

Comparing Keplerian and Galilean Telescopes

In this investigation the functional differences between a Keplerian telescope, with two converging lenses, and a Galilean telescope, with one converging lens and one diverging lens, are explored.

Question

What are the differences between Keplerian and Galilean telescopes?

Variables

manipulated: type of lens used
responding: magnification of the image
controlled: focal length of double concave and double convex lenses

Materials and Equipment

- long focal length converging lens
- short focal length converging lens
- short focal length diverging lens
- lens holders
- optical bench for measuring distances
- lamp
- paper, ruler, pencil, and tape

Procedure for Galilean Telescope

1. Place the long focal length converging lens at one end of the optical bench. This will serve as the objective lens for both telescopes.

2. If the long focal length is unknown, place a lamp in front of the lens and measure the distance between the lamp and the lens. Next, slide a sheet of paper or screen along the optical bench until a bright spot appears (image of the lamp). Record the distance between the paper and the lens. Calculate the focal length of the objective lens using the lens equation, and image and object distances.

3. Place the short focal length diverging lens halfway between the converging lens and its principal focus as illustrated in Figure 13.64.

▲ **Figure 13.64**   Galilean telescope

4. Draw a series of 5 vertical arrows, 1 cm apart, on a sheet of paper. Tape the sheet to a distant wall so that it will be visible in the telescope.

5. Look through the eyepiece with one eye and compare the image with the sheet seen with an unaided eye.

6. Estimate how many vertical arrows (viewed with the unaided eye) would fit in between two of the vertical arrows observed in the telescope. Record this as the estimated magnification.

Procedure for Keplerian Telescope

7. Remove the diverging lens from the optical bench.

8. If the focal length of the short focal length converging lens is not known, place a lamp in front of the lens and slide a sheet of paper or screen along the optical bench until a bright spot appears. Record the focal length for the short focal length lens.

9. Position the short focal length converging lens such that the distance between the two lenses is slightly less than the sum of the focal lengths, as shown in Figure 13.65.

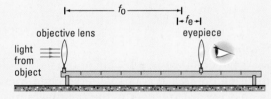

▲ **Figure 13.65**   Keplerian telescope

10. Estimate how many vertical arrows (viewed with the unaided eye) would fit in between two of the vertical arrows observed in the telescope. Record this as the estimated magnification.

Analysis

1. Prepare a table that compares the attitude, magnification, and brightness of the image in each telescope.

2. Complete a ray diagram to show how the image is formed in each telescope.

3. Suggest a different application for each telescope. Compare the telescopes' efficiency in looking at relatively close terrestrial objects, like mountains, or far away extraterrestrial objects, such as the Moon.

Knowledge

1. Is light bent toward or away from the normal line when it passes from a low-index medium to a high-index medium?

2. How is the index of refraction measured for a particular medium?

3. Construct a concept map using the following terms: incident ray, refracted ray, angle of incidence, angle of refraction, normal line.

4. What is the difference between the simple and general forms of Snell's Law?

5. Suggest an experimental design to determine the critical angle for an air-Lucite® boundary.

6. List five advantages of a fibre-optic network when compared to traditional electric networks used for data transmission.

7. How does a prism separate all the colours of white light?

8. Explain the effect of wavelength on the index of refraction for a particular medium, like glass. How does this lead to dispersion?

Applications

9. What is the speed of light in water ($n = 1.33$)?

10. A light ray is incident on a block of quartz glass ($n = 1.47$) at an angle of 35.0°. Determine the angle of refraction.

11. When a ray of light passes from water ($n = 1.33$) into a Lucite® block ($n = 1.52$) it is refracted at an angle of 28.0°. Determine the angle of incidence.

12. What is the critical angle for a Lucite®-air interface?

13. A light ray travelling in water approaches the water-air boundary at an angle of 50°. What happens to the light ray at the boundary?

14. Light with a wavelength of 540 nm enters a ruby crystal ($n = 1.54$) at an angle of 25.0°. Determine the angle of refraction and the wavelength of the light in the ruby.

15. Using ray diagrams, determine the image attributes for an object located at the following positions relative to a converging lens:
    (a) at C′
    (b) between 2F′ and F′
    (c) at F′

16. A camera with a converging lens ($f = 4.50$ cm) is used to take a picture of a 25.0-m-high tree that is 50.0 m from the camera. How tall is the image? Is it erect or inverted?

17. Red light of 700 nm and blue light of 475 nm are both incident on a Lucite® block. Which colour will be refracted to a greater extent?

18. The focal length of the converging lens in a computer projector is 8.00 cm. An LCD panel positioned inside the projector serves as the object for the lens.
    (a) If the LCD panel is located 8.10 cm from the lens inside the projector, how far away should the screen be placed so that a clear image is produced?
    (b) If the LCD panel is 1.75 cm high, how large is the image on the screen?
    (c) If the screen is moved 3.0 m closer to the projector, how far must the object now be from the lens in order to generate a focussed image?

Extensions

19. Explain why jewellery crystals, such as diamonds, sparkle.

20. Explain why you can start a fire with a magnifying glass.

21. If a diver is underwater and looks up, a circular "hole" appears on the surface of the water directly above the diver. Other than this hole, the surface appears as a mirror. Explain how this happens.

 e TEST

To check your understanding of refraction, fibre optics, dispersion, and lenses, follow the eTest links at www.pearsoned.ca/school/physicssource.

13.5 Diffraction and Interference

In section 8.3 you learned that there are many forms of interference patterns produced by mechanical waves that travel in a medium like water. And more importantly, you learned that the interference pattern contains information about the properties of the waves that created the pattern. In this section, we will investigate interference patterns produced by electromagnetic radiation and analyze the patterns to further our understanding of the wave model of light.

Huygens' Principle

Robert Hooke proposed the Wave Model of Light in his *Micrographica* of 1665. The first major improvement to this model was made by Christiaan Huygens (Figure 13.66), twenty years later. A Dutch physicist, Huygens contributed to the study of astronomy by advancing techniques in lens grinding and by discovering Saturn's rings and its largest satellite, Titan. He is also credited with producing the pendulum clock, originally proposed by Galileo. With regard to wave theory, Huygens described an elegant, conceptual model that predicted the motion of a wave front. This model is known as **Huygens' Principle.**

A wave front consists of many small point sources of tiny secondary waves, called wavelets, which propagate outward in a concentric circle at the same speed as the wave itself. The line tangent to all the wavelets constitutes the wave front.

To visualize Huygens' Principle, consider a point source of light that emits electromagnetic waves outward, in a concentric circle. At an instant in time, the wave front will form the line t_1. According to Huygens' Principle, all the points along line t_1 become secondary sources, producing wavelets that radiate outward to form the wave front at a future time t_2. Line t_2 is the tangent to all the wavelets that make up the wave front a short time later (Figure 13.67). The same analysis can be performed on a straight wave front, as shown in Figure 13.68.

▲ **Figure 13.66**
Christiaan Huygens

Huygens' Principle: a model of wave theory, which predicted the motion of a wave front as being many small point sources propagating outward in a concentric circle at the same speed as the wave itself

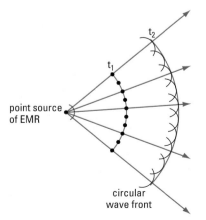

▲ **Figure 13.67** Circular wave front emitted by a light source

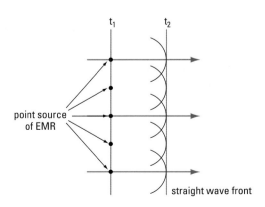

▲ **Figure 13.68** Straight wave front emitted by a distant light source

Concept Check

Use Huygens' Principle to predict the wave front shapes that occur after the straight waves pass through the openings shown in Figure 13.69 (a) and (b).

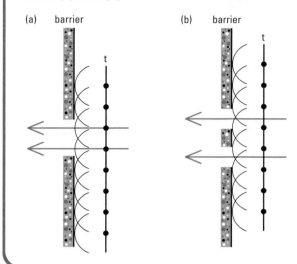

◄ **Figure 13.69**

At each opening, one or more secondary point sources exist. Draw the line tangent across the wavelets that would exist a short time after the secondary point sources pass through the opening. Explain what has happened to the shape and direction of the wave front after it passed through the barriers in Figure 13.69 (a) and (b).

*e***SIM**

Explore Huygens' Principle through simulations. Follow the eSim links at www.pearsoned.ca/school/physicssource.

According to Huygens' Principle, a periodic straight wave will continue to propagate in a straight line until it encounters a barrier. If the wave front encounters a small opening or aperture in the barrier, the wave front will change shape and direction. This process is called **diffraction**.

diffraction: the change in shape and direction of a wave front as a result of encountering a small opening or aperture in a barrier, or a corner

Young's Experiment

Huygens' wave theory can explain many of the properties of electromagnetic radiation, including reflection and refraction, but initially, the scientific reputation of Newton and his belief in the particle model of light dominated the scientific community. However, in 1801, an experiment by Thomas Young provided significant evidence in support of the wave model of light.

Problems Involved in the Design of the Experiment

In the years leading up to Young's groundbreaking work, scientists studying light were attempting to observe an **interference** pattern that was similar in nature to that of two point sources. They believed that if light were indeed a wave, then two side-by-side light sources should produce an interference pattern similar to that observed with water in a ripple tank (section 8.3). In these early light experiments, the light from the two sources was incident on a nearby screen that was observed for evidence of an interference pattern. What was not well understood at the time was that waves of high frequency and short wavelength result in a very short distance between nodal lines, the regions of destructive interference that appear dark. As we know today, light waves have an extremely high frequency and short wavelength, so the distance between nodal lines would be so small it could

interference: an effect resulting from the passage of two like waves through each other

*e***SIM**

Learn more about Young's classic experiment through simulations. Follow the eSim links at www.pearsoned.ca/school/physicssource.

▼ **Figure 13.70**

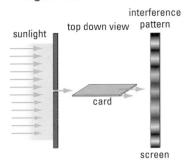

(a) Interference fringes

(b) Photo of two-slit pattern from Young's experiment

---

info **BIT**

The double-slit experiment works for water waves too! When a single wave front is incident on a barrier with two holes it will produce an interference pattern similar to the one observed by Young. This effect is explored in Unit IV.

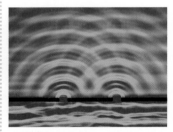

▲ **Figure 13.71** Interference pattern produced by water waves passing through two holes in a barrier

---

antinode: a point of interaction between waves, at which only constructive interference occurs; in an interference pattern, antinodes occur at path difference intervals of whole wavelengths

---

not be observed using traditional means. In addition, to produce an interference pattern, the waves must be in phase. When there are two incandescent lights, each source emits light in random bursts not necessarily in phase with the other source. These bursts of light have a variety of wavelengths that make up all the colours in the spectrum. Therefore, the interference pattern would not be constant, but would vary rapidly over time, making any observation of a pattern more difficult.

The Experiment

Thomas Young solved both of these problems and successfully observed an interference pattern produced by light. Young conducted his experiment using a pinhole in a window shutter and a card he described as "a slip of card, about one-thirtieth of an inch in breadth (thickness)." The card was positioned edgewise into a horizontal sunbeam directed into the room by using a mirror. The sunbeam had a diameter slightly greater than the thickness of the card. When the card was positioned edgewise in the centre of the sunbeam it split the sunbeam into two coherent beams separated by a very small distance (Figure 13.70(a)). The effect was equivalent to light passing through two slits that were very close together. The small distance of separation between the two beams of light expanded the interference pattern on the screen so that the distance between nodal lines was large enough that it could be observed. Light coming from both sides of the card was in phase and the wave fronts could create a fixed interference pattern of light and dark bands, called **interference fringes,** on the screen (Figure 13.70 and also Figure 13.9, page 640). **Bright fringes** or **antinodal lines** were regions of constructive interference and **dark fringes** or **nodal lines** were regions of destructive interference. Young's double-slit experiment provided the strong evidence needed for acceptance of the wave model of light.

The Interference Pattern

To understand how the interference pattern is created, consider three different points. The first point is the **central antinode** (Figure 13.72). This point occurs at the centre of the pattern, along the perpendicular bisector. The perpendicular bisector is an imaginary straight line that runs from the midpoint of a line joining the two slits to the area of constructive interference on the screen. This area of constructive interference may be called the central antinode, central bright fringe, or central maximum. At the central antinode, both waves travel the same distance from the slits and arrive at the screen in phase. Constructive interference will be observed as a bright band.

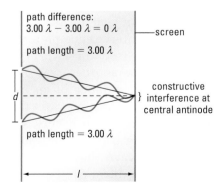

▶ **Figure 13.72** A path difference of zero at the central antinode results in constructive interference and a bright band on the screen.

The second point is the first **node,** also called the first dark fringe or the first minimum. At this location, one wave travels a distance of $\frac{1}{2}\lambda$ farther than the other so that the waves arrive out of phase, and destructive interference is observed as a dark band (Figure 13.73).

The third point is another antinode or bright fringe. At this location, one wave travels a distance of 1λ farther than the other, causing the waves to arrive at the screen in phase once again (Figure 13.74). This pattern of bright and dark fringes repeats as we move out in both directions from the central, perpendicular bisector.

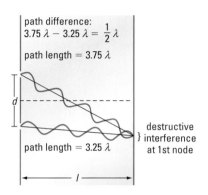

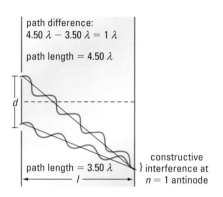

▲ **Figure 13.73** A path difference of $\frac{1}{2}\lambda$, at the first node results in destructive interference and a dark band on the screen.

▲ **Figure 13.74** A path difference of λ, at the first antinode results in constructive interference and a bright band on the screen.

Mathematical Analysis of Young's Experiment

Young's experiment and interference patterns in general contain mathematical information about the waves that create them. For instance, the interference pattern that Young observed can be used to determine the wavelength of the light that created it.

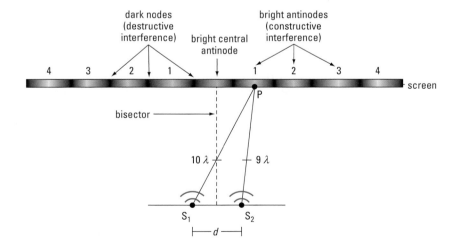

▲ **Figure 13.75** Two point sources, separated by a short distance, produce antinodal lines of constructive interference and nodal lines of destructive interference.

Point sources, S_1 and S_2, from the same original source, are separated by a short distance, d, and produce identical waves that are in phase.

PHYSICS INSIGHT

Compare Figures 13.74 and 13.75. The absolute path lengths (expressed in number of wavelengths) shown in Figure 13.74 and 13.75 are different, yet the waves are still causing constructive interference at the point where they meet. How can this be? If the distance separating the sources and the screen is constant, then the path length (expressed in number of wavelengths) to the antinodes can and will be different for different wavelengths of light. As long as the "difference" in path lengths is a whole number multiple of the wavelength of the light λ, constructive interference will occur where the waves meet and this will be observed as an antinode.

An equal number of antinodal lines, or lines of constructive interference, radiate outward on either side of the perpendicular bisector of the line joining S_1 and S_2. Beginning at the perpendicular bisector, antinodal lines on each side are numbered 1, 2, 3, etc., resulting in a duplicated series (Figure 13.75). For our analysis, we will chose a point, P, on the $n = 1$ antinodal line.

path length: the distance between a point source and a chosen point in space

difference in path length: the difference between two path lengths, each measured from a different origin and extending to a common point in space

The **path length** from S_1 to P and from S_2 to P can be measured in multiples of wavelengths. From Figure 13.75, the path S_1P is 10λ and the path S_2P is 9λ. The **difference in path length** from point P to the two sources is

$$10\lambda - 9\lambda = 1\lambda$$

Therefore, for any point along the first antinodal line (on either side of the bisector), the following relationship is true:

$$S_1P - S_2P = 1\lambda$$

Recall from section 8.3 that waves that are 1λ out of phase will constructively interfere. This explains why the antinodal lines are bright. A similar analysis for a point, P_2, on the $n = 2$ antinodal line generates a similar relationship

$$S_1P_2 - S_2P_2 = 2\lambda$$

An analysis of points on the $n = 3$ and $n = 4$, etc., antinodal lines follows a similar pattern, generating the following relationship between path difference and wavelength along the antinodal lines.

$$S_1P_n - S_2P_n = n\lambda, \text{ where } n = 1, 2, 3, 4, \ldots \text{ (1)}$$

If the wavelength is sufficiently large, the difference in path length can be calculated as in Equation (1). Light waves have extremely small wavelengths; therefore, another method of calculating path length becomes appropriate.

Difference in Path Length for Waves of Short Wavelength

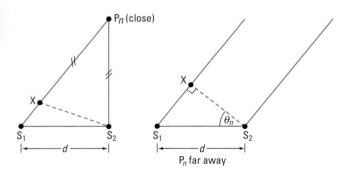

▲ **Figure 13.76** Two point sources, separated by a short distance, d, with path lengths to point P_n

Consider the triangles illustrated in Figure 13.76, showing the path length from two sources to point P_n.

For any point along the antinodal line P_n, the difference in path length will be equal to the segment S_1X. When P_n is selected to be very far away, the paths are nearly parallel. In such a case, S_1-X-S_2 forms a right triangle allowing the difference in path length to be expressed in terms of angle θ_n,

$$\sin \theta_n = \frac{S_1X}{d}$$

$$\sin \theta_n = \frac{\text{difference in path length}}{d}$$

Constructive interference

For constructive interference or antinodal lines, substitute the generalization for the difference in path length (Equation 1 above):

$$\sin \theta_n = \frac{n\lambda}{d}$$

$$\lambda = \frac{d \sin \theta_n}{n} \qquad \text{for } n = 1, 2, 3, 4, \ldots \text{ (2)}$$

Equation (2) can be used to determine the wavelength of the light used to produce the interference pattern, where n is the number of the nth antinodal line and d is the distance between the two sources. For a point P_n located far away from the two point sources, the angle θ_n is equivalent to the angle θ_α, located between the perpendicular bisector and the straight line drawn between the midpoint of the two sources and the point P_n. The angle θ_α is known as the **angle of diffraction** (Figure 13.77).

Destructive interference

The analysis for destructive interference, which occurs along the nodal lines, is done in an almost identical way. Recall that destructive interference occurs when the path difference between waves is a half number of wavelengths. Therefore, the generalization for the difference in path length becomes

$$\sin \theta_n = \frac{(n - \frac{1}{2})\lambda}{d}$$

$$\lambda = \frac{d \sin \theta_n}{(n - \frac{1}{2})} \qquad \text{for } n = 1, 2, 3, 4, \ldots \text{ (3)}$$

where n is the number of the nth nodal line relative to the perpendicular bisector, d is the distance between the two sources, and the angle θ_n is equivalent to the angle between the perpendicular bisector and the straight line drawn between the midpoint of the two sources and the point P_n.

angle of diffraction: the angle formed between the perpendicular bisector and the straight line to a nodal or antinodal point on the interference pattern

angle of diffraction: the angle formed between the perpendicular bisector and the straight line to a nodal or antinodal point on the interference pattern

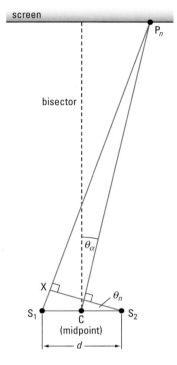

▲ **Figure 13.77** When P_n is far away, line S_1P_n is approximately parallel to CP_n, making θ_n and θ_α equal. θ_α is the angle of diffraction.

Example 13.8

Monochromatic light is incident on two slits separated by 0.30 mm, and the first bright fringe ($n = 1$ antinode) is located at an angle of 0.080° from the central antinode. What is the wavelength of the light?

Given
$d = 3.0 \times 10^{-4}$ m
$\theta_n = 0.080°$
$n = 1$

Required
Wavelength (λ)

Analysis and Solution
The angle given is relative to the central antinode, which occurs along the perpendicular bisector; therefore, the angle given is relative to the perpendicular bisector. The first bright fringe is a region of constructive

Practice Problems

1. Light of an unknown wavelength is incident on two slits separated by 0.20 mm. The second bright fringe is located at an angle of 0.26° from the central antinode. What is the light's wavelength?

2. Blue light of 460 nm is incident on two slits that are 0.55 mm apart. What is the angle of diffraction for the third antinodal line?

Chapter 13 The wave model can be used to describe the characteristics of electromagnetic radiation.   689

3. The second nodal line of an interference pattern occurs at 0.095° relative to the central antinode. The two slits are separated by 0.40 mm. What is the wavelength and colour of light producing this pattern?

Answers

1. 4.5×10^{-7}
2. $0.14°$
3. 4.4×10^{-7} m, violet

interference, where the path difference must be one full wavelength different. Therefore, Equation (2) above for constructive interference applies:

$$\lambda = \frac{d \sin \theta_n}{n}$$

$$\lambda = \frac{(30 \times 10^{-4} \, \text{m}) \sin 0.080°}{1}$$

$$\lambda = 4.2 \times 10^{-7} \, \text{m}$$

Paraphrase

Monochromatic light with a wavelength of 4.2×10^{-7} m will produce a bright fringe at an angle of 0.080° from the central antinode.

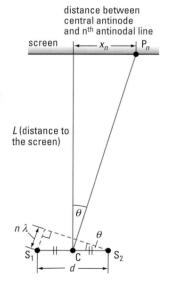

distance between central antinode and nth antinodal line

▲ Figure 13.78 Determining $\sin \theta$ using x and L

Finding Wavelength and the Angle of Diffraction Under Experimental Conditions

In experimental settings, it is often difficult to measure the angle of diffraction because this angle is very small relative to a point that is very far away from the two slits. It is easier to obtain a value for $\sin \theta$ by determining the ratio x/L, as shown in Figure 13.78. Here, x is the distance between the central antinode (where the perpendicular bisector intersects the screen) and the antinodal fringe. The length of the perpendicular bisector, L, is the distance from the midpoint between the slits to the screen, where the interference pattern is observed.

In Figure 13.78, $x/L = \tan \theta$, but when L is much greater than x, the ratio of x/L is very small (generally less than 0.2) making $\tan \theta$ nearly equal to $\sin \theta$ (see Infobit). Therefore, it is acceptable to assume $\sin \theta = x/L$ in this case. By replacing $\sin \theta$ with the ratio x/L, we arrive at the following equation for antinodal (bright) fringes:

$$\lambda = \frac{d\left(\dfrac{x}{L}\right)}{n}$$

$$\lambda = \frac{xd}{nL}$$

Applying the same analysis to nodal (dark) fringes gives:

$$\lambda = \frac{d\left(\dfrac{x}{L}\right)}{\left(n - \dfrac{1}{2}\right)}$$

$$\lambda = \frac{xd}{\left(n - \dfrac{1}{2}\right)L}$$

Example 13.9

A student measuring the wavelength of light emitted by a krypton gas sample directs the light through two slits separated by 0.264 mm. An interference pattern is created on a screen 3.0 m from the slits and the distance between the second bright ($n = 2$ antinode) fringe and the central antinode is measured to be 1.18 cm. What is one of the wavelengths of light emitted by the krypton gas sample?

Given
$d = 2.64 \times 10^{-4}$ m
$L = 3.0$ m
$x = 1.18 \times 10^{-2}$ m
$n = 2$

Required
wavelength (λ)

Analysis and Solution
The bright fringe is a region of constructive interference, where the path difference must be a whole number of wavelengths. Solve for the wavelength by using the equation:

$$\lambda = \frac{xd}{nL}$$

$$\lambda = \frac{(1.18 \times 10^{-2}\ \cancel{m})(2.64 \times 10^{-4}\ m)}{(2)(3.0\ \cancel{m})}$$

$$\lambda = 5.2 \times 10^{-7}\ m$$

Paraphrase
The krypton gas sample emits light with a wavelength of 5.2×10^{-7} m.

Practice Problems

1. Monochromatic light is incident on two slits separated by 0.15 mm. An interference pattern is observed on a screen 5.0 m away. The distance between the 3rd dark fringe and the central antinode is 4.50×10^{-2} m. What is the wavelength of the light?

2. Monochromatic light is incident on two slits separated by 3.00×10^{-5} m. The distance between antinodes is 3.10×10^{-2} m. If the screen is 1.50 m from the slits, what is the light's colour and wavelength ?

3. A student used light of wavelength 5.00×10^{-7} m and found that the distance between the third node and the central antinode was 1.00×10^{-1} m. If the screen was located 1.20 m away from the slits, how far apart are the slits?

Answers

1. 5.4×10^{-7} m
2. 6.20×10^{-7} m, red
3. 1.50×10^{-5} m

Poisson's Bright Spot

Using an analysis similar to that in Example 13.9, Young calculated the wavelength of various colours of light and announced his results in 1807. He was still overshadowed by Newton's reputation and support for the particle model of light. Thus, Young was not taken seriously by the scientific community until 1818, when Augustin Fresnel, a French physicist (Figure 13.79), proposed another mathematical wave theory. This new theory formed a critical turning point in the debate between the wave and particle models of the time. A mathematician by the name of Simon Poisson argued that the equations in Fresnel's theory could be used to predict a unique diffraction pattern that should be produced when light is incident on a small round disc. Poisson showed that Fresnel's equations should produce a central bright fringe at the centre of a shadow cast by a solid round disc when it is illuminated by a point source of monochromatic light (Figure13.80(a)). This predicted result was similar to the central bright fringe observed in Young's double-slit experiment.

▲ **Figure 13.79** Augustin Fresnel (1788–1827). Fresnel's analysis of diffraction provided the theoretical groundwork for the transverse wave model of light. He also designed the lenses that were used in lighthouses of the 19th century and in overhead projectors, solar collectors, and beacon lights of the 21st century.

diffraction grating: a sheet of glass or plastic etched with a large number of parallel lines. When light is incident on the grating, each line or slit acts as one individual light source.

▲ **Figure 13.81** Diffraction grating

info **BIT**

The concentric circles cut into a CD when it is made make it behave as a diffraction grating. So, the rainbow pattern you see when you look at a CD is the product of interference caused by diffraction.

▲ **Figure 13.82**

Fresnel's equations showed that the light that is diffracted around the edge of the disc should constructively interfere at the centre of the shadow. Poisson was unable to observe this bright spot experimentally and was of the opinion that he had refuted the wave model of light.

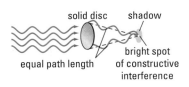

▲ **Figure 13.80** Poisson's Bright Spot
(a) Constructive interference at the bright spot   (b) Photograph of Poisson's Bright Spot

Poisson's prediction of a bright spot was retested by Dominique Arago in 1818, and this time, the bright spot was verified (Figure 13.80 (b)). The bright spot is known as "Poissson's Bright Spot" because, even though Poisson was a supporter of the particle model of light, he had predicted the spot's existence if the wave model of light was correct. Mainly as a result of this verification of Poisson's Bright Spot, by 1850 the wave model of light was generally accepted by the scientific community. The model was then successfully applied to many of the properties of light.

Diffraction Gratings

Young's experiment used only two small point sources of light that were in phase. A **diffraction grating** (Figure 13.81) has a very large number of equally spaced, parallel lines that act as individual light sources. When light is incident on a multi-slit diffraction grating, an interference pattern, similar to that of a double slit, is produced on a distant screen. But there are several key differences. First, the large number of lines in a diffraction grating can deliver more light energy to the distant screen, increasing the brightness of the interference pattern. Second, the antinodal, bright fringes are more defined, being sharper and narrower. And third, when line separation is very small, the separation between the lines (d) is inversely proportional to the distance between the fringes (x) in the interference pattern according to

$$\lambda = \frac{xd}{nL}$$

$$d = \frac{\lambda nL}{x}$$

Therefore, the extremely small separation distance between lines on a grating will cause an increase in the separation between the fringes in the pattern. For these reasons, a diffraction grating is a very precise apparatus for investigating the wavelength of light.

When a diffraction grating is used with monochromatic light, the interference pattern will have the same colour as the wavelength of light used to produce it. When full-spectrum, white light is used, each antinode will appear as a rainbow because each wavelength is diffracted at a slightly different angle. The relationship between the wavelength and the angle is:

$$\sin \theta_n = \frac{n\lambda}{d}$$

as was derived earlier for Young's double-slit experiment.

Diffraction gratings are produced by etching a large number of parallel lines on a sheet of glass or plastic. Each grating is defined by the number of lines per centimetre etched on it. Tens of thousands of lines per centimetre are common. The distance between lines is the inverse of the number of lines per centimetre, so as the number of lines increases, the distance between any two lines decreases accordingly.

Diffraction in Nature — Solar and Lunar Coronas

When the Sun is rising (Figure 13.83) or an overexposed photo of the Moon is taken (Figure 13.84), a pattern of rings appears. These are examples of diffraction in the atmosphere. When light from the Sun or Moon enters the atmosphere it encounters uniformly sized droplets of water and ice crystals. Diffraction occurs as the light bends around the edges of the particles at varying degrees depending upon the wavelength of the light. A series of coloured rings surrounding the astronomical object results.

e LAB
For a probeware activity, go to www.pearsoned.ca/school/physicssource.

e SIM
Investigate diffraction gratings through the use of simulations. Follow the eSim links at www.pearsoned.ca/school/physicssource.

e WEB
To learn more about diffraction effects in nature, follow the links at www.pearsoned.ca/school/physicssource.

▲ **Figure 13.83** A rising Sun

▲ **Figure 13.84** A ring around the Moon

Example 13.10

A diffraction grating has 1000 lines/1 cm. When light passes through the grating, an interference pattern is produced on a screen 4.00 m away. The first-order bright fringe is 19.2 cm away from the central antinode. What is the wavelength and colour of the light?

Given
$d = 1$ cm / 1000 lines $= 1.000 \times 10^{-3}$ cm/line
$\quad = 1.000 \times 10^{-5}$ m/line
$x = 1.92 \times 10^{-1}$ m
$n = 1$
$L = 4.00$ m

Required
wavelength of light (λ)

Analysis and Solution
The separation between lines is the inverse of the lines per centimetre given for the diffraction grating. Line separation is very small, and the first-order bright fringe is $n = 1$ because it is an antinode, or line of constructive interference. Therefore, this equation applies:

Practice Problems

1. An unknown wavelength of light is incident on a diffraction grating with 2500 lines/cm. The distance between the central antinode and the 3rd dark node is 20.0 cm when the screen is located 50.0 cm from the grating. Determine the wavelength of the light.

2. How many lines/cm are there in a diffraction grating if the 3rd dark fringe is located 5.00 cm from the central antinode when the screen is located 60 cm from the grating? Assume $\lambda = 500$ nm.

3. A diffraction grating has 1000 lines/cm. When red light ($\lambda = 750$ nm) is incident on the grating, what will be the separation between bright antinodes on a screen 3.0 m away?

$$\lambda = \frac{xd}{nL}$$

$$\lambda = \frac{(1.92 \times 10^{-1} \text{ m})(1.000 \times 10^{-5} \text{ m})}{(1)(4.00 \text{ m})}$$

$$\lambda = 4.80 \times 10^{-7} \text{ m}$$

$$\lambda = 480 \text{ nm}$$

Paraphrase

Based on the interference pattern, the incident light is 480 nm, which corresponds to the colour blue.

13-10 Inquiry Lab

Determining the Wavelength of Red, Green, and Blue Light

This investigation will verify the known wavelengths of different colours of light. According to the visible spectrum, red, green, and blue light have wavelengths in the following ranges:

- red: 650–750 nm
- green: 500–550 nm
- blue: 450–500 nm

Question

What are the wavelengths of red, green, and blue light?

Variables

manipulated: the distance between the diffraction grating and the screen will be indirectly manipulated
responding: the position of the first-order antinodes for red, blue, and green light on the "apparent" screen
controlled: single-filament incandescent light source and diffraction grating

Materials and Equipment

thin-film diffraction grating
two metre-sticks
single-filament lamp
masking tape and pen

Experimental Design

To investigate the position of the first- and second-order antinodes in an interference pattern produced by white light, a "simulated" screen will be used. Two metre-sticks and a lamp are arranged as shown in Figure 13.85.

In this design, observers look through the diffraction grating to see the antinodes as they would appear on a screen behind them. A screen is not needed as the angles θ are identical, so we can assume the distance to the hypothetical screen is identical to the distance between the lamp and the grating (1.0 m). While one person observes the antinode, a second person is directed to place an identification tape on the metre-stick where the antinode appears to be. This allows the distance between the central antinode and the position of the first-order antinode to be measured. This procedure can also be used to find the position of the second-order antinode.

Procedure

1. Set up the two metre-sticks such that they make a right angle with one another.

2. Place the lamp at the point where the metre-sticks join as shown in Figure 13.85.

3. Place the thin-film diffraction grating vertically upright at the end of one of the metre-sticks.

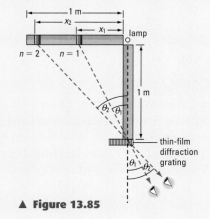

▲ **Figure 13.85**

4 Turn on the lamp and look through the grating, moving your head side to side until you can see the first-order antinode, which should appear as a rainbow. Your eye acts as the wavelength detector, in place of a screen.

5 While looking at the antinode, direct your lab partner to put a piece of tape labelled "B" on the metre-stick where the blue antinode band appears to be.

6 Repeat step 5 using tape labelled "G" for the green band of light and "R" for the red band of light.

7 Repeat steps 5 and 6 for the second-order antinode, if it is visible along the metre-stick.

8 Record the distance between the lamp and each piece of labelled tape.

Analysis

1. Using the first antinode ($n = 1$), calculate the wavelength of red, blue, and green light.

2. Determine the mean wavelength of each colour of light using the ranges given.

3. Calculate the percent difference between the mean wavelength of each colour and your experimentally determined value.

4. Explain why each antinode appears as a rainbow. Hint: What effect does the wavelength have on the angle of diffraction?

5. How many antinodes should appear in the diffraction grating on either side of the light source? Assume the largest angle of diffraction that could be visible is 89°.

 MINDS ON | **Comparing Spectra: Dispersion vs. Diffraction**

The rainbow produced when white light is refracted through a prism is similar to the rainbow produced at each antinode when white light passes through a thin-film diffraction grating.

In small groups, prepare a presentation to compare and contrast these two phenomena. Your presentation should consider:

1. The wave nature of light
2. The similarities of refraction and diffraction as they relate to Huygens' Principle of wavelets
3. The different wavelengths of the visible spectrum and how this leads to the separation of the colours in both dispersion and diffraction

4. The key differences in the causes of dispersion in a prism and the production of antinodes in an interference pattern
5. The reversed order of colours

Your presentation should also include:
· relevant images of both phenomena
· schematics of each phenomenon using ray diagrams where appropriate
· the use of animations and simulations found at www.pearsoned.ca/school/ physicssource
· a list of references

 e **LAB**

 For a probeware activity, go to www.pearsoned.ca/school/physicssource.

Polarization

Young's double-slit experiment, and interference in general, provided strong evidence that light does exhibit wave properties. However, evidence of interference alone could not distinguish whether the waves were transverse or longitudinal. Recall that in section 13.1 light, and electromagnetic radiation in general, was described by Maxwell as consisting of perpendicular electric and magnetic fields, propagating through space at the speed of light. In other words, Maxwell predicted that light was a transverse wave. Is there evidence that this is indeed the case?

Using a mechanical model, such as a rope, one can see that a transverse wave can be linearly polarized when vibrations only occur in one plane. The vertically polarized transverse waves shown in Figure 13.86 can pass through the vertical slit, but are blocked, or absorbed, by the horizontal slit. The longitudinal waves, on the other hand, can pass

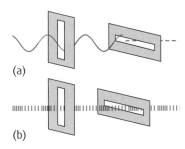

▲ **Figure 13.86** (a) A transverse wave passing through a vertical slit and being absorbed by a horizontal slit (b) A longitudinal wave passing through both a vertical and a horizontal slit

---

polarizing filter: a filter that allows only one plane of the electric field to pass through it; plane polarized EMR emerges

polarization: production of a state in which the plane of the electric field for each electromagnetic wave occurs only in one direction

plane polarized light: light resulting from polarization, in which only one plane of the electric field is allowed to pass through a filter

▲ **Figure 13.90** Two pairs of polarized sunglasses, at right angles

through both slits unaffected because longitudinal waves are not linearly polarized.

By a process similar to the mechanical model, electromagnetic waves can be blocked by two **polarizing filters** held at right angles to one another. In 13-1 QuickLab at the beginning of the chapter, you discovered that two polarizing filters, held at right angles to one another, can absorb light.

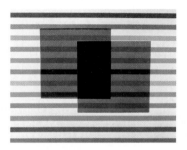

◀ **Figure 13.88** Two polarizing filters, one held vertically, the other held horizontally, partially overlap, showing the absorption of electromagnetic waves.

The photograph in Figure 13.88 can be explained by considering electromagnetic radiation as perpendicular magnetic and electric fields, with the plane of **polarization** arbitrarily defined by the direction of the electric field. When light is produced by an incandescent light bulb it is not polarized, meaning that the plane of the electric fields for each wave occurs randomly as light propagates outward from the source in all directions. When unpolarized light is incident on a polarizing filter, only one plane of the electric field is allowed to pass through, causing **plane polarized light** to emerge. If a second polarizing filter is held at right angles to the plane polarized light, then the plane polarized light also is absorbed (Figure 13.89).

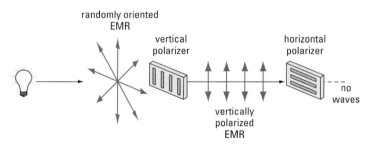

▲ **Figure 13.89** Unpolarized light incident on two polarizing filters at right angles to one another

The blue light in sunlight is partially polarized when it is scattered in the atmosphere. Therefore, in sunglasses and camera lenses, polarized filters are used to reduce the blue polarized light from the sky while allowing other non-polarized colours to pass through and appear brighter. To see this effect, tilt your head from side to side while looking at the blue sky with polarized glasses.

The polarizing effect supports the wave model of light in general and in particular, the concept that light is composed of perpendicular, oscillating electric and magnetic fields (Figure 13.90).

Knowledge

1. According to Huygens' Principle, what will happen to the shape of a straight wave front after it passes through a small opening in a barrier?

2. Use Huygens' Principle to describe how interference can occur when a straight wave front is incident on two narrow openings.

3. Two incandescent white lights are placed close to one another. Explain why an interference pattern is not observed on a nearby screen.

4. What parameters did Young need to control to enable him to observe an interference pattern from two point sources of light?

5. Construct a concept map to show the relationship between path length, nodal fringes, antinodal fringes, wave phase, and interference.

Applications

6. In an experiment similar to Young's, how far apart are two slits if the 3rd antinode is measured to be 20° from the central antinode, when light with a wavelength of 650 nm is used?

7. Determine the angle of diffraction to the 2nd node when light with a wavelength of 425 nm is incident on two slits separated by 6.00×10^{-6} m.

8. Light with a wavelength of 700 nm is diffracted by a diffraction grating with 5.00×10^3 lines/cm. If a screen is positioned 1.00 m away from the grating, what is the distance between the 1st and central antinodes?

9. Monochromatic light with a frequency of 5.75×10^{14} Hz is incident on a diffraction grating with 60 lines/cm. What is the distance between the 2nd and 3rd dark fringes when the screen is located 1.20 m away?

10. An unknown light source is directed at a diffraction grating with 6.00×10^4 lines/m. If the nodal lines are 5.50 cm apart when the screen is 1.50 m away, what is the wavelength and frequency of the light?

11. Light emitted from an unknown gas sample is incident on a diffraction grating with 5.00×10^2 lines/cm. The antinodes appear on a screen 1.50 m away and are separated by 3.10×10^{-2} m. What is the wavelength and frequency of the light?

Extensions

12. Design an experiment to determine the wavelength of an unknown monochromatic light. Include an experimental design, material list, and procedure.

13. Compare the wavelength of X rays to that of visible light and explain what should happen to the diffraction pattern if X rays were used instead of visible light.

14. Investigate how the process of diffraction, using radiation other than visible light, can be useful for determining the shapes of crystal lattices and structures too small to be seen with visible light.

 e TEST

To check your understanding of diffraction, interference, and polarization, follow the eTest links at www.pearsoned.ca/school/physicssource.

Key Terms and Concepts

electromagnetic radiation
frequency
wavelength
electromagnetic spectrum
particle model
wave model
photon
quantum model
electric field
magnetic field
capacitor
Maxwell's Equations

electromagnetic wave
rectilinear propagation
ray diagram
plane mirror
law of reflection
virtual image
real image
magnification
image attitude
converging mirror
diverging mirror
mirror equation

refraction
refractive index
Snell's Law
total internal reflection
critical angle
spectrum
dispersion
converging lens
diverging lens
thin lens equation
Huygens' Principle
diffraction

interference
antinode
node
path length
difference in path length
angle of diffraction
diffraction grating
polarizing filter
polarization
plane polarized light

Key Equations

$$m = \frac{h_i}{h_o} = -\frac{d_i}{d_o}$$

$$\frac{1}{d_o} + \frac{1}{d_i} = \frac{1}{f}$$

$$n = \frac{c}{v}$$

$$n_1 \sin \theta_1 = n_2 \sin \theta_2$$

$$\frac{\sin \theta_1}{\sin \theta_2} = \frac{v_1}{v_2} = \frac{\lambda_1}{\lambda_2} = \frac{n_2}{n_1}$$

$$\sin \theta_n = \frac{n\lambda}{d}$$

$$\lambda = \frac{xd}{nL}$$

Conceptual Overview

Summarize this chapter by explaining how the properties of electromagnetic radiation support either the wave model of light or the particle model of light, or both.

reflection

refraction

diffraction

Particle Model   polarization   Wave Model

interference

electric field

magnetic field

Knowledge

1. (13.1) Create a table to identify all the major categories of electromagnetic radiation, including the wavelengths and frequencies listed in the spectrum shown in Figure 13.4. Brainstorm common uses for each type of radiation.

2. (13.1) Compare and contrast the particle and wave models of electromagnetic radiation.

3. (13.1) What two critical insights were understood by Maxwell when he developed his theory of electromagnetic radiation?

4. (13.1) Consider two electric field lines on a transverse wave. One field line is up, and a moment later, another is down. What is produced as a result of this "changing" electric field?

5. (13.1) Describe how an electromagnetic wave is able to propagate in empty space.

6. (13.1) Describe the five predictions that Maxwell made regarding the properties of electromagnetic radiation.

7. (13.1) How did Hertz prove that the EMR observed at his antenna was, in fact, produced by the nearby spark gap and did not originate from another source?

8. (13.2) The first significant attempt to measure the speed of light was made by Christiaan Huygens, using the eclipse of Jupiter's moon Io. Describe this method.

9. (13.2) In addition to measuring the speed of light with a rotating toothed wheel, Armand Fizeau demonstrated that light travelled at different speeds in moving water. Explain how the results of his investigation support the wave model of light.

10. (13.3) Draw a ray diagram to demonstrate the law of reflection.

11. (13.3) Construct a ray diagram for a converging mirror and illustrate the following terms.
    (a) centre of curvature (C)
    (b) radius of curvature (r)
    (c) vertex (V)
    (d) principal axis (PA)
    (e) principal focal point (F)
    (f) focal length (f)

12. (13.3) Can a diverging mirror produce a real image? Explain.

13. (13.4) Using a ray diagram, illustrate partial reflection and partial refraction for a ray passing from air into water at an angle of 15°. On your ray diagram, label the normal line, the index of refraction, the angle of incidence, the angle of reflection, and the angle of refraction.

14. (13.4) Light passes from a medium with a high refractive index to one with a low refractive index. Is the light bent away from or toward the normal line?

15. (13.4) Contrast the simple and general forms of Snell's Law.

16. (13.4) Dispersion is the separation of white light into all the colours of the spectrum. Explain two different methods that could be used to separate all the colours in white light.

17. (13.5) Illustrate the process of refraction using a straight wave front that travels from air into water. Based on your diagram, does Huygens' Principle support the wave model or the particle model of light?

18. (13.5) A straight wave front is incident on two small holes in a barrier; illustrate the shape of the wave front a moment after it makes contact with the barrier. Does your drawing indicate that interference will occur?

19. (13.5) Why is an interference pattern not observed when two incandescent lights are located next to one another?

20. (13.5) How does the evidence from polarizing filters support the transverse nature of the wave model of light?

21. (13.5) Each antinode appears as a full spectrum when white light is incident on a diffraction grating. Explain this phenomenon.

22. (13.5) Explain how path length and diffraction are related to the production of Poisson's bright spot.

Applications

23. (13.1) High-voltage transmission lines that carry alternating current can interfere with radio waves. Explain how this interference can occur.

24. (13.2) Calculate the speed of yellow light, $\lambda = 589$ nm, in the following materials:
  (a) water
  (b) ethanol
  (c) Lucite®
  (d) quartz glass
  (e) diamond

25. (13.2) An 8-sided mirror is rotating at 5.50×10^2 Hz. At what distance should the fixed mirror be placed to replicate Michelson's experiment?

26. (13.2) A fixed mirror and a rotating mirror are separated by 30.0 km. The 8-sided rotating set of mirrors turns at 600 Hz when the light is able to pass through the experimental apparatus. Calculate the speed of light.

27. (13.3) When you look into a plane mirror, an image is formed. Describe the characteristics of the image based on attitude, type, and magnification.

28. (13.3) A student stands 30 cm from a plane mirror. If the student's face is 25 cm in length, what is the minimum length of mirror needed for the student to see her entire face?

29. (13.3) An object is located 25.0 cm from a converging mirror with a focal length of 15.0 cm. Draw a scale ray diagram to determine the following:
  (a) the image location and type
  (b) the image attitude
  (c) the magnification of the image

30. (13.3) Construct a ray diagram for a diverging mirror and illustrate the following terms:
  (a) centre of curvature (C)
  (b) radius of curvature (r)
  (c) vertex (V)

31. (13.3) Where must an object be placed relative to the focal point for a converging mirror such that the image produced is virtual?

32. (13.3) A 15.0-cm-high object is placed 20.0 cm from a diverging mirror with a virtual focal length of 10.0 cm. How high is the image and where is it located?

33. (13.3) A 20.0-cm-high, inverted image is produced when an object is placed 12.0 cm from a converging lens with a focal length of 11.0 cm. Calculate the height of the object.

34. (13.4) Light with a wavelength of 610 nm is incident on a quartz glass crystal at an angle of 35°. Determine the angle of refraction and the wavelength of the light in the quartz glass.

35. (13.4) Can total internal reflection occur when light travels from
  (a) air into water?
  (b) water into air?
  (c) Lucite® into water?
  (d) water into diamond?

36. (13.4) Light enters an unknown material and slows down to a speed of 2.67×10^8 m/s. What is the refractive index of the unknown material? Compare the refractive index of this material to that of water — which one has a higher index?

37. (13.4) Calculate the critical angle of the following boundaries:
  (a) water-air
  (b) diamond-air
  (c) diamond-water
  (d) Lucite®-air

38. (13.4) Use a ray diagram to determine the image attributes when the object is located between
  (a) 2F′ and F′ for a converging lens
  (b) F′ and a converging lens
  (c) F′ and a diverging lens

39. (13.4) A 4.00-cm-high object is located 5.00 cm from a diverging lens with a focal length of 10.0 cm. Using the thin lens equation, determine the image attributes and position. Verify your answer with a scale ray diagram.

40. (13.5) In an experiment similar to Young's, light with a wavelength of 630 nm is incident on two slits separated by 5.3×10^{-5} m. What is the angle to the 1st, 2nd, and 3rd antinodes?

41. (13.5) Monochromatic light is incident on two slits separated by 0.25 mm. The first dark fringe deviated an angle of 0.050° from the central antinode. What is the wavelength and colour of the light?

42. (13.5) Light from an unknown gas sample is incident on two slits separated by 1.4×10^{-4} m. On a screen 1.1 m away, the distance between the 7th node and the central antinode is measured to be 0.025 m. What is the wavelength of the light emitted by the unknown gas sample?

43. (13.5) A screen is located 4.5 m from two slits that are illuminated with a 490-nm light source. If the distance between the central antinode and the first-order antinode is 0.037 m, how far apart are the two slits?

Extensions

44. An X-ray machine operates by accelerating an electron through a large potential difference, generating a large amount of kinetic energy. The high-speed electron then collides with a metal barrier. Explain why the collision produces a high-frequency X ray.

45. Cable television wires have a metal shield surrounding the copper wire that carries the television signal. The shielding prevents interference from electromagnetic radiation and it must be grounded in order to effectively block interference. Explain how the shielding prevents interference and why it needs to be grounded.

46. Handheld two-way radios can communicate over relatively short distances. Suggest several ways to increase the radio's range.

47. When you place the concave side of a spoon on your nose and slowly pull it away from your face, your image disappears at a certain distance. What is the significance of this distance?

48. After light enters Earth's atmosphere it encounters a temperature gradient as it approaches the surface of Earth, causing a mirage. If the warm air near the surface of Earth has a lower index of refraction than the cooler air above, which way is the light bent? Show this with a ray diagram.

49. Explain why a fibre-optic network is much more efficient and powerful than a copper-wire network.

Consolidate Your Understanding

1. Explain how electromagnetic radiation is able to propagate in the absence of a medium, like air. Does your explanation support the wave model or particle model?

2. Why is an accelerating charge required to produce electromagnetic radiation and how does this relate to the word "changing" in Maxwell's explanation of EMR?

3. Is an electromagnetic wave one-dimensional, two-dimensional, or three-dimensional? Explain.

4. Has Maxwell's last prediction been verified by experimental evidence? If so, describe the evidence as it relates to reflection, refraction, diffraction, interference, and polarization.

5. Could Hertz have investigated the phenomenon of diffraction by using the same equipment as in his famous experiment? If so, how?

Think About It

Review your answers to the Think About It questions on page 635. How would you answer each question now?

 e TEST

To check your understanding of the nature and behaviour of electromagnetic radiation, follow the eTest links at www.pearsoned.ca/school/physicssource.

The wave-particle duality reminds us that sometimes truth really *is* stranger than fiction!

U p to this point in the course, you have studied what is known as *classical physics*. Classical physics includes most of the ideas about light, energy, heat, forces, and electricity and magnetism up to about 1900. The golden age of classical physics occurred at the very end of the 19th century. By this time, Newton's ideas of forces and gravitation were over 200 years old, and our knowledge of physics had been added to immensely by the work of James Clerk Maxwell, Michael Faraday, and others. It seemed as though nearly everything in physics had been explained. In the spring of 1900, in a speech to the Royal Institution of Great Britain, the great Irish physicist William Thomson (Figure 14.1) — otherwise known as Lord Kelvin — stated that "… the beauty and clearness of the dynamical theory of light and heat is overshadowed by two clouds…." You could paraphrase Kelvin as saying "the beauty and clearness of *physics* is overshadowed by two clouds." One "cloud" was the problem of how to explain the relationship between the temperature of a material and the colour of light the material gives off. The other "cloud" had to do with an unexpected result in an experiment to measure the effect of Earth's motion on the speed of light.

Kelvin was confident that these two clouds would soon disappear. He was wrong! Before the year was out, the first of these clouds "broke" into a storm the effects of which are still being felt today! In this chapter, you will meet one of the strangest ideas in all of science. In many ways, this chapter represents the end of classical physics. You will learn that light is not only a wave, but also a particle. Stranger still, you will learn that things you thought were particles, such as electrons, sometimes act like waves! Hang on!

◀ **Figure 14.1**

William Thomson (1824–1907) was named Lord Kelvin by Queen Victoria in 1892. He was the first British scientist to be honoured in this way. During his long and illustrious career, Lord Kelvin published over 600 books and papers, and filed more than 70 patents for his inventions. He was one of the driving forces behind the first transatlantic telegraph cable.

info **BIT**

This chapter is about the "cloud" that became quantum theory. In 1905, the other "cloud" became Einstein's theory of special relativity.

The Relationship Between Temperature and Colour of an Incandescent Object

Problem

What is the relationship between the temperature of a hot, glowing object and the colour of light emitted by the object?

Materials

incandescent (filament-style) light bulb
variable transformer, 0–120 V
transmission-type diffraction grating

Procedure

1 Attach a filament-style light bulb to a variable transformer and slowly increase the voltage.

2 Observe the spectrum produced by the light from the light bulb as it passes through the diffraction grating. For best results, darken the room.

Questions

1. What happens to the temperature of the filament in the light bulb as you increase the voltage output of the transformer?

2. How does the spectrum you observe through the diffraction grating change as you increase the voltage through the filament?

3. As you increase the temperature of the filament, what happens to the colour at which the spectrum appears brightest?

4. You may have noticed that the colour of a flashlight filament becomes reddish as the battery weakens. Suggest why.

Think About It

1. Describe the relationship between the colour of a hot object and its temperature. Note in particular the colour you would first see as the temperature of an object increases, and how the colour changes as the object continues to heat up.

2. What do we mean by the terms "red-hot" and "white-hot"?

3. Which is hotter: "red-hot" or "white-hot"?

4. Is it possible for an object to be "green-hot"? Explain.

Discuss your answers in a small group and record them for later reference. As you complete each section of this chapter, review your answers to these questions. Note any changes in your ideas.

info **BIT**

Even a great physicist can be wrong! Despite making extremely important contributions to many areas of physics and chemistry, Lord Kelvin has also become famous for less-than-accurate predictions and pronouncements. Here are a few:
- "I can state flatly that heavier-than-air flying machines are impossible." (1895)
- "There is nothing new to be discovered in physics now. All that remains is more and more precise measurement." (1900)
- "X rays will prove to be a hoax." (1899)
- "Radio has no future." (1897)
- "[The vector] has never been of the slightest use to any creature."

14.1 The Birth of the Quantum

▲ **Figure 14.2** The colour of molten bronze depends on its temperature.

incandescent: glowing with heat

We take for granted the relationship between the colour of a hot, glowing object and its temperature. You know from sitting around a campfire that the end of a metal wiener-roasting stick slowly changes from a dull red to a bright reddish-yellow as it heats up. For centuries, metalworkers have used the colour of molten metal to determine when the temperature is just right for pouring metal into molds in the metal-casting process (Figure 14.2). The association between colour and temperature is so common that you would expect the mathematical relationship between colour and temperature to be simple. That is certainly what classical physicists expected. Despite their best efforts, however, classical physicists were never able to correctly predict the colour produced by an **incandescent** object. What is the connection between temperature and a glowing object's colour?

Figure 14.3 shows three graphs that relate the colours produced by hot objects to their temperatures. The relationship between colour and temperature may be summarized as follows:

1. Hot, glowing objects emit a continuous range of wavelengths and hence a continuous spectrum of colours.

2. For a given temperature, the light emitted by the object has a range of characteristic wavelengths, which determine the object's colour when it glows (Figure 14.2).

3. The hotter an object is, the bluer the light it emits. The cooler an object is, the redder its light is.

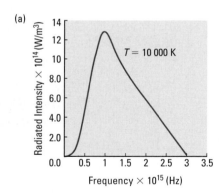

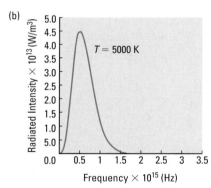

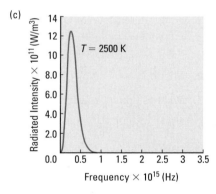

▲ **Figure 14.3** Blackbody curves for three different temperatures (Kelvin): 10 000 K, 5000 K, and 2500 K. Frequency is along the horizontal axis, and energy intensity emitted is along the vertical axis. Note that these graphs do not have the same vertical scale. If they did, graph (a) would be 256 times taller than graph (c)!

Concept Check

Next time you are under a dark, clear sky, look carefully at the stars. Some will appear distinctly bluish-white, while others will be reddish or orange in appearance. What do differences in colour tell you about the stars?

Physicists call the graphs in Figure 14.3 **blackbody radiation curves**. The term "blackbody," introduced by the German physicist Gustav Kirchhoff in 1862, refers to an object that completely absorbs any light energy that falls on it, from all parts of the electromagnetic spectrum. When this perfect absorber heats up, it becomes a perfect radiator. The energy it reradiates can be depicted as a blackbody curve, which depends on temperature only (Figure 14.3). Hot objects, such as the filament in an incandescent light bulb used in 14-1 QuickLab, or a glowing wiener-roast stick, are good approximations to a blackbody.

Not only did classical physics fail to explain the relationship between temperature and the blackbody radiation curve, it also made a completely absurd prediction: A hot object would emit its energy most effectively at short wavelengths, and that the shorter the wavelength, the more energy that would be emitted. This prediction leads to a rather disturbing conclusion: If you strike a match, it will emit a little bit of light energy at long wavelengths (e.g., infrared), a bit more energy in the red part of the spectrum, more yet in the blue, even more in the ultraviolet, a lot more in the X-ray region, and so on. In short, striking a match would incinerate the entire universe! This prediction was called the *ultraviolet catastrophe*. Fortunately for us, classical physics was incorrect. Figure 14.4 shows a comparison between the prediction made by classical physics and the blackbody radiation curve produced by a hot object.

Quantization and Planck's Hypothesis

In December 1900, Max Planck (Figure 14.5) came up with an explanation of why hot objects produce the blackbody radiation curves shown in Figures 14.3 and 14.4. Planck suggested that the problem with the classical model prediction had to do with how matter could absorb light energy. He discovered that, by limiting the *minimum* amount of energy that any given wavelength of light can exchange with its surroundings, he could reproduce the blackbody radiation curve exactly. The name **quantum** was given to the smallest amount of energy of a particular wavelength or frequency of light that could be absorbed by a body. Planck's hypothesis can be expressed in the following formula, known as **Planck's formula**:

$$E = nhf$$

where E is the energy of the quantum, in joules, $n = 1, 2, 3 \ldots$ refers to the *number* of quanta of a given energy, h is a constant of proportionality, called *Planck's constant*, which has the value 6.63×10^{-34} J·s, and f is the frequency of the light.

If energy is transferred in quanta, then the amount of energy transferred must be **quantized**, or limited to whole-number multiples of a smallest unit of energy, the quantum.

Even though Planck's hypothesis could reproduce the correct shape of the blackbody curve, there was no explanation in classical physics for his idea. The concept of the quantum marks the end of classical physics and the birth of quantum physics.

blackbody radiation curve: a graph of the intensity of light emitted versus wavelength for an object of a given temperature

blackbody: an object that completely absorbs any light energy that falls on it

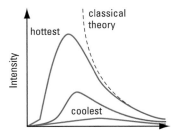

▲ **Figure 14.4** According to classical theory, as an object becomes hotter, the intensity of light it emits should increase and its wavelength should decrease. The graph shows a comparison of the classical prediction (dashed line) and what is actually observed for three objects at different temperatures.

▲ **Figure 14.5** Max Planck (1858–1947) is one of the founders of quantum physics.

quantum: the smallest amount or "bundle" of energy that a wavelength of light can possess (pl. quanta)

Planck's formula: light comes in quanta of energy that can be calculated using the equation $E = nhf$

quantized: limited to whole multiples of a basic amount (quantum)

Planck's constant can be expressed using two different units:
$h = 6.63 \times 10^{-34}$ J·s or
$h = 4.14 \times 10^{-15}$ eV·s
Recall that
1 eV = 1.60×10^{-19} J
or 1 J = 6.25×10^{18} eV.

photon: a quantum of light

Concept Check

Show that Planck's formula for one photon can be written as $E = \dfrac{hc}{\lambda}$.

Einstein, Quanta, and the Photon

In 1905, a young and not-yet-famous Albert Einstein made a very bold suggestion. Planck had already introduced the idea of quantization of energy and the equation $E = hf$. He thought that quantization applied only to matter and how matter could absorb or emit energy. Einstein suggested that this equation implied that light itself was quantized. In other words, Einstein reintroduced the idea that light could be considered a particle or a quantum of energy! This idea was troubling because, as you saw in Chapter 13, experiments clearly showed that light is a wave. In 1926, the chemist Gilbert Lewis introduced the term **photon** to describe a quantum of light. Planck's formula, $E = nhf$, can therefore be used to calculate the energy of one or more photons.

Examples 14.1 and 14.2 allow you to practise using the idea of the photon and Planck's formula.

Example 14.1

How much energy is carried by a photon of red light of wavelength 600 nm?

Given
$n = 1$
$\lambda = 600 \text{ nm} \times \dfrac{1 \times 10^{-9} \text{ m}}{1 \text{ nm}} = 6.00 \times 10^{-7} \text{ m}$

Required
photon energy (E)

Analysis and Solution
Since wavelength is given, first find the frequency using the equation $c = f\lambda$, where c is the speed of light, f is frequency, and λ is the wavelength.

$f = \dfrac{c}{\lambda}$

$= \dfrac{3.00 \times 10^8 \dfrac{\text{m}}{\text{s}}}{6.00 \times 10^{-7} \text{ m}}$

$= 5.00 \times 10^{14}$ Hz

Then substitute into Planck's formula:

$E = nhf$

$= (1)(6.63 \times 10^{-34} \text{ J·s})(5.00 \times 10^{14} \text{ s}^{-1})$

$= 3.32 \times 10^{-19}$ J

Practice Problems

1. What is the energy of a photon of light of frequency 4.00×10^{14} Hz?

2. What is the energy of a green photon of light of wavelength 555 nm?

3. What is 15.0 eV expressed in units of joules?

Answers

1. 2.65×10^{-19} J
2. 3.58×10^{-19} J
3. 2.40×10^{-18} J

It is often more convenient to express the energies of photons in units of electron volts. Since 1 eV = 1.60×10^{-19} J, the energy of the red photon is

$$3.32 \times 10^{-19}\ \cancel{J} \times \frac{1\ \text{eV}}{1.60 \times 10^{-19}\ \cancel{J}} = 2.07\ \text{eV}$$

Paraphrase
A red photon of light carries 3.32×10^{-19} J of energy, or about 2.07 eV.

Example 14.2

Your eye can detect as few as 500 photons of light. The eye is most sensitive to light having a wavelength of 510 nm. What is the minimum amount of light energy that your eye can detect?

Given
λ = 510 nm = 5.10×10^{-7} m
n = 500 photons

Required
minimum light energy (E)

Analysis and Solution
Since only wavelength is given, determine frequency using the equation $c = f\lambda$:

$$f = \frac{c}{\lambda}$$

$$= \frac{3.00 \times 10^{8}\ \dfrac{\cancel{m}}{s}}{5.10 \times 10^{-7}\ \cancel{m}}$$

$$= 5.88 \times 10^{14}\ \text{Hz}$$

Then apply Planck's formula:

$$E = nhf$$

$$= (500)(6.63 \times 10^{-34}\ \text{J}\cdot\text{s})(5.88 \times 10^{14}\ \text{s}^{-1})$$

$$= 1.95 \times 10^{-16}\ \text{J}$$

Paraphrase
Your eye is capable of responding to as little as 1.95×10^{-16} J of energy.

Practice Problems

1. What is the frequency of a 10-nm photon?

2. What is the energy of a 10-nm photon?

3. How many photons of green light (λ = 550 nm) are required to deliver 10 J of energy?

Answers

1. 3.0×10^{16} Hz

2. 2.0×10^{-17} J

3. 2.8×10^{19} photons

MINDS ON   What's Wrong with This Analogy?

Sometimes the idea of the quantum is compared to the units we use for money. A dollar can be divided into smaller units, where the cent is the smallest possible unit. In what way is this analogy for the quantum accurate and in what way is it inaccurate? Look very carefully at Planck's formula to find the error in the analogy. Try to come up with a better analogy for explaining quantization.

The next example involves rearranging Planck's formula and applying it to find the relationship between the power of a laser pointer and the number of photons it emits.

Example 14.3

Practice Problems

1. How much energy is delivered by a beam of 1000 blue-light photons ($\lambda = 400$ nm)?

2. How many 400-nm blue-light photons per second are required to deliver 10 W of power?

Answers

1. 4.97×10^{-16} J
2. 2.0×10^{19} photons/s

How many photons are emitted each second by a laser pointer that has a power output of 0.400 mW if the average wavelength produced by the pointer is 600 nm?

Given

$\lambda = 600$ nm $= 6.00 \times 10^{-7}$ m
$P = 0.400$ mW $= 4.00 \times 10^{-4}$ W

Required

number of photons (n)

Analysis and Solution

Since 1 W = 1 J/s, the laser pointer is emitting 4.00×10^{-4} J/s. Therefore, in 1 s the laser pointer emits 4.00×10^{-4} J of energy. By equating this amount of energy to the energy carried by the 600-nm photons, you can determine how many photons are emitted each second using the equation $E = nhf$.

First use the equation $c = f\lambda$ to determine the frequency of a 600-nm photon:

$$f = \frac{c}{\lambda}$$

Substitute this equation into Planck's formula.

$$E = nhf$$
$$= nh \left(\frac{c}{\lambda} \right)$$
$$n = \frac{E\lambda}{hc}$$
$$= \frac{(4.00 \times 10^{-4} \, \cancel{J})(6.00 \times 10^{-7} \, \cancel{m})}{(6.63 \times 10^{-34} \, \cancel{J \cdot s}) \left(3.00 \times 10^{8} \, \frac{\cancel{m}}{\cancel{s}} \right)}$$
$$= 1.21 \times 10^{15}$$

Paraphrase

A laser that emits 1.21×10^{15} photons each second has a power output of 0.400 mW.

Photons and the Electromagnetic Spectrum

Planck's formula provides a very useful way of relating the energy of a photon to its wavelength or frequency. It shows that a photon's energy depends on its frequency. An X-ray photon is more energetic than a microwave photon, just as X rays have higher frequencies than microwaves. Consequently, it takes a much more energetic process to create a gamma ray or X ray than it does to create a radio wave. Figure 14.6 gives the various photon energies along the electromagnetic spectrum.

X rays, for example, can only be emitted by a very hot gas or by a very-high-energy interaction between particles. Figure 14.7 shows images of the remnants of an exploded star, taken in different parts of the electromagnetic spectrum. Each image shows photons emitted by gases at different temperatures and locations in the remnant.

The Electromagnetic Spectrum

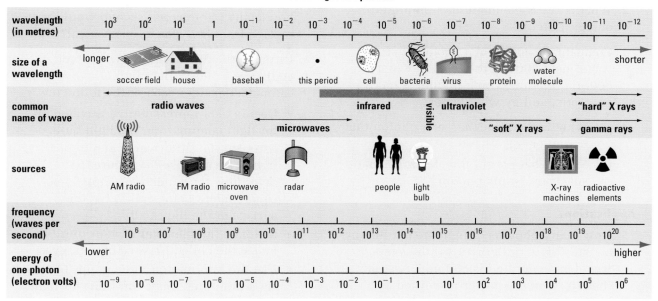

▲ **Figure 14.6** The energies of photons (in electron volts) along the electromagnetic spectrum

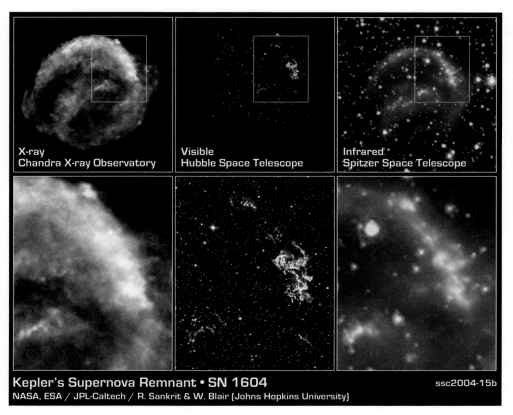

◀ **Figure 14.7** These images of a supernova remnant were taken by the Chandra X-ray space telescope, the Hubble space telescope (visible part of the spectrum), and the Spitzer space telescope (infrared). Each image is produced by gases at different temperatures. X rays are produced by very-high-temperature gases (millions of degrees), whereas infrared light is usually emitted by low-temperature gases (hundreds of degrees).

Chapter 14 The wave-particle duality reminds us that sometimes truth really *is* stranger than fiction!   709

Knowledge

1. What is the energy of a photon with wavelength 450 nm?

2. What is the wavelength of a photon of energy 15.0 eV?

3. Compare the energy of a photon of wavelength 300 nm to the energy of a 600-nm photon. Which photon is more energetic, and by what factor?

4. (a) What is the frequency of a photon that has an energy of 100 keV?

   (b) From what part of the electromagnetic spectrum is this photon?

Applications

5. How many photons of light are emitted by a 100-W light bulb in 10 s if the average wavelength emitted is 550 nm? Assume that 100% of the power is emitted as visible light.

6. The Sun provides approximately 1400 W of solar power per square metre. If the average wavelength (visible and infrared) is 700 nm, how many photons are received each second per square metre?

Extensions

7. Suppose that your eye is receiving 10 000 photons per second from a distant star. If an identical star was 10 times farther away, how many photons per second would you receive from that star in one second?

8. Estimate the distance from which you could see a 100-W light bulb. In your estimate, consider each of the following:

   • Decide on a representative wavelength for light coming from the light bulb.

   • Estimate the surface area of a typical light bulb and use this figure to determine the number of photons per square metre being emitted at the surface of the light bulb.

   • Estimate the diameter of your pupil and hence the collecting area of your eye.

   • Use the information in Example 14.2 to set a minimum detection limit for light from the light bulb.

Remember that your answer is an estimate. It will likely differ from other students' estimates based on the assumptions you made.

(Hint: The surface area of a sphere is $4\pi r^2$.)

e TEST

To check your understanding of Planck's formula, follow the eTest links at www.pearsoned.ca/school/physicssource.

14.2 The Photoelectric Effect

The secret agent cautiously inches forward and carefully steps over and around the thin, spidery outlines of laser beams focussed on light sensors scattered around Dr. Evil's secret lair.

Is this scenario only the stuff of spy movies? Perhaps, but every time you walk into a shopping mall or have your groceries scanned at the supermarket, you, like the secret agent, are seeing an application of the way in which photons and metals interact. This interaction is called the *photoelectric effect*.

14-2 QuickLab

Discharging a Zinc Plate Using UV Light

Problem

Does ultraviolet light cause the emission of electrons from a zinc metal plate?

Materials

electroscope
UV light source
zinc plate
glass plate

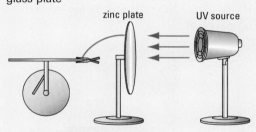

zinc plate   UV source

▲ **Figure 14.8**

Procedure

1. Attach the zinc plate so that it is in contact with the electroscope.

2. Apply a negative charge to the zinc plate and electroscope. What happens to the vanes of the electroscope? (If you are uncertain how to apply a negative charge, consult your teacher for assistance.)

3. Turn on the UV light source and shine it directly on the zinc plate (see Figure 14.8).

4. Place the glass plate between the UV light source and the zinc plate. Note any change in the behaviour of the vanes of the electroscope. Remove the plate and once again note any change in the response of the vanes.

Questions

1. Why did the vanes of the electroscope deflect when a negative charge was applied?

2. Explain what happened when UV light shone on the zinc plate. Why does this effect suggest that electrons are leaving the zinc plate?

3. Glass is a known absorber of UV light. What happened when the glass plate was placed between the UV source and the electroscope?

4. From your observations, what caused the emission of electrons from the zinc surface? Give reasons for your answer.

> ⚠ **CAUTION: UV light is harmful to your eyes. Do not look directly into the UV light source.**

In 1887, German physicist Heinrich Hertz conducted a series of experiments designed to test Maxwell's theory of electromagnetic waves. In one of the experiments, a spark jumping between the two metal electrodes of a spark gap was used to create radio waves that could be detected in a similar spark-gap receiver located several metres away. Hertz noticed that his spark-gap receiver worked much better if the small metal electrodes were highly polished. Eventually, it was recognized that it was not the polishing but the ultraviolet light being produced by the main spark in his transmitter that greatly enhanced the ability of sparks to jump in his receiver's spark-gap. Hertz had discovered that some metals emit electrons when illuminated by sufficiently short (high-energy) wavelengths of light. This process is called *photoemission of electrons*, or the **photoelectric effect**. Electrons emitted by this process are sometimes called **photoelectrons**.

How could light waves cause a metal to emit electrons? Experiments showed that the electrons required energies of a few electron volts in order to be emitted by the metal. Perhaps the atoms on the surface of the metal absorbed the energy of the light waves. The atoms would begin to vibrate and eventually absorb enough energy to eject an electron. There is a problem with this theory. According to classical physics, it should take minutes to hours for a metal to emit electrons. Experiments showed, however, that electron emission was essentially instantaneous: There was no measurable delay between the arrival of light on the metal surface and the emission of electrons. To further add to the puzzle, there was a minimum or **threshold frequency, f_0,** of incident light below which no photoemission would occur. If the light shining on the metal is of a frequency lower than this threshold frequency, no electrons are emitted, regardless of the brightness of the light shining on the metal (Figure 14.9).

photoelectric effect: the emission of electrons when a metal is illuminated by short wavelengths of light

photoelectron: an electron emitted from a metal because of the photoelectric effect

threshold frequency: the minimum frequency that a photon can have to cause photoemission from a metal

▼ **Table 14.1** Work Functions of Some Common Metals

Element	Work Function (eV)
Aluminium	4.08
Beryllium	5.00
Cadmium	4.07
Calcium	2.90
Carbon	4.81
Cesium	2.10
Copper	4.70
Magnesium	3.68
Mercury	4.50
Potassium	2.30
Selenium	5.11
Sodium	2.28
Zinc	4.33

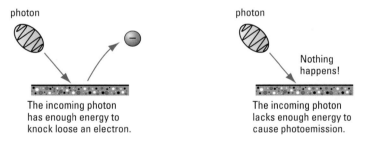

▲ **Figure 14.9** If an incident photon has a high enough frequency, an electron will be emitted by the metal surface. If the incoming photon frequency is not high enough, an electron will not be emitted.

Another puzzle was the lack of clear connection between the energy of the electrons emitted and the brightness of the light shining on the metal surface. For a given frequency of light, provided it was greater than the threshold frequency, the emitted electrons could have a range of possible kinetic energies. Increasing the intensity of the light had no influence on the maximum kinetic energy of the electrons.

Einstein's Contribution

The photoelectric effect remained an interesting but completely unexplained phenomenon until 1905. In 1905, Albert Einstein solved the riddle of the photoelectric effect by applying Planck's quantum hypothesis: Light energy arrives on the metal surface in discrete bundles, which are absorbed by atoms of the metal. This process takes very little time and all the energy needed to expel an electron is provided at once. However, photoemission only occurs if the frequency of the incident photons is greater than or equal to the threshold frequency of the metal. Since the frequency of a photon is directly proportional to its energy, as given by Planck's formula, $E = hf$, the incident photons must have the minimum energy required to eject electrons. This minimum energy is known as the **work function**, W. The work function is specific for every metal. Table 14.1 lists the work functions of some common metals. The work function, W, is related to threshold frequency, f_0, by the equation $W = hf_0$. Photons with a frequency greater than the threshold frequency have energy greater than the work function and electrons will be ejected.

work function: the minimum energy that a photon can have to cause photoemission from a metal; specific for every metal

MINDS ON   Light a Particle? Heresy!

Suggest reasons why a physicist might argue against Einstein's idea that light is a particle. One such physicist was Robert A. Millikan, whose important experiments on the photoelectric effect were viewed, ironically, as a brilliant confirmation of Einstein's "crazy" idea. How is skepticism both an advantage and a disadvantage to the progress of science?

Millikan's Measurement of Planck's Constant

When photons are absorbed by a metallic surface, either nothing will happen — the photons lack the minimum energy required to cause photoemission — or an electron will be emitted (Figure 14.10).

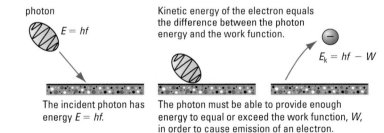

photon

$E = hf$

Kinetic energy of the electron equals the difference between the photon energy and the work function.

$E_k = hf - W$

The incident photon has energy $E = hf$.

The photon must be able to provide enough energy to equal or exceed the work function, W, in order to cause emission of an electron.

▲ **Figure 14.10** The kinetic energy of an electron emitted during photoemission is equal to the difference between the incident photon's energy and the work needed to overcome the work function for the surface.

One of the most successful experiments to investigate the photoelectric effect was conducted by American physicist Robert Millikan (Figure 14.11) and published in 1916. The main result from Millikan's work is given in Figure 14.12. The graph shows electron kinetic energy as a function of the frequency of the incident light. When the light frequency is

▲ **Figure 14.11** Robert Andrews Millikan (1868–1953) was awarded the Nobel Prize in physics in 1923 for his work on determining the charge of an electron, and for his work on the photoelectric effect. Despite his important work on the photoelectric effect, Millikan remained deeply skeptical of Einstein's particle view of light.

e MATH

Millikan graphed the kinetic energy of the photoelectons as a function of the incident frequency. To explore this relationship closer and to plot a graph like the one shown in Figure 14.12, visit www.pearsoned.com/school/physicssource.

below the threshold frequency, no electrons are ejected. When the light frequency equals the threshold frequency, electrons are ejected but with zero kinetic energy. The threshold frequency is therefore the *x*-intercept on the graph.

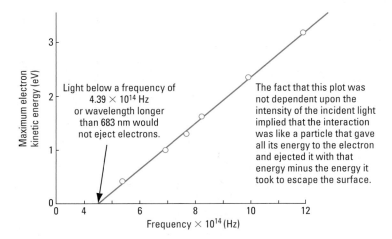

Light below a frequency of 4.39×10^{14} Hz or wavelength longer than 683 nm would not eject electrons.

The fact that this plot was not dependent upon the intensity of the incident light implied that the interaction was like a particle that gave all its energy to the electron and ejected it with that energy minus the energy it took to escape the surface.

▲ **Figure 14.12** A graph based on the 1916 paper in which Millikan presented the data from his investigation of the photoelectric effect

PHYSICS INSIGHT

$$E_k = hf - W$$
and
$$y = mx + b$$
Therefore,
$$x_{int} = f_0$$
and
$$y_{int} = -W$$

PHYSICS INSIGHT

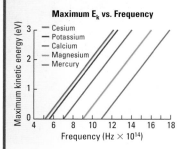

Maximum E_k vs. Frequency
— Cesium
— Potassium
— Calcium
— Magnesium
— Mercury

Different metals have different threshold frequencies, as shown in this graph. Which metal has the highest threshold frequency?

Once the frequency of the light exceeds the threshold frequency, photoemission begins. As the light frequency increases, the kinetic energy of the electrons increases proportionally. You can express this relationship in a formula by using the law of conservation of energy. The energy of the electron emitted by the surface is equal to the difference between the original energy of the photon, given by $E = hf$, minus the work needed to free the electron from the surface. The equation that expresses this relationship is

$$E_k = hf - W$$

where E_k is the maximum kinetic energy of the electrons and W is the work function of the metal. You may recall that this equation is an example of the straight-line relationship $y = mx + b$, where m is the slope of the line and b is the *y*-intercept. The graph in Figure 14.12 shows the linear relationship between the frequency of the incident light falling on a sodium metal surface and the maximum kinetic energy of the electrons emitted by the metal. The slope of this line shows that the energy of the photons is directly proportional to their frequency, and the proportionality constant is none other than Planck's constant. Millikan's photoelectric experiment provides an experimental way to measure Planck's constant. The *y*-intercept of this graph represents the negative of the work function of the photosensitive surface. The work function can also be determined by measuring the threshold frequency of photons required to produce photoemission of electrons from the metal.

Even though classical physics could not explain the photoelectric effect, this phenomenon still obeys the fundamental principle of conservation of energy, where $E_{\text{Total}_{\text{initial}}} = E_{\text{Total}_{\text{final}}}$. The energy of the photon is completely transferred to the electron and can be expressed by the following equation:

$$hf = W + E_k$$

Another way to interpret this equation is that the energy of the photon liberates the electron from the photosensitive surface, and any remaining energy appears as the electron's kinetic energy.

Stopping Potentials and Measuring the Kinetic Energy of Photoelectrons

How did Millikan determine the maximum kinetic energy of electrons emitted by a metal surface? Figure 14.13 shows a highly simplified version of his experimental set-up. An evacuated tube contains a photo-electron-emitting metal surface and a metal plate, called the collector. A power supply is connected to the collector and the electron-emitting metal surface. When the power supply gives the collector plate a positive charge, the ammeter registers an electric current as soon as the incoming photons reach the threshold frequency. Any electrons emitted by the metal surface are attracted to the collector and charge begins to move in the apparatus, creating a current.

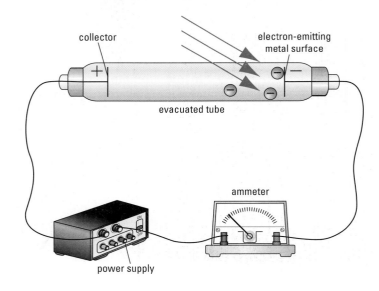

◀ **Figure 14.13** A simplified diagram depicting an experimental set-up used to investigate the photoelectric effect. When the power supply is connected as shown, the ammeter measures a current whenever the frequency of the incoming light exceeds the threshold frequency for the metal surface.

e SIM

Find out more about the photoelectric effect by doing this simulation. Follow the eSim links at www.pearsoned.ca/school/physicssource.

Now consider what happens if the collector plate is given a negative charge. Instead of being attracted toward the collector, electrons now experience an electric force directed away from the collector. This electric force does work on the photoelectron (Figure 14.14). Photoelectrons will arrive at the collector only if they leave the metal surface with enough kinetic energy to reach the collector.

You can express the final kinetic energy of the electrons in the following way:

$$E_{k_{final}} = E_{k_{initial}} - \Delta E$$

where $E_{k_{final}}$ is the final kinetic energy of the electron, $E_{k_{initial}}$ is its initial kinetic energy, and ΔE is the work done by the electric force.

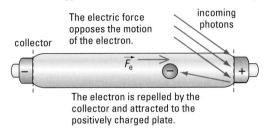

▲ **Figure 14.14** When the charges on the plates are reversed, the photoelectrons are repelled by the negatively charged collector and pulled back toward the positively charged plate. Only the most energetic electrons will reach the negative plate.

In Chapter 11, you saw that the work done in an electric field of potential V on a charge q is expressed by the equation $\Delta E = qV$. The final kinetic energy of an electron arriving at the collector can now be written as $E_{k_{final}} = E_{k_{initial}} - qV$, where q represents the charge of an electron. If the negative potential on the collector plate is increased, then eventually a point will be reached at which no electrons will be able to reach the collector. At this point, the current in the ammeter drops to zero and the potential difference is now equal to the **stopping potential**. In summary, the current drops to zero when $0 \leq E_{k_{max}} - qV_{stopping}$. The maximum kinetic energy of electrons may now be expressed as

$$E_{k_{max}} = qV_{stopping}$$

where $V_{stopping}$ is the stopping potential and q is the charge of the electron.

stopping potential: the potential difference for which the kinetic energy of a photoelectron equals the work needed to move through a potential difference, V

Example 14.4

Blue light shines on the metal surface shown in Figure 14.13 and causes photoemission of electrons. If a stopping potential of 2.6 V is required to completely prevent electrons from reaching the collector, determine the maximum kinetic energy of the electrons. Express your answer in units of joules and electron volts.

Given
$$V_{stopping} = 2.6 \text{ V}$$
$$q = 1.60 \times 10^{-19} \text{ C}$$

Required
maximum kinetic energy of electrons ($E_{k_{max}}$)

Practice Problems

1. What stopping potential will stop electrons of energy 5.3×10^{-19} J?

2. Convert 5.3×10^{-19} J to electron volts.

3. What is the maximum kinetic energy of electrons stopped by a potential of 3.1 V?

Analysis and Solution

Use the equation $E_{k_{max}} = qV_{stopping}$.

$$E_{k_{max}} = (1.60 \times 10^{-19} \text{ C})(2.6 \text{ V})$$
$$= 4.2 \times 10^{-19} \text{ J}$$
$$= 2.6 \text{ eV}$$

Paraphrase

A stopping potential of 2.6 V will stop electrons of kinetic energy 4.2×10^{-19} J or 2.6 eV.

Answers

1. 3.3 V
2. 3.3 eV
3. 3.1 eV or 5.0×10^{-19} J

Concept Check

Show that the idea of stopping potential can lead directly to the expression $h = \dfrac{qV_{stopping} + W}{f_0}$, where h is Planck's constant, $V_{stopping}$ is the stopping potential, W is the work function, and f_0 is the threshold frequency for emission of electrons from a metal surface.

14-3 *Design a Lab*

Using the Photoelectric Effect to Measure Planck's Constant

The Question

How can you use the photoelectric effect and the concept of stopping potential to determine Planck's constant?

Design and Conduct Your Investigation

You will need to decide on what equipment to assemble to enable you to relate frequency of incident light to kinetic energy of electrons and stopping potentials. In your design, be sure to address what you will need to measure and what variables will be involved, how to record and analyze your data, and how to use the data collected to answer the question. Prepare a research proposal for your teacher to determine whether your school laboratory has the necessary equipment for this lab, or if alternative approaches may work. Your proposal should include a worked-out sample of how the data you hope to collect will answer the question. Remember to work safely, to clearly identify tasks, and to designate which group members are responsible for each task.

The following example shows how to relate the concepts of threshold frequency and work function.

Example 14.5

Experiments show that the work function for cesium metal is 2.10 eV. Determine the threshold frequency and wavelength for photons capable of producing photoemission from cesium.

Given
$W = 2.10$ eV

Required
threshold frequency (f_0)
wavelength (λ)

Analysis and Solution
The work function is the amount of energy needed to just break the photoelectron free from the metal surface, but not give it any additional kinetic energy. Therefore, from $E_k = hf - W$, for threshold frequency, f_0, set $E_k = 0$ J.

First convert the work function to units of joules.

$$W = (2.10 \; \cancel{eV})\left(1.60 \times 10^{-19} \; \frac{J}{\cancel{eV}}\right)$$

$$= 3.36 \times 10^{-19} \; J$$

Now solve for the threshold frequency.

$$0 = hf_0 - W$$

$$f_0 = \frac{W}{h}$$

$$= \frac{3.36 \times 10^{-19} \; \cancel{J}}{6.63 \times 10^{-34} \; \cancel{J} \cdot s}$$

$$= 5.07 \times 10^{14} \; Hz$$

From $c = f\lambda$, the wavelength of this photon is

$$\lambda = \frac{c}{f}$$

$$= \frac{3.00 \times 10^8 \; \frac{m}{\cancel{s}}}{5.07 \times 10^{14} \; \cancel{s}^{-1}}$$

$$= 5.92 \times 10^{-7} \; m$$

$$= 592 \; nm$$

Paraphrase
The threshold frequency for photons able to cause photoemission from cesium metal is 5.07×10^{14} Hz. This frequency corresponds to photons of wavelength 592 nm, which is in the yellow-orange part of the visible spectrum.

You can also use the law of conservation of energy equation for the photoelectric effect to predict the energy and velocity of the electrons released during photoemission.

Example 14.6

Using Table 14.1, determine the maximum speed of electrons emitted from an aluminium surface if the surface is illuminated with 125-nm ultraviolet (UV) light.

Given
$\lambda = 125$ nm
metal = aluminium

Required
maximum speed of electrons (v)

Analysis and Solution
From Table 14.1, the work function for aluminium is 4.08 eV. Convert this value to joules.

$$W = 4.08 \text{ eV}$$
$$= (4.08 \text{ eV})\left(1.60 \times 10^{-19} \, \frac{\text{J}}{\text{eV}}\right)$$
$$= 6.53 \times 10^{-19} \text{ J}$$

To determine the energy of the incident photon, use the equation $E = hf = h\left(\dfrac{c}{\lambda}\right)$.

Incident photon energy is

$$E = h\left(\frac{c}{\lambda}\right)$$
$$= (6.63 \times 10^{-34} \text{ J} \cdot \text{s})\left(\frac{3.00 \times 10^8 \, \frac{\text{m}}{\text{s}}}{1.25 \times 10^{-7} \, \text{m}}\right)$$
$$= 1.59 \times 10^{-18} \text{ J}$$

To find the kinetic energy of the electrons, use the law of conservation of energy equation for the photoelectric effect, $E_k = hf - W$. Kinetic energy of the electron is

$$E_k = hf - W$$
$$= 15.9 \times 10^{-19} \text{ J} - 6.53 \times 10^{-19} \text{ J}$$
$$= 9.37 \times 10^{-19} \text{ J}$$

Finally, use $E_k = \dfrac{1}{2}mv^2$ to solve for speed. Recall that an electron has a mass of 9.11×10^{-31} kg.

The electron's speed is

$$v = \sqrt{\frac{2E_k}{m}}$$
$$= \sqrt{\frac{2(9.37 \times 10^{-19} \text{ J})}{9.11 \times 10^{-31} \text{ kg}}}$$
$$= 1.43 \times 10^6 \text{ m/s}$$

Paraphrase
The electrons emitted from the aluminium surface will have a maximum speed of 1.43×10^6 m/s.

Practice Problems

1. A photoelectron is emitted with a kinetic energy of 2.1 eV. How fast is the electron moving?

2. What is the kinetic energy of a photoelectron emitted from a cesium surface when the surface is illuminated with 400-nm light?

3. What is the maximum speed of the electron described in question 2?

Answers

1. 8.6×10^5 m/s

2. 1.0 eV

3. 5.9×10^5 m/s

Millikan's work on the photoelectric effect provided critical evidence in eventually demonstrating the particle or quantized nature of light. As you will see in the next chapter, Millikan also performed a key experiment that demonstrated the discrete or "quantized" nature of electrical charge: He showed that the electron is the smallest unit of electrical charge.

14.2 Check and Reflect

Knowledge

1. What is the energy, in eV, of a 400-nm photon?

2. Explain how the concepts of work function and threshold frequency are related.

3. What is the threshold frequency for cadmium? (Consult Table 14.1.)

4. Will a 500-nm photon cause the emission of an electron from a cesium metal surface? Explain why or why not.

5. What stopping voltage is needed to stop an electron of kinetic energy 1.25 eV?

6. Explain how stopping potential is related to the maximum kinetic energy of an electron.

7. True or false? The greater the intensity of the light hitting a metal surface, the greater the stopping potential required to stop photoelectrons. Explain your answer.

Applications

The following data are taken from an experiment in which the maximum kinetic energy of photoelectrons is related to the wavelength of the photons hitting a metal surface. Use these data to answer the following questions.

Wavelength (nm)	Kinetic Energy (eV)
500	0.36
490	0.41
440	0.70
390	1.05
340	1.52
290	2.14
240	3.025

8. Convert the wavelengths given in the data table to frequency units and graph them along with the kinetic energy of the photoelectrons. Be sure to plot frequency on the horizontal axis.

9. Give the value of the slope of the graph that you just drew. What is the significance of this value?

10. What metal do you think was used in the previous example? Justify your answer.

Extensions

11. Explain how the photon model of light correctly predicts that the maximum kinetic energy of electrons emitted from a metal surface does not depend on the intensity of light hitting the metal surface.

12. In several paragraphs, identify three common devices that use the photoelectric effect. Be sure to explain in what way these devices use the photoelectric effect.

13. How long would photoemission take from a classical physics point of view? Consider a beam of ultraviolet light with a brightness of 2.0×10^{-6} W and an area of 1.0×10^{-4} m^2 (about the area of your little fingernail) falling on a zinc metal plate. Use 3.5 eV as the energy that must be absorbed before photoemission can occur.
(Hint: Estimate the area of an atom and determine how much of the beam of UV light is being absorbed each second, on average.)

 *e*TEST

To check your understanding of the photoelectric effect, follow the eTest links at www.pearsoned.ca/school/physicssource.

14.3 The Compton Effect

Although Einstein's photon model provided an explanation of the photo-electric effect, many physicists remained skeptical. The wave model of light was so successful at explaining most of the known properties of light, it seemed reasonable to expect that a purely classical explanation of the photoelectric effect would eventually be found. In 1923, however, an experiment by American physicist Arthur Compton (Figure 14.15) provided an even clearer example of the particle nature of light, and finally convinced most physicists that the photon model of light had validity.

Compton studied the way in which electrons scattered X rays in a block of graphite. The X rays were observed to scatter in all directions. This effect was not surprising: Both the wave and particle models of light predicted this outcome. What the wave model could neither predict nor explain, however, was the small change in wavelength that Compton observed in the scattered X ray, and the relationship between the change in wavelength and the angle through which the X ray was scattered. The scattering of an X ray by an electron is now referred to as **Compton scattering**, and the change in wavelength of the scattered X-ray photon is called the **Compton effect** (Figure 14.16).

To understand the Compton effect, you will need to use two of the most central ideas of physics: the law of conservation of momentum and the law of conservation of energy. The interaction between an X-ray photon and an electron must still obey these laws.

By using the particle model of light and Einstein's mass-equivalence equation $E = mc^2$, Compton showed that the momentum of the X ray could be expressed as

$$p = \frac{h}{\lambda}$$

where p is momentum, h is Planck's constant, and λ is the wavelength of the X ray. Compton was also able to show exactly how the change in wavelength of the scattered X ray is related to the angle through which the X-ray photon is scattered.

Concept Check

Which of the following photons has the greater momentum: $\lambda_A = 500$ nm or $\lambda_B = 2$ nm? Explain your reasoning.

Compton found that the scattered X ray changed its momentum and energy in a way that was exactly what you would expect if it was a small particle undergoing an elastic collision with an electron. Recall from Chapter 9 that energy and momentum are conserved during an elastic collision.

▲ **Figure 14.15** Arthur Holly Compton (1892–1962) was a pioneer in high-energy physics. He was awarded the Nobel Prize in 1927 for his discovery of the Compton effect, which provided convincing evidence for the photon model of light.

Compton scattering: the scattering of an X ray by an electron

Compton effect: the change in wavelength of the scattered X-ray photon

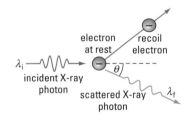

▲ **Figure 14.16** When an electron scatters an X ray, both momentum and energy are conserved. Compton scattering behaves like an elastic collision between a photon and an electron.

The laws of conservation of energy and of momentum can be applied to the X ray and the electron in the following way:

- The total momentum of the incident X-ray photon must equal the total momentum of the scattered X ray and the scattered electron.
- The total energy of the incident X-ray photon and the electron must equal the total energy of the scattered X ray and the scattered electron.

Concept Check

Study Figure 14.16. Define the direction of the incident X-ray photon as the positive x-direction and the upward direction as the positive y-direction. Suppose the incident X-ray photon has a wavelength of λ_i and the scattered X-ray photon has a wavelength λ_f.

1. Derive an expression for the x and y components of the momentum of the scattered photon.
2. Explain how your answer to question 1 gives you the x and y components of the electron's momentum.
3. How much energy was transferred to the electron in this interaction? Derive a simple expression for the electron's final energy.

Compton derived the following relationship between the change in the wavelength of the scattered photon and the direction in which the scattered photon travels:

$$\Delta\lambda = \lambda_f - \lambda_i$$
$$= \frac{h}{mc}(1 - \cos\theta)$$

where m is the mass of the scattering electron and θ is the angle through which the X ray scatters. The full derivation of this equation requires applying Einstein's theory of relativity and a lot of algebra! The central concepts behind this equation, however, are simply the laws of conservation of energy and of momentum. As well, this equation is exactly consistent with Einstein's idea that the X-ray photon collides with the electron as if it were a particle.

MINDS ON — Heisenberg's Microscope Problem

Suggest how Compton scattering shows that it is impossible to "see" an electron. In particular, why is it that we can only see where an electron was and not where it is?

(Hint: Think about what photons are doing when you look at something.) This question is sometimes referred to as Heisenberg's microscope problem.

Example 14.7

What is the maximum change in wavelength that a 0.010-nm X-ray photon can undergo by Compton scattering with an electron? Does initial wavelength (0.010 nm) matter in this example?

Given
$\lambda_i = 0.010$ nm

Required
change in wavelength ($\Delta\lambda$)

Analysis and Solution
Maximum change will occur when the X ray is scattered by the greatest possible amount, that is, when the X ray is *back-scattered*. From the Compton effect equation,

$\Delta\lambda = \lambda_f - \lambda_i = \dfrac{h}{mc}(1 - \cos\theta)$, the maximum value for

$\Delta\lambda$ occurs when the term $(1 - \cos\theta)$ is a maximum. This occurs when $\theta = 180°$ and $\cos\theta = -1$, so $(1 - \cos\theta)$ becomes $(1 - (-1)) = 2$. Use this relation to determine the largest possible change in wavelength of the scattered X-ray photon.

$$\Delta\lambda = \dfrac{h}{mc}(1 - \cos\theta)$$

$$= \dfrac{2h}{mc}$$

$$= \dfrac{2(6.63 \times 10^{-34} \text{ J·s})}{(9.11 \times 10^{-31} \text{ kg})(3.00 \times 10^8 \text{ m/s})}$$

$$= 4.85 \times 10^{-12} \text{ m}$$

Paraphrase
The maximum change in wavelength of a photon during Compton scattering is only 4.85×10^{-12} m. This change is independent of the initial wavelength of the photon.

Practice Problems

1. What is the energy of an X ray of wavelength 10 nm?

2. What is the momentum of an X ray of wavelength 10 nm?

3. If a 10-nm X ray scattered by an electron becomes an 11-nm X ray, how much energy does the electron gain?

Answers
1. 2.0×10^{-17} J
2. 6.6×10^{-26} N·s
3. 1.8×10^{-18} J

You can also use the Compton equation to determine the final wavelength of a photon after scattering, as you will see in the next example.

Example 14.8

An X-ray photon of wavelength 0.0500 nm scatters at an angle of 30°. Calculate the wavelength of the scattered photon.

Given
$\lambda_i = 0.0500$ nm
$\theta = 30°$

Required
final wavelength (λ_f)

Analysis and Solution
Rearrange the Compton equation to solve for final wavelength. Recall that the mass of an electron is 9.11×10^{-31} kg.

$$\Delta\lambda = \lambda_f - \lambda_i$$

$$= \frac{h}{mc}(1 - \cos\theta)$$

$$\lambda_f = \lambda_i + \Delta\lambda$$

$$= \lambda_i + \frac{h}{mc}(1 - \cos\theta)$$

$$= 0.0500 \text{ nm} + \frac{6.63 \times 10^{-34} \text{ J·s}}{(9.11 \times 10^{-31} \text{ kg})(3.00 \times 10^8 \text{ m/s})}(1 - \cos 30°)$$

$$= 0.0500 \text{ nm} + 0.000\ 325 \text{ nm}$$

$$= 0.0503 \text{ nm}$$

Paraphrase
The X-ray photon changes wavelength by 0.0003 nm to become a photon of wavelength 0.0503 nm.

Practice Problem

1. An X ray of wavelength 0.010 nm scatters at 90° from an electron. What is the wavelength of the scattered photon?

Answer

1. 0.012 nm

For many physicists, the Compton effect provided the final piece of evidence they needed to finally accept Einstein's idea of the particle nature of light. The Compton effect also describes one of the most fundamental phenomena — the interaction of light with matter.

14.3 Check and Reflect

Knowledge

1. What is the momentum of a 500-nm photon?

2. Photon A has a wavelength three times longer than photon B. Which photon has the greatest momentum and by what factor?

3. A photon has a momentum of 6.00×10^{-21} kg·m/s. What is the wavelength and energy of this photon?

4. Identify the part of the electromagnetic spectrum of the photon in question 3.

5. True or false? One of the major differences between classical physics and quantum physics is that the laws of conservation of energy and momentum do not always work for quantum physics. Explain your answer.

Applications

6. What is the wavelength of a 100-keV X-ray photon?

7. An X-ray photon of wavelength 0.010 nm strikes a helium nucleus and bounces straight back. If the helium nucleus was originally at rest, calculate its velocity after interacting with the X ray.

Extension

8. In order to see an object, it is necessary to illuminate it with light whose wavelength is smaller than the object itself. According to the Compton effect, why is illumination a problem if you wish to see a small particle, such as a proton or an electron?

 e **TEST**

To check your understanding of the Compton effect, follow the eTest links at www.pearsoned.ca/school/physicssource.

14.4 Matter Waves and the Power of Symmetric Thinking

If waves (light) can sometimes act like particles (photons), then why couldn't particles, such as electrons, sometimes act like waves? Louis de Broglie (pronounced "de Broy") (Figure 14.17), a young French Ph.D. student, explored this question in 1924 in a highly imaginative and perplexing thesis. The idea seemed so strange that despite no obvious errors in his argument, the examining committee was reluctant to pass de Broglie. Fortunately, a copy of his thesis was sent to Albert Einstein, who recognized at once the merit in de Broglie's hypothesis. Not only was de Broglie awarded his Ph.D., but his hypothesis turned out to be correct!

De Broglie's argument is essentially one of symmetry. As both the photoelectric effect and the Compton effect show, light has undeniable particle-like, as well as wave-like, properties. This dichotomy is called the **wave-particle duality**. In reality, light is neither a wave nor a particle. These ideas are classical physics ideas, but experiments were revealing subtle and strange results. What light is depends on how we interact with it. De Broglie's hypothesis completes the symmetry by stating that what we naturally assume to be particles (electrons, for example) can have wave-like properties as well. At the atomic level, an electron is neither a wave nor a particle. What an electron is depends on how we interact with it.

De Broglie arrived at his idea by tying together the concepts of momentum and wavelength. Using Compton's discovery relating momentum and wavelength for X-ray photons, de Broglie argued that anything that possessed momentum also had a wavelength. His idea can be expressed in a very simple form:

$$\lambda = \frac{h}{p}$$

where h is Planck's constant, p is momentum, and λ is de Broglie's wavelength.

De Broglie's Wave Equation Works for Both Light and Electrons

De Broglie's hypothesis states that anything that has momentum must obey the following wavelength-momentum equations:

For light: Maxwell's law of electromagnetism shows that the momentum of a light wave can be written as $p = \frac{E}{c}$, where E is the energy of the light and c is the speed of light. But Planck's formula states that $E = hf$. Therefore, $p = \frac{hf}{c}$. Substituting this equation into de Broglie's wave

▲ **Figure 14.17**   Louis de Broglie (1892–1987) was the first physicist to predict the existence of matter waves.

wave-particle duality: light has both wave-like and particle-like properties

Project LINK

How important is de Broglie's hypothesis to our current understanding of the nature of light and matter?

equation, you obtain $\lambda = \dfrac{h}{\dfrac{hf}{c}} = \dfrac{c}{f}$, which is the wavelength-frequency

relation. It tells you that a photon of light has a wavelength!

For electrons: If an electron is moving with a velocity, *v*, that is *much less than the speed of light*, then its momentum is $p = mv$ and de Broglie's

relationship is $\lambda = \dfrac{h}{p} = \dfrac{h}{mv}$. For electrons (or any other particles)

moving at velocities approaching the speed of light, the expression

$\lambda = \dfrac{h}{p}$ is still applicable.

THEN, NOW, AND FUTURE   The Electron Microscope

The Electron Microscope

The idea of matter waves is not simply abstract physics that has no practical application. The wave nature of electrons has been used to build microscopes capable of amazing magnification.

The reason for their amazing magnification lies in the extremely small wavelengths associated with electrons. The usable magnification of a microscope depends inversely on the wavelength used to form the image. In a transmission electron microscope (TEM, Figure 14.18), a series of magnets (magnetic lenses) focusses a beam of electrons and passes the beam through a thin slice of the specimen being imaged.

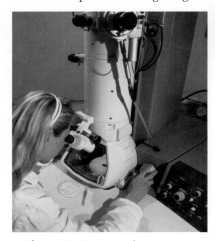

▲ **Figure 14.18**   A modern transmission electron microscope

Modern TEMs are capable of reaching very high magnification and imaging at the atomic level.

The scanning electron microscope (SEM) is similar to the TEM but differs in one important way: Electrons are reflected off the sample being imaged. SEM images have a remarkable three-dimensional appearance (Figure 14.19).

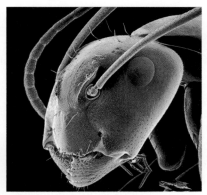

▲ **Figure 14.19**   An SEM view of an ant's head

Questions

1. Find out more about the varieties of electron microscopes in use. Search the Internet, using key words such as electron microscope, TEM, or SEM, to learn about at least three different kinds of electron microscopes. Summarize your findings in the following way:

- name (type) of microscope
- how it differs from other electron microscopes in use and operation
- typical applications and magnifications

2. The magnification of a microscope depends inversely on the wavelength used to image a specimen. The very best quality light microscopes typically have maximum magnifications of 1000 to 4000 times. Modern TEMs use electrons accelerated to energies of over 100 keV to observe specimens. Estimate the possible range of magnifications that can be achieved using a TEM by considering the following:

- What is a reasonable choice for the wavelength used in a light microscope?
- What is the wavelength of a 100-keV electron?
- How do the wavelengths of the light and of the electrons compare?

(Note: Your answer will likely be an overestimate. The actual magnification of electron microscopes is limited by the ability of the magnetic lenses to focus the electron beam. TEMs are capable of achieving magnifications as high as 500 000 times!)

The next two examples apply the de Broglie relationship between momentum and wavelength.

Example 14.9

What is the momentum of a 500-nm photon of green light?

Given
$\lambda = 500$ nm

Required
momentum (p)

Analysis and Solution
To find the photon's momentum, apply de Broglie's equation:

$$p = \frac{h}{\lambda}$$

$$= \frac{6.63 \times 10^{-34} \text{ J}\cdot\text{s}}{500 \times 10^{-9} \text{ m}}$$

$$= 1.33 \times 10^{-27} \text{ N}\cdot\text{s}$$

Paraphrase
The photon has a momentum of 1.33×10^{-27} N·s.

The next example shows how to calculate the wavelength of an electron, thus illustrating that particles have a wave nature.

Example 14.10

What is the wavelength of an electron moving at 1.00×10^4 m/s?

Given
$v = 1.00 \times 10^4$ m/s
$m_e = 9.11 \times 10^{-31}$ kg

Required
wavelength (λ)

Analysis and Solution
To find the electron's wavelength, first find its momentum and then rewrite de Broglie's equation:

$$mv = p = \frac{h}{\lambda}$$

$$\lambda = \frac{h}{mv}$$

$$= \frac{6.63 \times 10^{-34} \text{ J}\cdot\text{s}}{(9.11 \times 10^{-31} \text{ kg})(1.00 \times 10^4 \text{ m/s})}$$

$$= 7.28 \times 10^{-8} \text{ m} = 72.8 \text{ nm}$$

Paraphrase
The electron has a de Broglie wavelength of 7.28×10^{-8} m or 72.8 nm.

Practice Problem

1. What is the momentum of a 0.010-nm X ray?

Answer
1. 6.6×10^{-23} kg·m/s

e MATH

De Broglie showed how electrons can be thought of as waves and related the speed of an electron to its wavelength. Einstein's work showed that as the speed of the electron became greater than 10% of the speed of light, relativistic effects has to be taken into account (see Physics Insight p. 727) To explore how the wavelength of an electron is a function of its speed, including relativistic effects, visit www.pearsoned.ca/school/physicssource.

Practice Problems

1. What is the wavelength of a proton moving at 1.0×10^5 m/s?

2. What is the velocity of an electron that has a wavelength of 420 nm?

Answers
1. 4.0×10^{-12} m
2. 1.73×10^3 m/s

De Broglie's idea completes the concept of the wave-particle duality of light. Wave-particle duality combines two opposing ideas and teaches us that, at the atomic level, it is essential to use both ideas to accurately model the world.

De Broglie's Wave Hypothesis: Strange but True!

Experimental proof of de Broglie's hypothesis came very quickly and by accident. Between 1925 and 1927, American physicists C. J. Davisson and L. H. Germer, and British physicist G. P. Thomson (Figure 14.20, son of J. J. Thomson, discoverer of the electron) independently provided evidence that electrons can act like waves.

The original Davisson and Germer experiment was an investigation of how electrons scattered after hitting different kinds of metallic surfaces. To prevent an oxide layer from contaminating the surfaces, the scattering was done inside a vacuum tube. In one test on a nickel surface, the vacuum tube cracked and the vacuum was lost, unbeknownst to Davisson and Germer. The nickel surface oxidized into a crystalline pattern. What Davisson and Germer observed was a very puzzling pattern: Scattering occurred in some directions and not in others. It was reminiscent of a pattern of nodes and antinodes (Figure 14.21). A simplified version of a typical Davisson–Germer experiment is shown in Figure 14.22(a). The graph in Figure 14.22(b) shows the kind of data that Davisson and Germer found.

▲ **Figure 14.20** George Paget Thomson (1892–1975) was co-discoverer of matter waves with Davisson and Germer. One of the great ironies of physics is that Thomson played an instrumental role in showing that electrons can act like waves. Thirty years earlier, his father had shown that the electron was a particle!

 MINDS ON | **Interpret the Graph**

(a) Look at the graph in Figure 14.22(b). Explain why it makes sense to interpret the pattern as one of nodes and antinodes. What is happening at each of the nodes?
(b) What would you have to do to charge the wavelength of the elcetrons used in an electron differaction experiment?

When Davisson and Germer began their experiments, they were unaware of de Broglie's work. As soon as they learned of de Broglie's hypothesis, however, they realized that they had observed electron-wave interference! Over the next two years, they and G. P. Thomson in Scotland refined the study of electron-wave interference and provided beautiful experimental confirmation of de Broglie's hypothesis. In 1937, Davisson and Thomson received a Nobel Prize for the discovery of "matter waves."

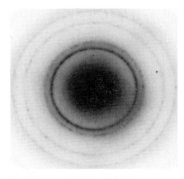

▲ **Figure 14.21** This image was produced by electrons scattered by gold atoms on the surface of a thin gold film. The bright concentric rings are antinodes produced by the constructive interference of electron waves.

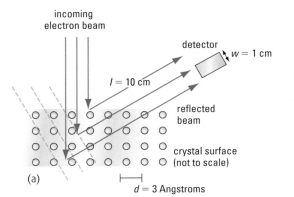

(a)

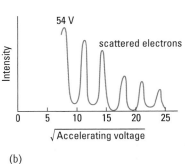

(b)

◀ **Figure 14.22** (a) A schematic of a typical Davisson–Germer experiment in which atoms on the surface of a metal scatter a beam of electrons. For specific angles, the electrons scatter constructively and the detector records a large number of electrons, shown in the graph in (b). (b) In this graph, a high intensity means that more electrons are scattered in that direction, creating an antinode, or constructive interference. Similarly, a low intensity can be interpreted as a node, or destructive interference.

Example 14.11

Explain conceptually how the wave properties of electrons could produce the interference pattern shown in Figure 14.21.

Given

You know that electrons have wavelike properties and that electrons are being scattered from atoms that are separated by distances comparable to the size of the electron wavelength.

Analysis

Figure 14.23 shows electron waves leaving from two different atomic scatterers. You can see that path 1 is a little longer than path 2, as denoted by the symbol δ. This difference means that a different number of electron wavelengths can fit along path 1 than along path 2. For example, if the path difference is $\frac{1}{2}\lambda$, $\frac{3}{2}\lambda$, or any odd half-multiple of λ, then, when the electron waves combine at the detector, a complete cancellation of the electron wave occurs, forming a node. On the other hand, if the path difference is a whole-number multiple of λ, then constructive interference occurs, forming an antinode. The Davisson–Germer experiment provided graphic evidence of the correctness of de Broglie's hypothesis.

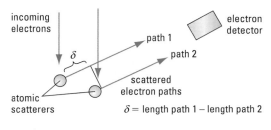

▲ **Figure 14.23**

De Broglie's Hypothesis — A Key Concept of Quantum Physics

Despite its simplicity, de Broglie's wave hypothesis heralded the true beginning of quantum physics. You will now explore two of the consequences that follow from de Broglie's equation.

De Broglie's Equation "Explains" Quantization of Energy

Imagine that you drop a small bead into a matchbox, close the matchbox, and then gently place the matchbox on a level tabletop. You then ask, "What is the kinetic energy of the bead?" The answer may seem obvious and not very interesting: The energy is 0 J because the bead is not moving. If, however, you could shrink the box down to the size of a molecule and replace the bead with a single electron, the situation becomes very different. You can sometimes model molecules as simple boxes. The particle-in-a-box model shows how the wave nature of electrons (and all other particles) predicts the idea of quantization of energy.

From a quantum point of view, explain why it becomes problematic to put a particle in a box.

In Chapter 8, section 8.3, you learned about standing waves and resonance. These concepts apply to all waves. Because an electron behaves like a wave as well as like a particle, it has a wavelength, so the ideas of resonance and standing waves also apply to the electron.

In order to fit a wave into a box, or finite space, the wave must have a node at each end of the box, and its wavelength must be related to the length of the box in the following way:

$$\lambda_n = \frac{2L}{n}$$

where n is a whole number ($n = 1, 2, 3, ...$). Since there is a node at each end of the box, you can think of n as equivalent to the number of half-wavelengths that can fit in the space L, or length of the box (Figure 14.24). The longest possible standing wave that can fit into the box has a wavelength of $\lambda = 2L$, where $n = 1$.

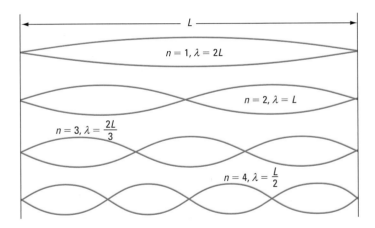

▲ **Figure 14.24** Standing wave patterns for waves trapped inside a box of length L

Because the electron is a standing wave, it cannot be at rest. Consequently, it must have a minimum amount of kinetic energy:

$$E_k = \frac{1}{2}mv^2 \times \frac{m}{m}$$

$$= \frac{m^2v^2}{2m}$$

$$= \frac{p^2}{2m} \qquad \text{since } p = mv$$

where p is the momentum and m is the mass of the electron. Recall that de Broglie's equation shows that the momentum of an electron is inversely related to its wavelength: $\lambda = \frac{h}{p}$.

The particle-in-a-box
model is very useful. It
can be used to describe
such diverse phenomena
as small-chain molecules,
tiny nano-scale electronics,
and the nucleus of an
atom. Depending on the
situation, the "box" can
have one dimension (for
a long-chain molecule),
two, or three dimensions.
Models and modelling
form an essential part
of the physicist's
imaginative "toolbox."

Using de Broglie's equation to relate the momentum of the electron to the length of the box, you can then write:

$$E_k = \frac{p^2}{2m}$$

$$= \frac{\left(\frac{h}{\lambda}\right)^2}{2m}$$

$$= \frac{h^2}{2m\lambda^2}$$

From $\lambda_n = \frac{2L}{n}$, when $n = 1$, $\lambda = 2L$. Therefore,

$$E_k = \frac{h^2}{2m(2L)^2}$$

$$= \frac{h^2}{8mL^2}$$

This equation represents the minimum kinetic energy of an electron.

What if you wanted to give the electron more energy? To have more energy, the electron must have the right momentum-wavelength relation to fit the next standing wave pattern (Figure 14.24). The electron's wavelength is, therefore,

$$\lambda_{n=2} = \frac{2L}{2} = L$$

Substituting into the equation for the kinetic energy of the electron,

$$E_{n=2} = \frac{p^2}{2m} = \frac{h^2}{2m(L)^2} = \frac{h^2}{2mL^2} = 4E_{n=1}$$

The energy of a particle in a box is given by the general formula

$$E_n = \frac{n^2 h^2}{8mL^2}, \, n = 1, 2, 3, \ldots$$

These equations demonstrate that energy is quantized for the particle-in-a-box model. As with photons, quantization means that the electron can have only specific amounts or quanta of energy. (Refer to section 14.1.)

Example 14.12

Nanotechnology is one of the hottest areas in physics today. It is now possible to create tiny electric circuits in which electrons behave like particles in a box. Imagine an electron confined to a tiny strip 5.0 nm long. What are three possible energies that the electron could have?

Given
$L = 5.0$ nm
$n = 1, 2, 3$

Required
electron energies (E_1, E_2, E_3)

Practice Problems

1. What is the maximum wavelength for an electron confined to a box of length $L = 1.0$ nm?

2. How much momentum does the electron in question 1 have?

Analysis and Solution

$$E_n = \frac{n^2h^2}{8mL^2}, \; n = 1, 2, 3, \ldots$$

Substitute $n = 1$ into the expression for energy:

$$E_1 = \frac{(1^2)h^2}{8mL^2}$$

$$= \frac{(1)(6.63 \times 10^{-34} \text{ J·s})^2}{8(9.11 \times 10^{-31} \text{ kg})(5.0 \times 10^{-9} \text{ m})^2}$$

$$= 2.4 \times 10^{-21} \text{ J}$$

Calculate any other energy by noting that

$$E_n = n^2 \frac{h^2}{8mL^2} = n^2E_1$$

$$E_2 = (2)^2 \, E_1 = 4(2.4 \times 10^{-21} \text{ J}) = 9.6 \times 10^{-21} \text{ J}$$

$$E_3 = (3)^2 \, E_1 = 9(2.4 \times 10^{-21} \text{ J}) = 2.2 \times 10^{-20} \text{ J}$$

$$E_n = n^2(2.4 \times 10^{-21} \text{ J})$$

Paraphrase

An electron confined to a space 5.0 nm long can only have energies that are whole-square multiples of 2.4×10^{-21} J. Three possible energies of the electron are, therefore, 2.4×10^{-21} J, 9.6×10^{-21} J, and 2.2×10^{-20} J.

3. What is the minimum energy that an electron can have when confined to a box of length $L = 1.0$ nm?

Answers

1. 2.0 nm
2. 3.3×10^{-25} kg·m/s
3. 6.0×10^{-20} J

Concept Check

Refer to Figure 14.24. What happens to the minimum possible energy of a particle in a box when you shrink the box? How would the minimum energy of particles in the nucleus of an atom (about 10^{-15} m across) compare to the minimum energy of an electron in the atom itself (about 10^{-10} m across)?

 MINDS ON **Planck in a Box**

Argue that the particle-in-a-box model illustrates Planck's discovery of quantization, and also demonstrates Planck's radiation law.

Heisenberg's Uncertainty Principle

▲ **Figure 14.25** Werner Heisenberg (1901–1976) was one of the most influential physicists of the 20th century and a key developer of modern quantum theory.

Consider what you have just learned about the minimum energy of a particle in a box. The smaller you make the box, the shorter is the wavelength of the particle. Furthermore, because wavelength and momentum are inversely related, the shorter the wavelength, the greater is the momentum of the particle. The greater the momentum, the faster, on average, the particle is moving at any instant.

In 1927, the young German physicist Werner Heisenberg (Figure 14.25) realized that the particle-in-a-box model of quantum mechanics has a troubling limitation built into it. Think of the size of the box as indicating the possible uncertainty in the location of the particle. The smaller the box is, the more precisely you know the location of the particle. At the same time, however, the smaller the box is, the greater the momentum and the greater the range of possible momentum values that the particle could have at any instant.

Figure 14.26 illustrates this idea by plotting the uncertainty in position of the particle, Δx (on the vertical axis), and the uncertainty in its momentum, Δp (on the horizontal axis), as strips that intersect. The shaded areas in Figure 14.26 represent the product of uncertainty in position (Δx) and uncertainty in momentum (Δp).

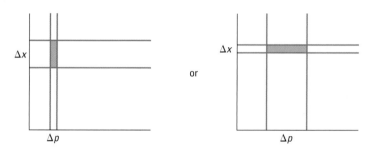

▲ **Figure 14.26** A graphical depiction of the uncertainty in both position and momentum for a particle in a box

Heisenberg's troubling finding was that, due to the wave nature of all particles, it is impossible to know both the position and momentum of a particle with unlimited precision *at the same time*. The more precisely you know one of these values, the less precisely you can know the other value.

To derive the formula for uncertainty in position and momentum of a particle, note that the length of the box is related to the wavelength of the particle:

$$\Delta x \approx \text{length of box} = L$$

$$\lambda = 2L \quad \text{(From } \lambda_n = \frac{2L}{n}, \lambda = 2L \text{ when } n = 1.\text{)}$$

$$\Delta x \approx \frac{\lambda}{2}$$

Similarly, from de Broglie's equation $\lambda = \dfrac{h}{p}$, the uncertainty in momentum is

$$\Delta p \approx \text{range in momentum} = \frac{h}{\lambda}$$

The product of uncertainty in position and uncertainty in momentum can be expressed as

$$\Delta x \Delta p \approx \left(\frac{\lambda}{2}\right)\left(\frac{h}{\lambda}\right)$$

$$\Delta x \Delta p \approx \frac{h}{2}$$

This formula represents **Heisenberg's uncertainty principle**. Note that the value of the product, $\dfrac{h}{2}$ (representing the shaded areas of the graphs in Figure 14.26), is constant. The symbol $\approx$ means that $\Delta x \Delta p$ is approximately $\dfrac{h}{2}$. A more sophisticated argument produces the following expression:

$$\Delta x \Delta p \geq \frac{h}{4\pi}$$

This version is a common form of Heisenberg's uncertainty principle. It tells you that the uncertainty in your knowledge of both the position and momentum of a particle must always be greater than some small, but non-zero, value. You can never know both of these quantities with certainty at the same time! This result was very troubling to many physicists, including Albert Einstein, because it suggests that, at the level of atoms and particles, the universe is governed by chance and the laws of probability.

De Broglie's matter-wave hypothesis and its confirmation by Davisson and Germer had an unsettling effect on physicists. Heisenberg's work represented a logical extension of these ideas and helped set the stage for the birth of modern quantum theory.

Heisenberg's uncertainty principle: It is impossible to know both the position and momentum of a particle with unlimited precision at the same time.

 MINDS ON | **Physics and Certainty**

Two physicists who were deeply troubled by de Broglie's, and especially Heisenberg's, work were Max Planck and Albert Einstein. Suggest why their reaction is ironic and why these discoveries were difficult for physicists to accept.

To help with your answer, consider the importance of precision in classical physics, and Einstein's famous quote concerning the uncertainty principle: "God does not play dice with the universe!"

Knowledge

1. What is the wavelength of an electron that is moving at 20 000 m/s?

2. Calculate the momentum of a 500-nm photon.

3. What is the uncertainty in momentum of a particle if you know its location to an uncertainty of 1.0 nm?

4. An electron is trapped within a sphere of diameter 2.5×10^{-12} m. What is the minimum uncertainty in the electron's momentum?

Applications

5. In your television set, an electron is accelerated through a potential difference of 21 000 V.

   (a) How much energy does the electron acquire?

   (b) What is the wavelength of an electron of this energy?

6. If an electron and a proton each have the same velocity, how do their wavelengths compare? Express your answer numerically as a ratio.

Extensions

7. According to classical physics, all atomic motion should cease at absolute zero. Is this state possible, according to quantum physics?

8. Derive the expression $E_n = \dfrac{n^2 h^2}{8mL^2}$, $n = 1, 2, 3, \ldots$ for the energy of a particle in a box, where m is the mass of the particle, L is the length of the box, and n is one of the possible quantum states. (Hint: Remember that the wavelength of the nth standing wave confined to a box of length L is $\lambda_n = \dfrac{2L}{n}$.)

e TEST

To check your understanding of matter waves and Heisenberg's uncertainty principle, follow the eTest links at www.pearsoned.ca/school/physicssource.

14.5 Coming to Terms with Wave-particle Duality and the Birth of Quantum Mechanics

These fifty years of conscious brooding have brought me no nearer to the question of "What are light quanta?" Nowadays every clod thinks he knows it, but he is mistaken.

Albert Einstein

The wave-particle duality represents a deep and troubling mystery. For some physicists, most notably Einstein, the duality was seen as a flaw in quantum theory itself. Others, including Bohr, learned to accept rather than understand the duality. In this section, we will opt to accept and work with the wave-particle duality.

14-4 QuickLab

The Two-slit Interference Experiment with Particles

Problem

To investigate the pattern that a stream of particles produces when passing through a pair of thin slits

Materials

marble
two-slit apparatus (see Figure 14.27)
graph paper (or plot on spreadsheet)

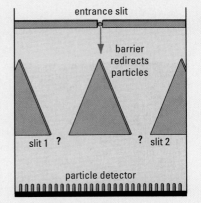

◀ **Figure 14.27**

Procedure

1 Place the two-slit apparatus on a level table surface and incline it by a small angle to allow the marble to roll down. Repeat this process 100 times.

2 Record your observations by noting how many times the marble lands in each bin.

3 Graph the results of your experiment by plotting the bin number along the horizontal axis and the number of times the marble landed in a given bin on the vertical axis.

Questions

1. Why is it important that the table surface be level for this experiment?

2. For 100 trials, how many times would you expect the marble to pass through slit 1? Did you observe this result? Explain.

3. Where did the marble land most of the time? Did you expect this result? Explain.

4. Where would you expect the marble to be found least often? Do your data support your answer?

5. Would the results of your experiment be improved by combining the data from all of the lab groups in the class? Explain.

The wave-particle duality of light presents us with many puzzles and paradoxes. Consider, for example, the famous two-slit interference experiment that Thomas Young used in 1801 to convince most physicists that light was a wave (see Chapter 13). This time, however, you are going to put a modern, quantum mechanical twist on the experiment. Since you know that light can behave as a particle (photons) and that particles can behave as matter waves (electrons), it does not matter what you choose to "shine" through the slits. Let us choose light, but reduce its intensity by inserting a filter so that only one photon at a time can enter the box (Figure 14.28). Let the light slowly expose a photographic film or enter the detector of your digital camera.

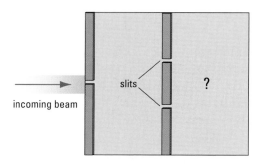

▲ **Figure 14.28** Young's double-slit experiment, modified such that the intensity of the beam entering the box is reduced to a level that allows only one photon at a time to enter

What will you observe? If you are impatient and let only a few photons through the slits, your result will be a random-looking scatter of dots where photons were absorbed by the film (Figure 14.29(a)). If you wait a little longer, the film will start to fill up (Figure 14.29(b)). Wait longer yet and something remarkable happens: You will see a two-slit interference pattern like the one in Figure 13.9 (Figure 14.29(c)). Why is this result so remarkable?

► **Figure 14.29** Three different results of the double-slit experiment. Image (a) shows the result of only a few photons being recorded. Image (b) shows the result of a few more photons, and image (c) shows the familiar double-slit interference pattern that forms when many photons are recorded.

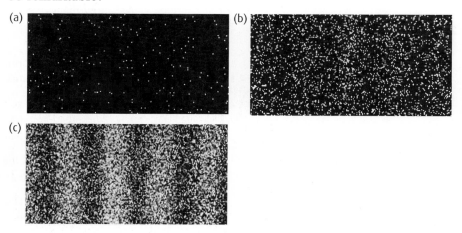

If light was *only* a wave, then the explanation would be that waves from the top slit in Figure 14.28 were slightly out of phase with waves from the bottom slit in some locations, causing nodes to form. In other places, the waves would combine in phase to produce antinodes. You arranged, however, to have only one photon at a time enter the apparatus. So, the photon would either go through the top slit or the bottom slit. But even a photon cannot be in two different places at once! If the photons can only go through one slit (either the top or bottom one), why does a two-slit interference pattern, such as the one shown in Figure 14.30, result? Even though the individual photons go through only one slit, they somehow "know" that there is another slit open somewhere else! American physicist Richard Feynman (Figure 14.31) often used this example to emphasize how strange the quantum world is.

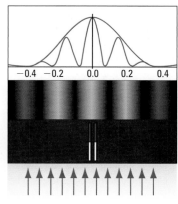

▲ **Figure 14.30** A two-slit interference pattern

▲ **Figure 14.31** Richard P. Feynman (1918–1988) was one of the founders of modern quantum theory. He once stated: "I think it is safe to say that no one understands quantum mechanics."

So what does it all mean? To try to understand the double-slit experiment as it applies to individual photons or electrons, it is useful to summarize the key points:

1. When the photon or electron is absorbed by the photographic film or the detector of your digital camera, it exhibits its *particle nature*.

2. The location where any one photon or electron is detected is random but distinct; that is, the photon or electron always arrives and is detected as a distinct particle.

3. Although the location of individual photons or electrons is random, the combined pattern that many photons form is the characteristic pattern of antinodes and nodes, as shown in Figure 14.30. This pattern shows the *wave nature* of the photons or electrons.

By the late 1920s, scientists developed a bold new interpretation of events. The wave-particle duality was showing that, at the level of atoms and molecules, the world was governed by the laws of probability and statistics. Although you cannot say much about what any one electron, for example, would do, you can make very precise predictions about the behaviour of very large numbers of electrons. In 1926, German physicist Max Born suggested that the *wave nature* of particles is best understood as a measure of the probability that the particle will be found at a particular location. The antinodes in the double-slit interference pattern exist because the particles have a high probability of being found at those locations after they pass through the double-slit apparatus. This measure of probability of a particle's

quantum indeterminacy: the probability of finding a particle at a particular location in a double-slit interference pattern

location is called **quantum indeterminacy**. This concept is the most profound difference between quantum physics and classical physics. According to quantum physics, nature does not always do exactly the same thing for the same set of conditions. Instead, the future develops probabilistically, and quantum physics is the science that allows you to predict the possible range of events that may occur.

Although you may think that quantum behaviour is remote and has nothing to do with your life, nothing could be further from the truth. As you will see in the next three chapters, quantum theory has become one of the most powerful scientific theories ever developed. Virtually all of the electronic equipment we use daily that improves our quality of life, and most of our current medical technologies and understanding, are possible because of the deep insights that quantum theory provides.

14.5 Check and Reflect

Knowledge

1. Explain which of the following choices is the best one.

   (a) The double-slit experiment demonstrates that light is a wave.

   (b) The double-slit experiment shows that light is a particle.

   (c) The double-slit experiment illustrates that light has both wave and particle characteristics.

2. True or false? Explain.

   (a) The results of the double-slit experiment described in this section apply only to photons.

   (b) The results of the double-slit experiment apply to photons as well as to particles such as electrons.

Applications

3. Which of the following examples illustrates the wave nature of a quantum, and which illustrates the particle nature?

   (a) Electrons hit a phosphor screen and create a flash of light.

   (b) Electrons scatter off a crystal surface and produce a series of nodes and antinodes.

   (c) Light hits a photocell and causes the emission of electrons.

Extension

4. Imagine that, one night as you slept, Planck's constant changed from 6.63×10^{-34} J·s to 6.63 J·s. Explain, from a quantum mechanical point of view, why walking through the doorway of your bedroom could be a dangerous thing to do.

e **TEST**

To check your understanding of quantum mechanics, follow the eTest links at www.pearsoned.ca/school/physicssource.

Key Terms and Concepts

incandescent

blackbody radiation
   curve

blackbody

quantum

Planck's formula

quantized

photon

photoelectric effect

photoelectron

threshold frequency

work function

stopping potential

Compton scattering

Compton effect

wave-particle duality

Heisenberg's
   uncertainty principle

quantum indeterminacy

Key Equations

$$E = nhf$$

$$hf = W + E_k$$

$$E_{k_{max}} = qV_{stopping}$$

$$p = \frac{h}{\lambda}$$

$$\Delta\lambda = \lambda_f - \lambda_i$$

$$= \frac{h}{mc}(1 - \cos\theta)$$

Conceptual Overview

Summarize this chapter by copying and completing the following concept map.

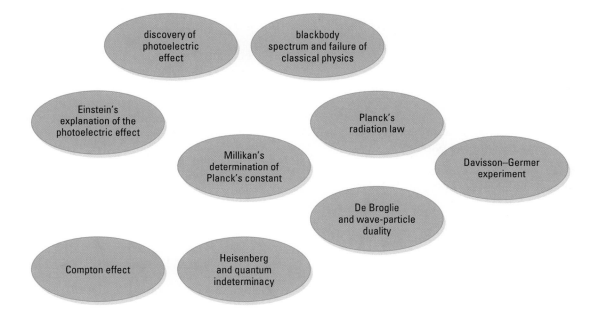

Knowledge

1. (14.1) Explain what is meant by the term "ultraviolet catastrophe."

2. (14.1) Write the equation for Planck's formula and briefly explain what it means.

3. (14.1) What is the energy of a 450-nm photon? Express the answer in both joules and electron volts.

4. (14.1) If an X-ray photon has a wavelength 100 times smaller than the wavelength of a visible light photon, how do the energies of the two photons compare? Give a numerical answer.

5. (14.2) Who is credited with discovering the photoelectric effect?

6. (14.2) Who provided the correct explanation of the photoelectric effect? In what way(s) was this explanation radical when first proposed?

7. (14.2) If the threshold frequency for photoemission from a metal surface is 6.0×10^{14} Hz, what is the work function of the metal?

8. (14.3) Explain why the Compton effect provides critical evidence for the particle model of light.

9. (14.3) If a 0.010-nm photon scatters 90° after striking an electron, determine the change in wavelength ($\Delta\lambda$) for the photon.

10. (14.4) What is the wavelength of an electron that has a momentum of 9.1×10^{-27} N·s?

11. (14.4) What is the momentum of a 100-nm UV photon?

12. (14.4) If a particle is confined to a region in space 10 fm across, could the particle also be at rest? Explain, using Heisenberg's uncertainty principle.

Applications

13. How many photons are emitted each second by a 1.0-W flashlight? Use 600 nm as the average wavelength of the photons.

14. A beam of 300-nm photons is absorbed by a metal surface with work function 1.88 eV. Calculate the maximum kinetic energy of the electrons emitted from the surface.

15. Modern transmission electron microscopes can accelerate electrons through a 100-keV potential difference and use these electrons to produce images of specimens. What is the wavelength of a 100-keV electron? Why are electron microscopes capable of much higher magnification than light microscopes?

16. A major league baseball pitcher can throw a 40-m/s fastball of mass 0.15 kg.
    (a) Calculate the wavelength of the ball.
    (b) Why can you safely ignore quantum effects in this case?

17. Imagine that you are 100 m from a 100-W incandescent light bulb. If the diameter of your pupil is 2 mm, estimate how many photons enter your eye each second. (Note: You will need to make estimates and provide additional information.)

18. How many photons are emitted each second by an FM radio station whose transmitted power is 200 kW and whose frequency is 90.9 MHz?

19. An electron is trapped in a box that is 0.85 nm long. Calculate the three lowest energies that this electron can have. Why can the electron not have energy values between the values you calculated?

20. Calculate the momentum of a 100-keV X-ray photon.

Extensions

21. Argue that photons exert pressure. (Hint: Newton's second law, $F = ma$, can also be written as $F = \dfrac{\Delta p}{\Delta t}$. In other words, force is a measure of the rate of change in momentum with respect to time. Also, remember that pressure is defined as force acting over an area: $P = \dfrac{F}{A}$.)

22. After you graduate from university, you take a job in a patent office, assessing the feasibility of inventions. Your boss hands you a file and skeptically tells you it is from a physicist who claims that a 1.0-km^2 sail made from highly reflecting Mylar film could produce about 10 N of force simply by reflecting sunlight. You are asked to check the physics. Do the following:

   (a) Estimate how many photons arrive from the Sun per second per square metre at a distance equal to the Earth-Sun separation. You know that the top of Earth's atmosphere gets 1.4 kW/m^2 of energy from the Sun.

   (b) Calculate the momentum of each photon and remember that the photons are reflected.

   (c) Multiply the pressure (force per unit area) by the total area of the sail.

   Does the physicist's claim make sense?

23. How many photons per second does your radio respond to? Consider receiving a 100-MHz radio signal. The antenna in an average radio receiver must be able to move a current of at least 1.0 μA through a 10-mV potential difference in order to be detectable.

24. Einstein thought there was a fundamental flaw in quantum physics because "God does not play dice."

   (a) What do you think he meant by this statement? What part of quantum theory was Einstein referring to?

   (b) Why is it ironic that Einstein made this statement?

Consolidate Your Understanding

1. Describe two significant failings of classical physics that challenged physics prior to 1900.

2. Provide evidence for quantization of energy, and explain this concept to a friend.

3. List and describe at least two crucial experimental findings that support Einstein's claim that light has a particle nature.

4. Explain why it is incorrect to state that light is either a wave or a particle. Comment on how quantum physics tries to resolve this duality.

5. What is meant by the term "quantum indeterminacy"? Provide experimental evidence for this idea.

Think About It

Review your answers to the Think About It questions on page 703. How would you answer each question now?

e **TEST**

To check your understanding of the wave-particle duality of light, follow the eTest links at www.pearsoned.ca/school/physicssource.

From Particle to Quantum — How did we arrive at our present understanding of light?

Scenario

In the past 500 years, our understanding of the nature of electromagnetic radiation has grown immensely, from the particle vs. wave controversy between Newton and Huygens, to the strange wave-particle duality described by de Broglie's hypothesis, and to Heisenberg's uncertainty principle. The key evidence and theories along the way have opened up a bounty of applications, from fibre-optic communication networks, to scanning and tunnelling electron microscopes. With our understanding of electromagnetic radiation has come a vast wealth of information and new technologies, which in turn, have furthered our ability to probe and investigate the nature of our universe. From humble beginnings with simple lenses, the scientific community has followed a long and difficult pathway to our present understanding. In this project, you will retrace this pathway, highlighting the theories, evidence, and experiments that have contributed to our present understanding of light and electromagnetic radiation.

Planning

Working in small groups or individually, prepare a presentation that summarizes the intellectual journey from the earliest theories of the particle nature of light, to the more modern theory of wave-particle duality. Your presentation should include simulations and illustrations that identify key experimental evidence, and descriptions of each model and theory, including the scientists who proposed them.

Your summary can be presented in chronological order, from early discoveries, to later ones, or it can be organized around models (particle, wave, quantum, wave-particle duality).

Materials

text and Internet resources

simulations, illustrations, photos of evidence collected in experiments

presentation software (PowerPoint, html editor, etc.)

Procedure

1 Define each of the following models: particle, wave, quantum, and wave-particle duality.

2 Identify each of the scientists involved with each model.

3 Using either a table or a timeline, place each model and the related scientists in order from earliest, to most recent.

4 On your table or a timeline, identify each key experiment and the evidence that was used to support each model. Include the following experimental evidence and theories:

- reflection, refraction, dispersion, diffraction, interference, polarization, blackbody radiation, photoelectric effect, Compton effect, de Broglie's hypothesis, and Heisenberg's uncertainty principle

5 Use your table or timeline as the basis for preparing your presentation. Use simulations, illustrations, and photographs where possible to describe experimental evidence.

Thinking Further

The evolution of an idea or theory can take place over hundreds of years, with one participant handing off evidence to the next participant. A sort of relay develops, because the race is simply too long for one person to complete alone. With this in mind, consider the following questions that could be answered at the end of your presentation.

- A relay race has an end. Is there an end in the race to fully understand the nature of electromagnetic radiation and light?
- If the relay is not over, where do you think we are going from here?
- How have we used the knowledge of our predecessors in determining where to look next? Explain.

*Note: Your instructor will assess the project using a similar assessment rubric.

Unit Concepts and Skills: Quick Reference

Concepts	Summary	Resources and Skill Building
Chapter 13	**The wave model can be used to describe the characteristics of electromagnetic radiation.**	
	13.1 What Is Electromagnetic Radiation?	
Types of electromagnetic radiation	Frequency, wavelength, and source are used to identify types of EMR.	Figure 13.4; Table 13.1
Models of EMR	Different models were used to explain the behaviour of EMR.	Figures 13.5–13.9
Maxwell's electromagnetic theory	Maxwell's theory linked concepts of electricity and magnetism.	Figures 13.10–13.15
	Electromagnetic radiation is produced by accelerating charges.	Figures 13.16-13.19; Minds On: Going Wireless
	13.2 The Speed of Electromagnetic Radiation	
Speed of electromagnetic radiation	Galileo, Roemer and Huygens, and Fizeau measured the speed of EMR, but Michelson's experiment made the definitive measurement.	Figures 13.21-13.24; Example 13.1; 13-2 QuickLab
	13.3 Reflection	
The Law of Reflection, image formation, and ray diagrams	The angle of reflection equals the angle of incidence and is in the same plane. Ray diagrams show a light ray interacting with a surface. Three rays predict the location and characteristics of the image.	Figures 13.28-13.30; 13-3 QuickLab; Minds On: Image in a Mirror; Figures 13.31–13.32; Figures 13.36–13.39; 13-4 QuickLab
Image formation/equations	The mirror equation relates the focal length of a curved mirror to the image and object distances.	13-5 Problem-Solving Lab; Example 13.2
	13.4 Refraction	
Refraction and Snell's Law	Snell's Law relates the refraction of a light wave to the speed with which light travels in different media.	Table 13.4; Examples 13.3–13.4; 13-6 Inquiry Lab
Total internal reflection	All light is internally reflected at an interface if the angle of refraction is 90° or greater.	Figures 13.49-13.53; Example 13.5, 13-7 Decision-Making Analysis
Dispersion and recomposition	White light can be separated into its component wavelengths.	Figures 13.54–13.56; Table 13.5; 13-8 QuickLab
Image formation with thin lenses	The lens equation relates the focal length of a curved lens to the image and object distances.	Figures 13.57–13.59; Example 13.6; Figure 13.61; Example 13.7; 13-9 Inquiry Lab
	13.5 Diffraction and Interference	
Huygens' Principle	Huygens predicted the motion of a wave front as many point sources.	Figures 13.67–13.69
Young's experiment, interference, and diffraction	Young's experiment showed that two beams of light produce an interference pattern and that light behaves as a wave.	Figures 13.70–13.78; Examples 13.8–13.9 Figure 13.80
Diffraction gratings	Light on a multi-slit diffraction grating produces an interference pattern.	Figure 13.81; Example 13.10; 13-10 Inquiry Lab
Polarization	EMR absorption by polarizing filters supports the wave model of light.	13-1 QuickLab; Figure 13.86; Figures 13.88–13.90
Chapter 14	**The wave–particle duality reminds us that sometimes truth really *is* stranger than fiction!**	
	14.1 The Birth of the Quantum	
Quantum	Classical physics was unable to explain the shape of the blackbody radiation curve.	14-1 QuickLab, Figures 14.3–14.4
	A quantum is the smallest amount of energy of a particular wavelength or frequency that a body can absorb, given by $E = hf$.	Examples 14.1, 14.2, 14.3; Minds On: What's Wrong with This Analogy? Figure 14.6
	14.2 The Photoelectric Effect	
Photoelectric effect	The work function is the minimum energy required to cause photoemission of electrons from a metal surface.	14-2 QuickLab, Table 14.1
Planck's constant	Millikan's photoelectric experiment provided a way to measure Planck's constant. The photoelectric effect obeys the law of conservation of energy.	Figure 14.12, 14-3 Design a Lab; Examples 14.5–14.6
	14.3 The Compton Effect	
Compton effect	When an electron scatters an X ray, the change in the X ray's wavelength relates to the angle of the X-ray photon's scattering.	Figure 14.16; Examples 14.7–14.8
	14.4 Matter Waves and the Power of Symmetric Thinking	
Wave–particle duality	Something that has momentum also has wavelength: Particles can act like waves.	Examples 14.9–14.10
Heisenberg's uncertainty principle	Particles have a wave nature, so it is impossible to precisely know their position at the same time as their momentum.	Figures 14.21, 14.22, 14.24, 14.26; Example 14.11
	14.5 Coming to Terms with Wave-particle Duality and the Birth of Quantum Mechanics	
Quantum indeterminacy	Wave-particle duality illustrates the probabilistic nature of atoms and molecules. Quantum indeterminacy is the measure of the probability of a particle's location.	14-4 QuickLab, Figures 14.28–14.30

Vocabulary

1. Use your own words to define these terms:
   angle of diffraction
   blackbody
   blackbody radiation curve
   Compton effect
   Compton scattering
   converging
   critical angle
   diffraction
   diffraction grating
   dispersion
   diverging
   electromagnetic radiation
   focal point
   frequency
   Heisenberg's uncertainty principle
   Huygens' Principle
   image attitude
   incandescent
   interference
   law of reflection
   magnification
   node, antinode
   particle model
   path length
   period
   photoelectric effect
   photoelectrons
   photon
   Planck's formula
   polarization
   quantized
   quantum
   quantum indeterminacy
   refraction
   refractive index
   Snell's Law
   spectrum
   stopping potential
   threshold frequency
   total internal reflection
   wave model
   wave-particle duality
   wavelength
   work function

Knowledge

CHAPTER 13

2. How does the quantum model reconcile the wave model and the particle model of light?

3. How did Maxwell's work with capacitors influence his theories on electromagnetism?

4. Describe the experimental evidence that supports all of Maxwell's predictions about electromagnetic radiation.

5. Discuss the significance of the word "changing" in Maxwell's original description of electromagnetic radiation.

6. Why does a spark produce electromagnetic radiation?

7. If a metal conductor, such as a spoon, is placed in an operating microwave oven, a spark is produced. Why?

8. Using a ray diagram, show three rays that are needed to identify and verify the characteristics of an image.

9. What is the relationship between the focal length and the radius of curvature for a curved mirror?

10. What is a virtual focal point and how is it different from a real focal point?

11. Explain, using a ray diagram, how a real image can be formed when using two concave mirrors.

12. When you place the concave side of a spoon on your nose and slowly pull it away from your face, your image disappears at a certain distance. What is the significance of this distance?

13. When an object such as a paddle is partially submerged in water, why does it appear bent?

14. Explain how Snell's Law supports the wave theory of light.

15. What happens to the wavelength of monochromatic light when it passes from air into water?

16. Several people holding hands run down the beach and enter the water at an angle. Explain what happens to the speed and direction of the people as they enter the water.

17. How was Newton able to show that a prism separates the colours in the spectrum, rather than adding the colours to white light?

18. What is Huygens' Principle?

19. A straight wave front is incident on a barrier with a small hole. Using a diagram, describe the shape of the wave front a moment after it makes contact with the barrier.

20. Using a schematic, illustrate Young's experiment.

21. Explain why diffraction supports the wave model of light.

22. What key evidence was observed by Dominique Arago in 1818? Why was this evidence crucial to the acceptance of the wave model of light?

23. How must two plane polarizing filters be aligned in order to fully block electromagnetic radiation?

24. Is an electromagnetic wave one-dimensional, two-dimensional, or three-dimensional? Explain.

CHAPTER 14

25. Is a quantum of blue light the same as a quantum of red light? Explain.

26. How much energy is carried by a photon of wavelength 550 nm?

27. Explain how you can estimate the surface temperature of a star by noting its colour.

28. Arrange the following photons from highest to lowest energy: ultraviolet photon, 10-nm photon, microwave photon, gamma-ray photon, 600-nm photon, infrared photon.

29. What is the frequency of blue light of wavelength 500 nm?

30. Ultraviolet light causes sunburn whereas visible light does not. Explain, using Planck's formula.

31. Explain what is meant by the term "threshold frequency."

32. How does the energy of photoelectrons emitted by a metal change as the intensity of light hitting the metal surface changes?

33. What is the minimum wavelength of light that will cause photoemission from a metal having a work function of 3.2 eV?

34. Explain the difference between the Compton effect and the photoelectric effect.

35. What is meant by the term "wave-particle duality"?

36. Even though photons have no mass, they still carry momentum. What is the momentum of a 300-nm ultraviolet photon?

37. What is the de Broglie wavelength of an electron moving at 3000 km/s?

38. A proton and a neutron are both moving at the same speed. Which particle has the shorter de Broglie wavelength?

39. Explain, using wave mechanics, why it is impossible for a particle to have zero kinetic energy when it is confined to a fixed region in space.

Applications

40. If visible light is a particle, predict what would be observed if light passed through two small holes in a barrier. Compare this prediction to what is actually observed when light passes through two small holes in a barrier. What does this suggest about the nature of light?

41. How many radio-frequency photons are emitted each second by a radio station that broadcasts at a frequency of 90.9 MHz and has a radiated power of 50 kW?

42. Explain how an antenna is able to "sense" electromagnetic radiation.

43. Detailed measurements of the Moon's orbit could be calculated after the Apollo mission placed large reflecting mirrors on the surface of the Moon. If a laser beam were directed at the mirrors on the Moon and the light was reflected back to Earth in 2.56 s, how far away, in kilometres, is the Moon?

44. When you increase the intensity of a green light, do you change the energy of the green-light photons? Why does the light get brighter?

45. A Michelson apparatus is used to obtain a value of 2.97×10^8 m/s for the speed of light. The sixteen-sided rotating mirror completes 1.15×10^4 revolutions in one minute. How far away was the flat reflecting mirror?

46. An eight-sided mirror like Michelson's is set up. The light reflects from the rotating mirror and travels to a fixed mirror 5.00 km away. If the rotating mirror turns through one-eighth of a rotation before the light returns from the fixed mirror, what is the rate of rotation?

47. A sixteen-sided mirror rotates at 4.50×10^2 Hz. How long does it take to make one-sixteenth of a rotation?

48. Why do police and search-and-rescue agencies use infrared cameras for night-time surveillance when looking for people? Explain why infrared is used and not some other part of the electromagnetic spectrum.

49. The speed of light in a material is determined to be 1.24×10^8 m/s. What is the material?

50. Light of wavelength 520 nm strikes a metal surface having a work function of 2.3 eV. Will the surface emit photoelectrons?

51. A student replicating Michelson's experiment uses an eight-sided mirror and a fixed mirror located 35.0 km away. Light is reflected through the system when the rotating mirror turns at 5.20×10^2 Hz. What is the experimentally determined speed of light and the percentage error in the measurement?

52. An electrically neutral 1-m² piece of aluminium is put in orbit high above Earth. Explain why, after a period of time, the piece of aluminium will become electrically charged. Predict the sign of the charge.

53. An object is located in front of a diverging mirror with a focal length of 5.0 cm. If the virtual image is formed 3.0 cm from the vertex of the mirror and is 1.0 cm high, determine the object's characteristics and position.

54. Photon A has four times the energy of photon B. Compare the wavelengths and the momenta of the two photons.

55. A light ray passes from water into ruby at an angle of 10°. What is the angle of refraction?

56. An X-ray photon of wavelength 0.025 nm collides elastically with an electron and scatters through an angle of 90°. How much energy did the electron acquire in this collision and in what important way did the X ray change?

57. A 3.0-cm-high object is placed 10.0 cm from a converging lens with a focal length of 5.0 cm. Using the thin lens equation, determine the image attributes and position.

58. Imagine that you are asked to review a patent application for a laser-powered deep space probe. The proposal you are reviewing calls for a 1-kW laser producing 500-nm photons. The total mass of the spacecraft, including the laser, is 1000 kg. Determine

    (a) if laser propulsion is possible, and the underlying principle of this form of propulsion.

    (b) how fast the spacecraft would be travelling after one year of "laser-drive" if it started from rest.

59. List two ways to recompose the spectrum into white light.

60. Calculate the wavelength of electrons used in a transmission electron microscope if the electrons are accelerated through an electric field of potential 75 kV.

61. In an experiment similar to Young's, two waves arrive at the screen one half-wavelength out of phase. What will be observed at this point on the screen?

62. What is the minimum or rest energy of an electron confined to a one-dimensional box 1 nm long?

63. A mixture of violet light ($\lambda = 420$ nm) and red light ($\lambda = 650$ nm) are incident on a diffraction grating with 1.00×10^4 lines/cm. For each wavelength, determine the angle of deviation that leads to the first antinode.

64. Light with a wavelength of 700 nm is directed at a diffraction grating with 1.50×10^2 slits/cm. What is the separation between adjacent antinodes when the screen is located 2.50 m away?

65. Your physics teacher, eager to get to class, was observed from a police spotting-plane to travel a distance of 222 m in 10 s. The speed limit was 60 km/h, and you can quickly determine that he was speeding. The police issued a ticket, but your teacher decided to argue the case, citing Heisenberg's uncertainty principle as his defence. He argued that the speed of his car was fundamentally uncertain and that he was not speeding. Explain how you would use Heisenberg's uncertainty principle in this case and comment on whether your teacher's defence was good. The combined mass of the car and your teacher is 2000 kg.

Extensions

66. Traditional radio technology blends a carrier signal and an audio signal with either frequency or amplitude modulation. This generates a signal with two layers of information—one for tuning and one containing the audio information. Describe the two layers of information that a cell phone signal must contain in order to establish and maintain constant communication with a cell phone network.

67. Use Heisenberg's uncertainty principle to estimate the momentum and kinetic energy of an electron in a hydrogen atom. Express the energy in electron volts. The hydrogen atom can be approximated by a square with 0.2-nm sides. (Hint: Kinetic energy is related to momentum via the equation $E_k = \dfrac{p^2}{2m}$.)

68. Global positioning satellites maintain an orbital altitude of 20 000 km. How long does it take for a time signal to travel from the satellite to a receiver located directly below the satellite?

69. Imagine ways the world would be different if Planck's constant were much larger than it is. Suggest why it would be difficult to do something as ordinary as walking through a doorway if $h = 1$ J·s rather than 6.63×10^{-34} J·s.

70. Explain how an optical fibre is able to transmit a light pulse over a long distance without a loss in intensity.

71. The human eye can detect as few as 500 photons of light, but in order to see, this response needs to occur over a prolonged period of time. Seeing requires approximately 10 000 photons per second. If the Sun emits 3.9×10^{26} W, mostly in the blue-green part of the spectrum, and if roughly half of the energy is emitted as visible light, estimate how far away a star like our Sun would be visible.

72. A beam of 200-eV electrons is made to pass through two slits in a metal film that are separated by 50 nm. A phosphor screen is placed 1 m behind the slits. Sketch what you would expect to see. Provide calculations to support your answer.

Skills Practice

73. An object is located 25.0 cm from a diverging mirror with a focal length of 10.0 cm. Draw a scale ray diagram to determine the following:

   (a) the image location and type

   (b) the image attitude

   (c) the magnification of the image

74. The following data are taken from an experiment in which the maximum kinetic energy of photo-electrons is related to the wavelength of the photons hitting a metal surface. Use these data to produce a graph that shows the energy of the incident photons on the horizontal axis and the kinetic energy of photoelectrons on the vertical axis. From this graph, determine the work function for the metal.

Wavelength (nm)	Kinetic Energy (eV)
200	3.72
250	2.47
300	1.64
350	1.05
400	0.61
450	0.26

75. Use a ray diagram to show why a double convex lens is called a converging lens and a double concave lens is called a diverging lens. Label the principal axis, principal focus, secondary focus, and optical centre.

76. Calculate the momentum and wavelength of an electron that has a kinetic energy of 50 keV.

77. Explain, with the aid of a ray diagram, why an image does not form when you place an object at the focal point of a converging lens.

78. Determine the momentum of an X ray of wavelength 10 nm.

79. Prepare a table in which you compare the wave and particle models of light. List as many phenomena as you can think of and decide whether light can be explained best using the wave or the particle model. How would you answer the question, "Is light a wave or a particle?"

Self-assessment

80. Describe to a classmate which concepts of electromagnetic radiation you found most interesting when studying this unit. Give reasons for your choices.

81. Identify one issue pertaining to the wave-particle duality of light that you would like to investigate in greater detail.

82. What concept in this unit did you find most difficult? What steps could you take to improve your understanding?

 e TEST

To check your understanding of electromagnetic radiation and the dual nature of light, follow the eTest links at www.pearsoned.ca/school/ physicssource.

UNIT
VIII

Atomic
Physics

A cluster of newly formed stars in a spiral arm of the Milky Way galaxy. Physicists are using atomic theories to understand the structure and evolution of the universe.

 e **WEB**

To learn more about the role of atomic physics in cosmology, follow the links at www.pearsoned.ca/school/physicssource.

Unit at a Glance

Unit Themes and Emphases

- Energy and Matter

Focussing Questions

The study of atomic structure requires analyzing how matter and energy are related. As you study this unit, consider these questions:

- What is the structure of atoms?
- How can models of the atom be tested?
- How does knowledge of atomic structure lead to the development of technology?

Unit Project

How Atomic Physics Affects Science and Technology

- Unit VIII discusses radical changes in the understanding of matter and energy. In this project, you will investigate how advances in atomic physics influenced the development of technology and other branches of science.

Electric force and energy quantization determine atomic structure.

Max Planck began undergraduate studies at the University of Munich in 1874. During his first term, he took primarily mathematics courses, although he also had considerable musical talent and an interest in physics. Wondering which field to pursue, the teenaged Planck asked his physics professor, Philipp von Jolly, about the prospects for a career in physics. Jolly told Planck that there would be few opportunities since almost everything in physics had already been discovered, leaving only a few minor gaps to fill in.

Despite Jolly's discouraging advice, Planck went on to complete a doctorate in physics, and became a renowned professor at the University of Berlin. As described in Chapter 14, one of the "gaps" in theoretical physics was the puzzling distribution of energy among the wavelengths of radiation emitted by a heated body. Planck concentrated on this problem for months, and by the end of 1900 concluded that this distribution is possible only if energy is quantized.

At first, Planck and his contemporaries did not realize the huge significance of his findings. As you will learn in this chapter, Planck's discovery led to quantum theory, a concept that revolutionized atomic physics. You will also see that Planck was just the first of many researchers who demonstrated that there was still a great deal to be discovered in physics.

Figure 15.1 shows how radically our concept of the atom changed during the 20th century. Planck's idea of quantization of energy led Bohr to propose his model of the atom in 1913. In this chapter, you will study in detail how the model of the atom evolved.

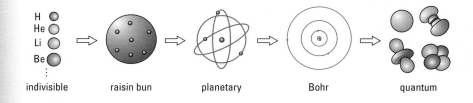

H
He
Li
Be
⋮

indivisible   raisin bun   planetary   Bohr   quantum

▲ **Figure 15.1**   The evolution of theories of atomic structure

Cathode Rays and Magnetic Fields

Problem

What is the charge of a cathode ray?

Materials

gas-discharge tube (Figure 15.2)
high-voltage power supply
bar magnet or electromagnet

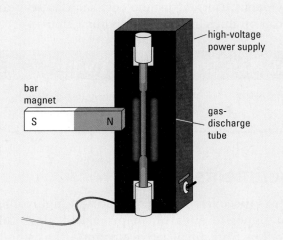

▲ **Figure 15.2** A gas-discharge tube

Procedure

1 Your teacher will give directions for setting up the particular tube and power supply that you will use. Follow these directions carefully.

2 Turn on the power supply and note the beam that appears in the tube. To see the beam clearly, you may need to darken the room.

3 Bring the bar magnet close to the tube surface. Note the direction of the magnetic field and the direction in which the beam moves.

4 Repeat step 3 at various positions along the tube.

Questions

1. How did you determine the direction of the magnetic field?

2. What do you think causes the visible beam in the tube?

3. What evidence suggests that the magnet causes the beam to deflect?

4. What can you conclude about the charge of the cathode rays? Explain your reasoning.

Think About It

1. What are atoms made of?

2. What holds atoms together?

3. How can physicists measure atomic structure when it is too small to be seen by even the most powerful microscope?

Discuss your answers in a small group and record them for later reference. As you complete each section of this chapter, review your answers to these questions. Note any changes in your ideas.

15.1 The Discovery of the Electron

info **BIT**

Dalton's research included important findings about the aurora borealis, atmospheric gases, and the formation of dew. He also made the first scientific study of colour blindness, which he had himself.

Around 1803, the English chemist John Dalton (1766–1844) developed an atomic theory to explain the ratios in which elements combine to form compounds. Although later discoveries required modifications to Dalton's theory, it is the cornerstone of modern atomic theory. This theory could explain the observations made by Dalton and other chemists, but their experiments did not provide any direct evidence that atoms actually exist. At the end of the 19th century, there was still some doubt about whether all matter was made up of atoms. By 1900, experiments were providing more direct evidence. Current technology, such as scanning tunnelling microscopes, can produce images of individual atoms.

 MINDS ON | **Evidence for Atoms**

How do you know that atoms exist? | Work with a partner to list evidence that matter is composed of atoms.

Cathode-ray Experiments

During the 1800s, scientists discovered that connecting a high voltage across the electrodes at opposite ends of an evacuated glass tube caused mysterious rays to flow from the negative electrode (the cathode) toward the positive electrode. These **cathode rays** caused the glass to glow when they struck the far side of the tube. The rays could be deflected by a magnetic field. In 1885, after several years of experiments with improved vacuum discharge tubes, William Crookes in England suggested that cathode rays must be streams of negatively charged particles. In 1895, Jean Baptiste Perrin in France showed that cathode rays entering a hollow metal cylinder built up a negative charge on the cylinder.

cathode ray: free electrons emitted by a negative electrode

In 1897, Joseph John Thomson (1856–1940) took these experiments a step further. First, he used an improved version of Perrin's apparatus to show even more clearly that cathode rays carry negative charge (Figure 15.3). Next, he tackled the problem of why no one had been able to deflect cathode rays with an electric field. Thomson's hypothesis was that the cathode rays ionized some of the air molecules remaining in the vacuum chamber and these ions then shielded the cathode rays from the electric field. By taking great care to get an extremely low pressure in his discharge tube, Thomson was able to demonstrate that cathode rays respond to electric fields just as negatively charged particles would. Thomson had discovered the electron.

info **BIT**

The Irish physicist G. Johnstone Stoney coined the term *electron* in 1891. Thomson called the particles in cathode rays "corpuscles."

cathode rays by an electrostatic force.
The apparatus used is represented in fig. 2.

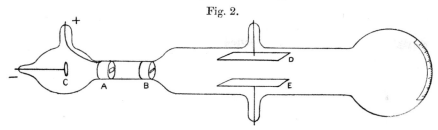

Fig. 2.

The rays from the cathode C pass through a slit in the anode A, which is a metal plug fitting tightly into the tube and connected with the earth; after passing through a second slit in another earth-connected metal plug B, they travel

MINDS ON	Are Electrons Positively or Negatively Charged?

Outline an experiment to test whether cathode rays consist of negatively or positively charged particles.	How could you tell that the particles have electric charge rather than magnetism?

Charge-to-mass Ratio of the Electron

Thomson did not have a method for measuring either the mass of an electron or the charge that it carried. However, he did find a way to determine the ratio of charge to mass for the electron by using both an electric field and a magnetic field.

Recall from Chapter 11 that the electric force acting on a charged particle is

$$\vec{F}_e = q\vec{E}$$

where $\vec{F}_e$ is the electric force, q is the magnitude of the charge on the particle, and $\vec{E}$ is the electric field.

Section 12.2 describes how the left-hand rule gives the direction of the magnetic force acting on a negative charge moving through a magnetic field. The magnitude of this force is

$$|\vec{F}_m| = qv_\perp B$$

where q is the magnitude of the charge on the particle, $v_\perp$ is the component of the particle's velocity perpendicular to the magnetic field, and B is the magnitude of the magnetic field.

For a particle moving perpendicular to a magnetic field, $v_\perp = v$ and

$$F_m = qvB$$

Consider the perpendicular electric and magnetic fields shown in Figure 15.4. The electric field exerts a downward force on the negative charge while the magnetic field exerts an upward force. The gravitational force acting on the particle is negligible. If the net force on the charged particle is zero, the electric and magnetic forces must be equal in magnitude but opposite in direction:

PHYSICS INSIGHT

Dots and ×s are a common way to show vectors directed out of or into the page. A dot represents the tip of a vector arrow coming toward you, and × represents the tail of an arrow moving away from you.

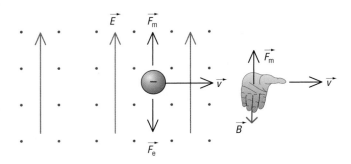

$$\vec{F}_{net} = \vec{F}_e + \vec{F}_m$$
$$\vec{F}_{net} = 0, \text{ so}$$
$$F_e = F_m$$
$$|\vec{E}|q = Bqv$$
$$|\vec{E}| = Bv$$

The speed of the particle is, therefore,

$$v = \frac{|\vec{E}|}{B}$$

▲ **Figure 15.4** Perpendicular electric and magnetic fields act on a moving negative charge. The red dots represent a magnetic field directed out of the page. Using the left-hand rule for magnetic force, your thumb points in the direction of electron flow (right), fingers point in the direction of the magnetic field (out of the page), and the palm indicates the direction of the magnetic force (toward the top of the page).

Example 15.1

Practice Problems

1. A beam of electrons passes undeflected through a 2.50-T magnetic field at right angles to a 60-N/C electric field. How fast are the electrons travelling?

2. What magnitude of electric field will keep protons from being deflected while they move at a speed of 10 m/s through a 0.05-T magnetic field?

3. What magnitude of magnetic field will stop ions from being deflected while they move at a speed of 75 m/s through an electric field with a magnitude of 150 N/C?

Answers

1. 24 m/s
2. 0.5 N/C
3. 2.0 T

A beam of electrons passes undeflected through a 0.50-T magnetic field combined with a 0.50-kN/C electric field. The electric field, the magnetic field, and the velocity of the electrons are all perpendicular to each other. How fast are the electrons travelling?

Given

$|\vec{E}| = 0.50$ kN/C $= 5.0 \times 10^2$ N/C $\qquad B = 0.50$ T

Required
speed (v)

Analysis and Solution
Since the electrons are not deflected, $\vec{F}_{net} = 0$, so the magnitude of $\vec{F}_e$ equals the magnitude of $\vec{F}_m$.

$$v = \frac{|\vec{E}|}{B}$$

$$= \frac{5.0 \times 10^2 \text{ N/C}}{0.50 \text{ T}}$$

$$= 1.0 \times 10^3 \text{ m/s}$$

Paraphrase
The electrons are travelling at a speed of 1.0×10^3 m/s.

Concept Check

What would happen to the beam of electrons in Example 15.1 if their speed decreased to 50 m/s?

Thomson used mutually perpendicular electric and magnetic fields to determine the speed of the cathode rays. He then measured the deflection of the rays when just one of the fields was switched on. These deflections depended on the magnitude of the field, the length of the path in the field, and the speed, charge, and mass of the cathode-ray particles. Thomson could determine only the first three quantities, but he could use his measurements to calculate the ratio of the two unknowns, the charge and mass of the particles. Thomson made measurements with a series of cathode-ray tubes that each had a different metal for the electrode that emitted the rays. Since he found reasonably consistent values for the charge-to-mass ratio, Thomson concluded that all cathode rays consist of identical particles with exactly the same negative charge.

Thomson's experiments showed that $\dfrac{q}{m}$ for an electron is roughly 10^{11} C/kg. This ratio is over a thousand times larger than the ratio for a hydrogen ion. Other physicists had shown that cathode rays can pass through thin metal foils and travel much farther in air than atoms do. Therefore, Thomson reasoned that electrons are much smaller than atoms. In his Nobel Prize lecture in 1906, he stated that "we are driven to the conclusion that the mass of the corpuscle is only about 1/1700 of that of the hydrogen atom." This value is within a few percent of the mass determined by the latest high-precision measurements.

Thomson put forward the daring theory that atoms were divisible, and the tiny particles in cathode rays were "the substance from which all the chemical elements are built up." Although he was incorrect about electrons being the *only* constituents of atoms, recognizing that electrons are subatomic particles was a major advance in atomic physics.

Determining Charge-to-mass Ratios

Thomson measured the deflection of cathode rays to determine the charge-to-mass ratio of the electron. You can also determine mass-to-charge ratios by measuring the path of charged particles in a uniform magnetic field.

When a charged particle moves perpendicular to a magnetic field, the magnetic force is perpendicular to the particle's velocity, so the particle's direction changes, but its speed is constant. In a uniform magnetic field, B is constant, so the magnitude of the magnetic force, Bqv, is also constant. As described in Chapter 6, a force of constant magnitude perpendicular to an object's velocity can cause uniform circular motion. A charged particle moving perpendicular to a uniform magnetic field follows a circular path, with the magnetic force acting as the centripetal force (Figure 15.5).

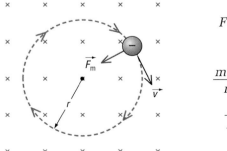

$$F_{net} = F_m$$

$$F_c = F_m$$

$$\frac{mv^2}{r} = Bqv$$

$$\frac{q}{m} = \frac{v}{Br}$$

▲ **Figure 15.5** The path of an electron travelling perpendicular to a uniform magnetic field. The red ×s represent a magnetic field directed into the page.

Concept Check

How do you know that the magnetic force on the particle is directed toward the centre of a circular path in Figure 15.5?

Example 15.2

When a beam of electrons, accelerated to a speed of 5.93×10^5 m/s, is directed perpendicular to a uniform 100-μT magnetic field, they travel in a circular path with a radius of 3.37 cm (Figure 15.6). Determine the charge-to-mass ratio for an electron.

Given

$v_e = 5.93 \times 10^5$ m/s

$B = 100\ \mu\text{T} = 1.00 \times 10^{-4}$ T

$r = 3.37\ \text{cm} = 3.37 \times 10^{-2}$ m

Required

charge-to-mass ratio $\left(\frac{q}{m}\right)$

Analysis and Solution

Since the magnetic force acts as the centripetal force,

$$F_m = F_c$$

$$Bqv = \frac{mv^2}{r}$$

$$Bq = \frac{mv}{r}$$

$$\frac{q}{m} = \frac{v}{Br}$$

Substituting the known values for the beam of electrons gives

$$\frac{q}{m} = \frac{5.93 \times 10^5\ \text{m/s}}{(1.00 \times 10^{-4}\ \text{T})(3.37 \times 10^{-2}\ \text{m})}$$

$$= 1.76 \times 10^{11}\ \text{C/kg}$$

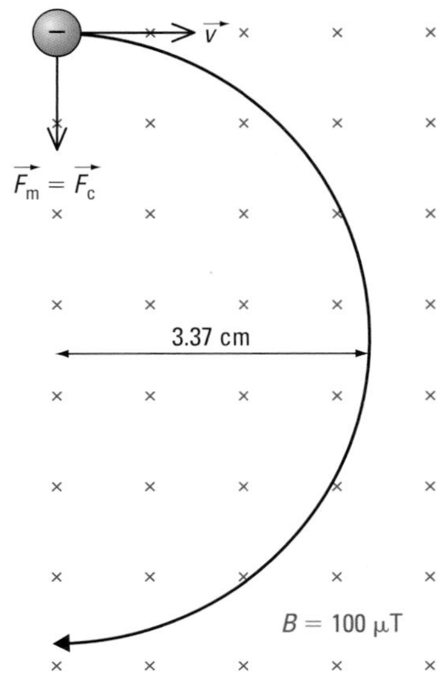

▲ **Figure 15.6**

Paraphrase

The charge-to-mass ratio for an electron is about 1.76×10^{11} C/kg.

Practice Problems

1. Find the charge-to-mass ratio for an ion that travels in an arc of radius 1.00 cm when moving at 1000 km/s perpendicular to a 1.0-T magnetic field.
2. Find the speed of an electron moving in an arc of radius 0.10 m perpendicular to a magnetic field with a magnitude of 1.0×10^{-4} T.
3. A carbon-12 ion has a charge-to-mass ratio of 8.04×10^6 C/kg. Calculate the radius of the ion's path when the ion travels at 150 km/s perpendicular to a 0.50-T magnetic field.

Answers

1. 1.0×10^8 C/kg
2. 1.8×10^6 m/s
3. 0.037 m

Thomson's Raisin-bun Model

Most matter is electrically neutral. If electrons are constituents of atoms, atoms must also contain some form of positive charge. Since no positively charged subatomic particles had yet been discovered, Thomson suggested that atoms might consist of electrons embedded in a blob of massless positive charge, somewhat like the way raisins are embedded in the dough of a raisin bun. Figure 15.7 shows Thomson's model of the atom.

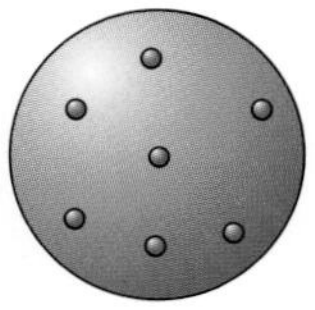

▲ **Figure 15.7** Thomson's raisin-bun model of the atom

What characteristics should a scientific model have? Does Thomson's raisin-bun model of the atom have these characteristics?

THEN, NOW, AND FUTURE   The Mass Spectrometer

Thomson used electric and magnetic fields to determine the charge-to-mass ratio of electrons. In later experiments, he made similar measurements for positive ions. These experiments led to the development of the mass spectrometer, an instrument that can detect compounds, measure isotope masses, and determine molecular structures (Figure 15.8).

Many mass spectrometers use a four-stage process enclosed in a vacuum chamber:

Ionization: If the sample is not already a gas, the ion source vaporizes it, usually by heating. Heating may also break complex compounds into smaller fragments that are easier to identify. Next, the neutral compounds in the sample are ionized so that they will respond to electric and magnetic fields. Usually, the ion source knocks one or two

electrons off the compound to produce a positive ion.

Acceleration: High-voltage plates then accelerate a beam of these ions into the velocity selector.

Velocity Selection: The velocity selector has crossed electric and magnetic fields arranged such that only the ions that have a speed of $v = \dfrac{|\vec{E}|}{B}$ pass straight through. Ions with slower or faster speeds are deflected away from the entrance to the detection chamber. Thus, all the ions entering the next stage of the mass spectrometer have the same known speed.

Detection: A uniform magnetic field in the detection chamber makes the ions travel in circular paths. The radius of each path depends on the charge and mass of the ion. Ions arriving at the detector produce an electrical current that is proportional

to the number of ions. The spectrometer can produce a graph of the charge-to-mass ratios for a sample by moving the detector or by varying the electric or magnetic fields.

Mass spectrometers can detect compounds in concentrations as small as a few parts per billion. These versatile machines have a huge range of applications in science, medicine, and industry.

Questions

1. Write an expression for the radius of the path of ions in a mass spectrometer.

2. How does the mass of an ion affect the radius of its path in the detection chamber?

3. Describe how you could use a mass spectrometer to detect an athlete's use of a banned performance-enhancing drug.

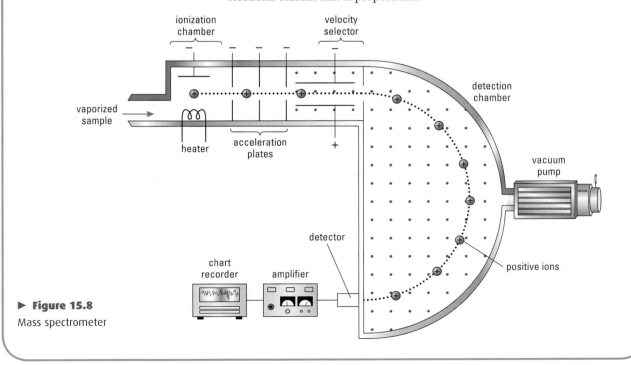

▶ **Figure 15.8**
Mass spectrometer

Knowledge

1. An electron moving at 5.0×10^5 m/s enters a magnetic field of magnitude 100 mT.

   (a) What is the maximum force that the magnetic field can exert on the electron? When will the magnetic field exert this maximum force?

   (b) What is the minimum force that the magnetic field can exert on the electron? When will the magnetic field exert this minimum force?

2. Explain why improved vacuum pumps were a key to the success of Thomson's experiments.

3. What experimental results led Thomson to conclude that all cathode rays consist of identical particles?

Applications

4. A beam of electrons enters a vacuum chamber that has a 100-N/C electric field and a 0.250-T magnetic field.

   (a) Sketch an orientation of electric and magnetic fields that will let the electrons pass undeflected through the chamber.

   (b) Find the speed of the electrons.

5. Electrons are observed to travel in a circular path of radius 0.04 m when placed in a magnetic field of strength 0.25 T. How fast are the electrons moving?

6. How large a magnetic field is needed to deflect a beam of protons moving at 1.50×10^5 m/s in a path of radius 1.00 m?

7. Use the appropriate hand rule to determine the direction of the magnetic field in question 6 if the protons rotate counterclockwise in the same plane as this page.

8. A mass spectrometer has the electric field in its velocity selector set to 30.0 N/C and the magnetic field set to 10.0 mT. Find the speed of the ions that travel straight through these fields.

9. This diagram shows a proton moving at 1.0×10^5 m/s through perpendicular electric and magnetic fields.

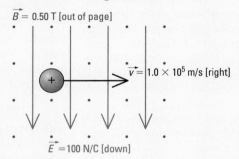

   (a) Calculate the net force acting on the particle.

   (b) Will the net force change over time? Explain your reasoning.

Extensions

10. Suppose that a typical physics professor accumulates 5 μC of negative charge while walking across the carpeted floor to the security gate at an airport.

    (a) If the metal detector at the security gate exerts an upward force on this charge, what is the direction of the magnetic field within the detector?

    (b) If the metal detector uses a 0.05-T magnetic field, roughly how fast does a physics professor have to run through the detector in order to feel weightless?

    (c) Explain whether it would be practical to use an airport metal detector as a levitation machine.

e TEST

To check your understanding of Thomson's experiments, follow the eTEST links at www.pearsoned.ca/school/physicssource.

15.2 Quantization of Charge

As you learned in Chapter 14, Planck and Einstein introduced the concept of quantization in physics in the early 20th century. The discovery of the electron raised the intriguing idea that electric charge might also be quantized.

15-2 QuickLab

Determining a Fundamental Quantity

Problem

Does a set of containers contain only identical items?

Materials

5 sealed containers
laboratory balance

Procedure

1. Measure the mass of each container to a precision of 0.1 g.

2. Discuss with your partner how to record and present your data.

3. Pool your data with the rest of the class.

Questions

1. Look for patterns in the pooled data. Discuss as a class the best way to tabulate and graph all of the data. How can you arrange the data to make it easier to analyze?

2. Consider the differences in mass between pairs of containers. Explain whether these differences indicate that the masses vary only by multiples of a basic unit. If so, calculate a value for this basic unit.

3. Can you be sure that the basic unit is not smaller than the value you calculated? Explain why or why not.

4. What further information do you need in order to calculate the number of items in each container?

The American physicist Robert Andrews Millikan (1868–1953) and his graduate student Harvey Fletcher made the next breakthrough in the study of the properties of the electron. In 1909, Millikan reported the results from a beautiful experiment that determined the charge on the electron and showed that it was a fundamental unit of electrical charge.

Millikan's Oil-drop Experiment

Millikan and Fletcher used an atomizer to spray tiny drops of oil into the top of a closed vessel containing two parallel metal plates (Figure 15.9). Some of the oil drops fell into the lower part of the vessel through a small hole in the upper plate. Friction during the spraying process gave some of the oil drops a small electric charge. Millikan also used X rays to change the charge on the oil drops.

Since these oil drops were usually spherical, Millikan could calculate the mass of each drop from its diameter and the density of the oil. He connected a high-voltage battery to the plates, then observed the motion of the oil drops in the uniform electric field between the plates. By analyzing this motion and allowing for air resistance, Millikan calculated the electric force acting on each drop, and thus determined the charge on the drop.

info **BIT**

Millikan won the Nobel Prize in physics in 1923. In his Nobel lecture on the oil-drop experiment, he did not mention Fletcher's work at all.

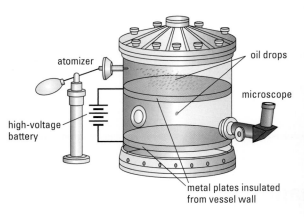

▲ **Figure 15.9** Millikan's oil-drop apparatus

 SIM

To see a simulation of Millikan's oil-drop experiment, follow the links at www.pearsoned.ca/school/physicssource.

elementary unit of charge, e:
the charge on a proton

info **BIT**

Thomson and others had tried to measure the charge on an electron using tiny droplets of water. However, evaporation and other problems made these measurements inaccurate.

 MATH

For a simple exercise to determine the fundamental unit of charge using a method similar to Millikan's, visit www.pearsoned.ca/school/physicssource.

Millikan made numerous measurements with oil drops of various sizes. He found that the charged oil drops had either 1.6×10^{-19} C of charge or an integer multiple of this value. Millikan reasoned that the smallest possible charge that a drop can have is the charge acquired either by gaining or losing an electron. Hence, the charge on the electron must be -1.6×10^{-19} C.

Millikan showed that charge is not a continuous quantity; it exists only in discrete amounts. This finding parallels Planck's discovery in 1900 that energy is quantized (see section 14.1).

Recent measurements have determined that the **elementary unit of charge, e**, has a value of $1.602\ 176\ 462 \pm 0.000\ 000\ 063 \times 10^{-19}$ C. A value of 1.60×10^{-19} C is accurate enough for the calculations in this textbook. Note that a proton has a charge of $+1e$ and an electron has a charge of $-1e$.

Since Thomson and others had already determined the charge-to-mass ratio for electrons, Millikan could now calculate a reasonably accurate value for the mass of the electron. This calculation confirmed Thomson's estimate that the mass of the electron is roughly 1700 times less than the mass of the lightest atom, hydrogen.

Millikan and Controversy

In the mid 1970s, historians of science made a disturbing discovery: Millikan had, on several occasions, stated that he used all of his data in coming to the conclusion that the charge of the electron was quantized. In fact, his notebooks contain 175 measurements of which he only reported 58! When all of Millikan's data are used, his evidence for the quantization of charge is far less conclusive! Was Millikan guilty of scientific fraud, or was it a deeper, intuitive insight that led him to select only the data that clearly supported his claim that the charge on the electron is quantized? Historians will debate this question for many years to come, but we still acknowledge Millikan as the first person to measure the charge of the electron and to establish the quantization of charge.

Why is it almost impossible to determine the mass of an electron without determining its charge first?

Example 15.3

An oil drop of mass 8.2×10^{-15} kg is suspended in an electric field of 1.0×10^5 N/C [down]. How many electrons has the oil drop gained or lost?

Given
$\vec{E} = 1.0 \times 10^5$ N/C [down]
$m = 8.2 \times 10^{-15}$ kg

Required
number of electrons gained or lost (n)

Analysis and Solution
To balance the gravitational force, the electric force must be directed upward (Figure 15.10). Since the electric force is in the opposite direction to the electric field, $\vec{E}$, the charge on the oil drop must be negative.

For the electric and gravitational forces to balance, their magnitudes must be equal. Since $\vec{F}_{net} = \vec{F}_e + \vec{F}_g$ and $\vec{F}_{net} = 0$, then $0 = F_e - F_g$.

$$F_e = F_g$$
$$q|\vec{E}| = mg$$

where q is the magnitude of the charge on the drop and g is the magnitude of the gravitational field.

Solving for q gives

$$q = \frac{mg}{|\vec{E}|}$$
$$= \frac{(8.2 \times 10^{-15}\ \text{kg})(9.81\ \text{m/s}^2)}{1.0 \times 10^5\ \text{N/C}}$$
$$= 8.04 \times 10^{-19}\ \text{C}$$

The net charge on the oil drop equals the number of electrons gained times the charge on each electron. Thus,

$$q = ne \quad \text{and} \quad n = \frac{q}{e}$$

Note that n must be a whole number.

$$n = \frac{q}{e}$$
$$= \frac{8.04 \times 10^{-19}\ \text{C}}{1.60 \times 10^{-19}\ \text{C}}$$
$$= 5$$

Paraphrase
The oil drop has gained five electrons.

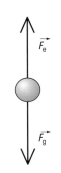

▲ **Figure 15.10**

Practice Problems

1. What can you conclude about a plastic sphere of mass 2.4×10^{-14} kg that is suspended by an electric field of 5.0×10^5 N/C [up]?

2. What electric field will suspend an oil drop with a mass of 3.2×10^{-14} kg and a charge of $+2e$?

Answers

1. The sphere has lost three electrons.

2. 9.8×10^5 N/C [up]

In Example 15.3, you studied what happens when the electric force on a charged droplet exactly balances the gravitational force on the same droplet. What happens if these two forces do not balance each other?

Example 15.4

An oil droplet of mass 8.2×10^{-15} kg is placed in an electric field of 1.0×10^5 N/C [down]. The droplet has 10 excess electrons and is, therefore, charged. Determine whether the oil droplet will accelerate, and if so, in which direction.

Given
Choose up to be positive.

$\vec{E} = 1.0 \times 10^5$ N/C [down] $= -1.0 \times 10^5$ N/C

$m = 8.2 \times 10^{-15}$ kg

$q = 10e^-$

$\vec{g} = 9.81$ m/s² [down] $= -9.81$ m/s²

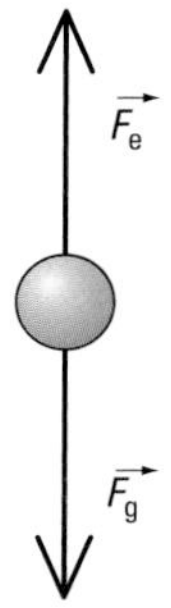

Required
acceleration of the oil droplet ($\vec{a}$)

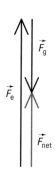

▲ **Figure 15.11 (a)**

Analysis and Solution
Determine the size of the charge on the oil droplet:

$q = 10e^- = -1.60 \times 10^{-18}$ C

Draw a free-body diagram of the forces acting on the droplet (Figure 15.11 (a)). Because the charge is negative, the electric force is in the opposite direction to the electric field, $\vec{E}$.
Calculate the magnitude of both the electric and gravitational forces acting on the oil droplet.

$$\vec{F}_g = m\vec{g}$$
$$= (8.2 \times 10^{-15} \text{ kg})(-9.81 \text{ m/s}^2)$$
$$= -8.04 \times 10^{-14} \text{ N}$$
$$\vec{F}_e = q\vec{E}$$
$$= (-1.60 \times 10^{-18} \text{ C})(-1.0 \times 10^5 \text{ N/C})$$
$$= +1.60 \times 10^{-13} \text{ N}$$

Determine the net force on the oil droplet. From Figure 15.11 (b),

$$\vec{F}_{net} = \vec{F}_g + \vec{F}_e$$
$$= -8.04 \times 10^{-14} \text{ N} + (+1.60 \times 10^{-13} \text{ N})$$
$$= +7.96 \times 10^{-14} \text{ N}$$

The acceleration of the oil droplet is:

$$\vec{F}_{net} = m\vec{a}$$
$$\vec{a} = \frac{\vec{F}_{net}}{m}$$
$$= \frac{+7.96 \times 10^{-14} \text{ N}}{8.2 \times 10^{-15} \text{ kg}}$$
$$= +9.7 \text{ m/s}^2$$

▲ **Figure 15.11 (b)**

Paraphrase
The oil droplet will accelerate upward at a rate of 9.7 m/s².

Practice Problems

1. Calculate the net force on a sphere of charge +5 electron charges and mass 2.0×10^{-14} kg when placed in an electric field of strength 1.0×10^5 N/C [up].

2. Calculate the acceleration of the sphere if the direction of the electric field in question 1 is reversed.

Answers

1. 1.2×10^{-13} N [down]
2. 14 m/s² [down]

Knowledge

1. Explain the term *quantization of charge*.

2. Which two properties of the electron was Millikan able to determine with his oil-drop experiment?

3. Calculate the charge, in coulombs, on an oil drop that has gained four electrons.

4. Determine the electric force acting on an oil drop with a charge of $-5e$ in a uniform electric field of 100 N/C [down].

Applications

5. (a) What is the net force acting on a charged oil drop falling at a constant velocity in the absence of an electric field? Explain your reasoning, using a free-body diagram to show the forces acting on the drop.

   (b) Describe the motion of the oil drop in an electric field that exerts an upward force greater than the gravitational force on the drop. Draw a diagram to show the forces acting on the drop.

6. An oil droplet with a mass of 6.9×10^{-17} kg is suspended motionless in a uniform electric field of 423 N/C [down].

   (a) Find the charge on this droplet.

   (b) How many electrons has the droplet either gained or lost?

   (c) Describe how the droplet will move if the direction of the electric field is suddenly reversed.

Extensions

7. A student attempting to duplicate Millikan's experiment obtained these results. Explain why you might suspect that there was a systematic error in the student's measurements.

Droplet #	Charge ($\times 10^{-19}$ C)
1	19.0
2	17.2
3	10.0
4	20.8
5	26.2
6	24.4
7	20.8
8	22.6
9	15.4
10	24.4

8. Some critics of Millikan have noted that he used only a third of his measurements when reporting the results of his oil-drop experiment. Use a library or the Internet to learn more about this issue. Explain whether you feel that Millikan was justified in presenting only his "best" data.

e **TEST**

To check your understanding of charge quantization, follow the eTEST links at www.pearsoned.ca/school/physicssource.

15.3 The Discovery of the Nucleus

By the beginning of the 20th century, the work of Thomson, Perrin, and others had provided strong evidence that atoms were not the smallest form of matter. Physicists then started developing models to describe the structure of atoms and devising experiments to test these models.

15-3 QuickLab

Using Scattering to Measure a Hidden Shape

Problem

What can scattering reveal about the shape of an unseen target?

Materials

cardboard tube 10–15 cm in diameter
small marbles or ball bearings
carbon paper
white letter-size paper

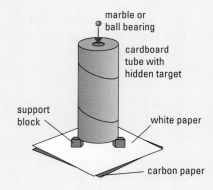

marble or ball bearing

cardboard tube with hidden target

support block

white paper

carbon paper

▲ **Figure 15.12**

Procedure

1 Your teacher will prepare several "beam tubes" containing a hidden target. A cover blocks the top of each tube, except for a small opening (Figure 15.12). No peeking!

2 Work with a small group. Place a sheet of carbon paper, carbon side up, on the desk, and put a piece of white paper on top of the carbon paper. Then carefully set the cardboard tube on blocks on top of the paper.

3 Drop a marble or ball bearing through the opening at the top of the cardboard tube. Retrieve the marble or bearing, then drop it through the tube again, for a total of 50 times.

4 Remove the piece of paper, and look for a pattern in the marks left on it.

Questions

1. Discuss with your group what the scattering pattern reveals about the shape and size of the target hidden in the cardboard tube. Sketch the likely shape of the target.
2. Explain how you can use your scattering results to estimate the dimensions of the target.
3. Compare your predictions to those made by groups using the other prepared tubes.
4. What is the smallest dimension that you could measure with the equipment in this experiment?

Rutherford's Scattering Experiment

Ernest Rutherford (1871–1937), a brilliant experimenter from New Zealand, was fascinated by radioactivity. By 1909, he had shown that some radioactive elements, such as radium and thorium, emitted positively charged helium ions, which are often called alpha (α) particles. Rutherford had also observed that a beam of these particles spread out somewhat when passing through a thin sheet of mica. So, he had two assistants, Hans Geiger and Ernest Marsden, measure the proportion of alpha particles scattered at different angles from various materials.

Figure 15.13 shows the technique Rutherford devised for these measurements. A few milligrams of radium in a lead block with a small opening produced a pencil-shaped beam of alpha particles. The experimenters positioned a sheet of thin gold foil at right angles to the beam of alpha particles and used a screen coated with zinc sulfide to detect particles scattered by the foil. When an alpha particle struck the screen, the zinc sulfide gave off a faint flash of light, just enough to be visible through the microscope. By rotating the screen and microscope around the gold film, Geiger and Marsden measured the rates at which alpha particles appeared at various angles.

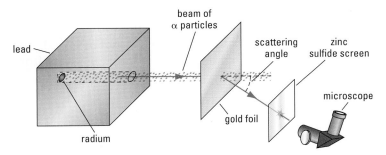

◀ **Figure 15.13** Rutherford's scattering experiment

Most of the alpha particles travelled through the foil with a deflection of a degree or less. The number of alpha particles detected dropped off drastically as the scattering angle increased. However, a few alpha particles were scattered at angles greater than 140°, and once in a while an alpha particle would bounce almost straight back. Figure 15.14 shows the relationship between the number of scattered alpha particles and the angle at which they scattered.

Rutherford was startled by these results. He knew that the deflections caused by attraction to the electrons in the gold atoms would be tiny because the alpha particles were fast-moving and roughly 8000 times heavier than electrons. He also calculated that deflection caused by repulsion of the alpha particles by the positive charge in the gold atoms would be no more than a degree if this charge were distributed evenly throughout each atom. So, Rutherford did not expect *any* alpha particles to be scattered at large angles. In a lecture describing the experiment, he said that seeing this scattering "was almost as incredible as if you had fired a 15-inch shell at a piece of tissue paper and it came back and hit you!"

Rutherford spent several weeks analyzing the scattering data. He concluded that the positive charge in a gold atom must be concentrated in an incredibly tiny volume, so most of gold foil was actually empty space!

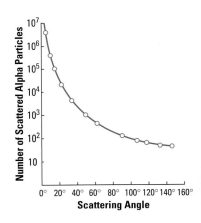

▲ **Figure 15.14** The scattering pattern observed by Geiger and Marsden

Rutherford's team then tried scattering alpha particles from other metals. Using data from scattering experiments with aluminium foil, Rutherford showed that the positive charge and most of the mass of an atom are contained in a radius of less than 10^{-14} m. Rutherford had discovered the nucleus—and disproved the raisin-bun model.

Concept Check

On average, atoms have a radius of roughly 10^{-10} m. Use Rutherford's estimate for the size of the nucleus to calculate the proportion of the human body that is just empty space.

The Planetary Model

planetary model: atomic model that has electrons orbiting a nucleus

Rutherford's discovery of the nucleus quickly led to the **planetary model** of the atom (Figure 15.15). In this model, the electrons orbit the nucleus much like planets orbiting the Sun. The electrostatic attraction between the positive nucleus and the negative electrons provides the centripetal force that keeps the electrons in their orbits. This model is also known as the solar-system, nuclear, or Rutherford model.

To calculate the size of the nucleus, Rutherford applied the law of conservation of energy and an equation for electric potential energy. He knew that the electric potential energy that a charge q_1 gains from the field around charge q_2 is

$$E_\mathrm{p} = \frac{kq_1q_2}{d}$$

where k is Coulomb's constant and d is the distance between the charges.

This equation can be derived from Coulomb's law using basic calculus.

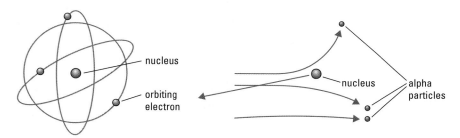

▲ **Figure 15.15** The planetary model of the atom can explain the results of Rutherford's scattering experiments. The extreme scattering of some alpha particles could only be explained by having most of the mass and positive charge of the atom concentrated in a very small nucleus.

Example 15.5

In a scattering experiment, some alpha particles are scattered almost straight back from a sheet of gold foil. Each of these particles had an initial kinetic energy of 1.6×10^{-12} J. The charge on an alpha particle is $+2e$, and the charge on a gold nucleus is $+79e$. Estimate the maximum possible size of a gold nucleus, given that the alpha particles do not hit the nucleus.

Given

$E_k = 1.6 \times 10^{-12}$ J $q_1 = q_\alpha = +2e$ $q_2 = q_{gold} = +79e$

Required

radius of the nucleus of a gold atom (r)

Analysis and Solution

Since energy is conserved, the total kinetic and potential energy of an alpha particle does not change during scattering.

As an alpha particle approaches a nucleus, the force of repulsion between the positive charges causes the alpha particle to slow down. This process converts the particle's kinetic energy to electric potential energy until the kinetic energy is zero. Then the particle starts moving away from the nucleus and regains its kinetic energy. At the point where the alpha particle is closest to the nucleus, all of the particle's kinetic energy has been converted to electric potential energy.

The electric potential energy of the alpha particle is $E_p = \dfrac{kq_1q_2}{d}$, where

k is Coulomb's constant and d is the distance between the alpha particle and the nucleus.

The initial distance between the alpha particle and the nucleus is vastly larger than the distance between them when they are closest together. Therefore, the initial electric potential energy of the alpha particle is negligible for this calculation.

Initially, kinetic energy + electric potential energy = 1.6×10^{-12} J + 0

When the alpha particle is closest to the nucleus,

kinetic energy + electric potential energy = $0 + \dfrac{kq_1q_2}{d}$

Since the total energy is conserved, $\dfrac{kq_1q_2}{d} = 1.6 \times 10^{-12}$ J

Solving for d gives

$$d = \frac{kq_1q_2}{1.6 \times 10^{-12} \text{ J}}$$

$$= \frac{\left(8.99 \times 10^9 \; \dfrac{\text{N·m}^2}{\text{C}^2}\right)(2 \times 1.60 \times 10^{-19} \text{ C})(79 \times 1.60 \times 10^{-19} \text{ C})}{1.6 \times 10^{-12} \text{ J}}$$

$$= 2.3 \times 10^{-14} \text{ m}$$

At its closest approach, the alpha particle is about 2.3×10^{-14} m from the centre of the nucleus.

Paraphrase

The radius of a gold nucleus cannot be larger than 2.3×10^{-14} m.

Practice Problems

1. The charge on a tin nucleus is $+50e$. How close can an alpha particle with an initial kinetic energy of 1.6×10^{-12} J approach the nucleus of a tin atom?

2. An iron nucleus has 56 protons. What is the electric potential energy of a proton located 5.6×10^{-13} m from the centre of an iron nucleus?

Answers

1. 1.4×10^{-14} m
2. 2.3×10^{-14} J

Knowledge

1. Explain how the results from Rutherford's gold-foil experiment disproved Thomson's model of the atom.

2. Briefly describe the planetary model of the atom.

3. Find the potential energy of an alpha particle that is

   (a) 1.0×10^{-10} m from the centre of a gold nucleus

   (b) 1.0×10^{-14} m from the centre of a gold nucleus

4. Why does the scattering angle increase as alpha particles pass closer to the nucleus?

Applications

5. Why did Rutherford conclude that it was just the nucleus that must be extremely tiny in an atom and not the entire atom?

6. (a) By 1900, physicists knew that 1 m³ of gold contains approximately 6×10^{28} atoms. Use this information to estimate the size of a gold atom. List any assumptions you make.

   (b) Compare this estimate to the estimate of the size of a gold nucleus in Example 15.5.

7. In scattering experiments with aluminium foil, Rutherford found that the alpha particles observed at angles close to 180° did not behave like they had been scattered only by electrostatic repulsion. Rutherford thought these alpha particles might have actually hit an aluminium nucleus.

   (a) Why did Rutherford see only electrostatic scattering when he used the same source of alpha particles with gold foil?

   (b) Rutherford used alpha particles with an energy of about 1.2×10^{-12} J. Estimate the radius of an aluminium nucleus.

Extension

8. According to Rutherford's calculations, the positive charges in an atom are packed tightly together in the nucleus. Why would physicists in 1900 expect such an arrangement to be highly unstable? What did Rutherford's results suggest about forces in the nucleus?

 eTEST

To check your understanding of atomic models, follow the eTEST links at www.pearsoned.ca/school/physicssource.

15.4 The Bohr Model of the Atom

In 1912, Niels Bohr (1885–1962), a Danish physicist, studied for a few months at Rutherford's laboratory. Both Bohr and Rutherford recognized a critical flaw in the planetary model of the atom. Experiments had shown that an accelerating charge emits electromagnetic waves, as predicted by the mathematical model for electromagnetism developed by the Scottish physicist James Clerk Maxwell (1831–1879). Electrons orbiting a nucleus are constantly accelerating, so they should emit electromagnetic waves. These waves would take energy from the orbiting electrons. As a result, the electrons in an atom should spiral into the nucleus in a few microseconds (Figure 15.16). But empirical evidence indicates that electrons do not spiral into their atomic nuclei. If they did, stable matter would not exist.

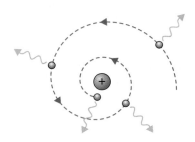

◀ **Figure 15.16** According to Maxwell's laws of electromagnetism, the orbiting electron should continuously radiate energy and spiral into the nucleus, which it does not do.

Bohr thought Planck's concept of quantized energy might provide a solution, and puzzled for months over how to fit this concept into a model of the atom. Then, a casual conversation with a colleague, his former classmate Hans Marius Hansen, gave Bohr the key to the answer. Hansen had recently returned from studying in Germany under an expert in **spectroscopy**. Hansen told Bohr that the wavelengths of the light in the spectrum of hydrogen have a mathematical pattern. No one had yet explained why this pattern occurs. Bohr found the explanation, and provided the first theoretical basis for spectroscopy.

spectroscopy: the study of the light emitted and absorbed by different materials

Spectroscopy

A prism or diffraction grating can spread light out into a spectrum with colours distributed according to their wavelengths. In 1814, Josef von Fraunhofer (1787–1826) noticed a number of gaps or dark lines in the spectrum of the Sun. By 1859, another German physicist, Gustav Kirchhoff (1824–1887), had established that each element or compound has a unique spectrum. Kirchhoff and others used spectra to identify a number of previously unknown elements. Kirchhoff's laws for spectra explain how temperature and pressure affect the light produced or absorbed by a material:

- A hot, dense material emits a continuous spectrum, without any dark or bright lines.
- A hot gas at low pressure has an **emission line spectrum** with bright lines at distinct characteristic wavelengths.
- A gas at low pressure absorbs light at the same wavelengths as the light it emits when heated. Shining white light through the gas produces an **absorption line spectrum** with dark lines that match the bright lines in the emission spectrum for the gas.

Figure 15.17 illustrates these three types of spectra.

emission line spectrum: a pattern of bright lines produced by a hot gas at low pressure

absorption line spectrum: a pattern of dark lines produced when light passes through a gas at low pressure

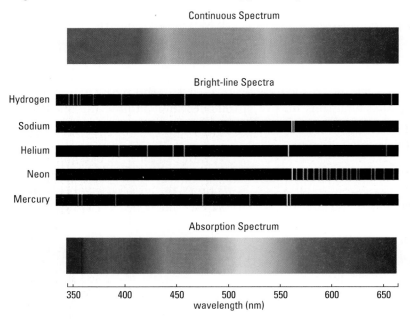

▶ **Figure 15.17**

Continuous, emission line, and absorption line spectra

15-4 *Design a Lab*

Emission Spectra of Elements

The Question

In what ways are emission line spectra characteristic of the elements that produce them?

Design and Conduct Your Investigation

Investigate the emission spectra produced by various elements. Here are some ways you can heat different elements enough to produce visible light:
- Use a Bunsen burner to vaporize a small amount of an element.
- Use commercially available discharge tubes containing gaseous elements.
- Observe forms of lighting that use a vaporized element, such as sodium or mercury arc lamps.

Often, a diffraction grating is the simplest method for observing a spectrum. Check with your teacher if you need directions for using a diffraction grating. Note the overall colour of the light from each element, and sketch or photograph its emission spectrum.

Extending

Investigate absorption lines. You could try comparing the spectra of direct sunlight and sunlight that passes through clouds. Alternatively, you could shine white light at coloured solutions and diffract the light that passes through. Why are distinct absorption lines generally more difficult to produce than emission lines?

Improvements in the resolution of **spectrometers** made them a powerful analytic tool. For example, scientists have painstakingly matched the dark **Fraunhofer lines** in the solar spectrum (Figure 15.18) to the spectral patterns of dozens of elements, thus proving that these elements are present in the Sun's atmosphere. However, at the start of the 20th century, the reasons why elements produce spectral lines were still a mystery.

spectrometer: a device for measuring the wavelengths of light in a spectrum

Fraunhofer line: a dark line in the spectrum of the Sun

▲ **Figure 15.18**   Fraunhofer lines are the dark lines in the visible part of the solar spectrum.

The first hint that spectral lines were not just randomly spaced came in 1885. Johann Jacob Balmer, a Swiss mathematics teacher with an interest in numerology, found a formula for the wavelengths of the lines in the hydrogen spectrum. In 1890, Johannes Robert Rydberg generalized Balmer's formula and applied it with varied success to other elements. Here is the formula for hydrogen:

$$\frac{1}{\lambda} = R_{\text{H}} \left(\frac{1}{2^2} - \frac{1}{n^2} \right)$$

where R_{H} is Rydberg's constant for hydrogen, $1.097 \times 10^7 \text{ m}^{-1}$, and n has the whole number values 3, 4, 5, ...

The emission line spectrum of hydrogen is given in Figure 15.19.

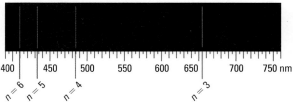

▲ **Figure 15.19**   Some of the bright lines in the spectrum of hydrogen

Hansen told Bohr about this formula. Bohr later remarked, "As soon as I saw Balmer's formula, the whole thing was immediately clear to me." Bohr had realized that the spectral lines corresponded to *differences* between quantized energy levels in the hydrogen atom. This concept was the foundation of a powerful new model of the atom.

 e **WEB**

To learn more about spectra, follow the links at www.pearsoned.ca/school/physicssource.

The Bohr Model of the Atom

In 1913, Bohr published a paper suggesting a radical change to the planetary model of the atom. Here are the basic principles of Bohr's model:

- Electrons can orbit the nucleus only at certain specific distances from the nucleus. These distances are particular multiples of the radius of the smallest permitted orbit (Figure 15.20). Thus, the orbits in an atom are quantized.

- Both the kinetic energy and the electric potential energy of an electron in orbit around a nucleus depend on the electron's distance from the nucleus. So, the energy of an electron in an atom is also quantized. Each orbit corresponds to a particular **energy level** for the electron.

- An electron can move from one energy level to another only by either emitting or absorbing energy equal to the difference between the two energy levels. An electron that stays in a particular orbit does not radiate any energy. Since the size and shape of the orbit remain constant along with the energy of the electron, the orbits are often called **stationary states**.

energy level: a discrete and quantized amount of energy

stationary state: a stable state with a fixed energy level

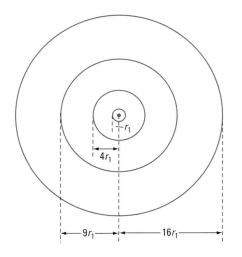

► **Figure 15.20** In Bohr's model of the atom, electrons can orbit only at specific distances from the nucleus.

Bohr reasoned that Balmer's formula shows that the energy of an orbiting electron depends inversely on the square of a quantum number n, now known as the **principal quantum number**. Bohr then used the equations for uniform circular motion, Coulomb's law, and electric potential energy to derive expressions for the size of the hydrogen atom and the energy of the electron in the atom.

Orbit Sizes

Bohr's model of the hydrogen atom states that electrons can orbit the nucleus only at specific locations given by the expression:

$$r_n = \frac{h^2}{4\pi^2 mke^2} n^2$$

where r_n is the radius of the nth possible orbit for an electron and n is the principal quantum number, which can have the values 1, 2, 3, ... The other symbols in the equation all represent constants: k is Coulomb's constant, h is Planck's constant, e is the elementary charge, and m is the mass of the electron.

By combining all the constants, this equation can be simplified to

$$r_n = r_1 n^2, \quad \text{where } r_1 = \frac{h^2}{4\pi^2 mke^2} = 5.29 \times 10^{-11} \text{ m}$$

The quantity r_1 is known as the **Bohr radius**. It is the radius of the lowest possible energy level or **ground state** of the hydrogen atom.

Concept Check

Sketch the first three orbits for a hydrogen atom to scale. Describe how the size of this atom changes as n increases.

Energy Levels

An orbiting electron has both kinetic energy and electric potential energy. By combining equations for kinetic and electric potential energies, Bohr derived this expression for E_n, the total energy of the electron in an energy level:

$$E_n = -\frac{1}{n^2} \left(\frac{2\pi^2 mk^2 e^4}{h^2} \right)$$

As with the expression for the orbit radii, the constants can be combined to simplify the equation:

$$E_n = -\frac{E_1}{n^2}, \text{ where } E_1 = \frac{2\pi^2 m k^2 e^4}{h^2} = 2.18 \times 10^{-18} \text{ J or } 13.6 \text{ eV}$$

E_1 is the ground-state energy of the hydrogen atom. When $n > 1$, the electron has greater energy and the atom is in an **excited state.** When $n = \infty$, the electron is no longer bound to the nucleus because $E_\infty = 0$. Thus, Bohr's model predicts that the **ionization energy** for hydrogen is 2.18×10^{-18} J or 13.6 eV, corresponding to E_1.

excited state: any energy level higher than the ground state

ionization energy: energy required to remove an electron from an atom

Concept Check

Does it make sense that the energy in the equation $E_n = -\frac{1}{n^2}\left(\frac{2\pi^2 m k^2 e^4}{h^2}\right)$ is negative? Consider what you have to do to remove an electron from an atom.

Example 15.6

How much energy must a hydrogen atom absorb in order for its electron to move from the ground state to the $n = 3$ energy level?

Given
$n_{\text{initial}} = 1$ $n_{\text{final}} = 3$

Required
energy absorbed by atom (ΔE)

Analysis and Solution
The energy the atom must absorb is equal to the difference between the two energy levels.
The energy for each energy level is

$$E_n = -\frac{2.18 \times 10^{-18} \text{ J}}{n^2}. \text{ Therefore,}$$

$$\Delta E = E_3 - E_1$$

$$= -\frac{2.18 \times 10^{-18} \text{ J}}{3^2} - \left(-\frac{2.18 \times 10^{-18} \text{ J}}{1^2}\right)$$

$$= (2.18 \times 10^{-18} \text{ J})\left(-\frac{1}{9} + 1\right)$$

$$= 1.94 \times 10^{-18} \text{ J}$$

Paraphrase
The electron in a hydrogen atom requires 1.94×10^{-18} J of energy to move from the ground state to the $n = 3$ level.

Practice Problems

1. How much energy does it take to move the electron in a hydrogen atom from the ground state to the $n = 4$ energy level?

2. How much energy does the electron in a hydrogen atom lose when dropping from the $n = 5$ energy level to the $n = 2$ energy level?

Answers
1. 2.04×10^{-18} J
2. 4.58×10^{-19} J

Energy Level Transitions and Line Spectra

The Bohr model explains why absorption and emission line spectra occur for hydrogen and other elements. To jump to a higher energy level, an electron in an atom must gain energy. The atom can gain this energy by absorbing a photon. For energy to be conserved, the photon's energy must match the difference between the electron's initial energy level and the higher one. Recall from section 14.1 that the energy and frequency of a photon are related by the equation $E = hf$. Thus, the atom can absorb only the frequencies that correspond to differences between the atom's energy levels. Absorption of light at these specific frequencies causes the discrete dark lines in absorption spectra.

Similarly, atoms can emit only photons that have energies corresponding to electron transitions from a higher energy level to a lower one. The arrows in Figure 15.21 illustrate all the possible downward transitions from the first six energy levels for hydrogen. Such energy level diagrams provide a way to predict the energies, and hence the wavelengths, of photons emitted by an atom.

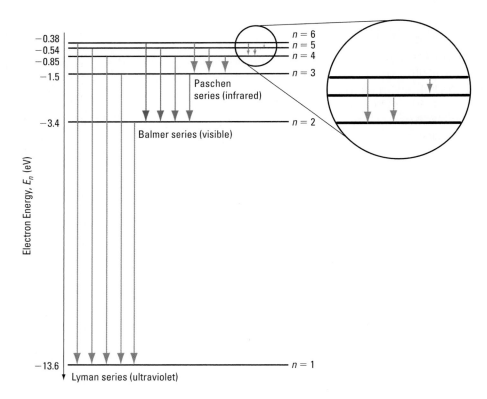

▲ **Figure 15.21** The first six energy levels for hydrogen. Which arrow represents the transition that releases the most energy?

An Emission Spectrum

Question

What is the energy difference between two energy states of atoms in a particular discharge tube?

Hypothesis

At a high temperature and low pressure, an atom emits light at the wavelengths predicted by the Bohr model.

Variables

- diffraction angle
- wavelength

Materials and Equipment

a discharge tube
high-voltage power supply
diffraction grating
12 straight pins
sheet of paper
cardboard or foam-core sheet
protractor and straightedge
masking tape

 CAUTION! Keep well clear of the power supply connections when the power is on.

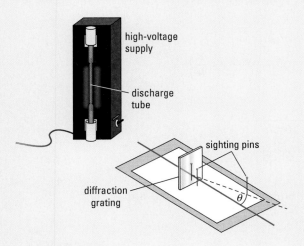

high-voltage supply

discharge tube

sighting pins

diffraction grating

θ

▲ **Figure 15.22**

Procedure

1 Draw an x-axis and a y-axis that intersect in the middle of the sheet of paper. Then tape the paper to the cardboard or foam-core sheet (Figure 15.22).

2 Connect the high-voltage power supply to the discharge tube.

3 Switch on the power supply and look at the discharge tube through the diffraction grating. Orient the grating so that the spectral lines are vertical. You may want to darken the room to see the spectrum more clearly.

4 Align the bottom edge of the diffraction grating with the x-axis on the paper. Hold the grating vertical by pressing a straight pin into the y-axis on either side of the grating.

5 Sight along the y-axis, and turn the cardboard or foam-core base so that the y-axis points directly toward the discharge tube. Now tape the base to the tabletop.

6 For each spectral line, position a sighting pin so that it is on the line between the spectral line and the origin of your axes. Draw a line from the sighting pin to the origin.

Analysis

1. Decide how to record your data. You could use a table similar to the one below.

Colour of Line	Diffraction Angle, θ	Wavelength (nm)

2. Use the diffraction formula $n\lambda = d \sin \theta$ to calculate the wavelengths of the spectral lines (see section 13.5). Sometimes the spacing of the slits, d, is marked on the grating. If not, ask your teacher for this information.

3. Determine the energy difference between the two energy states.

4. Draw an energy level diagram showing the electron transition.

When an electron in an atom absorbs a photon, the final energy level of the atom's electron is greater than its initial energy level. From the law of conservation of energy, the energy of the photon can be expressed as:

$$E_{photon} = E_{final} - E_{initial}$$

Since the energy of an electron in a hydrogen atom at a given energy level, n, is given by the formula $E_n = -\dfrac{1}{n^2}\left(\dfrac{2\pi^2 mk^2 e^4}{h^2}\right)$, it is possible (using algebra) to show that the expression $E_{photon} = E_{final} - E_{initial}$ becomes

$$\frac{1}{\lambda} = R_H\left(\frac{1}{n_{final}^2} - \frac{1}{n_{initial}^2}\right)$$

This result is impressive! Bohr's model not only explains spectral lines, but leads to a generalized form of Balmer's formula, and predicts the value of Rydberg's constant for hydrogen.

Example 15.7

Find the wavelength of the light emitted by a hydrogen atom when its electron drops from the $n = 3$ to the $n = 2$ energy level.

Given

$n_{initial} = 3$ $n_{final} = 2$

Required
wavelength (λ)

Analysis and Solution
Simply substitute the known values for n into the wavelength equation for an emitted photon:

$$\frac{1}{\lambda} = R_H\left(\frac{1}{n_{final}^2} - \frac{1}{n_{initial}^2}\right)$$

$$= R_H\left(\frac{1}{2^2} - \frac{1}{3^2}\right)$$

$$= (1.097 \times 10^7 \text{ m}^{-1})\left(\frac{1}{4} - \frac{1}{9}\right)$$

$$= 1.5236 \times 10^6 \text{ m}^{-1}$$

$$\lambda = \frac{1}{1.524 \times 10^6 \text{ m}^{-1}}$$

$$= 6.563 \times 10^{-7} \text{ m}$$

Paraphrase
The atom emits light with a wavelength of 656.3 nm.

Practice Problems

1. Find the wavelength of the light emitted by a hydrogen atom when its electron drops from the $n = 5$ to the $n = 2$ energy level.

2. Find the wavelength of light that a hydrogen atom will absorb when its electron moves from the $n = 3$ to the $n = 7$ energy level.

Answers

1. 434 nm
2. 1005 nm

What features do the Bohr model of the atom and the planetary model have in common? In what critical ways do these two models differ?

The Northern Lights and the Emission Line Spectrum of Oxygen

Alberta skies often display one of nature's most beautiful phenomena — the aurora borealis, or northern lights, which you first studied in Chapter 12. At altitudes between 100 km and 400 km above the surface of Earth, high-energy electrons, trapped by Earth's magnetic field, interact with oxygen and nitrogen atoms. During these interactions, the electrons in these atoms are excited and move into higher energy levels. Eventually, the excited electrons return to their ground states. In doing so, they emit light that forms the characteristic colours of the aurora borealis. Figure 15.23 shows a display of the aurora borealis above northern Alberta. You can use the Bohr model of the atom to help explain the characteristic green colour of the aurora (as well as the subtler shades of red and blue).

(a)

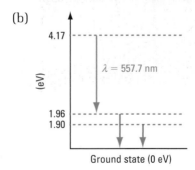

◄ **Figure 15.23** The photo in (a) shows a bright, mostly green aurora. The green colour is due to an energy level transition in oxygen atoms in Earth's atmosphere. The diagram in (b) shows some of the energy levels in the oxygen atom, including the one that produces the green light that is mostly seen in the aurora. In this diagram, the ground state energy equals 0 eV.

(b)

From Figure 15.23(b), the green colour of the aurora occurs when an excited electron drops from an energy level $E_{initial} = 4.17$ eV to a lower energy level $E_{final} = 1.96$ eV. Using the equations $\Delta E = E_{final} - E_{intial}$ and $\Delta E = \dfrac{hc}{\lambda}$, you can show that this change in energy level produces the colour you see.

Use the energy level diagram for oxygen, given in Figure 15.23(b), to verify that a transition from $E_{initial} = 4.17$ eV to $E_{final} = 1.96$ eV will produce green light ($\lambda = 558$ nm). Two other possible transitions are also shown in the diagram. What colours would these transitions produce? Determine their wavelengths.

15.4 Check and Reflect

Knowledge

1. Explain what the phrase "quantized process" means.

2. Sketch the first five orbits in a hydrogen atom. Indicate on your sketch which transitions cause the blue, green, and red lines shown in Figure 15.21.

3. List three quantities predicted by Bohr's model of the atom.

4. Why do electrons in hydrogen atoms emit infrared light when they make transitions to the $n = 3$ energy level, and ultraviolet light when they make transitions to the $n = 1$ energy level?

Applications

5. The wavelengths of the first four visible lines in the hydrogen spectrum are 410, 434, 486, and 656 nm.

   (a) Show that Balmer's formula predicts these wavelengths.

   (b) Which of the wavelengths corresponds to a transition from the $n = 4$ energy level to the $n = 2$ energy level?

   (c) Use this wavelength to calculate the energy difference between the $n = 4$ and the $n = 2$ stationary states.

6. A helium-neon laser produces photons of wavelength 633 nm when an electron in a neon atom drops from an excited energy state to a lower state. What is the energy difference between these two states? Express your answer in electron volts.

7. The diagram shown below shows some of the energy levels for the lithium atom. The designations 2s, 2p, etc., are a common notation used in spectroscopy.

   (a) Without doing any calculations, sort the four transitions shown from shortest wavelength to longest wavelength. Explain your reasoning.

   (b) Estimate the energy of each of the four energy levels shown.

   (c) Calculate the wavelengths produced in these transitions. Indicate which ones are in the visible part of the spectrum, along with their colours.

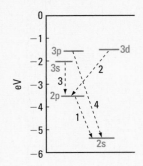

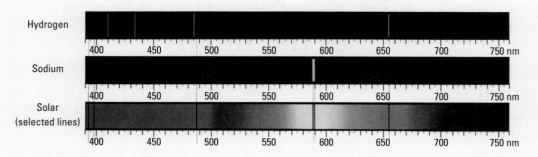

Hydrogen

400   450   500   550   600   650   700   750 nm

Sodium

400   450   500   550   600   650   700   750 nm

Solar
(selected lines)

400   450   500   550   600   650   700   750 nm

8. What can you conclude about the composition of the Sun from the spectra given above? Explain your reasoning.

9. (a) Find the difference in energy between the $n = 2$ and $n = 3$ energy levels in hydrogen.

   (b) Find the energy difference between the $n = 5$ and $n = 6$ energy levels in hydrogen.

   (c) What happens to the energy difference between successive orbits as the distance from the nucleus increases?

10. The ionization energy for an atom is the energy required to remove an electron completely from an atom. Show why the ionization energy for hydrogen is equal to E_1. (Hint: Consider going from the ground state to an energy level with $n > 1000$.)

11. When an atom's energy levels are closely spaced, the atom "de-excites" by having one of its electrons drop through a series of energy levels. This process is called fluorescence and is often seen when a high-energy photon, such as an X ray or a UV photon, excites an atom, which then de-excites through a series of longer-wavelength emissions. A common example of fluorescence occurs in the colours produced when rocks and minerals containing mercury and many other elements are illuminated by UV photons. Below is the energy level diagram for some of the energy levels in mercury (Hg). The ground state has been assigned an energy of 0 eV.

Determine:

(a) the wavelength of the photon needed to excite the mercury atom from its ground state to the $n = 5$ energy level

(b) the longest wavelength of photon that will be emitted as the mercury atom de-excites

(c) the number of possible downward transitions that can occur

(d) If an atom had 100 possible energy transitions that were very close together, what would the spectrum produced by this atom look like?

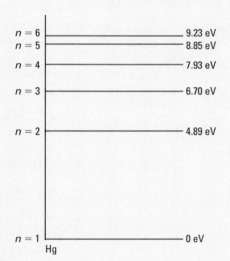

$n = 6$	9.23 eV
$n = 5$	8.85 eV
$n = 4$	7.93 eV
$n = 3$	6.70 eV
$n = 2$	4.89 eV
$n = 1$	0 eV

Hg

Extension

12. A laser produces light that is monochromatic, coherent, and collimated.

(a) Explain each of these three properties.

(b) Describe the spectrum of a laser.

e TEST

To check your understanding of Bohr's model of the atom, follow the eTEST links at www.pearsoned.ca/school/physicssource.

15.5 The Quantum Model of the Atom

PHYSICS INSIGHT

Recall from section 13.5 that for constructive interference to occur, the path difference between waves must be a whole number of wavelengths, or $n\lambda$.

Bohr's model explains the spectral lines of hydrogen and accurately predicts the size and ionization energy of the hydrogen atom. Despite these remarkable accomplishments, the theory has several serious failings:

- It does not really explain why energy is quantized, nor why orbiting electrons do not radiate electromagnetic energy.

- It is not accurate for atoms that have two or more electrons.

- It does not explain why a magnetic field splits the main spectral lines into multiple closely spaced lines. The Dutch physicist Pieter Zeeman discovered this effect in 1896. It is known as the Zeeman effect.

Physicists solved these problems within 15 years, but the solutions were even more radical than Bohr's theory!

The Wave Nature of Electrons

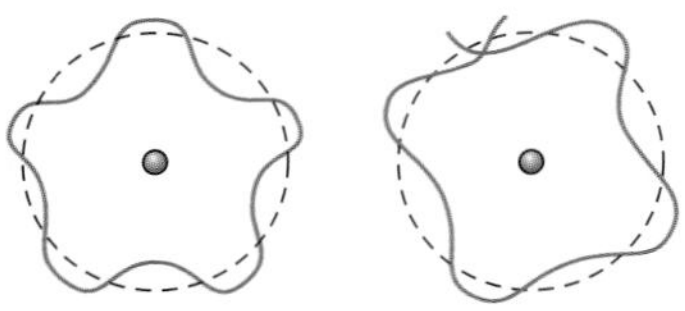

In 1924, Louis de Broglie developed his theory that particles have wave properties. As described in section 14.4, diffraction experiments confirmed that electrons behave like waves that have the wavelength predicted by de Broglie. So, the principles of interference and standing waves apply for electrons orbiting a nucleus.

For most sizes of orbit, successive cycles of the electron wave will be out of phase, and destructive interference will reduce the amplitude of the wave (Figure 15.24). For constructive interference to occur, the circumference of the orbit must be equal to a whole number of wavelengths:

$$2\pi r_n = n\lambda$$

where n is a positive integer, λ is the electron wavelength, and r_n is the radius of the nth energy level.

By substituting de Broglie's definition for wavelength, $\lambda = \dfrac{h}{mv}$, into the above equation, the condition for constructive interference becomes

$$2\pi r_n = \frac{nh}{mv} \qquad \text{or} \qquad mvr_n = \frac{nh}{2\pi}$$

This condition is fundamentally the same one that Bohr found was necessary for the energy levels in his model of the atom. Thus, the wave nature of matter provides a natural explanation for quantized energy levels. Figure 15.25 shows the standing waves corresponding to the first three energy levels in an atom. Note that the de Broglie wavelength is longer in each successive energy level because the electron's speed decreases as the radius of the orbit increases.

constructive   destructive
interference   interference

▲ **Figure 15.24** A standing wave is possible only if a whole number of electron wavelengths fit exactly along the circumference of an orbit.

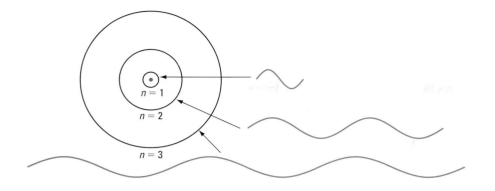

In 1926, Erwin Schrödinger (1887–1961) derived an equation for determining how electron waves behave in the electric field surrounding a nucleus. The solutions to Schrödinger's equation are functions that define the amplitude of the electron wave in the space around a nucleus. Max Born (1882–1970) showed that the square of the amplitude of these wave functions at any point is proportional to the probability of finding an electron at that point. Each wave function defines a different probability distribution or **orbital**.

Quantum Indeterminacy

Unlike the Bohr model, the quantum model does not have electrons orbiting at precisely defined distances from the nucleus. Instead, the electrons behave as waves, which do not have a precise location. The orbitals in the quantum model show the likelihood of an electron being at a given point. They are not paths that the electrons follow.

The idea that electrons within an atom behave as waves rather than as orbiting particles explains why these electrons do not radiate electromagnetic energy continuously.

Some physicists, including Einstein and Schrödinger, had difficulty accepting a quantum model that could predict only probabilities rather than clearly defined locations for electrons in an atom. As Niels Bohr noted, "Anyone who is not shocked by quantum theory has not understood a single word." Despite its challenging concepts, quantum theory is the most comprehensive and accurate model of atoms and molecules yet developed.

info **BIT**

Although Born won a Nobel Prize for his work on quantum theory, Schrödinger never accepted Born's interpretation of electron wave functions.

orbital: probability distribution of an electron in an atom

Concept Check

Soon after Bohr's model was published, physicists discovered that the spectral lines in hydrogen and other elements were not distinct, but could themselves be split into numerous, very closely spaced spectral lines. How does the splitting of spectral lines show that Bohr's concept of energy levels is incomplete?

Knowledge

1. Describe three failings of the Bohr model.

2. What is the Zeeman effect?

3. What is an orbital?

Applications

4. (a) Find the de Broglie wavelength for an electron in the ground state for hydrogen. Recall that the ground-state radius for hydrogen is 5.29×10^{-11} m.

   (b) Find the momentum of the electron in part (a). (Hint: Use the formula for the de Broglie wavelength.)

   (c) Find the kinetic energy and velocity for the electron in part (a).

5. (a) Express the de Broglie wavelength of the $n = 2$ and $n = 3$ energy levels of an atom in terms of λ_1, the de Broglie wavelength for the $n = 1$ energy level. (Hint: Apply Bohr's equation for the orbital radii.)

   (b) Make a scale diagram or model of the atom showing the electron waves for the first three energy levels.

Extensions

6. In more advanced treatments of quantum mechanics, the wave solutions to the Schrödinger equation can describe complex-looking orbitals around atoms. These solutions will sometimes have nodes. As you learned in Chapter 13, a node is a location where waves combine destructively and have zero amplitude. According to Born's interpretation of a wave function, what meaning would you give to a node in a wave function?

7. Radio astronomers use the 21-cm line to study hydrogen gas clouds in our galaxy. Use a library or the Internet to research this spectral line. What unusual transition causes the 21-cm line? Why does this transition occur naturally in hydrogen in deep space, but not in hydrogen on Earth?

 TEST

To check your understanding of the quantum model, follow the eTEST links at www.pearsoned.ca/school/physicssource.

Key Terms and Concepts

cathode ray
elementary unit of charge
planetary model
spectroscopy

emission line spectrum
absorption line spectrum
spectrometer
Fraunhofer line

energy level
stationary state
principal quantum
  number

Bohr radius
ground state
excited state
ionization energy
orbital

Key Equations

Velocity selection: no deflection if $v = \dfrac{|\vec{E}|}{B}$

Bohr model for hydrogen: $r_n = r_1 n^2$, where $r_1 = 5.29 \times 10^{-11}$ m $E_n = -\dfrac{E_1}{n^2}$, where $E_1 = 2.18 \times 10^{-18}$ J

Emission lines: $E_{\text{photon}} = E_{\text{final}} - E_{\text{initial}}$ and $\dfrac{1}{\lambda} = R_H\left(\dfrac{1}{n_{\text{final}}^2} - \dfrac{1}{n_{\text{initial}}^2}\right)$, where $R_H = 1.097 \times 10^7$ m^{-1}

Quantum model: $mvr_n = \dfrac{nh}{2\pi}$

Conceptual Overview

Summarize the chapter by copying and completing this concept map.

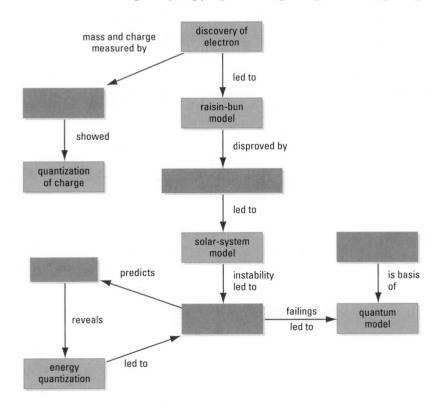

Knowledge

1. (15.1) What is a cathode ray? What type of electric charge does a cathode ray carry?

2. (15.1) (a) Describe the force acting on a cathode ray moving to the right in an electric field directed down.
   (b) Describe the force acting on a cathode ray moving to the right in a magnetic field directed down.
   (c) How could the electric and magnetic fields be directed so that the net force on the cathode ray is zero?

3. (15.1) The glowing gas shows the path of the electrons in this gas discharge tube. How can you tell that the beam of electrons is travelling through a magnetic field?

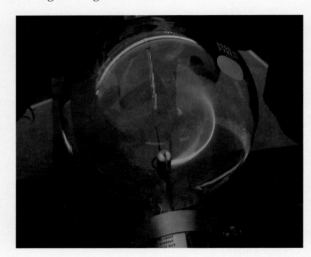

4. (15.1) Why was Thomson's experiment able to determine only the charge-to-mass ratio for an electron?

5. (15.2) Explain how the results of Millikan's oil-drop experiment also enabled physicists to determine the mass of the electron.

6. (15.2) What is the electrical charge on a dust particle that has lost 23 electrons?

7. (15.2) Calculate the electrical charge carried by 1.00 kg of electrons.

8. (15.3) What is an alpha particle?

9. (15.3) Why is the Rutherford gold-foil experiment sometimes called a "scattering experiment"?

10. (15.3) Explain how Thomson's model of the atom was inconsistent with the results of Rutherford's gold-foil experiment.

11. (15.4) (a) What is an emission line spectrum?
    (b) How could you produce an emission line spectrum?

12. (15.4) What are Fraunhofer lines?

13. (15.4) Explain how emission line spectra demonstrate Planck's concept of energy quantization.

14. (15.4) What is the difference between the ground state of an atom and an excited state?

15. (15.4) Here are four energy-level transitions for an electron in a hydrogen atom:
    $n_i = 1 \rightarrow n_f = 5$ $n_i = 4 \rightarrow n_f = 3$
    $n_i = 2 \rightarrow n_f = 5$ $n_i = 8 \rightarrow n_f = 3$
    (a) For which of these transition(s) does the atom gain energy?
    (b) For which transition does the atom gain the most energy?
    (c) Which transition emits the photon with the longest wavelength?

16. (15.4) Calculate the radius of a hydrogen atom in the $n = 3$ state.

17. (15.5) Describe the difference between an orbit in Bohr's model of the atom and an orbital in the quantum model.

18. (15.5) How does the quantum model explain why electrons in an atom do not continuously radiate energy?

Applications

19. An electron is moving at a speed of 1.0 km/s perpendicular to a magnetic field with a magnitude of 1.5 T. How much force does the magnetic field exert on the electron?

20. (a) Use the Bohr model to predict the speed of an electron in the $n = 2$ energy level of a hydrogen atom.
    (b) Explain why the quantum model can predict the energy of this electron, but not its speed.

21. Calculate the electric field that will suspend an oil droplet that has a mass of 2.0×10^{-15} kg and a charge of $+3e$.

22. Transitions to or from the $n = 3$ energy level produce the Paschen series of lines in the hydrogen spectrum.

(a) Find the change in energy level for the first three Paschen transitions.

(b) Find the wavelengths and frequencies of the first three Paschen transitions.

(c) Use $E = hf$ to calculate the energy of the photon produced by a transition from the $n = 5$ to the $n = 3$ energy level. Is your calculation consistent with your answer to part (a)? Why or why not?

(d) In what part of the electromagnetic spectrum would you find the Paschen lines?

23. The helium-neon laser produces a red-coloured light by exciting a gas that contains a mixture of both helium and neon atoms. The energy level diagram below shows three transitions, A, B, and C, that are involved. Two of these transitions are produced by collisions with other atoms or electrons, and the third is the result of photon emission.

(a) Explain which process is involved in transitions A, B, and C.

(b) For the transition that produces a photon, determine the wavelength of the photon.

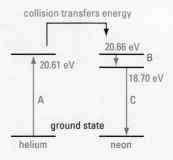

24. Determine the electric field that will stop this alpha particle from being deflected as it travels at 10 km/s through a 0.25-T magnetic field.

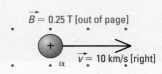

Extensions

25. Classical electromagnetic theory predicts that an electron orbiting a nucleus of charge q will radiate energy at a rate of $P = -\dfrac{2kq^2a^2}{3c^3}$, where k is Coulomb's constant, a is the electron's acceleration, and c is the speed of light.

(a) Determine the kinetic energy of the electron in the ground state.

(b) Use the Bohr model to calculate the acceleration of an electron in the ground state of a hydrogen atom. (Hint: Apply the equations for circular motion.)

(c) Show that P has the units of energy divided by time.

(d) How long will it take the electron to give off all of its kinetic energy as electromagnetic radiation, assuming that the electron's acceleration remains constant?

(e) Explain how your answer to part (d) shows that classical models of the atom are invalid.

Consolidate Your Understanding

1. Explain how the Rutherford gold-foil experiment radically changed the understanding of atomic structure.

2. Explain how Bohr linked spectral lines to Planck's idea of energy quantization.

3. Outline the successes and failures of the Bohr model.

4. Describe three fundamental differences between the quantum model of the atom and the Bohr model.

Think About It

Review your answers to the Think About It questions on page 753. How would you answer each question now?

e TEST

To check your understanding of atomic structure, follow the eTEST links at www.pearsoned.ca/school/physicssource.

Nuclear reactions are among the most powerful energy sources in nature.

"I believe a leaf of grass is no less than the journey-work of the stars"

— from *Leaves of Grass* by Walt Whitman

When the American poet Walt Whitman wrote this line in 1855, the reactions within stars were unknown, the nucleus had not been discovered, and there was no clear proof that atoms exist. By the late 1950s, however, a new interpretation of Whitman's words was possible. Astrophysicists had developed a theory that nuclear reactions inside massive stars created the heavy elements essential to life. Some of these stars exploded into supernovae, scattering heavy elements throughout the galaxy.

This chapter describes nuclear reactions, the enormous potential energy in some nuclei, and the hazards and benefits of radioactive materials. You will learn about the processes that power the stars and how every leaf of grass may indeed be "the journey-work of the stars."

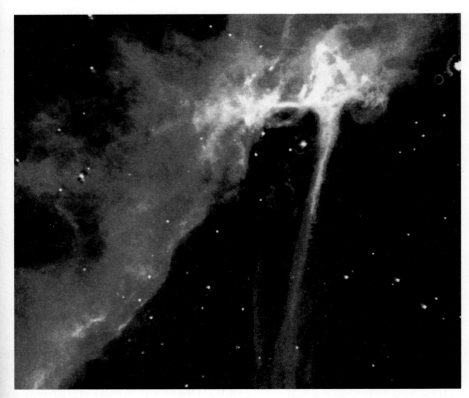

▲ **Figure 16.1** A portion of the Cygnus Loop, an expanding cloud of hot gas formed by a supernova explosion about 15 000 years ago. This composite image was made using photographs from the Hubble Space Telescope. The blue colour is light from oxygen, green is light from hydrogen, and red is light from sulfur.

Radiation Intensity

Question

Does the intensity of radiation depend on the distance from the source of the radiation?

Hypothesis

There is a mathematical relationship between the intensity of radiation and the distance from the radiation source.

Variables

- distance between radiation source and detector
- reading on radiation detector

Materials and Equipment

cobalt-60 radiation source
radiation detector
metre-stick
masking tape
optional: interface for computer or graphing calculator

> ⚠ **CAUTION: The radioactive material is enclosed in a durable casing to prevent accidental absorption into the body. Do not damage this casing.**

Procedure

1 Make sure the radiation source is at least 3 m away from the radiation detector. Switch on the detector and measure the background radiation level for 5 min or more. Record this measurement, including the units. If you are using an interface with a computer or graphing calculator, check with your teacher about recording your data electronically.

2 Centre the cobalt-60 radiation source over the zero mark on the metre-stick, and tape the source in place. If your radiation source is shielded so that it emits radiation only from one side, align the source to direct the radiation along the metre-stick (Figure 16.2).

3 Place the radiation detector on the metre-stick within a few centimetres of the radiation source. Measure the radiation level for at least 1 min. Record the radiation level and the distance between the source and the detector.

4 Increase the separation between the radiation source and the detector in steps of 5 cm. Measure the radiation level for at least 1 min at each distance. Record measurements for at least six distances.

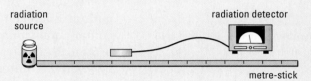

radiation source   radiation detector

metre-stick

▲ **Figure 16.2**

Analyzing and Interpreting

1. Which variable is the manipulated variable in this experiment?

2. Explain why you need to know the background radiation level in order to determine how the intensity of the radiation varies with distance.

3. Graph your data. What type of relationship do you think the graph shows?

4. Discuss with your lab partners how you could use a different graph to determine the exact relationship between the radiation intensity and the distance from the radiation source. Produce a graph using the method that you think will work best. Explain your choice.

5. List any assumptions you made when analyzing your data.

Forming Conclusions

6. Do your data support the hypothesis? Explain.

Think About It

1. What is radioactivity?

2. Where does the energy released in a nuclear reaction come from?

3. How can stars create elements?

Discuss your answers in a small group and record them for later reference. As you complete each section of this chapter, review your answers to these questions. Note any changes in your ideas.

16.1 The Nucleus

Section 15.3 described how scattering experiments directed by Rutherford showed that more than 99.9% of the mass of an atom is concentrated in a nucleus that is typically only a few **femto**metres (10^{-15} m) in diameter. In 1918, Rutherford began a new series of experiments in which he bombarded nitrogen gas with alpha particles. He found that some of the nitrogen transmuted into oxygen and that the process also produced hydrogen nuclei. Rutherford concluded that the hydrogen nucleus was a fundamental particle that is a constituent of all nuclei. He called these particles **protons**, from *protos*, the Greek word for "first."

However, protons could not account for all of the mass of nuclei. For example, the charge-to-mass ratio for protons is twice that of helium nuclei. In 1920, Rutherford suggested that nuclei might also contain **neutrons**, neutral particles with about the same mass as a proton. Neutral particles are difficult to detect or measure because they do not interact with electric or magnetic fields. A variety of experiments over the next decade failed to find any neutrons. The breakthrough came in 1932 when James Chadwick showed that alpha rays striking a beryllium target produced radiation consisting of neutral particles. In a similar experiment with a boron target, he determined that the mass of a neutron is about 0.1% greater than the mass of a proton.

femto: metric prefix meaning 10^{-15}

proton: a positively charged particle found in all nuclei

neutron: a neutral particle found in nuclei

info **BIT**

Chadwick made two earlier attempts to discover the neutron, in 1923 and 1928. In 1935, he received the Nobel Prize in physics for his discovery.

nucleon: a proton or neutron

Nuclear Terms and Notation

Protons and neutrons are called **nucleons** because they are both components of nuclei. Three numbers describe the composition of a nucleus:

Atomic Number, Z: the number of protons in a nucleus

Neutron Number, N: the number of neutrons in the nucleus

Atomic Mass Number, A: the number of nucleons in the nucleus, $Z + N$

Scientists often indicate the composition of a nucleus with the notation $^{A}_{Z}\text{X}$, where X is the chemical symbol for the element. For example, a carbon nucleus with 6 protons and 6 neutrons has $Z = 6$, $N = 6$, and $A = 6 + 6 = 12$. The notation for the carbon nucleus is $^{12}_{6}\text{C}$. Apply these terms and concepts in the next example.

Example 16.1

How many neutrons are contained in a gold nucleus $^{197}_{79}\text{Au}$?

Given

$Z = 79 \qquad A = 197$

Required

neutron number (N)

Analysis and Solution

Since $A = Z + N$,

$$N = A - Z$$
$$= 197 - 79$$
$$= 118$$

Paraphrase

There are 118 neutrons in a nucleus of $^{197}_{79}\text{Au}$.

Practice Problems

1. How many neutrons are in a nucleus of $^{24}_{12}\text{Mg}$?

2. Find the atomic mass number for a uranium atom that contains 92 protons and 146 neutrons.

Answers

1. 12
2. 238

Concept Check

How do the nuclei $^{12}_{6}\text{C}$, $^{13}_{6}\text{C}$, and $^{14}_{6}\text{C}$ differ? How are they the same?

Isotopes

Many elements have two or more **isotopes** — forms that have the same number of protons (Z) but differing numbers of neutrons (N). For example, ordinary hydrogen ($^{1}_{1}\text{H}$), deuterium ($^{2}_{1}\text{H}$), and tritium ($^{3}_{1}\text{H}$) are all isotopes of the element hydrogen. Specific isotopes can be indicated by the element name and the atomic mass number. For example, carbon-12 is another way of writing $^{12}_{6}\text{C}$.

All the isotopes of a particular element have the same number of protons and electrons. So, these isotopes have almost identical chemical properties. However, the physical properties can differ dramatically. In particular, one isotope of an element may be highly radioactive, while another is quite stable. Bombarding materials with electrons, neutrons, or other particles can create radioactive isotopes.

isotopes: atoms that have the same number of protons, but different numbers of neutrons

Atomic Mass Units

Atoms and nuclei are much, much smaller than everyday objects. So, even though a kilogram may be a convenient unit for expressing the mass of apples or oranges, it is not particularly useful for measuring the mass of a proton or a carbon nucleus. For calculations involving nuclei and subatomic particles, it is often convenient to use a mass unit that is much smaller than the kilogram. The **atomic mass unit (u)** is defined as exactly $\dfrac{1}{12}$ of the mass of the carbon-12 atom:

$$1 \text{ u} = 1.660\ 539 \times 10^{-27} \text{ kg}$$

Table 16.1 lists the masses of electrons and nucleons, in both kilograms and atomic mass units.

▼ **Table 16.1** Some Properties of Subatomic Particles (to Six Decimal Places)

Particle	Charge (C)	Mass (kg)	Mass (u)
Electron	$-1.602\,177 \times 10^{-19}$	$9.109\,383 \times 10^{-31}$	$5.485\,799 \times 10^{-4}$
Proton	$+1.602\,177 \times 10^{-19}$	$1.672\,622 \times 10^{-27}$	$1.007\,276$
Neutron	0	$1.674\,927 \times 10^{-27}$	$1.008\,665$

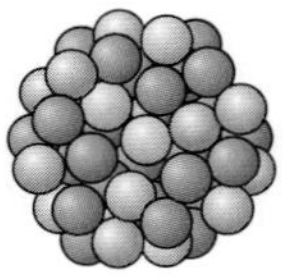

▲ **Figure 16.3** Any nucleus heavier than hydrogen has protons and neutrons packed closely together.

Forces in the Nucleus

Aside from hydrogen, all nuclei consist of two or more protons and a number of neutrons (Figure 16.3). Like charges repel each other, so what keeps these nuclei from flying apart?

Example 16.2

Can gravity bind the protons in a nucleus together?

Given
Rounding the values listed in Table 16.1 gives
proton mass $m = 1.67 \times 10^{-27}$ kg and proton charge $q = 1.60 \times 10^{-19}$ C.

Required
Comparison of the gravitational and electrostatic forces between protons in a nucleus

Analysis and Solution
The magnitude of the gravitational force is $F_g = \dfrac{Gm_1m_2}{r^2}$.

The magnitude of the electrostatic force is $F_e = \dfrac{kq_1q_2}{r^2}$.

So, $\dfrac{F_g}{F_e} = \dfrac{\dfrac{Gm_1m_2}{r^2}}{\dfrac{kq_1q_2}{r^2}} = \dfrac{Gm_1m_2}{kq_1q_2}$.

This ratio shows that the relative strength of the two forces does not depend on the distance between the protons. In order for the gravitational attraction between the protons to overcome the electrostatic repulsion, the ratio $\dfrac{F_g}{F_e}$ would have to be greater than 1.

Substituting the known values into the ratio of the forces gives

$$\frac{F_g}{F_e} = \frac{(6.67 \times 10^{-11} \text{ N·m}^2/\text{kg}^2)(1.67 \times 10^{-27} \text{ kg})^2}{(8.99 \times 10^9 \text{ N·m}^2/\text{C}^2)(1.60 \times 10^{-19} \text{ C})^2}$$

$$= 8.08 \times 10^{-37}$$

Paraphrase
The gravitational attraction is vastly weaker than the electrostatic repulsion, so gravity cannot be the force that holds a nucleus together.

Practice Problems

1. Calculate the gravitational force that two protons exert on each other when they are 5 fm apart.

2. Calculate the electrostatic force that two protons exert on each other when they are 5 fm apart.

Answers

1. 7×10^{-36} N

2. 9 N

Since gravity is far too weak, there must be some other force that holds the particles in a nucleus together. Physicists call this force the **strong nuclear force,** and think that it is a fundamental force of nature, like gravity and the electrostatic force. The strong nuclear force has a very short range. Although it is more powerful than the electrostatic force within a nucleus, the strong nuclear force has a negligible effect on particles that are more than a few femtometres apart. The strong nuclear force acts on both neutrons and protons, but does not affect electrons. Chapter 17 describes fundamental forces in more detail.

strong nuclear force: the force that binds together the protons and neutrons in a nucleus

Binding Energy and Mass Defect

PHYSICS INSIGHT

Measurements of interactions between subatomic particles suggest that there is a fourth fundamental force, the weak nuclear force. This force acts on electrons.

Removing a nucleon from a stable nucleus requires energy because work has to be done on the nucleon in order to overcome the strong nuclear force. The **binding energy**, E_b, of a nucleus is the energy required to separate all of its protons and neutrons and move them infinitely far apart. In other words, the binding energy is the difference between the total energy of the separate nucleons and the energy of the nucleus with the nucleons bound together:

binding energy: the net energy required to liberate all of the protons and neutrons in a nucleus

$$E_b = E_{nucleons} - E_{nucleus}$$

where $E_{nucleons}$ is the sum of the energies of the nucleons when they are free of the nucleus and $E_{nucleus}$ is the energy of the nucleus.

Mass-energy Equivalence

The equivalence of mass and energy is part of the theory of relativity that Albert Einstein developed in 1905. This theory correctly predicted that mass and energy are related by the equation

$$E = mc^2$$

where E is energy, m is mass, and c is the speed of light.

Earlier in this section, you learned that physicists use the atomic mass unit, u, for calculations involving nuclei and subatomic particles. Physicists also prefer to use a different unit for energy when dealing with nuclear change. For nuclear calculations, it is useful to know the energy equivalent for 1 u:

$$E = 1\ u \times c^2$$
$$= (1.660\ 539 \times 10^{-27}\ kg)(2.997\ 925 \times 10^8\ m/s)^2$$
$$= 1.492\ 418 \times 10^{-10}\ J \times \frac{1\ eV}{1.602\ 177 \times 10^{-19}\ J}$$
$$= 931.494\ 1\ MeV$$

Thus, 1 u is equivalent to about 149 pJ or 931.5 MeV. This unit is very useful because most nuclear changes consist of only a small fraction of an atomic mass unit or its energy equivalent.

Nuclear reactions can involve conversions between mass and energy. The law of conservation of energy still applies if the conversions are taken into account. For any closed system, the total of the energy and the energy equivalent of the mass in the system is constant.

Example 16.3

Calculate the energy equivalent for 0.0034 u of mass, in joules and in electron volts.

Analysis and Solution

Simply multiply 0.0034 u by the appropriate equivalence factors:

$$0.0034 \text{ u} \times \frac{1.49 \times 10^{-10} \text{ J}}{1 \text{ u}} = 5.1 \times 10^{-13} \text{ J}$$

$$0.0034 \text{ u} \times \frac{931.5 \text{ MeV}}{1 \text{ u}} = 3.2 \text{ MeV}$$

Paraphrase

The energy equivalent for 0.0034 u is 5.1×10^{-13} J or 3.2 MeV.

Mass Defect

mass defect: difference between the sum of the masses of the separate nucleons and the mass of the nucleus

Rearranging Einstein's equation for mass-energy equivalence gives $m = \dfrac{E}{c^2}$. Dividing the equation for binding energy by c^2 leads to a formula for the **mass defect**, Δm, of a nucleus:

$$\frac{E_b}{c^2} = \frac{E_{\text{nucleons}}}{c^2} - \frac{E_{\text{nucleus}}}{c^2}$$

$$\Delta m = m_{\text{nucleons}} - m_{\text{nucleus}}$$

where m_{nucleons} is the sum of the masses of the separate nucleons and m_{nucleus} is the mass of the nucleus.

Thus, the mass of a nucleus is equal to the total mass of its constituents, less the mass corresponding to the binding energy.

Physicists have determined the masses of atoms and nucleons with great accuracy. Tables of atomic data generally list the masses of neutral atoms rather than the masses of nuclei alone, without any electrons. The following formula uses atomic masses to calculate the mass defect for a nucleus:

PHYSICS INSIGHT

Nuclear calculations often involve very small differences in mass. Such calculations can require data with six or more significant digits.

$$\Delta m = Zm_{^1_1\text{H}} + Nm_{\text{neutron}} - m_{\text{atom}}$$

where $m_{^1_1\text{H}}$ is the mass of a neutral hydrogen atom, Z is the atomic number, and N is the neutron number.

Since $m_{^1_1\text{H}}$ includes the masses of both a proton and an electron, the term $Zm_{^1_1\text{H}}$ includes the mass of Z electrons, matching the mass of the electrons included in m_{atom}. The differences in the binding energy of the electrons are small enough to ignore in most nuclear calculations.

Show that $\Delta m = Zm_{proton} + Nm_{neutron} - m_{nucleus}$.

Example 16.4

Find the mass defect, expressed in kilograms, and the binding energy for a carbon-12 nucleus.

Given

$Z = 6$ $\qquad$ $A = 12$ $\qquad$ $m = 12.000\ 000$ u

Required

mass defect (Δm) $\qquad$ binding energy (E_b)

Analysis and Solution

The formula $N = A - Z$ gives the number of neutrons in the nucleus:

$N = 12 - 6$
$\quad = 6$

Thus, the $^{12}_{6}$C nucleus consists of 6 neutrons and 6 protons.
Now, use $\Delta m = Zm_{^1_1H} + Nm_{neutron} - m_{atom}$ to find the mass defect. See Table 7.5, Atomic Masses of Selected Isotopes, Student References 7, page 881.

$\Delta m = Zm_H + Nm_{neutron} - m_{atom}$
$\quad = 6(1.007\ 825$ u$) + 6(1.008\ 665$ u$) - 12.000\ 000$ u

$\quad = 0.098\ 940$ u $\times \dfrac{1.660\ 539 \times 10^{-27}\ \text{kg}}{1\ \text{u}}$

$\quad = 1.642\ 9 \times 10^{-28}$ kg

Use the equation for mass-energy equivalence to calculate the binding energy from the mass defect.

$E_b = \Delta m \times c^2$

$\quad = 0.098\ 940$ u $\times \dfrac{1.49 \times 10^{-10}\ \text{J}}{1\ \text{u}}$

$\quad = 1.47 \times 10^{-11}$ J or 92.0 MeV

Paraphrase

The mass defect for $^{12}_{6}$C is 0.098 940 u or $1.642\ 9 \times 10^{-28}$ kg. The binding energy of the carbon-12 nucleus is 1.47×10^{-11} J or 92.0 MeV.

Practice Problems

1. Sodium $^{23}_{11}$Na has an atomic mass of 22.989 769 u. Find the mass defect for this nucleus.

2. Find the binding energy for $^{23}_{11}$Na.

Answers

1. 0.200 286 u

2. 186.57 MeV

Binding Energy per Nucleon

You can compare the stability of different nuclei by dividing the binding energy of each nucleus by the number of nucleons it contains. The greater the binding energy per nucleon $\left(\dfrac{E_b}{A}\right)$, the more stable the nucleus is. Figure 16.4 is a graph of binding energy per nucleon versus atomic mass number for stable nuclei. This graph peaks at about 8.79 MeV per nucleon. The three most stable isotopes are nickel $^{62}_{28}$Ni, iron $^{58}_{26}$Fe, and iron $^{56}_{26}$Fe.

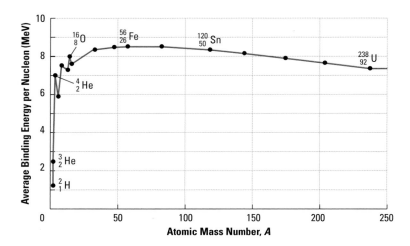

► **Figure 16.4** Binding energy per nucleon for stable isotopes

The graph also gives a hint about the process that causes the stars to shine. The binding energy per nucleon is much less for hydrogen than for helium. If hydrogen atoms combine to form helium, the nucleons move to a lower energy level and give off the difference in energy. In section 16.4, you will learn more about such nuclear reactions.

16.1 Check and Reflect

Knowledge

1. How many neutrons and protons do each of the following nuclei contain?
   (a) $^{90}_{38}$Sr   (b) $^{13}_{6}$C   (c) $^{56}_{26}$Fe   (d) $^{1}_{1}$H

2. Convert 1.6×10^{-10} J to electron volts.

3. Calculate the energy equivalent of 0.25 u.

4. How much mass is converted into energy by a nuclear reaction that produces 5.00 GJ of energy?

5. Define the term *isotope*.

6. Explain why the mass of a stable nucleus is a bit less than $Zm_{proton} + Nm_{neutron}$.

Applications

7. Determine the binding energy for $^{22}_{10}$Ne. The atomic mass of $^{22}_{10}$Ne is 21.991 385 u.

8. The $^{40}_{19}$K isotope of potassium has an atomic mass of 39.963 998 u.
   (a) Determine the mass defect for $^{40}_{19}$K.
   (b) Calculate the binding energy per nucleon for this isotope.

9. Use Figure 16.4 to estimate the binding energy for each of these nuclei:
   (a) $^{13}_{6}$C   (b) $^{56}_{26}$Fe   (c) $^{238}_{92}$U

10. Show that MeV/c^2 has the dimensions of mass.

Extensions

11. (a) Contrast the strength and range of the electromagnetic force and the strong nuclear force.
    (b) Explain how the nature of these forces limits the maximum possible size for nuclei.

12. Suppose that the electrostatic force were much stronger. Describe how this change would affect the stability of nuclei.

13. Experiments have shown that most nuclei are approximately spherical with a radius of $r = r_0 A^{\frac{1}{3}}$, where $r_0 = 1.20$ fm and A is the atomic number. Use this formula to determine the radius of the nucleus of a $^{90}_{38}$Sr atom. Then estimate the distance between adjacent nucleons in this nucleus. What can you conclude about the size of protons and neutrons?

e TEST

To check your understanding of nuclei, follow the eTEST links at www.pearsoned.ca/school/physicssource.

16.2 Radioactive Decay

The French physicist, Antoine Henri Becquerel (1852–1908), discovered radioactive decay in 1896 while conducting an experiment to see if a fluorescent compound of uranium would emit X rays when exposed to sunlight. During a period of cloudy weather, Becquerel put the uranium compound away in a drawer along with a photographic plate wrapped in black paper. When he developed the plate several days later, he was surprised to find that it was fogged even though the fluorescent compound had not been exposed to sunlight. Becquerel realized that the radiation that fogged the plate must be coming from the uranium in the compound. He also found that a magnetic field would deflect some of this radiation.

The husband and wife team of Marie Curie (1867–1934) and Pierre Curie (1859–1906) began an extensive study of this radiation. They showed that thorium was also radioactive, and discovered two new elements, radium and polonium, that were both much more radioactive than uranium. Indeed, Marie coined the term *radioactive*. She also demonstrated that the intensity of radiation from uranium compounds was not affected by the other elements in the compound or by processes such as being heated, powdered, or dissolved. The intensity depended only on the quantity of uranium. Therefore, the radioactivity must result from a process within the uranium nucleus.

Rutherford and others identified three forms of nuclear radiation:

Alpha (α): the emission of a helium nucleus
Beta (β): the emission of a high-energy electron
Gamma (γ): the emission of a high-energy photon

Initially, this classification was based on how much material each type of radiation could penetrate. In radiation from naturally occurring isotopes, the alpha particles typically do not penetrate much more than a thin metal foil or sheet of paper, whereas beta particles can pass through up to 3 mm of aluminium, and gamma rays can penetrate several centimetres of lead. The three types of radiation result from different processes within nuclei.

Concept Check

Figure 16.5 shows the paths that α, β, and γ rays take when passing through a magnetic field. What can you conclude about the electrical properties of these rays?

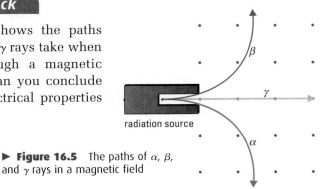

radiation source

▶ **Figure 16.5** The paths of α, β, and γ rays in a magnetic field

Stability of Isotopes

Figure 16.6 shows that stable isotopes form a relatively narrow band when plotted by their proton and neutron numbers. Other than hydrogen, all stable isotopes have at least as many neutrons as protons. As Z increases, the isotopes require an increasing ratio of neutrons to protons in order to be stable. There are no completely stable isotopes with more than 83 protons. Almost all of the stable isotopes have both an even number of protons and an even number of neutrons.

PHYSICS INSIGHT

β^+ decay consists of releasing a positron — a positively charged particle with its other properties the same as those of an electron. You will learn more about β^+ decay later in this section.

transmute: change into a different element

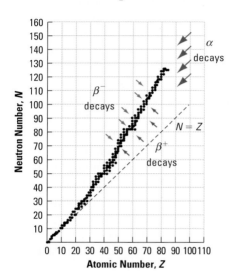

◄ **Figure 16.6** The black dots represent the band of stable isotopes.

The stable isotopes have greater binding energies than the unstable isotopes. Radioactive decay **transmutes** unstable nuclei into nuclei with higher binding energies. For example, heavy nuclei above and to the right of the stable band will emit alpha particles (larger red arrows), heavy nuclei below and to the right of the band will emit positrons, or β^+ particles (small red arrows), and lighter nuclei to the left of the band will emit electrons, or β^- particles (blue arrows). All of these decay processes produce isotopes that are either in the stable band or closer to it. As described later in this section, a nucleus may undergo several successive decays before it reaches the stable band.

Conservation Laws and Radioactive Decay

In addition to conserving momentum and energy, all radioactive decay processes obey these additional conservation laws:

* **Charge:** The net electrical charge cannot change in a decay process. Any change in the electrical charge of the nucleus must be exactly offset by an opposite change elsewhere in the system. For example, if the charge on a nucleus decreases by $+2e$, then a particle with a charge of $+2e$ must be emitted.

* **Atomic Mass Number:** The total of the atomic mass numbers for the final products must equal the atomic mass number of the original nucleus. In other words, the total number of nucleons remains constant.

Example 16.5

Determine which of these radioactive decay processes are possible.

(a) $^{214}_{84}\text{Po} \rightarrow ^{208}_{82}\text{Pb} + ^{4}_{2}\alpha$

(b) $^{230}_{90}\text{Th} \rightarrow ^{226}_{88}\text{Ra} + ^{4}_{2}\alpha$

(c) $^{60}_{27}\text{Co} \rightarrow ^{60}_{28}\text{Ni} + ^{1}_{0}\text{n}$ ($^{1}_{0}\text{n}$ represents a neutron)

Analysis and Solution

Compare the charge and atomic mass number of the original nucleus to those of the decay products.

(a) Charge: $84 = 82 + 2$
    Atomic mass number: $214 \neq 208 + 4$
    The decay process $^{214}_{84}\text{Po} \rightarrow ^{208}_{82}\text{Pb} + ^{4}_{2}\alpha$ is not possible.

(b) Charge: $90 = 88 + 2$
    Atomic mass number: $230 = 226 + 4$
    The decay process $^{230}_{90}\text{Th} \rightarrow ^{226}_{88}\text{Ra} + ^{4}_{2}\alpha$ is possible.

(c) Charge: $27 \neq 28 + 0$
    Atomic mass number: $60 \neq 60 + 1$
    The decay process $^{60}_{27}\text{Co} \rightarrow ^{60}_{28}\text{Ni} + ^{1}_{0}\text{n}$ is not possible.

Practice Problems

Determine whether these decay processes are possible.

1. $^{212}_{84}\text{Po} \rightarrow ^{210}_{86}\text{Rn} + ^{4}_{2}\alpha$

2. $^{233}_{91}\text{Pa} \rightarrow ^{233}_{92}\text{U} + ^{0}_{-1}\beta$

3. $^{14}_{6}\text{C} \rightarrow ^{14}_{7}\text{N} + ^{1}_{1}\text{H}$

Answers

1. Impossible
2. Possible
3. Impossible

Concept Check

Why are electrons *not* considered when applying the conservation law for atomic mass number?

Alpha Decay

In 1908, Rutherford showed that alpha particles are helium nuclei spontaneously emitted by unstable large nuclei. In these nuclei, the electromagnetic force repelling the outer protons is almost as great as the attractive strong nuclear force. Such nuclei can spontaneously emit alpha particles. Because a cluster of two protons and two neutrons forms a highly stable helium nucleus, these unstable large nuclei decay by emitting alpha particles rather than separate protons and neutrons.

The emission of an alpha particle decreases the atomic number by 2 and the atomic mass number by 4. For example, alpha decay of uranium-238 produces thorium:

$$^{238}_{92}\text{U} \rightarrow ^{234}_{90}\text{Th} + ^{4}_{2}\alpha$$

In this example, uranium is the **parent element** and thorium is the **daughter element**. Applying the conservation laws gives this general form for alpha decays:

$$^{A}_{Z}\text{X} \rightarrow ^{A-4}_{Z-2}\text{Y} + ^{4}_{2}\alpha$$

where X is the chemical symbol for the parent element and Y is the symbol for the daughter element. Here, A is the atomic mass number of the *parent* element and Z is its atomic number.

parent element: the original element in a decay process

daughter element: the element produced by a decay process

Example 16.6

Practice Problems

Write the α-decay process for these elements, and name the parent and daughter elements.

1. $^{230}_{90}\text{Th}$

2. $^{238}_{92}\text{U}$

3. $^{214}_{84}\text{Po}$

Answers

1. $^{230}_{90}\text{Th} \rightarrow {}^{226}_{88}\text{Ra} + {}^{4}_{2}\alpha$; thorium, radium

2. $^{238}_{92}\text{U} \rightarrow {}^{234}_{90}\text{Th} + {}^{4}_{2}\alpha$; uranium, thorium

3. $^{214}_{84}\text{Po} \rightarrow {}^{210}_{82}\text{Pb} + {}^{4}_{2}\alpha$; polonium, lead

Predict the daughter element that results from alpha decay of radium-226.

Analysis and Solution

From a periodic table, you can see that the atomic number for radium is 88. So, the parent element is $^{226}_{88}\text{Ra}$.

Since the alpha particle carries away four nucleons, including two protons, A decreases by 4 and Z decreases by 2:

$$^{A}_{Z}\text{X} \rightarrow {}^{A-4}_{Z-2}\text{Y} + {}^{4}_{2}\alpha$$

So, the daughter element is $^{226-4}_{88-2}\text{Y} = {}^{222}_{86}\text{Y}$.

The periodic table shows that the element with $Z = 86$ is radon.

Paraphrase

For alpha decay, the daughter element of radium-226 is radon-222.

Energy Released During Alpha Decay

You can apply the concepts of energy conservation and mass-energy equivalence to alpha decay, using a method similar to the calculation of nuclear binding energy:

The mass-energy of the parent nucleus is equal to the sum of the mass-energy and the kinetic energies of both the daughter nucleus and the alpha particle:

$$m_{\text{parent}}c^2 = m_{\text{daughter}}c^2 + m_{\alpha}c^2 + \Delta E$$

The difference in energy, ΔE, appears as the total kinetic energy of the alpha particle and of the daughter nucleus. If the parent nucleus was at rest, the law of conservation of momentum requires the momentum of the alpha particle to be equal in magnitude and opposite in direction to the momentum of the daughter nucleus. Usually, the mass of the daughter nucleus is much greater than the mass of the alpha particle. So, the speed of the alpha particle is correspondingly greater than the speed at which the daughter nucleus recoils:

$$m_{\alpha}v_{\alpha} = m_{\text{daughter}}v_{\text{daughter}}$$

$$v_{\alpha} = \frac{m_{\text{daughter}}v_{\text{daughter}}}{m_{\alpha}}$$

The kinetic energy of the alpha particle is also correspondingly greater than the kinetic energy of the daughter nucleus:

$$E_\alpha = \frac{1}{2} m_\alpha v_\alpha^2$$

$$= \frac{1}{2} m_\alpha \left(\frac{m_{\text{daughter}} v_{\text{daughter}}}{m_\alpha} \right)^2$$

$$= \frac{m_{\text{daughter}}}{m_\alpha} \times \frac{1}{2} m_{\text{daughter}} v_{\text{daughter}}^2$$

$$= \frac{m_{\text{daughter}}}{m_\alpha} \times E_{\text{daughter}}$$

Concept Check

Explain why ΔE must be positive in order for α-decay to occur. Give an example of a nucleus for which ΔE would be negative.

Example 16.7

Show that α-decay of radium-226 is possible, and estimate the maximum kinetic energy of the emitted alpha particle.

Given
Parent atom is radium-226.

Required
ΔE and kinetic energy of the alpha particle

Analysis and Solution
Example 16.6 showed that the daughter element is radon-222. Rearranging the formula $m_{\text{parent}} c^2 = m_{\text{daughter}} c^2 + m_\alpha c^2 + \Delta E$ gives $\Delta E = (m_{\text{parent}} - m_{\text{daughter}} - m_\alpha) c^2$.

Table 7.5, Atomic Masses of Selected Isotopes, Student References 7, page 881, lists the atomic masses for radium-226, radon-222, and helium-4. As in section 16.1, you can use atomic masses instead of nuclear masses because the masses of the electrons will balance out. A radon nucleus has over 50 times the mass of an alpha particle. So, the alpha particle will have over 98% of the total kinetic energy, ΔE.

$$\Delta E = (m^{226}_{88}\text{Ra} - m^{222}_{86}\text{Rn} - m^4_{2}\alpha) c^2$$

$$= (226.025\ 410\ \text{u} - 222.017\ 578\ \text{u} - 4.002\ 603\ \text{u}) c^2$$

$$= 0.005\ 229\ \text{u} \times \frac{1.49 \times 10^{-10}\ \text{J}}{1\ \text{u}}$$

$$= 7.79 \times 10^{-13}\ \text{J or 487 MeV}$$

Paraphrase
Since $\Delta E > 0$, alpha decay of radium-226 is possible. The maximum kinetic energy the alpha particle could have is 7.79×10^{-13} J.

Practice Problems

Calculate the energy released during α-decay of these nuclei:

1. $^{230}_{90}\text{Th}$
2. $^{238}_{92}\text{U}$
3. $^{214}_{84}\text{Po}$

Answers

1. 7.63×10^{-13} J
2. 6.83×10^{-13} J
3. 1.25×10^{-12} J

THEN, NOW, AND FUTURE   Ionization Smoke Detectors

Most household smoke detectors (Figure 16.7) contain a small amount of americium-241. This isotope emits α-particles, which ionize air molecules between two metal plates within the smoke detector. One of the plates has a positive charge, and the other plate has a negative charge. The plates attract the ions, so a small current flows between the plates.

If smoke particles enter the smoke detector, they absorb some of the α-particles. So, the alpha radiation ionizes fewer air molecules

and the current between the metal plates decreases. This drop in current triggers the alarm circuit in the smoke detector.

Questions

1. Why is it safer for a smoke detector to use alpha radiation, instead of beta or gamma radiation?

2. Explain why most manufacturers of smoke detectors recommend replacing them after 10 years.

▲ **Figure 16.7** This smoke detector uses alpha radiation to sense smoke particles.

Beta Decay

beta-negative (β^-) decay: nuclear decay involving emission of an electron

beta (β) particle: electron emitted by a nucleus

Sometimes, a nucleus decays by emitting an electron. This process is termed **beta-negative** or **β^- decay**. During β^- decay, a neutron in the nucleus transforms into a proton (Figure 16.8). So, the atomic number of the atom increases by 1, but the atomic mass number does not change. Charge is conserved because the charge on the new proton balances the charge on the electron emitted from the nucleus. This electron is often called a **beta (β) particle**, a name that originates from the early classification of types of radiation.

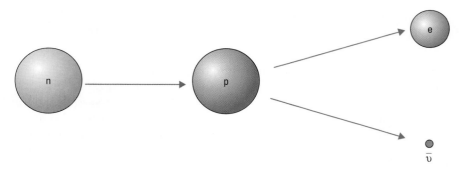

▲ **Figure 16.8** During β^- decay, a neutron changes into a proton.

Concept Check

Why is the mass of the neutron slightly larger than the sum of the proton and electron masses?

Example 16.8

What element will the β^- decay of thorium produce?

Analysis and Solution

A periodic table shows that the atomic number
for thorium is 90.
β^- decay increases the atomic number by 1,
so $A_{\text{daughter}} = 91$.
The element with an atomic number of 91 is
protactinium, the element immediately after
thorium in the periodic table.

Paraphrase

For β^- decay of thorium, the daughter element is protactinium.

As with alpha decays, you can use atomic masses to calculate how
much energy a beta decay will release.

Example 16.9

How much energy would you expect the β^- decay of a
thorium-234 nucleus to release?

Given

Parent element is $^{234}_{90}\text{Th}$.

Required

Energy released by β^- decay (ΔE)

Analysis and Solution

As shown in Example 16.8, the daughter element is
protactinium. However, this daughter atom has only the
90 electrons from the original thorium atom because the
electron emitted by the thorium nucleus leaves the atom as beta
radiation. The result is a positive ion, $^{234}_{91}\text{Pa}^+$. The energy released
is equivalent to the difference between the mass of the parent atom
and the total mass of the decay products. Together, the masses of the
protactinium ion and the beta particle equal the mass of a neutral
protactinium atom. Table 7.5, Atomic Masses of Selected Isotopes,
Student References 7, page 881, lists atomic masses.

$$\Delta m = m_{\text{parent}} - m_{\text{products}}$$
$$= m^{234}_{90}\text{Th} - (m^{234}_{91}\text{Pa}^+ + m^{0}_{-1}\beta)$$
$$= m^{234}_{90}\text{Th} - m^{234}_{91}\text{Pa}$$
$$= 234.043\ 601\ \text{u} - 234.043\ 308\ \text{u}$$
$$= 0.000\ 293\ \text{u}$$

1 u is equivalent to about 931.5 MeV, so

$$\Delta E = 0.000\ 293\ \text{u} \times \frac{931.5\ \text{MeV}}{1\ \text{u}}$$
$$= 0.273\ \text{MeV}$$

Paraphrase

The β^- decay of a $^{234}_{90}\text{Th}$ nucleus should release 0.273 MeV.

info **BIT**

The name *neutrino* comes from the Italian word for "little, neutral one." The word was coined by Enrico Fermi, a renowned physicist who developed a theory to explain beta decay.

neutrino: an extremely small neutral subatomic particle

e **WEB**

To learn more about the Sudbury Neutrino Observatory, follow the links at www.pearsoned.ca/school/physicssource.

info **BIT**

Each second, more than 100 trillion neutrinos pass through your body! Almost all of these neutrinos were formed by nuclear reactions in the core of the Sun.

weak nuclear force: fundamental force that acts on electrons and neutrinos

antimatter: form of matter that has a key property, such as charge, opposite to that of ordinary matter

positron (e^+ or $_{1}^{0}\beta$): an anti-electron; a positively charged particle with its other properties the same as those of an electron

The Elusive Neutrino

Since the daughter nucleus has vastly more mass than an electron, there is practically no recoil of the daughter nucleus during beta decay. Consequently, physicists expected that virtually all of the energy released during β^- decay would appear as the kinetic energy of the electron emitted by the nucleus. However, measurements found that most electrons emitted during β^- decay had somewhat less kinetic energy than expected, and a few had almost no kinetic energy. During β^- decay, small portions of the mass of the parent nuclei seemed to just disappear!

In 1930, the Austrian physicist Wolfgang Pauli (1900–1958) suggested that the missing energy was carried away by a tiny, as-yet-undiscovered neutral particle, now called the **neutrino**, ν. Neutrinos are so small that physicists have yet to determine their size and mass. These "ghost-like" particles can pass through Earth with only a slight chance of being absorbed! Indeed, it was 1956 before an experiment using the intense radiation at a nuclear power plant finally proved conclusively that neutrinos actually exist. Many astrophysicists now think that neutrinos play a critical role in the cores of stars and perhaps in the structure of the cosmos as well.

Concept Check

How did physicists know that the neutrino must be neutral?

Beta Decay, the Weak Nuclear Force, and Antimatter

Careful study of beta decays revealed two further important differences from alpha decay.

First, the transformation of a neutron into a proton involves a fundamental force called the **weak nuclear force**. Although it is less powerful than the strong nuclear force, the weak nuclear force acts on electrons and neutrinos, whereas the strong nuclear force does not.

The second difference is that beta decay involves **antimatter**. An antimatter particle has a key property, such as charge, opposite to that of the corresponding particle of ordinary matter. For example, an anti-electron, or **positron (e^+ or $_{1}^{0}\beta$)**, has a positive charge but the same mass as an electron. Section 17.2 presents antimatter in more detail.

In β^- decay, the transformation of a neutron into a proton produces an *antineutrino* rather than a neutrino:

$$n \rightarrow p^+ + e^- + \bar{\nu}$$

where $\bar{\nu}$ is the symbol for the antineutrino.

Thus, β^- decays have the general form

$$_{Z}^{A}X \rightarrow _{Z+1}^{A}Y + _{-1}^{0}\beta + \bar{\nu} \quad (Z \text{ increases by 1})$$

A second form of beta decay also produces an antiparticle. In β^+ **decay**, a proton transforms into a neutron, and the parent nucleus emits a positron and a neutrino:

$${}^A_Z X \rightarrow {}^{\ \ A}_{Z-1} Y + {}^{\ 0}_{1}\beta + \nu \quad (Z \text{ decreases by 1})$$

Sometimes, you will see the electron in these decay processes represented by the symbol e^-. For consistency, this textbook uses the standard symbol for an electron, ${}^{\ 0}_{-1}\beta$, throughout. Similarly, the symbol ${}^{\ 0}_{1}\beta$ is used to represent a positron.

Example 16.10

Identify the type of beta decay for each transmutation, then fill in the missing decay products for each process.

(a) ${}^{54}_{25}\text{Mn} \rightarrow {}^{54}_{24}\text{Cr}$

(b) ${}^{43}_{19}\text{K} \rightarrow {}^{43}_{20}\text{Ca}$

Analysis and Solution

(a) The atomic number decreases by 1, so the transmutation must be a β^+ decay. Therefore, the other decay products are a positron and a neutrino:
${}^{54}_{25}\text{Mn} \rightarrow {}^{54}_{24}\text{Cr} + {}^{\ 0}_{1}\beta + \nu$

(b) The atomic number increases by 1, so the transmutation must be a β^- decay. Therefore, the other decay products are an electron and an antineutrino:
${}^{43}_{19}\text{K} \rightarrow {}^{43}_{20}\text{Ca} + {}^{\ 0}_{-1}\beta + \overline{\nu}$

Practice Problems

1. (a) What isotope will β^+ decay of thallium-81 produce?
   (b) Write the process for this decay.

Answers

1. (a) mercury-80
   (b) ${}^{202}_{81}\text{Tl} \rightarrow {}^{202}_{80}\text{Hg} + {}^{\ 0}_{1}\beta + \nu$

Gamma Decay (γ-decay)

Many nuclei have a series of energy levels that correspond to different configurations of the nucleons. In the excited states, the nucleons are farther apart. As a result, their binding energy is less than when in the ground state, and the total energy of the nucleus is greater. When making a transition to a lower-energy state, a nucleus emits a gamma-ray photon, similar to the photon emitted when an electron in an atom moves to a lower energy level (Figure 16.9). However, the difference in energy is much greater for a nucleus.

e **WEB**
To learn more about nuclear energy levels, follow the links at www.pearsoned.ca/school/physicssource.

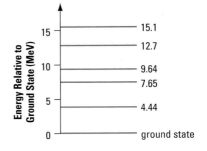

▲ **Figure 16.9** Nuclear energy levels for carbon-12: How do these energy levels differ from those for electrons in hydrogen?

Gamma (γ) decay does not change either the atomic number or the atomic mass number. Gamma decays can be written using this general form:

$$^A_Z X^* \to {}^A_Z X + \gamma,$$

where * indicates an excited state and γ represents a gamma ray.

Often, alpha or beta decay leaves the daughter nucleus in a highly excited state. The excited nucleus then makes a transition to its ground state, and emits a gamma ray. For example, when β^- decay of boron-12 produces carbon-12, the carbon nucleus is highly excited and quickly emits a gamma ray:

$$^{12}_{5}B \to {}^{12}_{6}C^* + {}^{0}_{-1}\beta + \bar{\nu}$$

$$^{12}_{6}C^* \to {}^{12}_{6}C + \gamma$$

The energy of a gamma ray depends on the energy levels and the degree of excitation of the particular nucleus. Gamma rays can have energies ranging from thousands to millions of electron volts.

16-2 *Design a Lab*

Radiation Shielding

The Question

What common materials provide effective shielding against α, β, and γ radiation?

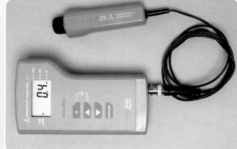

▲ **Figure 16.10** Radiation meters

Design and Conduct Your Investigation

Check with your teacher about the radiation sources and radiation meters (Figure 16.10) available for this investigation. Then design your experiment. List the materials you will need and outline the procedure.

Try this procedure and modify it if necessary. Keep careful records of your results. Then analyze your data, and explain your conclusions.

Radioactive Decay Series

Often, a radioactive nucleus will decay into a daughter nucleus that is itself radioactive. The daughter nucleus may then decay into yet another unstable nucleus. This process of successive decays continues until it creates a stable nucleus. Such a process is called a **radioactive decay series**.

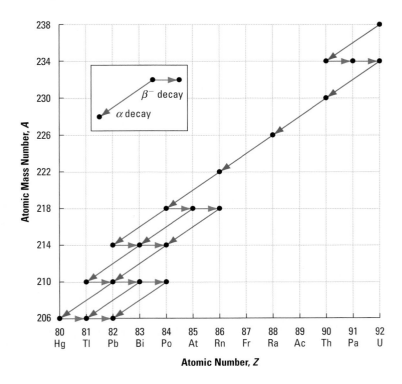

▲ **Figure 16.11**   Radioactive decay series beginning with $^{238}_{92}U$ and ending with $^{206}_{82}Pb$. How many different decay paths are there from uranium-238 to lead-206?

The dots in Figure 16.11 represent nuclei that are part of the decay series. A decay series can have several branches that lead to the same final product. Figure 16.11 shows that $^{218}_{84}Po$ can transmute into $^{214}_{84}Po$ by three different combinations of decays. All of the intermediate isotopes in a decay series are unstable, but the degree of instability is different for each isotope. For example, $^{218}_{86}Rn$ usually lasts for only a fraction of a second whereas $^{222}_{86}Rn$ takes several days to decay and $^{230}_{90}Th$ takes thousands of years. Although not shown in Figure 16.11, many of the intermediate isotopes undergo gamma decay.

Concept Check

Explain why gamma decays cannot be shown as paths on a decay series graph like the one in Figure 16.11.

Potential Hazards of Nuclear Radiation

info **BIT**

Both Marie and Pierre Curie suffered from radiation sickness. Some of Marie's laboratory notebooks are still dangerously radioactive.

Alpha, beta, and gamma radiation are all invisible, and most of their effects on the human body are not immediately apparent. As a result, it was not until years after the discovery of radioactive decay that researchers realized how dangerous radiation can be. Radiation poses two major types of risk:

- **Radiation Sickness:** Radiation can ionize cellular material. This ionization disrupts the intricate biochemistry of the body, resulting in radiation sickness. Large doses of ionizing radiation can kill cells. Blood cells and the lining of the intestine are particularly vulnerable. Symptoms include nausea, vomiting, diarrhea, headache, inflammation, and bleeding. Severe radiation sickness is often fatal.

- **Genetic Damage:** High-energy particles and gamma rays can alter DNA, and lead to the development of cancers or harmful mutations. These effects often appear 10 to 15 years after radiation exposure.

radioisotope: an isotope that is radioactive

Everywhere on Earth, there is some naturally occurring radiation from cosmic rays and from **radioisotopes** in the ground. This background radiation causes some minor damage, but normally the body can repair such damage without any lasting harm.

The effect of radiation on living organisms depends on the energy it carries, its ability to ionize atoms and molecules, and the depth to which it can penetrate living tissue. The charge and energy of the radiation determine how ionizing it is. The energy also affects how far the radiation can penetrate. The energy that a radiation has depends on the process that produces it. Table 16.2 compares the hazards posed by typical radiations from natural sources.

▼ **Table 16.2**   Radiation Hazards from Natural Sources Outside the Body

Radiation	Typical Penetration	Ionization	Hazard
alpha	Travels about 5 cm in air. Cannot penetrate skin.	high	low
beta	Travels about 30–50 cm in air. Penetrates about 1 cm into the body.	moderate	low
gamma	Travels great distances in air. Penetrates right through the body.	low	high

Although α and β particles are much less penetrating than gamma radiation, they can still be extremely harmful if emitted by material absorbed into the body, because the nearby tissue has a continuing exposure to the radiation. For example, health scientists have calculated that breathing in a speck of dust containing just 1 μg of plutonium is virtually certain to cause lung cancer within 30 years.

The introduction of radioactive isotopes into the food chain is also a serious concern because these materials can accumulate in the body. For example, strontium-90, a by-product of nuclear weapons and power reactors, is absorbed into bones because it is chemically similar to calcium. Radiation from strontium damages bone marrow, reduces the production of blood cells, and can lead to bone cancer and leukemia.

Despite its potential hazards, nuclear radiation is not always harmful. As you will see in section 16.3, nuclear radiation has many beneficial industrial and medical applications.

Measuring Radiation Exposure

The effects of a given dose of radiation depend on the type of radiation. For example, a dose of infrared radiation that delivered 1 J/kg to living tissue would do little more than heat the tissue slightly. The same quantity of energy from X rays would ionize some molecules within the tissue, whereas the same quantity of energy from alpha radiation would be far more ionizing and disruptive. For this reason, SI has two units for measuring radiation exposure: The gray is the unit for absorbed dose and the sievert is the unit for equivalent absorbed dose.

Gray (Gy): 1 gray is the dose of ionizing radiation that delivers 1 J of energy to each kilogram of material absorbing the radiation.

Sievert (Sv): 1 sievert is the absorbed dose of ionizing radiation that has the same effect on a person as 1 Gy of photon radiation, such as X rays or gamma rays. The absorbed dose in sieverts is equal to the dose in grays multiplied by the **relative biological effectiveness (RBE)**, a measure of how harmful the particular kind of radiation is. For example, the RBE for high-energy alpha particles is about 20, so an absorbed dose of 1 Gy of alpha radiation is equivalent to 20 Sv.

relative biological effectiveness (RBE): a factor indicating how much a particular type of radiation affects the human body

An equivalent dose of 6 Sv in a short time is usually fatal. Typical radiation exposure for North Americans is less than 0.5 mSv annually. Table 16.3 summarizes some common sources of radiation exposure.

▼ **Table 16.3** Common Sources of Radiation Exposure

Source	Typical Exposure (μSv/year)
Natural	
Radon from ground	200
Cosmic rays	44
Radioactive rocks/minerals, common building materials	40
Ingested from natural sources	18
Artificial	
Medical/dental X rays	73
Nuclear weapons testing	4
Consumer products	1
All other	2
Total	<400

▲ **Figure 16.12** Dosimeters: How do these devices measure exposure to radiation?

Knowledge

1. What are the three basic radioactive decay processes and how do they differ from each other?

2. What is the ratio of neutrons to protons for the heaviest stable isotopes?

3. (a) Write the alpha-decay process for $^{234}_{91}\text{Pa}$.

   (b) Identify the parent and daughter nuclei in this decay.

4. (a) Which type of beta decay transmutes carbon-14 into nitrogen?

   (b) Write the process for this decay.

5. (a) Which type of beta decay transmutes the sodium isotope $^{22}_{11}\text{Na}$ into $^{22}_{10}\text{Ne}$?

   (b) Write the process for this decay.

6. Explain why the daughter nucleus in an alpha decay often emits a gamma ray.

7. Which form of radioactive decay has the greatest penetrating power?

Applications

8. How much energy is released when $^{22}_{11}\text{Na}$ decays to $^{22}_{10}\text{Ne}$? The mass of $^{22}_{11}\text{Na}$ is 21.994 436 u and the mass of $^{22}_{10}\text{Ne}$ is 21.991 385 u.

9. Explain whether the atomic number can increase during nuclear decay. Support your answer with an example.

10. Compare the annual average radiation exposure from natural sources with the dose you would receive from a dental X ray.

11. Identify each type of decay in this series, and name the parent and daughter elements.

   (a) $^{232}_{90}\text{Th} \rightarrow {}^{228}_{88}\text{Ra}^* + {}^{4}_{2}\alpha$

   (b) $^{22}_{11}\text{Na} \rightarrow {}^{22}_{10}\text{Ne} + {}^{0}_{+1}\beta + \nu$

   (c) $^{228}_{88}\text{Ra}^* \rightarrow {}^{228}_{88}\text{Ra} + \gamma$

   (d) $^{228}_{88}\text{Ra} \rightarrow {}^{228}_{89}\text{Ac} + {}^{0}_{-1}\beta + \bar{\nu}$

   (e) $^{228}_{89}\text{Ac} \rightarrow {}^{228}_{90}\text{Th} + {}^{0}_{-1}\beta + \bar{\nu}$

   (f) $^{228}_{90}\text{Th} \rightarrow {}^{224}_{88}\text{Ra} + {}^{4}_{2}\alpha$

   (g) $^{0}_{1}\text{p} \rightarrow {}^{0}_{0}\text{n} + {}^{0}_{+1}\beta + \nu$

Extensions

12. In a process called electron capture, a nucleus absorbs an electron and emits a neutrino.

   (a) What effect does electron capture have on the atomic number?

   (b) Use nuclear notation to write the general form for electron capture.

   (c) Compare electron capture to beta decay.

13. Devise an experiment to test the hypothesis that gamma rays are emitted by nucleons jumping from higher energy levels to lower ones, similar to the energy-level transitions of electrons in an atom. What would you expect the spectrum of gamma rays emitted by a nucleus to look like?

14. Use library or Internet resources to learn how radon forms in the ground. Explain how radon can accumulate in basements in some areas. Why is this accumulation a health concern?

 e **TEST**

To check your understanding of radioactive decay, follow the eTEST links at www.pearsoned.ca/school/physicssource.

16.3 Radioactive Decay Rates

How can an archaeologist confidently tell you that a bison head found in southern Alberta provides evidence that First Nations peoples were here more than 5000 years ago? Why do doctors sometimes inject patients with radioactive dyes? In this section, you will be introduced to the concepts of radioactive decay rate and half-life, and begin to see how understanding the behaviour of radioactive elements can provide us with a glimpse into the past or give us powerful techniques to diagnose and combat disease.

16-3 QuickLab

Simulating Radioactive Decay

Problem

Are decay rates of atoms predictable?

Materials

container with 100 pennies
graph paper

Procedure

Work in groups of two or three.

1. (a) Pour the pennies onto a flat surface and spread them out. Put aside any pennies that are tails up. These pennies have "decayed."

   (b) Count the remaining pennies and put them back into the container. Record this count in a table.

2. Predict how many pennies will remain if you repeat step 1 two more times.

3. Repeat step 1 a total of eight times.

4. Pool your results with the other groups in the class.

5. Use the pooled data to draw a graph of how the number of pennies remaining varies with time.

Questions

1. How many pennies were left after you had done step 1 three times? Does this result match your prediction?

2. If you repeat the experiment, will you get exactly the same results each time? Explain.

3. Suppose that step 1 takes 2 min each time.

   (a) How long would it take for the number of pennies remaining to decrease by half? How long will it take until only about an eighth of the pennies remain? How are these two time intervals related?

   (b) Try to find a formula to predict how many pennies will remain at any given time.

Activity and Decay Constant

The radioactive decay of a specific nucleus is unpredictable. The nucleus could decay in the next minute, or tomorrow, or thousands of years from now. However, you can accurately predict how many nuclei in a sample will decay in a given time.

The **decay constant (λ)** is the probability of any given nucleus decaying in a unit of time. The decay constant is a property of each particular isotope. For example, radium-226 has a decay constant of 1.4×10^{-11} s^{-1}, indicating that each individual nucleus in a sample of radium-226 has a probability of 1.4×10^{-11} of decaying in 1 s. The greater the decay constant, the faster an isotope will decay.

decay constant: probability of a nucleus decaying in a given time

The **activity (A)** or **decay rate** is the number of nuclei in a sample that decay within a given time. Activity is usually measured in decays per second, or **becquerels (Bq).** A highly radioactive sample has many radioactive decays each second. Activity and the decay constant are related by this formula:

$$A = \frac{\Delta N}{\Delta t} = -\lambda N$$

where N is the number of radioactive nuclei, Δt is the time interval, and λ is the decay constant.

Example 16.11

Carbon-14 has a decay constant of 3.8×10^{-12} s^{-1}. What is the activity of a sample that contains 2.0×10^{15} carbon-14 nuclei?

Given
$\lambda = 3.8 \times 10^{-12}$ s^{-1}
$N = 2.0 \times 10^{15}$ atoms

Required
activity (A)

Analysis and Solution
Substitute the given values into the formula for activity:

$A = -\lambda N$

$\quad = -(3.8 \times 10^{-12}$ s$^{-1})(2.0 \times 10^{15})$

$\quad = -7.6 \times 10^3$ Bq

The negative sign indicates that the number of carbon-14 nuclei is decreasing.

Paraphrase
The initial activity of the sample is 7.6 kBq.

Practice Problems

1. Cobalt-60 has a decay constant of 4.1×10^{-9} s^{-1}. Find the activity of a sample containing 1.01×10^{22} cobalt-60 atoms.

2. A sample containing 5.00×10^{20} atoms has an activity of 2.50×10^{12} Bq. Find the decay constant of this sample.

Answers

1. 4.1×10^{13} Bq
2. 5.00×10^{-9} s^{-1}

The activity of a radioactive material decreases over time. The reason is simple: Radioactive decay "uses up" the unstable nuclei in the sample.

Half-life

Half-life is the time required for one-half of the radioactive nuclei in a sample to decay. For example, to diagnose thyroid problems, doctors sometimes inject patients with the radioactive isotope iodine-131, which has a half-life of about 192 h. Out of a dose of 20 μg of iodine-131, 10 μg will decay within 192 h. Only 5 μg of iodine-131 will remain after the next 192 h, then 2.5 μg after the next 192 h, and so on (see Figure 16.13). A common symbol for half-life is $t_{1/2}$.

e SIM

To see a simulation of half-life, follow the links at www.pearsoned.ca/school/physicssource.

The number of nuclei of the original radioisotope left in a sample is given by the equation

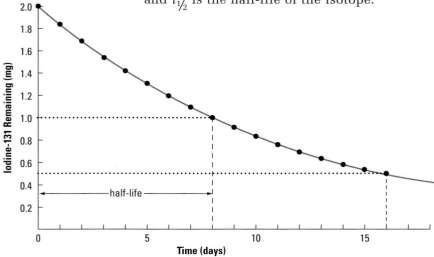

$$N = N_0\left(\frac{1}{2}\right)^{\frac{t}{t_{1/2}}}$$

where t is the time elapsed, N_0 is the number of nuclei of the original radioisotope when $t = 0$, and $t_{1/2}$ is the half-life of the isotope.

▲ **Figure 16.13**   A graph showing the radioactive decay of iodine-131

Example 16.12

Carbon-14 has a half-life of 5730 years. How long will it take for the quantity of carbon-14 in a sample to drop to one-eighth of the initial quantity?

Given
$t_{1/2} = 5730$ years
$N = \frac{1}{8}N_0$

Required
time (t)

Analysis and Solution
$$N = N_0\left(\frac{1}{2}\right)^{\frac{t}{t_{1/2}}} = \frac{1}{8}N_0$$

So, $\left(\frac{1}{2}\right)^{\frac{t}{t_{1/2}}} = \frac{1}{8} = \left(\frac{1}{2}\right)^3$

$\frac{t}{t_{1/2}} = 3$

$t = 3t_{1/2}$

$= 3 \times 5730$ years

$= 17\ 190$ years

Paraphrase
It will take just over 17 000 years for the amount of carbon-14 in a sample to drop to one-eighth of its original value.

Practice Problems

1. Astatine-218 has a half-life of only 1.6 s. About how long will it take for 99% of a sample of astatine-218 to decay?

2. Radium-226 has a half-life of 1600 years. What percentage of a sample of radium-226 will remain after 8000 years?

Answers
1. about 11 s
2. 3.125%

Example 16.13

Radon-222 has a half-life of 3.82 days. What proportion of a sample of this isotope will remain after 2 weeks?

Given

$t_{1/2} = 3.82$ days

$t = 14$ days

Required

proportion remaining after 14 days

Analysis and Solution

The proportion remaining is the ratio $\dfrac{N}{N_0}$.

$$N = N_0\left(\frac{1}{2}\right)^{\frac{t}{t_{1/2}}}$$

$$= N_0\left(\frac{1}{2}\right)^{\frac{14}{3.82}}$$

$$= N_0\left(\frac{1}{2}\right)^{3.66}$$

$$= 0.079N_0$$

$$\frac{N}{N_0} = 0.079 \text{ or } 7.9\%$$

Note that you can use the exponent or ^ key on a scientific or graphing calculator to evaluate powers of $\dfrac{1}{2}$. On a graphing calculator, you could enter (1/2)^(14/3.82).

Paraphrase

Only 7.9% of a sample of radon-222 will remain after 2 weeks.

Practice Problems

1. Strontium-90 has a half-life of 29.1 years. What proportion of a sample of this isotope will be left after 100 years?

2. Tritium ($^3_1$H) has a half-life of 12.3 years. How much of a 100-mg sample of tritium will be left after 5.0 years?

Answers

1. 9.2%

2. 75%

Applications of Radiation

The Rutherford gold-foil experiment that you learned about in Chapter 15 was one of the first examples of the use of nuclear energy (the release of alpha particles in the decay of radium nuclei) to study the inner working of atoms. Scientists apply radioactive decay in many other fields of scientific research, including archaeology. Radioactive compounds also have numerous industrial applications and are routinely used to diagnose and treat diseases.

During their first experiments with radium, Pierre and Marie Curie noticed that its radiation could burn the skin, but the wound would heal without forming scar tissue. They realized that radium could therefore be used to treat cancer. To ensure that this treatment was readily available to cancer patients, the Curies refused to patent their discovery.

Radiotherapy is particularly useful for treating cancer because cancer cells are more susceptible to the effects of radiation than healthy tissue is. Also, the radiation is concentrated on the cancer, and kept away from the surrounding tissue as much as possible (Figure 16.14).

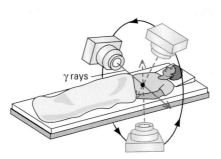

▲ **Figure 16.14** Rotating the radiation source around the patient minimizes damage to normal tissue.

There is now a wide variety of radiation treatments. Often, a carefully focussed beam of gamma rays is directed at the tumour. Another common method is to inject the tumour with a short-lived radioisotope that emits alpha-particles.

Questions

1. Give two reasons why gamma rays are used for the beam type of radiotherapy.

2. Why does injected radiotherapy use an isotope that undergoes alpha decay rather than one that gives off beta or gamma radiation?

Radioactive Dating

Nearly 6000 years ago, First Nations people of southwestern Alberta devised an ingenious method for hunting the vast herds of bison on the plains. By setting up barriers along a carefully chosen route, the First Nations people funnelled the bison toward a hidden cliff and then drove them over the edge. There were about 150 buffalo jumps in Alberta. The most famous, Head-Smashed-In Buffalo Jump, is now a United Nations World Heritage Site (see Chapter 2, Figure 2.68). By carefully measuring the ratio of carbon-12 to carbon-14 in bones found at this site, archaeologists have shown that it was used continuously for over 5500 years.

How did this carbon ratio indicate the age of these bones? High-energy neutrons in cosmic rays produce the radioisotope carbon-14 by colliding with nitrogen atoms high in the atmosphere:

$$^{1}_{0}n + {}^{14}_{7}N \rightarrow {}^{14}_{6}C + {}^{1}_{1}H$$

This carbon-14 diffuses throughout the atmosphere. Some of it is absorbed by plants and enters the food chain. So, a small proportion of all the carbon metabolized by plants and animals is carbon-14. Carbon-14 undergoes β^- decay to form nitrogen-14, whereas carbon-12 is completely stable. When living matter dies, it stops absorbing carbon, and the proportion of carbon-14 gradually decreases as it decays (see Figure 16.15). The half-life of carbon-14 is 5730 years.

e **MATH**

To plot the decay rate of carbon-14 and other radioactive elements, and to learn how to mathematically determine a radioactive sample's age based on the percentage of the sample remaining, visit www.pearsoned.ca/school/physicssource.

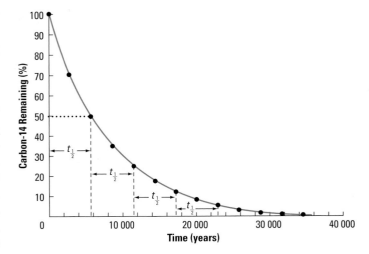

▲ **Figure 16.15** Carbon-14 content as a function of the age of an artifact

For archaeologists, bone fragments and other artifacts found at Head-Smashed-In Buffalo Jump are like clocks that show when the living matter stopped absorbing carbon. Suppose, for example, that the proportion of carbon-14 in a bone fragment is about 40% of that in living tissue. Since $\left(\dfrac{1}{2}\right)^{1.32} = 40\%$, the carbon-14 has been decaying for about 1.3 half-lives, provided that the ratio of carbon-14 to carbon-12 in the atmosphere is the same now as when the buffalo was alive. Thus, the age of the bone fragment is roughly $1.3 \times 5730 \approx 7500$ years. Accurate estimates require more detailed calculations that take into account factors such as variations in the proportion of carbon-14 in the atmosphere through the ages.

Geologists estimate the age of rocks and geological formations with calculations based on isotopes with much longer half-lives. Such calculations are one of the methods that scientists use to estimate the age of Earth.

Industrial Applications

Manufacturers of sheet materials such as paper, plastics, and metal foils often monitor the thickness of the material with a gauge that measures how much of the beta radiation from a calibrated source passes through the material. Unlike mechanical thickness gauges, such gauges need not touch the material they measure, so they do not get worn down and have less risk of marking the material. Gamma rays can pass through thick metal parts to expose a photographic plate. The resulting image can reveal hidden air bubbles or hairline cracks, similar to the way X rays produce images of the inside of a patient's body. Gamma-ray photographs are a non-destructive way of testing items that X rays cannot penetrate, including structural materials, jet engines, and welded joints in pipelines. Radioactive tracers are also used in pipelines to measure flow and to detect underground leaks.

Some uses of radiation are controversial. For example, beta radiation from tritium powers runway lights and emergency exit signs that require no electricity. However, several people have received harmful doses of radiation when tritium lights have been damaged. Critics of these lights argue that other technologies can provide reliable lighting during power failures without any risk of radiation exposure. Perhaps the most controversial application is the irradiation of food to kill bacteria, insects, and parasites. Although this process sterilizes the food and thereby prolongs its shelf life, there are concerns that the radiation might also alter the food in ways that make it harmful or less nutritious.

Concept Check

Why is beta radiation used for measuring the thickness of sheet materials, whereas gamma radiation is used for testing structural materials?

Knowledge

1. What fraction of a radioactive material remains after four half-lives?

2. How many decays per second occur in a radioactive sample containing 6.4×10^{23} atoms of a material that has a decay constant of 5.8×10^{-12} s^{-1}?

3. Which has the greater activity, 1 g of material with a half-life of 1 ms or 1 g of material with a half-life of 1 year? Explain your answer.

Applications

4. Analysis of a rock sample shows that only $\dfrac{1}{16}$ of the original amount of chlorine-36 remains in the rock. Estimate the age of the rock given that the half-life of chlorine-36 is 3.0×10^5 years.

5. A radioactive tracer used in a medical test has a half-life of 2.6 h. What proportion of this tracer will remain after 24 h?

6. An archaeologist finds a wooden arrow shaft with a proportion of carbon-14 that is about 25% of that in a living tree branch. Estimate the age of the arrow.

7. A radioactive sample has an activity of 2.5 MBq and a half-life of 12 h. What will be the activity of the sample a week later?

8. Graph the data in this table. Then use your graph to estimate
   (a) the half-life of the material
   (b) the activity of the sample at time $t = 0$

Time (h)	Activity (decays/min)
1	3027
2	2546
4	1800
6	1273
8	900
10	636

Extensions

9. A dealer in antiquities offers to sell you an "authentic" dinosaur bone for a mere $100. He shows you a certificate indicating that carbon-14 dating determined that the bone is 65 million years old. Why should you be suspicious?

10. Do a Web search on use of irradiation in food production and distribution. Prepare a summary of the arguments for and against this technology.

11. (a) What is depleted uranium?
    (b) Why is depleted uranium used in armour-piercing shells and in ballast for aircraft?
    (c) Why are these applications controversial?

e TEST

To check your understanding of radioactive decay, follow the eTEST links at www.pearsoned.ca/school/physicssource.

16.4 Fission and Fusion

▲ **Figure 16.16** The doomsday clock from the *Bulletin of the Atomic Scientists*

In 1945, a group of the scientists who had designed and built the atomic bomb founded a magazine as part of an ongoing campaign to prevent this weapon from ever being used again. The *Bulletin of the Atomic Scientists* features a doomsday clock that symbolizes their estimate of the risk of a nuclear war (Figure 16.16). Since 2002, the clock has showed just seven minutes to midnight — a sobering reminder of the dangers posed by the enormous energy that nuclear reactions can release.

The graph in Figure 16.4 (page 796) shows that binding energy per nucleon has a maximum value of about 8.7 MeV when the atomic mass number, *A*, is from 58 to 62 — the values for isotopes of iron and nickel. Up to this maximum, the binding energy per nucleon generally increases as *A* increases. Then, as *A* increases further, the binding energy per nucleon gradually decreases. The shape of this graph indicates that two distinct types of reactions can release energy from nuclei.

Fission: When a nucleus with $A > 120$ splits into smaller nuclei, they have greater binding energy per nucleon. This fission reaction gives off energy equal to the difference between the binding energy of the original nucleus and the total binding energy of the products.

Fusion: When two low-mass nuclei combine to form a single nucleus with $A < 60$, the resulting nucleus is more tightly bound. This fusion reaction gives off energy equal to the difference between the total binding energy of the original nuclei and the binding energy of the product.

For both nuclear fission and fusion, the energy released, ΔE, is

$$\Delta E = E_{b_f} - E_{b_i} = (\text{net change in mass defect}) \times c^2$$

where E_{b_i} is the total binding energy of the original nucleus or nuclei, and E_{b_f} is the total binding energy of the product(s).

Since the binding energies correspond to the mass defects for the nuclei, the energy released corresponds to the decrease in the total mass defect. This change in the total mass defect equals the change in the total mass. Thus, the energy released corresponds to the mass that the reaction transforms into energy:

$$\Delta E = (m_f - m_i) \times c^2$$

where m_i is the total mass of the original nucleus or nuclei, and m_f is the total mass of the product(s).

Concept Check

Why does a nuclear reaction that increases the binding energy per nucleon release energy? Use an analogy to help explain this release of energy.

Nuclear Fission

Often, fission results from a free neutron colliding with a large nucleus. The nucleus absorbs the neutron, forming a highly unstable isotope that breaks up almost instantly. Figure 16.17 shows one of the ways that uranium-235 can split into two lighter nuclei.

In the next example, you will calculate the energy released during a fission reaction. Note that because the mass differences are larger, atomic masses are given to three decimal places.

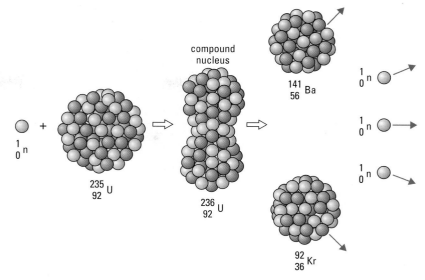

▲ **Figure 16.17** Absorbing a neutron causes uranium-235 to undergo fission in a CANDU nuclear reactor.

Example 16.14

Calculate the energy released by the fission reaction
$^{235}_{92}U + ^{1}_{0}n \rightarrow ^{141}_{56}Ba + ^{92}_{36}Kr + 3\,^{1}_{0}n$.

Given
Initial mass: $^{235}_{92}U$ plus one neutron
Final mass: $^{141}_{56}Ba$, $^{92}_{36}Kr$, and three neutrons

Required
energy released (ΔE)

Analysis and Solution
First, calculate the net change in mass resulting from the reaction. The initial neutron balances the mass of one of the product neutrons.

$m_i = 235.044$ u

$m_f = m_{^{141}_{56}Ba} + m_{^{92}_{36}Kr} + 2m_n$
$\quad = 140.914$ u $+ 91.926$ u $+ 2(1.009$ u$)$
$\quad = 234.858$ u

$m_i - m_f = 235.044$ u $- 234.858$ u
$\quad = 0.186$ u

Now, use mass-energy equivalence to calculate the energy released.
1 u is equivalent to 931.5 MeV, so

$\Delta E = 0.186$ u $\times \dfrac{931.5 \text{ MeV}}{1 \text{ u}}$

$\quad = 173$ MeV

Paraphrase
The fission of an atom of uranium-235 into barium-141 and krypton-92 releases 173 MeV of energy.

Practice Problems

1. Calculate the energy released by the reaction
$^{235}_{92}U + ^{1}_{0}n \rightarrow ^{94}_{40}Zr + ^{139}_{52}Te + 3\,^{1}_{0}n$.

2. A uranium-235 nucleus absorbs a neutron and then splits into a bromine nucleus ($^{87}_{35}Br$), a lanthanum nucleus ($^{146}_{57}La$), and additional neutrons. How many neutrons are released in this fission reaction? Express this reaction as a balanced equation.

3. How much energy is released in the reaction in question 2?

Answers

1. 172 MeV
2. $^{235}_{92}U + ^{1}_{0}n \rightarrow ^{87}_{35}Br + ^{146}_{57}La + 3\,^{1}_{0}n$
3. 167 MeV

Comparing Chemical Energy with Nuclear Energy

When you sit by a campfire, the warmth that you feel is due to the chemical energy released by the combustion of wood. All chemical processes, including combustion, involve electrons moving from one energy level to another. In Chapter 15, you learned that such transitions typically release no more than a few tens of electron volts. Example 16.15 shows that a nuclear process can release a vastly greater amount of energy.

Example 16.15

Burning 1 kg of gasoline releases about 4.4×10^7 J. Compare this energy to the energy released by the fission of 1 kg of uranium-235 into barium-141 and krypton-92.

Given
chemical energy content of gasoline = 4.4×10^7 J/kg

Required
ratio of the energy content of gasoline to that of uranium-235

Analysis and Solution
From Example 16.14, you know that uranium-235 has about 173 MeV of nuclear potential energy per atom, assuming fission into barium and krypton.

Use the atomic mass of uranium-235 to calculate the number of atoms in 1 kg of this isotope. Then calculate the potential energy per kilogram for comparison with gasoline.

$$m_{^{235}_{92}U} = 235.044 \text{ u} \times \frac{1.660\ 539 \times 10^{-27} \text{ kg}}{1 \text{ u}}$$

$$= 3.902\ 997 \times 10^{-25} \text{ kg}$$

$$\text{Number of atoms in 1 kg of } {}^{235}_{92}U = \frac{1 \text{ kg}}{3.902\ 997 \times 10^{-25} \text{ kg}}$$

$$= 2.562\ 133 \times 10^{24}$$

$$\text{Energy content of } {}^{235}_{92}U = (2.562\ 133 \times 10^{24} \frac{\text{atoms}}{\text{kg}})(173 \frac{\text{MeV}}{\text{atom}})$$

$$= 4.43 \times 10^{32} \frac{\text{eV}}{\text{kg}} \times \frac{1.60 \times 10^{-19} \text{ J}}{1 \text{ eV}}$$

$$= 7.09 \times 10^{13} \text{ J/kg}$$

$$\frac{\text{Energy content of } {}^{235}_{92}U}{\text{Energy content of gasoline}} = \frac{7.09 \times 10^{13} \text{ J/kg}}{4.4 \times 10^7 \text{ J/kg}}$$

$$= 1.6 \times 10^6$$

Paraphrase
The nuclear potential energy of 1 kg of uranium-235 is about 1.6 million times greater than the chemical potential energy of 1 kg of gasoline.

Practice Problems

1. A typical family car requires approximately 1600 MJ of energy to travel 500 km.
   (a) How many kilograms of gasoline does it take to provide this energy?
   (b) What mass of uranium-235 would provide the same energy?

Answers

1. (a) 36 kg
   (b) 22 mg

A nucleus is much smaller than an atom. How does this difference in size make nuclear reactions much more energetic than chemical reactions?

Fusion

What powers the Sun? The discovery of the nucleus and of mass-energy equivalence provided the key to this question, which had puzzled scientists for thousands of years. In the early 1920s, the British-American astrophysicist Cecilia Payne-Gaposchkin (1900–1979) showed that the Sun consists primarily of hydrogen (about 73%) and helium (about 27%). Noting that four protons have 0.7% more mass than a helium nucleus, the British astrophysicist Arthur Stanley Eddington (1882–1944) suggested that a fusion process might power the stars.

In the 1930s, the young German physicist Hans Bethe (1906–2005) worked out the details of how hydrogen nuclei could release energy by fusing together to form helium. In the Sun and smaller stars, the process, called the **proton-proton chain** (Figure 16.18), has three steps. First, two hydrogen nuclei combine to form deuterium (an isotope of hydrogen with one neutron), an antielectron, and a neutrino. Then, another hydrogen nucleus combines with the deuterium nucleus to produce a helium-3 nucleus and a gamma ray. Finally, two of the helium-3 nuclei combine to produce a helium-4 nucleus, two hydrogen nuclei, and a gamma ray. In order for these reactions to occur, the nuclei must have enough kinetic energy to overcome the electrostatic repulsion between them.

info **BIT**

In the mid-1930s, Hans Bethe won a $500 prize for a paper on fusion in stars. He used the money to get his mother out of Nazi Germany. Bethe won the Nobel Prize for physics in 1967 and helped found the *Bulletin of the Atomic Scientists*.

proton-proton chain:
fusion process in which four hydrogen nuclei combine to form a helium nucleus

Step	Reaction	Energy Released
1	$2\ {}_1^1\text{H} \rightarrow {}_1^2\text{H} + {}_1^0\beta + \nu$ (twice)	0.42 MeV (twice)
2	${}_1^1\text{H} + {}_1^2\text{H} \rightarrow {}_2^3\text{He} + \gamma$ (twice)	5.49 MeV (twice)
3	$2\ {}_2^3\text{He} \rightarrow {}_2^4\text{He} + 2\ {}_1^1\text{H} + \gamma$	12.85 MeV
Total	$4\ {}_1^1\text{H} \rightarrow {}_2^4\text{He} + 2\ {}_1^0\beta + 2\nu + 3\gamma$	24.67 MeV

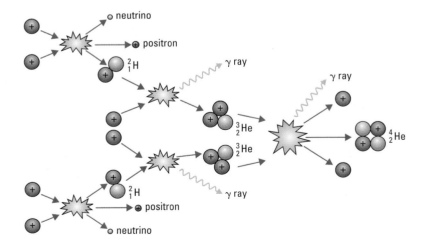

▲ **Figure 16.18**   The proton-proton chain

Example 16.16

The Sun radiates about 4×10^{26} W and has a mass of 1.99×10^{30} kg. Astronomers estimate that the Sun can convert only the innermost 10% of its hydrogen into helium. Estimate how long the Sun can continue to shine at its present intensity.

Given
Power $= 4 \times 10^{26}$ W $m_{\text{Sun}} = 1.99 \times 10^{30}$ kg
Hydrogen available for conversion = 10% of total hydrogen

Required
Time the Sun will take to convert 10% of its hydrogen into helium (t)

Analysis and Solution
The fusion of four hydrogen atoms produces 24.67 MeV. To find the rate at which helium nuclei are produced, divide the Sun's power by the energy released during the formation of each helium nucleus:

$$\text{Rate of helium production} = \frac{\text{power of Sun}}{\text{energy released per helium atom}}$$

$$= \frac{4 \times 10^{26} \text{ W}}{24.67 \text{ MeV/atom}}$$

$$= \frac{4 \times 10^{26} \; \frac{\cancel{J}}{\text{s}}}{\left(24.67 \; \frac{\cancel{\text{MeV}}}{\text{atom}}\right)\left(\frac{1.60 \times 10^{-13} \; \cancel{J}}{1 \; \cancel{\text{MeV}}}\right)}$$

$$= 1.01 \times 10^{38} \text{ atoms/s}$$

Multiply by 4 to find the rate at which the Sun converts hydrogen atoms into helium. Then, find the mass of hydrogen converted each second by multiplying the number of atoms converted each second by the mass of a hydrogen atom:

$$\text{Rate of hydrogen conversion} = 4\left(1.01 \times 10^{38} \; \frac{\cancel{\text{atoms}}}{\text{s}}\right)\left(1.67 \times 10^{-27} \; \frac{\text{kg}}{\cancel{\text{atom}}}\right)$$

$$= 6.77 \times 10^{11} \text{ kg/s}$$

Hydrogen makes up 73% of the mass of the Sun, but only 10% of this hydrogen can be converted into helium.
The lifespan of the Sun approximately equals the amount of hydrogen that can be converted divided by the conversion rate.

$$t = \frac{\text{amount of hydrogen available}}{\text{rate of conversion}}$$

$$= \frac{1.99 \times 10^{30} \text{ kg} \times 73\% \times 10\%}{6.77 \times 10^{11} \text{ kg/s}}$$

$$= 2 \times 10^{17} \text{ s} \quad \text{or} \quad 6 \times 10^{9} \text{ years}$$

Paraphrase
The Sun can continue to produce energy at its present rate for about 6 billion years.

Practice Problems

1. (a) How many helium nuclei does a star with a power of 1.6×10^{25} W produce every second?
   (b) Estimate how much helium this star has produced if it is four billion years old.

Answers
1. (a) 4.1×10^{36}
   (b) 3.4×10^{27} kg

Concept Check

Why can fusion reactions occur only at extremely high temperatures?

The cores of massive stars can reach temperatures high enough for helium nuclei to combine to form carbon and oxygen. In some stars, these elements can undergo further fusion. The extent of this **nucleosynthesis** depends on the star's density, temperature, and the concentration of the various elements. Current theory suggests that synthesis of elements heavier than iron and nickel occurs only during the explosion of **supernovae**. Such explosions distribute these elements throughout the cosmos. So, the uranium fuel for today's nuclear power stations may have come from the explosion of a massive star billions of years ago.

A hydrogen-fusion reactor might be an almost ideal energy source. Hydrogen is the most abundant of elements, and the end product, helium-4, is harmless. However, controlling and sustaining a fusion reaction for generating power is extremely difficult. To start the fusion process, the hydrogen has to be heated to a temperature between 45 million and 400 million kelvins, depending on which isotopes are used. Then, this extremely hot gas has to be contained so that the fusion reactions can continue. Researchers are using powerful lasers to generate the necessary temperatures and magnetic fields to contain the fusion reactions. However, the latest experiments have sustained fusion for only a few seconds and produced only slightly more energy than it took to run the reactor (see Figure 16.19). It will take major technological advances to make fusion power practical.

nucleosynthesis: formation of elements by the fusion of lighter elements

supernova: sudden, extremely powerful explosion of a massive star

e **WEB**

To learn more about fusion reactors, follow the links at www.pearsoned.ca/school/physicssource.

▲ **Figure 16.19** The Joint European Toroid (JET) fusion reactor

16.4 Check and Reflect

Knowledge

1. (a) Complete this nuclear reaction:
$$^{235}_{92}\text{U} \rightarrow ^{140}_{54}\text{Xe} + ? + 2\,^{1}_{0}\text{n}$$

   (b) Does this reaction involve fission or fusion?

2. What happens to the binding energy per nucleon in a nuclear reaction that releases energy?

3. An iron nucleus of binding energy 492 MeV fuses with a silicon nucleus of binding energy 237 MeV to form a nucleus with binding energy 718 MeV. Will this reaction release energy? Explain why or why not.

4. (a) Which elements are most likely to undergo fission?

   (b) Which elements are most likely to undergo fusion?

5. A neutron is emitted when aluminium-27 absorbs an alpha particle.

   (a) What isotope does this reaction create?

   (b) Write the process for the reaction.

Applications

6. (a) Write the reaction formula for the fusion of helium-4 with oxygen-16.

   (b) How much energy does this reaction release?

7. (a) What particle is emitted when deuterium ($^{2}_{1}\text{H}$) and tritium ($^{3}_{1}\text{H}$) fuse to form helium?

   (b) How much energy does this reaction release?

8. A CANDU-6 nuclear reactor can generate 700 MW of electrical power. A CANDU power plant transforms about 27% of its nuclear energy into electrical energy, with the rest being lost primarily as heat.

(a) If the plant uses uranium-235 as fuel and the average energy released per uranium nucleus is 200 MeV, how many nuclei undergo fission each second when the reactor is running at full power?

(b) Estimate how many kilograms of uranium-235 a CANDU-6 reactor uses in a year. List any assumptions you make.

Extensions

9. (a) In stars much more massive than the Sun, iron-56 will eventually be produced in their centres. Suppose that two iron-56 nuclei fuse. Complete the following reaction and identify the element produced: $^{56}_{26}\text{Fe} + ^{56}_{26}\text{Fe} \rightarrow$

   (b) The element formed in the reaction in (a) has a mass of 111.917 010 u. Show that this reaction absorbs rather than releases energy.

   (c) Explain why stars like the Sun do not produce elements heavier than iron.

10. (a) Research the radioactive wastes produced by nuclear reactors. List the major isotopes produced and their half-lives.

    (b) Briefly outline some of the methods for storing and disposing of these wastes.

11. Compare and contrast the risks and benefits of generating electricity with coal and with nuclear reactors.

e TEST

To check your understanding of fission and fusion, follow the eTest links at www.pearsoned.ca/school/physicssource.

Key Terms and Concepts

femto
proton
neutron
nucleon
atomic number
neutron number
atomic mass number
isotope
atomic mass unit (u)
strong nuclear force
binding energy

mass defect
alpha radiation
beta radiation
gamma radiation
transmute
parent element
daughter element
beta-negative (β^-) decay
beta (β) particle
neutrino
weak nuclear force

antimatter
positron (e+ or $^0_1\beta$)
beta-positive ($\beta+$) decay
gamma (γ) decay
radioactive decay series
radiation sickness
genetic damage
radioisotope
gray (Gy)
sievert (Sv)

relative biological
    effectiveness (RBE)
decay constant
activity (A) or decay rate
becquerel (Bq)
half-life
fission
fusion
proton-proton chain
nucleosynthesis
supernova

Key Equations

Binding energy: $E_b = E_{nucleons} - E_{nucleus}$

Mass defect: $\Delta m = m_{nucleons} - m_{nucleus}$
$$= Zm^1_{1H} + Nm_{neutron} - m_{atom}$$

α decay: $^A_Z X \rightarrow ^{A-4}_{Z-2}Y + ^4_2\alpha$

β^- decay: $^A_Z X \rightarrow_{Z+1}^A Y + _{-1}^0\beta + \bar{\nu}$

γ decay: $^A_Z X^* \rightarrow ^A_Z X + \gamma$

β^+ decay: $^A_Z X \rightarrow_{Z-1}^A Y + _1^0\beta + \nu$

Activity: $A = \dfrac{\Delta N}{\Delta t} = -\lambda N$

Half-life: $N = N_0\left(\dfrac{1}{2}\right)^{\frac{t}{t_{1/2}}}$

Nuclear energy released: $\Delta E = (m_i - m_f) \times c^2$

Conceptual Overview

Summarize this chapter by copying and completing this concept map.

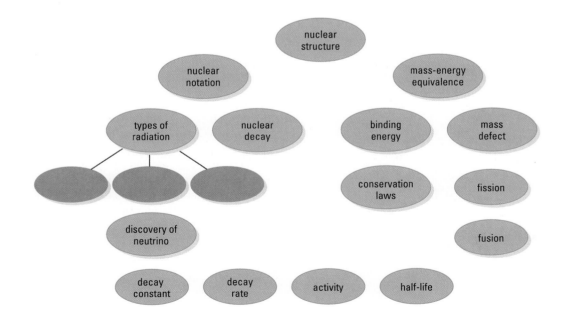

Chapter 16 Nuclear reactions are among the most powerful energy sources in nature.   825

Knowledge

1. (16.1) True or false? A nucleus always contains more neutrons than protons.

2. (16.1) True or false? The atomic mass number for an atom is always greater than the atomic number.

3. (16.1) What is the term for elements that have the same atomic number but different neutron numbers?

4. (16.1) Explain how these nuclei are similar and how they differ: $^{233}_{92}U$, $^{235}_{92}U$, $^{238}_{92}U$.

5. (16.1) How many neutrons are in a nucleus of $^{115}_{55}Cs$? How many protons?

6. (16.1) Convert 50 MeV to joules.

7. (16.1) Calculate the energy equivalent for 1 g of matter.

8. (16.1) Calculate the energy equivalent for 2.3 u of mass.

9. (16.1) Calculate the mass equivalent for 300 MeV.

10. (16.1) Calculate the binding energy for a nucleus that has a mass defect of 0.022 u.

11. (16.2) True or false? A decay process cannot change the atomic number of a nucleus.

12. (16.2) What is the charge on
    (a) a beta particle?
    (b) an alpha particle?
    (c) a gamma ray?

13. (16.2) Explain how each of these decay processes changes nuclear structure:
    (a) alpha decay
    (b) beta decay
    (c) gamma decay

14. (16.2) Describe this decay in words, identifying the parent element, the daughter element, and the type of decay: $^{43}_{19}K \rightarrow {}^{43}_{20}Ca + {}^{0}_{-1}\beta + \overline{\nu}$.

15. (16.2) Which of α, β, and γ radiation is the most penetrating, and which is the least penetrating?

16. (16.2) Explain why physicists think that radioactivity originates from nuclei.

17. (16.2) Compare the radiation dose that North Americans typically receive each year from radon and from diagnostic X rays. Which of these sources poses the greater health hazard?

18. (16.3) What is the activity of a sample that contains 1.5×10^{20} nuclei of an element with a decay constant of 1.2×10^{-12} s^{-1}?

19. (16.3) After 1.5 h, the number of radioactive nuclei in a sample has dropped from 5.0×10^{20} to 2.5×10^{20}. How many of these nuclei will remain after another 6 h?

20. (16.3) Explain why carbon-14 dating is not useful for determining the age of a rock sample.

21. (16.4) Why do all of the elements used as fuel in nuclear power plants have $A > 200$?

22. (16.4) What is the primary energy source for most stars?

23. (16.4) List the steps in the proton-proton chain.

Applications

24. Calculate the binding energy per nucleon for the following nuclei:
    (a) ^4_2He
    (b) $^{28}_{14}Si$
    (c) $^{58}_{26}Fe$
    (d) $^{235}_{92}U$

25. (a) Write the process for the β^+ decay of $^{52}_{26}Fe$.
    (b) Show that this process conserves charge and atomic mass number.

26. (a) What parent element decays into lead-208 by emitting an alpha particle?
    (b) Estimate the kinetic energy of the alpha particle.

27. (a) Write the complete decay process for the transmutation of $^{22}_{11}Na$ into $^{22}_{10}Ne$.
    (b) Calculate the energy released in this decay.

28. In the oldest campsites yet discovered in Alberta, archaeologists have found materials that contain about a quarter of their original carbon-14. Estimate the age of these campsites.

29. Until the early 1950s, a paint containing radium-226 was used to make the dials on some clocks, watches, and aircraft instruments glow in the dark. Radium-226 has a decay constant of 1.98×10^{-11} s^{-1}.

   (a) If the activity of one of these clocks is 0.10 MBq, how many atoms of radium-226 are on the dial?

   (b) Calculate the mass of radium on the dial.

   (c) The half-life of radium is 1600 years. Calculate the activity that the clock will have in 5000 years.

30. Graph the data in this table. Use your graph to estimate

   (a) the activity of the sample when $t = 5$ h

   (b) the half-life of the radioactive material in the sample

Time (h)	Activity (Bq)	Time (h)	Activity (Bq)
0	1000.0	14	80.5
2	697.7	16	56.1
4	486.8	18	39.2
6	339.6	20	27.3
8	236.9	22	19.1
10	165.3	24	13.3
12	115.3		

31. Calculate the energy released when three helium-4 nuclei combine to form a carbon-12 nucleus.

32. You are designing a thermoelectric power supply for a space probe. The probe will need 20 W of electricity for 14.5 years. The efficiency of thermal to electrical energy conversion is 15%. You are considering using polonium-208 as the fuel for the power supply.

   (a) What is the key advantage of polonium over a chemical fuel?

   (b) How much polonium will you need? Polonium-208 has a decay constant of 7.57×10^{-9} s^{-1} and a half-life of 2.9 years. $^{208}_{84}$Po decays into $^{204}_{82}$Pb.

Extensions

33. In 1918, Rutherford observed that bombarding nitrogen atoms with alpha particles produced oxygen and hydrogen. Use nuclear notation to write two reactions that could account for these products. Which reaction is more likely to occur? Explain your reasoning. How could you check your conclusion?

34. There have been over 2000 tests of nuclear weapons, including 711 conducted in the atmosphere or in the ocean. What radioactive products did these tests release? What health hazards result from this radioactive fallout?

35. Research nucleosynthesis in stars. List a sequence of fusion reactions that produces iron-56, and explain why smaller stars do not complete this sequence. How are the fusion reactions in the Sun likely to end?

Consolidate Your Understanding

1. Explain how atomic number, atomic mass number, and neutron number are related to the structure of the nucleus.

2. Use the concept of binding energy to explain why some nuclei are more stable than others.

3. Describe the differences between the alpha, beta, and gamma decays.

4. Explain how you can use conservation principles to predict the daughter elements created by a radioactive decay.

5. Distinguish between nuclear fission and nuclear fusion, and explain how to calculate the energy yield from either process.

Think About It

Review your answers to the Think About It questions on page 789. How would you answer each question now?

  TEST

To check your understanding of nuclear reactions, follow the eTEST links at www.pearsoned.ca/school/physicssource.

CHAPTER
17

The development of models of the structure of matter is ongoing.

Antimatter, quarks, particles appearing out of nowhere! Although these concepts may seem like science fiction, they are crucial for understanding the nature of matter.

You are about to enter the world of undetectable particles that blink in and out of existence. You will see that a calculation by a theoretical physicist in the 1920s led to sophisticated new medical technology that uses a previously unknown form of matter (Figure 17.1). You will learn about the peculiar properties of quarks, the elusive building blocks for protons, neutrons, and many other subatomic particles.

Quantum effects can make the subatomic world seem very strange indeed. This chapter introduces some of the most unusual and challenging ideas in all of physics. You will learn that experiments are showing that in some profound ways the universe is stranger than anyone could have imagined a century ago. The theories that you will explore next are exhilarating, difficult, weird, and yet elegant. They are a key to the next century of atomic physics.

Key Concepts

In this chapter, you will learn about:
- charge-to-mass ratio
- quantum mechanical model
- standard model of matter

Learning Outcomes

When you have completed this chapter, you will be able to:

Knowledge
- explain the discovery and identification of subatomic particles
- explain why high-energy particle accelerators are required
- describe the modern model of the proton and neutron
- compare and contrast elementary particles and their antiparticles
- describe beta decays

Science, Technology, and Society
- explain the use of concepts, models, and theories
- explain the link between scientific knowledge and new technologies

Skills
- observe relationships and plan investigations
- analyze data and apply models
- work as members of a team
- apply the skills and conventions of science

▲ **Figure 17.1** Recent findings in atomic physics may seem strange, but they have led to amazing advances in technology, as well as better models of the structure of matter.

Particle Tracking Simulation

Problem

What can magnetic tracking reveal about the properties and collisions of objects?

Materials

lid from shirt box or shoe box
magnetic metal marbles
glass marbles
iron filings
metre-sticks or wood slats

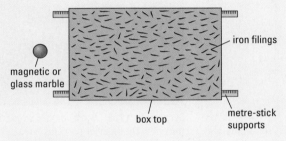

iron filings

magnetic or
glass marble

box top

metre-stick
supports

▲ **Figure 17.2**

Procedure

1 Turn the lid upside down and use metre-sticks or wood slats to support it above a smooth surface such as a tabletop. The gap should allow the marbles to roll freely under the lid.

2 Spread iron filings evenly over the lid (Figure 17.2).

3 Roll a glass marble and a magnetic marble under the lid and observe how they affect the filings.

4 Set the lid aside and place a line of five magnetic marbles spaced about 3 cm apart across the middle of the space between the supports. Estimate what percentage of glass marbles rolled between the supports will hit one of the five magnetic marbles.

5 Shake the lid to spread the filings evenly again and put it back on the supports. Then, roll glass marbles under the lid at least 10 times. After each collision, put the magnetic marbles back in line and spread the filings evenly. Note the number and shape of any tracks resulting from collisions between the glass marbles and the magnetic ones. Watch for any pattern in the formation of the tracks.

Questions

1. What can you conclude about the magnetic field from the glass marbles?

2. Calculate the percentage of glass marbles that appeared to collide with the magnetic marbles in step 5. How close was your estimate? Account for any difference between your estimate and your observations.

3. Did any factor appear to affect the length of the collision tracks?

4. How would you expect the tracks to change if you repeated step 5 using round plastic beads instead of glass marbles?

5. How could you use the electric field from charged particles to detect these particles? How could you detect uncharged particles?

Think About It

1. How can you tell if a particle is fundamental?

2. What did the measurement of beta decays reveal about the structure of matter?

3. How many fundamental particles are there?

Discuss your answers in a small group and record them for later reference.
As you complete each section of this chapter, review your answers to these questions. Note any changes in your ideas.

17.1 Detecting and Measuring Subatomic Particles

A skilled wilderness guide can tell a great deal about an animal from its tracks, not just identifying the animal but also estimating its age and how fast it was moving (Figure 17.3). In a similar way, physicists use tracks left by subatomic particles to identify the particles, study their interactions, and deduce the structure of matter (Figure 17.4).

▲ **Figure 17.3**   Tracks of an adult snowshoe hare. What do these tracks tell you about the hare's speed?

▲ **Figure 17.4**   Tracks of subatomic particles. The heavier particles have straighter tracks.

Cloud Chambers and Bubble Chambers

cloud chamber: a device that uses trails of droplets of condensed vapour to show the paths of charged particles

A **cloud chamber** contains dust-free air supersaturated with vapour from a liquid such as water or ethanol. The amount of vapour air can hold depends on temperature and pressure. Air is supersaturated when it contains more vapour than it would normally hold at a given temperature and pressure. So, the liquid and vapour in a cloud chamber are not in equilibrium, and a tiny disturbance can trigger condensation of vapour into droplets of liquid. A charged particle speeding through the supersaturated air will ionize some molecules along its path. The ions trigger condensation, forming a miniature cloud along the trajectory of the speeding particle. This cloud track shows the path of the particle the way a vapour trail formed by condensing exhaust gases shows the path of a jetliner through the sky.

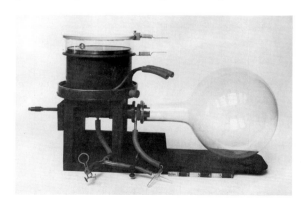

◀ **Figure 17.5**   One of Charles Wilson's cloud chambers. The large glass sphere is the expansion chamber, the rubber hoses are vacuum lines, the coiled wires are electrodes, and the black cylinder is the cloud chamber containing the supersaturated alcohol.

Charles Thomson Rees Wilson (1869–1969) made the first observations of particle tracks in a cloud chamber in 1910 (Figure 17.5). For the next 50 years, cloud chambers were the principal tools of atomic physics. They are to atomic physics what telescopes are to astronomy.

The **bubble chamber** (Figure 17.6) was developed in 1952 by the physicist Donald Glaser (b. 1926). It contains a liquefied gas, such as hydrogen, helium, propane, or xenon. Lowering the pressure in the chamber lowers the boiling point of this liquid. When the pressure is reduced so that the boiling point is just below the actual temperature of the liquid, ions formed by a charged particle zipping through the liquid cause it to boil. Thus, the particle forms a trail of tiny bubbles along its path. Bubble chambers reverse the process used in cloud chambers: particle tracks are formed by a liquid turning into vapour instead of a vapour turning into liquid.

info **BIT**

Charles Wilson built the first cloud chamber in 1894 to study how clouds form. He shared a Nobel Prize for his contribution to particle physics. Wilson was a renowned meteorologist and an avid mountaineer.

bubble chamber: a device that uses trails of bubbles in a superheated liquid to show the paths of charged particles

info **BIT**

CERN stands for *C*onseil *E*uropéen pour la *R*echerche *N*ucléaire. It is the world's largest particle physics laboratory.

◄ **Figure 17.6** One of the large bubble chambers at the CERN laboratory near Geneva, Switzerland

Only charged particles and ionizing photons, such as γ radiation, will create tracks in a cloud or bubble chamber. Neither neutral particles nor low-energy photons will show up. However, it is possible to calculate some of the properties of neutral particles from the tracks of charged particles that interact with them.

e **SIM**

To see an animation of particle tracks, follow the links at www.pearsoned.ca/school/physicssource.

Concept Check

Outline possible reasons why neutral particles will not show up in a bubble chamber. How could you tell if a neutron were involved in a particle collision in a bubble chamber?

Building a Cloud Chamber

Question

Can types of radiation be identified by the characteristics of their tracks?

Hypothesis

Since alpha, beta, and gamma radiations have different properties, the tracks they produce in a cloud chamber will be different.

Materials and Equipment

clear glass container
flat glass or plastic cover
black blotting paper to fit the bottom of the container
dry ice (frozen carbon dioxide)
reagent grade ethanol (ethyl alcohol)
foam plastic insulation
tape
silicone grease
lamp with reflector
radiation sources

 CAUTION: The temperature of dry ice is −78 °C. Handle it only with tongs or thick gloves.

Be careful not to damage the casing on the radioactive samples.

Variables

Identify the manipulated, responding, and controlled variables in this experiment.

Procedure

Work with a partner or a small group of classmates.

1. Cut a piece of black blotting paper to fit the bottom of the glass container.

2. Saturate this blotting paper with alcohol, but avoid having a pool of alcohol in the container.

3. Cover the container using silicone grease to ensure a good seal between the cover and the container.

4. Use a piece of foam plastic insulation as the base for your cloud chamber. Place a piece of dry ice at least 2.5 cm thick in the centre of this base, then put the glass container on top of the dry ice. Placing more insulation around the sides of the dry ice will make it last longer.

5. Position the lamp so it shines down from the side of the chamber (Figure 17.7). Darken the room and wait several minutes. Note any changes that you observe in the cloud chamber.

6. Now tape an alpha-radiation source onto the inside of the container near the bottom. Write a description of any tracks that appear. If the tracks have a consistent shape or pattern, sketch a typical track.

7. Repeat step 6 with beta- and gamma-radiation sources.

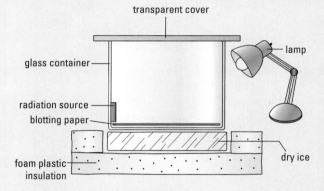

▲ **Figure 17.7** A simple cloud chamber

Analyzing and Interpreting

1. Were all of the tracks you observed produced by the three radiation sources? What else could produce tracks in your cloud chamber? Explain your reasoning.

2. Describe any relationship you see between the appearance of the tracks and the type of radiation that produced them.

3. Suggest improvements to the design of this experiment.

Forming Conclusions

4. Do your observations support the hypothesis? If so, which properties of the radiation might be responsible for any differences in the tracks?

5. Under what conditions will subatomic particles travelling through the ethanol cloud not produce observable tracks?

6. Hold a strong magnet against the side of the cloud chamber and observe the magnetic field's effect on tracks from the three radiation sources. Explain whether you could use the magnet to help distinguish between different types of radiation.

7. Make a hypothesis about how taping the radiation sources to the outside of the glass container would affect the tracks produced by each source. Test your hypothesis. Could your results help you distinguish between different types of radiation? What other methods could you use?

Analyzing Particle Tracks

Physicists use cloud and bubble chambers as a key part of a controlled environment for studying subatomic particles. Applying a magnetic field across the chamber causes charged particles to follow curved or spiral paths. Measurements of the resulting tracks can be used to determine the mass and charge of the particles.

For example, Figure 17.8 shows the path of a particle moving in a cloud chamber in which a magnetic field is coming out of the page. The particle entered the chamber from the left. Applying the right-hand rule to this track shows that the particle must have a positive charge.

Often, a photograph of a cloud or bubble chamber will show tracks from a number of particles entering the chamber. Once in a while, a single track will suddenly branch into several diverging tracks, as shown in Figure 17.9. Such tracks suggest that the original particle has transformed into two or more different particles.

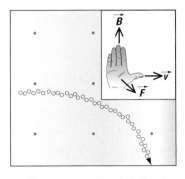

▲ **Figure 17.8** The right-hand rule shows that the particle must have a positive charge. Orient your right hand as shown and then rotate your hand so that your fingers point out of the page. Your palm points in the same direction as the force on a positively charged particle.

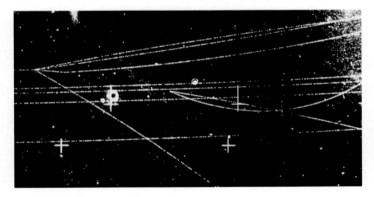

◀ **Figure 17.9** These tracks suggest that a particle interaction can form two or more different particles.

The following example demonstrates how a particle's track can reveal its charge-to-mass ratio.

Example 17.1

Assume that the tracks shown in Figure 17.10 were made by particles moving at a speed of $0.10c$ through a uniform magnetic field $\vec{B} = 30$ mT [out of the page]. The initial radius of each track is 5.7 mm. Determine the charge-to-mass ratio for the particles. Then, make a hypothesis about what the particles are. What is unusual about this pair of particles?

▲ **Figure 17.10** Why are these particle tracks spiral rather than circular?

Required

$\dfrac{q}{m}$ identification of each particle

Analysis and Solution

- Applying the right-hand rule shows that the particle spiralling clockwise has a positive charge. Similarly, the left-hand rule shows that the particle spiralling counterclockwise has a negative charge.
- Since there was no track before the two particles appeared, they must have originated from a photon or a neutral particle. For charge to be conserved, the net charge on the two new particles must be zero. Therefore, these particles must have equal but opposite charges.
- The charge-to-mass ratio for a particle moving perpendicular to a magnetic field is

$$F_m = F_c$$

$$Bqv = \frac{mv^2}{r}$$

$$Bq = \frac{mv}{r}$$

$$\frac{q}{m} = \frac{v}{Br}$$

- Since the values of q, v, r, and B are the same for both particles, their masses must also be equal.

> ## PHYSICS INSIGHT
>
> The tesla is a derived unit that can be expressed in terms of SI base units:
>
> $$1 \text{ T} = 1\, \frac{\text{kg}}{\text{A} \cdot \text{s}^2}$$

Substituting the known values gives

$$\frac{q}{m} = \frac{3.0 \times 10^7 \text{ m/s}}{0.030 \text{ T} \times 5.7 \text{ mm}}$$

$$= \frac{3.0 \times 10^7 \text{ m/s}}{0.030\, \dfrac{\text{kg}}{\text{A} \cdot \text{s}^2} \times 0.0057 \text{ m}}$$

$$= 1.8 \times 10^{11} \text{ A} \cdot \text{s/kg}$$

$$= 1.8 \times 10^{11} \text{ C/kg}$$

The charge-to-mass ratio for an electron is

$$\frac{1.60 \times 10^{-19} \text{ C}}{9.11 \times 10^{-31} \text{ kg}} = 1.76 \times 10^{11} \text{ C/kg}.$$

The ratios for protons or small ions are about four orders of magnitude smaller.

Practice Problems

1. Measurement of a particle track shows a radius of deflection of 8.66×10^{-4} m for a proton travelling at a speed of 4.23×10^5 m/s perpendicular to a 5.10-T magnetic field. Calculate the charge-to-mass ratio for a proton.

2. Determine the radius of the path of an electron moving at a speed of 3.2×10^5 m/s perpendicular to a 1.2-mT magnetic field.

Answers

1. 9.58×10^7 C/kg

2. 1.5 mm

Paraphrase

The charge-to-mass ratio of the negative particle is 1.8×10^{11} C/kg. Since this ratio matches the ratio for an electron, this particle very likely is an electron. However, the other particle has a charge-to-mass ratio of 1.8×10^{11} C/kg. This particle appears to be an "electron" with a positive charge!

Example 17.1 illustrates how a conservation law can be a powerful tool for understanding the interactions of subatomic particles. Physicists often apply the conservation laws for charge, momentum, and mass-energy in this way. Experiments and theoretical calculations have shown that several other quantities are also conserved when particles interact.

17.1 Check and Reflect

Knowledge

1. Compare the process for forming tracks in a cloud chamber with the process in a bubble chamber.

2. (a) List two subatomic particles that will leave tracks in a bubble chamber.

   (b) List two subatomic particles that will not leave tracks in a bubble chamber.

3. (a) Why does applying a magnetic field cause the particle tracks in a cloud or bubble chamber to curve?

   (b) What can the curvature of a particle's track in a magnetic field reveal about the particle?

Applications

4. Will X-ray photons produce tracks in a bubble chamber? Justify your answer.

5. (a) Determine the type of charge on each particle moving through the magnetic field in this diagram.

   (b) What information would you need to determine which particle is moving faster?

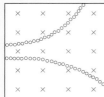

6. Describe and explain the differences in the tracks made in a bubble chamber by the particles in each pair:

   (a) protons and alpha particles

   (b) protons and electrons

7. In this bubble-chamber photograph, a particle enters from the bottom and collides with a helium nucleus.

   (a) Use conservation of momentum to show that the incoming particle was an alpha particle rather than a proton.

   (b) Describe how you could show that the particles have a positive charge.

Extension

8. Bubble chambers have replaced cloud chambers in many research laboratories. What advantages do bubble chambers have over cloud chambers?

 e **TEST**

To check your understanding of methods for detecting and measuring subatomic particles, follow the eTest links at www.pearsoned.ca/school/physicssource.

Quantum Theory and the Discovery of New Particles

Early in the 20th century, many scientists thought that there were just three **fundamental particles**: the electron, the proton, and the neutron. However, developments in quantum theory in the 1920s and 1930s suggested the possibility of other subatomic particles, some with peculiar properties.

fundamental particle: a particle that cannot be divided into smaller particles; an elementary particle

The Discovery of Antimatter

In 1928, British physicist Paul Adrien Maurice Dirac (1902–1984) predicted the existence of peculiar particles such as the positive electron in Example 17.1 (pages 833–834). Dirac combined Einstein's theory of relativity with Schrödinger's wave equation (described in section 15.5). Dirac's calculations, with the resulting relativistic wave equation, predicted that antimatter could exist. As mentioned in section 16.2, a particle of antimatter has a key property, such as charge, that is opposite to that of the corresponding particle of ordinary matter.

In 1932, the American physicist Carl Anderson (1905–1991) provided the first evidence that antimatter really does exist. He photographed a cloud chamber track of a positron, as shown in Figure 17.11. For this achievement, Anderson won the Nobel Prize for physics in 1936.

▲ **Figure 17.11** A picture worth a Nobel Prize: Anderson's photograph provided evidence for the existence of the positron. Anderson used this path (the white streak in the photo) to show that the particle that made it had a positive charge but a mass equal to that of the electron.

> ### Concept Check
>
> How could Anderson tell that the particle track in Figure 17.11 showed a positively charged particle going down rather than a negative particle going up? His ingenious solution was to pass the particle through a thin lead plate. This plate slowed the particle a bit. Explain how Anderson could use this change in speed to confirm that the particle had positive charge. (Hint: The magnetic field for the cloud chamber in the photograph was directed into the page.)

Quantum theory predicts that each kind of ordinary particle has a corresponding antiparticle. One of the startling properties of antimatter is that a collision between a particle and its antiparticle can annihilate both particles and create a pair of high-energy gamma-ray photons travelling in opposite directions. For example, an electron-positron collision can be written as

$$e^+ + e^- \rightarrow 2\gamma$$

Such electron-positron annihilations are part of the nuclear processes in stars. Note that e^+ is the symbol for a positron. In general, charged antiparticles are represented by simply reversing the sign of the charge on the symbol for the corresponding ordinary particles. Antiparticles for neutral particles are indicated by adding a bar over the symbol for the corresponding ordinary matter. Thus, the symbol for an antineutron is $\overline{n}$.

Consider the example of a head-on collision between a positron and an electron travelling at equal speeds. Explain why momentum would not be conserved if all the energy of the two particles transformed into a single photon.

Scientific Knowledge Can Lead to New Technologies

The discovery of the positron made it possible to develop a powerful new medical diagnostic instrument. Positron emission tomography (PET) is an imaging technique that uses gamma rays from electron-positron annihilations to produce images of cross sections through a patient's body. A computer can then generate a three-dimensional image by combining successive plane images (Figure 17.12).

The patient receives an injection of a radioactive tracer containing an isotope, usually fluorine-18, that gives off positrons as it decays. As these positrons meet electrons within the patient's body, they create pairs of gamma-ray photons. Several rings of gamma-ray detectors rotate around the patient. As the photon pairs register on diametrically opposite detectors, a computer builds up an image of the location and concentration of the radioactive tracer. These images can show a wide variety of vital information, such as blood flow, brain function, and the location of tumours.

▲ **Figure 17.12** A PET scanner

e **WEB**

To learn more about PET scanners, follow the links at www.pearsoned.ca/ school/physicssource.

Quantum Field Theory

By 1930, Dirac, Heisenberg, Born, and others had established the foundations of **quantum field theory**. In this theory, **mediating particles** are the mechanism by which the fundamental forces act over the distance between particles. Particles that mediate a force exist for such a brief time that they cannot be observed. For these **virtual particles**, energy, momentum, and mass are not related as they are for real particles.

To help understand this concept, imagine two people tossing a ball back and forth while standing on a very slippery surface, such as a smooth, wet sheet of ice. Throwing and catching the ball pushes the two people farther and farther apart (Figure 17.13(a)). In this analogy, the people correspond to ordinary particles and the ball corresponds to a mediating particle. For an attractive force, picture the same two people handing a somewhat sticky candy apple back and forth. The force that each person exerts to free the candy apple from the other person's hand pulls the two people toward each other (Figure 17.13(b)). Note, however, that quantum field theory is a complex mathematical model with aspects that cannot be explained by such analogies.

quantum field theory: a field theory developed using both quantum mechanics and relativity theory

mediating particle: a virtual particle that carries one of the fundamental forces

virtual particle: a particle that exists for such a short time that it is not detectable

(a)

(b)
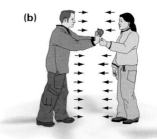

◄ **Figure 17.13** (a) Throwing a ball back and forth while on a slippery surface pushes these people apart. (b) Handing a sticky object back and forth pulls them together.

quantum electrodynamics:
quantum field theory dealing
with the interactions of
electromagnetic fields,
charged particles, and photons

The concept of mediating particles was first applied to the electromagnetic force, in a theory called **quantum electrodynamics**. This theory states that virtual photons exchanged between charged particles are the carriers of the attractive or repulsive force between the particles. For example, consider the electromagnetic repulsion between two electrons. One electron emits a virtual photon in the direction of the other electron. According to Newton's third law, the first electron will recoil and its momentum will change by an amount opposite to the momentum of the photon. Similarly, when the second electron absorbs the photon, this electron will gain momentum directed away from the first proton. You can think of the photon for an attractive force as acting a bit like the shared electron holding two atoms together in a covalent chemical bond.

In the latter part of the 20th century, calculations using a refined version of quantum electrodynamics gave results that matched observed values with amazing accuracy — sometimes to 10 significant digits.

Mediating Particles

By 1970, research with high-energy particle accelerators led physicists to suggest that the strong nuclear force is mediated by zero-mass particles called **gluons**. So far, there is only indirect evidence for the existence of gluons.

gluon: the mediating particle
for the strong nuclear force

Advances in quantum theory also led to the conjecture that the weak nuclear force is mediated by three particles, designated W^+, W^-, and Z^0. Experiments using extremely powerful accelerators detected these three particles in 1983. Some physicists think that the gravitational force also has a mediating particle, which they call the **graviton**. As yet, there is no experimental evidence that gravitons exist.

graviton: the hypothetical
mediating particle for the
gravitational force

Table 17.1 summarizes the current thinking about mediating particles.

▼ **Table 17.1**   The Fundamental Forces and Their Mediating Particles

Force	Range	Relative Strength for Protons in Nucleus	Mediating Particles	Particle Observed?
Electromagnetic	infinite	10^{-2}	photons	yes
Weak nuclear	<0.003 fm	10^{-6}	W^+, W^-, Z^0	yes
Strong nuclear	<1 fm	1	gluons	indirectly
Gravitational	infinite	10^{-38}	gravitons	no

Project **LINK**

For your unit project, you may want
to describe the search for gluons
and gravitons.

Knowledge

1. Describe the difference between ordinary matter and antimatter.

2. Outline how Anderson provided evidence for the existence of the positron.

3. (a) Which fundamental force is the strongest over large distances?

   (b) Which fundamental force is the weakest at nuclear distances?

4. (a) List the mediating particle for each of the fundamental forces.

   (b) Which of these mediating particles has not been detected at all?

5. Explain why a PET scan is like being X-rayed from the inside out.

Applications

6. (a) What event is represented by the equation $e^- + e^+ \rightarrow 2\gamma$?

   (b) Why is the event $e^- + e^+ \rightarrow \gamma$ not possible?

7. (a) Under what conditions will two protons attract each other?

   (b) Under what conditions will they repel each other?

8. The tracks in this diagram show the creation of two particles in a bubble chamber. Initially, the two particles have the same speed.

(a) What evidence suggests that a photon created the two particles?

(b) Describe the path of this photon.

(c) Which of the tracks shows the path of a positively charged particle?

(d) Give two reasons why the other track must show the path of a negatively charged particle.

(e) How are the mass and charge of the two particles related?

(f) Why is it likely that the interaction involves an antiparticle?

9. Explain how the stability of helium nuclei demonstrates that the electromagnetic force is weaker than the nuclear forces.

Extension

10. Research the Lamb shift and the Casimir effect at a library or on the Internet. Explain how these phenomena support the quantum field theory.

e TEST

To check your understanding of quantum theory and antimatter, follow the eTest links at www.pearsoned.ca/school/physicssource.

17.3 Probing the Structure of Matter

Our understanding of the structure of matter comes from a series of remarkable technological advances over the past century. For example, the first circular particle accelerator (Figure 17.14(a)) was about 12 cm in diameter and generated particles with energies up to 13 keV. Now, the most powerful accelerators are up to 8.5 km in diameter and can reach energies of a teraelectron volt (10^{12} eV). This huge increase in energy reflects an interesting overall trend: To probe matter at smaller and smaller scales, physicists need bigger and bigger machines! This trend results from the nature of matter: All of the fundamental forces become markedly stronger at distances less than the diameter of a nucleus.

▲ **Figure 17.14** (a) The first circular particle accelerator

(b) Fermilab near Chicago, Illinois. Its Tevatron accelerator ring is 2 km in diameter.

Energy Requirements

13.6 eV is sufficient to ionize a hydrogen atom. With energies of a few hundred electron volts, you can study electron shells of atoms and of molecules (using a spectrograph, for example). To determine the size of a nucleus, you need charged particles with enough energy to get close to it despite strong electrostatic repulsion. For his ground-breaking scattering experiment, Rutherford used alpha particles with energies in the order of 10 MeV. To examine the structure of the nucleus, the energy requirements are much greater because the probe particles have to overcome the strong nuclear force. Within the nucleus, this short-range force is about a hundred times stronger than the electromagnetic force. The fundamental forces within individual subatomic particles are stronger still. So, probing the structure of stable particles such as protons and neutrons requires even more energy.

With early, relatively low-energy accelerators, physicists could conduct experiments in which accelerated particles scattered from nuclei or split nuclei into lighter elements (hence the nickname "atom-smasher"). With high-energy particles, physicists can also study interactions that create new types of particles. Producing some of the heavier particles requires a minimum of several gigaelectron volts.

Natural Sources of Energetic Particles

Some naturally radioactive isotopes emit particles that are useful for probing the structure of the atom. For example, Rutherford used polonium and radium as particle sources for his experiments. However, the maximum energy of particles from natural radioactive decay is roughly 30 MeV, which is not enough to probe the structure of nuclei.

The other major natural particle source is cosmic radiation. Cosmic rays are high-energy particles that stream into Earth's atmosphere from outer space. Astronomers are not certain about the origin of these particles. Some of them may come from solar flares and from distant supernovae. About 90% of cosmic rays are protons and most of the rest are alpha particles with a few electrons, positrons, antiprotons, and other particles. The energies of these particles range from roughly 10^2 to 10^{14} MeV. The particles from space (**primary cosmic rays**) rarely reach the ground because they interact with atoms in the atmosphere, producing less energetic **secondary cosmic rays**.

primary cosmic rays: high-energy particles that flow from space into Earth's atmosphere

secondary cosmic rays: the shower of particles created by collisions between primary cosmic rays and atoms in the atmosphere

Particle Accelerators

The first particle accelerators were built around 1930. These accelerators, and the much more powerful ones developed since then, use electric and magnetic fields to accelerate and direct charged particles, usually in a vacuum chamber. Here is a brief description of some of the major types of particle accelerators.

- **Van de Graaff:** A moving belt transfers charge to a hollow, conductive sphere, building up a large potential difference. This potential difference then propels ions through an accelerator chamber.
- **Drift Tube:** An alternating voltage accelerates charged particles through a series of electrodes shaped like open tubes. The applied voltage reverses as the particles pass through each tube, so the particles are always attracted to the next tube in the line.
- **Cyclotron:** A magnetic field perpendicular to the paths of the charged particles makes them follow circular paths within two hollow semicircular electrodes. An alternating voltage accelerates the charged particles each time they cross the gap between the two electrodes. The radius of each particle's path increases with its speed, so the accelerated particles spiral toward the outer wall of the cyclotron.
- **Synchrotron:** This advanced type of cyclotron increases the strength of the magnetic field as the particles' energy increases, so that the particles travel in a circle rather than spiralling outward. Some of the largest and most powerful particle accelerators are synchrotron rings.

Concept Check

Explain the advantages and disadvantages of studying nuclei with protons from a large accelerator as opposed to alpha particles produced by radioactive decay.

*info*BIT

Marietta Blau published a number of papers on cosmic rays in the 1920s and 1930s. She was nominated for the Nobel Prize several times.

muon: an unstable subatomic particle having many of the properties of an electron but a mass 207 times greater

pion: an unstable subatomic particle with a mass roughly 270 times that of an electron

lepton: a subatomic particle that does not interact via the strong nuclear force

hadron: a subatomic particle that does interact via the strong nuclear force

meson: a hadron with integer spin

baryon: a hadron with half-integer spin

spin: quantum property resembling rotational angular momentum

fermion: particle with half-integer spin

boson: particle with integer spin

PHYSICS INSIGHT

How Small Are Electrons?

Experiments have shown that electrons are less than 10^{-18} m across, while protons are roughly 1.6×10^{-15} m in diameter. Leptons might be mathematical points with no physical size at all!

Although particle accelerators were originally developed for pure research, they now have medical and industrial uses as well. Many hospitals use accelerated particles for generating intense beams of X rays that can destroy cancerous tumours. Bombarding elements with particles from cyclotrons produces radioactive isotopes for diagnostic techniques, radiation therapy, testing structural materials, and numerous other applications. Particle accelerators can make a variety of specialized industrial materials by, for example, modifying polymers and implanting ions in semiconductors and ceramics. Accelerators are also powerful tools for analyzing the structure and composition of materials. Particle accelerators have even been used to verify the authenticity of works of art.

The Subatomic Zoo

In 1937, Carl Anderson and Seth Neddermeyer used a cloud chamber to discover **muons** in cosmic rays. These particles behave much like electrons, but have a mass 207 times greater and decay rapidly. Ten years later, Cecil Frank Powell discovered π-mesons, or **pions**, by using a photographic technology that Marietta Blau had developed. This method records tracks of particles on a photographic plate coated with a thick emulsion containing grains of silver bromide. Pions are much less stable than muons, and have some properties unlike those of electrons, protons, or neutrons.

Improved particle accelerators and detectors led to the discovery of many more subatomic particles. Over 300 have now been identified. Most of these particles are highly unstable and have lifetimes of less than a microsecond.

Studies of the interactions and decays of these particles show that there are two separate families of particles: **leptons**, which do not interact by means of the strong nuclear force, and **hadrons**, which do. The term *lepton* comes from *leptos*, a Greek word for "thin" or "small," and *hadron* comes from *hadros*, a Greek word for "thick." The diameters of leptons are much smaller than those of hadrons. The hadrons are divided into two subgroups, **mesons** (from *meso*, Greek for "middle") and **baryons** (from *barus*, Greek for "heavy").

One of the key quantum properties for classifying particles is their **spin**. This property is like angular momentum from rotation of the particle. The spin of a particle can be either an integer or half-integer multiple of Planck's constant divided by 2π. Particles that have half-integer spin (such as $\frac{1}{2}$ or $\frac{3}{2}$) are called **fermions**, while those that have integer spin (such as 0, 1, or 2) are called **bosons**. Leptons and baryons are fermions. Mesons and mediating particles are bosons. Spin can affect the interactions and energy levels of particles.

▼ **Table 17.2** Classification of Subatomic Particles

	Leptons	**Hadrons**	**Meditating Particles**
Fermions	all leptons	baryons	
Bosons		mesons	all mediating particles

There are far more types of hadrons than types of leptons. In fact, physicists have found only six leptons plus their corresponding anti-particles. Table 17.3 compares the mass and stability of the leptons and some of the more significant hadrons. You are not required to memorize this table. Its purpose is to show a tiny set of the dozens of particles that physicists had discovered by the 1960s. What they were desperately seeking, and what you will learn about in the next section, was an underlying theory that could help make sense of this "subatomic zoo."

▼ **Table 17.3** An Introduction to the Subatomic Zoo

	Particle	Symbol	Mass (MeV/c^2)	Lifetime (s)
Leptons	electron	e^-	0.511	stable
	electron neutrino	ν_e	$< 7 \times 10^{-6}$	stable?
	muon	μ^-	106	2.2×10^{-6}
	muon neutrino	ν_μ	< 0.17	stable?
	tauon	τ^-	1777	2.9×10^{-13}
	tauon neutrino	ν_τ	< 24	stable?
Mesons	pions	π^+	140	2.6×10^{-8}
		π^0	135	8.4×10^{-17}
	kaons	K^+	494	1.2×10^{-8}
		K^0	498	9×10^{-20}
	psi	ψ	3097	8×10^{-21}
	upsilon	Υ	9460	1.3×10^{-20}
Baryons	proton	ρ^+	938.3	10^{31}?
	neutron	n	939.6	885*
	lambda	Λ^0	1116	2.6×10^{-10}
	sigma	Σ^+	1189	8×10^{-11}
		Σ^0	1192	7.4×10^{-20}
	xi	Ξ^0	1315	2.9×10^{-10}
		Ξ^-	1321	1.6×10^{-10}
	omega	Ω^-	1672	8.2×10^{-11}

*lifetime for a free neutron; neutrons in nuclei are stable

info **BIT**

A pion will decay in the time it takes light to travel across a classroom.

Units for Subatomic Masses

Note that Table 17.3 lists masses in units of MeV/c^2. The kilogram is not always the most convenient unit for expressing the mass of subatomic particles. Physicists often deal with transformations between mass and energy using Einstein's famous equation $E = mc^2$. Rearranging this equation gives $m = \dfrac{E}{c^2}$. It follows that mass can be expressed in terms of units of $\dfrac{\text{energy}}{\text{speed squared}}$.

Particle physicists find it convenient to use a factor of c^2 to relate mass to electron volts, the traditional energy unit for particle physics. Conversion factors for such units are

$1 \text{ eV}/c^2 = 1.7827 \times 10^{-36} \text{ kg}$

$1 \text{ MeV}/c^2 = 1.7827 \times 10^{-30} \text{ kg}$
$1 \text{ GeV}/c^2 = 1.7827 \times 10^{-27} \text{ kg}$

e **MATH**

To better understand the relative sizes of subatomic particles, visit www.pearsoned.ca/school/physicssource.

For example, the mass of a proton expressed in these units is

$$m_p = 1.6726 \times 10^{-27} \text{ kg} \times \frac{1 \text{ MeV}/c^2}{1.7827 \times 10^{-30} \text{ kg}}$$
$$= 938.23 \text{ MeV}/c^2$$

The masses of the known subatomic particles range from 0.5 MeV/c^2 to 10 GeV/c^2, so exponent notation is usually not necessary with these units. Table 17.4 compares subatomic masses expressed in several common units.

▼ **Table 17.4** Comparison of Mass Units for Subatomic Particles (to Five Significant Digits)

Particle	Mass (kg)	Mass (u)	Mass (MeV/c^2)
Electron	9.1094×10^{-31}	5.4858×10^{-4}	0.51100
Proton	1.6726×10^{-27}	1.0073	938.23
Neutron	1.6749×10^{-27}	1.0087	939.52

17.3 Check and Reflect

Knowledge

1. Why do physicists require extremely high-energy particles for studying the structure of nucleons?

2. List two natural sources of energetic particles.

3. What is the advantage of high-altitude locations for performing experiments with cosmic rays?

4. List two uses of particle accelerators in
   (a) medicine
   (b) industry

5. Identify a major difference that distinguishes
   (a) leptons from hadrons
   (b) mesons from baryons

Applications

6. Can alpha particles from the radioactive decay of polonium be used to probe the nucleus? Explain your answer.

7. Calculate the momentum and kinetic energy of a proton that is accelerated to a speed of
   (a) 0.01c
   (b) 5.0×10^5 m/s

8. (a) Find the energy equivalent of the mass of an electron.
   (b) The mass of a psi particle is 3.097 GeV/c^2. Express this mass in kilograms.

9. Calculate the conversion factor between atomic mass units and MeV/c^2.

Extensions

10. How has the development of superconducting electromagnets aided research into the structure of matter?

11. (a) What relativistic effect limits the energy of particles accelerated in an ordinary cyclotron?
    (b) Describe three different ways this limit can be overcome.

 e TEST

To check your understanding of particle accelerators and subatomic particles, follow the eTest links at www.pearsoned.ca/school/physicssource.

Quarks and the Standard Model

By 1960, physicists faced a large and growing menagerie of subatomic particles. Since the leptons are small and there are only a few types of them, it seemed likely that they were fundamental particles. However, the number of hadrons was a puzzle: Could there really be a hundred or more fundamental particles?

The Quark Model

In the 19th century, chemists studied the properties and reactions of the elements. The patterns observed in these properties led to the development of the periodic table and an understanding of the electron structure in atoms. Physicists searched for similar patterns in the properties and interactions of subatomic particles.

In 1963, Americans Murray Gell-Mann (b. 1929) and George Zweig (b. 1937) independently proposed that *all* hadrons are composed of simpler particles, which Gell-Mann called **quarks**. By grouping the subatomic particles into distinct classes and families, Gell-Mann and Zweig showed that all the hadrons then known could be made from just three smaller particles and their antiparticles. These three particles are now called the up quark, the down quark, and the strange quark. This theory required that the quarks have fractional charges that are either one-third of the charge on an electron or two-thirds of the charge on a proton. Understandably, many physicists had trouble accepting this radical concept.

Using the quark model, Gell-Mann accurately predicted not only the existence of the omega (Ω^-) particle, but also the exact method for producing it. The quark model also accurately predicted key aspects of electron-positron interactions. Stronger evidence for the quark theory came in 1967 when Jerome Friedman, Henry Kendall, and Richard Taylor used the powerful Stanford Linear Accelerator to beam extremely high-energy electrons at protons. The electrons scattered off the protons, somewhat like the alpha particles that scattered off the gold nuclei in Rutherford's scattering experiment (Figure 17.15). The pattern of the scattered electrons suggested that the mass and charge of a proton are concentrated in three centres within the proton. Later experiments confirmed these results and showed a similar pattern for scattering from neutrons.

In the quark model, protons and neutrons contain only up and down quarks. The strange quark accounts for the properties of **strange particles**, hadrons that decay via the weak nuclear force even though they originate from and decay into particles that can interact via the strong nuclear force.

In 1974, the discovery of the psi meson confirmed the existence of a fourth quark, the charm quark. Then, in 1977, the heavy upsilon meson was detected and found to involve a fifth quark, the bottom quark. Since there are six leptons, physicists wondered if there might be an equal number of quarks. In 1995, a large team of researchers at Fermilab found evidence for the top quark. This discovery required a huge accelerator because the top quark is about 40 000 times heavier than the up quark.

info **BIT**

Gell-Mann coined the term "quark" from an obscure line in a novel by the Irish writer James Joyce. Zweig had called the new fundamental particles "aces."

quark: any of the group of fundamental particles in hadrons

info **BIT**

Richard Taylor was born in Medicine Hat and became interested in experimental physics while studying at the University of Alberta. In 1990, he shared the Nobel Prize in physics with Friedman and Kendall.

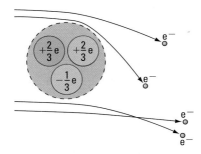

▲ **Figure 17.15** Scattering of high-energy electrons from a proton

strange particle: a particle that interacts primarily via the strong nuclear force yet decays only via the weak nuclear force

e **WEB**

To learn more about the strange particles, follow the links at www.pearsoned.ca/school/physicssource.

In the summer of 1936, Carl Anderson and his first graduate student, Seth Neddermeyer, lugged a cloud chamber and photographic equipment to the summit of Pikes Peak in Colorado, about 4300 m above sea level. They chose this location because the cosmic rays at that altitude were then the only source of the high-energy particles needed for their research. The work was lonely, uncomfortable, and poorly funded. It was also highly successful. Anderson and Neddermeyer discovered the muon with the cloud chamber photographs they took during their summer on Pikes Peak.

Flash forward 60 years. How particle physics has changed! In 1995, the Fermi National Accelerator Laboratory (Fermilab) near Chicago, Illinois, announced that a team of researchers there had discovered the elusive top quark. In all, 450 people worked on this project.

A key member of the team was Melissa Franklin (Figure 17.16), who has worked for over 18 years on the collider detector at Fermilab, a machine for studying the interactions resulting from colliding high-energy protons and antiprotons. A graduate of the University of Toronto and Stanford University, she is now a professor of physics at Harvard. Franklin is seeking to understand the structure of matter at the smallest scale, as Anderson did. However, Franklin collaborates with physicists from around the world and uses particle accelerators and detectors costing hundreds of millions of dollars. Although her work centres on tiny particles, she practises science on a big scale!

Questions

1. What other fields of scientific research require huge budgets and international cooperation?

2. What are some advantages and drawbacks of "big science"?

3. Teamwork skills are becoming increasingly important in many areas of research. What other skills would be useful for a career in science?

▲ **Figure 17.16** Melissa Franklin

Table 17.5 compares some properties of the six quarks. The mass of an individual quark cannot be measured directly. The masses given here were derived mainly by taking the total mass of various particles and subtracting estimates of the mass-energy the quarks gain from motion and interactions via the strong nuclear force within the particles. For each quark there is a corresponding antiquark with the opposite charge.

▼ **Table 17.5** Some Properties of Quarks

Generation	Name	Symbol	Mass (MeV/c^2)	Charge
First	up	u	1.5–4*	$+\frac{2}{3}e$
	down	d	4–8	$-\frac{1}{3}e$
Second	strange	s	80–130	$-\frac{1}{3}e$
	charm	c	1.15–1.35×10^3	$+\frac{2}{3}e$
Third	bottom (or beauty)	b	4.1–4.9×10^3	$-\frac{1}{3}e$
	top (or truth)	t	1.7–1.9×10^4	$+\frac{2}{3}e$

*Some physicists think the up quark may be essentially massless.

info **BIT**

To name quarks, physicists chose words that would not be mistaken for visible physical properties. In Europe, physicists commonly call the top quark "truth" and the bottom quark "beauty."

Individual quarks probably cannot be observed. The strong nuclear force binds the quarks in a particle very tightly. The energy required to separate quarks is large enough to create new quarks or antiquarks that bind to the quark being separated before it can be observed on its own.

Composition of Protons and Neutrons

The proton and the neutron contain only first-generation quarks. As shown in Figure 17.17, the proton consists of a down quark and two up quarks. The net charge of these three quarks is $\left(+\frac{2}{3}e\right) + \left(+\frac{2}{3}e\right) + \left(-\frac{1}{3}e\right) = +e$. The other quantum properties of the quarks also sum to those of a proton.

Similarly, a neutron consists of two down quarks and an up quark. In this combination, the positive charge on the up quark exactly balances the negative charge on the two down quarks.

Composition of Other Hadrons

All of the hadrons discovered in the 20th century can be accounted for with a combination of either two or three quarks:

- All the mesons consist of a quark and an antiquark.
- All the baryons consist of three quarks.
- All the antibaryons consist of three antiquarks.

However, experiments in 2003 produced strong evidence that the recently discovered theta particle (θ^+) consists of five quarks: two up quarks, two down quarks, and an antistrange quark.

Table 17.6 gives some examples of quark combinations.

*e*WEB

To learn more about the difficulties in measuring quarks, follow the links at www.pearsoned.ca/school/physicssource.

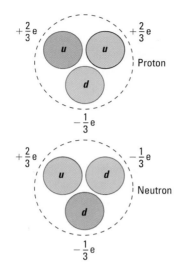

▲ **Figure 17.17** The quarks making up protons and neutrons

▼ **Table 17.6** Some Quark Combinations

Meson	Composition	Baryon	Composition	Antibaryon	Composition
pion (π^+)	u$\bar{\text{d}}$	proton (p)	uud	antiproton ($\bar{\text{p}}^-$)	$\bar{\text{u}}\bar{\text{u}}\bar{\text{d}}$
pion (π^0)	u$\bar{\text{u}}$	neutron (n)	udd	antineutron ($\bar{\text{n}}$)	$\bar{\text{u}}\bar{\text{d}}\bar{\text{d}}$
pion (π^-)	$\bar{\text{u}}$d	sigma-plus (Σ^+)	uus		
kaon (K^+)	u$\bar{\text{s}}$	sigma-minus (Σ^-)	dds		

Describing Beta Decay Using Quarks and Leptons

Recall from section 16.2 that during beta decays of elements, the nuclei emit either an electron or a positron. Since both these particles are leptons, beta decay must proceed via the weak nuclear force.

In β^- decay of nuclei, a neutron transforms into a proton, an electron, and an antineutrino. Figure 17.18 shows that a neutron consists of an up quark and two down quarks while a proton consists of two up quarks and a down quark. So, the decay can be written as:

$$\text{udd} \rightarrow \text{uud} + e^- + \bar{\nu}_e$$

Charge is conserved since the difference between the $-\frac{1}{3}e$ charge on the down quark and the $+\frac{2}{3}e$ charge on the new up quark equals the charge on the electron emitted by the neutron. Physicists think that the down

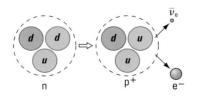

▲ **Figure 17.18** During β^- decay, a down quark changes into an up quark.

quark emits a virtual W⁻ particle (a mediator for the weak nuclear force) that then decays into an electron and an antineutrino:

$$d \rightarrow u + [W^-]$$
$$\rightarrow e^- + \bar{v}_e$$

The idea of mediating particles is essential to understanding beta decay and is a central idea in the standard model.

Similarly, in β^+ decay of nuclei, an up quark in a proton turns into a down quark by emitting a virtual W^+ particle that then decays into a positron and a neutrino:

$$uud \rightarrow udd + [W^+]$$
$$\rightarrow e^+ + v_e$$

The Standard Model

The term **standard model** now refers to a model originally proposed in 1978 to explain the nature of matter and the fundamental forces. Here are some key concepts of this model:

- All matter is composed of 12 fundamental particles — the 6 leptons and the 6 quarks — plus their antiparticles.
- The electromagnetic force and the weak nuclear force are both aspects of a single fundamental force. Sheldon Glashow, Abdus Salaam, and Steven Weinberg developed the theory for this **electroweak force** in the late 1960s. This theory accurately predicted the existence and masses of the W^+, W^-, and Z^0 particles.
- The electromagnetic and nuclear forces are mediated by virtual particles. As discussed in section 17.2, these mediating particles are the photon, the gluon, and the W^+, W^-, and Z^0 particles.
- All quarks have a quantum property, termed **colour**, which determines how the strong nuclear force acts between quarks. (Quantum colour is not related to visible colours at all.) The quantum field theory describing the strong nuclear force in this way is called **quantum chromodynamics**. It is analogous to quantum electrodynamics with colour instead of electric charge and gluons instead of photons.

Table 17.7 summarizes the fundamental particles in the standard model.

*e***WEB**

To learn more about the decay of subatomic particles, follow the links at www.pearsoned.ca/school/physicssource.

standard model: the current theory describing the nature of matter and the fundamental forces

electroweak force: a fundamental force that combines the electromagnetic force and the weak nuclear force

colour: a quantum property related to the strong nuclear force

quantum chromodynamics: quantum field theory that describes the strong nuclear force in terms of quantum colour

▼ **Table 17.7** Fundamental Particles in the Standard Model

Matter						
Generation	First		Second		Third	
Quarks	up	down	strange	charm	bottom	top
Leptons	electron	electron-neutrino	muon	muon-neutrino	tau	tau-neutrino
Fundamental Forces						
Force	Electromagnetic		Weak Nuclear		Strong Nuclear	
Mediating particle(s)	photon		W^+, W^-, and Z^0		gluon	

What's Next in Quantum Theory?

Many theorists are working to combine quantum chromodynamics and the electroweak force theory into a **grand unified theory**. One such theory suggests that the electromagnetic, strong nuclear, and weak nuclear forces would blend into a single force at distances less than 10^{-30} m, and leptons and quarks could transform from one into the other. However, it would take tremendously high energy to push particles so close together. Although of no relevance for everyday life, such theories could have a great effect on calculations about the origin of the universe.

Another challenge is to develop a theory that unifies gravity with the other three forces. One of the most promising approaches is **string theory**, which treats all particles as exceedingly tiny vibrating strings of mass-energy. The vibration of the strings is quantized (like standing waves). The various kinds of particles are just different modes of vibration, with the graviton being the lowest mode.

At present, these theories are highly speculative. The only thing known for sure is that the people who solve these problems will be in line for a Nobel Prize!

grand unified theory: quantum theory unifying the electromagnetic, strong nuclear, and weak nuclear forces

string theory: theory that treats particles as quantized vibrations of extremely small strings of mass-energy

Project **LINK**

For your unit project, you may want to describe theories that unify the fundamental forces.

17.4 Check and Reflect

Knowledge

1. What experimental evidence suggests that the proton contains three smaller particles?

2. Why is it probably impossible to observe an individual quark on its own?

3. Compare the quark composition of a proton to that of a neutron.

4. Describe the difference between mesons and baryons in terms of quarks.

5. State two differences between leptons and hadrons.

6. List the 12 fundamental particles of matter in the standard model.

Applications

7. (a) Using quark theory, write an equation for the beta decay of a neutron.

   (b) Show that charge is conserved in this decay process.

8. Is the beta decay $\mu^+ \rightarrow e^- + \nu_e + \bar{\nu}_\mu$ possible? Justify your answer.

9. Describe what happens in this decay process:

$$uud \rightarrow udd + [W^+]$$
$$ \longrightarrow e^+ + \nu_e$$

Extension

10. Explain why a grand unified theory could have a great effect on speculations about the origin of the universe.

 e **TEST**

To check your understanding of fundamental particles and the nature of matter, follow the eTest links at www.pearsoned.ca/school/physicssource.

Key Terms and Concepts

cloud chamber	graviton	pion	quark
bubble chamber	primary cosmic rays	lepton	strange particle
fundamental particle	secondary cosmic rays	hadron	standard model
quantum field theory	Van de Graaff accelerator	meson	electroweak force
mediating particle	drift tube accelerator	baryon	colour
virtual particle	cyclotron	spin	quantum chromodynamics
quantum electrodynamics	synchrotron	fermion	grand unified theory
gluon	muon	boson	string theory

Key Equations

Electron-positron annihilation: $e^+ + e^- \rightarrow 2\gamma$

Mass units: $1 \text{ eV}/c^2 = 1.7827 \times 10^{-36} \text{ kg}$

β^- decay: udd $\rightarrow$ uud + [W^-]
$\qquad \qquad \qquad \qquad \rightarrow e^- + \bar{\nu}_e$

β^+ decay: uud $\rightarrow$ udd + [W^+]
$\qquad \qquad \qquad \qquad \rightarrow e^+ + \nu_e$

Conceptual Overview

Summarize the chapter by copying and completing this concept map.

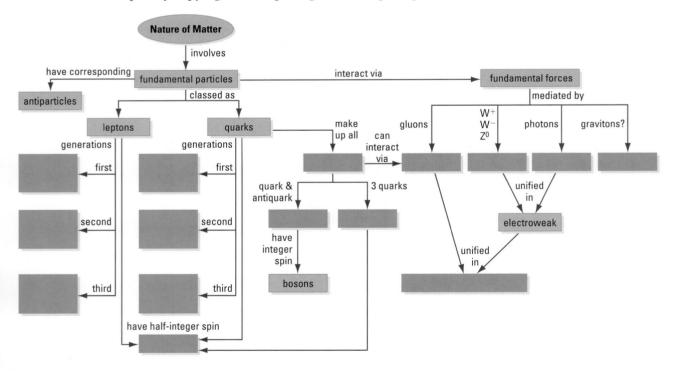

Knowledge

1. (17.1) How does a bubble chamber detect the path of a charged particle?

2. (17.1) Describe the technological advance in atomic physics made by

   (a) Charles Wilson   (b) Marietta Blau

   (c) Donald Glaser

3. (17.2, 17.4) (a) In the early 1900s, which three subatomic particles were thought to be the fundamental building blocks of matter?

   (b) Which of these particles is still thought to be fundamental?

4. (17.2) What theory predicted the existence of antimatter?

5. (17.2) For each of these particles, list the corresponding antimatter particle and explain how it differs from the ordinary matter particle.

   (a) electron   (b) proton

6. (17.2) How does quantum field theory account for fundamental forces acting over a distance?

7. (17.2, 17.3) Describe a similarity and a difference between a muon and a pion.

8. (17.3) What are two advantages of using units of MeV/c^2 to express the mass of subatomic particles?

9. (17.3) Compare the size of an electron to that of a proton.

10. (17.4) Describe an experiment that provided evidence for the existence of quarks.

11. (17.4) Give two reasons why Millikan did not detect any quarks with his oil-drop experiment.

12. (17.4) (a) Why did physicists suspect that there might be a sixth quark?

   (b) What is the name of this sixth quark?

   (c) Why was a huge accelerator necessary for the discovery of this quark?

13. (17.4) Compare the quark composition of antiprotons and antineutrons.

14. (17.4) Which two fundamental forces are united in the standard model?

15. (17.4) How does the string theory explain the various kinds of subatomic particles?

Applications

16. Sketch the paths that alpha, beta, and gamma radiation would follow when travelling perpendicular to a magnetic field directed out of the page.

17. The red tracks in this diagram show a high-speed proton colliding with a hydrogen atom in a bubble chamber, deflecting downward, and then colliding with another hydrogen atom. These tracks curve clockwise slightly.

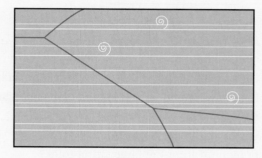

   (a) In which direction is the magnetic field oriented?

   (b) What conclusions can you make about the mass, speed, and charge of the particles involved in the first collision?

   (c) What conclusion can you make about the mass, speed, and charge of the particles that made the small spiral tracks?

18. (a) Write a nuclear decay equation to show how fluorine-18 can produce positrons for use in positron-emission tomography.

   (b) Describe the role that quarks play in this decay process.

   (c) Write an equation to describe what happens to the positrons within a patient undergoing a PET scan.

19. The mass of a top quark is about 176 GeV/c^2. Express this mass in kilograms.

20. (a) Determine the charge on a particle having the quark composition uus.

   (b) Estimate the mass of this particle.

21. The diagram shows a particle track recorded in a bubble chamber at the CERN particle accelerator. The magnetic field in the bubble chamber was 1.2 T directed out of the page.

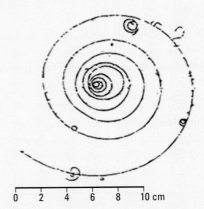

0   2   4   6   8   10 cm

(a) Does the particle have a positive or negative charge? Explain your reasoning.

(b) Estimate the initial radius of the particle's path.

(c) Determine the initial momentum of the particle.

(d) Why does the particle's path spiral inward?

(e) What could cause the short tracks that branch off from the large spiral track?

Extension

22. Research Pauli's exclusion principle at the library or on the Internet. Write a paragraph describing this principle and the classes of particles to which it applies.

Consolidate Your Understanding

1. Describe three experiments that discovered new subatomic particles. Explain how these experiments changed physicists' understanding of the nature of matter.

2. Give two examples of theories that accurately predicted the existence of previously unknown subatomic particles.

3. (a) Why was the quark theory first proposed?

(b) Outline the experimental evidence that supports this theory.

(c) Explain to a classmate why the standard model now includes six quarks instead of the three originally suggested by Gell-Mann and Zweig.

Think About It

Review your answers to the Think About It questions on page 829. How would you answer each question now?

e TEST

To check your understanding of the structure of matter, follow the eTest links at www.pearsoned.ca/school/physicssource.

How Atomic Physics Affects Science and Technology

Scenario

Atomic physics has enormously influenced the development of modern science and technology. Advances in atomic physics have profoundly changed scientists' understanding of chemistry, biology, and medicine. A century ago, technology that is taken for granted now would have seemed impossible even in principle. In this project, you will work with two or three classmates to research how the concepts presented in this unit affected an aspect of science or technology.

Planning

Brainstorm with your classmates to make a list of possible topics. Look for branches of science or technology that apply concepts of atomic physics. Here are some starting points:

- medical diagnostic technologies, such as X rays, magnetic resonance imaging (MRI), PET scans, and radioactive tracers
- chemistry applications, such as understanding molecular bonds and using spectroscopy to identify compounds
- biology topics such as quantum effects in photosynthesis and DNA replication
- computer and electronic devices, such as microchips, tunnel diodes, and quantum computers
- nanotechnologies such as nanotubes and atomic force microscopes
- power technologies, such as nuclear reactors, tokamaks, and radioisotope thermoelectric generators (RTGs)

Decide upon a topic to research. Often, you will find it easier to deal with a specific topic rather than a general one. For example, you could focus on nanotubes rather than trying to cover the whole field of nanotechnology. You may want to do some preliminary research on two or three promising ideas to see how much information is available.

Consider the best way to present your findings. You might use a written report, an oral presentation, slides, a poster, a model, a video, or a combination of methods. Consult with your teacher on the format of your presentation.

Materials

- library resources, including books and periodicals
- Web browser and Internet connection

Check with your teacher about any special resources, such as computer software, that you may need for your presentation.

Procedure

1 Assign tasks for each group member. Each member should do part of the research as well as some of the preparation for the presentation, such as writing, preparing graphics, or building a model. Clearly identify who is responsible for each part of your project.

2 Once you have gathered basic information about your topic, consider what further research you need to do. For example, you may be able to interview an expert either in person, or by telephone or e-mail. Many university departments have an outreach program that might suggest an expert you could consult.

3 Check whether the presentation method your group has chosen is suitable for the information you have found during your research. Consult with your teacher if you think you need to change to another type of presentation. If you will be making an oral presentation, practise. Having friends and family critique your presentation can often help you find ways to improve it.

Thinking Further

- Atomic physics often seems to be too abstract or theoretical to have any relevance to the "real world." How has your investigation changed your understanding of the relationship between atomic physics and other disciplines?

- Does the influence of atomic physics extend beyond science? Can you find ways in which atomic physics has influenced the arts or philosophy?

- Science fiction often employs ideas from physics. List several science-fiction books, movies, or television series that use some of the concepts in this unit. How accurate is their treatment of atomic physics?

*Note: Your instructor will assess the project using a similar assessment rubric.

Unit Concepts and Skills: Quick Reference

Concepts	Summary	Resources and Skill Building
Chapter 15	**Electric force and energy quantization determine atomic structure.**	
	15.1 The Discovery of the Electron	
cathode rays	Thomson's experiments showed that cathode rays are subatomic particles with a negative charge.	15-1 QuickLab
charge-to-mass ratio	You can use electric and magnetic fields to measure the charge-to-mass ratio of a particle.	Example 15.2
	15.2 Quantization of Charge	
charge quantization	Electric charge exists only in multiples of the fundamental unit of charge, e.	15-2 QuickLab
Millikan's experiment	Millikan's oil-drop experiment measured the charge on an electron and showed that charge is quantized.	Example 15.3 eSIM of Millikan's oil-drop experiment
	15.3 The Discovery of the Nucleus	
classical model of the atom	Rutherford's gold-foil experiment led to the solar-system model with electrons orbiting a tiny positively charged nucleus at the centre of the atom.	15-3 QuickLab Example 15.5
	15.4 The Bohr Model of the Atom	
spectra	Elements and compounds have characteristic emission and absorption line spectra.	15-4 Design a Lab
Bohr model	The Bohr model uses energy levels to account for stability of the atom and to explain line spectra. This model accurately predicts many properties of hydrogen, but has several serious failings.	Example 15.6
energy levels	An electron in an atom can occupy only orbits that give the electron discrete, quantized amounts of energy that are inversely proportional to the square of the principal quantum number.	Example 15.7 15-5 Inquiry Lab
	15.5 The Quantum Model of the Atom	
quantum mechanical model	The wave properties of electrons lead to a powerful new model based on probability distributions.	Figures 15.24–15.25
Chapter 16	**Nuclear reactions are among the most powerful energy sources in nature.**	
	16.1 The Nucleus	
nuclear structure	Nuclei contain protons and neutrons bound together by the strong nuclear force.	Examples 16.1 and 16.2
mass-energy equivalence	Mass and energy are equivalent, and the one can be transformed into the other.	Example 16.3
binding energy, mass defect	The binding energy and mass defect of a nucleus indicate how tightly its nucleons are bound together.	Figure 16.3 Example 16.4
	16.2 Radioactive Decay	
nuclear decay, transmutation	Some nuclei spontaneously transmute into a different element by emitting an alpha or beta particle. Nuclei can also give off gamma rays. All three types of radiation can be harmful.	Examples 16.5–16.10 16-1 Inquiry Lab 16-2 Design a Lab
	16.3 Radioactive Decay Rates	
half-life, activity	You can use the decay constant and the half-life of a radioisotope to predict the activity of a sample.	Examples 16.12 and 16.13
	16.4 Fission and Fusion	
nuclear reactions	Both the fission of a heavy nucleus into smaller nuclei and the fusion of light nuclei into a single heavier nucleus can release tremendous amounts of energy.	Figures 16.17 and 16.18 Examples 16.14–16.16
Chapter 17	**The development of models of the structure of matter is ongoing.**	
	17.1 Detecting and Measuring Subatomic Particles	
particle tracks	The existence and basic properties of subatomic particles can be determined by analyzing the paths of particles in magnetic and electric fields.	Example 17.1 17-1 QuickLab, 17-2 Inquiry Lab
	17.2 Quantum Theory and the Discovery of New Particles	
antimatter	Quantum theory predicted the existence of antimatter, which was confirmed by Anderson's discovery of the positron.	Figure 17.11
quantum field theory	According to this theory, the electromagnetic and nuclear forces are mediated by virtual particles.	Figure 17.13
	17.3 Probing the Structure of Matter	
particle accelerators	Particle accelerators produce high-energy particles, which are used to study the structure of matter.	Figure 17.14
families of particles	Hadrons interact via the strong nuclear force, whereas leptons do not. Bosons have integer spin and fermions have half-integer spin.	Tables 17.2 and 17.3
	17.4 Quarks and the Standard Model	
fundamental particles	The fundamental particles are the six leptons, the six quarks, and their antiparticles. All hadrons consist of a combination of quarks and/or antiquarks.	Tables 17.5,17.6, and 17.7

Vocabulary

1. Using your own words, define these terms:

absorption line spectrum
activity (A) or decay rate
alpha radiation
antimatter
atomic mass number
atomic mass unit (u)
atomic number
baryon
becquerel (Bq)
beta (β) particle
beta radiation
beta-negative (β^-) decay
beta-positive (β^+) decay
binding energy
Bohr radius
boson
bubble chamber
cathode ray
cloud chamber
colour
cyclotron
daughter element
decay constant
drift tube accelerator
electroweak force
elementary unit of charge
emission line spectrum
energy level
excited state
femto
fermion
fission
Fraunhofer line
fundamental particle
fusion
gamma (γ) decay
gamma radiation
gluon
grand unified theory
graviton
gray (Gy)
ground state
hadron

half-life
ionization energy
isotopes
lepton
mass defect
mediating particle
meson
muon
neutrino
neutron
neutron number
nucleon
nucleosynthesis
orbital
parent element
pion
planetary model
positron (e^+ or $^0_1\beta$)
primary cosmic rays
principal quantum number
proton
proton-proton chain
quantum chromodynamics
quantum electrodynamics
quantum field theory
quark
radioactive decay series
radioisotope
relative biological effectiveness (RBE)
secondary cosmic rays
sievert (Sv)
spectrometer
spectroscopy
spin
standard model
stationary state
strange particle
string theory
strong nuclear force
supernova
synchrotron
transmute
Van de Graaff accelerator
virtual particle
weak nuclear force

Knowledge

CHAPTER 15

2. Calculate the electrical charge carried by 1 kg of protons.

3. How many coulombs of charge are on a dust particle that has gained 10 electrons?

4. Calculate the force exerted by an electric field of strength 100 N/C [S] on a dust particle having a charge of $-10e$.

5. Explain how the path of this particle shows whether its charge is positive or negative.

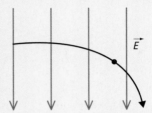

6. Determine whether the charge on this particle is positive or negative.

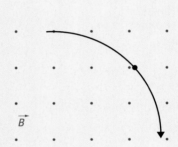

7. What is an alpha particle?

8. Here are four energy-level transitions for an electron in a hydrogen atom:

$n_i = 1 \rightarrow n_f = 5$ $n_i = 4 \rightarrow n_f = 1$

$n_i = 2 \rightarrow n_f = 6$ $n_i = 6 \rightarrow n_f = 2$

(a) For which transition(s) does the atom lose energy?

(b) For which transition does the atom gain the most energy?

(c) Which transition emits the shortest wavelength photon?

9. You are comparing the energy released by two different atomic transitions in a mercury atom. Transition A produces a very bright green line while transition B produces a fainter violet-coloured line. Which of these transitions releases more energy? Explain.

CHAPTER 16

10. How many neutrons are in a nucleus of gallium $^{64}_{31}Ga$? How many protons?

11. Why is the mass of an atom always less than $Zm_{1H} + Nm_{neutron}$?

12. Express the energy equivalent of 0.021 u of mass in electron volts.

13. Express the energy equivalent of 7.0 u in joules.

14. Calculate the binding energy for a nucleus that has a mass defect of 0.0072 u.

15. What is the activity of a sample that contains 1.5×10^{22} nuclei of an element with a decay rate of 1.5×10^{-13} Bq?

16. Write the β^+ decay process for $^{18}_9F$, and identify the daughter element.

17. The half-life of sulfur-35 is 87.51 days. How much of a 25-g sample of this isotope will be left after a year?

18. Write the alpha decay process for $^{228}_{90}Th$ and identify the daughter element.

19. Explain the difference between fission and fusion.

CHAPTER 17

20. What is a positron?

21. What is a pion?

22. If an electron and positron collide, they annihilate each other and are converted into energy.

(a) How much energy does the annihilation of a positron-electron pair produce?

(b) Explain why the annihilation must produce two gamma rays with the same wavelength.

(c) Estimate the wavelength of these gamma rays. Assume that the kinetic energy of the electron and positron was negligible.

23. What is a quark?

24. Describe this reaction in words:
$\bar{v}_e + p \rightarrow n + e$

25. Identify the particle formed by each of these combinations of quarks:

(a) uud   (b) u$\bar{s}$

(c) u$\bar{d}$ (d) dds

26. Use quarks to describe how a neutron decays into a proton and an electron.

Applications

27. A beam of protons enters a vacuum chamber where the electric field strength is 400 N/C and the magnetic field strength is 0.550 T.

   (a) Sketch an orientation of the electric and magnetic fields that could let the protons pass undeflected through the chamber.

   (b) What speed must the protons have if they are not deflected by this orientation of the fields?

28. Find the magnetic field strength that will deflect a sodium ion (Na^+) in an arc of radius 0.50 m when the ion has a speed of 1.0×10^6 m/s.

29. This diagram shows an electron moving at 2.5×10^6 m/s through perpendicular electric and magnetic fields.

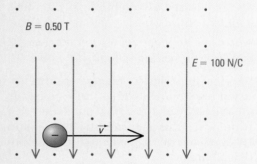

$B = 0.50$ T

$E = 100$ N/C

   (a) Calculate the electric and magnetic forces acting on the electron.

   (b) Calculate the net force acting on the particle.

30. An oil droplet with a mass of 1.6×10^{-16} kg is suspended motionless in a uniform electric field of strength 981 N/C [down].

   (a) Find the charge on this droplet.

   (b) How many electrons has the droplet either gained or lost?

31. (a) Find the wavelengths of the first four spectral lines produced by transitions into the $n = 3$ energy level of a hydrogen atom.

   (b) What part of the electromagnetic spectrum are these lines in?

32. (a) Use the Bohr model to calculate the radius of the $n = 2$ energy level in a hydrogen atom.

   (b) Find the de Broglie wavelength for an electron in this energy level.

   (c) Use the formula for the de Broglie wavelength to find the momentum of this electron.

   (d) Find the electron's speed and kinetic energy.

33. Calculate the binding energy for $^{40}_{20}Ca$.

34. Identify the nucleus produced in each reaction.

   (a) $^{12}_{6}C + \gamma \rightarrow ? + \alpha$

   (b) $^{14}_{7}N + \alpha \rightarrow ? + n$

   (c) $^{206}_{81}Tl \rightarrow ? + \beta^- + \bar{v}$

35. Explain why each of these reactions cannot occur.

   (a) $^{15}_{6}C \rightarrow ^{15}_{5}B + \beta^+ + \bar{v}_e$

   (b) $^{3}_{1}H \rightarrow ^{3}_{2}He + \beta^+ + v_e$

   (c) $^{23}_{11}Na + n \rightarrow ^{19}_{9}F + \alpha$

36. How much energy is released by β^- decay of $^{16}_{7}N$?

37. Some blood-flow tests use iodine-131 as a tracer. This isotope has a half-life of 8.04 days. Estimate the percentage of iodine-131 left after 30 days.

38. How much energy is given off in the alpha decay of neodymium isotope $^{144}_{60}Nd$? What daughter element does this decay produce?

39. A radioactive sample has an activity of 0.50 MBq and a half-life of 6 h. What will the activity of the sample be after 3.0 days?

40. The proportion of carbon-14 in charcoal used in a cave painting is only 12.5% of the proportion in living trees nearby. Estimate the age of this cave painting.

41. Calculate the amount of energy released when a carbon-12 nucleus absorbs an alpha particle and transmutes into oxygen-16.

42. Calculate the energy released by the reaction $^{2}_{1}H + ^{2}_{1}H \rightarrow ^{3}_{1}H + p$.

43. (a) What fundamental particles does a neutron contain, according to the standard model?

   (b) Show that this combination of particles has zero net charge.

44. The size of a nucleus is in the order of 1 fm.

    (a) Calculate the electrostatic force of repulsion between two protons separated by 1 fm.

    (b) Determine the potential energy of this pair of protons.

    (c) What keeps a nucleus together despite the electrostatic repulsion between protons?

Extensions

45. Two hydrogen atoms in the ground state collide head on and both ionize. Find the minimum speed at which the atoms could have been moving toward each other.

46. (a) Describe the reaction $\gamma + p \rightarrow \pi^0 + p$ in words.

    (b) Calculate the minimum energy the photon must have to produce this reaction.

47. In β^+ decay, a proton becomes a neutron and the nucleus emits a positron and a neutrino. A proton has less mass than a neutron, and the positron and the neutrino carry away some mass and energy. Explain how such decays conserve mass-energy despite this apparent imbalance.

48. A 5.0-GeV photon creates, via pair-production, an electron and a positron. Calculate the total momentum of the two particles and sketch their motion relative to the path of the original photon.

49. Imagine that protons and electrons were not charged but could still form a hydrogen atom through gravitational attraction. Calculate the size of such an atom by finding the radius of the ground state. (Hint: Assume that the electron travels in a circular orbit and has a total energy of $-\dfrac{Gm_p m_e}{2r}$.)

50. A typical banana contains about 0.40 g of potassium. Naturally occurring potassium is mainly $^{39}_{19}K$, but 0.012% of it is the radioactive isotope $^{40}_{19}K$, which has a decay constant of 1.8×10^{-17} s^{-1}. The average atomic mass for natural potassium is 39.1 u.

    (a) Calculate the activity of a typical banana.

    (b) Does the radiation exposure from bananas outweigh their health benefit as a source of potassium, fibre, and vitamins A, B6, and C? Explain your reasoning.

51. A spill of radioactive material at an industrial site emits 1.25 mGy per hour, measured at a distance of 1.0 m from the spill. The relative biological effectiveness of this radiation is 2.

    (a) Compare the radiation dose from this spill to exposure from background radiation.

    (b) At what distance from the spill would the annual absorbed dose be less than 0.1 mSv?

    (c) A newspaper headline reads "Dangerous Spill at Local Factory." Is this description fair? Explain why or why not.

52. (a) What is the fundamental difference between a fusion process and one that combines matter and antimatter?

    (b) Compare the energy released by the fusion of ordinary hydrogen into helium-4 with the energy released by combining two protons with two antiprotons.

    (c) Why can antimatter not be used for generating power or propelling a spaceship now?

53. Suppose that an electricity generator powered by the fusion reaction $^2_1H + {}^3_1H \rightarrow {}^4_2He + {}^1_0n$ has an overall efficiency of 20%. How much deuterium and tritium will this generator need to produce 10 MW·h of electricity, the annual consumption of a typical home?

Skills Practice

54. After two years, 6% remains of the original radioisotope in a sample. Estimate the half-life of this isotope.

55. A nucleus of boron $^{10}_5B$ absorbs an alpha particle and emits a proton. Use nuclear notation to write this reaction process, and identify the element that it produces.

56. Does an electron that moves from an energy level of −5.1 eV to an energy level of −6.7 eV emit or absorb a photon? Find the wavelength of the photon.

57. How much energy is produced by the conversion of 0.250 u of matter into energy?

58. Calculate the radius of a hydrogen atom in the $n = 2$ state.

59. An electron jumping from the $n = 3$ to the $n = 2$ state in a hydrogen atom emits a 656-nm photon.

   (a) Which state has the greater energy?

   (b) Find the energy difference between the two states.

60. Calculate the binding energy for $^{24}_{12}\text{Mg}$.

61. Find the parent atom for this decay:
$$? \rightarrow {}^{14}_{7}\text{N} + e^- + \bar{v}$$

62. Calculate the electrical charge of a particle composed of the quarks uus.

63. Find the activity of a sample containing 1.5×10^{20} radioactive atoms with a decay constant of 3.5×10^{-15} s^{-1}.

Self-assessment

64. Outline how you would describe Rutherford's gold-foil experiment to a friend. Explain why the results were startling for physicists in 1910.

65. (a) Explain why classical physics predicts that hydrogen will always produce a continuous spectrum rather than discrete spectral lines.

   (b) How does the Bohr model explain spectral lines?

66. Draw a concept map of the atomic physics topics that you find the most difficult. If you have trouble completing this concept map, discuss the concepts with a classmate or your teacher.

67. Explain why pair annihilation, such as $e + e^+ \rightarrow 2\gamma$, does not violate the law of conservation of mass.

68. List the four fundamental forces and explain which ones are involved in nuclear binding energy, decays, fission, and fusion.

  e **TEST**

To check your understanding of atomic physics, follow the eTEST links at www.pearsoned.ca/school/physicssource.

Contents

SR 1 Safety

In our modern society, safety has become much more than just protecting one's well being. Issues around safety have become extremely important to industry, business, governments, and all kinds of institutions including educational institutes. The understanding and application of safety in a broad sense has become an industry in itself. Today, even to be considered for many jobs, one must take safety courses or have a variety of safety-training certificates. Now is the time for you to continue developing an attitude and awareness of safety.

Safety is everyone's responsibility. The Provincial Government, the local school board, your teachers, and you all have an important role in keeping a safe environment. Alberta Education has prepared a detailed document, "Safety in the Science Classroom", outlining safety roles and responsibilities, and providing extensive information on potential hazards and safety procedures. This document is available online; go to www.pearsoned.ca/school/physicssource and follow the link to *Safety in the Science Classroom*. Of particular interest to you in this physics course is Chapter 6: Physical Hazards. For more technical information on issues, follow the link to *Health Canada Index* and search the topic alphabetically.

In general, your role in maintaining safety is to act responsibly by carefully following directions, learning how to recognize potential safety hazards, and how to respond to potentially unsafe situations and emergencies. If you are unsure about how to proceed, ask your teacher.

The Canadian Hazardous Products Act requires chemical manufacturers to include all hazard symbols and the degree of hazard on product labels. You may recognize hazard symbols on many household products. These symbols may indicate hazard(s), precaution, and first-aid treatment.

Hazardous Product and WHMIS Symbols

Household hazardous product symbols indicate the type of danger and the degree of danger. They appear in either a triangle (which means "caution"), a diamond (which means "warning"), or an octagon (which means "danger"). There are also numerous laboratory and industry hazard symbols in use.

Some symbols relevant to Physics 20 and 30 are shown below:

Flammable Hazard: The material could ignite (catch on fire) if exposed to flames, sparks, or friction.

Explosive Hazard: The material or equipment could explode.

Toxic Hazard: The material is very poisonous and could have immediate and serious effects.

Corrosive Hazard: The material may corrode ("eat away at") clothing, skin, or other materials.

Biological Hazard: Be alert to the possibility of poisoning or infection from microscopic and other organisms.

Electrical Hazard: Be alert to the possibility of an electric spark or shock.

Hot Surface: Skin or clothing may burn if touched.

Laser: Dangerous to eyes.

Radioactive Material: May pose hazard for short or long term exposure.

▲ **Figure SR 1.1** Laboratory and industry hazard symbols

Many of the chemical products used in Canadian schools are manufactured in the United States. To standardize the labelling systems, WHMIS (the Workplace Hazardous Materials Information System) was developed. The symbols belonging to this system appear on materials and products used both in workplaces and our schools.

compressed gas	dangerously reactive material	oxidizing material	poisonous and infectious causing immediate and serious toxic effects
flammable and combustible material	biohazardous infectious material	corrosive material	poisonous and infectious causing other toxic effects

▲ **Figure SR 1.2**

Laboratory Safety

Approach all investigations, especially in the laboratory, with maturity. Before you begin, read the instructions carefully, noting all safety precautions. In addition, your teacher may provide other safety reminders and rules pertaining to the laboratory activity. It is your responsibility to inform your teacher of medical conditions such as possible allergies to materials used (e.g., latex) or by-products of the activity. Inform your teacher if you wear contact lenses.

1. **General Precautions and Safety Equipment**
   a) Identify all safety equipment in the laboratory.
   b) Know the location of and how to operate safety equipment, including the fire extinguisher, fire blankets, eyewash fountains, sand, and the first-aid kit.
   c) Know how and where to get help if needed.
   d) Wear appropriate laboratory apparel, which may include safety goggles, gloves, and/or lab aprons.
   e) Tie back long hair and secure any loose clothing.

2. **Precautions with Mechanical Hazards**
   a) Rotating machinery or moving devices can catch loose clothing, fingers or hair; therefore, keep a safe distance away from moving parts.
   b) Strong magnets can snap on ferromagnetic materials and other magnets very quickly. Use caution to avoid pinching skin or cutting clothing.
   c) Projectile launchers should be used only with appropriate eye protection and a clear "line-of-fire." Be aware of the potential for a misfire or backfire.
   d) Model rockets with air, water, or solid-fuel motors can be a hazard. Wear eye protection and stay well clear of the launch area and potential trajectory. Make sure everyone watches for rocket parts falling back to the ground.

3. **Precautions with Electrical Sources**
   a) Do not use 110-V AC equipment if it has a damaged plug (e.g., missing the ground pin) or a frayed cord. Always disconnect the cord from the socket by pulling the plug, not the cord.
   b) Keep water and wet hands away from electrical cords.
   c) Do not touch a person in contact with live electrical currents. Disconnect the power source first. Then give artificial respiration if necessary. Call for help and treat burns.
   d) Make sure electrical cords are not placed where someone could trip over them.
   e) Do not allow a short circuit connection to a dry cell or battery. Dangerous amounts of heat can be generated in the wires and in the cells themselves, potentially causing an explosion or fire.
   f) Never attempt to recharge a non-rechargeable battery. Never cut open batteries. Their contents can be corrosive and poisonous.
   g) Keep flammable liquids away from electrical equipment. Sparks, in a motor for example, could ignite flammable vapours.

h) Spark timers create a very short but high voltage spark, which can give a minor electrical shock to anyone who touches a "live" part of the circuit. Although the shock itself is not dangerous, the surprise and sudden reaction can cause elbows to fly or objects to be dropped.

i) Some high voltage devices can cause nasty shocks or skin burns. Be aware of the potential danger of charged capacitors, tesla coils, electrostatic generators, and transformers. Use only under the guidance of your teacher.

j) When hooking up circuits, always have your teacher check the circuit before turning on the power.

4. **Precautions with Electromagnetic Radiation**

a) Never look directly into an infrared (IR) or an intense, visible ultraviolet (UV) light source. Intense light can harm the retina. UV and IR radiation are absorbed by the cornea and eye contents, and can cause burning and overheating or other damage.

b) Never look directly into the beam of an operating laser, even one with a low power. The eye focuses the laser light onto the retina, resulting in a power density of about 50 times that of direct sunlight. This can cause pinpoint burns to the retina.

c) Guard against stray reflections and turn the laser off when not in use.

d) Use radioactive sources only under the direction of your teacher.

e) In all cases, the potential for harm from radiation increases with exposure. Exposure can be minimized by limiting the time of use and maximizing the distance away from the source.

The Inquiry Process

Inquire: to seek knowledge of, to ask about, to investigate, or to seek information by asking.

Have you ever seen "sun dogs"? They are a common occurrence in Alberta, especially in the winter. Often they are coloured and associated with a coloured ring, or halo, around the sun. They seem to occur in thin clouds or in frosty air. You may have noticed that they are always the same distance from the sun and the colours are always in the same order: red closest to the sun and violet farther away. This set of observations can be the focus of an inquiry process.

▲ **Figure SR 2.1** Prairie sun dogs

The inquiry process is a model of learning incorporated in Alberta Education curricula; it is not a separate topic or option. The inquiry process is applicable to all learning, and is especially suited to learning physics. Learning an inquiry approach is more than a way to succeed in physics; it is a useful way to deal with problems and challenging situations throughout any future career.

The inquiry process is non-linear (there may be some side-tracks or dead ends), flexible (you can bend the rules or the process), individual (you can develop your own process), and recursive (you will need to revisit or loop through parts of the process as you go). An inquiry process model contains six components that connect together, all around your own thinking or reflection on the process. These components are:

- Planning
- Retrieving
- Processing
- Creating
- Sharing
- Evaluating

Planning

In order to inquire, you must have something in mind about which to inquire. Normally, the planning stage involves recognizing a situation, event, topic, or occurrence for which there is some unknown component. This leads to questions. In the planning stage, you (or your teacher) will need to look at the situation at hand and ask a question to be investigated. You may have many questions, but part of the process is to reflect on the situation and narrow (or in some cases, broaden) your question so that it is something you can actually investigate. From there, you will need to develop your process to lead through the other stages of the inquiry process. One way of working through the planning stage is to ask yourself the following questions:

- What do I want to know?
- What do I think the result might be?
- How can I find out?
- What do I need to do to find out?
- How will I know when I have found out?
- What form will my final results take?
- How can I best share my results with others?
- How can I evaluate what I have done?

In this stage, you will need to develop a clear inquiry question, propose a thesis or hypothesis, identify variables or related factors, create a data or information gathering process (experiment or research strategy), and recognize where your results may end up. Sometimes, this is the most difficult or lengthy part of the entire process, but very important.

Retrieving

Once you have an inquiry question, a hypothesis to test, and a plan to follow, you can begin the process of retrieving. This may involve experimentation or research. You may be gathering text information or numerical data from measurements. You may be using several different data sources including your own experimental data. In this stage, you may need to revisit *Planning* if you find difficulties or discrepancies during your information gathering.

Processing

The information or data you retrieve must be processed. You must evaluate the information, sort good data from poor data, decide what data is relevant, and perhaps re-identify variables. At this stage, you may find yourself looping through parts of the *Planning* and *Retrieving* stages again. Once you have good information, you need to decide how to display and analyze the data. What combination of data tables, graphs or graphic organizers should you use? Is there some mathematical analysis such as finding a slope, modelling a curve with an equation, or some statistical calculations that will be useful? Again, you may want to loop back to *Planning*, or ahead to *Creating* and *Sharing* to decide what detail of analysis you want to perform on your information. Ultimately, you need to be able to answer the question, "What does this information mean?"

Creating

You have asked a question, retrieved your information, and processed it. Now you must put the package together by creating a final product. Remember to look ahead to *Sharing*. In this product, you must clearly indicate your initial inquiry, provide a summary of your data or information, explain the meaning of your data, and state some conclusions regarding your inquiry question. At this point, you may find that you have more questions. This could lead you to another inquiry, and another, and another. This is the essence of how scientific knowledge continues to grow.

Sharing

This stage in the inquiry process is often devalued, yet it is a crucial step in the process. In science, if a new discovery is not communicated, then it is lost. In education, communicating ideas to others is one of the best learning processes. You don't really know or understand something until you can share the ideas with others. How you share will depend in part on how you created your final product. There are many modes of sharing: oral presentation, poster display, written report, demonstration, art work, working model, skit... Your job will be to choose a method that best fits you, your results, your classroom situation, and your audience. Again, you may need to loop back to *Planning* and *Creating* to get this in the most suitable form.

Evaluating

Now is the time to look at the whole process (not just the results or answers). Ask yourself these questions:

- What worked well?
- What became a challenge?
- Is there another or better way of doing any one of the stages in this process?
- What parts of the process were easier or more difficult, or more or less effective?
- How would I coach someone else to do this same inquiry in a more efficient way?
- Are there other questions or situations that might be resolved by the process I followed?
- What have I learned (about the inquiry question and about learning)?

By critically evaluating what you have done, you will learn process skills beyond physics or science; you will develop skills to last a lifetime.

A skeleton of a sample inquiry:

Planning

Situation: a solar halo display is very clear and colourful in the sky.

Question: Where do the sun dog's colours come from?

Hypothesis: This is the same effect as the rainbow. If I spray water into sunlight, then I should be able to see a halo.

What to do: Research rainbows and halos in print and online. Do an experiment with light rays and water drops to try to create a halo.

How do I know I have the answer: I can create a halo and a rainbow and match them together.

My final results: I will have a poster display with photos I have taken, and I will explain the results to my classmates.

Retrieving

Internet search informs me that halos and rainbows are different. From photos, I see that the colours are reversed. There are different types of halos. Sun dogs are part of ice crystal halos caused by refraction.

Revisit planning

Question: Does refraction of light through ice or other transparent solid crystals model the position of colours in sun dogs?

Hypothesis: If I shine a white light beam on a transparent solid crystal, then I will be able to see colours located in different directions.

Experiment: Shine light through ice crystals, prisms, or other transparent solids, and look for colours in different directions.

Processing

Can I see colours produced by light passing through the crystals? Is there a way for me to quantify my observations, e.g., can I measure directions?

To what degree of accuracy can I measure directions? Do I have enough data? Do I need to look at more variables such as the shape or material of the crystal? How can I record my observations in the most meaningful way for this context?

Creating

I will summarize my specific question and investigative process. My results include: data tables showing the approximate angles where I see different colours of light refracted through prisms of different shapes; three photos of my apparatus set-up and colours I could see; and internet photos of more sophisticated experiments. I will also create diagrams of what could be seen in my apparatus according to theory, and a poster display of the theory behind the experiment and actual halos. There are other questions arising from my work that I will pose on my poster. For example: What happens to the halo when an ice crystal tips on its side?

Sharing

I will give a short presentation to my class to explain my question and results, and model the path of light with white and coloured yarn through a foam block. Classmates will be able to see "colours" only at certain directions.

Evaluating

I will look critically at the entire process once I am finished.

The Problem-Solving Process: GRASP

Solving Numerical Problems

A significant amount of effort in physics is spent in solving problems that have a numerical component. Often these problems seem more difficult than they really are because they involve physics concepts, principles, and/or laws as well as mathematical operations. Research into the problem-solving abilities of professionals and novices shows that professionals have logical procedures they follow when solving problems while novices who are having difficulty do not. The more methods the problem-solver can apply, the more adept he/she is at problem solving.

The approach used in numerical problems throughout the textbook follows four basic steps. These steps are easy to remember and apply because combined, the first letters of the key words spell GRASP. A description of the four steps is provided below.

Step 1: List what is <u>G</u>iven

The first step in solving numerical problems involves answering the question, "What information are we given?" This is sometimes referred to as *data extraction*. To answer this question, read the problem carefully, study the information given, and represent physical quantities and numerical data with appropriate symbols, units, and directions (if necessary). Write the data in scientific notation to the correct number of significant digits (SR 6.3).

Step 2: List what you are <u>R</u>equired to find

The second step involves answering the question, "What am I required to find?" To answer this question, identify what the problem is asking you to do. Be sure to note the units requested, if specified, and, for vector quantities, the direction. Answering this question will point you in the right direction and prevent you from being distracted by irrelevant information.

Step 3: <u>A</u>nalysis and <u>S</u>olution — Analyze the problem carefully and work out the Solution

The third step requires a careful analysis of the problem before solving. To analyze the problem you must break it down into a series of logical steps. Begin by sketching a diagram. Many physics problems lend themselves to a diagram and the diagram often provides the key to solving the problem. Write down all the relationships you know involving the givens and the required. Also, write down any assumptions that must be made in order to solve the problem. An assumption is anything that must be taken for granted. Next, start with what you are trying to find, and answer the question, "What additional information do I need to calculate the unknown?" This may be a constant that you have to look up in a reference book or from a table of constants given in the textbook. Organize and sequence the information you have to form the solution. In physics, this often involves substituting appropriate data into an equation. It is good practice to rearrange an equation to solve for an unknown variable in terms of the other variables before substituting to obtain the final answer. Always be on the lookout for errors in the mathematical computations and check that the answer has the correct number of significant digits, and that appropriate units are included.

Step 4: <u>P</u>araphrase the solution

The numerical answer should be stated in a form that answers the original question. Since the original question was a sentence, the statement of the final answer should also be a complete sentence. Physical quantities should include units and directions, if appropriate.

You can use the following Numerical Problem Checklist to guide your work.

Numerical Problem Checklist

Given
☐ read problem carefully
☐ extract data
☐ represent physical quantities with appropriate symbols
☐ include units with physical quantities
☐ include directions where needed
☐ show the correct number of significant digits

Required
☐ identify what the problem is asking for
☐ identify units of the final answer
☐ identify direction of the final answer (for vector quantities)

Analysis and Solution
- [ ] draw a sketch
- [ ] write down possible relationships
- [ ] list viable assumptions
- [ ] write an appropriate equation containing the needed unknown variable and only other variables that are known or can be found from the given data
- [ ] identify and look up constants needed
- [ ] identify inconsistent units and perform needed unit conversions
- [ ] identify "red herrings" (i.e., extra bits of numerical information not needed to solve the problem)
- [ ] note the least number of significant digits in the given data
- [ ] note directions (for vector quantities)
- [ ] rearrange the equation to solve for the unknown
- [ ] substitute data into the rearranged equation
- [ ] simplify the mathematics: solve for the numerical answer and simplify the units
- [ ] check the mathematical calculations
- [ ] check the number of significant digits
- [ ] check the direction (if required)

Paraphrase
- [ ] write the final answer in a complete sentence
- [ ] check that units are included with numerals
- [ ] check accuracy of significant digits
- [ ] check accuracy of direction (if required)
- [ ] check that the original question has been answered and that the answer seems realistic

SR 4 Using Graphic Organizers

Graphic organizers are effective tools that can help you learn. They enable you to solve problems and think critically, through analyzing similarities and differences, inferring sequences, and establishing cause-and-effect relationships. They generate discussion and negotiation of ideas, extend comprehension of a concept, theme, or topic, and lead to organized representation and presentation of understandings. You can use them to brainstorm, demonstrate what you know, and organize your thoughts before planning a presentation or writing a report or essay. The following chart outlines a number of graphic organizers, their intended purposes, and how to use them as you study science.

Type of Graphic Organizer	Purpose	Method
Concept Map 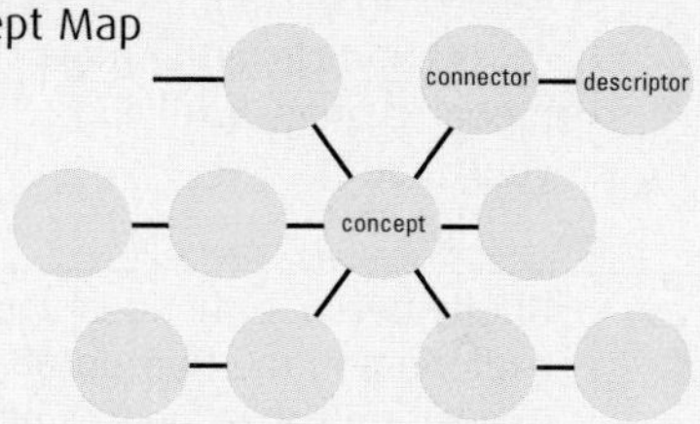	Used to clarify relationships and linkages between concepts, events, or ideas	Brainstorm ideas and link together from "big to small" with arrows or lines linking words.
Venn Diagram 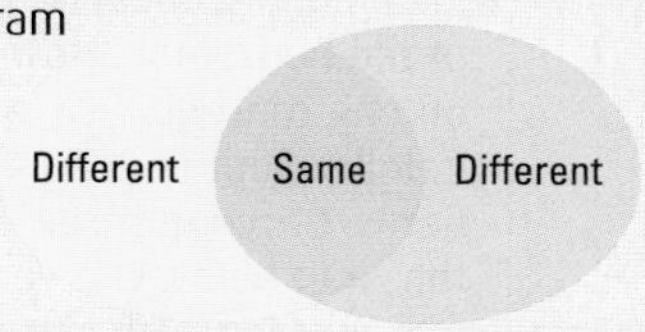	Used to visualize similarities and differences between two or more ideas, topics, or concepts	Brainstorm similarities, and list these in the overlapping section of the two circles. Then brainstorm differences and list these in the non-overlapping sections.
Web Diagram 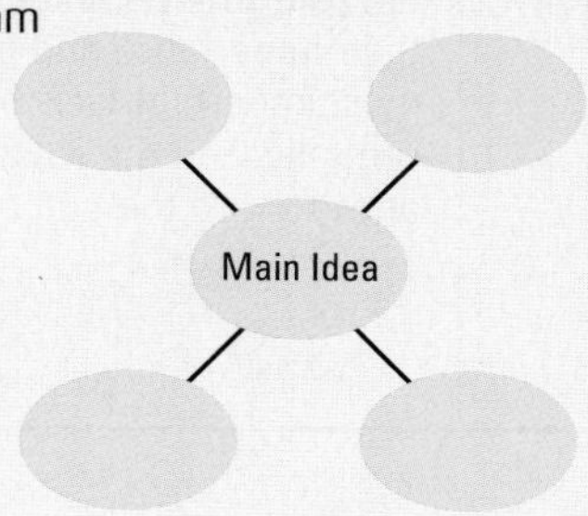	Used to clarify concepts and ideas by clustering them	Cluster words and/or information around a central object, concept, or idea.
Pie Chart	Used to estimate the relationship of parts to the whole	Estimate/research the importance or amount of proportionate time of each aspect of an event in relation to the whole.
Flowchart/Sequence Chart 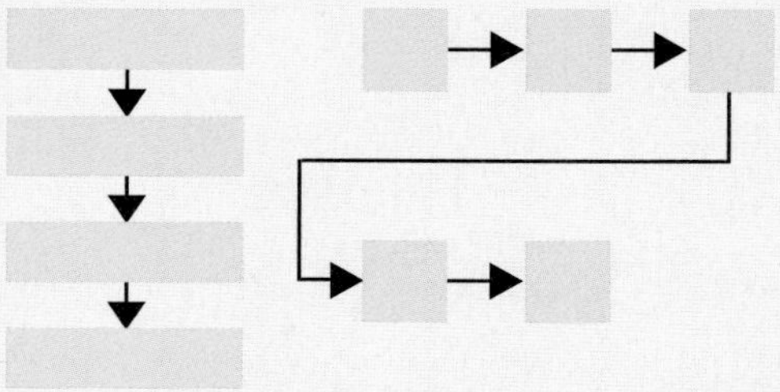	Used to map out your thinking about an issue or to organize ideas for an essay or report	Brainstorm aspects of the whole event. Select important aspects and put them into sequential order.

Type of Graphic Organizer	Purpose	Method
Ranking Ladder	Used to rank ideas in order of importance	Brainstorm ideas and rank them in order from least important (bottom rung) to most important (top rung).
Fishbone Diagram	Used to identify cause-and-effect relationships	Identify a problem to be solved. List the "effect" at the head of the fish. Brainstorm "possible causes" in each bone. Rank the causes and circle the most probable ones, justifying your choice.
Right-Angle Diagram	Used to explore the consequences of an idea and the impact of its application	Briefly describe the idea you are exploring on the horizontal arrow. Brainstorm consequences of the idea, and list these to the right of the horizontal arrow. Expand on one consequence, and list details about it along the vertical arrow. Describe social impacts of that trait below the vertical arrow.
Target Diagram	Used to weigh the importance of facts and ideas	Brainstorm facts and ideas. Rank their importance and place the most important facts or ideas centrally, and the least important ones toward the outer rings.

Type of Graphic Organizer	Purpose	Method
Agree/Disagree Chart 				Agree	Disagree		Used to organize data to support a position for or against an idea or decision	List a series of statements relating to a topic or issue. Survey agree-disagreement before discussion. Survey again after discussion and research.
PMI (Plus, Minus, Interesting) Chart 	Plus	Minus	Interesting		Used to summarize the positive and negative aspects of a topic or issue, as well as identify interesting aspects of the topic for possible further research	Sort ideas or information about a topic or issue in a three-column chart that has the following headings: Plus ($+$), Minus ($-$), and Interesting.
Gathering Grid	Used to make distinctions between ideas or events	Gather information on a number of ideas or events and arrange it on a grid. Each idea or event is assigned to a separate row. Analyze the information according to selected criteria in each specific column.
Concept Hierarchy Diagram	Used to identify and sequence the subordinate concepts needed to understand a higher-order concept	Place the higher-order concept at the top of a page. Then consider the question, "What concepts need to be understood before the higher-order concept above can be grasped?" The same question is then asked for each of the subordinate concepts identified and a hierarchy of connected concepts is created.

5.1 Graphing Techniques

▼ **Table SR 5.1**   Total mass of system as sand is added to a beaker

Total Volume of Sand Added V (mL)	Total Mass of System m (g)
28	188
55	258
84	333
106	391
148	500
174	567
210	661

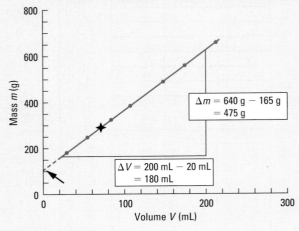

▲ **Figure SR 5.2**

Physicists make extensive use of graphs to convey information and to help determine how one physical quantity is affected by another. To review simple graphical analysis techniques, as an example, use the data from a simple measurement experiment where students added given volumes of sand as measured in a graduated cylinder to a beaker on a balance, recording the total volume of sand in the beaker and the total mass of the system as shown on the balance.

The Data Table
A data table is the most practical way to record quantitative data. Table SR 5.1 above shows the data from the student experiment of adding sand to a beaker on a balance. Note that the name of each variable, the symbol, and the unit of measurement (in round brackets) are recorded at the top of each column.

The Title of the Graph
Figure SR 5.2 shows a sample graph for a student's experiment. Every graph needs a title to describe what it is about. The title is placed at the top of the graph or in a box on a clear area above the graph.

The Axes of the Graph
Plot the independent variable on the horizontal x-axis and the dependent variable on the vertical y-axis. The variable that is changed intentionally is called the *manipulated* or *independent variable*. Volume of sand in the beaker was the manipulated or independent variable in the experiment

as students chose how much to add for each trial. The mass of the system depended on how much sand was added, thus the mass was the responding or *dependent* variable.

Label each axis with the name, symbol, and unit of the variable being plotted, as shown in Figure SR 5.2. Scales are chosen for each axis to spread the measured values across the graph paper without making the plotting difficult. The maximum values in the data table determine the maximum numbers on the scales of the axes.

To set a scale for an axis, analyze the data to be plotted and choose increments appropriate to the data.

In Table SR 5.1, the maximum volume value was 210 mL, and the minimum volume value was 28 mL. Increments of 20 mL on the x-axis would be appropriate for the data. As well, the maximum total mass of system was 661 g, and the minimum total mass of system was 188 g. Increments of 50 g on the y-axis would be appropriate for the data.

Plotting the Data and Drawing the Line of Best Fit
Use a pencil to plot the data points as accurately as possible by making a small visible dot. Accuracy is important. Use the actual data values and make your best estimate of values within the scale grid. Once all of the data points have been plotted, a line of best fit is drawn. A line of best fit is a line that shows the trend of the points. Make the smoothest curve you can, balancing points that do not fit the curve evenly above and

below the curve. Do not try to have the curve or straight line go through all the dots since most data points have some error. The scatter of the data points from the smooth line indicates the extent of the errors in the data.

Where a point is far off the line, a serious error may have been made. If this occurs, measure the data for that point again, if possible. If you believe an error was made, still plot the point, but ignore it while drawing your best fit curve.

Interpolating from the Graph

Interpolation is the process of estimating a value that is between two directly measured data points of a variable. To interpolate, first locate the point on the appropriate axis for the value of the variable in which you are interested. Next, draw a line perpendicular to this axis to intercept the line of best fit. From this point on the line of best fit, draw a second line perpendicular to the second axis. Read the value of the second variable from this axis. For example, in Figure SR 5.2, a volume of 70 mL of sand is interpolated to a total mass of 300 g (indicated by the small star).

There is some risk of inaccuracy involved in interpolation, since it is assumed that the trend of the line continues between the measured points. This assumption is not always valid.

Extrapolating from the Graph

Extrapolation is the process of estimating the values of a data point beyond the limits of the known or measured values. However, there is a considerable risk of inaccuracy, because it is assumed that the trend of the curve continues outside the range of the data. When the line is extended, a dotted line is used to show that the extension is little more than guesswork. The arrow in Figure SR 5.2 shows the process of extrapolating the curve to find the mass of the system without any sand in the beaker. What is this value and what does it represent? How valid is the value?

Calculating the Slope

If the line of best fit is straight, the *slope* of the line can be found. The slope of the line is defined as the rate of change of one variable with respect to the other and is found by the ratio of the rise to the run. To find the slope, find two points far apart on the line of best fit whose values are easily readable from the scales on the axes. On the graph, lightly draw a horizontal line from the lower point and a vertical line from the higher point so that they intersect. Use the axis scale to determine the change in vertical value (rise) and change in horizontal value (run) along these two line segments.

In Figure SR 5.2, the rise is shown as 475 g and the run as 180 mL.

The slope of this graph is thus:

slope = rise/run = 475 g/180 mL = 2.64 g/mL

Notice that the slope in this example has units; it also has some physical significance: it represents the density of the sand.

Writing the Equation of the Line

If the trend of the curve is a straight line, then changes in the plotted variables are directly proportional to each other. As the change in one variable doubles, the change in the other doubles, and vice versa. The general equation for a straight line is $y = mx + b$, where y is the variable on the vertical axis, x is the variable on the horizontal axis, m is the slope of the line, and b is the vertical axis intercept.

Figure SR 5.2 shows a straight line for volumes of sand at least up to 210 mL. For this range, the change in mass is directly proportional to the volume of sand added. The general equation for the linear graph in Figure SR 5.2 is: $m = \rho V + b$ where m is the total mass of the system, ρ is the density of the sand, V is the total volume of sand in the beaker, and b is the mass of the empty beaker. The specific equation for this graph is:

$m = (2.63 \text{ g/mL})V + 115 \text{ g}.$

Using the Equation of the Line

It is often more convenient to extrapolate or interpolate from the specific equation than from the graph. For example, the total mass of the system could be determined if 800 mL of sand is added, even though our beaker may not be that big and our graph does not extend that far. To do this, substitute 800 mL for V in the equation and calculate m. The accuracy of this result depends on the accuracy of the equation, which in turn depends on the accuracy of the determination of slope and vertical axis intercept.

5.2 Using the Graphing Tools

Graphing calculators make the process of plotting and interpreting graphs easy and efficient. Data from an experiment can be entered into the calculator and displayed as a scatterplot. The calculator can be used to determine the function that best models a given scatterplot. The information provided for this function can also be used to write the equation that best describes the relationship between the two plotted variables.

The graphing calculator can also be used to help us explore the graph of a given equation or relationship. It can be used to interpolate values between the plotted points or to extrapolate values beyond the plotted points. These uses make the graphing calculator a very powerful laboratory tool.

Data can also be stored and plotted in a computer spreadsheet such as Microsoft Excel.

The eMath activities in this textbook provide opportunities for you to use the graphing calculator or a computer spreadsheet.

6.1 Measurement: Accuracy and Precision

Measurement is a process of comparing some unknown characteristic, attribute, or quantity to some known or accepted scale or standard. Measurement involves tools and technique. If there is a problem with either, there can be problems with the quality of the measured data. A tape measure with the end broken off would give incorrect measurements if the problem was not noticed. Using a metre stick to measure the thickness of a hair would not work well. Forgetting to include the weight of the fuel when weighing in freight to load a plane could be disastrous. At best, a measurement is an estimate; there is always some amount of uncertainty to the value you record. To make a measurement, and to use measured values correctly, we must understand a number of important issues.

Accuracy

Accuracy is a means of describing the quality of measurements, or how closely a measurement agrees with the accepted or actual value of the quantity being measured. A broken tape measure will not give accurate values for length. The difference between an observed value (or the average of observed values) and the accepted value is called the *deviation*. The size of the deviation is an indication of the accuracy. Thus, the smaller the error, the greater is the accuracy.

The *percent deviation* is determined by subtracting the accepted value from the measured value, dividing this by the accepted value, and multiplying by 100. Thus,

$$\text{percent deviation} = \left| \frac{(\text{measured value} - \text{accepted value})}{\text{accepted value}} \right| \times 100\%$$

Precision

Precision is the degree of repeatability of measurements; it depends on your care and technique. If the same measurement is carefully made several times independently, we find that we may get variations in the last digit we read. This limitation defines the precision of the measurement. The precision of a measuring instrument depends on how finely the scale is divided. A ruler with mm divisions will not be useful in measuring the difference in hair thickness between blondes and red-heads. The smaller the divisions of its scale, the less uncertainty there will be in reading values.

Any measurement that falls between the smallest divisions on the measuring instrument is an estimate. We should always try to read any instrument by estimating tenths of the smallest division. For a ruler calibrated in centimetres, this means estimating to the nearest tenth of a centimetre, or to 1 mm. Using this procedure, the length of the object in Figure SR 6.1 is found to be 6.7 cm. We are certain of the 6, but the 0.7 is an estimate. In reality, it could easily be 0.6 or 0.8. It is however, unlikely that it would be 0.5.

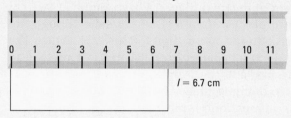

0   1   2   3   4   5   6   7   8   9   10   11

l = 6.7 cm

▲ **Figure SR 6.1**

Figure SR 6.2 shows the measurement of the same object using a ruler calibrated in millimetres. The reading estimated to the nearest tenth of a millimetre appears closest to 6.74 cm. It might be tempting to record the length as either 6.7 cm or 6.8 cm. This would be wrong. We can tell that the length is between the two divisions. The estimated digit is always shown when recording the measurement. The estimated digit in this reading is 0.04 cm.

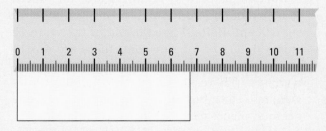

0   1   2   3   4   5   6   7   8   9   10   11

▲ **Figure SR 6.2**

Figure SR 6.3 shows a different object being measured with a ruler calibrated in centimetres. The length falls exactly on the 6-cm mark. Should the length be recorded as 6 cm or 6.0 cm? Remember that with a centimetre ruler we can estimate to tenths of a centimetre. With this ruler we can therefore distinguish readings of 5.9 cm and 6.1 cm. The object is right on a division mark, so the estimated digit is zero-tenths of a centimetre. Zero-tenths is indicated by 0.0 and the correct reading is 6.0 cm, not 6 cm.

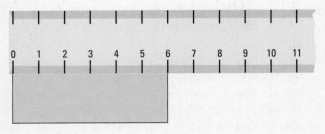

▲ **Figure SR 6.3**

Indicating the Precision of Measured Quantities

The *precision* of a measurement is indicated by the number of decimal places. For example, 2.861 cm is more precise than 581.86 cm even though the latter contains more digits. This is because the three decimal places in 2.861 make it precise to the nearest one-thousandth of a centimetre, while the two decimal places in 581.86 make it precise to the nearest one-hundredth of a centimetre. In this physics program, angle measures will have a precision no better than 0.1°.

Significant Digits

The accuracy of a measurement is indicated by the number of significant digits. *Significant digits* are the specific number of digits used to communicate the degree of uncertainty in a measurement. When we are expressing a physical quantity as a number, how many significant digits should we indicate? These rules should help you decide.

- Numbers obtained by counting are considered to be exact and contain an infinite number of significant digits. For example, if there are 12 stopwatches in a classroom, there are not 11 stopwatches, or 13 stopwatches, or 12.35 stopwatches. There are exactly 12.000... stopwatches. The zeros may be extended to as many decimal places as necessary in calculations.
- Numbers obtained from definitions are considered to be exact and contain an infinite number of significant digits. For example, 1 m = 100 cm, and 1 kW·h = 3600 kJ, are definitions of equalities. π ($\approx$ 3.141 592 654) has an infinite number of decimal places, as do numbers in formulae such as $P = 4s$, where P is perimeter of a square, and s is the length of a side.

- All of the digits from one to nine (1, 2, 3, ... 9) are significant, so 424.7 m or 0.4247 km each have four significant digits.
- All zeros to the left of the first non-zero digit are not significant. For example, 1.4 kg and 0.0014 kg each have two significant digits.
- Zeros between other non-zero digits are significant. Therefore, 501.009 s has six significant digits.
- Any zero to the right of a non-zero digit is significant. Therefore, the mass of an object written as 2000 kg has four significant digits. If the mass is a stated value, not a measured value, we can indicate that we know it to four significant digits by using scientific notation and writing the mass as 2.000×10^3 kg.

Good measurements have high degrees of both accuracy and precision. In order to assure better accuracy, instruments should be calibrated. *Calibration* involves making sure the scale divisions are spaced properly and that the zero reading is correct. Better precision is attained by using better tools, those with finer scales. Good technique, of course, is also necessary for both precision and accuracy.

6.2 Mathematical Operations with Data

When doing calculations with measured values, never keep more digits in the final answer than in the least accurate number in the calculation. For example, 0.6 + 0.32 = 0.9, not 0.92. This procedure for using only meaningful digits is called rounding off. The procedure for *rounding off* digits is as follows:

- When the first digit discarded is less than five, the last digit retained is left the same. Notice that we start rounding off at the digit immediately after the last digit we are retaining. For example, 14.248 kg rounded to three digits is 14.2 kg, since the fourth digit (4) is less than five.
- When the first digit discarded is a five or greater, we increase the last digit retained by one. Therefore, 7.8361 km rounded to three digits is 7.84 km, and 4.255 01 s rounded to three digits is 4.26 s.
- Consider numbers that are exact counts to be perfectly precise. For example, the average mass of three cars having masses of 1000 kg, 1250 kg, and 1165 kg is (1000 kg + 1250 kg + 1165 kg)/3 or 1138 kg. The denominator (3) in this example is an exact count, and therefore the answer includes four significant digits.

- Consider fractions and defined equalities to be perfectly precise. The fraction $\frac{1}{2}$ in the equation $E_k = \frac{1}{2}mv^2$ does not influence rounding off. Neither does the defined equality 10 mm = 1 cm.

Note: In the examples in this textbook, intermediate steps are shown rounded off to one extra significant digit. In reality, all digits are carried through the calculations until the final answer is reached, at which point the final answer is rounded off appropriately.

Rules for Significant Digits in Mathematical Operations

Adding or subtracting: the precision, as shown by the number of decimal places in the values being used, determines the number of significant digits in the answer. Round off the answer to the same precision as the least precise value used. For example, 11.2 kg + 0.24 kg + 0.336 kg = 11.776 kg, is rounded off to 11.8 kg because the least precise value, 11.2 kg, is only given to the first decimal place.

Multiplying or dividing: the value with the least number of significant digits determines the number of significant digits in the answer. For example, a distance of 34.28 m is travelled in a time of 4.8 s. The average speed is calculated by (34.28 m)/(4.8 s) = 7.141 666 m/s, rounded off to 7.1 m/s to two significant digits because the time of 4.8 s has only two significant digits.

Note: All quantities must have compatible units or prefixes before being used in calculations.

6.3 Exponential Notation and Scientific Notation

Exponential Notation

Exponential notation makes use of powers of ten to write large and small quantities and to convey the number of significant digits. The first part of the number is called the *coefficient,* and the power of ten is the *exponent.* The radius of Earth may be written in exponential notation to three significant digits as 638×10^4 m, 63.8×10^5 m, 6.38×10^6 m, or 0.638×10^7 m. The diameter of a typical atom may be expressed to one significant digit as 1×10^{-8} cm or 0.1×10^{-7} cm.

Scientific Notation

Any measurement that consists of a coefficient multiplied by a power of ten is expressed in exponential notation. Both 6.38×10^6 and 0.638×10^7 are in exponential notation. Scientific notation is a special kind of exponential notation. For a number to be in scientific notation, the coefficient must be greater than or equal to 1, and less than 10. This means that 6.38×10^6 is expressed in scientific notation and 0.638×10^7 is not.

Scientific notation enables us to show the correct number of significant digits. Remember that any zero to the right of the decimal point is significant. Therefore, if all four digits in the measurement 3400 J are significant, then it would be written in scientific notation as 3.400×10^3 J. However, if only two digits are significant, it would be as 3.4×10^3 J.

The results of all calculations should always be expressed in scientific notation, unless you are told otherwise. This involves moving the decimal point and changing the exponent until the coefficient is between 1 and 9. The exponent is decreased by one for each position the decimal point in the coefficient is moved to the right, and increased by one for each position the decimal point is moved to the left. For example,

a) $500 \times 10^4 = 5.00 \times 10^2 \times 10^4$
$$= 5.00 \times 10^{2+4}$$
$$= 5.00 \times 10^6$$

b) $0.068 \times 10^{-3} = 6.8 \times 10^{-2} \times 10^{-3}$
$$= 6.8 \times 10^{-2+(-3)}$$
$$= 6.8 \times 10^{-5}$$

Exponential Notation and Mathematical Operations

Multiplication

The product of exponential numbers is determined by multiplying the coefficients and adding the exponents. For example,

$(3.0 \times 10^2)(4.0 \times 10^{-6}) = (3.0 \times 4.0)(10^2 \times 10^{-6})$
$$= 12 \times 10^{2+(-6)}$$
$$= 12 \times 10^{-4}$$
$$= 1.2 \times 10^{-3}$$

Division

To divide numbers written in scientific notation, the coefficients are first divided, and then the exponent in the denominator is subtracted from the exponent in the numerator. For example,

$$\frac{3.3 \times 10^5}{6.6 \times 10^{-2}} = \frac{3.3}{6.6} \times \frac{10^5}{10^{-2}}$$
$$= 0.50 \times 10^{5-(-2)}$$
$$= 0.50 \times 10^{5+2}$$
$$= 0.50 \times 10^7$$
$$= 5.0 \times 10^6$$

Addition and Subtraction When the Exponents are the Same

When the exponents are the same, the coefficients are added or subtracted as in normal arithmetic. The exponent in the final answer remains the same. For example,

$$(2 \times 10^{-4}) + (3 \times 10^{-4}) - (1 \times 10^{-4})$$
$$= (2 + 3 - 1) \times 10^{-4}$$
$$= 4 \times 10^{-4}$$

Addition and Subtraction When the Exponents are Different

When the exponents are different, the numbers must first be converted to a form in which all exponents are the same. The decimal point is moved so that all have the same exponent as the largest number in the group. Then, the coefficients are added or subtracted accordingly. The exponent in the answer remains the same as the largest exponent. For example,

$$(1.00 \times 10^{-3}) - (2.00 \times 10^{-4}) + (400 \times 10^{-5})$$
$$= (1.00 \times 10^{-3}) - (0.200 \times 10^{-3}) + (4.00 \times 10^{-3})$$
$$= (1.00 - 0.200 + 4.00) \times 10^{-3}$$
$$= 4.80 \times 10^{-3}$$

6.4 Unit Conversions (Unit Factor Method)

Conversions are often necessary in both math and science problems. Whether you are working on a problem involving the metric system or converting moles to grams, the unit factor method is a useful tool.

The unit factor method is the sequential application of conversion factors expressed as fractions and arranged so that any dimensional unit appearing in both the numerator and denominator of any of the fractions can be cancelled out until only the desired set of dimensional units is obtained

Example 1: Convert a speed of 25 m/s to km/h.

The equivalent relationships are: 1000 m = 1 km, 60 s = 1 min, and 60 min = 1 h. Multiplying by unit factors and carefully analyzing the units results in

$$25 \, \frac{m}{s} \times \frac{1 \text{ km}}{1000 \text{ m}} \times \frac{60 \text{ s}}{1 \text{ min}} \times \frac{60 \text{ min}}{1 \text{ h}} = 90 \text{ km/h}$$

Example 2: 1 ng = 10^{-9} g, therefore,

$$\frac{\text{ng}}{10^{-9} \text{ g}} = 1 \text{ or } \frac{10^{-9} \text{ g}}{\text{ng}} = 1$$

This type of relation can be used to convert units from one to another.

Example 3: Convert 5.3 mL to μL.

Multiply by factors of 1 to remove the prefix "m" and to introduce "μ".

$$5.3 \text{ mL} \times \frac{10^{-3} \text{ L}}{\text{mL}} \times \frac{\mu\text{L}}{10^{-6} \text{ L}} = 5.3 \times 10^3 \, \mu\text{L}$$

mL "cancel" as do L, leaving the desired units of μL. Subtract the exponents for division:
$-3 - (-6) = 3$

This skill is also useful for drawing scale diagrams. For example, a force of 840 N is to be drawn at a scale of 1 cm = 50 N. The scale length, in centimetres, will be found thus,

$$840 \text{ N} \times \frac{1 \text{ cm}}{50 \text{ N}} = 16.8 \text{ cm}$$

6.5 Trigonometry for Solving Right Triangles

A right triangle is a special triangle with one right angle (90°). The side opposite the right angle is always the longest side and is called the hypotenuse. The other two sides are called the legs. There are several important relationships that allow us to solve right triangles as long as we know the lengths of any two sides, or the length of one side and the measure of one of the acute angles.

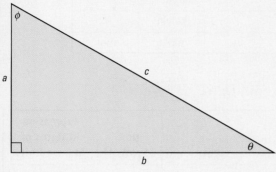

▲ **Figure SR 6.4**

In general, the relationships are:

Angle Sum
The angles of a plane triangle add to 180°; the acute angles of a plane right triangle add to 90°.

Pythagorean Theorem
The square of the length of the hypotenuse is equal to the sum of the squares of the length of each of the legs.

$$c^2 = a^2 + b^2$$

Sine Ratio
Sine of one of the acute angles is equal to the ratio of the length of the leg opposite the angle to the length of the hypotenuse.

$\sin \theta = \text{opp/hyp}$
$\sin \theta = a/c$

Cosine Ratio
Cosine of one of the acute angles is equal to the ratio of the length of the leg adjacent the angle to the length of the hypotenuse.

$\cos \theta = \text{adj/hyp}$
$\cos \theta = b/c$

Tangent Ratio
Tangent of one of the acute angles is equal to the ratio of the length of the leg opposite the angle to the length of the leg adjacent to the angle.

$\tan \theta = \text{opp/adj}$
$\tan \theta = a/b$

SR 7 Tables

7.1 SI Prefixes

Prefix	Symbol	Scientific Notation
yotta-	Y	10^{24}
zetta-	Z	10^{21}
exa-	E	10^{18}
peta-	P	10^{15}
tera-	T	10^{12}
giga-	G	10^{9}
mega-	M	10^{6}
kilo-	k	10^{3}
hecto-	h	10^{2}
deka-	da	10^{1}
deci-	d	10^{-1}
centi-	c	10^{-2}
milli-	m	10^{-3}
micro-	μ	10^{-6}
nano-	n	10^{-9}
pico-	p	10^{-12}
femto-	f	10^{-15}
atto-	a	10^{-18}
zepto-	z	10^{-21}
yocto-	y	10^{-24}

7.2 Fundamental Quantities and Base Units

Quantity	Quantity Symbol	Unit	Unit Symbol
Length or Distance	ℓ	metre	m
Mass	m	kilogram	kg
Time	t	second	s
Electrical current	I	ampere	A
Thermodynamic temperature	T	kelvin	K
Quantity of matter	n	mole	mol

7.3 Derived Quantities and Units

Quantity	Quantity Symbol	Unit	Unit Symbol	Expression in terms of SI Base Units
Area	A	square metre	m^2	—
Volume	V	cubic metre	m^3	—
Speed, Velocity	v	metre per second	m/s	—
Acceleration	a	metre per second squared	m/s^2	—
Frequency	f	hertz	Hz	s^{-1}
Force	F	newton	N	$kg \cdot m/s^2$
Momentum	p	kilogram·metre per second	$kg \cdot m/s$	—
Impulse	J	newton·second	N·s	$kg \cdot m/s$
Energy, Work	E, W	joule	J	$kg \cdot m^2/s^2$
Power	P	watt	W	$kg \cdot m^2/s^3$
Electric charge	Q	coulomb	C	A·s
Electric potential	V	volt	V	$kg \cdot m^2/s^3 \cdot A$
Electric resistance	R	ohm	Ω	$kg \cdot m^2/s^3 \cdot A^2$
Activity	A	becquerel	Bq	s^{-1}
Absorbed dose	D	gray	Gy	m^2/s^2
Equivalent absorbed dose	E	sievert	Sv	m^2/s^2

7.4 Numerical Constants

Name	Symbol	Value
Elementary unit of charge	e	1.60×10^{-19} C
Gravitational constant	G	6.67×10^{-11} N·m^2/kg^2
Coulomb's constant	k	8.99×10^9 N·m^2/C^2
Atomic mass unit	u	1.661×10^{-27} kg
Rest mass of an electron	m_e	9.109×10^{-31} kg
Rest mass of a proton	m_p	1.673×10^{-27} kg
Rest mass of a neutron	m_n	1.675×10^{-27} kg
Speed of light	c	3.00×10^8 m/s
Planck's constant	h	6.63×10^{-34} J·s
Rydberg's constant (hydrogen)	R_H	1.097×10^7 m^{-1}

7.5 Atomic Masses of Selected Isotopes

Isotope	Symbol	Atomic Mass (u)
hydrogen	H	1.007 825
deuterium	H (or D)	2.014 102
tritium	H (or T)	3.016 049
helium-3	He	3.016 029
helium-4	He	4.002 603
carbon-12	C	12 (by definition)
nitrogen-16	N	16.006 102
oxygen-16	O	15.994 915
neon-20	Ne	19.992 440
neon-22	Ne	21.991 385
sodium-22	Na	21.994 436
sodium-23	Na	22.989 769
magnesium-24	Mg	23.985 042
silicon-28	Si	27.976 927
potassium-39	K	38.963 707
potassium-40	K	39.963 998
calcium-40	Ca	39.962 591
iron-56	Fe	55.934 938
iron-58	Fe	57.933 276
cobalt-60	Co	59.933 817
nickel-60	Ni	59.930 786
bromine-87	Br	86.920 711
krypton-92	Kr	91.926 156
zirconium-94	Zr	93.906 315

Isotope	Symbol	Atomic Mass (u)
tellurium-112	Te	111.917 010
tellurium-139	Te	138.934 700
cesium-140	Cs	139.905 439
barium-141	Ba	140.914 412
neodymium-144	Nd	143.910 087
lanthanum-146	La	145.925 791
lead-204	Pb	203.973 044
lead-208	Pb	207.976 652
polonium-208	Po	207.981 246
lead-210	Pb	209.984 189
polonium-212	Po	211.988 868
polonium-214	Po	213.995 201
radon-222	Rn	222.017 578
radium-226	Ra	226.025 410
thorium-230	Th	230.033 134
thorium-234	Th	234.043 601
protactinium-234	Pa	234.043 308
uranium-235	U	235.043 930
uranium-238	U	238.050 788

Note: Measurements of the atomic mass of most stable isotopes are accurate to at least a millionth of an atomic mass unit. However, the masses of highly unstable isotopes are more difficult to measure. For such isotopes, measurement errors can be large enough that the last one or two digits listed for their masses are not known for certain.

GLOSSARY

Note: The number in parentheses at the end of each definition indicates the page number in this book where the term first appears.

A

acceleration vector quantity representing the change in velocity (magnitude and/or direction) per unit time; non-uniform motion (23)

> **acceleration due to gravity** constant acceleration of an object falling near Earth's surface (54)

activity (decay rate) number of nuclei in a sample that decay within a given time (812)

alpha radiation emission of a helium nucleus; symbol is α (797)

altitude elevation of the ground above sea level (221)

ampere flow of 1 C of charge past a point in a conductor in 1 s (602)

amplitude of oscillation maximum displacement of a body from its equilibrium position during oscillatory motion (355)

angle of diffraction angle formed between the perpendicular bisector and the straight line to a nodal or antinodal point on the interference pattern (689)

angle of incidence angle formed between the incident ray and the normal line (654)

angle of reflection angle formed between the reflected ray and the normal line (654)

angle of refraction angle formed between the normal line and the refracted ray (666)

antimatter form of matter that has a key property, such as charge, opposite to that of ordinary matter (804)

antinode point of interaction between waves on a spring or other medium at which only constructive interference occurs; in a standing wave, antinodes occur at intervals of $\frac{1}{2}\lambda$; in an interference pattern, antinodes occur at path difference intervals of whole wavelengths (417)

armature (rotor) fundamental component of a simple DC electric motor consisting of a rotating loop of conducting wire on a shaft (608)

artificial satellite artificially created object intended to orbit Earth or other celestial body to perform a variety of tasks; includes weather, communication, observation, science, broadcast, navigation, and military satellites (284)

at rest not moving; stationary (13)

atomic mass number number of nucleons in the nucleus, $Z + N$; symbol is A (790)

atomic mass unit exactly $\frac{1}{12}$ of the mass of the carbon-12 atom; symbol is u, where $1\ u = 1.660\ 539 \times 10^{-27}$ kg (791)

atomic number number of protons in a nucleus; symbol is Z (790)

axis of rotation imaginary line that passes through the centre of rotation perpendicular to circular motion (242)

axle shaft on which a wheel rotates (242)

B

ballistic pendulum type of pendulum used to determine the speed of bullets before electronic timing devices were invented (483)

baryon hadron with half-integer spin (842)

becquerel unit of activity equal to 1 decay per second; unit is Bq (812)

beta-negative decay nuclear decay involving emission of an electron; symbol is β^- (802)

beta-positive decay nuclear decay involving emission of a positron; symbol is β^+ (805)

beta radiation emission of a high-energy electron; symbol is β (797)

binding energy net energy required to liberate all of the protons and neutrons in a nucleus (793)

blackbody object that completely absorbs any light energy that falls on it (705)

blackbody radiation curve graph of the intensity of light emitted versus wavelength for an object of a given temperature (705)

Bohr radius radius of the smallest orbit in a hydrogen atom (774)

boson particle with integer spin (842)

bright fringe (antinodal line) region of constructive interference (686)

bubble chamber device that uses trails of bubbles in a superheated liquid to show the paths of charged particles (831)

C

capacitor two conductors, holding equal amounts of opposite charges, placed near one another without touching (642)

Cartesian method method commonly used to show direction for vector quantities in two dimensions; the positive x-axis is at 0° and angles are measured by moving counterclockwise about the origin (78)

cathode ray free electrons emitted by a negative electrode (754)

central maximum line of antinodes along the perpendicular bisector of the line joining the point sources (426)

centre of curvature (C) point in space representing the centre of the sphere from which a curved mirror was cut (657)

centre of mass point where the total mass of an object can be assumed to be concentrated (492)

centripetal acceleration acceleration acting toward the centre of a circle (244)

centripetal force force acting toward the centre of a circle causing an object to move in a circular path (244)

charge migration movement of electrons in a neutral object where one side of the object becomes positive and the other side becomes negative (520)

charge shift movement of electrons in an atom where one side of an atom becomes positive and the other side becomes negative (521)

charging by induction process of charging an object by first polarizing it by induction and then retaining the charge by grounding (521)

closed pipe (closed tube) pipe closed at one end; the longest wavelength that can resonate in a closed pipe is four times the length of the pipe (419)

closed-pipe (closed-tube) resonance if an antinode occurs at the open end of a pipe, a point of resonance (resulting from constructive interference) occurs at the open end of the pipe, and the sound appears to be amplified (419)

cloud chamber device that uses trails of droplets of condensed vapour to show the paths of charged particles (830)

collinear along the same straight line, either in the same or in opposite directions (71)

non-collinear not along the same straight line (80)

collision interaction between two objects involving an impulse with a large F_{net} and a very short Δt (469)

elastic collision collision in which the total kinetic energy of a system is conserved ($E_{k_i} = E_{k_f}$) (481)

inelastic collision collision in which the total kinetic energy of a system is not conserved ($E_{k_i} \neq E_{k_f}$) (483)

colour quantum property related to the strong nuclear force (848)

commutator fundamental component of a simple DC electric motor consisting of a mechanism for maintaining a properly polarized connection to the moving coil in a motor or generator (608)

components perpendicular parts (R_x and R_y) into which a vector can be separated (77)

Compton effect change in wavelength of the scattered X-ray photon (721)

Compton scattering scattering of an X ray by an electron (721)

conduction process of charging an object through the direct transfer of electrons when a charged object touches a neutral object (519)

conductor material in which electrons in the outermost regions of the atom are free to move (513)

conservative forces forces that act within systems but do not change

their mechanical energy; includes gravity and elastic forces (314)

non-conservative forces forces, such as friction, and forces applied from outside a system, that cause the energy of the system to change so that energy is not conserved (319)

converging lens lens that refracts rays travelling parallel to the principal axis inward to intersect at the principal focus (677)

converging mirror concave reflecting surface that causes parallel light rays to converge after being reflected (657)

coulomb SI unit for electric charge (C) (529)

Coulomb's law magnitude of the force of electrostatic attraction or repulsion ($|\vec{F}_e|$) is directly proportional to the product of the two charges q_1 and q_2 ($|\vec{F}_e| \propto q_1 q_2$) and inversely proportional to the square of the distance between their centres r (529)

crest region where the medium rises above the equilibrium position (394)

critical angle for any two media, the size of the incident angle for which the angle of refraction is 90° (672)

current quantity of charge that flows through a wire in a given unit of time (602)

cycle one complete back-and-forth motion or oscillation (249)

cyclotron particle accelerator Particle accelerator in which the magnetic field perpendicular to the paths of the charged particles makes them follow circular paths within two hollow semicircular electrodes. An alternating voltage accelerates the charged particles each time they cross the gap between the two electrodes. The radius of each particle's path increases with its speed, so the accelerated particles spiral toward the outer wall of the cyclotron. (841)

D

dark fringe (nodal line) region of destructive interference (686)

daughter element element produced by a decay process (799)

decay constant probability of a nucleus decaying in a given time; symbol is λ (811)

diffraction change in shape and direction of a wave front as a result of encountering a small opening or aperture in a barrier, or a corner (685)

diffraction grating sheet of glass or plastic etched with a large number of parallel lines; when light is incident on the grating, each line or slit acts as one individual light source (692)

diffuse (irregular) reflection behaviour describing parallel incident rays scattered in different directions when reflected from an irregular surface (653)

dispersion separation of white light into its components (675)

displacement straight line between initial and final positions; includes magnitude and direction (7)

distance length of the path taken to move from one position to another (7)

diverging lens lens that refracts rays travelling parallel to the principal axis outward to appear as though they have originated at a virtual principal focus (677)

diverging mirror convex reflecting surface that causes parallel light rays to spread out after being reflected (657)

diverging ray ray that spreads out as it moves away from the origin (397)

domain region of a material in which the magnetic fields of most of the atoms are aligned (589)

Doppler effect apparent change in frequency and wavelength of a wave that is perceived by an observer moving relative to the source of the wave (429)

drift tube particle accelerator particle accelerator in which alternating voltage accelerates charged particles through a series of electrodes shaped like open tubes; particles are always attracted to the next tube in the line (841)

dynamics branch of mechanics dealing with the cause of motion (126)

E

eccentricity degree to which an ellipse is elongated; number between 0 and 1, with 0 being a perfect circle and 1 being a parabola (269)

efficiency ratio of the energy output to the energy input of any system (324)

elastic potential energy energy resulting from an object being altered from its standard shape, without permanent deformation (300)

electric field lines lines drawn to represent the electric field; density of the lines represents the magnitude of the electric field (554)

electric potential (voltage) change in electric potential energy stored per unit charge; symbol is V (564)

electric potential difference change in electric potential experienced by a charge moving between two points in an electric field (565)

electric potential energy energy stored in a system of two charges a certain distance apart; change in electric potential energy equals work done to move a small charge ($\Delta E_p = W$) (561)

electromagnet magnet having its magnetic field produced by electric current flowing through a coil of wire (588)

electromagnetic radiation (EMR) radiant energy in the form of a wave produced by the acceleration of electrons or other charged particles; does not require a material medium; can travel through a vacuum (636)

electron volt change in energy of an electron when it moves through a potential difference of 1 V; unit is eV (564)

electrostatics study of electric charges at rest (513)

electroweak force fundamental force that combines the electromagnetic force and the weak nuclear force (848)

elementary unit of charge charge on a proton; symbol is e (762)

ellipse elongated circle; consists of two foci, a major, and a minor axis (269)

energy ability to do work (292)

energy level discrete and quantized amount of energy (773)

equilibrium position rest position or position of a medium from which the amplitude of a wave can be measured (394)

excited state any energy level higher than the ground state (775)

F

femto metric prefix meaning 10^{-15} (790)

fermion particle with half-integer spin (842)

ferromagnetic having magnetic properties, such as those of iron (589)

field three-dimensional region of influence surrounding an object (200)

　electric field three-dimensional region of electrostatic influence surrounding a charged object (641)

　gravitational field region of influence surrounding any object that has mass (200)

　magnetic field three-dimensional region of magnetic influence surrounding a magnet, in which other magnets or magnetic substances are affected by magnetic forces (584)

first order maximum line of antinodes resulting from a one-wavelength phase shift (427)

fission reaction in which a nucleus with $A > 120$ splits into smaller nuclei that have greater binding energy per nucleon (818)

focal length (f) distance from the vertex to the focal point, measured along the principal axis; related to the radius of curvature by $f = r/2$ (657)

force quantity measuring a push or a pull on an object; measured in newtons (127)

　action force force initiated by object A on object B (160)

　action-at-a-distance force force that acts even if the objects involved are not touching (200)

　applied force force exerted directly on an object by a person; symbol is $\vec{F}_{app}$ (130)

gravitational force attractive force between any two objects due to their masses; symbol is $\vec{F}_g$ (196)

　net force vector sum of two or more forces acting simultaneously on an object; symbol is $\vec{F}_{net}$ (131)

　normal force force on an object that is perpendicular to a common contact surface; symbol is $\vec{F}_N$ (130)

　reaction force force exerted by object B on object A (160)

　restoring force force acting opposite to the displacement to move an object back to its equilibrium position (353)

　strong nuclear force force that binds together the protons and neutrons in a nucleus (793)

　weak nuclear force fundamental force that acts on electrons and neutrinos (804)

forced frequency frequency at which an external force is applied to a resonating object (382)

Fraunhofer line dark line in the spectrum of the Sun (773)

free-body diagram vector diagram of an object in isolation showing all the forces acting on it (129)

free fall situation in which the only force acting on an object that has mass is the gravitational force (226)

frequency number of cycles per second measured in hertz (Hz) (249)

friction force that opposes either the motion of an object or the direction the object would be moving in if there were no friction; symbol is $\vec{F}_f$ (169)

fundamental forces basic forces of nature that physicists think underlie all interactions in the universe (194)

fundamental frequency lowest frequency produced by a particular instrument; corresponds to the standing wave having a single antinode, with a node at each end of the string (422)

fusion reaction in which two low-mass nuclei combine to form a single nucleus with $A < 60$; the resulting nucleus is more tightly bound (818)

G

gamma decay emission of a high-energy photon by a nucleus; symbol is γ (806)

gamma radiation emission of a high-energy photon; symbol is γ (797)

generator effect (electromagnetic induction) production of electricity by magnetism (611)

gluon mediating particle for the strong nuclear force (838)

grand unified theory quantum theory unifying the electromagnetic, strong nuclear, and weak nuclear forces (849)

gravimeter sensitive instrument used to detect small variations in the magnitude of the gravitational field strength on Earth's surface (222)

gravitational field strength gravitational force per unit mass at a specific location (201)

gravitational mass mass measurement based on comparing the known weight of one object to the unknown weight of another object (199)

gravitational potential energy energy of an object due to its position above the surface of Earth (295)

graviton hypothetical mediating particle for the gravitational force (838)

gravity assist use of the gravitational force exerted by celestial bodies to reduce interplanetary travel times (214)

gray dose of ionizing radiation that delivers 1 J of energy to each kilogram of material absorbing the radiation; unit is Gy (809)

ground state lowest possible energy level (774)

grounding process of transferring charge to and from Earth (521)

H

hadron subatomic particle that interacts via the strong nuclear force (842)

half-life time it takes for half of the radioactive nuclei in a sample to decay (812)

Heisenberg's uncertainty principle it is impossible to know both the position and momentum of a

particle with unlimited precision at the same time (735)

high tide highest level of ocean water that occurs near Earth's coastlines (211)

Hooke's Law relationship where the stretch produced by a force applied to a spring is proportional to the magnitude of the force (299)

horsepower (hp) unit used to identify the power output of motors, mainly in the automotive industry (324)

Huygens' Principle model of wave theory, which predicted the motion of a wave front as being many small point sources propagating outward in a concentric circle at the same speed as the wave itself (684)

I

image attitude orientation characteristic of an image, whether erect or inverted (656)

image position where the image forms relative to the surface of the mirror (656)

image type distinction between real and virtual images (656)

real image image from which light rays come; can be formed on a diffusely reflecting surface or screen (654)

virtual image image from which light rays appear to come; cannot be formed on a non-reflective surface or screen (654)

impulse product of the net force on an object and the time interval during an interaction (457)

incandescent glowing with heat (704)

induction movement of charge caused by an external charged object (520)

inertia property of an object that resists acceleration (138)

inertial mass mass measurement based on the ratio of a known net force on an object to the acceleration of the object (148)

insulator material in which the electrons are tightly bound to the nucleus and are not free to move within the substance (513)

interference effect of two pulses (or two waves) crossing within a

medium; the medium takes on a shape that is different from the shape of either pulse alone (411)

constructive interference overlap of pulses to create a pulse of greater amplitude (412)

destructive interference overlap of pulses to create a pulse of lesser amplitude (412)

interference fringes fixed interference pattern of light and dark bands (686)

interference pattern pattern of maxima and minima resulting from the interaction of waves, as crests and troughs overlap while the waves move through each other (425)

ionization energy energy required to remove an electron from an atom (775)

isotopes atoms that have the same number of protons, but different numbers of neutrons (791)

K

kinematics branch of physics that describes motion (6)

kinetic energy energy due to the motion of an object; symbol is E_k (302)

kinetic friction force exerted on an object in motion that opposes the motion of the object as it slides on another object; symbol is $\vec{F}_{f_{kinetic}}$ (176)

coefficient of kinetic friction proportionality constant relating $\vec{F}_{f_{kinetic}}$ and F_N (183)

L

latitude angular distance north or south of the equator (221)

law of conservation of charge net charge of an isolated system is conserved (517)

law of conservation of energy within an isolated system, energy may be transferred from one object to another or transformed from one form to another, but it cannot be increased nor decreased (312)

law of conservation of momentum momentum of an isolated system is constant (473)

law of magnetism like magnetic ends repel and unlike ends attract each other

law of reflection angle of reflection is equal to the angle of incidence and is in the same plane (654)

Lenz's law direction of a magnetically induced current is such as to oppose the cause of the current (618)

lepton subatomic particle that does not interact via the strong nuclear force (842)

low tide lowest level of ocean water that occurs near Earth's coastlines (211)

M

magnification relationship of the size of the image to the size of the object (656)

mass defect difference between the sum of the masses of the separate nucleons and the mass of the nucleus; symbol is Δm (794)

maximum (line of antinodes) line of points linking antinodes that occur as the result of constructive interference between waves (426)

Maxwell's Equations series of equations that summarized the relationships between electricity and magnetism, and predicted the existence of electromagnetic waves and their propagation through space (642)

mechanical energy sum of potential and kinetic energies; symbol is E_m (306)

mechanical resonance increase in amplitude of oscillation of a system as a result of a periodic force whose frequency is equal or very close to the resonant frequency of the system (382)

mechanics study of kinematics, statics, and dynamics (306)

medium material, for example, air or water through which waves travel; the medium does not travel with the wave (394)

meson hadron with integer spin (842)

minimum (nodal line) line of points linking nodes that occur as the result of destructive interference between waves (426)

mirror equation equation relating the focal length of a curved mirror to the image and object distances (662)

momentum product of the mass of an object and its velocity (449)

momentum (of a system) sum of the momenta of all the objects in the system (470)

motor effect force deflecting force acting on a charged particle moving in a magnetic field (593)

muon unstable subatomic particle having many of the properties of an electron but a mass 207 times greater (842)

N

natural satellite naturally formed body that revolves around a planet (moon) (273)

navigator method method commonly used to show direction for vector quantities in two dimensions; uses compass bearings north [N], south [S], east [E], and west [W] to identify vector directions (78)

net charge sum of all electric charges in the system (517)

neutrino extremely small neutral subatomic particle; symbol is v (804)

neutron neutral particle found in nuclei (790)

neutron number number of neutrons in the nucleus; symbol is N (790)

Newton's first law of motion an object will continue either being at rest or moving at constant velocity unless acted upon by an external non-zero net force (139)

Newton's law of universal gravitation Any two objects, A and B, in the universe exert gravitational forces of equal magnitude but opposite direction on each other. The forces are directed along the line joining the centres of both objects. (204)

Newton's second law of motion when an external non-zero net force acts on an object, the object accelerates in the direction of the net force; the magnitude of the acceleration is directly proportional to the magnitude of the net force and inversely proportional to the mass of the object (148)

Newton's third law of motion if object A exerts a force on object B, then B exerts a force on A that is equal in magnitude and opposite in direction (161)

node (nodal point) point on a spring or other medium at which only destructive interference occurs; in a standing wave, a point that never vibrates between supercrests and supertroughs; in a standing wave, nodes occur at intervals of $\frac{1}{2}\lambda$; in an interference pattern, nodes occur at path difference intervals of $\frac{1}{2}\lambda$ (417)

normal line imaginary line drawn perpendicular to the reflecting surface (652)

nucleon proton or neutron (790)

nucleosynthesis formation of elements by the fusion of lighter elements (823)

O

open pipe (open tube) pipe opened at both ends; the longest wavelength that can resonate in an open pipe is twice the length of the pipe (424)

optical fibre central core of glass with a refractive index of approximately 1.5, surrounded by a cladding material of a slightly lower refractive index (671)

orbital probability distribution of an electron in an atom (783)

orbital period time required for a planet to make one full orbit; may be measured in Earth days (271)

orbital perturbation irregularity or disturbance in the predicted orbit of a planet (282)

orbital radius distance between the centre of the ellipse and the planet; average orbital radius corresponds to the semi-major axis (269)

origin reference point (6)

oscillation repetitive back-and-forth motion (344)

oscillatory motion motion in which the period of each cycle is constant (344)

overtone any frequency of vibration of a string that may exist simultaneously with the fundamental frequency (423)

P

parent element original element in a decay process (799)

particle discrete unit of matter having mass, momentum, and the ability to carry an electric charge (639)

alpha particle two protons and two neutrons bound together to form a stable particle (497)

beta particle electron emitted by a nucleus; symbol is β (802)

fundamental particle particle that cannot be divided into smaller particles; an elementary particle (836)

mediating particle virtual particle that carries one of the fundamental forces (837)

strange particle particle that interacts primarily via the strong nuclear force yet decays only via the weak nuclear force (845)

virtual particle particle that exists for such a short time that it is not detectable (837)

particle model describes EMR as a stream of tiny particles radiating outward from a source (639)

path length distance between a point source and a chosen point in space (688)

difference in path length difference between two path lengths, each measured from a different origin and extending to a common point in space (688)

period time required for an object to make one complete oscillation (cycle); measured in s/cycle (249)

phase shift result of waves from one source having to travel farther to reach a particular point in the interference pattern than waves from another source (426)

photoelectric effect emission of electrons when a metal is illuminated by short wavelengths of light (712)

photoelectron electron emitted from a metal because of the photoelectric effect (712)

photon (from the Greek word meaning "light") quantum of light; discrete packet of energy associated with an electromagnetic field (640)

pion unstable subatomic particle with a mass roughly 270 times that of an electron (842)

Planck's formula light comes in quanta of energy that can be calculated using the equation $E = nhf$ (705)

plane mirror smooth, flat, reflecting surface (654)

plane polarized light light resulting from polarization, in which only one plane of the electric field is allowed to pass through a filter (696)

planetary model atomic model that has electrons orbiting a nucleus (768)

plasma highly ionized gas containing nearly equal numbers of free electrons and positive ions (522)

point of incidence point at which the incident ray contacts a polished, reflecting surface and is reflected from the surface as the reflected ray (652)

point source single point of disturbance that generates a circular wave (395)

polarization production of a state in which the plane of the electric field for each electromagnetic wave occurs only in one direction (696)

polarizing filter filter that allows only one plane of the electric field to pass through it; plane polarized EMR emerges (696)

position straight-line distance between the origin and an object's location; includes magnitude and direction (6)

positron antielectron; positively charged particle with its other properties the same as those of an electron; symbol is e^+ or $^0_1\beta$ (804)

potential energy energy that is stored and held in readiness; includes gravitational and elastic potential energies; symbol is E_p (807)

power rate of doing work (324)

primary cosmic rays high-energy particles that flow from space into Earth's atmosphere (841)

principal axis (PA) imaginary line drawn through the vertex, perpendicular to the surface of the curved mirror at this point (657)

principal focal point (F) point where light rays parallel to and close to the principal axis converge, or appear to diverge from, after being reflected (657)

principal quantum number quantum number that determines the size and energy of an orbit (774)

principle of superposition displacement of the combined pulse at each point of interference is the sum of the displacements of the individual pulses (412)

projectile object released or thrown into the air (54)

projectile motion motion in a vertical plane (54)

proton positively charged particle found in all nuclei (790)

proton–proton chain fusion process in which four hydrogen nuclei combine to form a helium nucleus (821)

pulse disturbance of short duration in a medium; usually seen as the crest or trough of a wave (401)

compression pulse region where the coils of a spring are more tightly compressed (404)

rarefaction pulse region where the coils of a spring are more widely spaced (404)

transverse pulse pulse in which the coils of the spring move at right angles to the direction of the pulse's motion (401)

Q

quanta discrete units of energy (638)

quantized limited to whole multiples of a basic amount (quantum) (705)

quantum smallest amount or "bundle" of energy that a wavelength of light can possess (pl. quanta) (705)

quantum chromodynamics quantum field theory that describes the strong nuclear force in terms of quantum colour (848)

quantum electrodynamics quantum field theory dealing with the interactions of electromagnetic fields, charged particles, and photons (838)

quantum field theory field theory developed using both quantum mechanics and relativity theory (837)

quantum indeterminacy probability of finding a particle at a particular location in a double-slit interference pattern (740)

quantum model combination of the particle and wave models; describes light and all other EMR as discrete bundles of energy, each of which is a massless particle that has wavelike characteristics (640)

quark any of the group of fundamental particles in hadrons (845)

R

radioactive decay series process of successive decays in which a radioactive nucleus decays into a daughter nucleus that is itself radioactive, and the daughter nucleus decays into another unstable nucleus until a stable nucleus is created (807)

radioisotope isotope that is radioactive (808)

radius of curvature (r) distance from the centre of curvature to the mirror surface (657)

range distance a projectile travels horizontally over level ground (105)

ray line that indicates only the direction of motion of the wave front at any point where the ray and the wave front intersect (397)

ray diagram diagram showing the result of a light ray interacting with a surface (653)

recomposition (of the spectrum) production of white light by a combination of light of all colours of the spectrum (674)

rectilinear propagation movement of light in straight lines through a uniform medium (653)

reference point arbitrarily chosen point from which distances are measured (297)

refracted ray path of a light ray after it has changed direction at an interface, due to a change in its speed (664)

refraction change in the direction of a light wave due to a change in its speed as it passes from one medium to another (666)

refractive index ratio comparing the speed of light in a vacuum to the measured speed of light in the medium (666)

relative biological effectiveness (RBE) factor indicating how much a particular type of radiation affects the human body (809)

relative motion motion measured with respect to an observer (91)

resonance increase in the amplitude of a wave due to a transfer of energy in phase with the natural frequency of the wave (418)

resonant frequencies natural frequencies of vibration of an object that will produce a standing wave pattern; at a resonant frequency, energy added is in phase with existing oscillations (418)

resultant vector sum of a series of vectors; drawn from the tail of the first vector to the tip of the last vector (71)

revolution one complete cycle for an object moving in a circular path (249)

rpm revolutions per minute; imperial unit used to measure frequency (249)

S

scalar quantity measurement that has magnitude only (6)

secondary cosmic rays shower of particles created by collisions between primary cosmic rays and atoms in the atmosphere (841)

semiconductor material that lies in the middle, between a good conductor and a good insulator; because of its nature, a semiconductor is a good conductor in certain situations, and a good insulator in other situations (514)

sievert absorbed dose of ionizing radiation that has the same effect on a person as 1 Gy of photon radiation, such as X rays or gamma rays; absorbed dose in sieverts is equal to the dose in grays multiplied by the relative biological effectiveness (RBE); unit is Sv (809)

simple harmonic motion (SHM) oscillatory motion where the restoring force is proportional to the displacement of the mass (355)

simple harmonic oscillator object that moves with simple harmonic motion (355)

Snell's Law For any angle of incidence greater than zero, the ratio $\sin \theta_i / \sin \theta_r$ is a constant for any light ray passing through the boundary between two media. (667)

solenoid electromagnet that operates a mechanical device (589)

sound barrier term applied to the increase in aerodynamic resistance as an aircraft approaches the speed of sound (433)

source charge charge that produces an electric field (546)

spectrometer device for measuring the wavelengths of light in a spectrum (773)

spectroscopy study of the light emitted and absorbed by different materials (771)

spectrum bands of colours making up white light; in order: red, orange, yellow, green, blue, and violet (675)

> **absorption line spectrum** pattern of dark lines produced when light passes through a gas at low pressure (772)
>
> **electromagnetic spectrum** all types of EMR considered in terms of frequency, wavelength, or energy (637)
>
> **emission line spectrum** pattern of bright lines produced by a hot gas at low pressure (772)

specular (regular) reflection behaviour describing parallel incident rays reflected from a flat, smooth, reflecting surface as parallel reflected rays (653)

spin quantum property resembling rotational angular momentum (842)

spring constant constant of proportionality k which appears in Hooke's Law for springs; represents the slope of the line and is measured in units of force per unit length; amount of stiffness of a spring (299)

standard model current theory describing the nature of matter and the fundamental forces (848)

static friction force exerted on an object at rest that prevents it from sliding on another object; symbol is $\vec{F}_{f_{static}}$ (171)

> **coefficient of static friction** proportionality constant relating $(F_{f_{static}})_{max}$ and F_N (182)

stationary state stable state with a fixed energy level (773)

stator fundamental component of a simple DC electric motor consisting of a frame with a coil or permanent magnet to provide a magnetic field (608)

stopping potential potential difference for which the kinetic energy of a photoelectron equals the work needed to move through a potential difference V (716)

string theory theory that treats particles as quantized vibrations of extremely small strings of mass-energy (849)

superconductor conductor that has no measurable resistance at very low temperatures (515)

supernova sudden, extremely powerful explosion of a massive star (823)

synchrotron particle accelerator particle accelerator in which an advanced type of cyclotron increases the strength of the magnetic field as the particles' energy increases, so that the particles travel in a circle rather than spiralling outward (841)

system two or more objects that interact with each other (470)

    isolated system (in the context of energy) group of objects assumed to be isolated from all other objects in the universe (311)

    isolated system (in the context of momentum) when mass of a system is constant and no external net force acts on the system (470)

    non-isolated system system in which there is an energy exchange with the surroundings (320)

T

tangent straight line that touches a curved-line graph at only one point (24)

tension (in a rope) magnitude of a force $\vec{F}_\mathrm{T}$ exerted by a rope on an object at the point where the rope is attached to the object (132)

test charge charge with a magnitude small enough that it does not disturb the charge on the source charge and thus change its electric field (546)

thin lens equation equation that relates object distance, image distance, and focal length of a curved lens (680)

threshold frequency minimum frequency that a photon can have to

cause photoemission from a metal; symbol is f_0 (712)

torsion balance device used to measure very small forces (205)

total internal reflection reflection of all incident light back into an optically more dense medium due to inability to refract beyond the maximum angle of 90° (672)

trajectory parabolic path or motion of a projectile (103)

transmute change into a different element (798)

trough region where the medium is lower than the equilibrium position (394)

tuning (a musical instrument) changing the tension in the string of a musical instrument (424)

U

uniform circular motion motion in a circular path at a constant speed (242)

uniform motion constant velocity (motion or rest) (13)

    non-uniform motion acceleration (23)

uniformly accelerated motion constant change in velocity per unit time (25)

universal gravitational constant constant in Newton's law of universal gravitation that is equal to $6.67 \times 10^{-11} \ \mathrm{N \cdot m^2/kg^2}$; symbol is G (204)

universal wave equation relationship between the speed, frequency, and wavelength of a wave: $v = f\lambda$ (408)

V

Van de Graaff particle accelerator particle accelerator in which a moving belt transfers charge to a hollow, conductive sphere, building up a large potential difference that propels ions through an accelerator chamber (841)

vector quantity measurement that has both magnitude and direction (6)

velocity rate of change in position; includes magnitude (speed) and direction (12)

    air velocity object's velocity relative to still air (92)

    ground velocity velocity relative to an observer on the ground (92)

    instantaneous velocity moment-to-moment measure of an object's velocity (24)

    wind velocity velocity of the wind relative to the ground (92)

vertex (V) geometric centre of the curved mirror surface (657)

W

wave disturbance that moves outward from its point of origin transferring energy through a medium by means of vibrations (394)

    bow wave V-shaped wave produced as a boat moves through water or an airplane moves through the atmosphere (433)

    electromagnetic wave periodic variation in perpendicular electric and magnetic fields, propagating at right angles to both fields (643)

    incident wave wave front moving out from the point of origin toward a barrier (395)

    longitudinal wave wave with the motion of the medium being parallel to the motion of the wave (401)

    reflected wave wave front moving away from a barrier (395)

    shock wave strong compression wave produced as an aircraft exceeds the speed of sound (433)

    standing wave condition in a spring or other medium in which a wave seems to oscillate around stationary points called nodes; wavelength of a standing wave is the distance between alternate nodes or alternate antinodes (417)

    transverse wave wave with the motion of the medium being perpendicular to the motion of the wave (401)

wave amplitude distance from the equilibrium position to the top of a crest or the bottom of a trough (395)

wave front imaginary line that joins all points reached by the wave at the same instant (395)

wave model describes EMR as a stream of transverse waves radiating outward from a source (639)

wave–particle duality light has both wave-like and particle-like properties (726)

wave train series of waves forming a continuous series of crests and troughs (395)

wavelength distance between two points on a wave that have identical status; usually measured from crest to crest or from trough to trough (395)

waves in phase occurs when crests or troughs from two waves occupy the same point in the medium; produces constructive interference (395)

waves out of phase occurs when a crest from one wave occupies the same point in the medium as a trough from a second wave; produces destructive interference (416)

weight gravitational force exerted on an object by a celestial body; symbol is $\vec{F}_g$ (198)

  apparent weight negative of the normal force acting on an object; symbol is $\vec{w}$ (224)

  true weight gravitational force acting on an object that has mass (222)

  true weightlessness situation in which $\vec{w} = 0$ for an object and $\vec{F}_g = 0$ on the object (228)

work measure of the amount of energy transferred when a force acts over a given displacement; calculated as the product of the magnitude of applied force and the displacement of the object in the direction of the force (293)

work–energy theorem work done on a system is equal to the sum of the changes in the potential and kinetic energies of the system (307)

work function minimum energy that a photon can have to cause photoemission from a metal; specific for every metal; symbol is W (713)

page 10, 1.1 Check and Reflect

4. **(e)** 13.0 m [right]

5. 45.0 km [W]

6. Distance = 11.0 m;
   Displacement = 5.0 m [right]

7. $\Delta \vec{d}_{groom}$ = 0.50 m [right]

   $\Delta \vec{d}_{best\ man}$ = 0.75 m [left]

   $\Delta \vec{d}_{maid\ of\ honour}$ = 1.25 m [right]

   $\Delta \vec{d}_{flower\ girl}$ = 1.50 m [left]

page 20, 1.2 Check and Reflect

3. **(i)** D   **(ii)** C   **(iii)** A   **(iv)** B

5. 7 km [W]

8. 2.5 m farther after 5.0 s

11. Time = 13 s; Distance = 26 m

12. Time = 20 s; Displacement = 45 m [N]

13. **(1)** 22 s   **(2)** 31 s   **(3)** 14 s

page 30, 1.3 Check and Reflect

1. **(a)** 5.6 m/s² [forward]
   (b) 2.8 m/s² [forward]
   (c) 0.30 m/s² [forward]

3. **(i)** A   **(ii)** B   **(iii)** C   **(iv)** D

4.

Time (s)	Velocity (m/s [forward])
0.0	1
2.0	4
4.0	8
6.0	0
8.0	−9

page 44, 1.4 Check and Reflect

7. 75 m/s [E]

8. 36 m [up]

11. 15 m/s² [E]

16. Acceleration = 1.25 m/s² [W];
    Time = 8.00 s

17. **(a)** 81 km/h [N]

18. 0.333 m/s² [right]

page 53, 1.5 Check and Reflect

1. −0.24 m/s² [forward]

2. 11 s

3. 20 cm [forward]

4. 0.064 m/s² [N]

5. 75.0 m/s² [W]

6. 19.6 m

7. 0.41 m/s²

8. 59.9 m

9. 3.52 m/s² [S]

10. 9.30 m/s²

11. 23.3 m/s²

12. 75 m [right]

13. 1.67×10^5 m/s² [forward]

14. 9.5 m

page 63, 1.6 Check and Reflect

3. 1.61 m/s² [down]

4. 2.8 m

5. **(1)** 33 m   **(2)** 26 m/s [down]

6. 0.365 s

7. 1.5 m

8. 47.9 m

9. 72.3 m

10. 1.6 s

11. 6.22 s

12. 9.27 m

13. 1.4 s

14. 2.4 m

15. 159 m, 5.69 s

16. 5.4 m/s [68°]

17. **(a)** 4.0 m/s² [up]
    (b) 5.0×10^3 m [up]
    (d) 7.0×10^3 m

18. 9.68 m/s [down]

page 65, Chapter 1 Review

3. **(a)** 1.0 m/s [forward]
   (b) 0.033 m/s [left]
   (c) 1.7 m/s [forward]

4. 27.0 km [W]

5. 42 min

6. **(1)** 3.75 m/s
   (2) −25.0 m [right] or 25.0 m [left]
   (3) 1.25 m/s [left]

8. 2.8 s

9. 7.0 s

10. 0 m/s

11. 1.5 m/s [W]

13. 60 m [N]

14. 7.2×10^7 m/s²

15. 18 km [forward]

16. 34.5 km

17. 72 times faster

18. 1.1×10^2 km/h or 31 m/s

19. **(1)** 22.5 m/s [downhill]
    (2) 2.81 m/s² [downhill]

20. **(1)** 1.3 m/s² [N]
    (2) 10 m/s [N]

21. 1.9×10^2 s

22. **(1)** 16.0 m/s [S]
    (2) 22.0 m/s [S]
    (3) 0.267 m/s² [S]

23. 35 m/s

24. **(1)** 12.1 s   **(2)** 39 m/s

26. **(1)** −20 km or 20 km [left]   **(2)** 0 m/s²

27. 9.03 s

28. 0.467 s

29. 0.298 m/s²

30. 25 km/h [E]

32. 11.2 m/s² [W]

33. 6.8 s

34. 1.17 s

35. 12 m

36. 9.29 m

37. 1.32 s

38. **(1)** 15.2 m   **(2)** 17.3 m/s

39. **(1)** 2.0 s   **(2)** 20 m/s

page 75, 2.1 Check and Reflect

3. 24 cm

4. 20 km

5. 2080 km

6. **(b)** 100 yards   **(c)** 1000 yards

7. 100 km [S], 150 km [S],
   and 200 km [S]

9. **(1)** 36.0 m   **(2)** 8.0 m [down]

page 90, 2.2 Check and Reflect

4. d_y = −48 cm; d_x = −28 cm

5. **(a)** Distance = 2.95 km;
       Displacement = 1.45 km [270°]
   (b) Distance = 11.5 km;
       Displacement = 3.4 km
       [27° N of W]
   (c) Distance = 522 m;
       Displacement = 522 m
       [16.7° E of N]

6. 2.0 km [45° S of E]

7. 178 m/s

8. 2.65 km [48° S of E]

9. Total displacement = 2.8 km
   [49° N of W];
   Average velocity = 3.0 km/h
   [49° N of W]

10. **(a)** 27 m in both the x and y directions
    (b) 54 m

11. 10.6 m [293°]

page 101, 2.3 Check and Reflect

5. **(a)** 79.0 s   **(b)** 47 m; 79.0 s

6. **(a)** 233 km/h [N]
   (b) 297 km/h [N]
   (c) 267 km/h [83.1° N of W]

7. 400 s

8. 8.4×10^2 km/h [3.0° N of E]

9. Ground velocity = 2.8 m/s
   [35° S of E]; Time = 19 min

10. 674 km/h [6.0° S of W]

11. **(a)** 4.7 m/s [32° W of N]   **(b)** 200 s

page 112, 2.4 Check and Reflect

5. 2.0 m

6. Initial horizontal velocity
   component = 22.1 m/s;
   Initial vertical velocity
   component = 15.5 m/s;
   Up 12.2 m; Out 69.8 m

7. 7.22 m/s

8. 11 m/s

9. **(a)** 10.0 s   **(b)** 543 m
  (c) 20.5 s   **(d)** 1.41 km
  (e) Horizontal component = 68.8 m/s;
     Vertical component = 103 m/s

page 114, Chapter 2 Review

2. x component $= -41$ m;
   y component $= -37$ m

3. 0

7. **(a)** $\Delta \vec{d} = 5.0$ m [N]
  (b) $\Delta \vec{d} = 140$ cm [E]
  (c) $\Delta \vec{d} = 2.5$ km [backward]
  (d) $\Delta \vec{d} = 80.0$ km [right]

8. 0

9. 3.9×10^2 km

10. Range = 86.3 m;
   Maximum height = 30.8 m

11. 2.23×10^2 m horizontally; 2.83 s

12. **(a)** 6.4 m/s [51° E of N]
  (b) 30 s

13. **(a)** 29 m/s   **(b)** 23 m
  (c) 7.5 m/s

14. 7.4 m/s [58°]

15. **(a)** 30° W of N   **(b)** 3.5 m/s
  (c) 1.4×10^2 s

16. 1.82 m

17. 39 s

18. 2.2 s

19. **(a)** 17° S of W   **(b)** 95 km/h

20. 42.2°

21. 5.0 m

22. 60.96 m

23. **(a)** 120 km/h   **(b)** east

24. 2.92 s; Distance = 59.9 m;
   Maximum height = 10.5 m

25. 39.8°

26. **(a)** 36 s   **(b)** 1.5 km

page 118, Unit I Review

3. **(a)** 0 m; 5.0 m
  (b) −15.0 m/s; −5.47 m/s

5. 9.8 km [30° S of E]

6. 2.70 m/s [W]

8. 3.0 s; Distance = 78 m horizontally;
   Maximum height = 11 m

13. 30 m/s

14. 32 km/h

16. **(a)** 30 m/s [90°]   **(b)** 40 m/s [90°]

17. 12.1 km

18. 0.944 h

19. 5.6 m/s

20. 9.56 m/s^2

21. 8.1×10^2 km/h [3.6° W of S]

22. 70.4 m/s^2

23. 2.2 s

24. 58 m

25. **(a)** 52 s   **(b)** 0.032 m/s^2

26. 13.5 m [forward]

27. 63 m

28. 99 km/h [W]

29. 1.5×10^2 m

30. 1.2 m/s [210°]; 4.4 m/s [210°];
   6.7 m/s [210°]

31. 1.1×10^2 km/h [6.5° N of E]

32. 13.2 m/s^2

33. 375 m [N]

35. 1.9 m

36. **(a)** 707 m [45°]   **(b)** 1600 m

37. 1.56 m/s [N]

38. 320 m [51.3° S of E]

40. 5.98 m/s^2

41. **(a)** 14.4 m/s [down]   **(b)** 10.6 m

42. **(a)** 347 m
  (b) 375 m
  (c) 82.6 m/s [down]

43. 13 m/s [30°]

page 136, 3.1 Check and Reflect

3. **(b)** 300 N [forward]

4. **(a)** 0°   **(b)** 180°

5. 1.47×10^2 N [13.1°]

6. 42 N [153°]

7. $\vec{F}_{T_1} = 1.5 \times 10^2$ N [125°],
   $\vec{F}_{T_2} = 1.5 \times 10^2$ N [55.0°]

page 139, 3.2 Concept Check

$\vec{v} = 17$ km/s [toward interstellar space]

page 146, 3.3 Concept Check

$\vec{F}_{net} = \vec{F}_{app}$ if $\vec{F}_f = 0$

page 148, 3.3 Concept Check

(a) a **(b)** a **(c)** $\left(\dfrac{1}{16}\right)a$ **(d)** 0

page 158, 3.3 Check and Reflect

5. **(a)** 26 kg   **(b)** 15 m/s^2 [up]

6. 0.11 m/s^2 [in direction of wind]

7. **(a)** 75 N [97°]   **(b)** 37 m/s^2 [97°]

8. 0.75 m/s^2 [right]

9. **(a)** (4.0-kg block) 1.3 m/s^2
   [toward pulley], (2.0-kg block)
   1.3 m/s^2 [down]
  (b) 17 N

page 168, 3.4 Check and Reflect

7. 10 N, 10 N [toward spring scale]

8. **(a)** $\vec{F}_{X \text{ on } Y} = 12$ N [right],
   $\vec{F}_{Y \text{ on } X} = 12$ N [left]
  (b) $\vec{F}_{X \text{ on } Y} = 12$ N [right],
   $\vec{F}_{Y \text{ on } X} = 12$ N [left]

page 178, 3.5 Concept Check

90°

page 190, 3.5 Check and Reflect

4. 2 N [backward]

5. 0.40

6. 2×10^3 N [backward]

7. 24°

9. 1.2 m/s^2 [uphill]

10. 16 m

11. 1.9 s

page 192, Chapter 3 Review

1. 5.00×10^{-2} m/s^2 [E]

3. 1850 N [W]

5. **(a)** 42 N [along rope connecting
   foot to pulley]

6. 1.2×10^3 N [forward]

7. $(\vec{L})$ 3.7×10^6 N, $(\vec{R})$ 3.3×10^6 N

8. 7.5 N [backward]

9. **(a)** 3.4×10^2 N
  (b) 1.4×10^3 N [forward]
  (c) 3.4×10^2 N [backward]

10. **(a)** $\vec{F}_{net_A} = 36$ N [W], $\vec{F}_{net_B} = 21$ N [E]
  (b) (curler A) 0.71 m/s^2 [W],
   (curler B) 0.26 m/s^2 [E]

11. 0.38

12. 0.423

13. **(a)** 9.8×10^2 N
  (b) **(i)** (60 kg) 2.0 m/s^2 [down],
     (40 kg) 2.0 m/s^2 [up]
   (ii) 4.7×10^2 N
  (c) 9.4×10^2 N

14. 7.3×10^2 kg

15. 2×10^3 kg

17. **(a)** dry asphalt   **(b)** either surface
  (c) dry concrete   **(d)** dry concrete

18. **(a)** 6.9 m/s^2 [backward]
  (b) 1.2 s

page 201, 4.1 Concept Check

(a) $16g$ **(b)** $\left(\dfrac{1}{4}\right)g$ **(c)** $\left(\dfrac{1}{2}\right)g$ **(d)** $2g$

page 202, 4.1 Check and Reflect

9. **(b)** 9.80 N/kg   **(c)** g_{Banff}

page 205, 4.2 Concept Check

(a) $4F_g$ **(b)** $4F_g$ **(c)** $\left(\dfrac{1}{16}\right)F_g$

page 215, 4.2 Check and Reflect

3. **(a)** $\left(\dfrac{1}{4}\right)F_g$ **(b)** $\left(\dfrac{1}{2}\right)F_g$

4. **(a)** **(i)** 162 N   **(ii)** 978 N

5. **(b)** (Deimos) 1.5×10^{14} N,
   (Phobos) 5.3×10^{15} N

6. **(a)** 132 N [toward Earth's centre]
  (b) about 13.4 times greater in
   magnitude

page 229, 4.3 Check and Reflect

5. 2.4 N/kg [toward Earth's centre]

6. **(b)** **(i)** 1.6 N/kg   **(ii)** 0.72 N/kg
   (iii) 0.40 N/kg
  (c) $4r_{Moon}$

7. 9.8 N/kg

8. 540 N [down]

9. **(b)** $(\vec{F}_g)$ 4.9×10^2 N [down],
   $(\vec{w})$ 2.9×10^3 N [down]

10. (Figure 4.38) 2.45 m/s^2 [up], (Figure 4.40) 1.23 m/s^2 [down]

page 231, Chapter 4 Review

2. (balance) 5.0 kg, (spring scale) 96 N

3. $g \propto M_{source}$

4. 3.8 N/kg [toward Earth's centre]

5. 1.4 s

7. (a) 222 N [toward centre of Mars]
(b) 625 N [toward centre of Saturn]

8. 2.0×10^{-7} N

9. (a) 2.4×10^2 N
(b) 7.1×10^2 N
(c) 6.8 N

10. (a) 7.3 m/s^2 [down]
(b) 12 s
(c) 4.9×10^2 N [down]

page 234, Unit II Review

2. 86 N [350°]

6. 0.50 kg

7. (a) $4a$ **(b)** $\left(\dfrac{1}{4}\right)a$ **(c)** 0

8. 39.9 N

10. 15 N [up]

21. (mass m) F_g, (mass $2m$) $2F_g$

24. 306 N [357°]

25. 2.097 m/s^2 [W]

27. 4.0 s

28. (b) 8.58 N [0°]

29. 0.56 m/s^2 [in same direction as train A]

30. 8.0×10^4 N [up]

31. 2.2 m/s^2 [forward]

32. 10 N [up]

33. (a) 5.3 m/s^2 [right]
(b) 4.8×10^2 N

34. 0.46

35. (a) 8×10^1 N [forward]
(b) 2×10^1 N [forward]
(c) 6×10^1 N [backward]

36. 3.2 m/s^2 [downhill]

37. 1.5 m/s^2 [up]

38. (a) 1.3 m/s^2 [toward object A]
(b) (string between A and B) 51 N, (string between B and C) 44 N

39. 8.00 N [toward Earth's centre]

41. 8.6 N/kg [toward Earth's centre]

42. 24.3 N less on Mars

43. (a) (i) and **(ii)** 5.9×10^2 N
(iii) 8.8×10^2 N **(iv)** 3.9×10^2 N
(b) (i) and **(ii)** $(\vec{F_g})$ 5.9×10^2 N [down], $(\vec{w})$ 5.9×10^2 N [down]
(iii) $(\vec{F_g})$ 5.9×10^2 N [down], $(\vec{w})$ 8.8×10^2 N [down]
(iv) $(\vec{F_g})$ 5.9×10^2 N [down], $(\vec{w})$ 3.9×10^2 N [down]

44. $(\vec{F_g})$ 5.9×10^2 N [down], $(\vec{a})$ 6.5 m/s^2 [down]

45. (a) 9.4 m/s^2 [down]
(b) 11 N [up]
(c) 11 N [down]

46. (Earth) 1.2 s, (Moon) 3.0 s

47. (a) 0.12 N [away from net]
(b) -0.78 m/s^2 [toward net]
(c) 8.9 s
(d) no

51. (a) 3.7×10^7 N [down]
(b) 1.3×10^7 N [forward]
(c) 3.3 m/s^2 [forward]

52. (a) F_g from person on you is 5.8 times greater

page 268, 5.2 Check and Reflect

6. 0.2 s

7. 1.88×10^2 m/s

8. 26 m/s

9. 8.57 m/s^2

10. 12

11. 1.21 m/s

12. 0.0337 m/s^2

13. 1.7 Hz

14. 1.3 Hz or 78 rpm

page 286, 5.3 Check and Reflect

9. 0.723 AU

10. 1.36×10^3 m/s

11. 3.547 d

12. 1.43×10^4 m/s

13. 1.98×10^{30} kg

page 288, Chapter 5 Review

14. $4\times$

17. 2.0×10^1 m/s

18. 7.8×10^2 N

19. 44.3 m/s

20. 68.0 N [down]

21. 50.4 km/h

22. 7.83×10^2 m/s^2

23. 3.0×10^3 rpm

24. 107 448 km/h

25. 13.1 m/s

26. (a) 6.00×10^7 m/s
(b) 1.20×10^{16} m/s^2

27. 18.0 AU

28. 1.09×10^{30} kg

29. (a) 1.16×10^{18} s or 3.68×10^{10} y
(b) 5.15×10^{36} kg
(c) 6.71×10^{-15} m/s^2

30. (a) 7.91×10^3 m/s
(b) 5.98×10^{24} kg
(c) 5.06×10^3 s

31. 2.01×10^{20} N

32. 0.430 d or 3.72×10^4 s

33. 5.50×10^3 m/s

34. (a) 4.01×10^{33} kg
(b) 6.38×10^{11} m

page 305, 6.1 Check and Reflect

5. (a) 3.60×10^4 J
(b) 1.18×10^4 J

6. 2.76×10^4 J

7. (a) -6.18×10^4 J
(b) 7.55×10^4 J
(c) 1.37×10^5 J

8. (a) 3.25 J
(b) 0.073 m

9. (a) A = 2.04×10^5 J; B = 3.49×10^5 J

10. (a) -110 J
(b) -33.8 J

11. (a) 160 J
(b) 12.6 m/s

page 310, 6.2 Check and Reflect

5. 1.79×10^6 J; k_e

6. 3.54×10^5 J

7. (a) 5.10×10^3 J
(b) 1.25×10^3 J
(c) 3.85×10^3 J
(d) 31.0 m/s [up]

8. (a) 288 J **(b)** 288 J
(c) 126 J **(d)** 126 J

page 323, 6.3 Check and Reflect

7. 12.4 J

10. (a) 0.482 m
(b) 3.08 m/s
(c) 2.13 m/s

page 330, 6.4 Check and Reflect

4. 164 W

5. 1.50×10^6 W

6. 4.05×10^6 J

7. 380 N

8. 1.04×10^7 W

page 332, Chapter 6 Review

5. 3.27×10^5 J

6. (a) increases by $4\times$

7. (a) 5.12 m/s **(b)** 5.59 m/s

8. 1.70×10^2 N/m

9. 12.7 m

10. 2.30×10^4 W

page 336, Unit III Review

16. 1 J = 1 kg·m^2/s^2

29. 0.017 s

30. 62.5 Hz

31. 0.200 s

32. 1.02×10^3 m/s

33. 1.6×10^1 s

34. 3.09 m/s^2

35. 1.40×10^2 m/s

36. 7.10×10^{-3} N

37. (a) 28.1 m **(b)** $4 \times$; 113 m

38. (a) 2.40×10^3 J **(b)** 1.41×10^3 J

39. (a) 2.80×10^3 N [0°]
(b) 1.54×10^3 J
(c) 3.79×10^5 J
(d) 19.5 m/s

40. 1.03 m

41. **(a)** 1.20×10^3 J **(b)** 15.5 m/s

42. **(a)** 35.9 J **(b)** 0.814 m

44. **(a)** 2.60 J **(b)** 0.065 m

45. 1.32 m/s

46. **(a)** 1.31×10^5 J
    (b) 917 m
    (c) 295 m/s

47. **(a)** -8.91 J **(b)** -1.78 N

48. 3.68×10^3 W

49. 1.62×10^4 W

50. 60.0 m/s (216 km/h)

51. 3.63 m/s

52. **(a)** 4.01×10^{30} kg
    (b) 4.27×10^{25} kg
    (c) 2.18×10^3 m/s

54. **(a)** 7.75 m/s **(b)** 4.38 m/s

page 347, 7.1 Check and Reflect

7. 20.0 Hz

9. 2.50×10^2 Hz

10. 0.026 s

11. 0.01250 s

12. **(a)** 0.400 s **(b)** 1.50×10^2 wags

page 365, 7.2 Check and Reflect

4. 6.0 N opposite to the displacement

5. 1.6 m [down]

6. 19 N

7. 1.5 N/m

8. 0.342 N [forward]

9. 0.028 N/m

page 380, 7.3 Check and Reflect

6. 19.4 m/s

7. 1.5 m

8. 1.08×10^3 m/s^2 [left]

9. 1.3×10^3 N/m

10. 11.0°

11. 3.47 s

12. **(a)** 1.88 s
    (b) 0.900 kg
    (c) 16.7 m/s^2

13. 3.14 m/s

14. 7.99 cm [east]

15. 0.898 s

page 390, Chapter 7 Review

11. **(a)** 2.5 N [forward]
    (b) 0.9 N

12. 250 Hz

13. 1.5 s

14. 10.0 Hz

15. 5.1 N [forward]

16. 2×10^2 N/m

17. **(a)** 2.00 N/m
    (b) -0.400 N
    (c) 0.33 m

18. 0.750 m

20. 24.8 cm

21. 3.00 s

22. 0.0379 m/s

23. 0.13 m/s^2 [down]

24. 1.02 s

25. 0.65 m/s^2

26. **(a)** l/g **(b)** 0.796 m

27. **(a)** 1.26 m/s **(b)** 0.993 s

28. **(a)** 0.566 Hz

page 410, 8.2 Check and Reflect

5. 1.20×10^3 Hz

6. 2.07 m

7. 0.135 m

9. **(a)** 0.911 m **(b)** 3.91 m

page 428, 8.3 Check and Reflect

7. 0.106 m

9. 0.60 cm

page 434, 8.4 Check and Reflect

4. 748 Hz

5. 15.7 m/s (56.5 km/h)

page 436, Chapter 8 Review

5. 0.133 s

7. 0.833 cm

8. 8.6 cm

9. 2.73×10^{-2} m

10. **(b)** 5.6 m/s

12. **(a)** 2.5 Hz **(b)** 0.50 Hz

13. **(a)** 435 m/s **(b)** 777 Hz

14. **(a)** 19.7 cm **(b)** 59.0 cm

16. 1.4 cm

17. 308 Hz

18. 86.9 km/h (24.1 m/s)

19. 1.26×10^3 km/h

20. 694 Hz

21. 175 m/s; $f = \dfrac{2}{3}$ original

page 440, Unit IV Review

11. 2.5, 3.5

28. 3.06 N

29. 7.9 g

32. $+1.25$ m/s^2

33. 4.0 mN/m

34. **(a)** 0.100 m
    (b) 2.24 m/s

35. 15 m/s

36. 6.73 s

37. 0.75 m/s

38. 15.9 m

41. 4.00×10^{14} Hz to 6.98×10^{14} Hz

42. 240 m

43. 0.294 m

44. 7.76 s

45. 120 m/s

46. **(a)** 9 antinodes and 10 nodes
    (b) 2.22 Hz

47. **(a)** 193 m/s
    (b) 440 Hz

48. **(a)** 0.552 m
    (b) 1.66 m

49. 8.62 m/s

50. **(a)** 1.28×10^3 Hz
    (b) 9.96×10^2 Hz

page 449, 9.1 Concept Check

(a) $2p$ **(b)** $\left(\dfrac{1}{3}\right)p$ **(c)** p [W]

page 453, 9.1 Check and Reflect

8. 13 kg•m/s [S]

9. 1.2×10^2 m/s [N]

10. **(a)** 39 kg•m/s [210°]
    (b) (bicycle) 42 kg•m/s [40.0° N of E];
    (rider) 2.3×10^2 kg•m/s [40.0° N
    of E]; (system) 2.7×10^2 kg•m/s
    [40.0° N of E]

11. 0.16 kg

12. 7.91 kg•m/s [214°]

13. 75 m/s [S]

14. **(a)** 4.28×10^5 kg•m/s [W]
    (b) 3.85×10^5 kg•m/s [W]

15. 1.36×10^5 kg

16. 32.6 m/s [W]

page 456, 9.2 Concept Check

$p_i \neq 0$

page 467, 9.2 Check and Reflect

4. **(a)** $2 \times$ (impulse)
   (b) $\dfrac{1}{3} \times$ (impulse)

7. **(a)** 2.3 N•s
   (b) 47 m/s [S]

8. 6.2 N•s [forward]

9. **(a)** 7.0×10^3 N•s [forward]
   (b) 11 m/s [forward]

10. 12 s

11. 560 N [W]

12. 545 N•s [W]

page 486, 9.3 Check and Reflect

6. 0.018 m/s [away from bag]

7. 3.1×10^3 m/s [down]

8. 1.2 m/s [S]

9. 0.47 m/s [E]

10. **(a)** 1.11 m/s [right] **(b)** inelastic

11. **(a)** 274 kg **(b)** inelastic

page 499, 9.4 Check and Reflect

5. 0.505 m/s [320°]

6. 0.625 m/s [48.1° N of W]

7. inelastic, 0.098 J

9. 0.603 m/s [49.6° S of W]

10. 27.4 m/s [37°]

11. 27.0 m/s [349°]

page 503, Unit V Review

11. $\vec{P}_{\text{sys}_i} = \vec{P}_{\text{sys}_f}$ where $(\vec{F}_{\text{net}})_{\text{sys}} = 0$,
(elastic collisions) $E_{k_i} = E_{k_f}$

15. $\Delta\vec{v}$

16. (a) $\vec{F}_{\text{net}}$ decreases **(b)** Δt increases

37. 1.4×10^4 kg·m/s [N]

38. 7.13 kg·m/s [26.0° S of E]

39. 1.85×10^4 kg·m/s [S]

40. 6.2 kg

41. 37 kg·m/s [W]

42. 2.4 kg·m/s [W]

43. (a) 7.5 N·s [S]
  (b) 0.26 kg

44. (a) 3.02 N·s [210°]
  (b) 6.9 m/s [210°]

45. 2.7×10^3 N [toward drop-off]

46. (a) 5.50×10^3 N·s [W]
  (b) 7.75 s

47. 11.3 m/s [6.4° S of W]

48. (a) 7.6×10^3 N·s [forward]
  (b) 22 m/s [forward]

49. (a) 3 N·s
  (b) 11 m/s

50. 6.5×10^7 N [toward rocket]

51. 8.7×10^2 N [down]

52. (a) 12 kg·m/s [toward pitcher]
  (b) 1.6×10^3 N [toward pitcher]

53. 2.1 m/s [225°]

54. (a) 1.29 m/s [S]
  (b) 1.29 m/s [S]

55. 0.750 m/s [backward]

56. 1.27×10^3 m/s [3.5°]

57. 3.5 m/s [65.3°]

58. 1.26 m/s [8.3° E of N]

59. (a) 1.8 m/s [1.8° E of N]
  (b) elastic

60. 1.3 m/s [downhill]

61. 15.6 m/s [34.1° S of W]

62. (a) 17 m/s

63. 4.90 m/s [2.0°]

64. (a) 13.4 m/s [0°]
  (b) inelastic

65. 4.21×10^{-25} kg·m/s [W]

66. (a) 3.46 m/s [4.7° W of N]
  (b) inelastic

67. (a) 40.0 kg

68. 33 m/s [72.5° N of W]

69. (a) 12 m/s
  (b) 61.8° E of N

70. (a) 5.95 m/s [E]
  (b) 2.76 s

71. 10 m/s [73.8° N of E]

72. 0.580 kg

73. 1.18 m/s [307.9°]

74. 0.641 m/s [S]

75. (a) S **(b)** NW **(c)** 248°

77. 10.5 m/s [46.4° W of S and 52.5° up]

80. (initial velocity of car) 90 km/h [W];
(initial velocity of truck) 88 km/h [N]

82. 6.1×10^2 m/s

page 538, 10.2 Check and Reflect

5. (a) 20 N **(b)** 40 N

6. (b) 3.1×10^{10} electrons

7. (a) 6.74 N—repulsive
  (b) 6.80 N—repulsive

8. (a) 1.21×10^{10} N toward charge B
  (b) 7.50×10^9 N toward charge A

page 540, Chapter 10 Review

11. 1.69 N—repulsive

12. 6.70×10^3 m

13. (a) 1.60×10^{10} N [left]
  (b) 1.24×10^{10} N [left]

22. (a) 160 N **(b)** 6.7 N

24. X—2.43×10^{12} N [90°];
Y—2.43×10^{12} N [210°];
Z—2.43×10^{12} N [330°]

25. (b) F_e varies as $1/r$ or $1/r^2$
  (e) 0.0360 N·m^2
  (f) kq_1q_2
  (g) 2.00×10^{-6} C

page 553, 11.1 Check and Reflect

7. (a) 4.50×10^5 N/C [right]
  (b) 9.00×10^{-3} N [right]

8. (a) 2.04×10^4 N/C [toward the
   larger sphere]
  (b) $+3.63 \times 10^{-9}$ C

9. (a) 2.50×10^{10} N/C [toward the
   3.00 C charge]
  (b) 0.661 m left of the -3.00 C charge

page 569, 11.2 Check and Reflect

4. (a) 2.40×10^{-17} N [downward]
  (b) 1.64×10^{-26} N [downward]

6. 1.60×10^3 N/C

7. 7.21×10^5 N/C
[toward the -6.4 μC charge]

8. 2.00×10^3 J

9. 1.78×10^6 N/C [left]

10. (a) 2.00×10^4 V/m
  (b) 3.86×10^{-5} J

page 575, 11.3 Check and Reflect

4. Speed of electron is 8.79×10^6 m/s;
speed of proton is 2.05×10^5 m/s

5. 9.4×10^7 m/s

6. 6.00×10^{-19} C

7. 2.40×10^{-4} J

8. (a) 1.38×10^6 m/s
  (b) 9.79×10^5 m/s

9. (a) 1.8×10^{-5} J
  (b) 1.8×10^{-5} J
  (c) 1.1 m/s

10. (b) 2.00×10^{-17} N [down]
  (c) 2.20×10^{13} m/s^2 [down]
  (d) 0.129 m

page 578, Chapter 11 Review

12. $E_p = W$

17. (a) 5.17×10^3 N/C
  (b) 1.03×10^{-2} N

18. (a) 7.50×10^{10} N/C [toward the
   -5.00 C charge]
  (b) 0.735 m from the -5.00 C charge

19. 1.2×10^7 N/C [90.0°]

20. (a) 3.0 J **(b)** 3.0 J

21. 5.62×10^4 J

22. (a) 160 V/m
  (b) 6.00 V

24. 7.0×10^5 V/m

25. 2.88×10^{-13} J or 1.80×10^6 eV

26. 6.40×10^{-15} J or 4.00×10^4 eV

page 601, 12.2 Check and Reflect

6. (a) 6.40×10^{-15} N
  (b) 3.67×10^{-15} N

7. 1.3×10^6 m/s

8. 6.53×10^{-26} N

9. 1.06×10^{-4} m

10. 8.31×10^{-9} T

page 613, 12.3 Check and Reflect

9. 1.04×10^{-2} C

11. 8.4×10^{-2} N

page 622, Chapter 12 Review

20. 9.86×10^{-14} N

21. (a) 2.3×10^4 m/s
  (b) 4.42×10^{-19} J or 2.76 eV

22. 4.08×10^{-3} m/s

23. (a) 4.13×10^{-16} N
  (b) 2.06×10^{-16} N
  (c) no force

24. 2.7×10^{-5} T

26. (b) B varies as $1/r$ or $1/r^2$

28. 25.0 N

page 626, Unit VI Review

40. (a) 1.4×10^8 V/m
  (b) 1.1×10^{-19} J

42. 2.56×10^{-9} m

43. 5.06×10^7 N—repulsive

46. 15 N/C

47. 3.2×10^{-15} J; maximum speed
is 1.96×10^6 m/s

48. 0.268 m to the right of the
first charge

49. 5.0×10^{-5} C

50. 0.73 A

51. (a) 2.6×10^6 N/C [left]
  (b) 1.62 N—attractive

53. 2.0×10^{-3} N

54. 1.67×10^{-4} m

55. (a) 3.63×10^{-47} N
  (b) 8.22×10^{-8} N
  (c) 2.27×10^{39} times greater

58. 1.53×10^{-3} m/s
59. (a) 3.17×10^{-12} N
(b) 1.89×10^{-2} m
60. (a) 113 N [right]
(b) 28.4 N [left]
(c) 30.8 N [69.4°]
61. 6.6×10^3 V
62. (a) 2.50×10^4 V
(b) 9.37×10^7 m/s
(c) 2.25×10^{-11} N
82. (b) B varies as 1/r
(c) Plot B vs 1/r
(f) 0.791
(g) 0.789

page 647, 13.1 Check and Reflect
8. 2.5×10^3 Hz

page 652, 13.2 Check and Reflect
4. 2.1×10^8 m/s
5. 6.67×10^{-2} s
6. 293 Hz
7. 2.7×10^3 Hz
8. 3.44×10^4 m
9. 1.86×10^3 Hz
10. 2.80×10^8 m/s
11. 2.85×10^8 m/s

page 665, 13.3 Check and Reflect
8. 50 cm

page 683, 13.4 Check and Reflect
9. 2.26×10^8 m/s
10. 23.0°
11. 32.4°
12. 41.1°
14. angle of refraction = 15.9°;
wavelength = 351 nm
16. -2.25×10^{-2} m; inverted
18. (a) 648 cm
(b) 140 cm
(c) 8.19 cm

page 697, 13.5 Check and Reflect
6. 5.7×10^{-6} m
7. 6.10°
8. 0.350 m
9. 3.76×10^{-3} m
10. wavelength = 6.11×10^{-7} m;
frequency = 4.91×10^{14} Hz
11. wavelength = 4.13×10^{-7} m;
frequency = 7.26×10^{14} Hz

page 699, Chapter 13 Review
24. (a) 2.26×10^8 m/s
(b) 2.19×10^8 m/s
(c) 1.97×10^8 m/s
(d) 2.04×10^8 m/s
(e) 1.24×10^8 m/s
25. 3.41×10^4 m
26. 2.88×10^8 m/s

28. 12.5 cm
32. 5.00 cm high, 6.67 cm from the mirror
33. 1.82 cm
34. angle of refraction = 23°;
wavelength = 415 nm
35. (a) no **(b)** yes **(c)** yes **(d)** no
36. 1.12, which is less than that of water
37. (a) 48.8° **(b)** 24.4°
(c) 33.3° **(d)** 41.1°
39. 2.67 cm high, 3.33 cm from the lens.
It is virtual, erect, and diminished.
40. 0.68°, 1.4°, 2.0°
41. 4.4×10^{-7} m; violet
42. 4.9×10^{-7} m; blue
43. 6.0×10^{-5} m

page 710, 14.1 Check and Reflect
1. 4.42×10^{-19} J
2. 8.29×10^{-8} m
4. (a) 2.4×10^{19} Hz
5. 2.8×10^{21} photons
6. 4.9×10^{21} photons
7. 100 photons/s

page 715, 14.2 Concept Check
$E_{\text{photon}} = hf > W$

page 720, 14.2 Check and Reflect
1. 3.11 eV
3. 9.82×10^{14} Hz
4. yes, $hf > W$
5. 1.25 V
9. 6.56×10^{-34} J•s; this is close to
Planck's constant

Page 725, 14.3 Check and Reflect
1. 1.33×10^{-27} N•s
3. wavelength = 1.11×10^{-13} m;
energy = 1.80×10^{-12} J
6. 0.0124 nm
7. 2.0×10^4 m/s

page 736, 14.4 Check and Reflect
1. 36.4 nm
2. 1.33×10^{-27} kg•m/s
3. 5.3×10^{-26} kg•m/s
4. 2.1×10^{-23} kg•m/s
5. (a) 3.36×10^{-15} J
(b) 8.47×10^{-12} m

page 742, Chapter 14 Review
3. 4.42×10^{-19} J or 2.76 eV
7. 4.0×10^{-19} J or 2.5 eV
9. It increases by 0.0024 nm.
10. 73 nm
11. 6.63×10^{-27} N•s
13. 3.0×10^{18} photons
14. 3.62×10^{-19} J or 2.26 eV
15. 0.00388 nm

16. (a) 1.1×10^{-34} m
17. 6.28×10^9 photons/s
18. 3.32×10^{30} photons/s
19. 0.52 eV, 2.1 eV, 4.7 eV
20. 5.33×10^{-23} kg·m/s
22. (a) 3.87×10^{21} photons/s/m²
(b) 2.41×10^{-27} kg·m/s
(c) 9.3 N
23. 1.5×10^{17}

page 746, Unit VII Review
26. 3.62×10^{-19} J
29. 6.00×10^{14} Hz
33. 3.88×10^{-7} m (388 nm)
36. 2.21×10^{-27} N·s
37. 0.243 nm
41. 8.3×10^{29} photons/s
43. 3.84×10^5 km
45. 4.84×10^4 m
46. 3.75×10^3 Hz
47. 1.39×10^{-4} s
49. refractive index = 2.42, therefore
the material is diamond
51. 2.91×10^8 m/s; error = 3%
53. 7.5 cm from mirror. It is erect and
2.5 cm high.
55. 8.6°
57. 10 cm from the lens
58.(b) 0.105 m/s
60. 0.0045 nm
62. 0.38 eV
63. for violet light 24.8°;
for red light 40.5°
64. 2.62×10^{-2} m
67. Energy = 0.24 eV;
momentum = 2.6×10^{-25} N•s
68. 6.67×10^{-2} s
71. 41 light years
76. momentum = 1.2×10^{-22} kg•m/s;
wavelength = 5.5×10^{-12} m
78. 6.63×10^{-26} N•s

page 760, 15.1 Check and Reflect
1. (a) 8.0×10^{-15} N
(b) 0 N
4. (b) 400 m/s
5. 1.8×10^9 m/s
6. 1.57×10^{-3} T
8. 3.00×10^3 m/s
9. (a) 8.0×10^{-15} N [downward]
10. (b) 3×10^9 m/s

page 765, 15.2 Check and Reflect
3. -6.40×10^{-19} C
4. 8.00×10^{-17} N [up]
5. (a) 0 N
6. (a) -1.6×10^{-18} C, or $-10e$
(b) 10
(c) It will accelerate downward at $2g$.

page 770, 15.3 Check and Reflect

3. **(a)** 3.6×10^{-16} J
   (b) 3.6×10^{-12} J
6. **(a)** 1.6×10^{-10} m
   (b) The gold atom is approximately 7000 times larger than the gold nucleus.
7. **(b)** 5.0×10^{-15} m

page 780, 15.4 Concept Check

634 nm, 654 nm

page 780, 15.4 Check and Reflect

5. **(b)** 486 nm
   (c) 4.09×10^{-19} J
6. 1.96 eV
7. **(b)** 1 = 1.9 eV; 2 = 2.1 eV; 3 = 1.5 eV; 4 = 3.9 eV
   (c) $\lambda_1 = 654$ nm, visible, red; $\lambda_2 = 592$ nm; visible, yellow-orange; $\lambda_3 = 829$ nm; $\lambda_4 = 319$ nm
9. **(a)** 3.03×10^{-19} J
   (b) 2.66×10^{-20} J
11. **(a)** 140 nm   **(b)** 3270 nm   **(c)** 15

page 784, 15.5 Check and Reflect

4. **(a)** 3.32×10^{-10} m
   (b) 2.00×10^{-24} kg·m/s
   (c) kinetic energy = 2.20 $\times 10^{-18}$ J; velocity = 2.20×10^6 m/s
5. **(a)** $\lambda_2 = 2\lambda_1$; $\lambda_3 = 3\lambda_1$

page 786, Chapter 15 Review

6. 3.68×10^{-18} C
7. -1.76×10^{11} C
16. 4.76×10^{-10} m
19. 2.4×10^{-16} N
20. **(a)** 1.09×10^6 m/s
21. 4.1×10^4 N/C directed upward
22. **(a)** 1.06×10^{-19} J; 1.55×10^{-19} J; 1.82×10^{-19} J
    (b) wavelengths: 1880 nm, 1280 nm, 1090 nm. Frequencies: 1.60×10^{14} Hz, 2.34×10^{14} Hz, 2.74×10^{14} Hz.
    (c) 1.55×10^{-19} J
23. **(b)** 634 nm
24. 2.5×10^3 N/C [up]
25. **(a)** 2.17×10^{-18} J
    (b) 9.0×10^{22} m/s^2
    (d) 4.7×10^{-11} s

page 796, 16.1 Check and Reflect

1. **(a)** 38 protons, 52 neutrons
   (b) 6 protons, 7 neutrons
   (c) 26 protons, 30 neutrons
   (d) 1 proton, 0 neutrons
2. 1.0×10^9 eV = 1.0 GeV
3. 233 MeV
4. 5.56×10^{-8} kg

7. 177.772 MeV
8. **(a)** 0.366642 u
   (b) 8.53818 MeV/nucleon
9. **(a)** 100 MeV
   (b) 476 MeV
   (c) 1737 MeV
13. Nuclear radius ≈ 5.4 fm. Approximate distance between nucleons = 1.9 fm

page 810, 16.2 Check and Reflect

8. 2.84 MeV

page 817, 16.3 Check and Reflect

1. $\frac{1}{16}$
2. 3.7×10^{12} atoms/s
3. 1.2 million years
4. 1.7×10^{-3} of the original quantity
5. 11500 years
7. 153 Bq
8. **(a)** 5 h
   (b) 3477 decays/min

Page 824, 16.4 Check and Reflect

6. **(b)** 4.73 MeV
7. **(b)** 17.6 MeV
8. **(a)** 8.10×10^{19}
   (b) 998 kg

Page 826, Chapter 16 Review

5. 60 neutrons, 55 protons
6. 8.0×10^{-12} J
7. 9×10^{13} J
8. 3.44×10^{-10} J
9. 0.322 u
10. 20.5 MeV
18. 180 MBq
19. 1.6×10^{19} nuclei
24. **(a)** 7.074 MeV
    (b) 8.448 MeV
    (c) 8.792 MeV
    (d) 7.591 MeV
26. **(b)** 8.95 MeV
27. **(b)** 2.33 MeV
28. 11500 years
29. **(a)** 5.05×10^{15} atoms
    (b) 1.90×10^{-9} kg
    (c) 1.15×10^4 Bq
30. **(a)** 400 Bq   **(b)** 3 h
31. 7.27 MeV
32. **(b)** 233 g

page 844, 17.3 Check and Reflect

7. **(a)** momentum = 5×10^{-21} kg·m/s; kinetic energy = 8×10^{-15} J
   (b) momentum = 8.4×10^{-22} kg·m/s; kinetic energy = 2.1×10^{-16} J
8. **(a)** 0.51100 MeV
   (b) 5.521×10^{-27} kg
9. 931.5

page 851, Chapter 17 Review

19. 3.14×10^{-25} kg
20. **(a)** +e
    (b) $83-138$ MeV/c^2
21. **(b)** 10 cm
    (c) $p = (1.2$ T$)q(0.10$ m$)$

page 855, Unit VIII Review

2. 9.6×10^7 C
3. -1.60×10^{-18} C
4. 1.60×10^{-16} N [N]
8. **(a)** $n_i = 4 \to n_f = 1$ and $n_i = 6 \to n_f = 2$
   (b) $n_i = 1 \to n_f = 5$
   (c) $n_i = 6 \to n_f = 2$
10. 33 neutrons, 31 protons
12. 1.96×10^7 eV
13. 1.0×10^{-9} J
14. 6.7 MeV
15. 2.3×10^9 decays/s
17. 1.4 g
22. **(c)** 2.4×10^{-12} m
25. **(a)** proton
    (b) kaon
    (c) pion
    (d) Σ^-
27. **(b)** 727 m/s
28. 0.48 T
29. **(a)** magnetic force = 2.0×10^{-13} N [up]; electric force = 1.60×10^{-17} N [up]
    (b) 2.0×10^{-13} N [up]
30. **(a)** -1.6×10^{-18} C
    (b) It has gained 10 electrons.
31. **(a)** 1005 nm, 1094 nm, 1282 nm, 1875 nm
    (b) infrared
32. **(a)** 2.12×10^{-10} m
    (b) 6.65×10^{-10} m
    (c) 9.97×10^{-25} kg·m/s
    (d) speed = 1.09 $\times 10^6$ m/s; kinetic energy = 5.46×10^{-19} J
33. 342.06 MeV
36. 10.42 MeV
37. 7.5%
38. 1.91 MeV; cesium-140
39. 122 Bq
40. 1.72×10^4 years old
41. 7.161 MeV
42. 4.033 MeV
44. **(a)** 2×10^2 N
    (b) 2×10^{-13} J
45. 51 km/s
46. **(b)** 135 MeV
48. 2.7×10^{-18} N·s
49. 2.33×10^{-50} m
50. **(a)** 13 Bq

51. (a) the level of 21.9 Sv is much higher than the background level of 400 μSv
  (b) 468 m

52. (b) The matter — anti-matter reaction is more than 150 times more powerful than nuclear fusion.

53. 0.22 g deuterium, 0.33 g tritium

54. 0.5 years

56. 777 nm photon emitted

57. 3.73×10^{-11} J

58. 2.12×10^{-10} m

59. (a) The $n = 3$ state
  (b) 1.89 eV

60. 198.3 MeV

62. +1

63. 5.25×10^5 Bq

page 131, Example 3.1 Practice Problems

1.

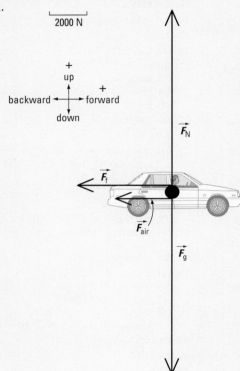

2.

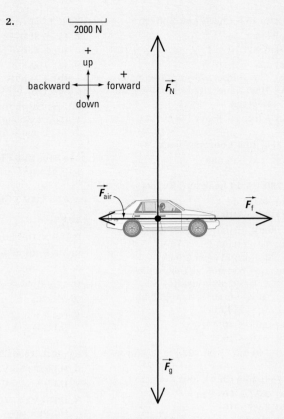

page 225, Example 4.7 Practice Problem

1.

Diagram is not to scale.

Le Verrier, Urbain, 282
Left-hand rule, 834
    for deflection of charged particles,
        594, 595
    for magnetic fields, 588
    for magnetic force, 604, 611, 756f
Lenses, 677–681
Lenz's law, **618**, 619
Leptons, **842**, 843t, 848t
Lewis, Gilbert, 706
Light (*see also* Electromagnetic radiation)
    from colliding objects, 481
    quantum theory of, 705–709,
        712–719, 721–724, 726–735
    reflection, 653–665
    refraction, 666–681
    speed of, 636, 648–651, 669, 670
Light waves, **712**–719
Lightning, 512, 513, 522, 529
Lightning rod, 554
Lodestone (*also* leading stone), 582, 583
Longitudinal waves, **401**, **404**–406, 695f
Lord Kelvin (*see* William Thomson)
Loudspeaker, 614t
Low tide, 210, **211**
Lyman series, 776f

M

Maglev, 587
Magnesium, 636f
Magnetic deflection, 593–597, 603, 604
Magnetic field, **584**–591, 593–600,
        602–611, **641**–643, 756f–758
    left-hand rule for, 588
Magnetic field strengths, 586t
Magnetic force,
    between two current carrying
        conductors, 607
    calculation of, 598–600
    on a current carrying conductor,
        603–606
Magnetic monopoles, 582
Magnetic poles, 582, 585
Magnetism, 512, 587–591
Magnetization, 589, 590
Magnetohydrodynamic propulsion, 614t
Magnetron, 599
Magnets, 583, 585, 586, 617, 618
Magnification, **656**, 662, 664
Magnitude, 6
Major axis, 269f
Marconi, Guglielmo, 646
Marsden, Ernest, 767
Mass, 220
    and conservation of momentum, 474
    due to gravity, 199
    in momentum, 448–452
    of celestial bodies, 218t, 280, 281
Mass defect, **794**, 795
Mass spectrometer, 759
Mass-energy equation, 793, 794
Mass-spring systems, 354–360, 366–376
Matter waves, 726–735, 729
Maximum, **426**

Maxwell, James Clerk, 641, 648, 695, 771
Maxwell's equations, **642**
Mechanical energy, **306**, 309, 311–322
Mechanical resonance, **382**
Mechanical waves (*see* Waves)
Mechanics, **306**
Mediating particles, **837**, 838
Medium, **394**, **395**, 404, 406, 411
Mesons, **842**, 843t, 845, 847
Michell, John, 205
Michelson, Albert, 650, 651
Microwaves, 637f, 638t
Millikan, Robert Andrews, 713f–715,
    761–763
Minor axis, 269f
Mirage, 667
Mirror equation, **662**, 664
Mirrors, 654–662
Momentum, **449**–452, **470**
    and impulse, 454–466
    and Newton's Second Law, 450–452,
        456
    and non-linear net forces, 461, 462
    conservation of, 473–479, 489–498
    in one-dimensional collisions,
        473–479
    in two-dimensional collisions,
        489–495
    of a photon, 728
Motion,
    in one dimension, 6–62, 70–75
    in two dimensions, 76–89
    of projectiles, 102–111
    sign conventions for, 8–10
Motor effect force, **593**
Muons, **842**, 843t

N

Nanotechnology, 619, 674
Navigator method, **77**, 78
Neddermeyer, Seth, 842, 846
Negative acceleration, 28, 29, 44
Net charge, **517**, 518
Net force, **131**–135, 139, 146, 152, 155,
        157, 164, 165, 171–189, 306, 307,
        356, 366, 456–466, 473, 474, 489
    in circular motion, 256
    on momentum, 450
Neutrino, **804**
Neutron, 497, 498, **790**, 792t, 844t, 847
Neutron number, **790**, 791, 794, 795
Newton (N), 127
Newton, Isaac, 194, 196, 214, 276–281,
    545, 634, 639, 675
Newton's first law of motion, 139, 140
Newton's law of gravitation, 524
Newton's law of universal gravitation,
    204–214, 216
Newton's second law of motion,
    143–157, 366, 367
    and horizontal motion, 149–151
    and momentum, 450–452, 456
    and single pulley system, 154, 155
    and two-body systems, 153, 154

    and two-pulley system, 156, 157
    and vertical motion, 152, 153
    on objects in systems, 470, 473
Newton's third law of motion, 161–167,
    459, 474
Newton-second (N•s), 457
Nodal lines (*also* Minimum; Dark
    fringes), **426**, **686**
Nodes (*also* Nodal points), **415**, **417**–419,
    423f, 424f, **687**
Non-collinear forces, 133, 134
Non-collinear vectors, **80**–89
Non-conservative forces, **319**
Non-isolated systems, **320**–322
Non-linear net force, 461, 462
Non-uniform motion, 22–28, 31
Non-zero net force, 307, 450
Normal (*also* Perpendicular) force, **130**, 131
Normal force, 258, 259, 260
Normal line (N), **653**, 654f, 666f
North pole, 582
Nuclear energy vs chemical energy, 820
Nuclear reactions, 818–823
Nucleon, **790**, 795, 796
Nucleosynthesis, **823**
Nucleus, 513, 766–769, 790–796
    decay rates of, 811–816
    reactions in, 818–823
    size of, 768, 769

O

Oersted, Hans Christian, 587
Oil-drop experiment, 761
Omega particle, 845
Open-pipe (*also* Open-tube) resonance, **424**
Opsin, 636
Optical centre, 678f
Optical fibres, **673**
Orbital height, 279, 280
Orbital period, 271–289
Orbital perturbations (also Wobbles),
    281, **282**, 283
Orbital radius, 271–289
Orbital, **783**
Origin, **6**
Oscillation, **344**
Oscillators, 640
Oscillatory motion, **344**, 345, 348–364,
    366–379, 381–387
Out of phase, **416**
Output energy, 324
Overtones, **422**, **423**, 424
Oxygen, 779f

P

Parabola, 61, 62
Parabolic mirror, 661
Parallel plates,
    electric field between, 567
    motion of charges between, 572, 573
Parallel-plate capacitors, 558, 559
    electric field between, 574, 575
    electric potential energy between, 563
Parent element, **799**

The publisher wishes to thank the following sources for photographs, illustrations, and other materials used in this book. Care has been taken to determine and locate ownership of copyright material used in this text. We will gladly receive information enabling us to rectify any errors or omissions in credits.

COVER: Olivier Grunewald/Oxford Scientific Films/First Light and Courtesy of EISCAT. **UNIT ONE:** Page 2 (left) Larry Macdougal/First Light; pp. 2-3 (top) CP-Adrian Wyld, (bottom) CP-Jeff McIntosh; p. 4 CP/Whitehorse Star-Vince Federoff; p. 6 (left) Elsa/Getty Images, (centre) CP-Adrian Wyld, (right) Bryan & Cherry Alexander Photography; p. 10 Richard Kellaway/PC Services; p. 11 JupiterImages Corporation; p. 21 (top right) Lightworks Media/Alamy, (bottom left) CP-Frank Gunn; p. 22 Frank Siteman/maXximages.com; p. 23 AP Photo/Brainerd Dispatch-Clint Wood; p. 26 blickwinkel/Alamy; p. 29 Courtesy of NHTSA; p. 31 (left) Antony Nettle/Alamy, (right) iStockphoto.com/Glenn Frank; p. 32 (left) Mike Robinson/ maXximages.com, (centre) JupiterImages Corporation, (right) Adam Pretty/AUS/Allsport/Getty Images; p. 46 Reuters/U.S. Navy/Landov; p. 51 Iain Cooper/Alamy; p. 54 dpa/Ingo Wagner/ Landov; p. 58 Wallace Garrison/maXximages.com; p. 68 CP-Larry MacDougal; p. 70 Steve Mason/Photodisc/Getty Images; p. 72 CP/Edmonton Sun-Darryl Dyck; p. 76 (left) CP/Edmonton Sun-Perry Mah, (right) CP-Adrian Wyld; p. 80 (left) Image 100/First Light, (right) Richard Megna/Fundamental Photographs, NYC; p. 86 CP/Calgary Herald-Ted Jacob; p. 88 Ryan McVay/Photodisc/Getty Images; p. 91 Courtesy of Syncrude Canada Ltd.; p. 92 Johnny Buzzerio/CORBIS; p. 102 (top left) CP/AP Photo-Jay LaPrete, (right) CP-Aaron Harris, (bottom left) CP/Edmonton Sun-Jason Franson; p. 104 Richard Megna/Fundamental Photographs, NYC; p. 107 Paul A. Souders/ CORBIS; p. 108 Cosmo Condina/Stone/Getty Images; p. 109 Jeff Carlick/Getty Images. **UNIT TWO:** Pages 122–123 Ian Tomlinson/Take Stock Inc.; p. 124 Rick Fischer/Masterfile; p. 126 Henry Westheim Photography/Alamy; p. 137 CP-Frank Gunn; p. 139 NASA-JPL; p. 140 (Figure 3.28) Courtesy of Autoliv Inc.; p. 141 Richard Kellaway/PC Services; p. 143 CP-Paul Chiasson; p. 150 CP/COC-Jonathan Hayward; p. 159 CP-Tom Hanson; p. 166 Photograph courtesy of the Canada Aviation Museum, Ottawa; p. 169 Angus McNee/Take Stock Inc.; p. 170 CP-Andrew Vaughan; p. 184 (top) Patrick Riviere/ Getty Images, (bottom left) Terje Rakke/The Image Bank/Getty Images, (bottom centre) Dorling Kindersley, (bottom right) Transtock Inc./Alamy; p. 194 The City of Calgary, Corporate Records (OCO-54-22-LF146#4); p. 195 Richard Kellaway/PC Services; p. 196 Anna Zieminski/AFP/Getty Images; p. 210 (left and right) Andrew J. Martinez/Photo Researchers, Inc./ First Light; p. 217 CP-Frank Gunn; p. 219 NASA; p. 222 (Figure 4.35) Reproduced with the permission of the Minister of Public Works and Government Services Canada, 2005 and Courtesy of Natural Resources Canada, Geological Survey of Canada; p. 228 NASA. **UNIT THREE:** Pages 238-239 NASA/ JSC; p. 243 CP/HO/Commonwealth Games Association-Dan Galbraith; p. 248 (left) Ian Waldie/Getty Images, (right) W. Cody/CORBIS; p. 249 JupiterImages Corporation; p. 250 Courtesy of Seagate Technology, Inc.; p. 252 (left and right) Dave Milcarek; p. 255 Mark Sykes/Alamy; p. 256 picturesbyrob/ Alamy; p. 260 CP/AP Photo-Keith Srakocic; p. 265 (left) Tom Stewart/CORBIS, (right) Hisham Ibrahim/Photodisc/Getty Images; p. 267 Eric M. Renard/Acclaim Images; p. 283 Dr. Seth Shostak/Science Photo Library; p. 284 CP/Rex Features; p. 290 (left) Dave King ©Dorling Kindersley, (right) CP/Toronto Star-Peter Power; p. 292 (top) Ker Robertson/Getty Images, (centre) [R376.3A] Copper Inuit sinew back bow, early 20th century, wood, sinew, ivory, sealskin, L:127 cm., Collection of Glenbow Museum, Calgary, Canada, (bottom) Karl Weatherly/Photodisc/ Getty Images; p. 295 Scooter Korek; p. 303 U.S. Geological Survey; p. 306 CP-Chuck Stoody; p. 324 Dave Milcarek; p. 329 (top) Xinhua/Sovfoto, (bottom) Vancouver Fuel Cell Vehicle Program, Government of Canada, Province of British Columbia, Ford Motor Company and Fuel Cells Canada. **UNIT FOUR:** Pages 340-341 (bkgd) AFP/AFP/Getty Images, (inset) Choo Youn-Kong/AFP/Getty Images; p. 342 NASA/JPL; p. 343 Richard Kellaway/PC Services; p. 344 Cecil Williams (www.cecilw.com); p. 349 (top) Adam Hart-Davis/Science Photo Library, (bottom) Science Photo Library; p. 351 Liu Liqun/CORBIS; p. 358 Per Eriksson/The Image Bank/Getty Images; p. 359 Clive Streeter ©Dorling Kindersley, Courtesy of The Science Museum, London; p. 367 Felix Velasquez Photography (photographersdirect.com); p. 369 Spectrum/ Robertstock.com; p. 373 Lori Adamski Peek/Stone/Getty Images; p. 374 iStockphoto.com/Dan Van Oss; p. 381 Science Museum/Science & Society Picture Library; p. 385 Dr. Wolfhard Schmidt (www.structurae.de); p. 386 (top left) CP/ AP Photo-Wally Santana, (top centre) Louie Psihoyos/Science Faction, (bottom centre) M. Szojka; p. 387 Richard Kellaway/ PC Services; p. 392 (top left) Josh Sher/Photo Researchers, Inc./First Light, (top right) Brand X Pictures/Alamy, (bottom left) Frank Greenaway ©Dorling Kindersley, (bottom right) Lawrence Sawyer/Photodisc/Getty Images; p. 394 CP/AP Photo-Ronen Zilberman; p. 395 Jeff Greenberg/Omni-Photo Communications; p. 397 Richard Megna/Fundamental Photographs, NYC; p. 401 Berenice Abbott/Photo Researchers, Inc.; p. 402 Richard Kellaway/PC Services; p. 417 Jim Richardson, Scotland 1986; p. 418 Keystone/Hulton Archive/ Getty Images; p. 423 (top) Altrendo/Getty Images, (bottom) Richard Megna/Fundamental Photographs, NYC; p. 424 (top) Michael C. Andrews/MCA Photography (photographersdirect.com), (centre) CP/Toronto Star-Steve Russell, (bottom) Philip Dowell ©Dorling Kindersley; p. 425 Richard Megna/Fundamental Photographs, NYC; p. 433 U.S. Navy Photo by Ensign John Gay; p. 434 GE Medical Systems/ Science Photo Library. **UNIT FIVE:** Pages 444-445 CP/Calgary Sun-Stuart Dryden; p. 446 CP-Andrew Vaughan; p. 448 Reuters/Dominique Favre/Landov; p. 449 (left) Michael Newman/PhotoEdit, (right) Matthias Kulka/CORBIS; p. 454 AP Photo/The Montana Standard-Meghan Brown; p. 461 Rhona Wise/epa/CORBIS; p. 464 Bryan & Cherry Alexander Photography; p. 465 (left) CP-Jacques Boissinot, (right) CP-Mike Sturk Photos; p. 466 CP-Frank Gunn; p. 468 W. Perry Conway/CORBIS; p. 473 Nigel Reed/Alamy; p. 474 CP/Peterborough Examiner-Clifford Skarstedt; p. 475 NASA Kennedy Space Center; p. 480 Richard Megna/Fundamental Photographs, NYC; p. 481 Tony Freeman/PhotoEdit; p. 487 CP/AP Photo; p. 496 Reuters/Gary Hershorn/Landov. **UNIT SIX:** Pages 508-509 Peter Menzel/menzelphoto.com; p. 510 (bkgd) PhotoLink/Photodisc/Getty Images, (inset) Ron Watts/ CORBIS; p. 513 (top right) The Granger Collection, New York, (centre left) The British Library Board. All rights reserved. Shelf#1608/5193, 538.f.7(1); p. 522 CORBIS; p. 528 (Figure 10.17) The Granger Collection, New York; p. 537 Courtesy of Ron Zezulka; p. 542 North Wind Picture Archives; p. 544 (top)

Mary Evans Picture Library; p. 545 NASA/Science Photo Library; p. 559 Courtesy of Koninklijke Philips Electronics N.V. All rights reserved.; p. 560 Mark Burnett/Stock Boston; p. 580 Carson Ganci/A.G.E. Foto Stock/First Light; p. 582 (Figure 12.3) Richard Kellaway/PC Services; p. 583 Richard Kellaway/ PC Services; p. 587 (left) Paul Silverman/ Fundamental Photographs, NYC, (right) Apollo News Services/PhotoEdit; p. 589 (left) Alex Bartel/Science Photo Library, (right) Dorling Kindersley, Courtesy of The Science Museum, London; p. 591 NASA; p. 593 (top right) Clive Streeter ©Dorling Kindersley, Courtesy of The Science Museum, (bottom left and right) Richard Megna/Fundamental Photographs, NYC; p. 598 SOHO/ESA/NASA/Science Photo Library; p. 602 (left) Courtesy of Sargent-Welch, (right) Gloria H. Chomica/Masterfile; p. 609 Dorling Kindersley, Courtesy of NASA; p. 610 (left) D. Falconer/PhotoLink/Photodisc/Getty Images, (right) Photodisc/Getty Images; p. 615 Michael Newman/PhotoEdit; p. 619 Courtesy of Dr. Hicham Fenniri, National Institute for Nanotechnology, NRC; p. 629 image100/ Alamy. **UNIT SEVEN:** Pages 632-633 NASA, ESA/JPL-Caltech/ R. Sankrit & W. Blair (John Hopkins University); p. 634 Bruce Roberts/Photo Researchers, Inc./First Light; p. 636 Tom Bochsler Photography Limited ©Prentice Hall, Inc.; p. 639 (top left) INSADCO Photography/Alamy, (top centre) Russell Illig/Photodisc/Getty Images, (bottom right) The Granger Collection, New York; p. 644 (Figure 13.16) Photo reference for illustration provided courtesy of John Jenkins, www.sparkmuseum.com; p. 646 Peter Lilja/maXximages.com; p. 653 (left and right) Richard Kellaway/PC Services; p. 656 (left and right) Frank Labua ©Prentice Hall, Inc.; p. 657 Paul Silverman/Fundamental Photographs, NYC; p. 666 Richard Kellaway/PC Services; p. 667 1994 Tom Bean/DRK PHOTO; p. 672 George B. Diebold/CORBIS; p. 675 Tom Skrivan Photography; p. 676 (top and bottom) Richard Megna/ Fundamental Photographs, NYC; p. 684 The Granger Collection, New York; p. 686 (Figure 13.70b) sciencephotos/ Alamy, (Figure 13.71) Erich Schrempp/Photo Researchers, Inc./First Light; p. 692 (top left) The Granger Collection, New York, (top right) Andrew Lambert Photography/Science Photo Library, (centre left) Courtesy of Sargent-Welch, (bottom left) PHOTOTAKE Inc./Alamy; p. 693 (left and right) Courtesy of

Tom Ruen; p. 696 (top left) Dave King ©Dorling Kindersley, Courtesy of the Museum of Mankind/British Museum, (bottom left) Diane Hirsch/Fundamental Photographs, NYC, (top right) Fundamental Photographs, NYC; p. 702 The Granger Collection, New York; p. 704 Vince Bucci/Getty Images; p. 705 AIP Emilio Segre Visual Archives, Landè Collection; p. 709 NASA/ESA/ R. Sankrit and W. Blair (John Hopkins University); p. 713, 721, 726 The Nobel Foundation; p. 727 (left) David Parker/Science Photo Library, (right) Susumu Nishinaga/Science Photo Library; p. 729 (top right) The Nobel Foundation, (centre right) Used with permission of Eastman Kodak Company; p. 734 The Nobel Foundation; p. 738 (Figure 14.29) Courtesy of Akira Tonomura of Hitachi, Ltd.; p. 739 Kevin Fleming/CORBIS. **UNIT EIGHT:** Pages 750-751 European Southern Observatory; p. 755 (Figure 15.3) Science Museum/Science & Society Picture Library; p. 762 (top right) Courtesy of the Archives, California Institute of Technology; p. 779 Courtesy of Brian Martin; p. 781 (top) Wabash Instrument Corp./Fundamental Photographs, NYC; p. 786 Courtesy of Brian Martin; p. 788 J.J. Hester/Arizona State University, et al/NASA; p. 802 Frank LaBua ©Prentice Hall, Inc.; p. 806 (left) Dorling Kindersley, (right) sciencephotos/Alamy; p. 809 Courtesy of Landauer, Inc.; p. 818 Reproduced by permission of the *Bulletin of the Atomic Scientists, copyright 2006 by the Bulletin of the Atomic Scientists: The Magazine of Global Security, Science, and Survival*, 6042 South Kimbark, Chicago, Illinois 60637, USA. It is illegal to copy, reproduce or alter this image. (www.thebulletin.org); p. 823 EFDA-JET; p. 830 (top left) Leonard Rue Enterprises/ maXximages.com, (top right) CERN, (bottom) Hulton Archive/ Getty Images; p. 831 CERN/Science Photo Library; p. 833 (left) CERN, (bottom right) Courtesy of Lawrence Berkeley National Laboratory; p. 835 Science Photo Library; p. 836 Carl Anderson/ Science Photo Library; p. 837 Dr. Henry Wagner/Peter Arnold/ Alpha Presse; p. 840 (left) Courtesy of Lawrence Berkeley National Laboratory, (right) Fermilab Photo; p. 846 Courtesy of Melissa Franklin. **APPENDIX:** Page 864 Dawn Goss/First Light.

Illustrations

ArtPlus Ltd.: Joelle Cottle, David Gray, Donna Guilfoyle Sacha Warunkiw